Weiss Ratings' Guide to Property and Casualty Insurers

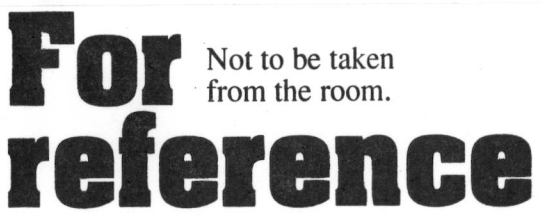

Weiss Ratings' Guide to Property and Casualty Insurers

A Quarterly Compilation of Insurance Company Ratings and Analyses

Winter 2016-17

GREY HOUSE PUBLISHING

Weiss Ratings
4400 Northcorp Parkway
Palm Beach Gardens, FL 33410
561-627-3300

Independent. Unbiased. Accurate. Trusted.

Published by Grey House Publishing, Inc., located at 4919 Route 22, Amenia, NY 12501; telephone 518-789-8700. Grey House Publishing neither guarantees the accuracy of the data contained herein nor assumes any responsibility for errors, omissions or discrepancies. Grey House Publishing accepts no payment for listing; inclusion in the publication of any organization, agency, institution, publication, service or individual does not imply endorsement of the publisher.

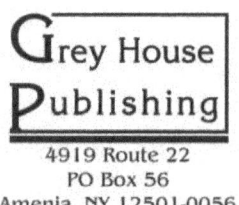

Grey House
Publishing
4919 Route 22
PO Box 56
Amenia, NY 12501-0056

Edition No. 91, Winter 2016-17

ISBN: 978-1-68217-430-2
ISSN: 2158-5989

Contents

Terms and Conditions

This document is prepared strictly for the confidential use of our customer(s). It has been provided to you at your specific request. It is not directed to, or intended for distribution to or use by, any person or entity who is a citizen or resident of or located in any locality, state, country or other jurisdiction where such distribution, publication, availability or use would be contrary to law or regulation or which would subject Weiss Ratings or its affiliates to any registration or licensing requirement within such jurisdiction.

No part of the analysts' compensation was, is, or will be, directly or indirectly, related to the specific recommendations or views expressed in this research report.

This document is not intended for the direct or indirect solicitation of business. Weiss Ratings and its affiliates disclaims any and all liability to any person or entity for any loss or damage caused, in whole or in part, by any error (negligent or otherwise) or other circumstances involved in, resulting from or relating to the procurement, compilation, analysis, interpretation, editing, transcribing, publishing and/or dissemination or transmittal of any information contained herein.

Weiss Ratings has not taken any steps to ensure that the securities or investment vehicle referred to in this report are suitable for any particular investor. The investment or services contained or referred to in this report may not be suitable for you and it is recommended that you consult an independent investment advisor if you are in doubt about such investments or investment services. Nothing in this report constitutes investment, legal, accounting or tax advice or a representation that any investment or strategy is suitable or appropriate to your individual circumstances or otherwise constitutes a personal recommendation to you.

The ratings and other opinions contained in this document must be construed solely as statements of opinion from Weiss Ratings, and not statements of fact. Each rating or opinion must be weighed solely as a factor in your choice of an institution and should not be construed as a recommendation to buy, sell or otherwise act with respect to the particular product or company involved.

Past performance should not be taken as an indication or guarantee of future performance, and no representation or warranty, expressed or implied, is made regarding future performance. Information, opinions and estimates contained in this report reflect a judgment at its original date of publication and are subject to change without notice. Weiss Ratings offers a notification service for rating changes on companies you specify. For more information visit WeissRatings.com or call 1-877-934-7778. The price, value and income from any of the securities or financial instruments mentioned in this report can fall as well as rise.

This document and the information contained herein is copyrighted by Weiss Ratings, LLC. Any copying, displaying, selling, distributing or otherwise reproducing or delivering this information or any part of this document to any other person entity is prohibited without the express written consent of Weiss Ratings, LLC, with the exception of a reviewer or editor who may quote brief passages in connection with a review or a news story, is prohibited.

Message To Insurers

All survey data received on or before October 11, 2016 has been considered or incorporated into this edition of the Directory. If there are particular circumstances which you believe could affect your rating, please use the online survey (http://weissratings.com/survey/) or e-mail Weiss Ratings, LLC (insurancesurvey@weissinc.com) with documentation to support your request. If warranted, we will make every effort to incorporate the changes in our next edition.

Welcome to Weiss Ratings'

Guide to Property and Casualty Insurers

Most people automatically assume their insurance company will survive, year after year. However, prudent consumers and professionals realize that in this world of shifting risks, the solvency of insurance companies can't be taken for granted.

If you are looking for accurate, unbiased ratings and data to help you choose property and casualty insurance for yourself, your family, your company or your clients, Weiss Ratings' *Guide to Property and Casualty Insurers* gives you precisely what you need.

In fact, it's the only source that currently provides ratings and analyses on over 2,400 property and casualty insurers.

Weiss Ratings' Mission Statement

Weiss Ratings' mission is to empower consumers, professionals, and institutions with high quality advisory information for selecting or monitoring a financial services company or financial investment.

In doing so, Weiss Ratings will adhere to the highest ethical standards by maintaining our independent, unbiased outlook and approach to advising our customers.

Why rely on Weiss Ratings?

Weiss Ratings provides fair, objective ratings to help professionals and consumers alike make educated purchasing decisions.

At Weiss Ratings, integrity is number one. Weiss Ratings never takes a penny from insurance companies for issuing a rating. We publish Weiss Safety Ratings without regard for insurers' preferences. However, other rating agencies like A.M. Best, Fitch, Moody's and Standard & Poor's are paid by insurance companies for their ratings and may even suppress unfavorable ratings at an insurer's request.

Our ratings are reviewed and updated more frequently than the other agencies' ratings. You can be sure that the information you receive is accurate and current, providing you with advance warning of financial vulnerability early enough to do something about it.

Other rating agencies focus primarily on a company's current claims paying ability and consider only mild economic adversity. Weiss Ratings also considers these issues, but our analysis also covers a company's ability to deal with severe economic adversity and a sharp increase in claims.

Our use of more rigorous standards stems from the viewpoint that an insurance company's obligations to its policyholders should not depend on favorable business conditions. An insurer must be able to honor its policy commitments in bad times as well as good.

Our rating scale, from A to F, is easy to understand. Only a few outstanding companies receive an A (Excellent) rating, although there are many to choose from within the B (Good) category. An even larger group falls into the broad average range which receives C (Fair) ratings. Companies that demonstrate marked vulnerabilities receive either D (Weak) or E (Very Weak) ratings.

How to Use This Guide

The purpose of the *Guide to Property and Casualty Insurers* is to provide policyholders and prospective policy purchasers with a reliable source of insurance company ratings and analyses on a timely basis. We realize that the financial strength of an insurer is an important factor to consider when making the decision to purchase a policy or change companies. The ratings and analyses in this Guide can make that evaluation easier when you are considering:

- Homeowners insurance

- Business insurance

- Auto insurance

- Workers' compensation insurance

- Product liability insurance

- Medical malpractice and other professional liability insurance

This Guide does not include companies that strictly provide life and health insurance or annuities. For information on those companies, please refer to our *Guide to Life and Annuity Insurers*. Also, only a few of the property and casualty companies in this Guide provide any form of health insurance. For a complete listing of health insurance providers, please refer to our *Guide to Health Insurers*.

The rating for a particular company indicates our opinion regarding that company's ability to meet its commitments to the policyholder – not only under current economic conditions, but also during a declining economy or in the event of a sharp increase in claims. Such an increase in claims and related expenses may be triggered by any number of occurrences including a strong earthquake or hurricane, rising medical or legal costs, or large court awards. The safest companies, however, should be prepared to deal with harsh and unforeseen circumstances.

To use this Guide most effectively, we recommend you follow the steps outlined below:

Step 1 To ensure you evaluate the correct company, verify the company's exact name and state of domicile as it was given to you or appears on your policy. Many companies have similar names but are not related to one another, so you want to make sure the company you look up is really the one you are interested in evaluating.

Step 2 Turn to Section I, the Index of Companies, and locate the company you are evaluating. This section contains all companies analyzed by Weiss Ratings including those that did not receive a Safety Rating. It is sorted alphabetically by the name of the company and shows the state of domicile following the name for additional verification. Once you have located your specific company, the first column after the state of domicile shows its Weiss Safety Rating. Turn to *About Weiss Safety Ratings* for information about what this rating means. If the rating has changed since the last issue of this Guide, a downgrade will be indicated with a down triangle ▼ to the left of the company name; an upgrade will be indicated with an up triangle ▲.

Step 3   Following Weiss Safety Rating are some of the various indexes that our analysts used in rating the company. Refer to the Critical Ranges In Our Indexes table for an interpretation of which index values are considered strong, good, fair or weak. You can also turn to the introduction of Section I to see what each of these factors measures. In most cases, lower-rated companies will have a low index value in one or more of the factors shown. Bear in mind, however, that the Safety Rating is the result of a complex qualitative and quantitative analysis which cannot be reproduced using only the data provided here.

Step 4   Our analysts evaluate a great number of ratios and performance measures when assigning a rating. The right hand page of Section I shows you some of the key financial ratios we consider. Again, refer to the introduction of Section I for a description of each ratio.

Step 5   Some insurers have a bullet ● preceding the company name on the right hand page of Section I. This means that more detailed information about the company is available in Section II. If the company you are evaluating is identified with a bullet, turn to Section II, the Analysis of Largest Companies, and locate it there (otherwise skip to step 8). Section II contains the largest insurers rated by Weiss Ratings, regardless of rating. It too is sorted alphabetically by the name of the company.

Step 6   Once you have identified your company in Section II, you will find its Safety Rating and a description of the rating immediately to the right of the company name. Then, below the company name is a description of the various rating factors that were considered in assigning the company's rating. These factors and the information below them are designed to give you a better feel for the company and its strengths and weaknesses. See the Section II introduction to get a better understanding of what each of these factors means.

Step 7   To the right, you will find a five-year summary of the company's Safety Rating, capitialization and income. Look for positive or negative trends in these data. Below the five-year summary, we have included a graphic illustration of the most critical factor or factors impacting the company's rating. Again, the Section II introduction provides an overview of the content of each graph or table.

Step 8   If the company you are evaluating is not highly rated and you want to find an insurer with a higher rating, turn to the page in Section V that has your state's name at the top. This section contains those Recommended Companies (rating of A+, A, A- or B+) that are licensed to underwrite insurance in your state, sorted by rating. Then turn to the page in Section IV that shows the type of insurance you are interested in at the top. Insurers appearing on both lists will be those Recomended Companies which are licensed to sell that particular type of insurance in your state. From here you can select a company and then refer back to Sections I and II to analyze it.

Step 9   If you decide that you would like to contact one of Weiss Recommended Companies about obtaining a policy or for additional information, refer to Section III. Following each company's name is its address and phone number to assist you in making contact.

Step 10 In order to use Weiss Safety Ratings most effectively, we strongly recommend you consult the Important Warnings and Cautions listed. These are more than just "standard disclaimers"; they are very important factors you should be aware of before using this Guide. If you have any questions regarding the precise meaning of specific terms used in the Guide, refer to the Glossary.

Step 11 The Appendix contains information about State Guaranty Associations and the types of coverage they provide to policyholders when an insurance company fails. Keep in mind that while guaranty funds have now been established in all states, many do not cover all types of insurance. Furthermore, all of these funds have limits on their amount of coverage. Use the table to determine whether the level of coverage is applicable to your policy and the limits are adequate for your needs. You should pay particular attention to the notes regarding coverage limitations.

Step 12 If you want more information on your state's guaranty fund, call the State Commissioner's Office directly.

Step 13 Keep in mind that good coverage from a state guaranty association is no substitute for dealing with a financially strong company. Weiss Ratings only recommends those companies which we feel are most able to stand on their own, without regard to what might happen in case the company does fail.

Step 14 Make sure you stay up to date with the latest information available since the publication of this Guide. For information on how to set up a rating change notification service, acquire follow-up reports, or receive a more in-depth analysis of an individual company, call 1-877-934-7778 or visit www.weissratings.com.

Data Sources: Annual and quarterly statutory statements filed with state insurance commissioners and data provided by the insurance companies being rated. The National Association of Insurance Commissioners has provided some of the raw data. Any analyses or conclusions are not provided or endorsed by the NAIC.

Date of data analyzed June 30, 2016 unless otherwise noted.

About Weiss Safety Ratings

The Weiss Ratings of insurers are based upon the annual and quarterly financial statements obtained from state insurance commissioners. This data may be supplemented by information that we request from the insurance companies themselves. However, if a company chooses not to provide supplemental data, we reserve the right to rate the company based exclusively on publicly available data.

The Weiss Ratings are based on a complex analysis of hundreds of factors that are synthesized into a series of indexes: capitalization, investment safety (life, health and annuity companies only), reserve adequacy (property and casualty companies only), profitability, liquidity, and stability. These indexes are then used to arrive at a letter grade rating. A weak score on any one index can result in a low rating, as financial problems can be caused by any one of a number of factors, such as inadequate capital, unpredictable claims experience, poor liquidity, speculative investments, inadequate reserving, or consistent operating losses.

Our **Capital Index** gauges capital adequacy in terms of each insurer's ability to handle a variety of business and economic scenarios as they may impact investment performance, claims experience, persistency, and market position. The index combines two Risk-Adjusted Capital ratios as well as a leverage test that examines pricing risk.

Our **Investment Safety Index** measures the exposure of the company's investment portfolio to loss of principal and/or income due to default and market risks. Each investment area is rated by a factor that takes into consideration both quality and liquidity. (This factor is measured as a separate index only for life, health, and annuity insurers.)

Our **Reserve Adequacy Index** measures the adequacy of the company's reserves and its ability to accurately anticipate the level of claims it will receive. (This factor is measured as a separate index only for property and casualty insurers.)

Our **Profitability Index** measures the soundness of the company's operations and the contribution of profits to the company's financial strength. The profitability index is a composite of five sub-factors: 1) gain or loss on operations; 2) consistency of operating results; 3) impact of operating results on surplus; 4) adequacy of investment income as compared to the needs of policy reserves (life, health and annuity companies only); and 5) expenses in relation to industry norms for the types of policies that the company offers.

Our **Liquidity Index** evaluates a company's ability to raise the necessary cash to settle claims and honor cash withdrawal obligations. We model various cash flow scenarios, applying liquidity tests to determine how the company might fare in the event of an unexpected spike in claims and/or a run on policy surrenders.

Our **Stability Index** integrates a number of sub-factors that affect consistency (or lack thereof) in maintaining financial strength over time. These sub-factors will vary depending on the type of insurance company being evaluated but may include such things as 1) risk diversification in terms of company size, group size, number of policies in force, types of policies written, and use of reinsurance; 2) deterioration of operations as reported in critical asset, liability, income and expense items, such as surrender rates and premium volume; 3) years in operation; 4) former problem areas where, despite recent improvement, the company has yet to establish a record of stable performance over a suitable period of time; 5) a substantial shift in the company's operations; 6) potential instabilities such as reinsurance quality, asset/liability matching, and sources of capital; and 7) relationships with holding companies and affiliates.

In order to help guarantee our objectivity, we reserve the right to publish ratings expressing our opinion of a company's financial stability based exclusively on publicly available data and our own proprietary standards for safety.

Each of these indexes is measured according to the following range of values.

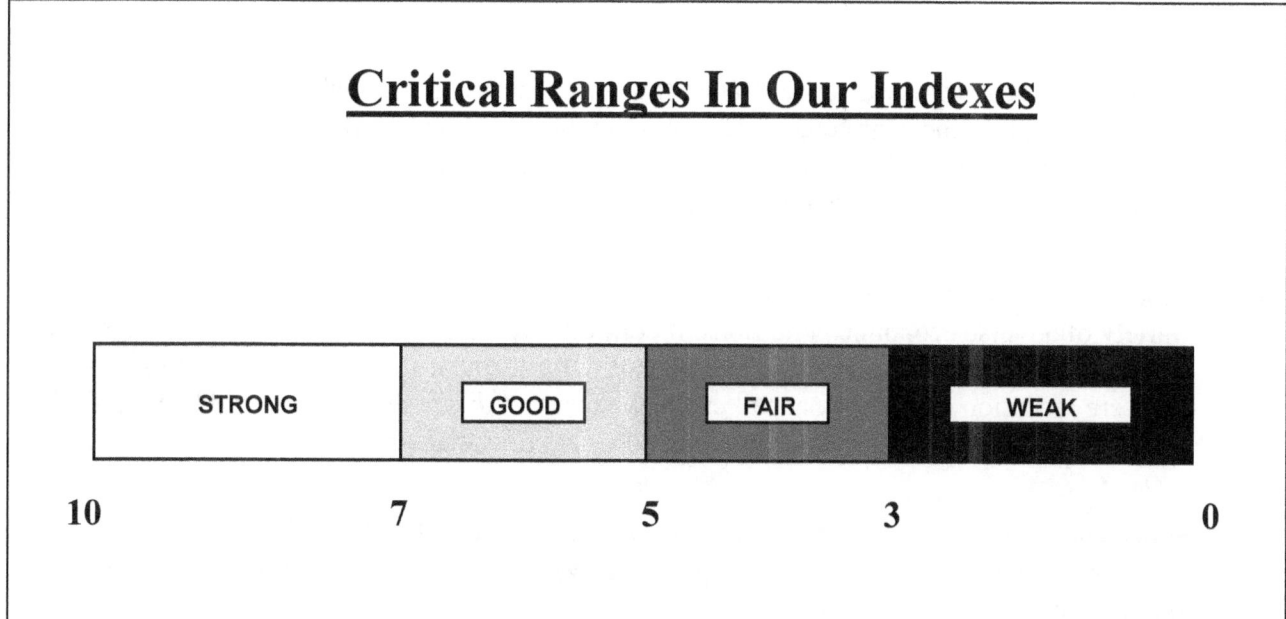

What Our Ratings Mean

A   **Excellent.** The company offers excellent financial security. It has maintained a conservative stance in its investment strategies, business operations and underwriting commitments. While the financial position of any company is subject to change, we believe that this company has the resources necessary to deal with severe economic conditions.

B   **Good.** The company offers good financial security and has the resources to deal with a variety of adverse economic conditions. It comfortably exceeds the minimum levels for all of our rating criteria, and is likely to remain healthy for the near future. However, in the event of a severe recession or major financial crisis, we feel that this assessment should be reviewed to make sure that the firm is still maintaining adequate financial strength.

C   **Fair.** The company offers fair financial security and is currently stable. But during an economic downturn or other financial pressures, we feel it may encounter difficulties in maintaining its financial stability.

D   **Weak.** The company currently demonstrates what, in our opinion, we consider to be significant weaknesses which could negatively impact policyholders. In an unfavorable economic environment, these weaknesses could be magnified.

E   **Very Weak.** The company currently demonstrates what we consider to be significant weaknesses and has also failed some of the basic tests that we use to identify fiscal stability. Therefore, even in a favorable economic environment, it is our opinion that policyholders could incur significant risks.

F   **Failed.** The company is deemed failed if it is either 1) under supervision of an insurance regulatory authority; 2) in the process of rehabilitation; 3) in the process of liquidation; or 4) voluntarily dissolved after disciplinary or other regulatory action by an insurance regulatory authority.

+   The **plus sign** is an indication that the company is in the upper third of the letter grade.

-      The **minus sign** is an indication that the company is in the lower third of the letter grade.

U   **Unrated.** The company is unrated for one or more of the following reasons: (1) total assets are less than $1 million; (2) premium income for the current year was less than $100,000; or (3) the company functions almost exclusively as a holding company rather than as an underwriter; or, (4) in our opinion, we do not have enough information to reliably issue a rating.

How Our Ratings Differ From Those of Other Services

Weiss Safety Ratings are conservative and consumer-oriented. We use tougher standards than other rating agencies because our system is specifically designed to inform risk-averse consumers about the safety strength of property and casualty insurers.

Our rating scale (A to F) is easy to understand by the general public. Users can intuitively understand that an A+ rating is at the top of the scale rather than in the middle like some of the other rating agencies.

Other rating agencies give top ratings more generously so that most companies receive excellent ratings.

More importantly, other rating agencies focus primarily on a company's *current* claims paying ability or consider only relatively mild economic adversity. We also consider these scenarios but extend our analyses to cover a company's ability to deal with severe economic adversity and potential liquidity problems. This stems from the viewpoint that an insurance company's obligations to its policyholders should not be contingent upon a healthy economy. The company must be capable of honoring its policy commitments in bad times as well.

Looking at the insurance industry as a whole, we note that several major rating firms have poor historical track records in identifying troubled companies. The 1980s saw a persistent decline in capital ratios, increased holdings of risky investments in the life and health industry as well as recurring long-term claims liabilities in the property and casualty industry. Despite these clear signs that insolvency risk was rising, other rating firms failed to downgrade at-risk insurance companies. Instead, they often rated companies by shades of excellence, understating the gravity of potential problems.

They have not issued clear warnings that the ordinary consumer can understand. Few, if any, companies receive "weak" or "poor" ratings. Surely, weak companies do exist. However, the other rating agencies apparently do not view themselves as consumer advocates with the responsibility of warning the public about the risks involved in doing business with such companies.

Additionally, these firms will at times agree *not* to issue a rating if a company denies them permission to do so. In short, too often insurance rating agencies work hand-in-glove with the companies they rate.

At Weiss Ratings, although we seek to maintain good relationships with the firms, we owe our primary obligation to the consumer, not the industry. We reserve the right to rate companies based on publicly available data and make the necessary conservative assumptions when companies choose not to provide the additional data we request.

Comparison of Insurance Company Rating Agency Scales

Weiss Ratings [a]	Best [a,b]	S&P [c]	Moody's	Fitch [d]
A+, A, A-	A++, A+	AAA	Aaa	AAA
B+, B, B-	A, A-	AA+, AA AA-	Aa1, Aa2, Aa3	AA+, AA, AA-
C+, C, C-	B++, B+,	A+, A, A-, BBB+, BBB, BBB-	A1, A2, A3, Baa1, Baa2, Baa3	A+, A, A-, BBB+, BBB, BBB-
D+, D, D-	B, B- C++, C+, C, C-	BB+, BB, BB-, B+, B, B-	Ba1, Ba2, Ba3, B1, B2, B3	BB+, BB, BB-, B+, B, B-
E+, E, E- F	D E, F	CCC R	Caa, Ca, C	CCC+, CCC, CCC- DD

[a] Weiss Ratings and Best use additional symbols to designate that they recognize an insurer's existence but do not provide a rating. These symbols are not included in this table.

[b] Best added the A++, B++ and C++ ratings in 1992. In 1994, Best classified its ratings into "secure" and "vulnerable" categories, changed the definition of its "B" and "B-" ratings from "good" to "adequate" and assigned these ratings to the "vulnerable" category. This table contains GAO's assignment of Best's ratings to bands based on our interpretation of their rating descriptions prior to 1994.

[c] S&P discontinued CCC "+" and "-" signs, CC, C and D ratings and added the R rating in 1992.
Source: 1994 GAO *Insurance Ratings* study.

[d] Duff & Phelps Credit Rating Co. merged with Fitch IBCA in 2000, and minor changes were made to the rating scale at that time. These changes were not reflected in the GAO's 1994 study, but *are* reflected in the chart.

Rate of Insurance Company Failures

Weiss Ratings provides quarterly Safety Ratings for thousands of insurance companies each year. Weiss Ratings strives for fairness and objectivity in its ratings and analyses, ensuring that each company receives the rating that most accurately depicts its current financial status, and more importantly, its ability to deal with severe economic adversity and a sharp increase in claims. Weiss Ratings has every confidence that its Safety Ratings provide an accurate representation of a company's stability.

In order for these ratings to be of any true value, it is important that they prove accurate over time. One way to determine the accuracy of a rating is to examine those insurance companies that have failed, and their respective Weiss Safety Ratings. A high percentage of failed companies with "A" ratings would indicate that Weiss Ratings is not being conservative enough with its "secure" ratings, while conversely, a low percentage of failures with "vulnerable" ratings would show that Weiss Ratings is overly conservative.

Over the past 27 years (1989–2015) Weiss Ratings has rated 615 insurance companies, for all industries, that subsequently failed. The chart below shows the number of failed companies in each rating category, the average number of companies rated in each category per year, and the percentage of annual failures for each letter grade.

	Safety Rating	Number of Failed Companies	Average Number of Companies Rated per year	Percentage of Failed Companies per year (by ratings category)*
Secure	A	1	155	0.02%
	B	6	1,102	0.02%
	C	69	1,615	0.16%
Vulnerable	D	268	756	1.31%
	E	271	217	4.62%

A=Excellent, B=Good, C=Fair, D=Weak, E=Very Weak

On average, only 0.10% of the companies Weiss Ratings rates as "secure" fail each year. On the other hand, an average of 2.05% of the companies Weiss Ratings rates as "vulnerable" fail annually. That means that a company rated by Weiss Ratings as "Vulnerable" is 20.9 times more likely to fail than a company rated as "Secure".

When considering a Weiss Safety Rating, one can be sure that they are getting the most fair, objective, and accurate safety rating available anywhere.

*Percentage of Failed Companies per year = (Number of Failed Companies) / [(Average Number of Companies Rated per year) x (years in study)]

Data as of December 2015 for Life and Annuity Insurers and Property, Casualty Insurers and Health Insurers

What Does Average Mean?

At Weiss Ratings, we consider the words average and fair to mean just that – average and fair. So when we assign our ratings to insurers, the largest percentage of companies receives an average C rating. That way, you can be sure that a company receiving Weiss B or A rating is truly above average. Likewise, you can feel confident that companies with D or E ratings are truly below average.

Percentage for Property and Casualty Insurers in Each Rating Category

Current Weiss Ratings Distribution

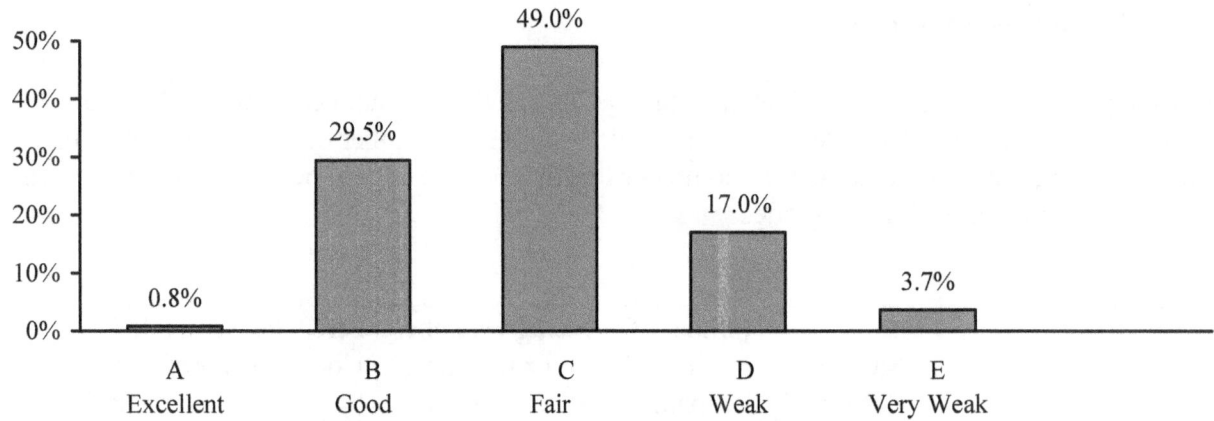

Important Warnings and Cautions

1.   A rating alone cannot tell the whole story. Please read the explanatory information contained in this publication. It is provided in order to give you an understanding of our rating philosophy, as well as paint a more complete picture of how we arrive at our opinion of a company's strengths and weaknesses.

2.   Weiss Safety Ratings represent our opinion of a company's insolvency risk. As such, a high rating means we feel that the company has less chance of running into financial difficulties. A high rating is not a guarantee of solvency nor is a low rating a prediction of insolvency. Weiss Safety Ratings are not deemed to be a recommendation concerning the purchase or sale of the securities of any insurance company that is publicly owned.

3.   Company performance is only one factor in determining a rating. Conditions in the marketplace and overall economic conditions are additional factors that may affect the company's financial strength. Therefore, a rating upgrade or downgrade does not necessarily reflect changes in the company's profits, capital or other financial measures, but may be due to external factors. Likewise, changes in Weiss indexes may reflect changes in our risk assessment of business or economic conditions as well as changes in company performance.

4.   All firms that have the same Safety Rating should be considered to be essentially equal in strength. This is true regardless of any differences in the underlying numbers which might appear to indicate greater strengths. Weiss Safety Rating already takes into account a number of lesser factors which, due to space limitations, cannot be included in this publication.

5.   A good rating requires consistency. If a company is excellent on four indicators and fair on one, the company may receive a fair rating. This requirement is necessary due to the fact that fiscal problems can arise from any *one* of several causes including speculative investments, inadequate capital resources or operating losses.

6.   We are an independent rating agency and do not depend on the cooperation of the companies we rate. Our data are derived, for the most part, from annual and quarterly financial statements that we obtain from federal banking regulators and state insurance commissioners. The latter may be supplemented by information insurance companies voluntarily provide upon request. Although we seek to maintain an open line of communication with the companies, we do not grant them the right to stop or influence publication of the ratings. This policy stems from the fact that this publication is designed for the protection of the consumer.

7.   Affiliated companies do not automatically receive the same rating. We recognize that a troubled company may expect financial support from its parent or affiliates. Weiss Safety Ratings reflect our opinion of the measure of support that may become available to a subsidiary, if the subsidiary were to experience serious financial difficulties. In the case of a strong parent and a weaker subsidiary, the affiliate relationship will generally result in a higher rating for the subsidiary than it would have on a stand-alone basis. Seldom, however, would the rating be brought up to the level of the parent. This treatment is appropriate because we do not assume the parent would have either the resources or the will to "bail out" a troubled subsidiary during a severe economic crisis. Even when there is a binding legal obligation for a parent corporation to honor the policy obligations of its subsidiaries, the possibility exists that the subsidiary could be sold and lose its parental support. Therefore, it is quite common for one affiliate to have a higher rating than another. This is another reason why it is especially important that you have the precise name of the company you are evaluating.

Section I

Index of Companies

An analysis of all rated and unrated

U.S. Property and Casualty Insurers.

Companies are listed in alphabetical order.

Section I Contents

This section contains the key rating factors and performance measures for all rated and unrated insurers analyzed by Weiss Ratings. An explanation of each of the footnotes and stability factors appears at the end of this section.

Left Pages

1. **Insurance Company Name**   The legally registered name, which can sometimes differ from the name that the company uses for advertising. If you cannot find the company you are interested in, or if you have any doubts regarding the precise name, verify the information with the company before looking the name up in this Guide. Also, determine the domicile state for confirmation. (See column 2.)

2. **Domicile State**   The state which has primary regulatory responsibility for the company. It may differ from the location of the company's corporate headquarters. You do not have to be living in the domicile state to purchase insurance from this firm, provided it is licensed to do business in your state.

3. **Safety Rating**   Our rating is measured on a scale from A to F and considers a wide range of factors. Please see *What Our Ratings Mean* for specific descriptions of each letter grade. Also, refer to how our ratings differ from those of other rating agencies. Most important, when using this rating, please be sure to consider the warnings regarding the ratings' limitations and the underlying assumptions. Notes in this column refer to the date of the data included in the rating evaluation and are explained.

4. **Total Assets**   All assets admitted by state insurance regulators in millions of dollars through the most recent quarter available. This includes investments and current business assets such as receivables from agents and reinsurers.

    The overall size is an important factor which affects the ability of a company to manage risk. Generally speaking, risks can be more effectively diversified by large companies. Because the insurance business is based on probability, the number of policies must be large enough so that actuarial statistics are valid. The larger the number of policyholders, the more reliable the actuarial projections will be. A large company with a correspondingly large policy base can spread its risk and minimize the effects of claims experience that exceeds actuarial expectations.

5. **Capital and Surplus**   The company's statutory net worth in millions of dollars through the most recent quarter available. Consumers may wish to limit the size of any policy so that the policyholder's maximum potential claims do not exceed approximately 1% of the company's capital and surplus. For example, when buying a policy from a company with capital and surplus of $10,000,000, the 1% limit would be $100,000. (When performing this

calculation, do not forget that figures in this column are expressed in millions of dollars.)

6. Net Premium   The amount of insurance premiums received from policyholders less any premiums that have been transferred to other companies through reinsurance agreements. This figure is updated through the most recent annual report available.

Generally speaking, companies with large net premium volume generally have more predictable claims experience.

Critical Ranges In Our Indexes and Ratios

Indicators	Strong	Good	Fair	Weak
Risk-Adjusted Capital Ratio #1	—	1.0 or more	0.75 - 0.99	0.74 or less
Risk-Adjusted Capital Ratio #2	1.0 or more	0.75 - 0.99	0.5 - 0.74	0.49 or less
Capitalization Index	6.9 – 10	4.9 - 6.8	2.9 - 4.8	Less than 2.9
Reserve Adequacy Index	6.9 – 10	4.9 - 6.8	2.9 - 4.8	Less than 2.9
Profitability Index	6.9 – 10	4.9 - 6.8	2.9 - 4.8	Less than 2.9
Liquidity Index	6.9 – 10	4.9 - 6.8	2.9 - 4.8	Less than 2.9
Stability Index	6.9 – 10	4.9 - 6.8	2.9 - 4.8	Less than 2.9

---

7. Net Income   The company's profit for the period. Profit is defined as revenues minus expenses. In the case of an insurance company, revenues include premiums and investment income, and expenses include claims payments and underwriting expenses.

8. Capitalization Index   An index that measures the adequacy of the company's capital resources to deal with a variety of business and economic scenarios. It combines Risk-Adjusted Capital Ratios #1 and #2 as well as a leverage test that examines pricing risk. (See the table above for the ranges which we believe are critical.)

9. **Reserve Adequacy Index**

An index that uses annual and quarterly data to measure the adequacy of the company's reserves. Reserves are funds the company sets aside to cover unsettled claims it estimates each year. Included are claims that the company has already received but have not yet been settled and claims that they expect to receive, but which have not yet been reported.

If a company consistently estimates its claims accurately, that is good. Or if it errs on the side of being conservative and overestimates its claims from time to time, that is even better. Either case will cause this index to move higher.

On the other hand, some companies may have trouble accurately predicting the claims they will have to pay. Others may intentionally underestimate their claims to inflate their profits for stockholders or to make their capital appear higher than it really is. In either case, inadequate reserve levels will result in a low Reserve Adequacy Index.

If a company has chronically deficient reserves, it calls into question the company's ability to manage its policy risk effectively.

10. **Profitability Index**

An index that uses annual and quarterly data to measure the soundness of the company's operations and the contribution of profits to the company's fiscal strength. The Profitability Index is a composite of five factors: (1) gain or loss on underwriting; (2) gain or loss on overall operations; (3) consistency of operating results; (4) impact of operating results on surplus; and (5) expenses in relation to industry averages for the types of policies that the company offers.

11. **Liquidity Index**

An index which uses annual and quarterly data to measure the company's ability to raise the necessary cash to settle claims. Sometimes a company may appear to have the necessary resources to pay claims on paper, but in reality, it may be unable to raise the necessary cash. This can occur, for example, when a company is owed a great deal of money from its agents or reinsurers, or when it cannot sell its investments at the prices at which they are valued in the company's financial statements.

We look at various cash flow scenarios. Then we apply liquidity tests which tell us how the company might fare in each of those circumstances.

12. **Stability Index**

An index which uses annual and quarterly data to integrate a number of factors such as: (1) risk diversification in terms of company size, number of policies in force, use of reinsurance, and single largest risk exposure; (2) deterioration of operations as reported in critical asset, liability, income, or expense items such as premium volume and/or surplus (See the table prior page for the levels which we believe are critical.)

13. **Stability Factors**

Indicates those specific areas that have negatively impacted the company's Stability Index.

Right Pages

1. Risk-Adjusted Capital Ratio #1

This ratio examines the adequacy of the company's capital base and whether the company has sufficient capital resources to cover potential losses which might occur in an average recession or other moderate loss scenario. Specifically, the figure, calculated from annual and quarterly data, answers the question: For every dollar of capital that we feel would be needed, how many dollars in capital resources does the company actually have?

You may find that some companies have unusually high levels of capital. This often reflects special circumstances related to the small size or unusual operations of the company.

See the table prior page for the levels which we believe are critical. See the Appendix for more details on how this ratio is calculated.

2. Risk-Adjusted Capital Ratio #2

This is similar to the Risk-Adjusted Capital Ratio #1. But in this case, the question relates to whether the company has enough capital cushion to withstand a *severe* recession or other severe loss scenario.

See the table prior page for the levels which we believe are critical. See the Appendix for more details on how this ratio is calculated.

3. Premium to Surplus

The ratio of net premiums written compared to the company's capital and surplus level. This ratio, calculated from the company's annual report, answers the question: For every dollar of capital and surplus, how many dollars of premium does the company take in? Results of over 300% are considered perilous and could indicate that the insurer does not have adequate capital to support the volume of business that it is underwriting. A large figure could also help explain why a company has poor results on its risk-adjusted capital tests.

4. Reserves to Surplus

The ratio of reserves for expected claims compared to the company's capital and surplus level. If a company does not set aside enough reserves, it may have to withdraw capital to pay claims. This ratio, calculated from the annual report, is a rough measure of how much capital cushion the company has against claims reserves. The industry average is around 180%.

High ratios signify that reserve deficiencies would have a strong impact on capital and could help explain why a company has poor risk-adjusted capital results.

5. One-Year Reserve Development

The percentage increase or decrease in the company's annual reserve estimate compared to the previous year. If last year's estimate is below that of this year, this will result in a positive ratio meaning that the company underestimated its future claims and set aside insufficient reserves. Making this error consistently is viewed negatively because it means the company is inflating its income and capital.

6. Two-Year Reserve Development

This ratio is similar to the One-Year Reserve Development ratio. However, instead of comparing the latest estimates with those from the prior year, it compares them to the estimates from two years ago.

Again, a positive ratio means the company underestimated its reserve needs while a negative ratio indicates that reserve needs were overestimated.

7. Loss Ratio

The ratio of claims paid to premiums collected, calculated from the annual report, measures the company's underwriting profits. Needless to say, if an insurer pays out a very high percentage of what it collects, there may not be enough left over for other expenses, let alone enough to build the company's capital and financial strength over time.

8. Expense Ratio

The ratio of overhead expenses to premiums collected, calculated from the annual report, and answers the question: How many cents is the company paying out in executive salaries, agents' commissions, and other administrative expenses for every dollar in premiums that it collects from policyholders? A low Expense Ratio is good for both the company and its policyholders because it means that the company is efficient and can utilize more of each premium dollar to pay claims. A high Expense Ratio is a bad sign because it signals that too much of the company's premiums are being used for things which do not directly benefit its policyholders.

9. Combined Ratio

The sum of the Loss Ratio and the Expense Ratio. The Combined Ratio shows how much the company is paying out in administrative expenses and claims for every dollar of premium collected.

Values over 100% indicate that the company is losing money on its underwriting. This is very common in the industry, but it's still a sign of possible weakness.

Underwriting losses can often be offset by income the company realizes on its investments. This is especially true for companies that issue policies on which they do not have to pay claims for several years (long-tail policies). With these policies, the premiums can be invested in order to earn income for the company until the claims are paid.

10. Cash from Underwriting

The ratio of cash received from premiums (net of reinsurance) to cash outlays for claims and underwriting expenses, compiled from the annual report. A figure under 100% indicates that the company is paying out more in claims and expenses than it is receiving in premiums, whereas a figure over 100% indicates a positive cash flow. A negative figure generally indicates that the company has sold more business to a reinsurance company than it has taken in during the current year.

When a company has a positive net cash flow from its underwriting, it can generate additional funds for investing. On the other hand, if net cash flow is negative, the company may have to rely on its investment income to make up the shortfall. And if that isn't enough, it may even have to sell assets to meet its obligations.

11. Net Premium Growth

The annual percentage change in net premiums compared to the previous year. A company can increase its premium volume by: (1) issuing more new policies; (2) raising its rates; or (3) selling less of its insurance to other insurance companies. Slow and steady growth is healthy but rapid growth is often an indicator of trouble ahead. It may mean that the company is underpricing as a means of gaining market share. Indeed, a high percentage of insurance company failures are related to rapid growth. Regulators consider a fluctuation of more than 33% as a cautionary flag.

A rapid decline in premium volume is also a negative sign. It indicates that the company is losing its customer base. However, if the decline is the result of premium redistribution among a group of affiliates, the significance of the decline is minimal.

12. Investments In Affiliates

The percentage of the company's investment portfolio from the annual report dedicated to investments in affiliates. These investments can be bonds, preferred and common stocks, as well as other vehicles which many insurance companies use to invest in – and establish a corporate link with – affiliated companies. Large investments of this type can pose problems as these investments often produce no income and can be difficult to sell.

Footnotes:

(1)   Data items shown are from the company's 2015 annual statutory statement except for Risk-Adjusted Capital Indexes 1 and 2, Profitability Index, Investment Safety Index, Liquidity Index and Stability Index which have been updated using the company's March 2016 quarterly statutory statement. Other more recent data may have been factored into the rating when available.

(2)   Data items shown are from the company's 2015 annual statutory statement. Other more recent data may have been factored into the rating when available.

(3)   Data items shown are from the company's 2014 annual statutory statement except for Risk-Adjusted Capital Indexes 1 and 2, Profitability Index, Investment Safety Index, Liquidity Index and Stability Index which have been updated using the company's September 2015 quarterly statutory statement. Other more recent data may have been factored into the rating when available.

(4)   Data items shown are from the company's 2014 annual statutory statement except for Risk-Adjusted Capital Indexes 1 and 2, Profitability Index, Investment Safety Index, Liquidity Index and Stability Index which have been updated using the company's June 2015 quarterly statutory statement. Other more recent data may have been factored into the rating when available.

(5)   These companies have data items that are older than March 31, 2015. They will be unrated (U) if they are not failed companies (F).

Stability Factors

(A)   Stability Index was negatively impacted by the financial problems or weaknesses of a parent or **affiliate** company.

(C)   Stability Index was negatively impacted by past results on our Risk-Adjusted **Capital** tests. In general, the Stability Index of any company can be affected by past results even if current results show improvement. While such improvement is a plus, the improved results must be maintained for a period of time to assure that the improvement is not a temporary fluctuation. During a five-year period, the impact of poor past results on the Stability Index gradually diminishes.

(D)   Stability Index was negatively impacted by limited **diversification** of general business, policy, and/or investment risk. This factor especially affects smaller companies that do not issue as many policies as larger firms. It can also affect firms that specialize in only one line of business.

(E)   Stability Index was negatively impacted due to a lack of operating **experience**. The company has been in operation for less than five years. Consequently, it has not been able to establish the kind of stable track record that we believe is needed to demonstrate financial permanence and strength.

(F)   Stability Index was negatively impacted by negative cash **flow**. In other words, the company paid out more in claims and expenses than it received in premiums and investment income.

(G)   Stability Index was negatively impacted by fast asset or premium **growth**. Fast growth can pose a serious problem for insurers. It is generally achieved by offering policies with premiums that are too low, benefits that are too costly, or agents commissions that are too high. Due to the highly competitive nature of the insurance marketplace, rapid growth has been a factor in many insurance insolvencies.

(L)   Stability Index was negatively impacted by results on our **liquidity** tests. While the company may have sufficient cash flow to meet its current obligations, it could encounter difficulties under adverse scenarios, such as a dramatic increase in claims.

(O)   Stability Index was negatively impacted by significant changes in the company's business **operations**. These changes can include shifts in the kinds of insurance offered by the company, a temporary or permanent freeze on the sale of new policies, or recent release from conservatorship. In these circumstances, past performance cannot be a reliable indicator of future financial strength.

(R)   Stability Index was negatively impacted by concerns about the financial strength of its **reinsurers**.

(T)   Stability Index was negatively impacted by significant **trends** in critical asset, liability, income or expense items. Examples include fluctuations in premium volume, changes in the types of investments the company makes, and changes in the types of policies the company writes.

(Z)   This company is unrated due to data, as received by Weiss Ratings, that are either incomplete in substantial ways or contains items that, in the opinion of Weiss Ratings analysts, may not be reliable.

INSURANCE COMPANY NAME	DOM. STATE	RATING		TOTAL ASSETS ($MIL)	CAPITAL & SURPLUS ($MIL)	ANNUAL NET PREMIUM ($MIL)	NET INCOME ($MIL)	CAPITAL-IZATION INDEX (PTS)	RESERVE ADQ INDEX (PTS)	PROFIT-ABILITY INDEX (PTS)	LIQUIDITY INDEX (PTS)	STAB. INDEX (PTS)	STABILITY FACTORS
1ST ATLANTIC SURETY CO	NC	D+		3.8	2.1	1.1	0.1	7.5	3.6	2.5	9.2	1.7	DGT
1ST AUTO & CASUALTY INS CO	WI	C		29.3	11.8	21.1	-0.1	7.3	6.7	3.5	5.5	3.0	DFGR
1ST CHOICE AUTO INS CO	PA	C+		20.1	8.3	11.7	0.0	7.7	6.3	3.8	5.7	3.0	DGRT
21ST CENTURY ADVANTAGE INS CO	MN	B		29.3	29.1	0.0	0.2	10.0	6.0	6.6	10.0	4.2	GT
21ST CENTURY ASR CO	DE	B		70.1	69.5	0.0	0.3	10.0	5.0	6.5	10.0	4.3	T
21ST CENTURY AUTO INS CO OF NJ	NJ	U		25.5	25.1	0.0	0.0	N/A	6.0	5.6	10.0	5.7	FGT
21ST CENTURY CASUALTY CO	CA	B		12.4	12.0	0.0	0.0	10.0	5.0	5.6	10.0	4.3	DGT
21ST CENTURY CENTENNIAL INS CO	PA	B		587.9	582.5	0.0	2.4	8.3	6.0	6.9	8.9	4.8	T
21ST CENTURY INDEMNITY INS CO	PA	B		67.2	66.6	0.0	0.8	10.0	6.0	6.9	10.0	4.1	T
21ST CENTURY INS CO	CA	B		940.0	921.9	0.0	19.0	10.0	5.0	6.0	10.0	4.9	T
21ST CENTURY INS CO OF THE SW	TX	U		6.1	6.1	0.0	0.7	N/A	N/A	6.2	10.0	4.6	GT
21ST CENTURY NATIONAL INS CO INC	NY	B		24.5	24.2	0.0	0.1	10.0	6.0	6.0	9.7	4.1	DFGT
21ST CENTURY NORTH AMERICA INS	NY	B		577.2	560.4	0.0	3.5	10.0	6.0	6.7	10.0	4.7	RT
21ST CENTURY PACIFIC INS	CO	B		44.5	43.9	0.0	0.1	10.0	6.0	6.0	10.0	4.2	DT
21ST CENTURY PINNACLE INS CO	NJ	B		42.9	42.2	0.0	0.2	10.0	6.0	6.0	10.0	4.2	DT
21ST CENTURY PREFERRED INS CO	PA	B		41.9	41.4	0.0	0.3	10.0	6.0	6.4	10.0	4.0	DT
21ST CENTURY PREMIER INS CO	PA	B-		281.7	279.8	0.0	2.2	10.0	6.0	6.9	10.0	4.6	T
21ST CENTURY SECURITY INS CO	PA	B		198.7	196.5	0.0	0.8	10.0	6.0	6.3	10.0	4.6	DT
21ST CENTURY SUPERIOR INS CO	CA	U		30.8	30.5	0.0	0.1	N/A	6.0	6.6	10.0	5.7	GT
360 INS CO	WY	B-		27.3	23.8	2.5	0.3	10.0	5.4	6.6	10.0	3.8	DGOT
7710 INS CO	SC	U		9.3	7.1	0.5	-0.2	N/A	N/A	3.3	7.0	3.7	DFGT
A CENTRAL INS CO	NY	D	(1)	104.9	39.0	46.9	0.2	8.5	7.3	2.9	6.5	2.0	T
A-ONE COMM INS RRG GROUP INC	TN	D		11.0	3.2	7.7	0.2	0.7	3.6	4.0	6.7	2.0	CDGT
ACA FINANCIAL GUARANTY CORP	MD	U		316.4	21.8	0.1	-19.6	N/A	4.3	0.4	9.2	0.0	FT
ACADEMIC HLTH PROFESSIONALS INS	NY	E-		312.0	-77.7	71.6	-3.6	0.0	4.1	0.9	7.0	0.0	CDRT
ACADEMIC MEDICAL PROFESSIONALS RRG	VT	E		4.2	2.8	0.6	0.1	7.1	5.7	6.1	9.3	0.0	DGT
ACADIA INS CO	NH	C		167.0	52.7	0.0	0.3	10.0	N/A	6.1	6.9	4.0	FT
ACCC INS CO	TX	D		315.4	55.2	333.0	-2.8	1.6	4.3	3.6	0.0	2.3	CLT
ACCEPTANCE CASUALTY INS CO	NE	D		73.6	51.7	11.7	1.6	7.7	5.9	5.6	7.3	2.1	DRT
ACCEPTANCE INDEMNITY INS CO	NE	C-		269.7	128.1	66.4	5.7	7.0	4.6	4.4	6.4	2.7	RT
ACCEPTANCE INS CO	NE	F		15.0	2.6	0.0	-0.6	3.2	0.1	0.1	10.0	0.0	DFGR
ACCESS HOME INS CO	LA	C-		44.8	11.4	15.5	0.5	4.6	5.8	7.2	7.8	2.4	DGT
ACCESS INS CO	TX	C		181.7	31.3	55.2	0.1	4.8	2.5	4.2	6.3	3.2	RT
ACCIDENT FUND GENERAL INS CO	MI	B		264.2	68.0	42.5	2.5	7.9	3.9	8.4	6.3	4.1	GRT
ACCIDENT FUND INS CO OF AMERICA	MI	B-		3,099.4	872.7	812.6	42.8	7.0	3.7	7.2	6.9	4.6	RT
ACCIDENT FUND NATIONAL INS CO	MI	B		271.3	76.4	63.7	5.9	7.8	3.8	6.9	6.7	4.2	RT
ACCIDENT INS CO	SC	E		119.0	8.5	31.5	-6.8	0.0	0.5	1.7	5.4	0.1	CDFR
ACCREDITED SURETY & CAS CO INC	FL	C		26.3	22.2	9.3	0.5	8.8	6.1	8.7	7.7	2.6	DGRT
ACE AMERICAN INS CO	PA	B-		12,643.3	2,758.5	1,760.5	82.8	7.1	7.7	6.6	6.7	4.0	RT
ACE FIRE UNDERWRITERS INS CO	PA	C		115.2	75.9	9.5	0.9	10.0	4.6	7.1	7.4	3.9	RT
ACE INS CO OF THE MIDWEST	IN	C		97.8	66.1	5.0	0.8	10.0	5.0	7.9	7.4	3.9	T
ACE P&C INS CO	PA	B-		8,959.9	2,051.1	1,665.3	84.6	8.2	7.8	7.8	6.9	3.8	RT
ACIG INS CO	IL	D+		474.3	128.2	93.0	7.3	6.7	6.9	6.7	6.8	2.2	RT
ACSTAR INS CO	IL	C+		61.0	28.1	1.7	1.1	8.8	8.6	3.8	9.7	3.3	DRT
ACUITY A MUTUAL INS CO	WI	B+		3,483.6	1,521.1	1,269.9	81.1	9.2	9.3	8.9	6.7	5.1	T
ADDISON INS CO	IA	C+		116.8	45.5	35.5	0.9	8.5	8.8	7.7	6.9	3.9	T
ADIRONDACK INS EXCHANGE	NY	C-		252.9	82.1	89.8	8.7	7.3	6.9	4.2	5.4	3.3	RT
ADM INS CO	AZ	C		222.3	23.4	0.0	0.2	8.0	4.1	5.7	7.0	3.6	T
ADMIRAL INDEMNITY CO	DE	C		61.3	41.3	0.0	0.5	10.0	3.8	8.0	7.0	3.9	RT
ADMIRAL INS CO	DE	C		732.7	641.9	0.0	4.1	8.4	3.8	3.4	10.0	3.9	ART
ADRIATIC INS CO	ND	C		84.0	66.9	24.2	2.5	10.0	7.7	8.3	8.5	3.5	DGRT
ADVANCED PHYSICIANS INS RRG INC	AZ	D		1.6	1.4	0.2	0.1	10.0	3.9	3.1	8.1	1.2	DGT

See Page 27 for explanation of footnotes and   30   www.weissratings.com
Page 28 for explanation of stability factors.
Arrows denote recent upgrades ▲ or downgrades ▼   (see Section VII for explanations)

RISK ADJ. RATIO #1	CAPITAL RATIO #2	PREMIUM TO SURPLUS (%)	RESV. TO SURPLUS (%)	RESV. DEVELOP. 1 YEAR (%)	2 YEAR (%)	LOSS RATIO (%)	EXP. RATIO (%)	COMB RATIO (%)	CASH FROM UNDER-WRITING (%)	NET PREMIUM GROWTH (%)	INVEST. IN AFFIL (%)	INSURANCE COMPANY NAME
1.7	1.4	54.7	6.8	10.0	-0.1	31.2	69.1	100.3	142.1	50.6	0.0	1ST ATLANTIC SURETY CO
1.5	1.1	177.2	78.5	0.1	-2.9	66.6	33.6	100.2	93.7	0.9	0.0	1ST AUTO & CASUALTY INS CO
2.0	1.4	148.7	40.8	0.9	3.7	80.1	25.4	105.5	101.5	13.8	0.0	1ST CHOICE AUTO INS CO
171.1	86.2	N/A	1.0	-0.2	0.1	N/A	N/A	N/A	13.9	0.0	0.0	21ST CENTURY ADVANTAGE INS CO
241.2	121.7	N/A	0.8	-0.2	0.1	N/A	N/A	N/A	N/A	0.0	0.0	21ST CENTURY ASR CO
N/A	N/A	N/A	1.7	-0.3	0.2	N/A	N/A	N/A	N/A	0.0	0.0	21ST CENTURY AUTO INS CO OF NJ
73.0	65.7	N/A	0.6	-0.1	0.1	N/A	N/A	N/A	N/A	0.0	0.0	21ST CENTURY CASUALTY CO
1.8	1.8	N/A	1.0	-0.2	0.1	N/A	N/A	N/A	-3.4	0.0	59.5 ●	21ST CENTURY CENTENNIAL INS CO
229.2	115.6	N/A	0.9	-0.2	0.1	N/A	N/A	N/A	N/A	0.0	0.0	21ST CENTURY INDEMNITY INS CO
101.4	46.0	N/A	0.6	-0.1	0.1	N/A	N/A	N/A	N/A	0.0	0.0 ●	21ST CENTURY INS CO
N/A	N/A	N/A	N/A	N/A	N/A	N/A	N/A	N/A	N/A	0.0	0.0	21ST CENTURY INS CO OF THE SW
160.7	96.4	N/A	1.2	-0.2	0.1	N/A	N/A	N/A	N/A	0.0	0.0	21ST CENTURY NATIONAL INS CO INC
5.9	5.7	N/A	1.2	-0.2	0.1	N/A	N/A	N/A	N/A	0.0	17.8 ●	21ST CENTURY NORTH AMERICA INS
181.4	113.3	N/A	1.3	-0.2	0.2	N/A	N/A	N/A	N/A	0.0	0.0	21ST CENTURY PACIFIC INS
141.5	93.3	N/A	1.2	-0.2	0.1	N/A	N/A	N/A	N/A	0.0	0.0	21ST CENTURY PINNACLE INS CO
158.5	80.3	N/A	1.4	-0.3	0.2	N/A	N/A	N/A	N/A	0.0	0.0	21ST CENTURY PREFERRED INS CO
4.5	4.4	N/A	1.0	-0.2	0.1	N/A	N/A	N/A	-3.1	0.0	24.1 ●	21ST CENTURY PREMIER INS CO
8.7	8.5	N/A	1.2	-0.2	0.1	N/A	N/A	N/A	N/A	0.0	12.2 ●	21ST CENTURY SECURITY INS CO
N/A	N/A	N/A	0.9	-0.2	0.1	N/A	N/A	N/A	N/A	0.0	0.0	21ST CENTURY SUPERIOR INS CO
14.6	10.6	10.8	3.9	0.1	-0.4	98.3	12.8	111.1	14.9	263.1	0.0	360 INS CO
N/A	N/A	6.8	1.3	N/A	N/A	60.9	58.6	119.5	-88.8	0.0	0.0	7710 INS CO
3.0	2.3	121.1	74.9	-1.5	-0.2	67.1	31.7	98.8	104.9	0.4	0.0	A CENTRAL INS CO
0.2	0.1	265.8	101.3	1.8	N/A	74.0	17.3	91.3	483.9	N/A	0.0	A-ONE COMM INS RRG GROUP INC
N/A	N/A	0.2	278.9	-4.4	13.7	266.9	999 +	999 +	0.1	0.8	0.0	ACA FINANCIAL GUARANTY CORP
-0.1	-0.1	-92.6	-444.4	38.4	-627.9	100.1	-1.5	98.6	127.8	17.4	-0.3	ACADEMIC HLTH PROFESSIONALS INS
1.6	1.0	21.3	23.0	-4.6	-3.2	30.2	36.2	66.4	186.1	49.8	0.0	ACADEMIC MEDICAL PROFESSIONALS
5.7	5.1	N/A	N/A	N/A	N/A	N/A	N/A	N/A	90.2	0.0	0.0	ACADIA INS CO
0.3	0.3	577.3	281.5	30.7	26.3	89.0	17.2	106.2	97.0	5.3	0.0	ACCC INS CO
2.5	1.5	23.2	24.1	2.3	4.9	70.6	31.2	101.8	112.7	2.5	0.0	ACCEPTANCE CASUALTY INS CO
1.3	1.0	53.6	50.7	3.8	7.6	74.1	31.2	105.3	114.1	3.9	21.6	ACCEPTANCE INDEMNITY INS CO
0.9	0.3	N/A	304.4	28.9	109.7	N/A	N/A	N/A	N/A	0.0	0.0	ACCEPTANCE INS CO
1.4	0.9	141.5	11.2	-0.6	-10.6	32.1	45.6	77.7	138.0	1.3	0.0	ACCESS HOME INS CO
0.9	0.8	175.0	96.5	-1.3	17.4	74.8	25.2	100.0	102.5	-10.1	0.0	ACCESS INS CO
1.8	1.4	65.2	72.8	-0.4	9.0	64.4	17.7	82.1	137.2	13.3	0.0	ACCIDENT FUND GENERAL INS CO
1.2	1.0	99.9	111.5	-0.5	9.7	64.5	19.9	84.4	132.6	13.3	17.5 ●	ACCIDENT FUND INS CO OF AMERICA
1.9	1.4	90.4	100.9	-0.5	9.6	64.4	18.3	82.7	122.3	13.3	0.0	ACCIDENT FUND NATIONAL INS CO
0.0	0.0	190.6	330.7	86.0	127.7	114.4	15.7	130.1	48.9	-13.0	0.2	ACCIDENT INS CO
3.2	2.7	43.0	0.8	0.4	0.5	1.1	77.2	78.3	119.2	-0.6	0.0	ACCREDITED SURETY & CAS CO INC
1.4	1.1	68.3	123.0	-1.0	-0.2	72.8	24.9	97.7	125.7	6.3	19.8 ●	ACE AMERICAN INS CO
13.5	10.4	12.7	22.9	-0.2	N/A	72.8	19.5	92.3	79.2	6.3	0.0	ACE FIRE UNDERWRITERS INS CO
13.8	12.4	7.7	2.9	N/A	0.2	71.5	-22.2	49.3	705.0	80.1	0.0	ACE INS CO OF THE MIDWEST
2.6	1.7	83.4	150.3	-1.4	-0.3	72.8	23.8	96.6	111.6	6.3	3.3 ●	ACE P&C INS CO
1.6	1.0	81.5	224.8	-13.8	-10.5	69.3	31.4	100.7	123.1	0.5	0.0	ACIG INS CO
3.5	2.1	6.6	48.0	-5.7	-8.5	-30.0	69.3	39.3	154.1	-4.9	0.0	ACSTAR INS CO
4.4	2.6	88.8	81.8	-4.5	-8.2	61.9	29.5	91.4	120.5	6.8	0.0 ●	ACUITY A MUTUAL INS CO
3.8	2.4	80.1	84.8	-2.1	-6.1	61.2	31.7	92.9	121.0	10.3	0.0	ADDISON INS CO
2.0	1.4	120.7	80.9	0.5	2.8	69.6	13.0	82.6	136.2	-22.4	11.0	ADIRONDACK INS EXCHANGE
2.3	1.4	N/A	N/A	N/A	N/A	N/A	N/A	N/A	113.4	0.0	0.0	ADM INS CO
11.7	10.6	N/A	N/A	N/A	N/A	N/A	N/A	N/A	-292.5	0.0	0.0	ADMIRAL INDEMNITY CO
1.6	1.6	N/A	N/A	N/A	N/A	N/A	N/A	N/A	N/A	0.0	50.4 ●	ADMIRAL INS CO
8.5	5.3	37.5	7.9	-3.8	-2.6	47.1	26.5	73.6	159.4	52.2	0.0	ADRIATIC INS CO
4.3	3.9	13.9	7.2	-4.0	-9.8	27.9	135.9	163.8	90.7	-15.0	0.0	ADVANCED PHYSICIANS INS RRG INC

999 + Denotes number greater than 999.9%
999 - Denotes number less than -999.99%
● Bullets denote a more detailed analysis is available in Section II.

INSURANCE COMPANY NAME	DOM. STATE	RATING	TOTAL ASSETS ($MIL)	CAPITAL & SURPLUS ($MIL)	ANNUAL NET PREMIUM ($MIL)	NET INCOME ($MIL)	CAPITAL-IZATION INDEX (PTS)	RESERVE ADQ INDEX (PTS)	PROFIT-ABILITY INDEX (PTS)	LIQUIDITY INDEX (PTS)	STAB. INDEX (PTS)	STABILITY FACTORS
ADVANTAGE WORKERS COMP INS CO	IN	C+	484.6	194.1	14.1	-8.2	9.0	3.6	2.9	7.7	3.7	GT
AEGIS HEALTHCARE RRG INC	DC	D-	5.5	2.6	0.9	-0.1	7.4	9.9	3.8	7.5	1.3	DGRT
AEGIS SECURITY INS CO	PA	B-	120.9	57.7	64.0	0.8	5.3	8.9	8.6	5.8	3.7	CRT
AETNA INS CO OF CT	CT	C+	15.9	15.4	0.0	0.1	10.0	7.4	5.1	10.0	3.2	DGRT
AF&L INS CO	PA	E-	141.3	5.1	21.1	5.1	0.0	0.1	1.9	0.0	0.0	CDFL
AFFILIATED FM INS CO	RI	C	2,889.7	1,520.6	420.5	26.2	9.2	6.5	6.5	6.9	2.6	RT
AFFILIATES INS CO	IN	U	62.5	48.8	0.1	0.7	N/A	4.6	7.5	8.0	4.3	GT
AFFILIATES INS RECIPROCAL A RRG	VT	B-	7.1	5.1	0.4	-0.3	9.7	4.9	3.9	7.9	3.5	DFGT
AFFINITY MUTUAL INS CO	OH	C-	14.2	7.7	4.2	0.3	7.5	6.0	2.0	7.1	2.2	DFGR
AFFIRMATIVE CASUALTY INS CO	LA	F (3)	35.4	28.0	0.0	0.0	10.0	4.6	3.9	7.0	0.0	FGRT
AFFIRMATIVE DIRECT INS CO	NY	F (1)	5.3	5.2	0.0	-0.1	10.0	N/A	3.8	10.0	0.0	DGT
AFFIRMATIVE INS CO	IL	F (3)	179.4	-13.5	101.8	-65.6	0.9	1.8	0.1	0.0	0.0	ACDF
AFFIRMATIVE INS CO OF MI	MI	U	9.4	7.3	0.0	-0.2	N/A	N/A	3.8	7.0	4.9	GRT
AGCS MARINE INS CO	IL	D+	383.8	187.4	0.0	0.2	10.0	4.9	4.7	0.0	2.8	LRT
AGENCY INS CO OF MD INC	MD	C+	131.6	38.6	85.9	1.5	7.3	5.1	6.4	5.9	3.4	RT
AGENT ALLIANCE INS CO	AL	C	50.5	49.4	0.0	0.5	10.0	2.8	4.1	7.0	3.7	DGT
AGENTS MUTUAL INS CO	AR	D	3.9	2.1	1.6	0.0	3.8	9.7	6.5	7.8	1.7	DGRT
AGIC INC	FL	D+	2.6	1.8	0.7	-0.2	7.9	3.6	1.6	6.9	1.6	DGT
AGRI GENERAL INS CO	IA	C-	112.3	106.4	0.0	1.0	10.0	4.7	1.9	9.8	3.1	RT
AGRI INS EXCHANGE RRG	IN	C	17.0	13.9	0.9	0.5	7.5	8.6	8.7	9.2	2.6	DGT
AGRICULTURAL WORKERS MUT AUTO INS	TX	B-	89.1	34.3	37.3	-0.3	6.6	6.0	5.6	5.8	3.5	FRT
AGRINATIONAL INS CO	VT	D	658.6	248.1	287.3	25.0	4.0	9.6	5.7	5.4	1.3	DFRT
AGSECURITY INS CO	OK	C+	57.7	31.6	13.8	-0.6	10.0	9.3	5.3	7.9	3.6	T
AIG ASR CO	PA	C+	33.9	32.8	0.0	0.3	10.0	N/A	3.4	7.0	3.8	DGT
AIG INS CO - PR	PR	C+	143.2	84.6	16.0	0.8	10.0	7.6	2.8	8.0	4.3	T
AIG PROPERTY CASUALTY CO	PA	C	4,187.6	1,103.1	927.5	487.9	7.5	3.8	4.5	6.3	2.8	AFT
AIG SPECIALTY INS CO	IL	C+	104.9	47.4	0.0	1.5	10.0	4.7	1.9	7.0	3.9	AT
AIG STRUCTURED MORTGAGE INS CO	NC	U	10.1	9.3	0.0	-0.8	N/A	N/A	3.6	7.0	4.8	FGT
AIMCO MUTUAL INS CO	NC	U	8.1	5.4	0.0	-0.2	N/A	9.4	3.0	10.0	3.4	FGT
AIOI NISSAY DOWA INS CO LTD	GU	D+	30.9	12.8	10.3	1.1	6.9	5.0	9.0	8.9	1.3	DGT
AIOI NISSAY DOWA INS CO OF AMERICA	NY	C+	133.6	61.0	31.9	0.2	10.0	9.0	7.3	10.0	3.4	GRT
AIU INS CO	NY	C+	87.6	69.8	0.0	0.4	10.0	5.0	1.9	7.0	4.1	ADFR
AIX SPECIALTY INS CO	DE	B-	55.8	48.4	0.0	0.6	10.0	N/A	4.1	8.3	3.9	RT
ALABAMA MUNICIPAL INS CORP	AL	C+	105.6	45.4	32.0	0.7	7.9	7.0	8.8	7.1	3.4	RT
ALAMANCE FARMERS MUTUAL INS CO	NC	B-	8.2	5.3	2.8	-0.2	7.2	6.5	3.8	6.4	3.5	DGT
ALAMANCE INS CO	IL	C-	485.5	378.9	32.8	4.3	7.7	7.8	7.4	8.1	2.6	RT
ALASKA NATIONAL INS CO	AK	B	916.1	410.9	228.5	18.8	9.1	9.4	8.7	7.4	4.7	T
ALASKA TIMBER INS EXCHANGE	AK	C	15.6	7.0	4.9	-2.0	8.2	9.5	2.9	6.9	2.3	DFGR
ALEA NORTH AMERICA INS CO	NY	U	99.4	79.6	0.0	-0.6	N/A	6.2	2.8	10.0	5.3	FGT
▲ALFA ALLIANCE INS CORP	VA	B	28.8	13.0	11.4	0.2	8.5	7.6	3.0	7.1	4.3	DGT
ALFA GENERAL INS CORP	AL	B	95.0	50.2	45.5	1.0	8.7	7.9	3.3	6.4	4.5	T
ALFA INS CORP	AL	B	97.0	50.7	34.2	1.2	10.0	7.9	3.6	6.7	4.6	T
ALFA MUTUAL FIRE INS CO	AL	B	715.5	408.4	341.5	2.7	8.0	7.7	5.1	6.3	4.9	T
ALFA MUTUAL GENERAL INS CO	AL	B+	103.4	56.3	45.5	0.5	8.0	7.5	5.6	6.6	5.0	T
ALFA MUTUAL INS CO	AL	B	1,251.2	487.1	592.0	2.3	7.2	6.5	2.9	3.6	4.6	LT
ALFA SPECIALTY INS CORP	VA	B	51.1	25.8	22.8	0.4	7.6	6.5	5.1	6.9	4.6	FT
ALFA VISION INS CORP	VA	B	96.5	43.7	45.5	0.5	8.6	7.6	3.9	6.9	4.0	T
ALINSCO INS CO	TX	C-	62.2	10.4	0.0	1.5	7.8	N/A	9.9	10.0	2.3	DGT
ALL AMERICA INS CO	OH	B+	280.0	147.0	93.0	0.8	10.0	9.3	7.6	6.8	5.0	T
ALLEGANY CO-OP INS CO	NY	C+	52.3	35.6	13.3	1.7	9.6	6.4	8.7	6.9	3.4	DRT
ALLEGHENY CASUALTY CO	NJ	C	37.8	22.9	30.2	0.2	4.2	6.2	7.6	7.1	2.6	CDGT
ALLEGHENY SURETY CO	PA	D	3.8	1.8	1.5	-0.2	6.2	3.8	1.4	6.8	1.6	DGRT

See Page 27 for explanation of footnotes and
Page 28 for explanation of stability factors.
Arrows denote recent upgrades ▲ or downgrades ▼   (see Section VII for explanations)

32

www.weissratings.com

RISK ADJ. CAPITAL RATIO #1	RATIO #2	PREMIUM TO SURPLUS (%)	RESV. TO SURPLUS (%)	RESV. DEVELOP. 1 YEAR (%)	2 YEAR (%)	LOSS RATIO (%)	EXP. RATIO (%)	COMB RATIO (%)	CASH FROM UNDER-WRITING (%)	NET PREMIUM GROWTH (%)	INVEST. IN AFFIL (%)	INSURANCE COMPANY NAME
4.0	2.2	26.8	88.5	2.1	11.4	77.8	23.6	101.4	96.4	51.9	0.0	ADVANTAGE WORKERS COMP INS CO
1.7	1.2	32.7	63.2	4.8	-18.6	107.7	48.7	156.4	153.2	-9.8	0.0	AEGIS HEALTHCARE RRG INC
1.0	0.7	113.4	33.6	-0.6	-1.9	42.5	48.7	91.2	110.1	2.8	17.4	AEGIS SECURITY INS CO
70.4	62.9	N/A	1.8	-0.2	-2.0	999 +	999 +	999 +	1.3	99.9	0.0	AETNA INS CO OF CT
0.2	0.1	999 +	999 +	999 +	999 +	145.3	-7.8	137.5	53.8	-8.5	0.0	AF&L INS CO
3.9	2.4	28.4	27.6	1.5	-1.8	58.8	26.9	85.7	118.8	8.8	0.0 ●	AFFILIATED FM INS CO
N/A	N/A	0.2	5.3	0.4	-0.2	53.9	583.5	637.4	106.9	-91.8	0.0	AFFILIATES INS CO
5.1	3.0	7.3	11.9	1.4	1.4	93.8	10.8	104.6	25.8	-0.9	0.0	AFFILIATES INS RECIPROCAL A RRG
2.1	1.3	59.5	27.0	-3.8	4.1	55.8	59.0	114.8	90.3	-15.6	0.0	AFFINITY MUTUAL INS CO
4.8	4.2	N/A	-0.1	N/A	N/A	N/A	N/A	N/A	193.2	0.0	29.1	AFFIRMATIVE CASUALTY INS CO
87.5	46.0	N/A	N/A	N/A	N/A	N/A	N/A	N/A	6.2	0.0	0.0	AFFIRMATIVE DIRECT INS CO
-0.0	-0.0	419.4	191.0	52.9	48.4	119.5	41.1	160.6	67.1	-20.9	41.2	AFFIRMATIVE INS CO
N/A	N/A	N/A	N/A	N/A	N/A	N/A	N/A	N/A	-51.0	0.0	0.0	AFFIRMATIVE INS CO OF MI
19.4	17.5	N/A	N/A	N/A	N/A	N/A	N/A	N/A	119.2	100.0	2.8	AGCS MARINE INS CO
1.5	1.3	233.4	99.3	-10.3	-8.3	70.9	25.2	96.1	113.0	23.8	0.0	AGENCY INS CO OF MD INC
49.9	20.9	N/A	N/A	N/A	N/A	N/A	N/A	N/A	89.2	0.0	0.0	AGENT ALLIANCE INS CO
0.8	0.6	77.2	4.2	6.2	-45.0	35.3	11.6	46.9	880.7	0.8	0.0	AGENTS MUTUAL INS CO
4.5	4.0	36.6	41.9	-8.2	-9.0	58.7	-70.3	-11.6	71.7	-53.2	0.0	AGIC INC
52.0	25.4	N/A	0.9	N/A	N/A	N/A	N/A	N/A	-187.0	100.0	0.0	AGRI GENERAL INS CO
2.1	1.2	6.8	15.4	-5.0	-10.5	-7.6	28.0	20.4	295.9	4.8	0.0	AGRI INS EXCHANGE RRG
1.6	1.1	109.1	25.8	3.4	-0.1	71.1	17.5	88.6	104.5	-14.1	14.2	AGRICULTURAL WORKERS MUT AUTO
0.9	0.7	113.0	101.9	-9.0	-32.6	72.3	14.5	86.8	100.1	35.5	53.2 ●	AGRINATIONAL INS CO
8.0	5.8	43.0	26.8	-7.9	-12.0	56.6	25.5	82.1	102.7	-16.8	0.0	AGSECURITY INS CO
71.6	46.2	N/A	N/A	N/A	N/A	N/A	N/A	N/A	N/A	0.0	0.0	AIG ASR CO
6.2	4.1	19.2	15.6	-2.5	-1.4	16.7	102.3	119.0	115.8	-27.5	1.8	AIG INS CO - PR
2.2	1.5	70.6	163.2	9.5	14.3	88.8	30.1	118.9	83.8	-10.4	0.1 ●	AIG PROPERTY CASUALTY CO
8.5	7.6	N/A	N/A	N/A	N/A	N/A	N/A	N/A	N/A	100.0	0.0	AIG SPECIALTY INS CO
N/A	N/A	N/A	N/A	N/A	N/A	N/A	N/A	N/A	N/A	0.0	0.0	AIG STRUCTURED MORTGAGE INS CO
N/A	N/A	N/A	47.7	-3.1	-7.8	999 +	999 +	999 +	0.2	-9.0	0.0	AIMCO MUTUAL INS CO
1.8	1.1	87.6	19.3	-13.8	-27.5	32.6	37.1	69.7	165.3	22.0	0.0	AIOI NISSAY DOWA INS CO LTD
5.4	3.7	52.7	84.2	-3.3	-7.8	71.2	19.7	90.9	-260.0	598.2	0.0	AIOI NISSAY DOWA INS CO OF AMERICA
7.6	7.1	N/A	N/A	N/A	N/A	N/A	N/A	N/A	N/A	100.0	18.7	AIU INS CO
24.5	22.1	N/A	N/A	N/A	N/A	N/A	N/A	N/A	N/A	0.0	0.0	AIX SPECIALTY INS CO
2.3	1.9	71.3	93.3	-4.1	-15.4	61.7	24.5	86.2	119.8	5.6	0.0	ALABAMA MUNICIPAL INS CORP
1.8	1.1	53.3	13.3	1.1	-3.1	55.9	48.8	104.7	100.2	19.8	0.0	ALAMANCE FARMERS MUTUAL INS CO
1.4	1.4	8.8	23.6	-1.5	-2.2	44.4	51.8	96.2	92.1	-10.5	57.8 ●	ALAMANCE INS CO
3.4	2.4	58.9	95.6	-7.7	-15.8	56.3	25.7	82.0	130.5	7.7	0.0 ●	ALASKA NATIONAL INS CO
1.9	1.4	52.8	83.8	-14.5	-21.4	51.2	20.2	71.4	110.3	-0.3	0.0	ALASKA TIMBER INS EXCHANGE
N/A	N/A	N/A	19.5	-0.4	-2.2	999 +	999 +	999 +	-0.3	54.5	0.0	ALEA NORTH AMERICA INS CO
2.8	1.9	86.1	35.3	-1.4	-1.9	70.6	32.1	102.7	106.4	1.6	0.0	ALFA ALLIANCE INS CORP
3.2	2.1	91.3	34.6	-1.5	-1.6	70.6	29.5	100.1	99.3	1.6	0.0	ALFA GENERAL INS CORP
4.9	3.3	68.6	26.3	-1.3	-1.3	70.5	27.5	98.0	97.6	1.6	0.0	ALFA INS CORP
2.4	1.9	83.3	30.4	-1.6	-1.8	70.6	29.9	100.5	99.8	1.6	28.1 ●	ALFA MUTUAL FIRE INS CO
3.1	2.0	80.1	29.3	-1.5	-1.6	70.7	30.0	100.7	99.2	1.6	0.8 ●	ALFA MUTUAL GENERAL INS CO
1.3	1.0	118.9	46.6	-2.3	-2.3	70.5	29.6	100.1	97.1	1.6	41.2 ●	ALFA MUTUAL INS CO
2.9	1.9	87.0	31.8	-1.6	-2.3	70.7	30.1	100.8	91.7	1.6	0.0	ALFA SPECIALTY INS CORP
2.9	1.9	102.6	37.6	-1.8	-1.8	70.7	30.1	100.8	97.5	1.6	0.0	ALFA VISION INS CORP
1.5	1.3	N/A	0.6	N/A	N/A	N/A	N/A	N/A	N/A	0.0	0.0	ALINSCO INS CO
6.0	4.1	63.7	47.1	-4.2	-7.3	57.8	33.3	91.1	110.4	9.0	0.1 ●	ALL AMERICA INS CO
4.3	2.7	40.1	18.5	-3.4	-1.9	53.0	38.4	91.4	107.5	-2.9	0.0	ALLEGANY CO-OP INS CO
0.6	0.6	133.6	N/A	-0.3	-0.3	-0.2	98.3	98.1	104.5	2.1	0.0	ALLEGHENY CASUALTY CO
1.0	0.9	75.5	40.7	-1.6	3.3	64.6	90.2	154.8	94.7	-13.8	0.0	ALLEGHENY SURETY CO

999 + Denotes number greater than 999.9%
999 - Denotes number less than -999.99%
● Bullets denote a more detailed analysis is available in Section II.

INSURANCE COMPANY NAME	DOM. STATE	RATING	TOTAL ASSETS ($MIL)	CAPITAL & SURPLUS ($MIL)	ANNUAL NET PREMIUM ($MIL)	NET INCOME ($MIL)	CAPITAL-IZATION INDEX (PTS)	RESERVE ADQ INDEX (PTS)	PROFIT-ABILITY INDEX (PTS)	LIQUIDITY INDEX (PTS)	STAB. INDEX (PTS)	STABILITY FACTORS
ALLEGIANT INS CO INC A RRG	HI	E	23.5	7.7	4.9	0.2	1.3	0.4	2.9	9.0	0.0	CDGT
ALLIANCE INDEMNITY CO	KS	C+	10.5	6.7	3.8	0.1	10.0	7.7	5.3	6.8	3.3	DGRT
ALLIANCE INS CO	KS	C	26.2	10.9	15.1	0.3	7.8	8.5	6.1	6.6	2.9	DGRT
ALLIANCE NATIONAL INS CO	NY	E	48.3	6.5	8.1	-0.3	0.0	5.1	2.9	3.8	0.1	CDFL
ALLIANCE OF NONPROFITS FOR INS RRG	VT	C-	94.2	36.1	29.6	0.8	7.0	6.1	6.8	7.1	3.2	RT
ALLIANCE UNITED INS CO	CA	C-	519.6	124.0	443.4	-19.3	3.7	5.6	2.8	2.9	3.3	GLT
ALLIANZ GLOBAL RISKS US INS CO	IL	C	8,012.3	1,767.9	1,093.4	-193.7	4.9	8.4	3.2	6.9	3.5	FGRT
ALLIANZ UNDERWRITERS INS CO	IL	C-	91.5	69.8	0.0	0.6	10.0	N/A	6.7	8.8	3.1	RT
ALLIED EASTERN INDEMNITY CO	PA	C+	91.1	16.3	21.1	0.3	6.2	4.4	8.9	5.8	3.3	DRT
ALLIED INS CO OF AMERICA	OH	C	39.4	14.1	0.0	0.1	10.0	N/A	8.0	6.9	3.1	DGT
ALLIED P&C INS CO	IA	B	402.1	58.6	0.0	0.4	10.0	N/A	5.8	7.6	4.1	FT
ALLIED PREMIER INS A RRG	CT	D (2)	6.4	1.9	4.2	-0.7	1.9	N/A	1.7	8.6	0.6	CDT
ALLIED PROFESSIONALS INS CO RRG	AZ	C-	49.7	19.3	14.2	-0.5	7.1	2.2	4.8	7.6	2.9	DRT
ALLIED SERVICES RRG	SC	E	6.6	4.2	1.0	0.1	4.4	5.0	5.6	7.2	0.0	DGT
ALLIED TRUST INS CO	TX	U	10.4	9.6	0.0	-0.5	N/A	N/A	3.2	7.0	4.0	FGT
ALLIED WORLD ASR CO (US) INC	DE	C+	365.1	139.8	47.7	-0.8	10.0	7.7	5.9	8.5	4.5	ART
ALLIED WORLD INS CO	NH	C	1,802.4	1,038.1	214.6	7.8	7.8	7.4	7.3	7.0	3.4	ART
ALLIED WORLD NATL ASR CO	NH	B-	330.4	148.8	47.7	-0.7	10.0	7.8	4.5	8.5	4.5	ART
ALLIED WORLD SPECIALTY INS CO	DE	B	837.0	412.5	119.2	5.6	9.2	7.6	7.9	6.9	4.7	RT
ALLIED WORLD SURPLUS LINES INS	AR	C	284.7	96.5	47.7	-0.5	8.9	8.1	5.9	7.3	4.2	RT
ALLMERICA FINANCIAL ALLIANCE INS CO	NH	C+	20.0	20.0	0.0	0.2	10.0	N/A	7.2	7.0	3.4	DGRT
ALLMERICA FINANCIAL BENEFIT INS CO	MI	C+	37.7	37.6	0.0	0.3	10.0	N/A	7.4	7.0	3.8	GRT
ALLSTATE COUNTY MUTUAL INS CO	TX	B	14.7	14.6	0.0	0.0	10.0	N/A	6.1	7.0	4.9	DGT
ALLSTATE F&C INS CO	IL	C+	224.6	212.4	0.0	1.2	10.0	N/A	7.3	9.4	4.3	T
ALLSTATE INDEMNITY CO	IL	B	128.5	120.5	0.0	0.8	10.0	N/A	3.4	7.0	4.5	T
ALLSTATE INS CO	IL	B	43,881.3	14,856.0	27,774.3	271.8	7.8	6.3	3.9	4.4	5.1	LT
ALLSTATE NJ INS CO	IL	B	2,550.9	822.0	1,157.5	45.1	8.2	6.7	3.9	6.3	4.9	T
ALLSTATE NJ P&C INS CO	IL	C	66.2	63.4	0.0	0.4	10.0	N/A	7.4	7.0	4.1	GT
ALLSTATE NORTH AMERICAN INS CO	IL	U	10.7	10.6	0.0	0.1	N/A	N/A	4.4	7.0	4.9	GT
ALLSTATE NORTHBROOK INDEMNITY CO	IL	B-	44.1	42.6	0.0	0.4	10.0	N/A	7.5	7.0	3.9	T
ALLSTATE P&C INS CO	IL	B	249.7	230.2	0.0	1.3	10.0	N/A	7.4	10.0	4.7	FT
ALLSTATE TEXAS LLOYDS	TX	B	17.3	17.0	0.0	0.1	10.0	N/A	6.3	7.0	4.9	DFGT
ALLSTATE VEHICLE & PROPERTY INS CO	IL	B	52.6	49.4	0.0	0.3	10.0	N/A	7.5	7.0	4.7	GT
ALPHA P&C INS CO	WI	B	30.9	13.7	0.0	0.2	10.0	N/A	5.6	10.0	4.0	DGRT
ALPS PROPERTY & CASUALTY INS CO	MT	C+	113.1	36.8	30.5	1.1	7.8	9.2	6.3	7.4	3.4	RT
ALTERRA AMERICA INS CO	DE	B-	454.4	163.1	103.6	4.4	4.9	6.0	3.7	7.0	3.6	CGT
AMALGAMATED CASUALTY INS CO	WA	C+	54.4	42.4	9.0	0.2	10.0	8.0	6.8	7.6	3.4	DT
AMBAC ASR CORP SEGREGATED ACCT	WI	U	11.0	385.6	0.0	0.0	N/A	N/A	0.8	7.0	0.0	CGT
AMBAC ASSURANCE CORP	WI	E	5,367.0	754.6	53.2	136.7	1.4	2.5	1.9	9.2	-0.5	CFRT
AMCO INS CO	IA	C+	940.5	201.7	0.0	1.8	10.0	N/A	2.5	7.7	4.5	FT
AMERICA FIRST INS CO	NH	C+	14.6	14.6	0.0	0.1	10.0	N/A	7.4	7.0	3.3	DGRT
AMERICA FIRST LLOYD'S INS CO	TX	C	6.7	6.4	0.0	0.0	10.0	N/A	6.3	7.0	2.7	DGRT
AMERICAN ACCESS CASUALTY CO	IL	D+	308.3	54.2	243.4	1.4	2.5	2.5	3.8	2.7	2.8	CLT
AMERICAN AGRI BUSINESS INS CO	TX	C+	1,052.9	30.9	0.0	1.4	7.6	3.6	8.9	7.0	3.7	RT
AMERICAN AGRICULTURAL INS CO	IN	B	1,247.8	554.6	304.9	8.8	7.8	7.0	5.1	6.9	4.4	RT
AMERICAN ALLIANCE CASUALTY CO	IL	D	21.0	5.4	11.1	0.0	2.0	1.7	3.3	7.0	2.0	CDFG
AMERICAN ALTERNATIVE INS CORP	DE	C	518.5	183.5	0.0	13.4	10.0	N/A	8.4	10.0	3.7	RT
AMERICAN ASSOC OF ORTHODONTIST RRG	AZ	C-	45.3	13.5	6.7	0.3	6.5	10.0	7.8	7.7	2.5	DRT
AMERICAN AUTOMOBILE INS CO	MO	C	124.7	75.2	0.0	0.9	10.0	3.6	4.4	6.8	4.2	RT
AMERICAN BANKERS INS CO OF FL	FL	B	1,972.7	526.5	867.5	90.4	7.3	6.7	4.8	6.1	4.7	AT
AMERICAN BUILDERS INS CO	DE	C	130.5	38.5	20.2	0.3	8.6	8.9	8.8	6.9	3.5	RT
AMERICAN BUILDERS INS CO RRG INC	MT	U	0.8	0.7	0.0	0.1	N/A	1.9	1.6	10.0	0.0	FGT

See Page 27 for explanation of footnotes and
Page 28 for explanation of stability factors.
Arrows denote recent upgrades ▲ or downgrades ▼   (see Section VII for explanations)

34

www.weissratings.com

RISK ADJ. RATIO #1	CAPITAL RATIO #2	PREMIUM TO SURPLUS (%)	RESV. TO SURPLUS (%)	RESV. DEVELOP. 1 YEAR (%)	RESV. DEVELOP. 2 YEAR (%)	LOSS RATIO (%)	EXP. RATIO (%)	COMB RATIO (%)	CASH FROM UNDER-WRITING (%)	NET PREMIUM GROWTH (%)	INVEST. IN AFFIL (%)	INSURANCE COMPANY NAME
0.4	0.2	65.5	126.4	29.8	58.0	53.5	17.1	70.6	104.5	8.5	0.0	ALLEGIANT INS CO INC A RRG
5.2	3.8	57.2	20.4	-2.8	-2.4	63.1	31.0	94.1	109.3	2.1	0.0	ALLIANCE INDEMNITY CO
2.1	1.6	143.2	51.2	-7.3	-6.4	63.1	31.0	94.1	109.3	2.1	0.0	ALLIANCE INS CO
0.0	0.0	120.0	391.2	29.1	-96.0	90.4	27.5	117.9	42.9	-20.7	0.0	ALLIANCE NATIONAL INS CO
1.3	1.0	87.8	113.4	-2.1	-0.4	67.6	28.8	96.4	143.5	12.1	0.0	ALLIANCE OF NONPROFITS FOR INS
0.8	0.6	327.9	152.7	17.7	0.8	92.6	22.9	115.5	113.4	111.4	0.0	ALLIANCE UNITED INS CO
0.8	0.6	58.7	78.0	-17.9	-8.1	71.9	31.3	103.2	74.4	-11.6	39.2 ●	ALLIANZ GLOBAL RISKS US INS CO
18.9	17.0	N/A	N/A	N/A	N/A	N/A	N/A	N/A	86.8	0.0	0.0	ALLIANZ UNDERWRITERS INS CO
1.0	0.8	129.5	108.2	2.8	1.5	73.1	14.5	87.6	126.6	7.5	0.0	ALLIED EASTERN INDEMNITY CO
3.4	3.1	N/A	N/A	N/A	N/A	N/A	N/A	N/A	488.8	0.0	0.0	ALLIED INS CO OF AMERICA
5.2	4.7	N/A	N/A	N/A	N/A	N/A	N/A	N/A	68.0	0.0	6.0	ALLIED P&C INS CO
0.5	0.3	219.0	118.1	N/A	N/A	87.9	25.8	113.7	349.8	0.0	0.0	ALLIED PREMIER INS A RRG
1.4	0.9	72.9	93.2	11.0	38.4	62.0	39.3	101.3	112.7	13.9	0.0	ALLIED PROFESSIONALS INS CO RRG
0.9	0.7	25.5	49.7	-0.6	-13.6	56.2	23.1	79.3	126.2	0.0	0.0	ALLIED SERVICES RRG
N/A	N/A	N/A	N/A	N/A	N/A	N/A	N/A	N/A	N/A	0.0	0.0	ALLIED TRUST INS CO
5.6	3.6	34.4	59.6	-0.1	-1.6	69.0	28.4	97.4	120.7	8.3	0.0	ALLIED WORLD ASR CO (US) INC
1.7	1.5	19.8	34.4	N/A	-0.9	69.0	28.5	97.5	120.4	8.3	46.9 ●	ALLIED WORLD INS CO
6.1	3.9	35.5	61.6	-0.1	-1.7	69.0	28.3	97.3	131.8	8.3	0.0	ALLIED WORLD NATL ASR CO
3.1	2.6	29.4	51.0	-0.1	-1.4	69.0	28.6	97.6	120.4	8.3	21.4 ●	ALLIED WORLD SPECIALTY INS CO
3.9	2.5	49.3	85.5	-0.1	-3.3	69.0	28.3	97.3	120.0	8.3	0.0	ALLIED WORLD SURPLUS LINES INS
83.4	38.3	N/A	N/A	N/A	N/A	N/A	N/A	N/A	N/A	0.0	0.0	ALLMERICA FINANCIAL ALLIANCE INS CO
92.9	44.3	N/A	N/A	N/A	N/A	N/A	N/A	N/A	N/A	0.0	0.0	ALLMERICA FINANCIAL BENEFIT INS CO
98.6	49.3	N/A	N/A	N/A	N/A	N/A	N/A	N/A	N/A	0.0	0.0	ALLSTATE COUNTY MUTUAL INS CO
79.5	56.1	N/A	N/A	N/A	N/A	N/A	N/A	N/A	999 +	0.0	0.0 ●	ALLSTATE F&C INS CO
58.5	45.0	N/A	N/A	N/A	N/A	N/A	N/A	N/A	171.3	0.0	0.0	ALLSTATE INDEMNITY CO
1.8	1.4	181.3	101.2	1.0	-0.2	70.1	25.1	95.2	108.4	5.0	12.5 ●	ALLSTATE INS CO
2.4	1.8	149.4	157.7	0.8	-2.1	70.2	23.2	93.4	108.5	-0.5	4.8 ●	ALLSTATE NJ INS CO
67.8	61.0	N/A	N/A	N/A	N/A	N/A	N/A	N/A	62.4	0.0	0.0	ALLSTATE NJ P&C INS CO
N/A	N/A	N/A	N/A	N/A	N/A	N/A	N/A	N/A	N/A	0.0	0.0	ALLSTATE NORTH AMERICAN INS CO
70.7	60.9	N/A	N/A	N/A	N/A	N/A	N/A	N/A	999 +	0.0	0.0	ALLSTATE NORTHBROOK INDEMNITY CO
66.5	56.4	N/A	N/A	N/A	N/A	N/A	N/A	N/A	-16.1	0.0	0.0 ●	ALLSTATE P&C INS CO
100.2	50.0	N/A	N/A	N/A	N/A	N/A	N/A	N/A	N/A	0.0	0.0	ALLSTATE TEXAS LLOYDS
46.8	42.1	N/A	N/A	N/A	N/A	N/A	N/A	N/A	999 +	0.0	0.0	ALLSTATE VEHICLE & PROPERTY INS CO
4.2	3.8	N/A	N/A	N/A	N/A	N/A	N/A	N/A	-166.1	0.0	0.0	ALPHA P&C INS CO
2.3	1.6	82.0	133.6	-1.2	-6.5	69.1	29.7	98.8	146.9	4.8	0.0	ALPS PROPERTY & CASUALTY INS CO
0.9	0.5	65.9	135.4	-5.3	1.4	72.9	40.7	113.6	133.4	366.1	0.0	ALTERRA AMERICA INS CO
6.5	4.2	21.3	13.9	-0.4	-3.4	81.3	32.4	113.7	85.9	50.6	0.0	AMALGAMATED CASUALTY INS CO
N/A	N/A	N/A	N/A	N/A	N/A	N/A	N/A	N/A	N/A	0.0	0.0	AMBAC ASR CORP SEGREGATED ACCT
0.7	0.3	8.5	299.4	-537.4	-96.4	-159.7	561.6	401.9	30.3	-16.4	8.9 ●	AMBAC ASSURANCE CORP
5.2	4.5	N/A	N/A	N/A	N/A	N/A	N/A	N/A	8.1	0.0	15.6 ●	AMCO INS CO
107.7	53.8	N/A	N/A	N/A	N/A	N/A	N/A	N/A	N/A	0.0	0.0	AMERICA FIRST INS CO
40.9	36.8	N/A	N/A	N/A	N/A	N/A	N/A	N/A	N/A	0.0	0.0	AMERICA FIRST LLOYD'S INS CO
0.5	0.4	481.1	256.0	24.3	30.5	73.7	28.5	102.2	109.9	19.1	0.0	AMERICAN ACCESS CASUALTY CO
1.6	0.8	N/A	N/A	N/A	N/A	N/A	N/A	N/A	N/A	0.0	0.0	AMERICAN AGRI BUSINESS INS CO
2.2	1.5	56.4	90.3	-3.3	-10.0	71.4	19.4	90.8	132.3	3.2	0.1 ●	AMERICAN AGRICULTURAL INS CO
0.5	0.4	293.5	143.2	25.8	35.1	70.3	33.6	103.9	96.8	54.7	0.0	AMERICAN ALLIANCE CASUALTY CO
16.5	12.3	N/A	N/A	N/A	N/A	N/A	N/A	N/A	-5.1	0.0	0.0 ●	AMERICAN ALTERNATIVE INS CORP
1.2	0.9	53.5	200.7	-44.8	-57.9	69.5	33.6	103.1	126.4	6.4	0.0	AMERICAN ASSOC OF ORTHODONTIST
11.2	10.1	N/A	N/A	N/A	N/A	N/A	N/A	N/A	105.8	0.0	0.0	AMERICAN AUTOMOBILE INS CO
2.1	1.2	179.5	30.9	-4.7	-4.1	39.9	38.6	78.5	127.0	-0.3	0.9 ●	AMERICAN BANKERS INS CO OF FL
3.8	2.7	54.0	76.2	-7.9	-9.2	54.4	17.4	71.8	164.9	5.1	0.0	AMERICAN BUILDERS INS CO
N/A	N/A	N/A	45.0	0.3	0.7	N/A	N/A	N/A	N/A	0.0	0.0	AMERICAN BUILDERS INS CO RRG INC

999 + Denotes number greater than 999.9%
999 - Denotes number less than -999.99%
● Bullets denote a more detailed analysis is available in Section II.

INSURANCE COMPANY NAME	DOM. STATE	RATING		TOTAL ASSETS ($MIL)	CAPITAL & SURPLUS ($MIL)	ANNUAL NET PREMIUM ($MIL)	NET INCOME ($MIL)	CAPITAL-IZATION INDEX (PTS)	RESERVE ADQ INDEX (PTS)	PROFIT-ABILITY INDEX (PTS)	LIQUIDITY INDEX (PTS)	STAB. INDEX (PTS)	STABILITY FACTORS
AMERICAN BUS & MERCANTILE INS MUT	DE	C-		65.1	31.4	2.8	-1.3	1.6	3.0	3.3	7.4	2.9	CDRT
AMERICAN CAPITAL ASR CORP	FL	B		121.0	60.6	67.3	5.7	8.6	9.3	6.3	7.5	4.7	FRT
AMERICAN CASUALTY CO OF READING	PA	C		141.6	138.5	0.0	8.8	8.7	N/A	7.4	9.1	3.8	ART
AMERICAN COASTAL INS CO	FL	C		329.6	163.5	156.8	19.2	8.3	6.7	7.8	7.3	4.0	T
AMERICAN COLONIAL INS CO	FL	C		46.5	21.9	16.6	-0.6	7.2	6.0	2.7	6.8	3.3	DFT
AMERICAN COMMERCE INS CO	OH	C+		345.4	106.3	189.8	-0.2	8.5	4.0	2.8	2.1	4.0	FLT
AMERICAN COMPENSATION INS CO	MN	D		74.9	52.8	0.0	0.2	10.0	N/A	6.2	9.5	2.1	FRT
AMERICAN CONTRACTORS INDEMNITY CO	CA	B		298.8	103.0	15.5	5.0	9.3	7.1	7.7	9.0	4.1	T
AMERICAN CONTRACTORS INS CO RISK	TX	D-		60.2	9.3	0.0	0.4	8.5	N/A	8.6	9.5	1.2	DGRT
AMERICAN COUNTRY INS CO	IL	C		93.5	30.1	42.3	2.2	3.6	4.2	5.3	6.7	3.6	RT
AMERICAN ECONOMY INS CO	IN	C+		67.9	66.5	0.0	-0.3	10.0	3.9	3.0	7.0	4.1	ART
AMERICAN EMPIRE INS CO	OH	C		49.3	21.1	10.1	0.0	7.5	5.9	5.4	8.1	3.5	DRT
AMERICAN EMPIRE SURPLUS LINES INS CO	DE	C		381.3	126.1	91.1	-0.5	7.2	4.9	7.7	7.0	4.0	RT
AMERICAN EQUITY INS CO	AZ	U		102.7	102.5	0.0	1.0	N/A	N/A	6.0	7.0	5.4	T
AMERICAN EQUITY SPECIALTY INS CO	CT	B		78.8	30.2	20.8	1.4	8.1	8.2	6.3	7.0	4.1	DT
AMERICAN EUROPEAN INS CO	NH	B-		132.3	58.4	28.9	-0.8	8.3	6.4	2.7	6.9	3.6	FRT
AMERICAN EXCESS INS EXCHANGE RRG	VT	C-		325.9	162.6	22.2	-2.1	8.4	9.2	3.3	7.6	2.2	DRT
AMERICAN FAMILY HOME INS CO	FL	C+		562.9	186.7	210.4	2.7	8.0	8.0	8.1	6.1	4.4	FT
AMERICAN FAMILY INS CO	OH	B		34.5	23.3	0.0	0.3	10.0	N/A	8.1	6.7	4.8	DFGT
AMERICAN FAMILY MUT INS CO	WI	B+		16,216.1	6,554.3	6,854.8	108.9	8.1	8.2	6.9	6.3	5.2	T
AMERICAN FARMERS & RANCHERS INS CO	OK	U		8.8	8.7	0.1	0.0	N/A	6.5	4.0	10.0	4.8	FGRT
AMERICAN FARMERS & RANCHERS	OK	C		141.7	60.4	110.5	1.7	7.5	7.1	4.1	5.5	3.5	RT
AMERICAN FEDERATED INS CO	MS	C		43.6	19.9	17.7	2.8	6.0	7.8	8.2	6.9	2.9	DT
AMERICAN FEED INDUSTRY INS CO RRG	IA	U	(5)	1.5	1.3	0.0	0.0	N/A	9.6	1.9	7.0	0.0	FRT
AMERICAN FIRE & CASUALTY CO	NH	C-		40.6	39.9	0.0	0.3	10.0	3.8	4.6	7.0	3.1	ART
AMERICAN FOREST CASUALTY CO RRG	VT	D+		9.0	4.3	1.6	0.1	7.2	9.6	4.8	6.9	2.0	DGRT
AMERICAN FREEDOM INS CO	IL	C+		53.8	18.3	31.4	1.6	7.2	7.0	7.3	6.5	3.4	DT
AMERICAN GUARANTEE & LIABILITY INS	NY	C+		286.9	181.8	0.0	1.5	10.0	N/A	6.1	9.1	4.5	FRT
AMERICAN HALLMARK INS CO OF TX	TX	B-		427.2	140.3	127.4	1.9	7.6	5.0	5.4	6.8	4.1	RT
AMERICAN HEALTHCARE INDEMNITY CO	OK	U		22.1	21.2	0.0	-0.1	N/A	6.9	2.1	6.8	3.3	FGRT
AMERICAN HEARTLAND INS CO	IL	D		17.6	2.5	10.4	-0.2	2.4	7.0	2.9	6.2	1.6	CDGT
AMERICAN HOME ASR CO	NY	C		29,633.5	7,317.2	5,708.9	685.2	7.8	3.3	5.1	6.5	2.8	AFT
AMERICAN INDEPENDENT INS CO	PA	C-		56.3	20.5	17.2	0.1	7.6	2.2	2.4	4.4	2.9	DFLT
▼AMERICAN INS CO	OH	C-		140.2	63.4	0.0	0.0	10.0	3.3	1.9	6.7	3.1	FRT
AMERICAN INTEGRITY INS CO OF FL	FL	C		218.9	73.0	108.5	5.8	7.1	3.7	9.3	5.8	3.6	T
AMERICAN INTER FIDELITY EXCHANGE	IN	C		69.2	23.5	30.0	0.6	3.1	5.0	8.8	7.0	3.1	CDRT
AMERICAN INTERSTATE INS CO	NE	B-		1,291.5	409.4	301.8	33.9	7.7	9.3	8.5	7.2	4.3	RT
AMERICAN INTERSTATE INS CO OF TEXAS	TX	B-		69.0	26.8	18.4	2.1	6.5	9.2	8.8	7.1	3.7	DRT
AMERICAN LIBERTY INS CO	UT	E	(1)	10.6	1.8	7.4	0.1	0.1	0.3	1.7	1.3	0.0	CDFG
AMERICAN MEDICAL ASR CO	IL	U		3.3	2.7	0.0	0.0	N/A	6.2	2.5	10.0	3.0	FGRT
AMERICAN MERCURY INS CO	OK	B		368.8	158.8	170.3	6.3	8.4	5.7	5.4	6.7	4.8	RT
AMERICAN MERCURY LLOYDS INS CO	TX	B		6.5	5.0	0.0	0.0	10.0	N/A	6.5	10.0	4.9	DFGT
AMERICAN MILLENNIUM INS CO	NJ	C-		35.1	8.8	6.3	0.8	3.3	2.2	3.1	7.4	2.2	CDFG
AMERICAN MINING INS CO	IA	B-		37.5	25.9	0.0	0.2	10.0	N/A	6.5	7.0	3.7	FGT
AMERICAN MODERN HOME INS CO	OH	C+		1,295.2	419.9	370.2	9.0	7.9	7.8	7.4	2.3	4.3	FLRT
AMERICAN MODERN INS CO OF FLORIDA	FL	C+		35.7	10.5	15.6	0.1	5.5	8.4	6.1	4.5	3.0	CDGL
AMERICAN MODERN LLOYDS INS CO	TX	C		9.1	3.9	0.0	0.1	8.9	N/A	3.9	7.0	2.5	DGT
AMERICAN MODERN PROPERTY &	OH	B		20.7	16.8	3.9	0.1	10.0	7.6	7.7	6.9	4.0	DGT
AMERICAN MODERN SELECT INS CO	OH	C		329.2	55.0	39.0	1.9	9.3	7.8	8.4	6.9	3.9	FT
AMERICAN MODERN SURPLUS LINES INS	OH	B		70.6	30.5	39.0	0.1	7.1	8.1	6.8	5.2	4.1	CFT
AMERICAN MUTUAL SHARE INS CORP	OH	C-		255.4	221.8	0.2	-1.9	10.0	6.9	4.7	10.0	1.5	DFGT
AMERICAN NATIONAL GENERAL INS CO	MO	B		103.6	66.4	31.4	0.8	9.7	6.4	5.4	6.7	4.2	RT

See Page 27 for explanation of footnotes and Page 28 for explanation of stability factors.

Arrows denote recent upgrades ▲ or downgrades ▼   (see Section VII for explanations)

36

www.weissratings.com

RISK ADJ. RATIO #1	CAPITAL RATIO #2	PREMIUM TO SURPLUS (%)	RESV. TO SURPLUS (%)	RESV. DEVELOP. 1 YEAR (%)	RESV. DEVELOP. 2 YEAR (%)	LOSS RATIO (%)	EXP. RATIO (%)	COMB RATIO (%)	CASH FROM UNDER-WRITING (%)	NET PREMIUM GROWTH (%)	INVEST. IN AFFIL (%)	INSURANCE COMPANY NAME
0.4	0.3	9.5	98.7	11.0	15.3	211.9	38.8	250.7	65.7	28.9	39.0	AMERICAN BUS & MERCANTILE INS MUT
2.9	2.4	71.6	19.7	-14.9	-15.9	6.5	48.6	55.1	105.1	-24.6	10.9	AMERICAN CAPITAL ASR CORP
2.0	1.9	N/A	N/A	N/A	N/A	N/A	N/A	N/A	N/A	0.0	51.5	AMERICAN CASUALTY CO OF READING
2.6	1.8	89.7	14.9	2.9	0.3	24.4	51.1	75.5	148.2	-13.2	0.0	AMERICAN COASTAL INS CO
1.6	1.0	73.7	13.1	0.5	1.8	57.5	40.3	97.8	89.8	22.0	0.0	AMERICAN COLONIAL INS CO
2.5	2.0	181.0	83.6	3.4	8.1	84.1	24.4	108.5	85.5	8.4	0.0	AMERICAN COMMERCE INS CO
4.1	4.0	N/A	N/A	N/A	N/A	N/A	N/A	N/A	-213.2	0.0	43.8	AMERICAN COMPENSATION INS CO
5.9	4.3	13.7	30.7	-15.8	-24.9	8.3	92.3	100.6	105.9	-75.9	0.0	AMERICAN CONTRACTORS INDEMNITY
1.3	1.2	N/A	N/A	N/A	N/A	N/A	N/A	N/A	-217.5	0.0	0.0	AMERICAN CONTRACTORS INS CO RISK
1.8	1.2	150.7	86.1	3.6	12.2	58.5	25.4	83.9	115.8	26.5	0.0	AMERICAN COUNTRY INS CO
7.4	7.3	N/A	N/A	N/A	N/A	N/A	N/A	N/A	N/A	0.0	17.3	AMERICAN ECONOMY INS CO
1.5	1.2	47.8	94.7	5.9	6.3	86.0	13.0	99.0	207.5	6.3	0.0	AMERICAN EMPIRE INS CO
1.3	1.0	72.7	144.1	10.0	11.1	86.0	13.0	99.0	194.6	6.3	6.6	AMERICAN EMPIRE SURPLUS LINES INS
N/A	N/A	N/A	N/A	N/A	N/A	N/A	N/A	N/A	0.5	0.0	28.9	AMERICAN EQUITY INS CO
2.8	1.7	72.1	123.7	-2.3	-5.5	58.7	30.2	88.9	108.8	2.9	0.0	AMERICAN EQUITY SPECIALTY INS CO
2.2	1.7	47.1	88.8	-1.0	-2.9	84.6	38.5	123.1	70.5	-2.3	15.9	AMERICAN EUROPEAN INS CO
2.3	1.7	11.9	78.2	6.2	-0.9	139.9	23.9	163.8	97.2	-4.0	0.0 ●	AMERICAN EXCESS INS EXCHANGE RRG
2.9	1.9	114.4	26.8	-2.6	-1.2	48.2	46.1	94.3	98.2	-25.4	9.4	AMERICAN FAMILY HOME INS CO
9.0	8.1	N/A	N/A	N/A	N/A	N/A	N/A	N/A	6.2	0.0	0.0	AMERICAN FAMILY INS CO
2.1	1.6	105.4	55.1	-4.3	-3.3	63.5	31.0	94.5	107.9	3.0	16.7 ●	AMERICAN FAMILY MUT INS CO
N/A	N/A	0.9	0.1	-7.6	-8.7	-712.3	115.5	-596.8	N/A	229.5	0.0	AMERICAN FARMERS & RANCHERS INS
2.4	1.7	184.1	35.6	-28.6	-60.6	57.0	30.0	87.0	116.6	10.5	9.9	AMERICAN FARMERS & RANCHERS
1.4	1.2	106.2	3.2	-1.1	-2.1	6.7	77.5	84.2	117.4	-5.3	0.0	AMERICAN FEDERATED INS CO
N/A	N/A	N/A	N/A	-7.9	-22.0	N/A	N/A	N/A	N/A	0.0	0.0	AMERICAN FEED INDUSTRY INS CO RRG
129.2	87.1	N/A	N/A	N/A	N/A	N/A	N/A	N/A	N/A	0.0	0.0	AMERICAN FIRE & CASUALTY CO
1.7	1.2	39.7	74.3	-8.8	-13.4	55.1	39.7	94.8	68.4	110.5	0.0	AMERICAN FOREST CASUALTY CO RRG
1.2	1.1	191.1	86.5	-8.4	-15.0	50.5	35.2	85.7	117.6	16.6	0.0	AMERICAN FREEDOM INS CO
20.0	18.0	N/A	N/A	N/A	N/A	N/A	N/A	N/A	-66.7	0.0	0.0	AMERICAN GUARANTEE & LIABILITY INS
1.8	1.5	91.5	84.4	-2.0	-1.7	65.6	26.9	92.5	101.0	31.8	27.6	AMERICAN HALLMARK INS CO OF TX
N/A	N/A	N/A	N/A	12.4	6.6	999 +	999 +	999 +	N/A	102.6	0.0	AMERICAN HEALTHCARE INDEMNITY CO
0.4	0.3	358.9	369.4	N/A	0.1	61.1	40.0	101.1	107.1	1.5	0.0	AMERICAN HEARTLAND INS CO
2.3	1.6	86.0	198.3	12.6	17.6	90.5	29.9	120.4	84.4	3.8	0.9 ●	AMERICAN HOME ASR CO
1.7	1.6	87.4	68.6	19.1	34.7	84.3	15.4	99.7	75.1	-33.5	27.0	AMERICAN INDEPENDENT INS CO
8.1	7.3	N/A	N/A	N/A	N/A	N/A	N/A	N/A	43.5	0.0	0.0 ●	AMERICAN INS CO
2.2	1.6	160.4	46.2	5.0	1.6	50.3	34.3	84.6	136.9	2.1	0.0	AMERICAN INTEGRITY INS CO OF FL
0.9	0.6	129.3	99.1	-4.0	N/A	61.7	27.7	89.4	143.5	1.7	0.0	AMERICAN INTER FIDELITY EXCHANGE
1.9	1.5	81.3	141.7	-10.4	-16.6	57.1	22.5	79.6	137.7	-1.2	12.6 ●	AMERICAN INTERSTATE INS CO
1.8	1.4	74.2	119.2	-10.9	-18.0	58.0	22.7	80.7	137.9	-1.6	0.0	AMERICAN INTERSTATE INS CO OF
0.2	0.1	450.2	406.2	13.8	74.6	75.4	37.7	113.1	94.2	-31.9	0.0	AMERICAN LIBERTY INS CO
N/A	N/A	N/A	20.5	-0.1	0.4	N/A	N/A	N/A	N/A	0.0	0.0	AMERICAN MEDICAL ASR CO
2.6	1.8	104.5	34.1	3.4	2.1	79.2	27.5	106.7	92.1	2.8	9.5	AMERICAN MERCURY INS CO
8.7	7.9	N/A	N/A	N/A	N/A	N/A	N/A	N/A	9.2	0.0	0.0	AMERICAN MERCURY LLOYDS INS CO
0.6	0.5	77.8	60.3	13.8	22.3	100.2	-7.9	92.3	60.9	131.3	0.0	AMERICAN MILLENNIUM INS CO
9.9	8.9	N/A	N/A	N/A	N/A	N/A	N/A	N/A	-299.3	0.0	0.0	AMERICAN MINING INS CO
2.0	1.6	84.9	19.9	-1.9	-0.9	48.2	46.2	94.4	108.3	-25.4	34.5 ●	AMERICAN MODERN HOME INS CO
1.7	1.0	165.5	38.7	-3.8	-1.7	48.2	46.5	94.7	106.9	-25.4	0.0	AMERICAN MODERN INS CO OF FLORIDA
2.5	2.2	N/A	N/A	N/A	N/A	N/A	N/A	N/A	79.4	0.0	0.0	AMERICAN MODERN LLOYDS INS CO
11.1	6.6	23.2	5.4	-0.5	-0.6	48.2	46.9	95.1	114.9	-25.4	0.0	AMERICAN MODERN PROPERTY &
5.0	2.9	73.9	17.3	-1.7	-0.8	48.2	38.4	86.6	63.0	-25.4	0.0	AMERICAN MODERN SELECT INS CO
2.0	1.2	127.9	29.9	-2.8	-1.3	48.2	46.9	95.1	95.0	-25.4	0.0	AMERICAN MODERN SURPLUS LINES
9.0	7.9	0.1	11.0	-11.5	-19.8	999 +	999 +	999 +	2.3	-9.8	9.1 ●	AMERICAN MUTUAL SHARE INS CORP
5.9	4.1	48.4	31.0	-2.3	-5.2	72.4	24.2	96.6	90.9	-7.8	0.0	AMERICAN NATIONAL GENERAL INS CO

999 + Denotes number greater than 999.9%
999 - Denotes number less than -999.99%
● Bullets denote a more detailed analysis is available in Section II.

INSURANCE COMPANY NAME	DOM. STATE	RATING	TOTAL ASSETS ($MIL)	CAPITAL & SURPLUS ($MIL)	ANNUAL NET PREMIUM ($MIL)	NET INCOME ($MIL)	CAPITAL-IZATION INDEX (PTS)	RESERVE ADQ INDEX (PTS)	PROFIT-ABILITY INDEX (PTS)	LIQUIDITY INDEX (PTS)	STAB. INDEX (PTS)	STABILITY FACTORS
AMERICAN NATIONAL LLOYDS INS CO	TX	B	86.7	64.6	19.2	-2.6	10.0	5.9	5.9	6.9	4.7	T
AMERICAN NATIONAL PROPERTY & CAS CO	MO	B	1,292.6	628.9	496.5	-1.0	8.0	8.4	6.8	6.2	4.9	T
AMERICAN NATL COUNTY MUT INS CO	TX	B	22.3	9.1	0.0	0.0	8.1	N/A	6.5	6.9	4.7	DGT
AMERICAN PACIFIC INS CO	HI	U	11.6	11.5	0.0	-1.3	N/A	6.0	4.6	10.0	5.0	GT
AMERICAN PET INS CO	NY	D	47.2	27.7	116.6	1.7	1.9	6.1	8.9	0.0	2.3	LT
AMERICAN PHYSICIANS ASR CORP	MI	U	344.1	249.0	0.4	6.8	N/A	10.0	8.5	9.9	6.5	FGT
AMERICAN PLATINUM PROP & CAS INS CO	FL	C+	20.5	14.8	3.5	0.0	9.7	4.6	4.8	7.4	3.2	DGT
AMERICAN PROPERTY INS	NJ	D+	18.2	7.2	6.9	0.4	4.4	7.0	1.9	7.0	2.2	DGRT
AMERICAN RELIABLE INS CO	AZ	B	273.8	89.1	-13.3	0.2	8.8	4.7	5.1	6.6	4.2	FRT
AMERICAN RESOURCES INS CO INC	OK	D	23.9	6.2	9.9	-0.2	0.9	7.0	1.6	6.8	1.6	CDGR
AMERICAN RISK INS CO	TX	D+	33.1	10.5	13.8	-0.6	5.0	1.8	5.1	2.3	2.4	DGLT
AMERICAN RISK MGMT RRG INC	TN	U	2.0	1.4	0.0	0.0	N/A	0.0	2.8	0.0	0.0	LT
AMERICAN ROAD INS CO	MI	C+	663.4	237.2	134.6	-15.2	10.0	7.4	5.6	9.1	3.0	RT
AMERICAN SAFETY INS CO	GA	C	18.1	17.4	0.0	0.3	10.0	N/A	3.9	7.0	3.3	DGRT
AMERICAN SAFETY RRG INC	VT	D+	8.3	6.1	0.5	-0.3	8.1	9.8	2.0	8.7	2.1	DFGR
AMERICAN SECURITY INS CO	DE	B-	1,506.1	553.3	1,047.3	78.2	7.8	6.1	3.3	6.5	4.7	AT
AMERICAN SELECT INS CO	OH	C	244.7	109.5	88.5	3.8	8.8	9.2	6.1	6.6	3.8	T
AMERICAN SENTINEL INS CO	PA	C	36.3	17.3	21.3	0.4	3.5	9.1	8.4	5.7	3.2	CDGT
AMERICAN SERVICE INS CO	IL	D	156.6	55.7	70.5	4.1	7.1	4.3	5.8	6.6	1.8	RT
AMERICAN SOUTHERN HOME INS CO	FL	C	182.1	46.6	31.2	1.6	8.8	7.7	8.4	7.5	3.8	FT
AMERICAN SOUTHERN INS CO	KS	C+	114.2	39.9	55.6	2.5	7.5	9.0	5.8	6.0	3.3	RT
AMERICAN SPECIAL RISK INS CO	DE	U	0.8	0.8	0.0	0.0	N/A	3.6	3.3	7.0	2.4	FGT
AMERICAN STANDARD INS CO OF OH	OH	B	9.6	8.1	0.0	0.1	10.0	N/A	7.9	6.9	4.7	DGT
AMERICAN STANDARD INS CO OF WI	WI	B+	433.2	341.5	0.0	3.1	10.0	N/A	7.7	8.7	5.0	T
AMERICAN STATES INS CO	IN	C+	132.1	127.8	0.0	-0.5	10.0	3.9	3.2	7.0	4.5	ART
AMERICAN STATES INS CO OF TX	TX	B	12.2	12.0	0.0	0.1	10.0	N/A	3.4	7.0	4.0	DGRT
AMERICAN STATES LLOYDS INS CO	TX	B	3.6	3.6	0.0	0.0	10.0	N/A	6.7	7.0	4.1	DGRT
AMERICAN STATES PREFERRED INS CO	IN	B-	21.8	21.7	0.0	0.0	10.0	3.9	3.7	7.0	3.5	ADGR
AMERICAN STEAMSHIP O M PROT & IND AS	NY	D+	302.0	61.7	77.8	-3.9	6.3	6.9	3.8	6.5	2.0	DFRT
AMERICAN STRATEGIC INS CO	FL	C	999.2	432.6	576.1	-7.1	8.4	9.3	5.7	6.6	3.9	T
AMERICAN SUMMIT INS CO	TX	C+	48.4	29.4	26.3	1.1	8.7	6.5	6.1	7.1	3.6	RT
AMERICAN SURETY CO	IN	C	14.1	10.8	10.2	1.1	7.1	8.7	3.8	7.0	2.4	DGT
AMERICAN TRADITIONS INS CO	FL	C	50.7	19.8	27.0	-1.2	6.0	4.6	5.7	6.9	3.1	DRT
AMERICAN TRANSIT INS CO	NY	E+	311.8	56.5	227.5	5.8	1.6	0.1	3.6	5.2	0.4	CGRT
AMERICAN TRUCKING & TRANSP INS RRG	MT	E+	34.3	5.7	6.6	0.2	0.3	7.0	1.3	7.8	0.5	CDGR
AMERICAN UNDERWRITERS INS CO	AR	D+	6.1	4.9	0.0	0.0	10.0	N/A	2.6	7.0	2.5	DFGR
AMERICAN WEST INS CO	ND	C	18.5	12.0	6.9	0.7	7.5	5.6	6.0	6.1	3.0	DGT
AMERICAN WESTERN HOME INS CO	OK	C	180.4	72.4	70.1	1.0	8.6	7.9	8.3	6.4	3.9	FT
AMERICAN ZURICH INS CO	IL	C+	348.7	228.1	0.0	1.5	10.0	N/A	7.6	10.0	4.5	FRT
AMERICAS INS CO	DC	C	22.2	8.3	8.1	-0.4	7.1	6.4	2.7	7.1	2.3	DFGR
AMERIGUARD RRG INC	VT	D	14.9	8.4	2.7	0.5	6.7	6.9	6.7	9.4	2.2	DGT
AMERIHEALTH CASUALTY INS CO	DE	C+	293.6	62.9	110.3	-0.3	4.2	5.7	5.2	6.2	3.5	CRT
AMERIPRISE INS CO	WI	B	48.6	47.9	0.0	1.7	10.0	N/A	6.9	10.0	4.0	T
AMERISURE INS CO	MI	B-	821.3	237.2	232.8	-0.3	8.3	6.4	6.8	6.8	4.4	RT
AMERISURE MUTUAL INS CO	MI	B-	2,192.8	882.9	519.9	6.4	8.1	6.3	6.8	6.9	4.7	T
AMERISURE PARTNERS INS CO	MI	C+	79.5	23.6	23.3	0.0	7.4	6.7	5.5	6.9	3.7	DT
AMERITRUST INS CORP	MI	C-	115.2	28.6	35.1	2.2	7.5	2.2	4.9	6.6	3.0	FRT
AMEX ASSURANCE CO	IL	B	265.9	215.4	188.2	31.1	10.0	8.8	3.9	6.7	4.5	RT
AMFED CASUALTY INS CO	MS	D	5.7	5.1	0.0	0.0	10.0	N/A	7.1	10.0	2.3	DFGR
AMFED NATIONAL INS CO	MS	D-	72.8	30.5	22.6	0.7	0.8	0.5	8.2	7.0	0.9	CT
AMFIRST SPECIALTY INS CO	MS	U	2.0	2.0	0.0	0.0	N/A	0.0	3.9	0.0	0.0	LT
AMGUARD INS CO	PA	C	569.6	126.1	97.0	2.0	7.3	9.6	8.3	6.9	2.9	RT

See Page 27 for explanation of footnotes and
Page 28 for explanation of stability factors.
Arrows denote recent upgrades ▲ or downgrades ▼   (see Section VII for explanations)

38

www.weissratings.com

RISK ADJ. RATIO #1	CAPITAL RATIO #2	PREMIUM TO SURPLUS (%)	RESV. TO SURPLUS (%)	RESV. DEVELOP. 1 YEAR (%)	RESV. DEVELOP. 2 YEAR (%)	LOSS RATIO (%)	EXP. RATIO (%)	COMB RATIO (%)	CASH FROM UNDER-WRITING (%)	NET PREMIUM GROWTH (%)	INVEST. IN AFFIL (%)	INSURANCE COMPANY NAME
7.7	6.4	28.7	6.8	0.2	1.3	62.2	20.7	82.9	132.9	-0.4	0.0	AMERICAN NATIONAL LLOYDS INS CO
2.1	1.7	78.1	40.8	-2.7	-6.1	70.4	26.4	96.8	105.7	3.2	21.5 ●	AMERICAN NATIONAL PROPERTY & CAS
2.8	1.6	N/A	N/A	N/A	N/A	N/A	999 +	999 +	999 +	0.0	0.0	AMERICAN NATL COUNTY MUT INS CO
N/A	N/A	N/A	1.2	-0.2	0.1	N/A	N/A	N/A	-1.0	0.0	0.0	AMERICAN PACIFIC INS CO
0.9	0.5	447.4	20.6	0.6	-1.9	70.7	27.1	97.8	104.9	23.9	0.0	AMERICAN PET INS CO
N/A	N/A	0.2	37.1	-17.9	-51.2	999 +	999 +	999 +	-1.5	134.8	2.1	AMERICAN PHYSICIANS ASR CORP
5.9	4.0	23.6	4.8	-1.9	-0.3	19.1	55.3	74.4	127.6	-23.8	0.0	AMERICAN PLATINUM PROP & CAS INS
0.7	0.5	101.5	18.0	-1.7	-8.7	37.9	32.5	70.4	224.8	184.9	0.0	AMERICAN PROPERTY INS
4.7	3.4	-15.0	81.7	-6.4	0.3	60.5	-110.9	-50.4	39.1	-107.3	1.3	AMERICAN RELIABLE INS CO
0.4	0.2	156.7	150.7	-9.6	-18.8	51.1	47.9	99.0	106.1	11.8	0.0	AMERICAN RESOURCES INS CO INC
0.8	0.5	124.5	41.4	4.1	29.1	51.2	28.5	79.7	119.6	19.6	0.0	AMERICAN RISK INS CO
N/A	N/A	N/A	N/A	N/A	N/A	N/A	N/A	N/A	N/A	0.0	0.0	AMERICAN RISK MGMT RRG INC
10.4	6.2	53.6	2.3	-0.4	-0.8	65.0	2.4	67.4	132.9	7.0	0.0 ●	AMERICAN ROAD INS CO
22.8	8.3	N/A	N/A	N/A	N/A	N/A	N/A	N/A	N/A	0.0	0.0	AMERICAN SAFETY INS CO
2.0	1.6	7.5	30.9	-18.4	-21.3	-196.0	514.9	318.9	9.7	236.6	0.0	AMERICAN SAFETY RRG INC
2.1	1.5	187.4	40.5	-3.3	2.1	36.6	43.7	80.3	111.6	-23.5	9.5 ●	AMERICAN SECURITY INS CO
3.6	2.4	86.0	75.1	-2.8	-6.5	62.7	33.3	96.0	108.4	2.1	0.0	AMERICAN SELECT INS CO
0.8	0.5	134.9	39.9	-0.7	-2.2	42.4	48.6	91.0	119.6	2.8	0.0	AMERICAN SENTINEL INS CO
3.5	2.2	137.9	78.8	3.5	11.4	58.5	25.5	84.0	115.3	26.5	0.0	AMERICAN SERVICE INS CO
3.5	2.5	69.7	16.3	-1.5	-0.7	48.2	45.4	93.6	62.3	-25.4	8.2	AMERICAN SOUTHERN HOME INS CO
1.8	1.3	145.2	103.3	-3.8	-0.3	64.3	32.4	96.7	103.7	10.5	17.5	AMERICAN SOUTHERN INS CO
N/A	N/A	N/A	N/A	N/A	N/A	N/A	N/A	N/A	N/A	0.0	0.0	AMERICAN SPECIAL RISK INS CO
14.3	12.9	N/A	N/A	N/A	N/A	N/A	N/A	N/A	177.6	0.0	0.0	AMERICAN STANDARD INS CO OF OH
39.5	35.6	N/A	N/A	N/A	N/A	N/A	N/A	N/A	337.8	0.0	0.0 ●	AMERICAN STANDARD INS CO OF WI
111.2	97.4	N/A	N/A	N/A	N/A	N/A	N/A	N/A	N/A	0.0	0.0	AMERICAN STATES INS CO
86.7	46.9	N/A	N/A	N/A	N/A	N/A	N/A	N/A	N/A	0.0	0.0	AMERICAN STATES INS CO OF TX
227.2	113.7	N/A	N/A	N/A	N/A	N/A	N/A	N/A	N/A	0.0	0.0	AMERICAN STATES LLOYDS INS CO
234.0	117.0	N/A	N/A	N/A	N/A	N/A	N/A	N/A	N/A	0.0	0.0	AMERICAN STATES PREFERRED INS CO
1.1	0.8	96.7	207.4	-5.0	-12.5	68.6	35.2	103.8	88.8	-14.2	2.5	AMERICAN STEAMSHIP O M PROT & IND
2.4	2.1	130.4	39.1	-12.2	-19.0	57.9	30.1	88.0	116.1	15.1	1.4 ●	AMERICAN STRATEGIC INS CO
2.6	2.2	85.9	11.6	-2.7	-2.8	61.2	30.2	91.4	108.5	4.1	0.0	AMERICAN SUMMIT INS CO
1.1	1.0	99.5	16.2	-7.8	-6.1	6.3	79.2	85.5	112.4	15.1	0.0	AMERICAN SURETY CO
1.4	1.3	130.2	34.8	-1.6	-1.7	55.1	40.8	95.9	108.8	2.1	0.0	AMERICAN TRADITIONS INS CO
0.4	0.3	452.3	120.6	200.9	377.1	68.6	27.5	96.1	108.9	39.7	0.0	AMERICAN TRANSIT INS CO
0.2	0.2	203.5	533.9	25.3	6.7	139.1	16.2	155.3	130.0	-11.5	0.0	AMERICAN TRUCKING & TRANSP INS
9.5	8.6	N/A	N/A	N/A	N/A	N/A	N/A	N/A	255.1	0.0	0.0	AMERICAN UNDERWRITERS INS CO
1.3	1.1	61.4	8.9	-3.6	-4.7	65.8	27.5	93.3	107.6	1.8	0.0	AMERICAN WEST INS CO
3.9	2.3	98.5	23.0	-2.1	-1.0	48.2	46.7	94.9	93.7	-25.4	0.0	AMERICAN WESTERN HOME INS CO
6.9	6.5	N/A	N/A	N/A	N/A	N/A	N/A	N/A	-849.6	0.0	14.9 ●	AMERICAN ZURICH INS CO
1.3	0.9	92.0	25.6	3.3	5.0	61.7	52.8	114.5	93.7	36.4	6.8	AMERICAS INS CO
1.2	1.0	34.4	53.4	-4.8	-2.3	54.7	9.0	63.7	162.4	2.8	0.0	AMERIGUARD RRG INC
0.9	0.7	186.1	249.5	-14.5	-14.9	62.0	31.2	93.2	116.0	9.4	0.0	AMERIHEALTH CASUALTY INS CO
72.3	32.7	N/A	N/A	N/A	N/A	N/A	N/A	N/A	N/A	0.0	0.0	AMERIPRISE INS CO
2.5	1.8	97.5	159.1	1.5	1.8	64.5	30.7	95.2	104.8	8.1	0.0 ●	AMERISURE INS CO
2.2	1.7	59.4	96.9	0.9	1.1	64.5	30.6	95.1	112.0	8.1	14.6 ●	AMERISURE MUTUAL INS CO
1.7	1.2	97.5	159.0	1.5	1.7	64.5	30.7	95.2	105.7	8.1	0.0	AMERISURE PARTNERS INS CO
1.9	1.2	114.3	206.7	14.5	23.1	77.1	35.3	112.4	71.7	0.7	0.0	AMERITRUST INS CORP
12.0	6.8	102.1	16.8	-5.9	-8.6	36.6	19.0	55.6	186.7	2.6	0.0	AMEX ASSURANCE CO
19.7	17.7	N/A	N/A	N/A	N/A	N/A	N/A	N/A	999 +	0.0	0.0	AMFED CASUALTY INS CO
0.3	0.2	76.8	111.7	12.8	139.0	58.6	19.9	78.5	149.4	-26.3	8.2	AMFED NATIONAL INS CO
N/A	N/A	N/A	N/A	N/A	N/A	N/A	N/A	N/A	N/A	0.0	0.0	AMFIRST SPECIALTY INS CO
1.9	1.3	82.6	125.9	-18.2	-8.1	53.2	33.8	87.0	123.4	-17.4	0.0	AMGUARD INS CO

999 + Denotes number greater than 999.9%
999 - Denotes number less than -999.99%
● Bullets denote a more detailed analysis is available in Section II.

INSURANCE COMPANY NAME	DOM. STATE	RATING	TOTAL ASSETS ($MIL)	CAPITAL & SURPLUS ($MIL)	ANNUAL NET PREMIUM ($MIL)	NET INCOME ($MIL)	CAPITAL-IZATION INDEX (PTS)	RESERVE ADQ INDEX (PTS)	PROFIT-ABILITY INDEX (PTS)	LIQUIDITY INDEX (PTS)	STAB. INDEX (PTS)	STABILITY FACTORS
AMICA MUTUAL INS CO	RI	B+	4,974.1	2,549.3	1,942.8	18.5	8.3	8.1	6.0	5.8	5.4	FT
AMICA P&C INS CO	RI	C	83.2	78.4	0.0	0.2	10.0	7.0	3.1	10.0	4.3	DGT
AMICA TEXAS INS CO	TX	B (3)	77.8	74.4	-0.3	1.6	10.0	6.2	8.1	8.0	4.8	DT
AMSHIELD INS CO	MO	U	4.6	4.6	0.0	-0.1	N/A	N/A	2.8	7.0	4.0	FGT
AMTRUST INS CO OF KANSAS INC	KS	B-	91.6	27.5	21.4	1.9	7.4	6.4	9.3	7.3	3.9	GRT
ANCHOR GENERAL INS CO	CA	C	108.6	23.2	50.4	-1.8	6.1	6.5	3.6	1.7	3.2	FLRT
ANCHOR P&C INS CO	FL	B-	70.8	26.0	54.0	-0.8	3.3	N/A	3.6	6.9	3.5	CGT
ANCHOR SPECIALTY INS CO	TX	C	18.5	9.1	9.6	-0.2	4.3	4.0	2.9	7.1	2.8	CDGR
ANPAC LOUISIANA INS CO	LA	B	126.4	68.2	50.4	-3.3	8.4	6.9	4.6	6.3	4.3	T
ANSUR AMERICA INS CO	MI	B	111.4	41.9	46.2	2.5	9.2	9.3	6.7	6.5	4.6	T
ANTHRACITE MUTUAL FIRE INS CO	PA	C-	3.9	3.9	0.4	0.1	10.0	5.0	8.1	9.3	2.5	DGT
ANTILLES INS CO	PR	C-	72.2	46.2	30.8	1.8	2.8	7.9	2.9	1.6	3.1	CLRT
APOLLO CASUALTY CO	IL	D+	19.1	5.4	5.3	-0.5	7.6	1.8	2.7	6.4	2.7	DFGT
APOLLO MUTUAL FIRE INS CO	PA	C- (2)	3.9	3.8	0.2	0.1	10.0	4.6	5.7	10.0	2.0	DGT
APPALACHIAN INS CO	RI	C	320.8	208.9	65.2	3.0	9.3	2.6	6.1	8.1	2.4	RT
APPLIED MEDICO LEGAL SOLUTIONS RRG	AZ	C-	134.3	38.4	42.0	0.7	7.0	7.0	6.9	7.3	3.3	RT
APPLIED UNDERWRITERS CAPTIVE RISK	IA	D	952.8	58.7	0.0	2.6	10.0	3.1	5.6	10.0	2.3	T
ARAG INS CO	IA	B-	79.4	60.3	69.2	6.9	9.5	8.9	9.3	6.2	3.7	RT
ARBELLA INDEMNITY INS CO	MA	C	50.1	15.3	24.0	0.7	7.4	7.9	2.9	6.1	3.1	DRT
ARBELLA MUTUAL INS CO	MA	C+	1,399.1	530.4	609.1	20.5	8.2	7.8	4.0	6.0	4.3	RT
ARBELLA PROTECTION INS CO	MA	C+	330.3	93.9	128.2	4.2	8.7	8.1	4.3	5.7	4.1	FRT
ARCH EXCESS & SURPLUS INS CO	MO	U	65.1	64.8	0.0	0.4	N/A	6.1	6.8	7.0	6.1	T
ARCH INDEMNITY INS CO	MO	B-	62.7	27.1	0.0	0.5	10.0	N/A	4.7	9.1	3.7	DGRT
ARCH INS CO	MO	C	3,619.7	875.3	772.9	38.5	7.1	7.5	6.7	6.8	3.4	RT
ARCH MORTGAGE ASR CO	WI	U	15.0	14.8	0.1	-0.1	N/A	6.4	3.6	9.2	4.8	GT
ARCH MORTGAGE GUARANTY CO	WI	B	51.7	49.9	-0.1	0.4	10.0	3.6	6.0	10.0	4.6	DFGT
ARCH MORTGAGE INS CO	WI	C+	451.7	119.6	60.7	-12.9	7.1	4.1	2.6	6.2	4.5	FRT
▲ARCH MORTGAGE REINS CO	WI	C-	20.8	14.6	0.2	1.0	8.2	4.4	2.9	9.2	3.1	DFGT
ARCH REINS CO	DE	C-	1,963.4	1,249.9	219.0	17.2	7.8	8.1	7.6	7.2	2.7	RT
ARCH SPECIALTY INS CO	MO	B	515.4	300.0	0.3	-8.0	10.0	6.0	5.5	9.3	4.7	FGRT
ARCHITECTS & ENGINEERS INS CO RRG	DE	C	21.5	9.1	1.4	0.1	10.0	6.6	4.4	8.4	2.3	DGRT
ARCOA RRG INC	NV	E	15.9	6.2	10.2	0.6	0.3	2.8	2.9	6.9	0.3	CDGT
ARECA INS EXCHANGE	AK	C+	28.4	20.0	3.9	0.4	8.9	5.4	3.8	8.1	3.1	DGRT
ARGONAUT GREAT CENTRAL INS CO	IL	D+	42.7	25.4	0.0	0.3	10.0	N/A	6.9	6.9	2.4	RT
ARGONAUT INS CO	IL	C	1,616.4	795.7	192.2	28.5	7.1	2.8	5.5	6.9	3.3	FRT
ARGONAUT LTD RISK INS CO	IL	U	11.7	11.6	0.0	0.1	N/A	N/A	6.6	7.0	5.0	GT
ARGONAUT-MIDWEST INS CO	IL	D	22.1	17.4	0.0	0.2	10.0	N/A	6.3	7.0	2.2	DGRT
ARGONAUT-SOUTHWEST INS CO	IL	D	18.2	18.1	0.0	0.1	10.0	N/A	6.5	7.0	2.3	DGRT
ARGUS FIRE & CASUALTY INS CO	FL	F	3.6	3.1	0.0	-0.1	10.0	4.7	2.8	10.0	0.0	DFGT
ARI CASUALTY CO	NJ	U	8.1	8.1	0.0	0.1	N/A	3.6	3.6	7.0	4.8	GRT
ARI INS CO	PA	D	108.3	16.3	6.8	-6.1	1.0	1.9	0.8	5.7	1.7	CDFR
ARISE BOILER INSPECT & INS CO RRG	KY	B-	4.1	3.1	0.8	0.1	10.0	8.6	8.6	7.9	3.5	DGT
ARIZONA AUTOMOBILE INS CO	AZ	C-	23.0	9.6	9.1	0.0	9.1	8.5	8.1	6.7	2.9	DFGR
ARIZONA HOME INS CO	AZ	D	26.2	17.0	9.4	0.1	6.3	8.2	8.4	6.5	2.1	DGRT
ARK ROYAL INS CO	FL	C	114.2	37.0	49.1	-7.0	7.2	8.8	3.8	6.8	3.3	T
ARKANSAS MUTUAL INS CO	AR	C-	5.7	3.4	-4.1	-0.7	8.7	7.0	2.0	8.9	2.5	DFGT
ARMED FORCES INS EXCHANGE	KS	B-	145.1	69.5	69.9	-9.0	8.9	9.0	3.0	6.7	3.7	RT
ARROW MUTUAL LIABILITY INS CO	MA	B-	49.1	31.3	6.9	0.8	8.6	8.8	4.4	7.3	3.7	DRT
ARROWOOD INDEMNITY CO	DE	D+	1,294.8	235.0	-1.8	-6.1	0.7	4.6	1.8	9.1	2.4	CFRT
ARROWOOD SURPLUS LINES INS CO	DE	U	91.3	83.4	0.0	0.8	N/A	7.7	2.2	7.0	3.4	FT
ARTISAN & TRUCKERS CASUALTY CO	WI	C	324.4	62.1	44.5	3.4	10.0	5.9	8.8	8.0	3.6	RT
ASCENDANT COMMERCIAL INS INC	FL	E+	45.8	10.5	29.1	0.1	1.6	0.5	5.8	7.4	0.5	DGT

RISK ADJ. RATIO #1	CAPITAL RATIO #2	PREMIUM TO SURPLUS (%)	RESV. TO SURPLUS (%)	RESV. DEVELOP. 1 YEAR (%)	2 YEAR (%)	LOSS RATIO (%)	EXP. RATIO (%)	COMB RATIO (%)	CASH FROM UNDER-WRITING (%)	NET PREMIUM GROWTH (%)	INVEST. IN AFFIL (%)	INSURANCE COMPANY NAME
2.6	1.8	74.4	43.4	-3.6	-6.6	80.9	24.0	104.9	99.6	5.5	8.6 ●	AMICA MUTUAL INS CO
40.3	16.5	N/A	N/A	-0.8	-0.7	999 +	999 +	999 +	-594.0	0.0	0.0	AMICA P&C INS CO
68.6	59.9	-0.4	2.4	-0.7	-0.4	38.0	999 +	999 +	136.2	-101.6	0.0	AMICA TEXAS INS CO
N/A	N/A	N/A	N/A	N/A	N/A	N/A	N/A	N/A	N/A	0.0	0.0	AMSHIELD INS CO
1.6	1.0	86.8	45.5	-0.2	-3.7	64.6	-17.6	47.0	915.7	153.4	4.0	AMTRUST INS CO OF KANSAS INC
0.9	0.7	202.8	78.7	2.5	1.6	73.0	25.8	98.8	97.4	22.5	25.6	ANCHOR GENERAL INS CO
0.7	0.5	202.6	23.8	N/A	N/A	52.2	21.8	74.0	278.7	0.0	0.0	ANCHOR P&C INS CO
0.8	0.6	102.7	22.7	4.8	7.6	105.4	28.9	134.3	135.6	861.5	0.0	ANCHOR SPECIALTY INS CO
4.0	2.7	69.0	37.4	-0.2	-5.2	74.7	20.9	95.6	109.1	9.9	0.0	ANPAC LOUISIANA INS CO
4.0	2.9	118.0	81.4	-10.4	-13.8	62.1	30.8	92.9	108.6	5.3	0.0	ANSUR AMERICA INS CO
12.2	7.3	9.3	0.1	0.2	0.6	24.3	42.7	67.0	122.7	3.1	0.0	ANTHRACITE MUTUAL FIRE INS CO
0.7	0.5	68.7	7.0	-1.3	-2.9	40.2	70.1	110.3	95.9	-27.1	0.0	ANTILLES INS CO
1.4	1.1	88.5	69.5	19.2	32.7	84.3	24.3	108.6	60.4	-33.5	0.0	APOLLO CASUALTY CO
7.7	5.3	5.3	0.1	-0.1	-0.1	32.2	57.8	90.0	116.8	118.8	0.0	APOLLO MUTUAL FIRE INS CO
4.2	2.5	31.7	39.6	7.1	14.2	58.1	28.6	86.7	163.1	2.4	0.0 ●	APPALACHIAN INS CO
1.5	1.0	118.4	175.5	4.5	0.5	72.5	27.7	100.2	127.3	7.7	0.0	APPLIED MEDICO LEGAL SOLUTIONS
3.6	3.1	N/A	9.2	-4.2	0.1	N/A	N/A	N/A	-243.3	0.0	0.0	APPLIED UNDERWRITERS CAPTIVE RISK
4.9	3.2	129.9	28.9	-3.6	-7.3	43.6	33.0	76.6	129.8	2.7	0.0	ARAG INS CO
1.8	1.2	163.3	90.0	-2.3	-3.1	82.2	30.4	112.6	104.3	5.8	0.0	ARBELLA INDEMNITY INS CO
2.4	1.8	119.3	65.7	-1.7	-2.3	82.2	29.3	111.5	99.8	5.5	14.4 ●	ARBELLA MUTUAL INS CO
3.2	2.1	141.8	78.1	-2.1	-3.0	82.2	30.3	112.5	94.2	6.5	0.0	ARBELLA PROTECTION INS CO
N/A	N/A	N/A	0.3	0.1	0.4	999 +	999 +	999 +	-0.4	100.0	40.2	ARCH EXCESS & SURPLUS INS CO
5.2	4.6	N/A	2.0	N/A	N/A	N/A	N/A	N/A	-126.9	0.0	0.0	ARCH INDEMNITY INS CO
1.6	1.2	93.5	178.4	0.7	-1.3	68.5	26.5	95.0	132.5	-1.6	15.0 ●	ARCH INS CO
N/A	N/A	0.5	0.6	-0.2	-0.6	110.9	225.5	336.4	24.5	-29.4	84.1	ARCH MORTGAGE ASR CO
76.7	61.7	-0.1	0.1	N/A	-0.2	20.9	-518.1	-497.2	-7.8	-121.5	0.0	ARCH MORTGAGE GUARANTY CO
1.0	0.9	45.1	39.2	-5.8	-3.4	23.3	136.6	159.9	71.9	15.4	5.5	ARCH MORTGAGE INS CO
7.9	5.5	1.7	34.3	-6.6	-8.0	90.3	-397.5	-307.2	3.2	-44.5	0.0	ARCH MORTGAGE REINS CO
1.6	1.5	18.2	30.8	-2.7	-4.9	49.2	36.9	86.1	134.0	-10.8	49.3 ●	ARCH REINS CO
5.5	4.4	0.1	14.8	0.3	0.6	999 +	999 +	999 +	-207.3	-71.1	0.0 ●	ARCH SPECIALTY INS CO
3.4	3.1	15.2	37.1	-1.9	-4.1	70.0	-13.6	56.4	177.1	-33.9	0.0	ARCHITECTS & ENGINEERS INS CO RRG
0.2	0.2	190.1	150.0	-9.5	-28.5	39.8	43.8	83.6	136.2	-4.2	0.0	ARCOA RRG INC
6.3	3.3	19.1	33.3	-6.3	-3.5	59.3	39.3	98.6	126.5	-17.7	0.0	ARECA INS EXCHANGE
7.8	7.0	N/A	N/A	N/A	N/A	N/A	N/A	N/A	999 +	0.0	2.6	ARGONAUT GREAT CENTRAL INS CO
2.4	1.5	46.2	116.2	4.2	15.6	70.4	31.0	101.4	81.5	3.8	11.5 ●	ARGONAUT INS CO
N/A	N/A	N/A	N/A	N/A	N/A	N/A	N/A	N/A	N/A	0.0	0.0	ARGONAUT LTD RISK INS CO
11.9	10.7	N/A	N/A	N/A	N/A	N/A	N/A	N/A	N/A	0.0	0.0	ARGONAUT-MIDWEST INS CO
90.8	43.8	N/A	N/A	N/A	N/A	N/A	N/A	N/A	17.1	0.0	0.0	ARGONAUT-SOUTHWEST INS CO
14.2	12.8	N/A	10.0	3.6	-11.7	N/A	N/A	N/A	N/A	100.0	0.0	ARGUS FIRE & CASUALTY INS CO
N/A	N/A	N/A	N/A	N/A	N/A	N/A	N/A	N/A	N/A	0.0	0.0	ARI CASUALTY CO
0.4	0.3	51.9	321.8	36.2	42.8	123.0	51.8	174.8	27.7	-82.3	14.9	ARI INS CO
5.6	4.5	28.6	5.2	-6.0	-7.0	N/A	54.4	54.4	185.6	-1.3	0.0	ARISE BOILER INSPECT & INS CO RRG
3.3	2.3	95.0	68.8	-5.0	-4.7	65.2	29.5	94.7	53.9	19.5	0.0	ARIZONA AUTOMOBILE INS CO
1.5	0.9	56.3	16.5	-2.5	-5.5	70.4	22.8	93.2	103.6	9.2	0.0	ARIZONA HOME INS CO
2.4	1.8	114.3	26.9	-5.6	-17.0	39.5	33.9	73.4	124.7	10.1	0.0	ARK ROYAL INS CO
4.8	4.3	-99.2	N/A	-99.3	-37.7	90.0	-32.0	58.0	-66.2	-240.7	0.0	ARKANSAS MUTUAL INS CO
3.0	2.1	91.9	18.0	-3.6	-6.7	57.6	37.1	94.7	106.8	4.4	3.5	ARMED FORCES INS EXCHANGE
3.5	2.2	22.7	43.1	1.4	-3.6	113.4	7.0	120.4	96.7	6.7	0.0	ARROW MUTUAL LIABILITY INS CO
0.3	0.2	-0.8	421.2	-4.8	12.0	999 +	999 +	999 +	-0.1	5.6	7.4 ●	ARROWOOD INDEMNITY CO
N/A	N/A	N/A	9.0	-0.4	-2.5	N/A	N/A	N/A	N/A	0.0	0.0	ARROWOOD SURPLUS LINES INS CO
6.0	4.2	76.1	48.3	-1.7	-0.1	71.7	17.8	89.5	126.2	1.4	0.0	ARTISAN & TRUCKERS CASUALTY CO
0.5	0.3	280.2	186.1	40.5	59.1	71.0	22.8	93.8	100.2	49.2	0.0	ASCENDANT COMMERCIAL INS INC

999 + Denotes number greater than 999.9%
999 - Denotes number less than -999.99%
● Bullets denote a more detailed analysis is available in Section II.

INSURANCE COMPANY NAME	DOM. STATE	RATING	TOTAL ASSETS ($MIL)	CAPITAL & SURPLUS ($MIL)	ANNUAL NET PREMIUM ($MIL)	NET INCOME ($MIL)	CAPITAL-IZATION INDEX (PTS)	RESERVE ADQ INDEX (PTS)	PROFIT-ABILITY INDEX (PTS)	LIQUIDITY INDEX (PTS)	STAB. INDEX (PTS)	STABILITY FACTORS
ASHLAND MUTUAL FIRE INS CO OF PA	PA	U	0.5	0.5	0.0	0.0	N/A	5.2	2.3	10.0	1.5	FGT
ASHMERE INS CO	IL	U	9.4	9.3	0.0	-0.1	N/A	4.6	2.1	7.0	3.3	FGRT
ASI ASR CORP	FL	B	129.5	65.8	58.6	7.2	9.4	9.4	8.1	7.0	4.2	T
ASI HOME INS CORP	FL	B-	18.8	16.9	0.7	0.2	10.0	N/A	4.4	10.0	3.8	DGRT
▼ASI LLOYDS	TX	D+	205.7	76.1	108.5	-21.3	9.1	8.8	2.9	6.6	2.7	RT
ASI PREFERRED INS CORP	FL	B-	109.7	34.1	51.9	1.1	7.0	8.9	6.1	7.2	3.8	GT
ASI SELECT INS CORP	DE	D	22.5	21.0	0.5	0.0	10.0	4.7	4.8	10.0	2.3	DFGT
ASOC DE SUSCRIPCION CONJUNTA DEL	PR	C	169.7	96.1	101.3	2.8	10.0	6.6	2.6	6.2	3.5	FT
ASPEN AMERICAN INS CO	TX	B-	606.7	278.4	69.4	8.8	10.0	6.9	3.6	8.3	4.2	GRT
ASPEN SPECIALTY INS CO	ND	C	374.7	144.8	64.3	-7.2	4.7	6.2	3.4	7.0	4.1	CRT
ASPEN SPECIALTY RRG INC	DC	U	0.7	0.7	0.0	-0.1	N/A	3.6	1.4	9.8	2.1	FGT
ASPIRE GENERAL INS CO	CA	C-	15.8	8.4	5.9	-0.7	6.6	3.6	1.8	6.1	2.3	DFGT
ASSET PROTECTION PROGRAM RRG INC	SC	U	1.2	1.1	0.0	-0.1	N/A	5.0	2.9	10.0	1.7	FGT
ASSN CASUALTY INS CO	TX	C	46.7	19.4	17.2	0.3	8.2	5.9	4.4	6.6	3.4	DT
ASSN OF CERTIFIED MTG ORIG RRG	NV	D	2.5	1.1	0.1	0.0	9.5	N/A	4.1	9.9	1.0	DGT
ASSOCIATED EMPLOYERS INS CO	MA	C	5.3	4.5	0.0	0.0	10.0	N/A	6.5	10.0	2.6	DGRT
ASSOCIATED INDEMNITY CORP	CA	C	122.0	87.8	0.0	0.6	10.0	3.6	6.5	9.2	4.2	RT
ASSOCIATED INDUSTRIES INS CO INC	FL	C-	290.4	84.5	36.5	11.5	5.6	7.0	4.5	6.6	3.3	GRT
ASSOCIATED INDUSTRIES OF MA MUT INS	MA	C+	583.3	199.1	132.8	4.6	8.0	9.4	8.4	6.8	4.0	RT
ASSOCIATED INTL INS CO	IL	C-	213.7	116.9	1.8	8.8	6.9	3.2	5.7	9.2	2.9	DFRT
ASSOCIATED LOGGERS EXCHANGE	ID	C	33.3	13.8	11.7	0.5	5.5	9.3	5.7	6.7	2.5	DGRT
ASSOCIATED MUTUAL INS CO	NY	C	26.9	9.6	7.6	0.2	5.1	5.8	2.6	7.1	2.3	CDFG
ASSURANCEAMERICA INS CO	SC	D+	51.8	12.2	32.5	-0.1	5.3	4.4	3.3	6.0	2.4	DRT
ASSURED GUARANTY CORP	MD	C-	3,022.8	1,435.1	45.2	67.1	9.0	2.2	5.3	7.0	2.1	AFGR
ASSURED GUARANTY MUNICIPAL CORP	NY	D+	5,665.6	2,440.8	141.8	122.1	7.9	4.4	8.6	9.5	1.9	ACRT
ASURE WORLDWIDE INS CO	MI	C+	40.7	16.8	17.3	1.0	8.8	9.3	6.7	6.5	3.3	DGT
ATAIN INS CO	TX	C	80.8	49.7	14.5	1.5	9.0	8.3	8.7	7.9	3.7	DRT
ATAIN SPECIALTY INS CO	MI	C	351.5	176.8	81.9	7.1	7.6	8.6	8.9	7.0	3.8	RT
ATHENS FINANCIAL INS CO	OK	B-	2.3	2.0	0.3	0.1	10.0	N/A	8.5	10.0	3.5	DGT
ATLANTA INTERNATIONAL INS CO	NY	U	42.5	19.8	0.0	0.2	N/A	4.3	2.7	10.0	3.9	FRT
ATLANTIC BONDING CO	MD	D	9.8	9.0	0.8	0.5	7.8	5.0	3.3	6.9	1.4	DFGT
ATLANTIC CASUALTY INS CO	NC	B-	254.4	92.4	72.1	3.8	7.6	9.3	8.0	6.9	4.4	RT
ATLANTIC CHARTER INS CO	MA	B-	190.7	50.1	59.8	0.6	5.2	9.8	7.3	7.0	3.6	CRT
▲ATLANTIC SPECIALTY INS CO	NY	B-	2,256.9	603.6	590.1	7.8	7.6	5.7	4.4	6.8	4.7	FRT
ATLANTIC STATES INS CO	PA	B-	740.8	220.1	393.1	8.7	8.6	5.8	6.1	6.3	4.2	RT
ATRADIUS TRADE CREDIT INS CO	MD	C	110.6	64.8	18.2	-1.8	10.0	6.6	4.2	7.5	2.9	FRT
ATRIUM INS CORP	NY	U	1.7	1.6	0.0	0.0	N/A	0.2	2.7	7.0	0.5	FGT
ATTORNEYS INS MUTUAL	DC	C-	11.6	6.7	2.1	-0.3	8.3	9.4	2.3	8.3	2.2	DFGR
ATTORNEYS INS MUTUAL RRG	HI	D	15.6	8.7	3.6	0.1	4.1	5.8	5.8	8.1	2.3	DGRT
ATTORNEYS LIAB ASR SOCIETY INC RRG	VT	D	2,096.8	568.8	222.9	3.9	1.1	1.1	4.3	7.0	1.5	CRT
ATTORNEYS LIABILITY PROTECTION SOCIE (See ALPS PROPERTY & CASUALTY INS CO)												
ATTPRO RRG RECIPROCAL RRG	DC	D-	2.7	1.2	0.0	-0.1	8.6	3.6	2.1	9.0	1.3	DGT
AUSTIN MUTUAL INS CO	MN	D-	55.3	42.1	0.0	2.0	10.0	3.3	2.9	10.0	1.3	RT
AUTO CLUB CASUALTY CO	TX	U	2.9	2.9	0.0	0.0	N/A	N/A	6.3	7.0	4.0	GT
AUTO CLUB COUNTY MUTUAL INS CO	TX	D+	91.3	8.3	0.0	0.0	6.6	N/A	6.4	6.5	2.7	DFT
AUTO CLUB FAMILY INS CO	MO	C	113.3	43.1	31.8	-0.5	8.7	7.4	5.4	6.6	3.8	T
AUTO CLUB GROUP INS CO	MI	C+	336.6	122.7	135.5	5.4	9.4	4.3	5.0	6.5	4.5	T
AUTO CLUB INDEMNITY CO	TX	B+	27.2	5.4	0.0	0.0	7.8	N/A	6.4	6.7	5.0	DGT
AUTO CLUB INS ASSN	MI	B	3,921.9	1,690.0	1,432.8	46.4	7.7	4.5	4.6	6.3	4.9	RT
AUTO CLUB INS CO OF FL	FL	B-	369.7	162.8	175.9	7.6	8.9	6.9	8.9	6.6	4.3	T
AUTO CLUB PROPERTY & CASUALTY INS	MI	C	85.3	31.3	38.7	1.0	8.3	4.2	4.5	6.4	3.7	T
▲AUTO CLUB SOUTH INS CO	FL	B-	116.1	55.4	45.5	0.4	9.5	6.4	8.4	6.5	3.6	FT

See Page 27 for explanation of footnotes and Page 28 for explanation of stability factors.
Arrows denote recent upgrades ▲ or downgrades ▼ (see Section VII for explanations)

42

www.weissratings.com

RISK ADJ. RATIO #1	CAPITAL RATIO #2	PREMIUM TO SURPLUS (%)	RESV. TO SURPLUS (%)	RESV. DEVELOP. 1 YEAR (%)	RESV. DEVELOP. 2 YEAR (%)	LOSS RATIO (%)	EXP. RATIO (%)	COMB RATIO (%)	CASH FROM UNDER-WRITING (%)	NET PREMIUM GROWTH (%)	INVEST. IN AFFIL (%)	INSURANCE COMPANY NAME
N/A	N/A	0.4	0.6	-0.4	-0.6	N/A	999 +	999 +	3.5	151.2	0.0	ASHLAND MUTUAL FIRE INS CO OF PA
N/A	N/A	N/A	N/A	N/A	N/A	N/A	N/A	N/A	N/A	-100.0	0.0	ASHMERE INS CO
6.2	5.1	97.6	33.0	-18.1	-24.4	31.1	32.3	63.4	114.1	-7.6	0.0	ASI ASR CORP
24.5	22.0	4.5	0.8	N/A	N/A	74.8	21.9	96.7	242.9	903.5	0.0	ASI HOME INS CORP
2.4	2.1	111.9	28.3	-9.2	-9.2	55.6	30.0	85.6	108.7	8.5	0.0	ASI LLOYDS
1.5	1.2	155.4	19.3	-16.3	-13.5	28.8	34.9	63.7	197.5	119.8	0.0	ASI PREFERRED INS CORP
29.8	19.3	2.4	0.3	-0.5	-3.8	-6.6	76.2	69.6	100.2	N/A	0.0	ASI SELECT INS CORP
8.1	4.9	102.1	17.6	0.1	-5.0	75.9	19.9	95.8	82.7	-24.3	0.0	ASOC DE SUSCRIPCION CONJUNTA DEL
4.1	2.6	25.9	20.7	1.9	0.4	83.5	44.2	127.7	129.0	8.6	0.0 •	ASPEN AMERICAN INS CO
0.7	0.5	42.2	48.2	4.1	7.1	75.3	12.0	87.3	193.2	45.5	0.0	ASPEN SPECIALTY INS CO
N/A	N/A	0.5	1.0	-0.5	N/A	61.5	999 +	999 +	23.6	-70.7	0.0	ASPEN SPECIALTY RRG INC
1.4	1.0	69.3	27.2	-0.9	N/A	106.4	26.5	132.9	81.6	339.5	0.0	ASPIRE GENERAL INS CO
N/A	N/A	N/A	11.1	-37.0	-67.6	N/A	N/A	N/A	N/A	0.0	0.0	ASSET PROTECTION PROGRAM RRG INC
2.7	2.0	89.8	74.1	-3.9	-5.5	64.4	30.2	94.6	100.1	8.6	0.0	ASSN CASUALTY INS CO
1.8	1.6	10.7	3.0	N/A	N/A	22.2	42.5	64.7	334.5	312.2	0.0	ASSN OF CERTIFIED MTG ORIG RRG
12.0	10.8	N/A	N/A	N/A	N/A	N/A	N/A	N/A	-443.3	0.0	0.0	ASSOCIATED EMPLOYERS INS CO
17.4	15.6	N/A	N/A	N/A	N/A	N/A	N/A	N/A	-1.6	0.0	0.0	ASSOCIATED INDEMNITY CORP
1.4	0.8	52.6	160.8	5.0	3.9	69.5	8.0	77.5	287.1	153.0	3.9	ASSOCIATED INDUSTRIES INS CO INC
2.3	1.7	68.5	136.3	-8.6	-14.5	71.7	23.1	94.8	121.9	2.8	2.3 •	ASSOCIATED INDUSTRIES OF MA MUT
2.5	1.6	1.7	120.2	3.0	7.7	96.0	113.8	209.8	13.6	-94.2	0.0	ASSOCIATED INTL INS CO
1.3	0.7	87.8	137.2	-9.2	-7.5	74.9	20.3	95.2	120.9	1.3	1.6	ASSOCIATED LOGGERS EXCHANGE
1.0	0.6	80.5	114.9	5.0	3.1	72.7	35.6	108.3	94.4	13.3	0.0	ASSOCIATED MUTUAL INS CO
0.9	0.7	257.7	105.6	-5.4	-4.5	75.4	25.6	101.0	107.5	10.6	0.0	ASSURANCEAMERICA INS CO
3.0	2.5	3.3	15.4	25.2	116.3	93.2	403.7	496.9	-69.4	6.4	13.1 •	ASSURED GUARANTY CORP
2.8	1.7	5.8	18.0	1.8	1.4	59.6	13.3	72.9	48.1	-18.4	12.0 •	ASSURED GUARANTY MUNICIPAL CORP
3.2	2.4	109.7	75.7	-9.7	-12.9	62.1	30.8	92.9	109.6	5.3	0.0	ASURE WORLDWIDE INS CO
3.2	2.3	30.3	39.0	1.0	-1.0	65.4	23.6	89.0	140.9	8.6	0.0	ATAIN INS CO
1.7	1.3	49.4	63.6	1.7	-1.5	64.9	21.3	86.2	124.2	8.6	15.8	ATAIN SPECIALTY INS CO
8.5	5.1	17.0	N/A	N/A	N/A	N/A	38.1	38.1	241.6	95.6	0.0	ATHENS FINANCIAL INS CO
N/A	N/A	N/A	102.6	N/A	-2.4	N/A	N/A	N/A	N/A	-100.0	0.0	ATLANTA INTERNATIONAL INS CO
2.7	1.6	8.9	1.9	0.7	0.2	8.9	60.9	69.8	133.5	-34.4	0.0	ATLANTIC BONDING CO
1.7	1.4	82.1	139.3	-8.3	-9.7	59.1	36.6	95.7	116.9	-1.0	0.0	ATLANTIC CASUALTY INS CO
1.1	0.6	121.3	209.9	-10.1	-47.1	62.1	26.2	88.3	118.8	-1.7	0.0	ATLANTIC CHARTER INS CO
1.7	1.3	94.8	151.5	0.5	14.4	65.9	36.0	101.9	81.4	-46.8	11.6 •	ATLANTIC SPECIALTY INS CO
2.9	2.1	189.3	104.4	0.6	3.9	66.0	31.4	97.4	108.3	5.9	0.0 •	ATLANTIC STATES INS CO
5.7	4.4	27.3	11.4	-1.1	-2.1	45.8	54.4	100.2	73.7	-11.8	0.0	ATRADIUS TRADE CREDIT INS CO
N/A	N/A	N/A	N/A	N/A	127.5	N/A	N/A	N/A	N/A	0.0	0.0	ATRIUM INS CORP
2.1	1.7	30.6	40.5	-13.0	-16.5	13.8	99.2	113.0	68.8	-8.9	0.0	ATTORNEYS INS MUTUAL
0.7	0.5	41.7	62.9	5.7	-4.1	61.4	34.1	95.5	166.4	0.5	0.0	ATTORNEYS INS MUTUAL RRG
0.3	0.2	40.0	179.0	1.8	69.6	115.2	10.2	125.4	95.6	-8.4	31.6 •	ATTORNEYS LIAB ASR SOCIETY INC
1.9	1.7	-0.6	2.8	1.3	2.5	-450.0	999 +	999 +	273.1	-115.7	0.0	ATTPRO RRG RECIPROCAL RRG
12.3	5.5	N/A	N/A	N/A	N/A	N/A	N/A	N/A	N/A	0.0	0.0	AUSTIN MUTUAL INS CO
N/A	N/A	N/A	N/A	N/A	N/A	N/A	N/A	N/A	237.0	0.0	0.0	AUTO CLUB CASUALTY CO
1.0	0.9	N/A	N/A	N/A	N/A	N/A	N/A	N/A	62.3	0.0	0.0	AUTO CLUB COUNTY MUTUAL INS CO
3.2	2.1	73.9	25.5	-0.7	-1.4	71.9	21.8	93.7	106.8	5.3	0.0	AUTO CLUB FAMILY INS CO
3.4	2.6	114.2	94.0	-0.2	1.6	70.5	27.4	97.9	103.5	5.7	0.0	AUTO CLUB GROUP INS CO
1.4	1.3	N/A	N/A	N/A	N/A	N/A	N/A	N/A	122.9	0.0	0.0 •	AUTO CLUB INDEMNITY CO
1.9	1.5	90.0	75.1	-0.2	1.1	70.5	27.3	97.8	106.3	5.7	19.9 •	AUTO CLUB INS ASSN
3.5	2.5	114.9	55.6	-5.0	-9.3	61.9	23.4	85.3	123.7	5.8	0.0	AUTO CLUB INS CO OF FL
2.4	1.9	127.8	93.9	0.3	3.0	69.5	28.1	97.6	101.3	4.1	0.0	AUTO CLUB PROPERTY & CASUALTY INS
3.4	2.9	83.5	51.5	0.1	1.7	79.1	22.8	101.9	94.6	-10.2	0.0	AUTO CLUB SOUTH INS CO

999 + Denotes number greater than 999.9%
999 - Denotes number less than -999.99%
• Bullets denote a more detailed analysis is available in Section II.

INSURANCE COMPANY NAME	DOM. STATE	RATING	TOTAL ASSETS ($MIL)	CAPITAL & SURPLUS ($MIL)	ANNUAL NET PREMIUM ($MIL)	NET INCOME ($MIL)	CAPITAL-IZATION INDEX (PTS)	RESERVE ADQ INDEX (PTS)	PROFIT-ABILITY INDEX (PTS)	LIQUIDITY INDEX (PTS)	STAB. INDEX (PTS)	STABILITY FACTORS
AUTO-OWNERS INS CO	MI	A-	13,712.2	9,342.7	2,873.1	279.5	8.7	6.0	8.1	6.9	5.7	T
AUTO-OWNERS SPECIALTY INS CO	DE	U	28.5	28.2	0.0	0.0	N/A	4.6	3.3	7.0	4.2	GT
AUTOMOBILE CLUB INTERINSURANCE	MO	C	419.5	209.8	127.0	-1.6	8.7	7.4	4.6	6.4	4.2	T
AUTOMOBILE INS CO OF HARTFORD CT	CT	B	1,034.2	340.6	284.7	17.8	8.3	8.6	7.0	6.7	4.7	T
AVATAR P&C INS CO	FL	C+	51.0	24.3	21.5	0.5	5.1	4.2	8.0	6.4	3.2	DGT
AVEMCO INS CO	MD	C+	83.9	48.8	27.9	1.5	9.1	9.3	3.1	6.7	3.2	RT
AVIATION ALLIANCE INS RRG INC	MT	E	3.6	1.2	1.2	-0.1	0.8	4.3	2.4	9.4	0.0	CDFG
AVIVA INS CO OF CANADA (US BR)	NY	U	18.0	13.1	0.0	0.0	N/A	4.4	3.8	10.0	4.4	FGT
AWBURY INS CO	DE	U	1.0	1.0	0.0	0.0	N/A	N/A	3.9	7.0	1.5	GT
AXA ART INS CORP	NY	C	25.7	18.0	0.7	-0.4	10.0	6.6	2.7	9.6	3.1	DGRT
AXA INS CO	NY	C-	226.4	119.3	49.0	4.2	10.0	6.0	6.6	7.5	3.3	FRT
AXIS INS CO	IL	B	1,528.9	577.2	307.5	-2.5	7.4	6.6	4.6	6.9	4.3	ART
AXIS REINS CO	NY	C+	3,136.3	860.6	513.4	-20.4	7.9	9.4	5.3	7.0	4.2	ART
AXIS SPECIALTY INS CO	CT	U	66.4	52.6	0.0	-0.1	N/A	8.7	3.1	10.0	5.2	FGT
AXIS SURPLUS INS CO	IL	C	480.5	194.3	41.4	1.4	10.0	8.5	3.9	8.5	4.2	FRT
BADGER MUTUAL INS CO	WI	C+	176.1	68.1	91.0	4.9	8.2	3.4	5.7	6.4	3.5	RT
BALBOA INS CO	CA	C-	99.8	77.5	-0.5	0.0	10.0	6.0	1.9	7.0	3.1	DRT
BALDWIN MUTUAL INS CO	AL	D	12.1	8.8	4.5	0.4	8.7	6.1	2.9	7.5	2.3	DGT
BALTIMORE EQUITABLE SOCIETY	MD	U	151.3	89.4	-1.4	2.1	N/A	5.1	4.9	9.4	5.9	FT
BANKERS INDEPENDENT INS CO	PA	C	26.5	7.7	8.0	-0.4	7.5	2.0	2.2	5.8	2.8	DFGR
BANKERS INS CO	FL	C	146.1	78.0	45.0	0.7	5.8	5.1	5.6	6.9	3.9	FRT
BANKERS SPECIALTY INS CO	LA	C	58.3	47.9	9.7	-0.3	5.9	8.2	4.8	6.0	3.7	DFT
BANKERS STANDARD FIRE & MARINE CO	PA	C	203.0	85.1	42.8	2.0	9.8	7.6	8.4	7.4	4.0	RT
BANKERS STANDARD INS CO	PA	C	502.6	158.9	99.9	3.5	7.7	7.7	8.3	7.3	4.0	RT
BAR PLAN MUTUAL INS CO	MO	C	44.2	17.5	10.3	0.2	5.0	5.5	2.5	6.4	2.9	DFRT
BAR PLAN SURETY & FIDELITY CO	MO	C	5.5	4.3	0.4	0.1	10.0	7.7	7.0	9.8	2.9	DGOR
BAR VERMONT RRG INC	VT	D+	25.0	17.2	1.8	0.1	8.0	8.8	6.7	9.2	2.0	DFGR
BARNSTABLE COUNTY INS CO	MA	C	23.2	20.7	1.6	0.7	10.0	6.1	8.2	9.3	3.4	DGRT
BARNSTABLE COUNTY MUTUAL INS CO	MA	B	101.3	80.6	17.1	0.7	8.8	7.5	7.2	7.0	4.0	RT
BATTLE CREEK MUTUAL INS CO	NE	C-	9.6	5.6	0.0	0.1	10.0	4.8	4.7	9.0	2.6	DFGR
BAY INS RRG INC	SC	U	0.7	0.6	0.0	0.1	N/A	N/A	2.9	7.0	1.5	FGT
BAY STATE INS CO	MA	B-	453.0	289.1	77.8	6.9	8.4	6.4	5.5	7.0	4.5	T
BCS INS CO	OH	B	287.0	168.4	95.3	6.6	10.0	6.3	7.5	6.8	4.3	RT
BEACONHARBOR MUTUAL RRG	ME	U	1.0	1.0	0.0	0.0	N/A	N/A	3.8	10.0	2.3	FGT
BEAR RIVER MUTUAL INS CO	UT	B	247.7	116.4	120.0	-3.8	8.9	8.1	5.1	6.1	4.1	T
BEARING MIDWEST CASUALTY CO	KS	C	6.2	5.7	0.0	0.0	10.0	N/A	4.9	7.0	2.6	DGT
BEAZLEY INS CO	CT	B-	310.6	120.5	64.7	1.1	8.8	6.9	3.7	6.9	3.7	GRT
BEDFORD GRANGE MUTUAL INS CO	PA	C-	8.9	4.5	4.5	0.3	7.1	6.2	6.9	6.7	2.0	DGT
BEDFORD PHYSICIANS RRG INC	VT	D+	52.7	7.4	6.1	0.3	2.8	9.5	4.5	9.1	2.2	CDRT
BEDIVERE INS CO	PA	D+	268.7	103.6	0.2	0.9	1.2	5.7	1.9	10.0	2.3	CFGR
BELL UNITED INS CO	NV	C+	37.6	22.5	5.9	-0.1	9.9	9.6	6.5	9.5	3.1	DGT
BENCHMARK INS CO	KS	B-	234.6	73.1	32.2	3.3	8.5	6.0	8.9	8.1	3.7	RT
BENEFIT SECURITY INS CO	IL	B-	8.2	3.8	1.6	0.1	7.3	4.9	6.6	6.9	3.5	DGT
BERKLEY ASR CO	IA	C-	68.7	53.4	0.0	0.5	10.0	4.0	6.7	10.0	2.9	RT
BERKLEY INS CO	DE	B-	17,317.1	5,027.4	5,338.8	196.4	7.3	8.0	7.4	6.8	5.1	AT
BERKLEY NATIONAL INS CO	IA	C	111.7	51.2	0.0	0.5	10.0	3.6	6.1	10.0	4.0	T
BERKLEY REGIONAL INS CO	DE	C+	723.4	692.7	0.0	4.9	8.3	3.9	6.1	7.0	4.5	ART
BERKLEY REGIONAL SPECIALTY INS CO	DE	C	60.6	55.3	0.0	0.7	10.0	N/A	6.9	10.0	4.0	DT
BERKSHIRE HATHATWAY DIRECT INS CO	NE	U	123.7	112.9	-36.7	1.5	N/A	4.0	2.7	10.0	5.8	FGT
BERKSHIRE HATHAWAY ASR CORP	NY	A+	2,220.4	1,483.1	12.9	37.2	9.3	3.6	8.5	10.0	7.6	GT
BERKSHIRE HATHAWAY HOMESTATE INS	NE	C+	2,128.3	1,105.5	461.5	22.2	7.4	6.0	6.0	7.8	3.9	GRT
BERKSHIRE HATHAWAY SPECIALTY INS CO	NE	C+	3,479.8	2,998.0	95.5	-12.8	8.6	4.2	5.0	10.0	3.8	GRT

See Page 27 for explanation of footnotes and
Page 28 for explanation of stability factors.
Arrows denote recent upgrades ▲ or downgrades ▼ (see Section VII for explanations)

44

www.weissratings.com

RISK ADJ. RATIO #1	CAPITAL RATIO #2	PREMIUM TO SURPLUS (%)	RESV. TO SURPLUS (%)	RESV. DEVELOP. 1 YEAR (%)	RESV. DEVELOP. 2 YEAR (%)	LOSS RATIO (%)	EXP. RATIO (%)	COMB RATIO (%)	CASH FROM UNDER-WRITING (%)	NET PREMIUM GROWTH (%)	INVEST. IN AFFIL (%)	INSURANCE COMPANY NAME
2.4	2.1	32.7	25.8	-0.4	-0.6	51.7	30.0	81.7	129.0	13.1	27.3 ●	AUTO-OWNERS INS CO
N/A	N/A	N/A	N/A	N/A	N/A	N/A	N/A	N/A	N/A	0.0	0.0	AUTO-OWNERS SPECIALTY INS CO
2.7	2.0	60.5	20.8	-0.6	-1.1	71.9	21.8	93.7	106.3	5.3	14.3 ●	AUTOMOBILE CLUB INTERINSURANCE
3.0	1.9	88.3	151.5	-2.8	-6.9	58.7	30.4	89.1	108.1	2.9	0.0 ●	AUTOMOBILE INS CO OF HARTFORD CT
1.2	0.8	90.6	28.9	-0.3	1.9	34.9	43.7	78.6	158.8	8.3	0.0	AVATAR P&C INS CO
2.5	2.4	59.1	27.7	-6.5	-13.5	36.4	34.4	70.8	135.2	-4.8	23.5	AVEMCO INS CO
0.3	0.2	91.1	102.0	25.7	37.2	80.1	48.7	128.8	145.0	1.4	0.0	AVIATION ALLIANCE INS RRG INC
N/A	N/A	N/A	29.4	1.5	3.2	N/A	N/A	N/A	N/A	0.0	0.0	AVIVA INS CO OF CANADA (US BR)
N/A	N/A	N/A	N/A	N/A	N/A	N/A	N/A	N/A	N/A	0.0	0.0	AWBURY INS CO
5.4	4.9	3.9	11.9	-2.7	-4.1	-113.1	343.5	230.4	-15.0	-15.7	0.0	AXA ART INS CORP
4.6	2.9	40.9	26.4	1.7	-0.2	45.7	46.0	91.7	43.8	9.1	0.0	AXA INS CO
1.9	1.3	54.4	103.4	-2.9	-7.9	62.2	39.6	101.8	87.7	8.9	20.2 ●	AXIS INS CO
2.5	1.5	59.6	159.1	-6.0	-14.9	68.1	36.7	104.8	97.5	-2.8	0.0 ●	AXIS REINS CO
N/A	N/A	N/A	26.3	2.7	-8.3	999 +	999 +	999 +	3.4	71.7	0.0	AXIS SPECIALTY INS CO
6.7	4.4	21.5	38.3	-1.2	-4.2	53.9	35.9	89.8	74.3	9.7	0.0 ●	AXIS SURPLUS INS CO
3.1	1.9	141.8	85.2	7.0	5.8	69.6	28.1	97.7	102.5	-2.2	0.0	BADGER MUTUAL INS CO
8.6	5.1	-0.6	5.3	1.7	0.7	-654.6	955.0	300.4	-23.2	56.7	27.7	BALBOA INS CO
2.6	2.3	53.2	4.5	-1.6	-4.6	23.8	45.8	69.6	128.9	-13.3	2.6	BALDWIN MUTUAL INS CO
N/A	N/A	-1.5	1.0	-0.1	-0.4	-183.1	-171.4	-354.5	-23.1	0.1	0.0	BALTIMORE EQUITABLE SOCIETY
1.4	1.2	99.3	78.0	22.2	39.9	84.3	15.6	99.9	68.5	-33.5	0.0	BANKERS INDEPENDENT INS CO
1.1	1.0	58.7	57.5	-2.1	4.2	34.0	58.8	92.8	76.4	-17.1	51.4	BANKERS INS CO
1.0	0.9	20.5	4.2	-1.7	-5.0	42.6	57.5	100.1	90.3	-3.9	72.6	BANKERS SPECIALTY INS CO
4.2	2.8	51.6	92.9	-0.9	-0.2	72.8	20.1	92.9	120.4	6.3	0.0	BANKERS STANDARD FIRE & MARINE CO
1.7	1.4	65.2	117.4	-1.2	-0.3	72.8	20.1	92.9	122.2	6.3	24.0	BANKERS STANDARD INS CO
0.9	0.7	59.8	112.2	-8.2	-8.5	61.4	38.9	100.3	76.2	-2.4	13.4	BAR PLAN MUTUAL INS CO
8.5	7.7	10.2	9.4	-2.2	-1.2	32.2	33.4	65.6	116.0	2.3	0.0	BAR PLAN SURETY & FIDELITY CO
2.6	1.6	10.7	23.4	-4.6	-2.0	14.5	75.8	90.3	49.4	-6.7	0.0	BAR VERMONT RRG INC
7.5	4.6	7.9	1.1	-0.4	-0.5	21.0	50.9	71.9	151.5	11.0	0.0	BARNSTABLE COUNTY INS CO
2.9	2.4	21.4	4.8	-1.0	-2.2	57.9	46.7	104.6	97.1	2.9	21.8	BARNSTABLE COUNTY MUTUAL INS CO
4.3	3.9	N/A	N/A	N/A	N/A	N/A	N/A	N/A	343.1	0.0	0.0	BATTLE CREEK MUTUAL INS CO
N/A	N/A	N/A	N/A	N/A	N/A	N/A	N/A	N/A	N/A	0.0	0.0	BAY INS RRG INC
3.2	1.9	27.3	14.5	-1.2	-2.5	68.5	37.6	106.1	92.0	-1.0	0.0 ●	BAY STATE INS CO
9.7	5.5	59.1	30.9	-7.5	-2.5	60.5	30.9	91.4	109.4	-26.4	0.9	BCS INS CO
N/A	N/A	N/A	N/A	N/A	N/A	N/A	999 +	999 +	38.2	130.0	0.0	BEACONHARBOR MUTUAL RRG
3.1	2.1	97.7	44.2	-1.5	-2.3	82.7	26.0	108.7	99.5	10.4	0.0	BEAR RIVER MUTUAL INS CO
27.0	18.7	N/A	N/A	N/A	N/A	N/A	N/A	N/A	N/A	0.0	0.0	BEARING MIDWEST CASUALTY CO
2.7	2.1	54.3	66.5	-0.2	-6.0	64.7	44.6	109.3	98.0	43.4	0.0	BEAZLEY INS CO
1.5	1.0	107.1	11.5	-7.4	-6.1	40.0	40.7	80.7	115.0	23.8	9.4	BEDFORD GRANGE MUTUAL INS CO
0.7	0.5	89.0	368.7	-26.9	-21.4	93.6	8.8	102.4	193.0	-11.0	0.0	BEDFORD PHYSICIANS RRG INC
0.5	0.3	0.2	150.2	17.2	1.2	999 +	999 +	999 +	1.9	388.3	13.9	BEDIVERE INS CO
6.1	4.0	26.3	54.5	-13.4	-21.7	22.0	20.0	42.0	162.2	-0.7	0.0	BELL UNITED INS CO
3.5	2.5	48.6	66.0	-2.0	-3.0	54.4	23.7	78.1	140.4	12.4	0.0	BENCHMARK INS CO
1.5	1.1	41.6	61.8	N/A	-1.3	36.4	70.4	106.8	108.8	-0.7	0.0	BENEFIT SECURITY INS CO
17.8	16.0	N/A	N/A	N/A	N/A	N/A	N/A	N/A	N/A	0.0	0.0	BERKLEY ASR CO
1.3	1.0	100.8	164.2	-1.8	-4.4	56.5	32.3	88.8	118.8	5.3	19.2 ●	BERKLEY INS CO
7.0	6.3	N/A	N/A	N/A	N/A	N/A	N/A	N/A	70.5	0.0	0.0	BERKLEY NATIONAL INS CO
1.5	1.5	N/A	N/A	N/A	N/A	N/A	N/A	N/A	-206.1	0.0	47.2 ●	BERKLEY REGIONAL INS CO
34.8	31.3	N/A	N/A	N/A	N/A	N/A	N/A	N/A	-923.0	0.0	0.0	BERKLEY REGIONAL SPECIALTY INS CO
N/A	N/A	-32.6	N/A	-261.0	-276.1	100.0	-3.2	96.8	999 +	0.0	0.0	BERKSHIRE HATHATWAY DIRECT INS
4.5	2.7	0.9	N/A	-0.7	-0.8	-3.1	15.4	12.3	140.1	450.2	0.0 ●	BERKSHIRE HATHAWAY ASR CORP
2.7	1.6	39.5	49.5	-2.4	-5.4	70.4	22.1	92.5	181.8	22.6	0.0 ●	BERKSHIRE HATHAWAY HOMESTATE
4.2	2.5	3.1	4.4	N/A	N/A	75.7	32.2	107.9	175.2	N/A	0.0 ●	BERKSHIRE HATHAWAY SPECIALTY INS

999 + Denotes number greater than 999.9%
999 - Denotes number less than -999.99%
● Bullets denote a more detailed analysis is available in Section II.

INSURANCE COMPANY NAME	DOM. STATE	RATING	TOTAL ASSETS ($MIL)	CAPITAL & SURPLUS ($MIL)	ANNUAL NET PREMIUM ($MIL)	NET INCOME ($MIL)	CAPITAL-IZATION INDEX (PTS)	RESERVE ADQ INDEX (PTS)	PROFIT-ABILITY INDEX (PTS)	LIQUIDITY INDEX (PTS)	STAB. INDEX (PTS)	STABILITY FACTORS
BITCO GENERAL INS CORP	IL	B	844.8	291.0	237.6	10.0	8.4	9.1	5.6	6.8	4.8	AT
BITCO NATIONAL INS CO	IL	B	501.0	150.4	149.4	3.6	7.8	9.3	3.8	6.7	4.5	AT
BLACK DIAMOND INS CO	NV	U (5)	0.0	0.0	0.0	0.0	N/A	N/A	3.9	10.0	2.1	DFT
BLOOMFIELD MUTUAL INS CO	MN	C-	11.4	8.9	3.4	0.2	10.0	7.5	8.5	6.8	2.3	DGT
BLOOMINGTON COMP INS CO	MN	C+	17.9	13.8	0.0	0.1	10.0	N/A	6.7	7.6	3.3	DFGR
BLUE CROSS BLUE SHIELD OF INDIANA (See ANTHEM INS COMPANIES INC)												
BLUE CROSS BLUE SHIELD OF OHIO (See COMMUNITY INS CO)												
BLUE HILL SPECIALTY INS CO	IL	U	15.6	15.3	0.0	0.0	N/A	N/A	4.9	7.0	5.2	GT
BLUE RIDGE INDEMNITY CO	WI	C	8.4	6.7	7.0	0.1	7.1	3.8	4.8	7.7	2.7	DFGR
BLUESHORE INS CO	CO	U	77.5	16.4	11.4	-0.4	N/A	3.7	3.6	8.6	4.8	DGT
BOND SAFEGUARD INS CO	SD	D	81.8	34.0	42.3	1.2	6.2	1.4	4.1	6.9	2.3	RT
BONDED BUILDERS INS CO RRG	NV	D	3.1	1.7	0.8	0.1	6.5	5.8	6.9	6.9	1.4	DGT
BONDEX INS CO	NJ	B-	7.1	3.5	1.7	0.1	7.0	8.8	7.9	8.6	3.5	DGT
BOSTON INDEMNITY CO INC	SD	U	7.8	5.1	0.0	0.1	N/A	4.7	3.7	7.3	0.0	T
BREMEN FARMERS MUTUAL INS CO	KS	C	42.7	18.5	25.2	1.2	7.5	6.9	6.2	5.4	2.9	DGRT
BRETHREN MUTUAL INS CO	MD	B	250.6	123.2	109.4	-0.3	9.6	4.6	5.3	6.8	4.5	RT
BRIAR CREEK MUTUAL INS CO	PA	C	13.3	10.4	2.2	0.3	10.0	6.1	7.8	8.3	2.3	DGRT
BRICKSTREET MUTUAL INS CO	WV	C	1,931.4	724.9	245.0	20.7	7.4	9.5	8.7	7.1	4.3	RT
BRIDGEFIELD CASUALTY INS CO	FL	C	65.1	50.5	0.0	0.4	10.0	N/A	7.4	8.9	4.0	RT
BRIDGEFIELD EMPLOYERS INS CO	FL	B-	125.9	122.3	0.0	0.8	9.4	N/A	7.3	10.0	4.5	RT
BRIERFIELD INS CO	MS	C-	13.1	8.8	0.0	0.1	10.0	N/A	6.7	10.0	2.8	DGRT
BRISTOL WEST CASUALTY INS CO	OH	D+	18.0	8.8	0.0	0.0	10.0	4.9	5.1	10.0	2.5	DFGR
BRISTOL WEST INS CO	OH	D+	134.0	47.0	0.0	-1.1	10.0	5.5	4.9	9.0	2.6	RT
BRISTOL WEST PREFERRED INS CO	MI	C-	24.6	11.6	0.0	0.1	10.0	5.7	4.4	7.0	3.0	DGRT
BRITISH AMERICAN INS CO	TX	C+	55.6	33.1	4.5	0.5	5.5	4.4	7.5	9.2	3.4	DRT
BROADLINE RRG INC	VT	C+	85.9	32.3	18.6	-2.3	8.1	7.0	5.3	5.8	3.4	DFT
BROADWAY INS & SURETY CO	NJ	D (2)	2.2	1.4	0.8	0.4	7.9	3.6	8.2	9.4	1.2	DFT
BROOKWOOD INS CO	IA	U	7.4	7.2	0.0	0.0	N/A	N/A	3.8	10.0	4.7	FGT
BROOME CO OPERATIVE INS CO	NY	C	20.6	13.5	6.3	0.7	9.7	6.6	5.4	6.8	2.5	DGT
BROTHERHOOD MUTUAL INS CO	IN	B	553.8	228.9	304.9	-1.4	8.0	5.8	5.7	6.1	4.9	RT
BTTS INS RRG GROUP INC	SC	U	0.7	0.5	0.0	0.0	N/A	N/A	3.4	7.0	1.5	FGT
BUCKEYE STATE MUTUAL INS CO	OH	C+	65.4	21.8	36.5	-1.5	7.4	9.3	3.8	5.6	3.2	DRT
BUCKS COUNTY CONTRIBUTIONSHIP	PA	U	6.4	5.7	0.0	-0.1	N/A	N/A	4.6	10.0	3.4	FGRT
BUILD AMERICA MUTUAL ASR CO	NY	D+	485.9	432.5	6.3	-15.9	10.0	N/A	2.2	10.0	1.1	DFGT
BUILDERS INS (A MUTUAL CAPTIVE CO)	GA	C	546.3	239.1	144.7	7.4	7.8	9.3	8.4	6.8	3.5	RT
BUILDERS MUTUAL INS CO	NC	B+	736.0	295.6	246.8	10.6	8.0	9.0	8.4	6.8	5.1	T
BUILDERS PREMIER INS CO	NC	C	11.8	11.7	0.0	0.1	10.0	N/A	6.9	10.0	3.0	DGT
BUILDING INDUSTRY INS ASSN INC	VA	E	17.8	4.7	10.9	0.9	0.1	0.5	2.9	0.0	0.3	CDGL
BUNKER HILL INS CAS CO	MA	C-	15.3	6.7	5.1	0.3	7.5	9.2	5.4	6.3	2.7	DFGT
BUNKER HILL INS CO	MA	C	56.8	28.1	16.3	1.2	7.4	8.7	3.6	6.7	3.6	DFRT
BURLINGTON INS CO	IL	C-	367.0	179.4	46.4	3.5	9.3	9.0	6.2	8.3	2.6	FRT
BUS ALLIANCE INS CO	CA	C	24.2	17.4	5.5	0.3	9.0	5.6	4.6	8.7	2.7	DGRT
BUSINESSFIRST INS CO	FL	C	41.1	16.0	11.1	0.3	7.6	6.4	6.8	6.5	3.2	DGRT
CA CASUALTY COMP INS CO	CA	C+	73.0	70.4	0.5	0.5	7.3	4.7	5.9	10.0	3.9	DGRT
CALIFORNIA AUTOMOBILE INS CO	CA	B	640.6	173.5	634.4	7.0	7.1	5.9	3.5	3.0	4.0	GLT
CALIFORNIA CAPITAL INS CO	CA	B-	588.7	315.0	218.1	1.8	8.1	6.0	6.3	6.6	4.2	FRT
CALIFORNIA CAS GEN INS CO OF OREGON	OR	C	108.2	25.6	40.9	-0.8	7.5	7.8	2.1	6.3	2.8	RT
CALIFORNIA CASUALTY & FIRE INS CO	CA	C	66.4	21.3	34.1	-0.7	7.5	7.8	2.1	6.4	2.8	DRT
CALIFORNIA CASUALTY INDEMNITY EXCH	CA	C+	575.5	276.7	238.6	-3.3	7.9	7.5	2.5	6.4	3.4	RT
CALIFORNIA CASUALTY INS CO	OR	C+	105.4	70.9	27.3	-0.4	7.9	7.3	2.7	6.8	4.0	RT
CALIFORNIA GENERAL UNDERWRITERS INS	CA	B	22.5	20.0	0.4	-0.1	10.0	5.8	4.7	10.0	4.9	DGT
CALIFORNIA HEALTHCARE INS CO INC RRG	HI	C+	122.7	54.3	16.7	0.6	10.0	9.7	8.5	7.3	3.4	RT

See Page 27 for explanation of footnotes and
Page 28 for explanation of stability factors.
Arrows denote recent upgrades ▲ or downgrades ▼   (see Section VII for explanations)

46

www.weissratings.com

RISK ADJ. RATIO #1	CAPITAL RATIO #2	PREMIUM TO SURPLUS (%)	RESV. TO SURPLUS (%)	RESV. DEVELOP. 1 YEAR (%)	RESV. DEVELOP. 2 YEAR (%)	LOSS RATIO (%)	EXP. RATIO (%)	COMB RATIO (%)	CASH FROM UNDER-WRITING (%)	NET PREMIUM GROWTH (%)	INVEST. IN AFFIL (%)	INSURANCE COMPANY NAME
3.0	1.8	86.3	152.6	-2.3	-5.5	71.9	22.6	94.5	116.0	3.2	0.0 •	BITCO GENERAL INS CORP
2.3	1.4	106.7	211.2	0.2	-5.7	72.0	32.5	104.5	109.9	3.0	0.0	BITCO NATIONAL INS CO
N/A	N/A	2.3	N/A	N/A	N/A	N/A	202.9	202.9	75.3	-45.8	0.0	BLACK DIAMOND INS CO
9.8	5.8	39.0	2.8	-4.2	-1.5	18.5	33.9	52.4	159.3	2.7	0.0	BLOOMFIELD MUTUAL INS CO
10.6	9.5	N/A	N/A	N/A	N/A	N/A	N/A	N/A	-1.0	0.0	0.0	BLOOMINGTON COMP INS CO
N/A	N/A	N/A	N/A	N/A	N/A	N/A	N/A	N/A	N/A	0.0	0.0	BLUE HILL SPECIALTY INS CO
7.6	5.3	108.7	116.6	1.4	2.9	63.9	35.8	99.7	89.9	-24.7	0.0	BLUE RIDGE INDEMNITY CO
N/A	N/A	71.5	1.9	0.4	N/A	51.2	36.4	87.6	179.4	2.2	0.0	BLUESHORE INS CO
1.1	0.9	117.3	40.9	-1.6	9.5	23.0	56.5	79.5	117.7	14.4	0.0	BOND SAFEGUARD INS CO
2.1	1.2	45.7	9.5	-5.7	-9.1	-0.7	71.5	70.8	133.8	9.1	0.0	BONDED BUILDERS INS CO RRG
1.6	1.2	50.8	23.4	-6.7	-7.2	8.5	82.3	90.8	113.9	9.4	0.0	BONDEX INS CO
N/A	N/A	N/A	N/A	N/A	N/A	N/A	N/A	N/A	N/A	-100.0	0.0	BOSTON INDEMNITY CO INC
1.7	1.6	145.7	20.9	-2.8	-8.2	59.4	27.7	87.1	109.7	3.0	0.0	BREMEN FARMERS MUTUAL INS CO
4.4	2.7	90.1	37.7	2.7	N/A	66.9	34.1	101.0	98.5	-7.0	0.0	BRETHREN MUTUAL INS CO
5.8	3.6	22.1	7.8	-0.3	-0.3	38.9	41.3	80.2	135.5	-2.4	0.0	BRIAR CREEK MUTUAL INS CO
3.1	2.0	34.7	145.4	-10.7	-22.1	69.2	32.3	101.5	99.5	-15.6	1.9 •	BRICKSTREET MUTUAL INS CO
17.2	15.4	N/A	N/A	N/A	N/A	N/A	N/A	N/A	225.8	0.0	0.0	BRIDGEFIELD CASUALTY INS CO
2.6	2.6	N/A	N/A	N/A	N/A	N/A	N/A	N/A	-772.9	0.0	40.9	BRIDGEFIELD EMPLOYERS INS CO
6.6	5.9	N/A	N/A	N/A	N/A	N/A	N/A	N/A	-88.7	0.0	0.0	BRIERFIELD INS CO
3.8	3.4	N/A	N/A	0.2	0.4	N/A	N/A	N/A	-90.6	0.0	0.0	BRISTOL WEST CASUALTY INS CO
5.5	5.0	N/A	3.8	-0.4	-1.7	N/A	N/A	N/A	999 +	0.0	0.0	BRISTOL WEST INS CO
4.2	3.7	N/A	3.0	-0.1	-0.5	N/A	N/A	N/A	-8.2	0.0	0.0	BRISTOL WEST PREFERRED INS CO
1.1	0.8	13.2	63.2	-2.7	10.0	35.4	21.8	57.2	158.9	-1.1	0.0	BRITISH AMERICAN INS CO
2.2	1.4	40.3	105.5	-7.7	-8.6	73.9	7.5	81.4	87.4	-1.6	0.0	BROADLINE RRG INC
1.9	1.6	54.9	9.8	-0.1	N/A	-8.5	71.9	63.4	99.4	-41.2	0.0	BROADWAY INS & SURETY CO
N/A	N/A	N/A	2.8	N/A	N/A	N/A	N/A	N/A	36.1	0.0	0.0	BROOKWOOD INS CO
4.3	2.9	50.4	18.3	-1.9	-3.1	68.9	33.1	102.0	96.9	2.0	0.0	BROOME CO OPERATIVE INS CO
2.1	1.7	133.1	47.9	2.6	2.0	61.0	32.1	93.1	113.7	10.0	0.0 •	BROTHERHOOD MUTUAL INS CO
N/A	N/A	N/A	N/A	N/A	N/A	N/A	N/A	N/A	-16.4	0.0	0.0	BTTS INS RRG GROUP INC
1.6	1.2	159.0	44.8	-3.0	-8.9	63.0	33.7	96.7	101.2	-4.7	15.6	BUCKEYE STATE MUTUAL INS CO
N/A	N/A	N/A	N/A	N/A	N/A	N/A	999 +	999 +	0.7	-19.0	0.0	BUCKS COUNTY CONTRIBUTIONSHIP
8.4	8.1	1.4	N/A	N/A	N/A	N/A	585.5	585.5	18.4	73.8	0.0 •	BUILD AMERICA MUTUAL ASR CO
2.3	1.7	63.6	99.6	-10.3	-12.2	54.6	31.4	86.0	128.4	2.4	13.5 •	BUILDERS INS (A MUTUAL CAPTIVE CO)
2.2	1.6	87.6	109.7	-2.8	-6.0	63.1	30.3	93.4	126.4	14.5	1.9 •	BUILDERS MUTUAL INS CO
100.2	50.1	N/A	N/A	N/A	N/A	N/A	N/A	N/A	N/A	0.0	0.0	BUILDERS PREMIER INS CO
0.1	0.1	236.5	138.6	65.2	69.4	63.3	34.0	97.3	97.3	-2.1	0.0	BUILDING INDUSTRY INS ASSN INC
1.9	1.3	82.2	26.2	-0.9	-9.8	92.4	25.6	118.0	84.9	2.3	0.0	BUNKER HILL INS CAS CO
2.2	1.6	66.3	21.2	-0.7	-7.1	92.4	24.7	117.1	84.7	2.3	16.4	BUNKER HILL INS CO
3.5	2.8	26.0	70.1	-4.0	-5.8	43.4	59.0	102.4	82.7	-10.5	0.0	BURLINGTON INS CO
3.2	2.2	32.7	18.2	0.3	5.3	33.1	44.6	77.7	107.2	-9.9	0.0	BUS ALLIANCE INS CO
1.7	1.3	71.6	88.8	-2.4	-3.9	68.0	30.8	98.8	100.8	0.1	0.0	BUSINESSFIRST INS CO
2.0	1.2	0.7	33.7	0.2	0.4	93.8	-0.4	93.4	24.6	3.7	0.0	CA CASUALTY COMP INS CO
1.4	1.1	383.9	121.7	4.0	2.3	77.5	23.7	101.2	117.4	32.9	3.7	CALIFORNIA AUTOMOBILE INS CO
2.1	1.7	69.4	47.4	0.7	1.0	69.9	33.5	103.4	96.9	-11.0	26.3 •	CALIFORNIA CAPITAL INS CO
1.6	1.1	154.7	59.6	-0.6	-0.9	84.1	27.5	111.6	110.5	45.6	0.0	CALIFORNIA CAS GEN INS CO OF
1.7	1.1	154.6	59.5	-0.6	-0.9	84.1	27.5	111.6	108.3	45.6	0.0	CALIFORNIA CASUALTY & FIRE INS CO
1.8	1.5	83.9	32.3	-0.3	-0.5	84.1	27.5	111.6	108.2	45.6	33.5 •	CALIFORNIA CASUALTY INDEMNITY
1.5	1.5	37.4	14.4	-0.1	-0.2	84.1	27.5	111.6	109.6	45.6	55.7	CALIFORNIA CASUALTY INS CO
5.9	4.9	2.0	4.9	3.3	3.7	182.3	29.9	212.2	130.3	-13.1	0.0	CALIFORNIA GENERAL UNDERWRITERS
4.4	3.2	31.6	96.9	-10.3	-29.7	88.3	10.1	98.4	104.0	27.5	0.4	CALIFORNIA HEALTHCARE INS CO INC

999 + Denotes number greater than 999.9%
999 - Denotes number less than -999.99%
• Bullets denote a more detailed analysis is available in Section II.

INSURANCE COMPANY NAME	DOM. STATE	RATING	TOTAL ASSETS ($MIL)	CAPITAL & SURPLUS ($MIL)	ANNUAL NET PREMIUM ($MIL)	NET INCOME ($MIL)	CAPITAL-IZATION INDEX (PTS)	RESERVE ADQ INDEX (PTS)	PROFIT-ABILITY INDEX (PTS)	LIQUIDITY INDEX (PTS)	STAB. INDEX (PTS)	STABILITY FACTORS
CALIFORNIA INS CO	CA	B-	775.7	495.7	255.3	30.2	9.1	8.7	9.2	8.5	4.7	RT
CALIFORNIA MEDICAL GROUP INS CO RRG	AZ	E	16.5	4.3	3.7	-0.4	7.5	10.0	3.2	8.0	0.0	DGRT
CALIFORNIA MUTUAL INS CO	CA	D	14.5	10.6	4.0	-0.1	9.0	6.5	4.5	6.9	2.3	DGRT
CALLICOON CO-OPERATIVE INS CO	NY	C+	30.2	24.9	5.2	0.9	10.0	7.5	8.6	6.9	3.2	DGRT
CAMBRIA COUNTY MUTUAL INS CO	PA	U (2)	0.5	0.4	0.0	0.0	N/A	3.6	2.3	10.0	1.4	T
CAMBRIDGE MUTUAL FIRE INS CO	MA	B-	848.0	502.6	181.5	21.6	8.5	6.5	5.8	7.0	4.6	FT
CAMERON MUTUAL INS CO	MO	C+	81.4	35.2	49.3	-0.4	7.3	6.7	4.6	5.8	3.3	RT
CAMERON NATIONAL INS CO	MO	C-	12.1	10.2	0.0	0.3	10.0	N/A	6.2	10.0	2.9	DGRT
CAMICO MUTUAL INS CO	CA	C	91.4	39.2	30.4	-0.6	7.9	5.9	5.2	6.7	2.9	FRT
CAMPMED CAS & INDEM CO INC OF MD	NH	C+	20.8	20.6	0.0	0.2	10.0	3.6	6.9	10.0	3.5	DGRT
CANAL INDEMNITY CO	SC	B	46.8	43.4	0.0	0.4	10.0	N/A	7.8	10.0	4.9	DT
CANAL INS CO	SC	B	800.7	447.1	185.5	6.8	8.4	6.0	4.8	6.9	4.6	FRT
CANOPIUS US INS INC	DE	B-	217.3	103.0	55.4	-1.5	7.6	5.5	2.8	7.0	4.2	T
CAPACITY INS CO	FL	D	21.4	9.9	8.5	0.5	1.8	4.4	5.8	5.4	2.1	CDGT
CAPITOL CASUALTY CO	NE	C+	28.7	25.5	0.4	0.5	8.2	7.4	6.8	9.3	3.2	DGT
CAPITOL COUNTY MUTUAL FIRE INS CO	TX	C	11.7	6.9	0.0	-1.8	8.0	3.6	1.5	9.9	2.8	DFGR
CAPITOL INDEMNITY CORP	WI	C	508.9	226.6	154.2	2.8	7.3	4.0	5.3	6.7	4.0	RT
▼CAPITOL INS CO	PA	E	15.3	1.5	9.8	-0.5	0.2	1.3	0.5	0.8	0.1	CDFG
CAPITOL PREFERRED INS CO	FL	C-	58.9	28.5	13.0	2.2	8.2	6.3	8.9	7.7	3.1	RT
CAPITOL SPECIALTY INS CORP	WI	C+	135.1	54.6	33.0	0.7	9.2	4.0	5.4	6.9	3.7	RT
CAPSON PHYSICIANS INS CO	TX	D	24.8	7.1	13.3	0.1	3.6	4.7	2.3	6.8	2.2	DGT
CAR RRG INC	TN	U	1.1	1.0	0.0	0.0	N/A	0.0	2.8	0.0	0.0	LT
CARE RRG INC	DC	D+(1)	20.9	4.5	8.1	0.0	2.5	9.6	2.9	6.9	2.0	CDGR
CARE WEST INS CO	CA	D	127.9	31.0	27.5	4.7	3.2	2.3	3.9	6.6	2.3	RT
CARECONCEPTS INS INC A RRG	MT	E (1)	3.8	0.4	1.3	-0.3	0.7	3.9	0.9	4.1	0.0	CDFG
CAREGIVERS UNITED LIAB INS CO RRG	SC	D	41.2	25.7	5.1	1.9	9.5	9.4	7.7	8.3	2.3	DRT
CARIBBEAN AMERICAN PROPERTY INS CO	PR	C	42.3	23.7	27.4	2.2	4.0	9.2	6.9	6.0	3.6	CDT
CARING COMMUNITIES RECIP RRG	DC	C	81.4	48.6	8.2	0.8	8.4	8.2	8.9	9.4	3.4	DRT
CAROLINA CASUALTY INS CO	IA	C	181.1	100.0	0.0	1.4	10.0	N/A	3.3	9.1	4.1	RT
CAROLINA FARMERS MUTUAL INS CO	NC	C-	9.1	6.4	3.3	-0.3	7.8	6.4	3.9	7.1	2.1	DGRT
CAROLINA MUTUAL INS INC	NC	B-	88.5	39.4	29.9	0.7	7.8	9.7	8.9	7.3	3.5	T
CASCO INDEMNITY CO	ME	C	29.8	12.9	15.9	0.6	8.3	9.4	7.7	6.7	3.0	DGRT
CASSATT RISK RETENTION GROUP INC	VT	D	13.4	3.7	0.1	0.0	7.5	7.0	2.8	7.4	2.0	DGRT
CASTLE KEY INDEMNITY CO	IL	B	11.7	10.9	0.0	0.1	10.0	N/A	3.8	10.0	4.9	DGT
CASTLE KEY INS CO	IL	B-	388.5	213.1	123.0	6.3	8.1	6.7	5.4	6.8	3.9	T
CASTLEPOINT FLORIDA INS	FL	D (3)	10.0	7.3	-1.0	0.4	7.3	3.5	2.3	0.0	2.2	DFGL
CASTLEPOINT INS CO	NY	E (3)	178.4	17.4	-33.8	0.2	2.0	0.9	0.1	3.0	0.1	CDFL
CASTLEPOINT NATIONAL INS CO	CA	C- (3)	355.2	44.7	-32.3	4.8	4.0	1.2	0.5	9.6	3.1	CFRT
CASUALTY CORP OF AMERICA	OK	D-	10.1	2.4	12.3	0.3	1.0	0.5	3.5	0.0	1.2	CDGL
CASUALTY UNDERWRITERS INS CO	UT	D+	4.5	4.3	0.0	0.0	10.0	4.6	2.6	10.0	2.0	DGRT
CATASTROPHE REINS CO	TX	D	1,953.6	1,749.4	165.5	68.2	10.0	5.0	7.3	9.4	2.3	T
CATAWBA INS CO	SC	U	6.1	5.6	0.0	0.0	N/A	4.1	2.1	10.0	3.3	FGRT
CATERPILLAR INS CO	MO	B	690.3	305.7	142.5	13.7	9.3	6.9	8.9	6.9	4.2	RT
CATLIN INDEMNITY CO	DE	C	124.3	67.2	6.4	0.4	7.4	5.9	3.1	6.8	3.6	FT
CATLIN INS CO	TX	C	250.6	55.8	44.8	3.5	5.7	3.9	2.9	6.6	2.1	DRT
CATLIN SPECIALTY INS CO	DE	C+	656.3	222.1	76.8	5.8	7.9	4.4	4.5	7.2	3.2	RT
CATTLEMANS INS CO A RRG	MT	U (2)	0.6	0.6	0.0	0.0	N/A	5.9	1.9	7.0	2.0	FT
CBIA COMP SERVICES INC	CT	C-	24.5	7.6	5.1	0.0	3.8	9.8	5.2	6.8	2.2	DGRT
CELINA MUTUAL INS CO	OH	C	70.3	31.8	37.9	1.8	7.7	8.2	6.5	6.0	3.5	RT
CEM INS CO	IL	D	33.6	10.9	11.3	0.3	4.4	1.7	5.2	5.7	2.1	DGRT
CENSTAT CASUALTY CO	NE	C	23.2	17.1	2.0	0.0	10.0	7.8	7.8	9.1	3.3	DGRT
CENTAURI SPECIALTY INS CO	FL	C-	118.6	28.3	61.9	-3.1	4.3	4.6	3.8	6.8	3.2	CGOR

Arrows denote recent upgrades ▲ or downgrades ▼   (see Section VII for explanations)

RISK ADJ. RATIO #1	CAPITAL RATIO #2	PREMIUM TO SURPLUS (%)	RESV. TO SURPLUS (%)	RESV. DEVELOP. 1 YEAR (%)	RESV. DEVELOP. 2 YEAR (%)	LOSS RATIO (%)	EXP. RATIO (%)	COMB RATIO (%)	CASH FROM UNDER-WRITING (%)	NET PREMIUM GROWTH (%)	INVEST. IN AFFIL (%)	INSURANCE COMPANY NAME
3.8	3.0	54.4	39.9	-3.9	-3.5	21.1	29.4	50.5	191.9	5.7	0.0 ●	CALIFORNIA INS CO
1.5	1.1	88.1	153.7	-22.2	-55.6	40.4	20.7	61.1	261.1	-0.4	0.0	CALIFORNIA MEDICAL GROUP INS CO
3.4	2.1	37.1	11.4	-1.2	0.4	47.2	51.6	98.8	112.6	13.4	2.3	CALIFORNIA MUTUAL INS CO
12.8	9.4	21.8	7.5	-1.6	-1.5	42.2	35.6	77.8	115.1	-2.2	0.0	CALLICOON CO-OPERATIVE INS CO
N/A	N/A	4.5	N/A	N/A	N/A	11.4	185.6	197.0	62.2	38.9	0.0	CAMBRIA COUNTY MUTUAL INS CO
3.3	2.0	38.3	20.3	-1.7	-3.7	68.5	37.6	106.1	93.0	-1.0	0.0 ●	CAMBRIDGE MUTUAL FIRE INS CO
1.8	1.2	140.1	55.5	-0.9	1.5	67.4	34.9	102.3	103.8	3.2	15.4	CAMERON MUTUAL INS CO
14.9	13.4	N/A	N/A	N/A	N/A	N/A	N/A	N/A	23.1	0.0	0.0	CAMERON NATIONAL INS CO
2.5	1.6	75.5	71.5	6.0	5.7	64.7	33.0	97.7	82.8	0.0	1.8	CAMICO MUTUAL INS CO
75.8	33.9	N/A	N/A	N/A	N/A	N/A	N/A	N/A	999 +	0.0	0.0	CAMPMED CAS & INDEM CO INC OF MD
5.8	3.3	N/A	N/A	N/A	N/A	N/A	N/A	N/A	60.8	0.0	0.0	CANAL INDEMNITY CO
2.8	1.9	43.3	51.9	2.4	1.7	71.6	32.7	104.3	85.8	4.6	6.1 ●	CANAL INS CO
2.9	1.4	54.6	84.2	8.3	7.3	118.1	34.9	153.0	111.1	21.6	0.0	CANOPIUS US INS INC
0.5	0.3	88.9	47.7	9.1	10.3	53.5	41.4	94.9	113.9	2.5	0.0	CAPACITY INS CO
3.1	1.8	1.8	0.7	-0.7	-0.8	46.4	108.3	154.7	72.1	15.2	0.0	CAPITOL CASUALTY CO
1.3	1.3	N/A	N/A	1.3	0.5	N/A	N/A	N/A	-11.0	0.0	43.4	CAPITOL COUNTY MUTUAL FIRE INS CO
1.5	1.1	68.4	64.9	1.3	1.7	54.8	45.7	100.5	103.6	14.5	22.3 ●	CAPITOL INDEMNITY CORP
0.1	0.0	464.0	346.4	46.8	47.9	95.5	22.2	117.7	75.9	-19.2	0.0	CAPITOL INS CO
2.8	1.9	49.8	27.8	-0.7	1.6	114.0	-43.3	70.7	206.2	1.2	0.0	CAPITOL PREFERRED INS CO
4.1	2.4	61.4	54.7	1.1	1.2	54.8	44.9	99.7	138.5	14.5	0.0	CAPITOL SPECIALTY INS CORP
0.8	0.5	180.1	167.3	9.5	4.3	58.0	41.6	99.6	102.9	11.5	0.0	CAPSON PHYSICIANS INS CO
N/A	N/A	N/A	N/A	N/A	N/A	N/A	N/A	N/A	N/A	0.0	0.0	CAR RRG INC
0.6	0.4	184.9	264.8	22.8	-16.2	80.7	26.0	106.7	104.3	2.1	0.0	CARE RRG INC
1.3	0.9	103.6	283.3	-14.0	-13.1	58.0	19.5	77.5	98.2	1.4	0.0	CARE WEST INS CO
0.1	0.1	202.6	370.2	28.7	-7.5	73.4	65.4	138.8	82.2	-9.5	0.0	CARECONCEPTS INS INC A RRG
4.2	2.7	19.6	45.6	-8.3	-10.5	42.8	15.8	58.6	202.4	-4.0	0.0	CAREGIVERS UNITED LIAB INS CO RRG
0.8	0.5	122.2	16.7	-9.1	-12.9	31.9	42.0	73.9	120.8	-8.4	0.0	CARIBBEAN AMERICAN PROPERTY INS
2.1	1.8	17.1	28.9	-2.3	-7.0	45.6	24.0	69.6	199.4	0.1	32.8	CARING COMMUNITIES RECIP RRG
12.2	11.0	N/A	N/A	N/A	N/A	N/A	N/A	N/A	999 +	0.0	0.0	CAROLINA CASUALTY INS CO
2.4	1.5	53.9	10.2	-0.6	-1.4	61.7	33.8	95.5	121.0	1.3	0.0	CAROLINA FARMERS MUTUAL INS CO
2.0	1.6	78.5	82.8	-19.9	-30.6	45.9	27.6	73.5	123.0	14.6	0.0	CAROLINA MUTUAL INS INC
3.2	2.3	128.8	63.0	-4.7	-9.1	61.6	33.9	95.5	109.6	3.1	0.0	CASCO INDEMNITY CO
1.5	1.4	2.7	1.2	-0.1	-0.1	102.2	283.8	386.0	726.8	0.0	0.0	CASSATT RISK RETENTION GROUP INC
34.0	30.6	N/A	N/A	N/A	N/A	N/A	N/A	N/A	N/A	0.0	0.0	CASTLE KEY INDEMNITY CO
4.6	3.3	59.6	24.1	-0.6	2.0	60.5	28.5	89.0	106.2	-13.7	4.9 ●	CASTLE KEY INS CO
7.8	7.0	-14.3	N/A	-7.0	9.7	13.1	-156.6	-143.5	46.3	-119.4	0.0	CASTLEPOINT FLORIDA INS
1.2	0.8	-418.8	N/A	253.5	71.5	108.5	-15.2	93.3	-35.1	-122.8	9.4	CASTLEPOINT INS CO
0.9	0.8	-90.0	N/A	25.7	60.8	108.5	-15.2	93.3	-35.1	-122.6	12.4	CASTLEPOINT NATIONAL INS CO
0.3	0.2	587.0	105.1	28.5	85.3	82.5	13.1	95.6	104.2	21.0	0.0	CASUALTY CORP OF AMERICA
3.8	2.6	0.3	N/A	N/A	N/A	142.4	999 +	999 +	3.9	15.0	6.5	CASUALTY UNDERWRITERS INS CO
14.6	9.0	10.0	1.9	-0.1	-2.7	-1.7	0.4	-1.3	999 +	-7.0	0.0 ●	CATASTROPHE REINS CO
N/A	N/A	N/A	12.4	1.8	3.2	N/A	N/A	N/A	N/A	0.0	0.0	CATAWBA INS CO
4.4	3.0	49.7	4.7	-0.8	1.4	63.5	21.3	84.8	93.9	-30.4	0.0 ●	CATERPILLAR INS CO
1.3	1.2	10.1	17.9	1.6	2.1	90.9	26.5	117.4	80.5	-11.5	67.1	CATLIN INDEMNITY CO
1.3	0.8	85.3	151.8	13.6	17.7	90.9	26.2	117.1	127.8	-11.5	0.0	CATLIN INS CO
2.3	1.7	36.0	64.1	7.2	9.7	90.9	26.2	117.1	111.0	-11.5	15.2 ●	CATLIN SPECIALTY INS CO
N/A	N/A	-7.0	N/A	N/A	-1.6	N/A	152.7	152.7	-36.3	-114.4	0.0	CATTLEMANS INS CO A RRG
1.1	0.7	66.6	200.9	-35.5	-42.3	49.9	26.9	76.8	111.8	-8.2	0.0	CBIA COMP SERVICES INC
2.8	1.8	126.8	39.0	-3.2	-4.2	61.0	31.6	92.6	103.0	-1.0	0.0	CELINA MUTUAL INS CO
1.3	1.0	108.6	39.7	4.2	16.8	68.1	27.9	96.0	108.9	1.6	0.0	CEM INS CO
7.0	5.6	11.9	3.7	-0.8	-1.7	39.1	24.9	64.0	286.9	5.6	0.0	CENSTAT CASUALTY CO
0.8	0.5	193.4	25.1	-1.4	-1.3	52.5	37.5	90.0	148.2	50.6	0.0	CENTAURI SPECIALTY INS CO

999 + Denotes number greater than 999.9%
999 - Denotes number less than -999.99%
● Bullets denote a more detailed analysis is available in Section II.

INSURANCE COMPANY NAME	DOM. STATE	RATING	TOTAL ASSETS ($MIL)	CAPITAL & SURPLUS ($MIL)	ANNUAL NET PREMIUM ($MIL)	NET INCOME ($MIL)	CAPITAL-IZATION INDEX (PTS)	RESERVE ADQ INDEX (PTS)	PROFIT-ABILITY INDEX (PTS)	LIQUIDITY INDEX (PTS)	STAB. INDEX (PTS)	STABILITY FACTORS
CENTENNIAL CASUALTY CO	AL	B-	110.2	68.2	10.9	3.9	8.0	7.4	8.9	8.3	3.8	DRT
CENTER MUTUAL INS CO	ND	C+	54.4	30.0	27.2	1.4	8.9	8.6	7.2	6.5	3.3	RT
CENTER VALLEY MUTUAL FIRE INS CO	PA	D+(2)	2.5	2.4	0.1	0.0	10.0	N/A	5.2	10.0	1.9	DT
CENTRAL CO-OPERATIVE INS CO	NY	C-	16.0	9.9	5.8	0.5	9.3	6.7	8.4	7.0	2.3	DGRT
CENTRAL MUTUAL INS CO	OH	B	1,468.5	712.1	488.0	4.0	8.6	9.3	7.6	6.8	4.6	RT
CENTRAL PA PHYSICIANS RRG INC	SC	C-	58.7	22.7	12.4	-0.5	7.2	4.3	5.9	7.2	3.0	DFT
CENTRAL STATES INDEMNITY CO OF	NE	C+	395.5	340.4	55.0	3.0	9.3	7.5	6.8	7.3	4.5	RT
CENTRE COUNTY MUTUAL FIRE INS CO	PA	D+	5.6	3.3	2.6	-0.1	7.0	9.3	5.2	5.9	2.0	DGT
CENTRE INS CO	DE	U	89.0	50.0	0.0	0.1	N/A	8.3	7.0	10.0	6.0	FT
CENTURION CASUALTY CO	IA	B+	157.1	156.6	11.7	4.6	10.0	7.3	8.2	9.2	5.0	DT
CENTURION MEDICAL LIAB PROTECT RRG	AZ	D (1)	22.8	10.7	4.3	0.1	8.4	9.7	8.5	7.4	2.0	DGRT
CENTURY CASUALTY CO	GA	D+	5.5	3.0	0.8	0.0	8.3	7.0	1.5	7.4	2.0	DFGR
CENTURY INDEMNITY CO	PA	U	708.4	25.0	0.0	-0.2	N/A	0.3	0.9	7.0	0.0	CFRT
CENTURY INS CO GUAM LTD	GU	D-	22.7	11.1	7.3	0.8	7.5	2.8	7.3	6.9	1.3	DGT
CENTURY MUTUAL INS CO	NC	C- (1)	9.3	7.7	2.1	0.1	7.3	6.0	4.3	6.9	2.2	DGT
CENTURY SURETY CO	OH	C-	561.5	174.8	172.8	9.7	2.6	2.8	4.1	6.7	3.1	CFRT
CENTURY-NATIONAL INS CO	CA	B	485.4	241.7	165.1	16.1	8.9	6.6	5.1	6.9	4.3	T
▲CGB INS CO	IN	D-	337.6	146.3	0.0	0.9	10.0	4.7	6.8	7.0	1.0	T
CHARITABLE SERVICE PROVIDERS RRG	AZ	U (5)	3.5	2.7	0.9	0.0	N/A	8.4	5.3	7.3	3.0	DR
CHARTER INDEMNITY CO	TX	B	12.0	8.3	0.0	0.1	10.0	N/A	5.5	7.0	4.1	DGRT
CHARTER OAK FIRE INS CO	CT	B	944.7	269.1	263.9	15.0	7.9	8.8	7.5	6.8	4.6	T
CHAUTAUQUA PATRONS INS CO	NY	C	21.4	11.2	8.0	0.1	8.2	8.0	5.8	6.8	2.4	DGRT
▼CHEROKEE GUARANTEE CO INC A RRG	AZ	E	14.3	2.4	5.0	-1.6	3.6	5.1	2.5	6.7	0.0	GT
CHEROKEE INS CO	MI	C	469.7	164.3	181.8	3.6	7.5	4.3	6.6	4.9	4.0	LRT
CHERRY VALLEY COOPERATIVE INS CO	NY	D	1.7	1.4	0.3	0.1	9.0	7.5	2.6	8.8	1.5	DGRT
CHESAPEAKE EMPLOYERS INS CO	MD	B	2,168.9	499.1	231.1	32.5	6.2	9.3	6.2	7.5	4.4	CT
CHICAGO INS CO	IL	C	101.5	61.6	0.0	0.2	10.0	3.5	7.4	7.0	4.1	DRT
CHUBB CUSTOM INS CO	NJ	B-	396.9	206.2	48.9	5.9	10.0	7.9	8.8	7.7	4.6	T
CHUBB INDEMNITY INS CO	NY	B	408.4	152.3	48.9	5.3	10.0	8.0	8.8	7.0	4.6	T
CHUBB INS CO OF NJ	NJ	B (2)	76.5	34.5	0.0	0.8	10.0	N/A	7.4	7.0	4.0	T
CHUBB INS CO OF PR	PR	U	141.9	49.8	0.0	-1.2	N/A	9.5	7.2	7.0	0.0	T
CHUBB LLOYDS INS CO OF TX	TX	B	39.1	5.3	0.0	0.0	6.6	N/A	6.8	7.0	4.9	DGT
CHUBB NATIONAL INS CO	IN	B	342.0	156.7	48.9	5.1	10.0	8.0	8.8	7.0	4.6	T
CHUNG KUO INS CO LTD GUAM BRANCH	GU	C+	39.5	23.3	15.9	3.1	7.4	8.9	8.5	8.7	3.0	DGT
CHURCH INS CO	NY	U	24.7	15.4	0.0	-0.2	N/A	9.1	2.7	9.3	1.2	FGT
CHURCH MUTUAL INS CO	WI	B	1,566.3	615.7	615.7	19.0	8.7	8.8	6.2	6.7	4.9	T
CIM INS CORP	MI	C	17.7	17.5	0.0	0.1	10.0	N/A	6.3	7.0	3.3	DFGR
CINCINNATI CASUALTY CO	OH	B	391.5	349.5	0.0	5.5	10.0	N/A	7.9	10.0	4.7	T
CINCINNATI EQUITABLE INS CO	OH	U	3.1	3.1	0.0	-0.1	N/A	6.1	2.5	7.0	3.7	GRT
CINCINNATI INDEMNITY CO	OH	A-	123.8	91.4	0.0	2.4	10.0	N/A	7.9	10.0	5.5	T
CINCINNATI INS CO	OH	A-	11,749.4	4,600.1	4,189.4	226.0	8.1	8.7	7.3	6.4	5.7	T
CINCINNATI SPECIALTY UNDERWRITER	DE	B	669.5	332.7	174.7	22.2	7.8	9.4	8.7	6.8	4.9	RT
CIRCLE STAR INS CO A RRG	VT	D	7.8	2.1	0.4	0.3	10.0	5.9	9.3	10.0	1.6	DGT
CITATION INS CO (MA)	MA	C+	258.2	78.3	158.0	0.6	8.2	4.2	2.7	4.3	3.8	FLT
CITIES & VILLAGES MUTUAL INS CO	WI	C	51.9	28.8	13.6	0.6	7.6	8.0	6.5	6.9	3.2	DFT
CITIZENS INS CO OF AM	MI	B	1,545.0	734.7	680.7	62.9	10.0	7.8	5.6	6.2	4.8	RT
CITIZENS INS CO OF IL	IL	C+	4.8	4.7	0.0	0.0	10.0	N/A	6.4	7.0	3.0	DGRT
CITIZENS INS CO OF OHIO	OH	C	15.8	15.6	0.0	0.2	10.0	N/A	7.2	7.0	3.2	DGT
CITIZENS INS CO OF THE MIDWEST	IN	C	51.5	51.4	0.0	0.5	10.0	N/A	7.5	7.0	4.0	T
CITIZENS PROPERTY INS CORP	FL	A+	12,538.0	7,568.5	578.0	140.8	10.0	5.8	8.4	9.3	8.4	FT
CITIZENS UNITED RECIP EXCH	NJ	D	88.3	18.5	41.6	-5.3	2.4	1.4	1.4	5.5	2.2	CDFT
CIVIC PROPERTY & CASUALTY CO INC	CA	C+	280.2	115.5	149.3	-2.3	9.3	6.1	6.1	6.6	4.5	RT

See Page 27 for explanation of footnotes and   50   www.weissratings.com
Page 28 for explanation of stability factors.
Arrows denote recent upgrades ▲ or downgrades ▼   (see Section VII for explanations)

RISK ADJ. CAPITAL RATIO #1	CAPITAL RATIO #2	PREMIUM TO SURPLUS (%)	RESV. TO SURPLUS (%)	RESV. DEVELOP. 1 YEAR (%)	RESV. DEVELOP. 2 YEAR (%)	LOSS RATIO (%)	EXP. RATIO (%)	COMB RATIO (%)	CASH FROM UNDER-WRITING (%)	NET PREMIUM GROWTH (%)	INVEST. IN AFFIL (%)	INSURANCE COMPANY NAME
3.3	1.9	16.5	1.9	-0.7	-1.3	41.9	16.5	58.4	152.8	9.8	0.0	CENTENNIAL CASUALTY CO
3.6	2.5	94.2	24.2	-4.5	-6.3	63.1	26.7	89.8	113.5	-13.6	0.0	CENTER MUTUAL INS CO
20.4	19.0	4.6	N/A	N/A	N/A	34.5	96.9	131.4	72.1	-26.3	0.0	CENTER VALLEY MUTUAL FIRE INS CO
3.5	2.4	61.5	11.9	-2.8	-3.8	46.9	40.8	87.7	112.7	9.2	0.0	CENTRAL CO-OPERATIVE INS CO
2.8	2.1	69.1	51.2	-4.7	-7.7	57.8	33.1	90.9	111.0	9.0	11.9 ●	CENTRAL MUTUAL INS CO
1.6	1.1	55.1	115.0	-3.3	-7.9	64.0	28.5	92.5	80.0	-4.0	0.0	CENTRAL PA PHYSICIANS RRG INC
4.2	2.7	15.5	1.5	-0.2	-0.6	55.4	48.9	104.3	98.0	9.5	3.5 ●	CENTRAL STATES INDEMNITY CO OF
1.5	0.9	78.8	13.5	-0.5	-5.2	73.0	36.5	109.5	96.8	14.4	0.0	CENTRE COUNTY MUTUAL FIRE INS CO
N/A	N/A	N/A	80.0	-0.1	-2.5	N/A	N/A	N/A	N/A	100.0	0.0	CENTRE INS CO
51.1	23.6	7.7	0.4	-0.2	-0.3	4.0	15.7	19.7	455.9	-13.3	0.0 ●	CENTURION CASUALTY CO
2.9	1.9	40.4	33.1	-7.1	-34.4	42.4	34.3	76.7	142.8	33.6	0.0	CENTURION MEDICAL LIAB PROTECT
3.7	2.8	25.0	83.5	1.3	7.2	165.4	50.6	216.0	35.2	-62.8	0.0	CENTURY CASUALTY CO
N/A	N/A	N/A	999 +	396.8	874.3	N/A	N/A	N/A	N/A	0.0	13.0	CENTURY INDEMNITY CO
2.1	1.3	64.4	27.1	-2.2	5.8	39.9	46.3	86.2	106.4	-9.5	0.0	CENTURY INS CO GUAM LTD
1.7	1.2	26.7	3.3	-0.5	-0.3	49.4	46.4	95.8	105.5	7.3	0.0	CENTURY MUTUAL INS CO
0.6	0.4	99.6	180.2	12.2	18.8	77.1	37.2	114.3	85.6	0.7	8.8	CENTURY SURETY CO
2.3	1.5	44.9	30.7	-0.7	-1.7	70.3	33.0	103.3	99.8	17.1	0.0 ●	CENTURY-NATIONAL INS CO
14.9	10.4	N/A	N/A	N/A	N/A	N/A	N/A	N/A	N/A	100.0	0.0	CGB INS CO
N/A	N/A	30.9	13.7	1.7	-5.6	28.8	47.8	76.6	206.0	-4.1	0.0	CHARITABLE SERVICE PROVIDERS RRG
7.0	6.3	N/A	N/A	N/A	N/A	N/A	N/A	N/A	-2.7	0.0	0.0	CHARTER INDEMNITY CO
2.6	1.6	103.2	177.0	-3.3	-8.2	58.7	30.6	89.3	113.8	2.9	0.0 ●	CHARTER OAK FIRE INS CO
2.5	1.7	72.6	30.0	-0.4	-2.8	70.9	36.5	107.4	93.4	7.9	0.0	CHAUTAUQUA PATRONS INS CO
0.4	0.3	148.0	210.4	-24.3	-61.1	71.0	17.3	88.3	136.2	45.7	0.0	CHEROKEE GUARANTEE CO INC A RRG
2.3	1.3	119.0	144.0	3.0	2.1	91.9	9.5	101.4	117.3	0.7	0.0	CHEROKEE INS CO
2.9	1.9	22.4	13.1	2.5	-1.4	105.6	36.9	142.5	109.6	7.9	0.0	CHERRY VALLEY COOPERATIVE INS CO
1.7	1.0	49.9	289.0	-10.3	-18.8	73.1	25.1	98.2	101.7	1.4	0.0 ●	CHESAPEAKE EMPLOYERS INS CO
10.8	9.8	N/A	N/A	N/A	N/A	N/A	N/A	N/A	-5.3	0.0	0.0	CHICAGO INS CO
9.4	5.9	24.4	40.5	-1.5	-2.9	55.1	29.3	84.4	122.9	4.1	0.0 ●	CHUBB CUSTOM INS CO
7.2	4.5	32.4	54.0	-1.5	-3.4	56.5	29.2	85.7	113.2	4.1	0.0	CHUBB INDEMNITY INS CO
5.8	5.2	N/A	N/A	N/A	N/A	N/A	N/A	N/A	N/A	0.0	0.0	CHUBB INS CO OF NJ
N/A	N/A	N/A	N/A	N/A	N/A	N/A	N/A	N/A	N/A	-100.0	0.0	CHUBB INS CO OF PR
1.0	0.9	N/A	N/A	N/A	N/A	N/A	N/A	N/A	N/A	0.0	0.0	CHUBB LLOYDS INS CO OF TX
7.5	4.7	32.1	53.4	-1.5	-3.4	56.5	29.3	85.8	112.7	4.1	0.0	CHUBB NATIONAL INS CO
2.2	1.4	78.7	20.3	-12.1	-13.2	34.8	55.9	90.7	110.4	6.9	0.0	CHUNG KUO INS CO LTD GUAM BRANCH
N/A	N/A	N/A	46.7	-4.2	-0.9	999 +	999 +	999 +	N/A	131.9	0.0	CHURCH INS CO
2.9	2.0	105.2	77.6	-1.4	-5.5	57.7	31.1	88.8	120.2	4.5	3.7 ●	CHURCH MUTUAL INS CO
202.3	182.0	N/A	N/A	N/A	N/A	N/A	N/A	N/A	345.5	0.0	0.0	CIM INS CORP
10.6	6.1	N/A	N/A	N/A	N/A	N/A	N/A	N/A	-236.6	0.0	0.0 ●	CINCINNATI CASUALTY CO
N/A	N/A	N/A	0.4	-0.8	-0.3	N/A	N/A	N/A	N/A	0.0	0.0	CINCINNATI EQUITABLE INS CO
10.9	6.3	N/A	N/A	N/A	N/A	N/A	N/A	N/A	-28.1	0.0	0.0 ●	CINCINNATI INDEMNITY CO
2.3	1.7	94.9	94.3	-3.3	-3.7	60.9	30.0	90.9	117.0	4.9	9.8 ●	CINCINNATI INS CO
2.9	1.5	57.0	72.2	-13.0	-21.8	41.9	30.0	71.9	196.1	14.0	0.0 ●	CINCINNATI SPECIALTY UNDERWRITER
1.2	1.1	23.9	32.1	-3.8	-7.1	41.8	-154.4	-112.6	-77.9	21.7	0.0	CIRCLE STAR INS CO A RRG
2.2	1.8	206.1	94.4	3.4	8.4	84.1	25.5	109.6	96.3	11.0	0.0	CITATION INS CO (MA)
2.1	1.3	48.4	51.1	-3.0	-7.5	63.0	28.5	91.5	97.6	4.4	6.1	CITIES & VILLAGES MUTUAL INS CO
4.9	3.3	103.1	63.5	-5.0	-5.0	58.3	27.0	85.3	114.6	0.8	0.0 ●	CITIZENS INS CO OF AM
273.3	136.7	N/A	N/A	N/A	N/A	N/A	N/A	N/A	N/A	0.0	0.0	CITIZENS INS CO OF IL
74.5	33.2	N/A	N/A	N/A	N/A	N/A	N/A	N/A	N/A	0.0	0.0	CITIZENS INS CO OF OHIO
78.3	35.3	N/A	N/A	N/A	N/A	N/A	N/A	N/A	N/A	0.0	0.0	CITIZENS INS CO OF THE MIDWEST
32.4	16.5	7.8	9.9	1.5	2.2	64.3	46.0	110.3	54.3	-41.0	0.0 ●	CITIZENS PROPERTY INS CORP
0.5	0.4	222.0	199.4	11.3	34.8	99.4	24.7	124.1	77.1	-12.2	0.0	CITIZENS UNITED RECIP EXCH
3.8	2.7	127.0	73.2	1.3	1.5	68.4	33.7	102.1	104.0	6.2	0.0	CIVIC PROPERTY & CASUALTY CO INC

999 + Denotes number greater than 999.9%
999 - Denotes number less than -999.99%
● Bullets denote a more detailed analysis is available in Section II.

INSURANCE COMPANY NAME	DOM. STATE	RATING	TOTAL ASSETS ($MIL)	CAPITAL & SURPLUS ($MIL)	ANNUAL NET PREMIUM ($MIL)	NET INCOME ($MIL)	CAPITAL-IZATION INDEX (PTS)	RESERVE ADQ INDEX (PTS)	PROFIT-ABILITY INDEX (PTS)	LIQUIDITY INDEX (PTS)	STAB. INDEX (PTS)	STABILITY FACTORS
CIVIL SERVICE EMPLOYEES INS CO	CA	C+	212.6	116.4	99.8	0.9	8.4	6.2	4.2	6.2	4.0	FRT
CLAIM PROFESSIONALS LIAB INS CO RRG	VT	D	4.3	2.2	0.6	-0.2	7.5	7.0	6.2	9.3	1.9	DGRT
CLARENDON NATIONAL INS CO	IL	C	814.8	204.0	-204.8	-8.0	7.7	10.0	3.0	7.0	4.3	FGRT
CLAVERACK CO-OPERATIVE INS CO	NY	U	3.4	0.8	1.8	0.1	N/A	0.0	4.9	0.0	0.3	CGLT
CLEAR BLUE INS CO	IL	C	18.0	18.0	-0.2	0.0	10.0	7.2	2.0	7.0	3.2	DGT
CLEAR BLUE SPECIALTY INS CO	NC	C+	64.4	64.2	0.0	0.1	10.0	3.5	5.2	10.0	3.5	DFGR
CLEARFIELD CTY GRNGE MUT FIRE INS CO	PA	C-	2.9	2.3	0.7	-0.1	9.0	5.0	1.7	7.5	1.9	DFGT
CLEARWATER INS CO	DE	D-	1,129.5	276.2	0.1	-10.4	4.8	0.7	1.5	9.4	1.3	FGRT
CLEARWATER SELECT INS CO	CT	D	1,223.4	479.8	200.4	35.5	4.4	0.7	8.7	6.2	1.7	RT
CLERMONT INS CO	IA	C	26.0	22.5	0.0	0.2	10.0	N/A	7.2	10.0	3.5	DGRT
CLINIC MUTUAL INS CO RRG	HI	U (5)	4.1	4.1	0.0	0.0	N/A	4.7	3.8	10.0	3.2	FGRT
CLOISTER MUTL CAS INS CO	PA	C-	9.6	9.6	0.1	0.1	10.0	7.2	3.8	9.4	2.9	DFGT
CM REGENT INS CO	PA	C	170.8	63.2	40.9	4.0	7.5	5.0	4.1	7.2	3.5	FRT
CM VANTAGE SPECIALTY INS CO	WI	U	53.3	52.0	0.0	-0.1	N/A	N/A	3.9	7.0	5.4	T
CMIC RRG	DC	C+	5.2	2.7	0.1	0.1	10.0	4.9	3.0	9.4	3.3	DGT
CO-OPERATIVE INS COS	VT	B-	128.2	70.9	61.3	4.6	9.8	7.9	7.3	6.4	3.7	RT
COAST NATIONAL INS CO	CA	D+	603.8	424.7	0.0	5.4	10.0	6.0	6.7	10.0	2.7	FRT
COASTAL AMERICAN INS CO	MS	C-	8.3	4.6	4.2	0.3	5.7	5.7	5.0	6.5	2.1	DGT
COASTAL INS CO	AL	D	40.7	18.1	4.9	-1.1	8.8	9.7	3.4	8.5	2.3	DFGR
COASTAL SELECT INS CO	CA	C-	108.3	39.7	32.8	3.5	1.5	7.6	3.8	1.0	2.9	CLRT
CODAN INS CO LTD	NY	U	2.1	2.1	0.0	-0.1	N/A	9.4	2.1	10.0	1.2	FGRT
COFACE NORTH AMERICA INS CO	MA	C	157.9	49.3	52.3	-5.6	9.9	9.7	3.9	7.3	2.6	RT
COLISEUM REINS CO	DE	U	295.8	193.8	0.2	12.0	N/A	5.0	3.1	9.6	4.6	GRT
COLLEGE LIAB INS CO LTD RRG	HI	D-	15.2	7.2	2.6	-0.5	7.1	9.3	2.4	6.9	0.4	DGT
COLLEGE RRG INC	VT	C-	20.9	9.9	5.7	0.3	5.9	7.0	8.6	7.4	2.3	DGT
COLONIAL AMERICAN CAS & SURETY CO	MD	C+	30.2	22.5	0.0	0.2	10.0	N/A	5.5	10.0	3.5	DGRT
COLONIAL COUNTY MUTUAL INS CO	TX	B	168.4	13.9	0.0	0.0	7.5	N/A	3.9	6.5	4.3	DFT
COLONIAL LLOYDS	TX	D+	8.8	6.3	1.2	0.7	8.9	4.2	1.6	7.0	2.5	DFGT
COLONIAL MORTGAGE INS CO	TX	D+	3.0	1.9	0.3	-0.2	7.8	1.3	3.9	9.1	2.2	DGT
COLONIAL SURETY CO	PA	C	55.5	33.6	9.6	1.9	9.3	9.3	8.7	8.5	3.2	DRT
COLONY INS CO	VA	C	1,450.9	346.0	278.8	11.4	7.2	9.4	7.9	6.9	3.3	RT
COLONY SPECIALTY INS CO	OH	D+	62.4	21.0	0.0	0.0	8.9	N/A	3.4	7.0	2.4	DRT
COLORADO CASUALTY INS CO	NH	C+	24.5	24.5	0.0	0.1	10.0	N/A	7.1	7.0	3.7	DGRT
COLORADO FARM BUREAU MUTUAL INS CO	CO	C	86.7	36.4	25.9	2.5	8.4	9.3	2.5	6.5	3.2	T
COLUMBIA CASUALTY CO	IL	C	236.2	234.8	0.0	3.5	10.0	N/A	6.7	10.0	3.9	ART
COLUMBIA FEDERAL INS CO	DC	D+	3.1	2.1	0.8	0.0	7.2	9.4	5.4	7.0	1.8	DGT
COLUMBIA INS CO	NE	C+	19,039.1	14,203.1	448.9	699.4	7.7	8.2	7.7	9.8	3.4	RT
COLUMBIA LLOYDS INS CO	TX	C	51.9	21.8	22.3	1.1	3.7	4.5	5.4	3.2	3.1	CDLR
COLUMBIA MUTUAL INS CO	MO	B-	380.8	183.3	126.3	1.3	7.9	6.1	5.0	6.6	4.1	RT
COLUMBIA NATIONAL INS CO	NE	C+	91.6	39.1	32.5	0.7	8.9	5.9	4.9	6.6	3.7	T
COLUMBIA NATIONAL RRG INC	VT	E	1.8	1.2	0.2	0.0	10.0	N/A	6.9	10.0	0.0	DGT
COMCARE PRO INS RECIPROCAL RRG	VT	D	4.5	3.7	1.7	0.3	7.2	4.1	6.1	6.8	2.0	DGT
COMMERCE & INDUSTRY INS CO	NY	C	482.6	465.2	927.4	156.3	7.5	3.9	1.9	6.4	2.8	AFT
COMMERCE INS CO	MA	C	2,244.5	674.4	1,157.6	19.9	8.4	4.2	3.1	2.9	4.3	FLT
COMMERCE WEST INS CO	CA	C	173.5	55.0	108.5	1.8	8.3	4.1	3.2	5.2	3.5	T
COMMERCIAL ALLIANCE INS CO	TX	C	76.7	39.0	33.8	2.7	6.8	3.8	6.0	6.3	3.6	RT
COMMERCIAL CASUALTY INS CO	CA	U	113.6	57.9	0.0	0.4	N/A	3.6	3.1	10.0	5.4	FGT
COMMERCIAL GUARANTY INS CO	DE	U	33.6	33.5	0.0	0.4	N/A	N/A	5.8	7.0	5.4	GT
COMMERCIAL HIRECAR INS CO RRG	TN	U	2.0	1.4	0.0	-0.1	N/A	N/A	2.9	7.0	2.0	FGT
COMMERCIAL MUT INS CO	GA	F (5)	0.0	0.0	7.9	0.0	0.0	2.3	0.1	0.0	0.0	CDFL
COMMONWEALTH CASUALTY CO	AZ	E	12.6	3.8	4.2	-0.9	0.3	4.2	1.9	0.0	0.2	CDFG
COMMONWEALTH INS CO OF AMERICA	DE	U	11.2	9.4	0.0	0.0	N/A	7.0	2.0	7.0	3.2	FGRT

See Page 27 for explanation of footnotes and Page 28 for explanation of stability factors.

Arrows denote recent upgrades ▲ or downgrades ▼   (see Section VII for explanations)

52

www.weissratings.com

RISK ADJ. CAPITAL RATIO #1	RATIO #2	PREMIUM TO SURPLUS (%)	RESV. TO SURPLUS (%)	RESV. DEVELOP. 1 YEAR (%)	RESV. DEVELOP. 2 YEAR (%)	LOSS RATIO (%)	EXP. RATIO (%)	COMB RATIO (%)	CASH FROM UNDER-WRITING (%)	NET PREMIUM GROWTH (%)	INVEST. IN AFFIL (%)	INSURANCE COMPANY NAME
2.5	2.0	87.5	41.7	0.5	-0.2	69.5	33.0	102.5	92.6	3.1	20.7	CIVIL SERVICE EMPLOYEES INS CO
1.3	1.0	24.7	29.2	-3.5	-10.9	32.8	12.7	45.5	206.8	10.1	0.0	CLAIM PROFESSIONALS LIAB INS CO
7.5	4.3	-97.6	60.6	-96.4	-90.8	103.6	5.2	108.8	-849.5	N/A	0.0 •	CLARENDON NATIONAL INS CO
N/A	N/A	281.8	125.5	-9.0	-11.9	57.7	38.6	96.3	139.9	51.0	0.0	CLAVERACK CO-OPERATIVE INS CO
250.4	125.1	-1.2	N/A	-0.2	-0.3	116.5	-62.4	54.1	-293.6	-238.9	0.0	CLEAR BLUE INS CO
7.7	4.7	N/A	11.2	2.8	13.7	999 +	999 +	999 +	-132.1	100.0	0.0	CLEAR BLUE SPECIALTY INS CO
3.6	2.5	31.5	11.6	-1.0	1.8	83.7	75.3	159.0	70.7	13.8	0.0	CLEARFIELD CTY GRNGE MUT FIRE INS
0.8	0.6	N/A	246.6	25.6	51.3	999 +	999 +	999 +	-1.8	-22.6	14.4 •	CLEARWATER INS CO
0.8	0.7	42.0	131.0	-4.0	-7.4	58.3	25.0	83.3	107.2	-9.9	14.8 •	CLEARWATER SELECT INS CO
19.7	17.7	N/A	N/A	N/A	N/A	N/A	N/A	N/A	121.7	0.0	0.0	CLERMONT INS CO
N/A	N/A	N/A	N/A	-1.9	N/A	1.5	999 +	999 +	0.4	-98.0	0.0	CLINIC MUTUAL INS CO RRG
11.3	6.7	1.4	0.3	-1.2	-0.1	24.1	614.6	638.7	16.6	-12.8	0.0	CLOISTER MUTL CAS INS CO
3.7	2.3	71.8	181.5	-21.8	-42.0	57.2	28.6	85.8	89.8	-18.7	0.0	CM REGENT INS CO
N/A	N/A	N/A	N/A	N/A	N/A	N/A	N/A	N/A	N/A	0.0	0.0	CM VANTAGE SPECIALTY INS CO
3.1	2.8	3.7	15.1	-1.8	1.2	-209.4	-172.7	-382.1	-234.6	68.1	0.0	CMIC RRG
4.5	3.1	92.5	28.3	-5.2	-2.4	61.0	34.9	95.9	101.0	5.3	1.0	CO-OPERATIVE INS COS
7.8	7.1	N/A	N/A	0.2	0.3	N/A	N/A	N/A	-207.3	0.0	12.4 •	COAST NATIONAL INS CO
1.8	1.2	94.3	11.1	-4.4	-2.5	31.3	49.7	81.0	112.2	-3.0	0.0	COASTAL AMERICAN INS CO
2.3	1.9	25.6	85.8	-14.6	-26.8	63.5	73.8	137.3	55.2	2.0	0.2	COASTAL INS CO
0.4	0.3	83.4	17.5	-1.3	-2.2	27.9	34.4	62.3	166.2	-2.9	0.0	COASTAL SELECT INS CO
N/A	N/A	N/A	242.3	-7.6	-16.3	999 +	999 +	999 +	0.2	0.0	0.0	CODAN INS CO LTD
3.1	2.0	92.2	52.4	-1.8	-21.0	56.6	33.8	90.4	134.1	-2.7	0.0	COFACE NORTH AMERICA INS CO
N/A	N/A	0.1	41.6	1.8	1.6	999 +	999 +	999 +	1.7	132.9	7.3	COLISEUM REINS CO
1.4	0.9	33.2	62.1	1.8	-4.6	139.7	22.8	162.5	100.5	18.1	0.0	COLLEGE LIAB INS CO LTD RRG
1.3	1.2	58.9	91.3	6.7	3.3	74.6	22.8	97.4	116.7	8.4	0.0	COLLEGE RRG INC
11.1	10.0	N/A	N/A	N/A	N/A	N/A	N/A	N/A	23.0	0.0	0.0	COLONIAL AMERICAN CAS & SURETY CO
1.4	1.3	N/A	N/A	N/A	N/A	N/A	N/A	N/A	62.7	0.0	0.0	COLONIAL COUNTY MUTUAL INS CO
7.0	6.3	21.4	15.5	3.4	10.7	94.2	8.4	102.6	80.8	-59.6	0.0	COLONIAL LLOYDS
2.7	2.3	15.6	13.8	0.6	7.6	3.7	58.6	62.3	107.7	-29.4	0.0	COLONIAL MORTGAGE INS CO
4.1	2.9	30.2	39.3	-8.0	-13.1	7.0	40.6	47.6	160.7	6.2	0.0	COLONIAL SURETY CO
1.6	1.1	79.7	120.5	-0.2	-11.8	56.1	34.1	90.2	130.3	18.8	5.5 •	COLONY INS CO
3.6	2.3	N/A	N/A	N/A	N/A	N/A	N/A	N/A	-5.1	0.0	0.0	COLONY SPECIALTY INS CO
211.6	105.8	N/A	N/A	N/A	N/A	N/A	N/A	N/A	N/A	0.0	0.0	COLORADO CASUALTY INS CO
2.9	2.0	76.4	42.0	-8.6	-11.8	72.2	28.0	100.2	95.2	-3.9	2.0	COLORADO FARM BUREAU MUTUAL INS
65.8	27.2	N/A	N/A	N/A	N/A	N/A	N/A	N/A	N/A	0.0	0.0 •	COLUMBIA CASUALTY CO
1.8	1.1	38.5	48.1	-9.5	-11.4	78.2	21.3	99.5	104.3	-5.1	0.0	COLUMBIA FEDERAL INS CO
1.9	1.5	3.2	11.4	-0.5	-6.7	62.0	16.1	78.1	205.1	191.7	25.2 •	COLUMBIA INS CO
0.8	0.6	112.3	20.1	-0.4	6.7	62.6	25.4	88.0	120.5	22.7	33.3	COLUMBIA LLOYDS INS CO
2.0	1.7	69.8	57.5	-3.2	-4.6	64.4	30.8	95.2	100.5	8.6	26.1	COLUMBIA MUTUAL INS CO
3.5	2.5	85.6	70.6	-3.7	-5.2	64.4	29.3	93.7	101.7	8.6	0.0	COLUMBIA NATIONAL INS CO
4.1	3.7	19.8	N/A	N/A	N/A	N/A	55.0	55.0	186.8	0.4	0.0	COLUMBIA NATIONAL RRG INC
2.3	1.4	48.9	25.9	4.9	2.2	78.2	26.5	104.7	112.4	13.6	0.0	COMCARE PRO INS RECIPROCAL RRG
3.9	3.0	95.2	224.1	9.3	8.8	91.2	30.2	121.4	84.4	57.1	1.7 •	COMMERCE & INDUSTRY INS CO
2.5	1.9	175.2	88.1	3.4	7.2	84.1	25.1	109.2	89.8	-15.5	3.5 •	COMMERCE INS CO
2.3	1.9	207.3	92.2	3.4	8.5	84.1	20.7	104.8	103.0	22.6	0.0	COMMERCE WEST INS CO
1.4	1.0	93.1	60.5	10.2	14.9	67.2	31.1	98.3	139.0	1.0	0.0	COMMERCIAL ALLIANCE INS CO
N/A	N/A	N/A	100.2	N/A	N/A	999 +	999 +	999 +	N/A	N/A	0.0	COMMERCIAL CASUALTY INS CO
N/A	N/A	N/A	N/A	N/A	N/A	N/A	N/A	N/A	N/A	0.0	0.0	COMMERCIAL GUARANTY INS CO
N/A	N/A	N/A	N/A	N/A	N/A	N/A	N/A	N/A	N/A	0.0	0.0	COMMERCIAL HIRECAR INS CO RRG
0.0	0.0	544.6	674.2	9.5	40.7	76.4	80.1	156.5	91.3	-17.7	0.0	COMMERCIAL MUT INS CO
0.1	0.1	157.7	71.1	12.8	10.8	117.0	92.5	209.5	82.8	15.9	0.0	COMMONWEALTH CASUALTY CO
N/A	N/A	-0.1	10.2	0.8	1.2	999 +	999 +	999 +	-0.8	-375.5	0.0	COMMONWEALTH INS CO OF AMERICA

999 + Denotes number greater than 999.9%
999 - Denotes number less than -999.99%
• Bullets denote a more detailed analysis is available in Section II.

INSURANCE COMPANY NAME	DOM. STATE	RATING	TOTAL ASSETS ($MIL)	CAPITAL & SURPLUS ($MIL)	ANNUAL NET PREMIUM ($MIL)	NET INCOME ($MIL)	CAPITAL-IZATION INDEX (PTS)	RESERVE ADQ INDEX (PTS)	PROFIT-ABILITY INDEX (PTS)	LIQUIDITY INDEX (PTS)	STAB. INDEX (PTS)	STABILITY FACTORS
COMMUNITIES OF FAITH RRG INC	SC	C-	14.6	12.7	0.9	0.0	10.0	8.0	4.9	9.4	2.5	DGRT
COMMUNITY BLOOD CENTERS EXCHANGE	IN	C	20.7	16.3	2.7	0.3	10.0	9.6	8.7	9.2	2.7	DFGR
COMMUNITY CARE RRG INC	DC	U	5.0	2.6	2.5	0.1	N/A	N/A	5.9	9.0	0.0	DGT
COMMUNITY HEALTH ALLIANCE RECIP RRG	VT	U	57.9	11.1	0.0	-0.2	N/A	1.0	1.3	7.6	0.0	CFRT
COMMUNITY HOSPITAL ALTERNATIVE RRG	VT	C	266.1	121.2	41.4	11.0	9.0	9.7	9.3	7.4	3.9	RT
COMMUNITY INS CORP	WI	C	8.7	6.0	0.0	0.0	10.0	3.6	4.4	5.0	2.8	DFGR
COMMUNITY MUTUAL INS CO	NY	D+	2.7	1.0	0.0	0.0	10.0	9.8	2.9	7.0	1.2	DGRT
COMP OPTIONS INS CO	FL	C	115.1	38.4	34.4	-0.3	6.5	4.6	2.9	7.0	3.9	T
COMPASS INS CO	NY	U	12.2	10.3	0.0	0.1	N/A	3.9	5.0	7.0	4.0	GRT
COMPASS SPCLTY INS RRG INC	TN	U	1.6	1.1	0.0	-0.1	N/A	0.0	2.5	0.0	0.0	LT
COMPSOURCE MUTUAL INS CO	OK	U	--	--	--	--	N/A	--	--	--	--	Z
COMPTRUST AGC MUT CAPTIVE INS CO	GA	C	32.8	14.3	12.5	1.2	4.9	9.4	3.1	6.8	2.5	DGT
COMPUTER INS CO	RI	U	23.5	24.0	0.0	-0.1	N/A	4.6	3.5	7.0	4.7	FGT
COMPWEST INS CO	CA	C	258.3	131.5	42.5	3.5	10.0	4.5	8.2	7.0	4.3	RT
CONCORD GENERAL MUTUAL INS CO	NH	B-	449.3	228.8	164.1	1.7	8.1	8.7	4.6	6.5	4.1	FT
CONEMAUGH VALLEY MUTUAL INS CO	PA	C-	8.6	4.1	1.8	0.1	8.5	8.0	6.7	7.1	2.5	DGRT
CONIFER INS CO	MI	D	83.1	28.7	41.1	-2.1	1.9	6.7	3.9	6.0	2.2	CT
CONNECTICUT MEDICAL INS CO	CT	B	493.4	292.0	31.8	2.7	7.5	9.4	8.1	8.1	4.2	FRT
CONSOLIDATED INS ASSN	TX	C-	3.0	2.8	-0.2	0.0	10.0	7.9	3.2	10.0	2.3	FGT
CONSOLIDATED INS CO	IN	C	13.4	13.0	0.0	0.1	10.0	N/A	3.4	7.0	3.1	DGRT
CONSOLIDATED LLOYDS	TX	U	1.6	1.4	0.0	0.0	N/A	7.6	3.2	10.0	3.0	FGRT
CONSTITUTION INS CO	NY	C	24.8	19.7	7.0	1.0	9.2	3.6	8.3	8.1	2.7	DGT
CONSUMER SPECIALTIES INS CO RRG	VT	D+	4.6	2.8	0.5	-0.2	8.1	8.7	2.3	9.2	2.0	DFGR
CONSUMERS COUNTY MUTUAL INS CO	TX	D	187.8	2.3	0.0	0.0	0.8	N/A	6.2	0.0	1.9	CDGL
CONSUMERS INS USA INC	TN	B-	70.2	31.5	21.5	0.2	8.3	4.6	4.0	7.0	3.8	RT
CONTINENTAL CASUALTY CO	IL	C+	43,522.7	10,583.9	6,036.8	495.8	7.8	6.2	5.7	7.0	3.2	ART
CONTINENTAL DIVIDE INS CO	CO	C+	15.7	12.7	0.0	0.6	10.0	N/A	7.2	10.0	3.3	DGT
CONTINENTAL HERITAGE INS CO	FL	C	7.5	7.1	1.9	0.1	10.0	7.3	7.7	8.9	2.2	DGRT
CONTINENTAL INDEMNITY CO	IA	C	177.9	90.7	57.3	6.3	8.2	9.0	9.4	8.1	3.8	RT
CONTINENTAL INS CO	PA	C	1,685.8	1,478.7	0.0	27.8	10.0	3.7	6.2	7.0	4.2	ART
CONTINENTAL INS CO OF NJ	NJ	C (2)	18.4	18.3	0.0	0.4	10.0	N/A	6.0	10.0	3.3	ADRT
CONTINENTAL MUTUAL INS CO	PA	D	1.6	1.3	1.7	0.0	6.7	5.9	6.9	6.0	1.4	DGRT
CONTINENTAL RISK UNDERWRITERS RRG	NV	U (4)	0.4	0.4	0.0	0.0	N/A	N/A	2.1	7.0	1.7	FGT
CONTINENTAL WESTERN INS CO	IA	C	230.0	91.3	0.0	1.1	10.0	N/A	7.0	7.7	4.3	T
▼CONTINUING CARE RRG INC	VT	E	4.8	1.2	4.1	-1.1	4.0	6.5	0.9	0.5	0.1	DFGL
CONTRACTORS BONDING & INS CO	IL	B	209.9	113.1	63.0	4.3	10.0	9.4	5.3	7.0	4.0	RT
CONTRACTORS INS CO OF NORTH AMER	HI	D	37.2	27.5	3.5	0.9	9.7	5.1	2.9	9.1	2.3	DFGT
CONTROLLED RISK INS CO OF VT RRG	VT	C+	105.7	38.7	17.0	2.1	9.3	8.6	8.3	7.6	3.4	RT
CONVENTUS INTER-INS	NJ	C+(2)	88.8	39.7	12.8	1.0	10.0	9.5	7.0	7.9	3.3	DRT
COOPERATIVA D SEGUROS MULTIPLES D	PR	C+	509.1	169.8	176.3	3.6	8.1	5.9	4.7	7.2	3.4	RT
COPIC A RRG	DC	U	0.7	0.6	0.0	0.0	N/A	N/A	2.6	10.0	1.8	FGT
COPIC INS CO	CO	B	690.9	403.5	82.1	5.9	10.0	9.4	8.2	7.9	4.7	RT
COPPERPOINT AMERICAN INS CO	AZ	C+	6.9	5.3	0.0	-0.1	10.0	N/A	3.3	10.0	3.0	DGT
COPPERPOINT CASUALTY INS CO	AZ	C+	6.8	4.2	0.0	-0.1	10.0	3.6	2.5	10.0	2.9	DFGT
COPPERPOINT GENERAL INS CO	AZ	B-	15.1	9.3	0.0	-0.3	10.0	3.6	3.2	10.0	3.5	DGT
COPPERPOINT INDEMNITY INS CO	AZ	C	10.9	7.4	0.0	-0.2	10.0	N/A	3.4	10.0	2.8	DFGT
COPPERPOINT MUTUAL INS CO	AZ	A+	3,573.1	1,290.5	242.1	26.4	8.4	6.9	6.6	8.4	7.7	T
COPPERPOINT NATIONAL INS CO	AZ	C	6.6	4.6	0.0	-0.1	10.0	N/A	2.7	7.0	2.6	DGT
COPPERPOINT PREMIER INS CO	AZ	C+	19.6	19.4	0.0	-0.5	8.0	3.6	3.7	10.0	3.4	DGT
COPPERPOINT WESTERN INS CO	AZ	B-	9.0	5.0	0.0	0.0	10.0	3.6	3.6	10.0	3.5	DGT
COREPOINTE INS CO	MI	C-	101.4	57.5	-9.4	0.3	10.0	8.9	1.9	9.1	2.9	FRT
CORNERSTONE MUTUAL INS CO	GA	F (5)	0.0	0.0	7.9	0.0	0.3	3.2	0.8	0.1	0.3	CDFL

See Page 27 for explanation of footnotes and   54   www.weissratings.com
Page 28 for explanation of stability factors.

Arrows denote recent upgrades ▲ or downgrades ▼   (see Section VII for explanations)

RISK ADJ. RATIO #1	CAPITAL RATIO #2	PREMIUM TO SURPLUS (%)	RESV. TO SURPLUS (%)	RESV. DEVELOP. 1 YEAR (%)	RESV. DEVELOP. 2 YEAR (%)	LOSS RATIO (%)	EXP. RATIO (%)	COMB RATIO (%)	CASH FROM UNDER-WRITING (%)	NET PREMIUM GROWTH (%)	INVEST. IN AFFIL (%)	INSURANCE COMPANY NAME
4.8	2.9	7.6	10.2	-1.9	-1.8	42.9	48.5	91.4	136.6	0.9	0.0	COMMUNITIES OF FAITH RRG INC
8.6	5.2	16.8	10.2	-9.7	-24.4	-31.5	31.4	-0.1	75.5	-2.3	0.0	COMMUNITY BLOOD CENTERS
N/A	N/A	98.3	41.7	N/A	N/A	79.0	9.3	88.3	907.6	0.0	0.0	COMMUNITY CARE RRG INC
N/A	N/A	N/A	281.1	7.2	37.2	N/A	N/A	N/A	N/A	-100.0	0.0	COMMUNITY HEALTH ALLIANCE RECIP
3.7	2.9	35.3	107.3	-21.0	-45.0	39.5	16.9	56.4	137.6	-6.2	0.0	COMMUNITY HOSPITAL ALTERNATIVE
6.6	6.0	N/A	N/A	N/A	N/A	N/A	N/A	N/A	76.6	0.0	0.0	COMMUNITY INS CORP
1.7	1.5	N/A	N/A	N/A	-1.0	N/A	N/A	N/A	49.2	0.0	8.1	COMMUNITY MUTUAL INS CO
1.6	1.0	87.0	129.1	-19.6	8.4	39.1	30.1	69.2	132.7	-39.4	4.7	COMP OPTIONS INS CO
N/A	N/A	N/A	26.1	5.4	11.9	N/A	N/A	N/A	N/A	0.0	0.0	COMPASS INS CO
N/A	N/A	N/A	N/A	N/A	N/A	N/A	N/A	N/A	N/A	0.0	0.0	COMPASS SPCLTY INS RRG INC
N/A	N/A	--	--	--	--	--	--	--	--	--	--	COMPSOURCE MUTUAL INS CO
1.2	0.9	95.8	102.6	-7.6	-9.8	57.5	45.2	102.7	103.7	38.0	0.0	COMPTRUST AGC MUT CAPTIVE INS CO
N/A	N/A	N/A	N/A	N/A	N/A	N/A	N/A	N/A	N/A	0.0	0.0	COMPUTER INS CO
5.0	3.8	33.3	37.1	-0.2	3.1	64.4	17.4	81.8	135.2	13.3	0.0	COMPWEST INS CO
2.5	1.7	74.0	34.2	-1.8	-5.0	74.6	32.2	106.8	92.3	-2.1	6.4 •	CONCORD GENERAL MUTUAL INS CO
2.9	2.6	46.3	19.5	-2.1	-3.5	50.4	48.7	99.1	99.4	-7.4	0.0	CONEMAUGH VALLEY MUTUAL INS CO
0.5	0.3	134.3	62.6	5.8	5.3	61.1	38.7	99.8	106.3	20.2	0.0	CONIFER INS CO
1.5	1.3	11.1	45.2	-3.6	-8.9	67.5	34.2	101.7	72.2	2.4	0.0 •	CONNECTICUT MEDICAL INS CO
29.8	26.8	-6.4	3.1	-2.4	-3.3	4.1	-305.8	-301.7	-25.3	-157.7	0.0	CONSOLIDATED INS ASSN
82.4	74.2	N/A	N/A	N/A	N/A	N/A	N/A	N/A	N/A	0.0	0.0	CONSOLIDATED INS CO
N/A	N/A	-0.8	2.2	-2.4	-2.2	68.5	-399.4	-330.9	-15.6	-178.5	0.0	CONSOLIDATED LLOYDS
5.8	3.6	40.7	10.1	-3.0	N/A	12.0	37.8	49.8	250.1	0.9	0.0	CONSTITUTION INS CO
2.2	1.5	16.8	51.2	-2.6	-4.8	58.5	95.3	153.8	69.3	-8.9	0.0	CONSUMER SPECIALTIES INS CO RRG
0.2	0.2	N/A	N/A	N/A	N/A	N/A	N/A	N/A	104.9	0.0	0.0	CONSUMERS COUNTY MUTUAL INS CO
3.7	2.7	69.5	50.5	-2.0	-5.4	64.4	36.7	101.1	104.3	34.6	0.0	CONSUMERS INS USA INC
1.9	1.4	56.3	171.1	-1.8	-1.2	83.1	30.0	113.1	93.8	0.5	10.5 •	CONTINENTAL CASUALTY CO
12.7	11.4	N/A	6.1	N/A	N/A	N/A	N/A	N/A	9.0	0.0	0.0	CONTINENTAL DIVIDE INS CO
4.6	4.1	26.2	0.3	-0.2	-0.4	-0.2	73.1	72.9	120.2	7.6	0.0	CONTINENTAL HERITAGE INS CO
3.2	2.6	67.6	47.1	-4.9	-4.4	24.6	28.1	52.7	140.6	18.6	0.0	CONTINENTAL INDEMNITY CO
6.0	3.2	N/A	55.2	2.0	1.2	N/A	N/A	N/A	-73.4	0.0	10.8 •	CONTINENTAL INS CO
63.6	28.1	N/A	N/A	N/A	N/A	N/A	N/A	N/A	N/A	0.0	0.0	CONTINENTAL INS CO OF NJ
1.3	1.2	131.5	5.0	-6.1	1.4	22.3	65.0	87.3	113.4	4.1	0.0	CONTINENTAL MUTUAL INS CO
N/A	N/A	N/A	N/A	N/A	N/A	N/A	N/A	N/A	N/A	0.0	0.0	CONTINENTAL RISK UNDERWRITERS
9.7	8.7	N/A	N/A	N/A	N/A	N/A	N/A	N/A	95.3	0.0	0.0	CONTINENTAL WESTERN INS CO
0.5	0.4	179.4	103.9	37.1	-0.5	86.3	30.8	117.1	65.5	19.5	0.0	CONTINUING CARE RRG INC
5.3	4.4	55.2	38.8	-7.8	-13.8	27.0	47.5	74.5	135.3	12.8	0.0	CONTRACTORS BONDING & INS CO
4.3	3.6	13.3	27.5	11.6	-62.2	137.4	28.5	165.9	32.2	3.9	0.0	CONTRACTORS INS CO OF NORTH
2.9	2.4	46.4	41.9	0.3	-2.9	39.8	60.8	100.6	102.1	-1.6	0.0	CONTROLLED RISK INS CO OF VT RRG
5.2	4.2	32.2	68.3	-5.9	-18.3	68.4	33.0	101.4	106.8	2.5	0.0	CONVENTUS INTER-INS
2.4	1.7	107.4	21.7	-3.5	1.7	62.0	34.7	96.7	100.3	6.5	8.5	COOPERATIVA D SEGUROS MULTIPLES
N/A	N/A	0.2	0.1	N/A	N/A	74.0	999 +	999 +	8.6	102.8	0.0	COPIC A RRG
6.1	4.0	20.7	45.8	-6.8	-15.8	56.3	25.8	82.1	131.9	1.2	0.0 •	COPIC INS CO
8.8	7.9	N/A	N/A	N/A	N/A	N/A	N/A	N/A	48.0	0.0	0.0	COPPERPOINT AMERICAN INS CO
4.7	4.2	N/A	N/A	N/A	N/A	N/A	N/A	N/A	43.7	0.0	0.0	COPPERPOINT CASUALTY INS CO
5.5	4.9	N/A	N/A	N/A	N/A	N/A	N/A	N/A	300.6	0.0	0.0	COPPERPOINT GENERAL INS CO
6.5	5.9	N/A	N/A	N/A	N/A	N/A	N/A	N/A	33.9	0.0	0.0	COPPERPOINT INDEMNITY INS CO
3.1	1.9	19.2	166.9	0.2	-7.3	78.5	26.0	104.5	84.8	1.1	1.7 •	COPPERPOINT MUTUAL INS CO
6.1	5.5	N/A	N/A	N/A	N/A	N/A	N/A	N/A	76.8	0.0	0.0	COPPERPOINT NATIONAL INS CO
1.4	1.4	N/A	N/A	N/A	N/A	N/A	N/A	N/A	3.9	0.0	76.0	COPPERPOINT PREMIER INS CO
3.9	3.5	N/A	N/A	N/A	N/A	N/A	N/A	N/A	-97.8	0.0	0.0	COPPERPOINT WESTERN INS CO
6.9	5.0	-16.5	23.7	-21.5	-11.3	-146.2	-108.8	-255.0	-36.4	-121.7	4.2	COREPOINTE INS CO
0.1	0.1	172.5	213.5	6.7	29.5	76.4	86.4	162.8	67.9	-17.7	0.0	CORNERSTONE MUTUAL INS CO

999 + Denotes number greater than 999.9%
999 - Denotes number less than -999.99%

• Bullets denote a more detailed analysis is available in Section II.

INSURANCE COMPANY NAME	DOM. STATE	RATING	TOTAL ASSETS ($MIL)	CAPITAL & SURPLUS ($MIL)	ANNUAL NET PREMIUM ($MIL)	NET INCOME ($MIL)	CAPITAL-IZATION INDEX (PTS)	RESERVE ADQ INDEX (PTS)	PROFIT-ABILITY INDEX (PTS)	LIQUIDITY INDEX (PTS)	STAB. INDEX (PTS)	STABILITY FACTORS
CORNERSTONE NATIONAL INS CO	MO	C	31.7	10.8	26.2	-0.9	5.6	6.5	3.9	4.6	2.5	DFGL
COUNTRY CASUALTY INS CO	IL	B+	83.4	69.3	0.0	0.5	10.0	N/A	6.6	10.0	5.0	T
COUNTRY MUTUAL INS CO	IL	A-	4,421.1	2,143.9	2,023.5	67.1	9.6	6.2	6.2	6.2	5.9	T
COUNTRY PREFERRED INS CO	IL	B	237.3	67.8	0.0	1.0	10.0	N/A	6.3	10.0	4.6	FT
COUNTRY-WIDE INS CO	NY	D-	250.0	34.7	88.4	-6.9	2.1	0.4	3.2	6.5	0.9	CRT
COUNTRYWAY INS CO	NY	C	27.9	23.9	0.0	0.3	10.0	3.8	6.8	10.0	3.6	DGT
COUNTY HALL INS CO INC A RRG	HI	U	1.0	1.0	0.0	0.0	N/A	0.0	3.7	0.0	0.0	CLT
COURTESY INS CO	FL	B	785.7	368.4	135.6	5.6	10.0	6.1	8.9	7.6	4.2	RT
COVENANT INS CO	CT	C	91.4	25.0	40.1	1.3	7.4	8.1	4.0	5.5	3.6	DT
COVENTRY INS CO	RI	U	1.6	1.6	0.0	0.0	N/A	N/A	3.7	7.0	2.1	GT
COVERYS RRG INC	DC	D+	9.2	3.9	0.7	-0.6	7.5	3.6	2.9	9.1	2.1	DGT
COVERYS SPECIALTY INS CO	NJ	U	61.8	51.2	0.0	0.5	N/A	N/A	4.9	7.0	5.4	DT
COVINGTON SPECIALTY INS CO	NH	B	107.1	50.6	16.1	0.7	10.0	6.0	6.8	8.3	4.2	T
CPA MUTL INS CO OF AM (A RRG)	VT	C-	18.5	5.5	3.8	0.2	7.1	6.9	2.2	7.3	2.3	DFGR
CRESTBROOK INS CO	OH	B	127.9	89.0	0.0	0.7	10.0	N/A	3.6	9.1	4.5	AT
CROSSFIT RRG INC	MT	C	6.8	2.7	2.2	0.0	2.0	1.9	5.9	7.7	2.3	CDGT
CROWN CAPTIVE INS CO	GA	D	1.5	0.8	0.4	0.0	7.3	6.7	6.5	9.1	1.2	DGT
CROWN CAPTIVE INS CO INC	DC	D	5.3	1.7	3.3	0.1	3.8	4.7	1.7	5.8	1.6	DFGT
CRUDEN BAY RRG INC	VT	D	15.7	6.6	3.0	0.5	7.5	10.0	3.6	7.1	2.1	DGT
CRUM & FORSTER INDEMNITY CO	DE	D+	51.0	15.9	16.6	1.2	7.2	5.7	5.7	7.8	2.7	DRT
CRUM & FORSTER INS CO	NJ	D+(2)	50.2	17.6	16.6	1.8	7.4	5.8	6.0	7.5	2.7	DT
CRUM & FORSTER SPECIALTY INS CO	DE	D+	64.5	48.3	0.0	0.0	10.0	3.5	6.9	10.0	2.7	RT
CRUSADER INS CO	CA	B-	119.7	59.9	31.0	0.5	10.0	9.3	5.4	7.2	3.6	RT
CRYSTAL RUN RECIPROCAL RRG	VT	D-	24.7	3.3	3.1	0.7	0.8	1.6	3.2	9.3	1.1	CDGT
CSAA AFFINITY INS CO	AZ	C	212.4	149.2	49.7	1.1	10.0	6.1	4.3	6.8	3.5	FRT
CSAA FIRE & CASUALTY INS CO	IN	C	106.5	46.0	16.6	0.4	10.0	6.2	6.6	6.5	3.9	FT
CSAA GENERAL INS CO	IN	C	296.4	151.0	99.4	2.0	10.0	6.2	6.4	6.6	4.3	T
CSAA INS EXCHANGE	CA	B-	6,651.6	3,319.5	3,116.8	-25.7	8.8	6.2	2.9	5.9	4.8	RT
CSAA MID-ATLANTIC INS CO	AZ	C-	35.5	23.6	9.9	0.3	10.0	6.1	5.4	6.8	3.2	DFGR
CSAA MID-ATLANTIC INS CO OF NJ	NJ	C-	50.3	25.2	19.9	0.2	10.0	6.2	4.2	6.6	3.2	FT
CSE SAFEGUARD INS CO	CA	C+	91.5	40.2	49.8	0.9	8.6	6.3	5.0	6.3	3.7	FRT
CUBE INS CO	OH	U	21.6	5.5	22.6	-0.2	N/A	N/A	2.5	6.5	0.0	DGT
CUMBERLAND INS CO	NJ	B-	103.8	52.8	22.6	1.0	9.8	8.8	8.6	6.9	3.7	DRT
CUMBERLAND MUTUAL FIRE INS CO	NJ	B-	273.3	151.9	96.0	1.4	8.4	8.0	5.0	6.6	4.0	RT
CUMIS INS SOCIETY INC	IA	B	1,789.0	844.0	826.3	40.1	10.0	8.9	8.8	6.3	4.9	RT
CUMIS MORTGAGE REINS CO	WI	C	11.3	9.8	1.0	-0.1	10.0	N/A	3.9	9.0	2.9	DGT
CUMIS SPECIALTY INS CO INC	IA	B	54.1	52.0	-70.7	0.9	10.0	4.8	3.5	7.0	4.1	T
CYPRESS INS CO	CA	C+	1,363.6	313.8	327.0	41.3	5.7	9.1	5.5	7.3	4.4	T
CYPRESS P&C INS CO	FL	C+	100.2	25.5	61.8	-6.2	7.1	9.5	2.9	6.8	3.3	FT
CYPRESS TEXAS INS CO	TX	C-	50.6	10.2	14.5	-2.6	3.7	9.2	1.7	8.2	2.4	CDT
DAILY UNDERWRITERS OF AMERICA	PA	C+	42.0	30.6	12.3	1.4	8.3	3.2	8.6	7.6	3.2	DGT
DAIRYLAND COUNTY MUTUAL INS CO OF TX	TX	B	13.5	12.6	0.0	0.0	10.0	N/A	5.2	8.1	4.9	DFGT
DAIRYLAND INS CO	WI	B+	1,282.3	491.1	328.5	8.9	9.9	8.1	6.0	6.9	5.3	T
DAKOTA FIRE INS CO	ND	C	231.0	64.7	98.5	2.3	7.8	8.6	6.6	6.6	4.1	T
DAKOTA TRUCK UNDERWRITERS	SD	C+	109.5	45.1	34.4	2.6	7.9	6.0	8.7	6.8	3.4	RT
DAN RRG INC	SC	U	2.2	1.0	0.0	0.0	N/A	0.0	3.9	0.0	0.0	LT
DANBURY INS CO	MA	C	11.8	7.2	4.3	0.1	8.7	8.5	3.9	6.8	2.7	DFGR
DANIELSON NATIONAL INS CO	CA	U	6.0	5.5	0.0	0.0	N/A	5.7	2.4	10.0	3.6	FGRT
DE SMET FARM MUTUAL INS CO OF SD	SD	C+	28.7	17.3	12.6	0.9	7.5	5.9	4.5	6.1	3.0	DGRT
DE SMET INS CO OF SD	SD	C-	15.1	7.3	10.1	0.5	7.7	8.2	2.6	5.6	2.6	DGRT
DEALERS ASR CO	OH	B-	103.7	58.7	14.5	2.1	10.0	3.6	8.8	9.4	3.6	RT
DEALERS CHOICE MUTUAL INS INC	NC	C-	24.7	6.1	6.3	-0.4	3.3	7.0	1.7	6.4	2.1	CDFG

See Page 27 for explanation of footnotes and Page 28 for explanation of stability factors.

Arrows denote recent upgrades ▲ or downgrades ▼ (see Section VII for explanations)

56

www.weissratings.com

RISK ADJ. RATIO #1	CAPITAL RATIO #2	PREMIUM TO SURPLUS (%)	RESV. TO SURPLUS (%)	RESV. DEVELOP. 1 YEAR (%)	RESV. DEVELOP. 2 YEAR (%)	LOSS RATIO (%)	EXP. RATIO (%)	COMB RATIO (%)	CASH FROM UNDER-WRITING (%)	NET PREMIUM GROWTH (%)	INVEST. IN AFFIL (%)	INSURANCE COMPANY NAME
1.1	0.9	212.6	102.7	-5.2	0.7	73.1	30.1	103.2	85.2	-21.2	0.0	CORNERSTONE NATIONAL INS CO
24.1	21.7	N/A	N/A	N/A	N/A	N/A	N/A	N/A	-66.9	0.0	0.0 •	COUNTRY CASUALTY INS CO
4.4	3.1	97.7	51.0	-1.2	-1.6	70.7	29.9	100.6	98.5	-1.5	4.0 •	COUNTRY MUTUAL INS CO
7.0	5.6	N/A	N/A	N/A	N/A	N/A	N/A	N/A	-149.8	0.0	0.0	COUNTRY PREFERRED INS CO
0.3	0.2	199.2	278.4	26.0	62.1	90.8	7.0	97.8	92.5	9.1	1.7	COUNTRY-WIDE INS CO
19.5	17.5	N/A	N/A	N/A	N/A	N/A	N/A	N/A	-272.8	0.0	0.0	COUNTRYWAY INS CO
N/A	N/A	N/A	N/A	N/A	N/A	N/A	N/A	N/A	N/A	0.0	0.0	COUNTY HALL INS CO INC A RRG
9.9	5.6	37.6	3.9	0.6	0.2	67.6	16.3	83.9	136.3	11.4	0.0 •	COURTESY INS CO
1.9	1.2	165.9	91.4	-2.4	-3.2	82.2	30.4	112.6	102.9	5.8	0.0	COVENANT INS CO
N/A	N/A	N/A	N/A	N/A	N/A	N/A	N/A	N/A	N/A	0.0	0.0	COVENTRY INS CO
1.0	0.8	16.2	24.1	N/A	1.1	176.6	-29.3	147.3	-157.5	342.5	0.0	COVERYS RRG INC
N/A	N/A	N/A	N/A	N/A	N/A	N/A	N/A	N/A	85.4	0.0	0.0	COVERYS SPECIALTY INS CO
5.7	3.0	32.3	29.1	1.1	0.6	67.9	28.2	96.1	171.6	1.6	0.0	COVINGTON SPECIALTY INS CO
0.8	0.6	45.9	88.4	-2.8	6.0	106.7	22.0	128.7	95.7	17.0	0.0	CPA MUTL INS CO OF AM (A RRG)
16.0	14.4	N/A	N/A	N/A	N/A	N/A	N/A	N/A	-314.6	0.0	0.0	CRESTBROOK INS CO
0.6	0.4	80.0	61.7	15.4	46.0	47.8	47.3	95.1	135.3	-5.4	0.0	CROSSFIT RRG INC
1.9	1.1	48.4	66.2	-4.2	-5.2	52.9	28.7	81.6	170.2	21.2	0.0	CROWN CAPTIVE INS CO
0.8	0.6	212.7	210.3	14.7	1.1	85.3	36.9	122.2	93.1	4.9	0.0	CROWN CAPTIVE INS CO INC
2.1	1.6	49.2	122.9	-123.6	-38.2	31.5	9.0	40.5	247.1	50.0	0.0	CRUDEN BAY RRG INC
1.6	1.0	103.5	151.3	-0.6	-0.9	64.1	34.2	98.3	120.9	23.2	0.0	CRUM & FORSTER INDEMNITY CO
1.9	1.2	94.2	137.6	-0.5	-0.8	64.1	34.2	98.3	107.3	23.2	0.0	CRUM & FORSTER INS CO
15.5	14.0	N/A	N/A	N/A	N/A	N/A	N/A	N/A	-482.5	0.0	0.0	CRUM & FORSTER SPECIALTY INS CO
3.6	3.1	50.6	64.3	-4.3	-7.5	64.4	30.4	94.8	108.2	11.7	0.0	CRUSADER INS CO
0.3	0.2	119.5	321.7	58.1	84.9	120.1	17.5	137.6	204.4	-35.0	0.0	CRYSTAL RUN RECIPROCAL RRG
3.2	3.0	33.7	15.5	-0.4	-0.1	81.6	31.1	112.7	81.1	7.5	25.5	CSAA AFFINITY INS CO
6.3	5.7	36.6	16.8	-0.5	-0.1	81.6	19.2	100.8	74.0	7.5	0.0	CSAA FIRE & CASUALTY INS CO
7.1	5.2	66.9	30.7	-0.9	-0.1	81.6	23.7	105.3	94.8	7.5	0.0	CSAA GENERAL INS CO
3.1	2.1	92.3	42.4	-1.0	-0.2	81.6	29.0	110.6	96.5	7.5	6.4 •	CSAA INS EXCHANGE
7.4	5.4	42.7	19.6	-0.5	-0.1	81.6	28.0	109.6	77.1	7.5	0.0	CSAA MID-ATLANTIC INS CO
4.0	2.9	79.7	36.6	-1.0	-0.2	81.6	27.4	109.0	85.3	7.5	0.0	CSAA MID-ATLANTIC INS CO OF NJ
3.6	2.5	126.7	59.5	0.4	-0.5	68.7	33.0	101.7	90.9	3.1	0.0	CSE SAFEGUARD INS CO
N/A	N/A	372.2	117.8	N/A	N/A	84.1	17.6	101.7	206.6	0.0	0.0	CUBE INS CO
5.9	3.5	44.0	71.4	-3.1	-4.9	66.5	29.8	96.3	98.0	-1.6	0.0	CUMBERLAND INS CO
2.4	2.0	64.9	34.1	0.7	-2.8	63.9	34.0	97.9	103.0	0.8	20.9	CUMBERLAND MUTUAL FIRE INS CO
5.3	3.8	103.2	48.8	-6.7	-11.4	64.4	26.1	90.5	111.9	26.7	4.2 •	CUMIS INS SOCIETY INC
7.2	6.4	10.4	0.5	N/A	N/A	5.0	81.9	86.9	223.6	359.7	0.0	CUMIS MORTGAGE REINS CO
71.4	47.6	-138.6	N/A	N/A	N/A	99.9	N/A	99.9	-23.0	-197.6	0.0	CUMIS SPECIALTY INS CO INC
1.0	0.7	107.0	223.9	-8.3	-14.1	77.3	16.2	93.5	139.7	28.6	0.0 •	CYPRESS INS CO
1.2	0.9	192.3	59.5	-15.7	-19.7	46.4	50.7	97.1	98.9	18.4	0.0	CYPRESS P&C INS CO
0.6	0.4	110.2	71.6	7.7	-4.5	38.8	74.2	113.0	132.0	-27.8	0.0	CYPRESS TEXAS INS CO
3.3	2.5	43.5	15.1	3.7	9.9	34.2	33.5	67.7	144.8	4.5	0.0	DAILY UNDERWRITERS OF AMERICA
29.0	26.1	N/A	N/A	N/A	N/A	N/A	N/A	N/A	-67.3	0.0	0.0	DAIRYLAND COUNTY MUTUAL INS CO OF
4.4	2.8	68.1	109.6	-2.5	-3.9	72.7	27.5	100.2	108.3	3.5	0.0 •	DAIRYLAND INS CO
2.3	1.5	159.5	163.3	-4.4	-3.8	65.5	31.4	96.9	112.6	4.8	0.0	DAKOTA FIRE INS CO
2.1	1.7	78.8	101.9	-1.2	-3.5	69.0	23.5	92.5	119.4	12.1	7.3	DAKOTA TRUCK UNDERWRITERS
N/A	N/A	N/A	N/A	N/A	N/A	N/A	N/A	N/A	N/A	0.0	0.0	DAN RRG INC
3.9	2.6	60.8	21.5	-0.5	-2.0	67.0	40.7	107.7	90.0	-5.0	0.0	DANBURY INS CO
N/A	N/A	0.8	9.0	0.2	-3.4	77.3	373.7	451.0	7.0	-90.0	0.0	DANIELSON NATIONAL INS CO
1.9	1.7	79.6	17.4	-0.3	0.6	72.8	24.8	97.6	101.1	-3.6	26.9	DE SMET FARM MUTUAL INS CO OF SD
2.0	1.5	150.0	70.2	-1.9	-5.1	89.3	14.5	103.8	97.2	0.8	0.0	DE SMET INS CO OF SD
9.4	6.8	25.8	0.1	0.7	N/A	16.0	25.6	41.6	271.4	20.4	0.0	DEALERS ASR CO
0.7	0.4	99.3	279.3	-17.5	-18.7	77.3	32.3	109.6	81.0	9.9	0.0	DEALERS CHOICE MUTUAL INS INC

999 + Denotes number greater than 999.9%
999 - Denotes number less than -999.99%
• Bullets denote a more detailed analysis is available in Section II.

INSURANCE COMPANY NAME	DOM. STATE	RATING	TOTAL ASSETS ($MIL)	CAPITAL & SURPLUS ($MIL)	ANNUAL NET PREMIUM ($MIL)	NET INCOME ($MIL)	CAPITAL-IZATION INDEX (PTS)	RESERVE ADQ INDEX (PTS)	PROFIT-ABILITY INDEX (PTS)	LIQUIDITY INDEX (PTS)	STAB. INDEX (PTS)	STABILITY FACTORS
DELAWARE GRANGE MUTUAL FIRE INS CO	DE	D	1.4	1.3	0.2	0.0	8.7	7.3	7.6	8.1	1.2	DFGR
DELAWARE PROFESSIONAL INS CO	DE	D (2)	5.1	1.4	0.9	-0.5	2.8	10.0	0.7	5.7	1.4	CDFT
DELPHI CASUALTY CO	IL	D	2.6	2.5	2.7	0.3	6.1	1.4	2.4	6.1	2.2	DFGT
DELTA FIRE & CAS INS CO	GA	C-	7.3	5.7	1.9	0.2	7.9	8.4	4.5	6.8	2.4	DFGR
DELTA LLOYDS INS CO OF HOUSTON	TX	D+	6.8	5.1	1.0	-0.7	8.1	6.0	1.4	6.7	2.1	DFGR
DENTISTS BENEFITS INS CO	OR	C	17.3	12.4	4.7	0.1	8.7	7.0	6.1	6.9	2.8	DFGT
DENTISTS INS CO	CA	B	328.6	178.4	61.2	1.7	9.2	9.0	6.8	7.0	4.1	RT
DEPOSITORS INS CO	IA	B-	309.3	36.8	0.0	0.3	10.0	N/A	6.1	7.7	3.8	FT
DEVELOPERS SURETY & INDEMNITY CO	IA	C	130.9	91.5	27.4	1.2	8.4	8.1	6.8	7.5	3.0	RT
DIAMOND INS CO	IL	D-	46.1	8.4	22.0	0.3	1.2	9.6	3.9	7.1	1.3	CDRT
DIAMOND STATE INS CO	IN	B-	133.3	57.6	32.7	-0.9	8.3	6.1	3.7	7.8	3.9	GRT
DIRECT AUTO INS CO	IL	D	45.1	8.4	25.9	0.1	1.7	10.0	8.8	7.3	2.0	CDGT
DIRECT GENERAL INS CO	IN	C+	411.0	123.1	339.8	-0.5	7.0	3.3	5.7	0.6	4.0	FLRT
DIRECT GENERAL INS CO OF LA	LA	C-	25.9	10.6	20.0	0.2	6.4	5.9	2.3	1.9	2.9	DFGL
DIRECT GENERAL INS CO OF MS	MS	C-	36.9	11.9	27.1	0.5	7.2	8.5	3.4	1.8	3.0	DFGL
DIRECT INS CO	TN	C	84.3	25.2	64.3	-0.2	6.2	8.4	5.7	1.1	3.6	LRT
DIRECT NATIONAL INS CO	AR	C+	16.8	5.8	12.9	-0.9	7.3	9.3	2.7	3.1	3.4	DFGL
DISCOVER P&C INS CO	CT	C+	135.3	65.0	29.1	1.8	10.0	7.9	5.7	7.4	4.1	T
DISCOVER SPECIALTY INS CO	CT	C+	109.2	40.8	29.1	1.8	8.7	8.3	6.6	6.7	3.9	T
DISCOVERY INS CO	NC	D+	24.3	10.9	17.5	0.0	4.4	7.0	3.2	1.0	2.4	DFGL
DIST-CO INS CO INC RRG	HI	E	3.4	2.8	0.4	0.1	10.0	4.6	4.0	10.0	0.0	DFGT
DISTRICTS MUTUAL INS	WI	D	21.3	12.9	5.5	-0.3	8.2	9.5	4.8	7.5	2.3	DGT
DOCTORS & SURGEONS NATL RRG IC	VT	E+	9.1	1.1	5.4	0.0	1.0	4.3	0.6	7.3	0.7	CFGT
DOCTORS CO AN INTERINS	CA	B-	4,063.5	1,824.0	622.9	-2.1	7.7	9.1	4.5	7.5	4.7	RT
DOCTORS CO RRG A RECIPROCAL	DC	D	12.9	3.5	0.9	-0.8	9.0	N/A	2.8	7.9	2.3	DGT
DOCTORS DIRECT INS INC	IL	C	14.2	6.5	2.4	0.2	7.6	9.5	5.8	8.3	2.1	DGRT
DOCTORS PROF LIAB RRG INC	NC	U	1.1	1.0	0.0	0.0	N/A	0.0	3.6	0.0	0.0	LT
DONEGAL MUTUAL INS CO	PA	B-	451.0	223.9	109.8	6.3	6.2	6.0	7.2	6.5	4.2	T
DONGBU INS CO LTD	HI	D	248.3	58.1	89.9	-9.5	4.9	1.6	2.8	6.2	2.3	RT
DONGBU INS CO LTD US GUAM BRANCH	GU	B-	62.7	39.5	16.1	3.0	8.6	8.5	8.8	8.7	3.8	T
DORCHESTER INS CO LTD	VI	C	21.3	11.8	3.9	0.7	9.9	9.5	6.1	7.3	3.0	DGRT
DORCHESTER MUTUAL INS CO	MA	C	85.7	39.5	26.9	0.1	8.2	5.9	6.1	6.8	3.7	RT
DORINCO REINS CO	MI	C-	1,575.2	553.9	153.7	51.4	7.0	6.9	5.1	6.8	2.6	T
DRIVE NEW JERSEY INS CO	NJ	C+	206.7	34.1	28.7	1.3	9.5	6.2	5.0	7.6	3.8	RT
DRYDEN MUTUAL INS CO	NY	B	191.6	123.8	58.8	7.1	10.0	7.6	8.8	7.0	4.1	RT
DTRIC INS CO LTD	HI	C	100.4	25.5	45.0	-0.2	5.7	9.3	2.2	6.2	3.5	RT
DTRIC INS UNDERWRITERS LTD	HI	C	11.7	4.6	0.0	0.1	8.5	N/A	8.0	7.0	2.6	DGRT
DUBOIS MEDICAL RRG	DC	C-	11.7	9.3	1.0	0.1	10.0	7.0	8.8	9.3	2.3	DGT
EAGLE POINT MUTUAL INS CO	WI	D	4.9	3.5	1.0	0.1	7.3	3.6	6.4	7.0	2.0	DGT
EAGLE WEST INS CO	CA	C+	123.7	52.9	57.2	1.4	7.8	6.0	6.7	6.4	3.9	FT
EAGLESTONE REINS CO	PA	B	6,494.1	1,812.0	40.4	-42.7	7.2	2.4	4.2	7.7	4.4	T
EASTERN ADVANTAGE ASR CO	PA	C+	51.6	14.6	16.8	0.5	5.2	4.6	8.9	6.5	3.2	CDT
EASTERN ALLIANCE INS CO	PA	D	302.9	100.4	96.3	2.9	8.0	4.4	8.9	6.5	1.9	RT
EASTERN ATLANTIC INS CO	PA	C-	66.8	32.6	18.8	-0.9	8.1	8.7	3.3	7.1	3.2	DT
EASTERN DENTISTS INS CO RRG	VT	C	54.8	23.8	11.1	0.1	7.7	9.6	8.4	7.1	3.1	DT
EASTERN MUTUAL INS CO	NY	C	24.3	14.7	5.9	-0.1	10.0	9.3	8.1	7.2	3.1	DGT
EASTGUARD INS CO	PA	D+	127.6	39.4	37.9	0.5	1.5	9.5	8.7	2.7	1.2	CDGL
ECHELON P&C INS CO	IL	C	15.5	5.6	7.4	-0.1	7.2	3.7	3.2	6.2	2.5	DGRT
ECOLE INS CO	AZ	C	11.3	6.9	2.9	0.2	2.4	4.9	5.0	7.0	2.2	CDGT
ECONOMY FIRE & CAS CO	IL	B-	486.0	383.8	0.0	7.3	10.0	N/A	6.4	10.0	4.7	T
ECONOMY PREFERRED INS CO	IL	B	40.3	10.9	0.0	0.2	8.8	N/A	7.8	7.0	4.9	DGT
ECONOMY PREMIER ASR CO	IL	B	84.5	48.3	0.0	0.9	10.0	N/A	8.0	10.0	4.3	T

See Page 27 for explanation of footnotes and
Page 28 for explanation of stability factors.   58   www.weissratings.com
Arrows denote recent upgrades ▲ or downgrades ▼   (see Section VII for explanations)

RISK ADJ. RATIO #1	CAPITAL RATIO #2	PREMIUM TO SURPLUS (%)	RESV. TO SURPLUS (%)	RESV. DEVELOP. 1 YEAR (%)	RESV. DEVELOP. 2 YEAR (%)	LOSS RATIO (%)	EXP. RATIO (%)	COMB RATIO (%)	CASH FROM UNDER-WRITING (%)	NET PREMIUM GROWTH (%)	INVEST. IN AFFIL (%)	INSURANCE COMPANY NAME
3.9	2.3	17.3	4.9	N/A	-0.4	65.9	38.1	104.0	86.5	-3.0	0.0	DELAWARE GRANGE MUTUAL FIRE INS
0.5	0.4	63.7	190.5	-60.3	-57.8	58.0	103.7	161.7	36.5	31.8	0.0	DELAWARE PROFESSIONAL INS CO
3.1	2.9	125.8	98.8	36.6	48.0	84.3	23.3	107.6	73.4	-33.5	0.0	DELPHI CASUALTY CO
1.8	1.6	32.6	5.5	-5.3	-6.2	32.6	94.9	127.5	77.2	2.1	23.3	DELTA FIRE & CAS INS CO
2.4	1.5	17.3	20.6	15.0	2.5	153.5	75.6	229.1	41.0	-50.5	0.0	DELTA LLOYDS INS CO OF HOUSTON
3.5	2.3	37.9	18.3	-7.7	-4.6	41.0	41.6	82.6	90.4	2.7	0.0	DENTISTS BENEFITS INS CO
3.9	2.3	34.3	48.2	-4.0	-8.4	77.3	25.8	103.1	108.7	5.1	0.0	DENTISTS INS CO
3.4	3.1	N/A	N/A	N/A	N/A	N/A	N/A	N/A	25.8	0.0	4.7	DEPOSITORS INS CO
2.9	2.1	30.5	30.6	-2.4	-5.4	31.0	50.6	81.6	126.8	-38.5	16.0	DEVELOPERS SURETY & INDEMNITY CO
0.4	0.3	336.0	381.9	4.3	-11.1	75.0	21.8	96.8	102.6	-5.8	0.0	DIAMOND INS CO
2.2	1.9	56.1	59.4	-3.7	0.2	60.5	23.9	84.4	117.7	116.6	20.8	DIAMOND STATE INS CO
0.6	0.4	312.6	282.9	-82.1	-88.7	51.6	38.1	89.7	160.6	29.5	0.0	DIRECT AUTO INS CO
1.1	1.0	272.9	86.3	-4.5	-0.4	80.0	18.0	98.0	92.4	4.4	12.5	DIRECT GENERAL INS CO
1.3	1.1	191.8	105.3	14.4	4.8	110.6	9.6	120.2	88.1	-6.0	0.0	DIRECT GENERAL INS CO OF LA
1.3	1.1	241.0	72.5	3.5	-0.7	81.3	21.2	102.5	93.6	9.9	0.0	DIRECT GENERAL INS CO OF MS
0.9	0.8	257.4	77.8	6.3	-0.2	78.6	21.6	100.2	96.2	11.9	0.0	DIRECT INS CO
1.1	1.0	194.9	49.7	2.9	-6.0	76.2	25.9	102.1	98.1	17.1	0.0	DIRECT NATIONAL INS CO
5.5	3.5	46.1	79.0	-1.4	-3.5	58.7	35.2	93.9	150.5	2.9	0.0	DISCOVER P&C INS CO
3.4	2.1	74.4	127.7	-2.4	-5.7	58.7	30.2	88.9	110.4	2.9	0.0	DISCOVER SPECIALTY INS CO
1.0	0.8	154.8	38.2	-9.8	-23.9	83.5	16.7	100.2	85.7	9.9	0.0	DISCOVERY INS CO
6.3	4.0	15.1	1.6	-0.5	-0.8	6.4	30.5	36.9	10.3	432.6	0.0	DIST-CO INS CO INC RRG
2.7	1.7	42.1	53.1	-10.6	-24.4	62.3	48.3	110.6	114.2	6.8	0.0	DISTRICTS MUTUAL INS
0.2	0.2	302.1	366.1	-138.9	-29.6	67.7	32.1	99.8	80.1	44.6	0.0	DOCTORS & SURGEONS NATL RRG IC
1.9	1.4	34.4	78.3	-4.1	-7.4	74.5	24.1	98.6	109.6	-3.3	18.7 •	DOCTORS CO AN INTERINS
1.5	1.3	20.2	31.5	N/A	N/A	203.7	-101.2	102.5	-398.7	0.0	0.0	DOCTORS CO RRG A RECIPROCAL
2.1	1.5	39.4	87.3	-9.6	-16.5	53.6	63.4	117.0	91.3	-14.9	0.0	DOCTORS DIRECT INS INC
N/A	N/A	N/A	N/A	N/A	N/A	N/A	N/A	N/A	N/A	0.0	0.0	DOCTORS PROF LIAB RRG INC
0.9	0.9	52.4	28.6	0.5	1.4	65.7	28.0	93.7	130.2	7.0	69.8 •	DONEGAL MUTUAL INS CO
0.7	0.4	132.0	139.1	28.5	62.5	85.6	25.5	111.1	135.7	-3.8	0.0	DONGBU INS CO LTD
6.3	3.8	41.8	18.9	N/A	-5.1	24.5	34.3	58.8	295.6	-2.4	0.0	DONGBU INS CO LTD US GUAM BRANCH
4.6	3.0	34.5	41.3	-6.1	-22.4	42.4	54.1	96.5	98.0	21.3	0.0	DORCHESTER INS CO LTD
2.7	1.8	71.0	44.7	N/A	2.9	74.4	34.9	109.3	96.5	4.1	6.3	DORCHESTER MUTUAL INS CO
1.5	1.1	29.9	164.3	-8.1	-11.4	60.1	16.8	76.9	111.4	-10.5	0.0 •	DORINCO REINS CO
3.3	2.5	87.6	71.5	0.5	-1.4	73.0	19.5	92.5	117.1	2.3	0.0	DRIVE NEW JERSEY INS CO
7.1	5.0	49.9	25.1	0.3	-0.1	46.3	38.0	84.3	118.9	8.4	0.0	DRYDEN MUTUAL INS CO
1.2	0.8	177.4	160.7	-4.9	-9.9	73.6	30.9	104.5	100.5	2.1	6.1	DTRIC INS CO LTD
2.4	2.2	N/A	N/A	N/A	N/A	N/A	N/A	N/A	33.6	0.0	0.0	DTRIC INS UNDERWRITERS LTD
5.8	3.5	11.1	21.9	-8.8	-9.2	12.4	25.0	37.4	231.9	-5.5	0.0	DUBOIS MEDICAL RRG
2.0	1.2	31.7	0.7	1.2	N/A	29.8	42.7	72.5	119.8	0.0	0.0	EAGLE POINT MUTUAL INS CO
2.7	1.7	111.1	75.8	1.3	1.7	69.9	33.5	103.4	96.9	-11.0	0.0	EAGLE WEST INS CO
1.6	1.0	2.2	338.9	22.5	27.7	999 +	-869.0	149.2	N/A	N/A	0.0 •	EAGLESTONE REINS CO
1.3	0.7	117.9	86.1	1.2	-0.3	65.0	23.7	88.7	154.7	-1.3	0.0	EASTERN ADVANTAGE ASR CO
2.1	1.7	100.5	77.5	-0.5	0.2	68.1	22.9	91.0	108.6	-1.6	0.0	EASTERN ALLIANCE INS CO
2.7	1.6	59.2	68.2	-1.9	-4.2	69.0	34.4	103.4	110.7	-8.5	0.0	EASTERN ATLANTIC INS CO
1.8	1.5	47.9	96.0	-9.7	-17.7	42.9	43.4	86.3	118.2	5.6	0.0	EASTERN DENTISTS INS CO RRG
4.1	2.9	40.9	30.5	-3.8	-9.8	57.6	37.2	94.8	119.2	9.8	0.3	EASTERN MUTUAL INS CO
0.3	0.2	104.1	114.5	0.2	-0.9	60.0	18.9	78.9	232.1	59.0	0.0	EASTGUARD INS CO
1.3	0.9	129.0	55.7	13.3	24.5	67.8	32.5	100.3	111.7	17.7	1.4	ECHELON P&C INS CO
0.3	0.2	39.8	16.0	-1.3	2.8	47.1	26.5	73.6	192.6	100.5	0.0	ECOLE INS CO
6.7	6.1	N/A	N/A	N/A	N/A	N/A	N/A	N/A	827.2	0.0	14.6 •	ECONOMY FIRE & CAS CO
2.4	2.1	N/A	N/A	N/A	N/A	N/A	N/A	N/A	999 +	0.0	0.0	ECONOMY PREFERRED INS CO
9.1	8.2	N/A	N/A	N/A	N/A	N/A	N/A	N/A	N/A	0.0	0.0	ECONOMY PREMIER ASR CO

999 + Denotes number greater than 999.9%
999 - Denotes number less than -999.99%
• Bullets denote a more detailed analysis is available in Section II.

INSURANCE COMPANY NAME	DOM. STATE	RATING	TOTAL ASSETS ($MIL)	CAPITAL & SURPLUS ($MIL)	ANNUAL NET PREMIUM ($MIL)	NET INCOME ($MIL)	CAPITAL-IZATION INDEX (PTS)	RESERVE ADQ INDEX (PTS)	PROFIT-ABILITY INDEX (PTS)	LIQUIDITY INDEX (PTS)	STAB. INDEX (PTS)	STABILITY FACTORS
EDISON INS CO	FL	C	39.3	21.8	7.3	1.6	6.4	1.3	3.9	6.8	3.2	DGT
ELECTRIC INS CO	MA	C+	1,643.4	562.7	346.5	9.3	8.6	7.0	6.7	6.7	3.4	RT
ELEMENTS PROPERTY INS CO	FL	C	62.3	24.6	31.3	-3.2	3.7	3.6	2.8	6.7	3.1	CFGT
ELEPHANT INS CO	VA	C	162.2	50.9	47.2	-14.5	7.0	4.9	2.2	7.7	3.5	FGT
ELITE TRANSPORTATION RRG INC	VT	E+	12.6	2.7	3.9	0.4	0.8	0.5	2.6	2.6	0.8	CDFG
ELIZABETHTOWN INS CO	DE	U (2)	3.9	3.7	0.0	0.1	N/A	6.9	4.5	10.0	4.3	FRT
ELLINGTON MUTUAL INS CO	WI	D+	6.0	3.5	2.2	-0.1	7.3	6.9	3.2	6.6	2.0	DGRT
EMC PROPERTY & CASUALTY CO	IA	C	122.8	87.7	53.0	7.6	10.0	7.7	7.4	7.0	4.2	T
EMC REINS CO	IA	C+	465.6	201.7	124.5	10.2	7.8	9.4	7.0	6.9	3.4	T
EMCASCO INS CO	IA	B-	482.2	138.2	204.5	4.7	7.9	8.6	6.8	6.5	4.5	T
EMERGENCY CAP MGMT LLC A RRG	VT	D	6.9	2.2	1.0	0.2	1.5	3.4	2.0	6.6	1.3	CDGT
EMERGENCY MEDICINE PROFESSIONAL	NV	C-	19.4	7.2	5.6	-0.2	7.3	6.0	5.1	7.0	2.7	DFGR
EMERGENCY MEDICINE RRG INC	SC	E	7.4	3.0	1.2	0.1	2.6	4.5	2.2	8.3	0.0	DGT
EMERGENCY PHYSICIANS INS RRG	VT	C-	31.5	10.8	4.2	0.1	4.2	4.9	6.5	7.7	2.3	DFGR
EMPIRE BONDING & INS CO	NY	B-	3.5	2.1	0.8	0.1	10.0	5.4	6.4	9.8	3.5	DGT
EMPIRE FIRE & MARINE INS CO	NE	C+	46.6	41.0	0.0	0.4	10.0	N/A	3.4	7.7	3.9	FRT
EMPIRE INDEMNITY INS CO	OK	C+	60.1	51.1	0.0	0.3	10.0	N/A	8.2	10.0	4.0	RT
EMPIRE INS CO	NY	U	24.4	10.7	0.0	0.0	N/A	4.7	2.0	10.0	3.2	FGRT
EMPLOYERS ASSURANCE CO	FL	C	489.8	171.1	88.6	4.0	9.0	8.3	6.5	7.0	3.3	RT
EMPLOYERS COMPENSATION INS CO	CA	B	1,063.5	326.2	265.0	11.8	7.4	8.3	7.8	6.8	4.6	FRT
EMPLOYERS FIRE INS CO	PA	U	13.1	11.1	0.0	0.0	N/A	3.7	2.2	7.0	3.4	GRT
▲EMPLOYERS INS CO OF NV	NV	B-	839.8	462.9	20.4	44.1	5.2	9.1	8.1	6.2	4.5	CRT
EMPLOYERS INS OF WAUSAU	WI	B-	5,526.4	1,513.3	2,050.6	-0.4	7.9	5.7	6.2	6.3	3.6	AT
EMPLOYERS MUTUAL CAS CO	IA	B-	3,116.3	1,331.3	946.0	22.3	8.0	7.8	5.6	6.6	4.8	RT
EMPLOYERS PREFERRED INS CO	FL	C	1,089.3	292.6	315.3	39.2	5.6	8.0	8.3	6.5	3.3	GRT
ENCOMPASS FLORIDIAN INDEMNITY CO	IL	U	4.9	4.8	0.0	0.1	N/A	N/A	5.7	7.0	4.5	GT
ENCOMPASS FLORIDIAN INS CO	IL	U	4.9	4.8	0.0	0.1	N/A	N/A	5.7	7.0	4.5	GT
ENCOMPASS HOME & AUTO INS CO	IL	B-	20.1	19.6	0.0	0.1	10.0	N/A	7.3	7.0	3.5	DGT
ENCOMPASS INDEMNITY CO	IL	B	30.2	26.0	0.0	0.2	10.0	N/A	6.3	7.0	4.6	GT
ENCOMPASS INDEPENDENT INS CO	IL	B-	7.3	7.1	0.0	0.1	10.0	N/A	4.6	7.0	3.5	DGT
ENCOMPASS INS CO	IL	C	9.6	9.4	0.0	0.1	10.0	3.6	3.5	7.0	2.9	DGT
ENCOMPASS INS CO OF AM	IL	C+	20.5	20.3	0.0	0.3	10.0	N/A	4.9	7.0	3.4	DGT
ENCOMPASS INS CO OF MA	MA	C	6.5	6.4	0.0	0.1	10.0	N/A	4.3	7.0	2.7	DGT
ENCOMPASS INS CO OF NJ	IL	C+	30.1	29.2	0.0	0.3	10.0	N/A	4.5	7.0	3.7	GT
ENCOMPASS PROP & CAS INS CO OF NJ	IL	C+	13.8	13.1	0.0	0.1	10.0	N/A	4.5	7.0	3.2	DGT
ENCOMPASS PROPERTY & CASUALTY CO	IL	C+	10.7	10.1	0.0	0.1	10.0	N/A	4.6	10.0	3.1	DGT
ENDEAVOUR INS CO	MA	C+	6.1	6.0	0.0	0.1	10.0	N/A	7.8	7.0	3.1	DGRT
ENDURANCE AMERICAN INS CO	DE	C+	1,660.6	267.9	233.1	3.3	5.9	6.5	3.9	2.5	3.9	CLRT
ENDURANCE AMERICAN SPECIALTY INS CO	DE	C+	404.1	99.5	118.7	1.4	4.9	6.6	3.9	2.0	3.7	CFLR
ENDURANCE ASR CORP	DE	B	1,801.5	753.5	262.4	1.8	8.1	8.3	5.1	7.2	4.6	ART
ENDURANCE RISK SOLUTIONS ASR CO	DE	C+	254.9	67.9	88.0	1.2	4.0	6.6	3.9	1.6	3.7	CLRT
ENUMCLAW P&C INS CO	OR	C+	8.5	7.9	0.0	0.0	10.0	N/A	6.4	9.0	3.0	DFGT
EQUITABLE LIABILITY INS CO	DC	D	2.8	1.1	1.1	0.0	8.0	9.8	2.7	8.7	1.3	DFGT
EQUITY INS CO	TX	C	82.0	30.2	48.7	0.1	7.4	6.2	4.1	5.9	3.2	RT
ERIE & NIAGARA INS ASSN	NY	B-	199.2	132.6	63.4	5.6	10.0	6.1	8.8	6.9	4.0	RT
ERIE INS CO	PA	B-	944.4	347.4	294.6	11.8	10.0	8.1	7.1	6.6	4.7	T
ERIE INS CO OF NEW YORK	NY	B	110.3	30.9	29.5	0.9	9.0	8.3	5.1	6.7	4.0	T
ERIE INS EXCHANGE	PA	B	14,449.8	7,412.0	5,567.1	260.6	9.3	8.0	7.1	6.6	5.1	T
ERIE INS P&C CO	PA	B-	102.0	12.2	0.0	0.1	7.5	N/A	7.5	10.0	3.9	DT
ESSENT GUARANTY INC	PA	A-	1,194.6	545.7	299.0	100.0	10.0	4.6	5.1	7.8	5.7	GT
ESSENT GUARANTY OF PA INC	PA	B	85.8	45.5	18.0	7.0	10.0	4.6	9.2	8.3	4.0	DT
ESSENTIA INS CO	MO	C	80.3	27.3	0.0	-3.8	10.0	3.6	3.2	5.8	3.7	AFRT

RISK ADJ. CAPITAL RATIO #1	RATIO #2	PREMIUM TO SURPLUS (%)	RESV. TO SURPLUS (%)	RESV. DEVELOP. 1 YEAR (%)	2 YEAR (%)	LOSS RATIO (%)	EXP. RATIO (%)	COMB RATIO (%)	CASH FROM UNDER-WRITING (%)	NET PREMIUM GROWTH (%)	INVEST. IN AFFIL (%)	INSURANCE COMPANY NAME
0.9	0.6	36.4	4.5	-1.1	13.1	55.0	4.8	59.8	626.1	N/A	0.0	EDISON INS CO
3.5	2.1	63.5	147.7	-3.0	-10.2	81.6	20.7	102.3	95.2	14.8	1.8 ●	ELECTRIC INS CO
1.0	0.6	125.6	31.9	1.4	-0.1	61.2	56.8	118.0	90.3	-14.6	0.0	ELEMENTS PROPERTY INS CO
1.4	1.0	83.4	30.4	0.1	1.7	98.2	46.2	144.4	55.7	41.5	0.0	ELEPHANT INS CO
0.3	0.2	185.2	319.7	6.0	62.3	77.7	18.7	96.4	94.3	6.8	0.0	ELITE TRANSPORTATION RRG INC
N/A	N/A	N/A	2.5	-2.8	-3.1	N/A	N/A	N/A	N/A	0.0	0.0	ELIZABETHTOWN INS CO
1.8	1.2	70.7	11.5	-1.1	-11.6	55.3	46.1	101.4	90.8	3.3	0.0	ELLINGTON MUTUAL INS CO
17.1	14.9	64.7	66.3	-1.7	-1.5	65.5	31.4	96.9	112.6	4.8	0.0	EMC PROPERTY & CASUALTY CO
2.5	1.7	65.1	102.9	-12.0	-14.9	64.1	24.3	88.4	107.4	4.7	0.0 ●	EMC REINS CO
2.4	1.6	154.4	158.1	-4.2	-3.7	65.5	31.4	96.9	112.6	4.8	0.0	EMCASCO INS CO
0.6	0.4	74.0	221.9	25.1	26.2	144.0	12.7	156.7	228.6	23.2	0.0	EMERGENCY CAP MGMT LLC A RRG
1.7	1.2	78.8	102.3	-6.0	-11.2	59.5	42.2	101.7	88.1	4.9	0.0	EMERGENCY MEDICINE PROFESSIONAL
0.6	0.5	39.7	154.4	-8.9	-3.4	60.4	48.5	108.9	142.2	-11.3	0.0	EMERGENCY MEDICINE RRG INC
1.0	0.7	40.8	160.1	-7.2	-8.8	75.2	40.8	116.0	52.1	0.4	0.0	EMERGENCY PHYSICIANS INS RRG
3.8	3.4	39.2	4.2	-1.6	-1.9	7.9	53.3	61.2	184.4	29.0	0.0	EMPIRE BONDING & INS CO
24.7	22.3	N/A	N/A	N/A	N/A	N/A	N/A	N/A	27.2	0.0	0.0	EMPIRE FIRE & MARINE INS CO
22.6	20.4	N/A	N/A	N/A	N/A	N/A	N/A	N/A	267.5	0.0	0.0	EMPIRE INDEMNITY INS CO
N/A	N/A	N/A	132.3	N/A	N/A	N/A	N/A	N/A	-1.4	0.0	0.0	EMPIRE INS CO
2.7	1.8	42.2	98.3	0.1	-1.3	65.1	26.8	91.9	107.3	28.9	0.0 ●	EMPLOYERS ASSURANCE CO
1.8	1.2	79.1	179.6	0.2	-2.4	65.1	27.7	92.8	35.6	42.7	0.0 ●	EMPLOYERS COMPENSATION INS CO
N/A	N/A	N/A	N/A	N/A	N/A	N/A	N/A	N/A	N/A	0.0	0.0	EMPLOYERS FIRE INS CO
1.3	1.2	4.8	72.8	0.1	-1.2	65.1	158.4	223.5	126.0	-94.4	44.8 ●	EMPLOYERS INS CO OF NV
2.4	1.6	135.4	178.7	-1.0	-1.2	68.4	30.2	98.6	103.4	1.0	3.4 ●	EMPLOYERS INS OF WAUSAU
2.0	1.6	74.1	77.5	-1.5	-1.3	65.7	31.3	97.0	109.2	4.9	20.8 ●	EMPLOYERS MUTUAL CAS CO
1.0	0.8	112.4	214.4	0.3	-2.9	65.1	20.8	85.9	241.1	358.6	24.9 ●	EMPLOYERS PREFERRED INS CO
N/A	N/A	N/A	N/A	N/A	N/A	N/A	N/A	N/A	N/A	0.0	0.0	ENCOMPASS FLORIDIAN INDEMNITY CO
N/A	N/A	N/A	N/A	N/A	N/A	N/A	N/A	N/A	N/A	0.0	0.0	ENCOMPASS FLORIDIAN INS CO
88.7	79.8	N/A	N/A	N/A	N/A	N/A	N/A	N/A	999 +	0.0	0.0	ENCOMPASS HOME & AUTO INS CO
19.6	17.6	N/A	N/A	N/A	N/A	N/A	N/A	N/A	15.0	0.0	0.0	ENCOMPASS INDEMNITY CO
126.9	106.9	N/A	N/A	N/A	N/A	N/A	N/A	N/A	999 +	0.0	0.0	ENCOMPASS INDEPENDENT INS CO
91.3	67.4	N/A	N/A	N/A	N/A	N/A	N/A	N/A	N/A	0.0	0.0	ENCOMPASS INS CO
111.6	55.8	N/A	N/A	N/A	N/A	N/A	N/A	N/A	999 +	0.0	0.0	ENCOMPASS INS CO OF AM
105.7	95.1	N/A	N/A	N/A	N/A	N/A	N/A	N/A	999 +	0.0	0.0	ENCOMPASS INS CO OF MA
70.2	63.2	N/A	N/A	N/A	N/A	N/A	N/A	N/A	112.7	0.0	0.0	ENCOMPASS INS CO OF NJ
41.4	37.2	N/A	N/A	N/A	N/A	N/A	N/A	N/A	171.5	0.0	0.0	ENCOMPASS PROP & CAS INS CO OF NJ
37.3	33.5	N/A	N/A	N/A	N/A	N/A	N/A	N/A	-48.1	0.0	0.0	ENCOMPASS PROPERTY & CASUALTY
74.4	34.8	N/A	N/A	N/A	N/A	N/A	N/A	N/A	N/A	0.0	0.0	ENDEAVOUR INS CO
1.3	0.9	88.7	85.1	-0.9	-3.2	78.4	16.8	95.2	108.1	-25.3	20.5 ●	ENDURANCE AMERICAN INS CO
1.0	0.6	121.3	116.3	-1.2	-4.4	78.4	16.8	95.2	93.9	-25.3	0.0	ENDURANCE AMERICAN SPECIALTY INS
2.2	1.9	35.5	67.6	-4.8	-8.0	47.7	36.0	83.7	102.3	4.6	26.4 ●	ENDURANCE ASR CORP
0.9	0.6	132.1	126.7	-1.3	-4.8	78.4	16.8	95.2	99.9	-25.3	0.0	ENDURANCE RISK SOLUTIONS ASR CO
29.8	26.8	N/A	N/A	N/A	N/A	N/A	N/A	N/A	N/A	0.0	0.0	ENUMCLAW P&C INS CO
1.8	1.6	101.1	156.7	-7.4	-31.4	72.8	31.0	103.8	83.4	9.6	0.0	EQUITABLE LIABILITY INS CO
1.4	1.2	162.8	74.1	-1.5	-1.3	89.4	12.8	102.2	92.5	8.6	0.0	EQUITY INS CO
7.0	4.8	50.4	15.3	0.2	-0.2	47.0	38.2	85.2	110.6	3.9	0.1	ERIE & NIAGARA INS ASSN
5.1	3.5	88.0	58.2	-1.7	-3.4	69.4	27.9	97.3	107.5	7.4	5.0 ●	ERIE INS CO
3.7	2.5	99.1	66.2	-1.9	-4.5	68.6	27.9	96.5	107.1	7.4	0.0	ERIE INS CO OF NEW YORK
4.0	2.7	78.0	51.5	-1.5	-2.9	69.4	27.9	97.3	107.6	7.4	5.3 ●	ERIE INS EXCHANGE
1.4	1.2	N/A	N/A	N/A	N/A	N/A	N/A	N/A	999 +	0.0	0.0	ERIE INS P&C CO
7.6	4.6	57.3	2.9	-0.6	-0.3	3.6	29.5	33.1	365.3	24.8	0.0 ●	ESSENT GUARANTY INC
7.9	5.2	38.3	3.4	-0.8	-0.1	4.3	25.8	30.1	376.5	-13.6	0.0	ESSENT GUARANTY OF PA INC
3.9	3.5	N/A	N/A	0.1	N/A	N/A	N/A	N/A	65.9	0.0	0.0	ESSENTIA INS CO

999 + Denotes number greater than 999.9%
999 - Denotes number less than -999.99%
● Bullets denote a more detailed analysis is available in Section II.

INSURANCE COMPANY NAME	DOM. STATE	RATING	TOTAL ASSETS ($MIL)	CAPITAL & SURPLUS ($MIL)	ANNUAL NET PREMIUM ($MIL)	NET INCOME ($MIL)	CAPITAL-IZATION INDEX (PTS)	RESERVE ADQ INDEX (PTS)	PROFIT-ABILITY INDEX (PTS)	LIQUIDITY INDEX (PTS)	STAB. INDEX (PTS)	STABILITY FACTORS
ESURANCE INS CO	WI	C	195.2	163.3	0.0	0.6	10.0	3.6	2.8	10.0	3.9	RT
▲ESURANCE INS CO OF NJ	WI	C	14.5	11.8	0.0	0.0	10.0	3.6	3.2	7.0	3.0	DGRT
▲ESURANCE P&C INS CO	WI	C-	98.0	42.1	0.0	0.3	10.0	3.7	3.5	7.0	3.2	FRT
ETHIO-AMERICAN INS CO	GA	D	10.2	3.3	5.9	-0.2	6.0	3.6	2.2	6.3	2.0	DGT
EULER HERMES NORTH AMERICA INS CO	MD	B	423.1	133.6	87.0	5.2	10.0	9.4	6.1	6.8	4.1	RT
EVANSTON INS CO	IL	C	4,264.1	1,207.5	838.4	85.4	6.8	6.0	8.4	7.3	3.8	ART
EVER-GREENE MUTUAL INS CO	PA	C	5.8	5.8	0.4	0.2	10.0	7.3	8.9	9.3	2.1	DGT
EVEREST INDEMNITY INS CO	DE	C	167.1	61.4	0.0	3.4	10.0	3.9	8.4	7.0	3.9	RT
EVEREST NATIONAL INS CO	DE	C+	884.3	144.9	0.0	15.9	10.0	3.1	5.6	8.6	4.5	RT
EVEREST REINS CO	DE	B-	9,863.2	3,442.3	2,079.5	252.0	7.5	5.3	5.6	6.7	4.7	RT
EVEREST SECURITY INS CO	GA	C	39.9	22.1	0.0	1.3	10.0	4.6	5.4	10.0	3.5	DGRT
EVERETT CASH MUTUAL INS CO	PA	C+	118.4	60.4	59.5	-1.0	8.1	8.0	6.9	6.3	3.6	RT
EVERGREEN NATIONAL INDEMNITY CO	OH	C	45.2	30.8	11.5	-0.5	8.5	8.7	3.8	7.3	2.5	RT
EVERGREEN USA RRG INC	VT	U	9.4	6.8	-0.2	-0.2	N/A	5.9	4.6	7.0	3.6	FGRT
EVERSPAN FINANCIAL GUARANTEE CORP	WI	U	227.6	224.9	0.0	2.0	N/A	4.6	7.0	7.0	5.7	GT
EXACT PROPERTY & CASUALTY CO INC	CA	C+	279.3	115.1	149.3	-2.3	9.3	6.1	6.2	6.6	4.5	RT
EXCALIBUR NATIONAL INS CO	LA	U	8.6	8.6	0.0	-0.2	N/A	0.0	2.9	0.0	0.0	CLT
EXCALIBUR REINS CORP	PA	U (2)	9.0	0.1	0.1	0.0	N/A	5.1	1.0	10.0	0.0	CFRT
EXCELA RECIPROCAL RRG	VT	D	9.9	2.9	2.9	0.5	2.5	3.6	3.7	9.1	1.9	DGT
EXCELSIOR INS CO	NH	C	36.3	35.2	0.0	0.3	10.0	N/A	3.7	7.0	3.8	GRT
EXCESS SHARE INS CORP	OH	C	51.7	21.0	1.6	0.1	10.0	8.9	5.4	9.8	2.4	DT
EXECUTIVE INS CO	NY	U	1.7	1.6	0.0	-0.1	N/A	3.6	1.5	7.0	2.3	FGT
EXECUTIVE RISK INDEMNITY INC	DE	B	3,093.7	1,261.8	782.7	116.3	8.9	8.5	8.5	6.8	4.3	T
EXECUTIVE RISK SPECIALTY INS CO	CT	B-	299.7	170.5	48.9	5.2	10.0	7.9	8.8	6.9	4.5	T
EXPLORER AMERICAN INS CO	CA	U	2.7	2.7	0.0	0.0	N/A	N/A	5.6	7.0	4.0	GT
EXPLORER INS CO	CA	C	336.6	113.7	133.7	9.5	6.1	4.6	8.5	6.4	3.7	RT
FACILITY INS CORP	TX	U	101.2	96.9	0.0	1.6	N/A	N/A	5.1	8.2	5.4	FRT
FACTORY MUTUAL INS CO	RI	B-	16,582.9	10,849.0	2,782.1	198.3	8.4	6.2	8.0	6.9	3.7	RT
FAIR AMERICAN INS & REINS CO	NY	B	255.8	242.4	3.5	3.0	10.0	5.2	5.2	10.0	4.6	T
FAIR AMERICAN SELECT INS CO	DE	B	53.7	47.7	0.9	0.4	10.0	3.6	4.7	10.0	4.2	DGT
FAIRMONT FARMERS MUTUAL INS CO	MN	C	32.9	18.3	14.7	0.3	10.0	8.1	8.7	6.9	2.8	DGT
FAIRWAY PHYSICIANS INS CO RRG	DC	D	22.0	4.8	10.5	0.3	1.7	1.7	1.6	5.6	1.7	CDFG
FAITH AFFILIATED RRG INC	VT	E+	9.3	5.7	1.5	0.6	3.0	4.0	3.8	6.6	0.7	DGT
FALCON INS CO	IL	C-	36.3	8.7	13.4	-1.6	3.4	3.6	2.8	6.6	2.3	CDGT
FALLS LAKE FIRE & CASUALTY CO	CA	U	17.9	15.1	0.0	0.1	N/A	0.0	4.7	0.0	0.0	LT
FALLS LAKE GENERAL INS CO	OH	C	6.6	4.2	0.9	0.0	10.0	8.3	6.7	9.0	2.9	DGT
FALLS LAKE NATIONAL INS CO	OH	B-	325.6	57.8	11.6	0.0	7.3	7.0	3.9	6.5	3.8	FT
FAMILY SECURITY INS CO	HI	C	33.3	15.5	17.0	0.2	6.0	3.7	4.7	7.0	3.2	DGT
FARM BU TOWN & COUNTRY INS CO OF MO	MO	B	384.3	177.6	187.9	11.6	8.6	7.8	6.6	5.4	4.6	T
FARM BUREAU CNTY MUTUAL INS CO OF	TX	C	19.9	5.8	0.0	0.0	8.2	N/A	3.6	7.0	2.9	DGT
FARM BUREAU GENERAL INS CO OF MI	MI	B	661.8	286.9	312.7	12.5	9.4	6.5	6.7	5.8	4.9	RT
FARM BUREAU INS OF NC INC	NC	B	9.6	9.4	0.0	0.1	10.0	N/A	7.1	7.0	4.1	DGT
FARM BUREAU MUTUAL INS CO OF AR	AR	B	399.9	229.8	201.9	4.3	9.8	8.2	6.5	6.1	4.2	T
FARM BUREAU MUTUAL INS CO OF ID	ID	B	458.5	243.2	169.0	4.4	9.1	5.9	4.2	6.3	4.1	T
FARM BUREAU MUTUAL INS CO OF MI	MI	B	725.2	349.3	345.3	17.8	9.2	8.5	5.5	6.0	4.6	T
FARM BUREAU NEW HORIZONS INS CO MO	MO	C-	45.8	23.5	28.1	0.9	7.2	8.7	3.8	6.6	3.3	DT
FARM BUREAU P&C INS CO	IA	B+	2,379.2	1,066.5	1,209.0	41.6	9.5	8.2	8.7	5.9	5.3	T
FARM CREDIT SYS ASSOC CAPTIVE INS CO	CO	B-	112.6	81.4	16.8	5.7	10.0	9.3	8.9	7.1	3.8	DT
FARM FAMILY CASUALTY INS CO	NY	B+	1,160.0	389.7	407.6	7.4	9.1	9.3	6.5	6.3	5.3	T
FARMERS & MECH MU I ASN OF CECIL CTY	MD	D	1.1	0.6	0.4	0.0	7.7	7.5	1.9	7.0	1.0	DGRT
FARMERS & MECH MUTUAL INS CO	PA	B	5.6	4.6	0.2	0.2	8.5	5.0	8.6	9.4	4.5	ADGT
FARMERS & MECHANICS FIRE & CAS INS	WV	C-	11.3	4.9	4.9	0.1	7.1	4.2	5.0	6.6	2.5	DGRT

See Page 27 for explanation of footnotes and
Page 28 for explanation of stability factors.
Arrows denote recent upgrades ▲ or downgrades ▼   (see Section VII for explanations)

62

www.weissratings.com

RISK ADJ. RATIO #1	CAPITAL RATIO #2	PREMIUM TO SURPLUS (%)	RESV. TO SURPLUS (%)	RESV. DEVELOP. 1 YEAR (%)	RESV. DEVELOP. 2 YEAR (%)	LOSS RATIO (%)	EXP. RATIO (%)	COMB RATIO (%)	CASH FROM UNDER-WRITING (%)	NET PREMIUM GROWTH (%)	INVEST. IN AFFIL (%)	INSURANCE COMPANY NAME
3.2	3.1	N/A	N/A	N/A	N/A	N/A	N/A	N/A	999 +	0.0	38.2	ESURANCE INS CO
13.0	11.7	N/A	N/A	N/A	N/A	N/A	N/A	N/A	N/A	0.0	0.0	ESURANCE INS CO OF NJ
6.1	5.5	N/A	N/A	N/A	N/A	N/A	N/A	N/A	999 +	0.0	0.0	ESURANCE P&C INS CO
1.1	0.7	162.1	117.5	0.2	18.9	69.7	27.5	97.2	125.9	34.0	0.0	ETHIO-AMERICAN INS CO
6.4	4.0	59.6	33.4	-4.1	-20.6	59.0	24.2	83.2	116.1	-6.6	0.0	EULER HERMES NORTH AMERICA INS
1.7	1.1	116.5	198.7	-17.1	-22.0	46.2	38.7	84.9	119.4	18.0	0.0 •	EVANSTON INS CO
74.2	38.2	7.2	0.6	-0.3	-0.4	15.1	22.9	38.0	316.8	39.1	0.0	EVER-GREENE MUTUAL INS CO
6.7	6.0	N/A	N/A	N/A	N/A	N/A	N/A	N/A	42.6	0.0	0.0	EVEREST INDEMNITY INS CO
8.6	4.3	N/A	N/A	N/A	N/A	N/A	N/A	N/A	-62.1	0.0	0.0	EVEREST NATIONAL INS CO
2.7	1.8	64.8	130.1	-0.4	0.8	58.8	26.4	85.2	101.3	-2.0	2.8 •	EVEREST REINS CO
6.7	6.0	N/A	N/A	N/A	N/A	N/A	N/A	N/A	-0.5	0.0	0.0	EVEREST SECURITY INS CO
2.5	1.9	99.6	34.7	0.7	-1.1	57.5	28.8	86.3	114.6	9.5	8.2	EVERETT CASH MUTUAL INS CO
2.7	2.0	37.5	11.9	-6.8	-7.4	1.3	76.9	78.2	134.2	-4.4	0.0	EVERGREEN NATIONAL INDEMNITY CO
N/A	N/A	-2.5	43.2	-20.7	-16.7	-236.3	-634.8	-871.1	2.7	-107.4	0.0	EVERGREEN USA RRG INC
N/A	N/A	N/A	N/A	N/A	N/A	N/A	999 +	999 +	-0.3	46.4	0.0	EVERSPAN FINANCIAL GUARANTEE
3.8	2.7	127.3	73.4	1.3	1.6	68.5	33.7	102.2	104.2	6.2	0.0	EXACT PROPERTY & CASUALTY CO INC
N/A	N/A	N/A	N/A	N/A	N/A	N/A	N/A	N/A	N/A	0.0	0.0	EXCALIBUR NATIONAL INS CO
N/A	N/A	148.4	999 +	999 +	999 +	999 +	999 +	-784.6	2.7	-93.4	0.0	EXCALIBUR REINS CORP
0.7	0.5	123.4	197.5	35.4	N/A	109.9	9.4	119.3	263.2	16.1	0.0	EXCELA RECIPROCAL RRG
72.1	64.9	N/A	N/A	N/A	N/A	N/A	N/A	N/A	N/A	0.0	0.0	EXCELSIOR INS CO
4.6	4.1	7.4	10.3	-6.1	-9.0	1.9	105.3	107.2	93.9	8.0	0.0	EXCESS SHARE INS CORP
N/A	N/A	N/A	N/A	N/A	N/A	N/A	N/A	N/A	N/A	0.0	0.0	EXECUTIVE INS CO
3.6	2.4	61.8	102.8	-2.6	-5.7	56.5	29.3	85.8	119.8	4.1	5.9 •	EXECUTIVE RISK INDEMNITY INC
6.0	3.8	29.5	49.1	-1.3	-3.1	56.5	29.3	85.8	124.0	4.1	0.0	EXECUTIVE RISK SPECIALTY INS CO
N/A	N/A	N/A	N/A	N/A	N/A	N/A	N/A	N/A	N/A	0.0	0.0	EXPLORER AMERICAN INS CO
1.3	0.9	131.7	164.7	-5.2	-1.7	63.0	22.9	85.9	159.9	19.7	0.0	EXPLORER INS CO
N/A	N/A	N/A	N/A	N/A	N/A	N/A	N/A	N/A	N/A	-100.0	0.0	FACILITY INS CORP
2.6	1.9	26.4	19.8	0.4	-1.1	58.0	29.2	87.2	130.7	-2.0	18.2 •	FACTORY MUTUAL INS CO
76.3	46.9	1.5	1.9	-0.3	-0.2	52.8	33.5	86.3	183.9	-4.4	0.0 •	FAIR AMERICAN INS & REINS CO
27.9	25.1	1.9	0.4	-0.1	N/A	41.0	91.5	132.5	34.3	144.6	0.0	FAIR AMERICAN SELECT INS CO
5.2	3.0	82.5	5.2	-1.0	-5.7	41.2	32.4	73.6	142.0	9.9	0.0	FAIRMONT FARMERS MUTUAL INS CO
0.6	0.4	245.8	266.6	48.3	58.7	85.7	27.6	113.3	63.8	-2.4	0.0	FAIRWAY PHYSICIANS INS CO RRG
4.2	3.0	29.5	90.2	10.7	10.6	128.8	18.4	147.2	109.1	13.7	0.0	FAITH AFFILIATED RRG INC
0.7	0.5	132.1	68.7	5.9	0.4	78.3	27.4	105.7	122.1	21.5	0.0	FALCON INS CO
N/A	N/A	N/A	N/A	N/A	N/A	N/A	N/A	N/A	N/A	0.0	0.0	FALLS LAKE FIRE & CASUALTY CO
4.5	3.2	21.1	38.4	-2.0	-4.6	65.2	27.1	92.3	109.1	21.6	0.0	FALLS LAKE GENERAL INS CO
1.2	1.1	20.4	36.9	-2.2	-5.1	65.2	27.1	92.3	78.0	21.6	66.6	FALLS LAKE NATIONAL INS CO
1.5	1.0	109.5	9.0	-16.4	-1.5	28.3	48.6	76.9	147.5	19.5	0.0	FAMILY SECURITY INS CO
3.6	2.4	114.7	41.1	-1.2	-5.5	71.8	20.5	92.3	111.8	4.7	3.7	FARM BU TOWN & COUNTRY INS CO OF
2.0	1.8	N/A	N/A	N/A	N/A	N/A	N/A	N/A	N/A	0.0	0.0	FARM BUREAU CNTY MUTUAL INS CO OF
4.5	3.1	114.5	54.8	1.1	-3.3	72.1	24.2	96.3	107.0	8.9	0.0 •	FARM BUREAU GENERAL INS CO OF MI
102.6	51.3	N/A	N/A	N/A	N/A	N/A	N/A	N/A	N/A	0.0	0.0	FARM BUREAU INS OF NC INC
5.1	3.5	89.7	13.1	-4.2	-4.9	60.6	20.3	80.9	125.8	3.4	0.5 •	FARM BUREAU MUTUAL INS CO OF AR
2.9	2.3	70.9	33.1	-0.3	1.4	82.1	27.0	109.1	97.4	4.1	18.0 •	FARM BUREAU MUTUAL INS CO OF ID
4.3	2.8	104.3	58.4	-1.9	-8.8	65.5	28.2	93.7	110.4	6.3	0.0 •	FARM BUREAU MUTUAL INS CO OF MI
1.9	1.2	124.4	34.3	-0.9	-1.0	38.0	43.3	81.3	133.9	2.3	0.0	FARM BUREAU NEW HORIZONS INS CO
4.0	3.0	118.5	48.7	-3.3	-5.4	62.2	26.4	88.6	118.9	3.6	5.4 •	FARM BUREAU P&C INS CO
10.1	6.4	20.3	31.4	-2.4	-14.8	53.5	7.7	61.2	259.1	0.4	0.0	FARM CREDIT SYS ASSOC CAPTIVE INS
3.8	2.5	108.3	126.4	-6.9	-7.3	71.0	30.0	101.0	96.9	3.8	0.0 •	FARM FAMILY CASUALTY INS CO
2.4	1.5	70.7	10.0	-1.2	-0.3	53.0	53.0	106.0	98.3	-6.2	0.0	FARMERS & MECH MU I ASN OF CECIL
2.8	1.7	5.6	3.4	-0.5	0.3	48.5	18.7	67.2	147.0	-1.2	0.0	FARMERS & MECH MUTUAL INS CO
1.3	1.1	100.2	48.5	-14.8	-2.0	50.2	20.7	70.9	130.8	-5.4	0.0	FARMERS & MECHANICS FIRE & CAS INS

999 + Denotes number greater than 999.9%
999 - Denotes number less than -999.99%
• Bullets denote a more detailed analysis is available in Section II.

INSURANCE COMPANY NAME	DOM. STATE	RATING	TOTAL ASSETS ($MIL)	CAPITAL & SURPLUS ($MIL)	ANNUAL NET PREMIUM ($MIL)	NET INCOME ($MIL)	CAPITAL- IZATION INDEX (PTS)	RESERVE ADQ INDEX (PTS)	PROFIT- ABILITY INDEX (PTS)	LIQUIDITY INDEX (PTS)	STAB. INDEX (PTS)	STABILITY FACTORS
FARMERS & MECHANICS MUTUAL IC OF WV	WV	B-	63.1	45.7	21.0	-0.2	10.0	5.0	8.3	6.9	3.5	DRT
FARMERS & MERCHANTS MUTUAL FIRE I C	MI	C+	29.1	23.6	3.7	0.7	9.7	6.1	7.8	7.6	3.1	DGRT
FARMERS ALLIANCE MUTUAL INS CO	KS	B-	319.8	171.5	132.2	4.0	10.0	7.9	6.5	6.6	4.0	RT
FARMERS ALLIANCE MUTUAL INS CO	MI	D-	2.0	1.0	1.2	0.0	5.6	6.0	1.2	1.3	1.0	DFGL
FARMERS AUTOMOBILE INS ASN	IL	B+	1,283.7	503.9	480.8	-7.7	8.4	8.8	4.9	6.4	5.0	T
FARMERS FIRE INS CO	PA	C	26.3	12.1	15.5	-0.1	7.4	6.0	2.0	6.2	2.5	DGRT
FARMERS INS CO	KS	C+	301.0	105.3	112.0	-1.9	10.0	6.0	4.3	6.5	4.5	FRT
FARMERS INS CO OF AZ	AZ	C+	44.1	4.2	0.0	0.0	4.5	N/A	3.7	0.0	3.2	CDFL
FARMERS INS CO OF FLEMINGTON	NJ	C+(2)	64.1	25.5	22.7	2.5	7.1	9.4	8.2	7.1	3.4	T
FARMERS INS CO OF IDAHO	ID	C+	198.5	70.5	112.0	-1.9	8.9	6.1	4.3	6.3	4.2	RT
FARMERS INS CO OF OREGON	OR	B	1,713.8	518.9	1,045.1	-10.0	8.2	6.0	4.8	6.1	4.7	RT
FARMERS INS CO OF WA	WA	B-	557.5	203.1	298.6	-0.5	9.1	6.1	5.0	6.3	4.6	RT
FARMERS INS EXCHANGE	CA	C	16,189.6	4,108.1	7,726.6	-150.3	5.6	5.9	3.6	2.7	4.3	FLRT
FARMERS INS HAWAII INC	HI	B	99.5	91.9	0.0	-21.8	10.0	6.0	3.1	10.0	4.3	T
FARMERS INS OF COLUMBUS INC	OH	C+	272.1	99.8	149.3	-2.2	9.1	6.1	4.6	6.3	4.5	RT
FARMERS MUTUAL F I C OF MCCANDLESS	PA	C-	10.2	5.6	5.4	0.3	7.2	8.2	8.3	6.6	2.1	DGRT
FARMERS MUTUAL F I C OF OKARCHE OK	OK	C	18.2	12.7	8.3	0.2	8.6	6.1	5.8	6.4	2.5	DGT
FARMERS MUTUAL F I C OF SALEM CTY	NJ	B-	142.5	69.8	39.0	1.1	9.6	9.3	8.6	6.9	3.7	RT
FARMERS MUTUAL FIRE INS CO OF	PA	C	29.4	19.1	8.6	0.6	8.4	9.0	8.8	7.1	2.8	DGRT
FARMERS MUTUAL HAIL INS CO OF IA	IA	B-	792.3	373.0	360.4	-0.2	7.4	7.7	3.7	6.5	4.1	RT
FARMERS MUTUAL INS CO	WV	C	14.8	10.4	5.5	0.3	10.0	5.2	8.7	7.4	2.3	DGRT
FARMERS MUTUAL INS CO OF ELLINWOOD	KS	D-	4.0	1.8	2.9	0.2	6.3	3.7	3.9	4.2	1.2	DGLR
FARMERS MUTUAL INS CO OF NE	NE	B	624.1	327.5	315.3	18.4	9.9	7.9	6.1	6.7	4.8	RT
FARMERS MUTUAL OF TENNESSEE	TN	C (1)	23.1	13.9	11.0	0.2	7.9	6.2	4.5	6.8	2.7	DGRT
FARMERS NEW CENTURY INS CO	IL	C+	195.5	70.9	112.0	-1.9	8.9	6.1	4.5	6.2	4.2	RT
FARMERS REINS CO	CA	C	591.9	484.5	158.5	9.2	10.0	5.1	2.2	6.7	3.4	FT
FARMERS SPECIALTY INS CO	MI	B-	58.4	16.8	0.0	0.2	9.3	N/A	6.4	6.7	3.8	DGT
FARMERS TEXAS COUNTY MUTUAL INS CO	TX	C+	165.8	48.5	0.0	1.4	10.0	N/A	8.7	3.5	3.9	LRT
FARMERS UNION MUTUAL INS CO	MT	C+	58.2	35.8	20.7	0.4	9.3	6.9	5.9	6.9	3.4	RT
▲FARMERS UNION MUTUAL INS CO	ND	B-	112.6	64.1	62.3	2.4	10.0	8.0	8.8	6.8	3.6	RT
FARMERS UNION MUTUAL INS CO	AR	D	4.7	1.8	1.7	-0.3	5.3	6.0	2.7	7.2	1.7	DGT
FARMINGTON CASUALTY CO	CT	B	1,033.6	309.8	307.5	16.8	7.9	8.8	6.9	6.6	4.6	T
FARMINGTON MUTUAL INS CO	WI	E	7.9	7.0	1.1	0.2	9.1	6.1	5.8	8.1	0.0	DGRT
FARMLAND MUTUAL INS CO	IA	B	566.1	170.3	186.9	-0.1	9.9	6.3	4.1	6.2	4.6	AT
FB INS CO	KY	U	1.3	1.3	0.0	0.0	N/A	3.7	4.9	7.0	2.7	GT
FBALLIANCE INS CO	IL	U	49.2	48.9	0.0	-0.8	N/A	N/A	3.6	7.0	5.4	FT
FBALLIANCE INS INC	VA	U	4.5	4.5	0.0	0.0	N/A	0.0	4.9	0.0	0.0	LT
FCCI ADVANTAGE INS CO	FL	U	7.2	6.3	0.0	0.1	N/A	N/A	6.2	9.0	4.7	GRT
FCCI COMMERCIAL INS CO	FL	C-	14.6	17.2	0.0	0.2	10.0	N/A	5.6	8.3	3.2	DGRT
FCCI INS CO	FL	C+	1,915.8	584.1	711.1	-2.5	8.2	9.3	6.9	6.6	4.2	RT
FD INS CO	FL	C	43.9	20.5	22.0	1.9	5.9	7.0	3.2	7.4	2.8	DFT
FDM PREFERRED INS CO	NY	D+	9.9	2.5	2.0	0.0	4.0	9.3	7.3	8.1	2.1	CDGT
FEDERAL INS CO	IN	B	30,306.0	12,782.6	7,338.2	1,520.7	7.2	8.2	3.9	6.8	4.5	T
FEDERATED MUTUAL INS CO	MN	B	5,260.8	2,988.8	1,301.0	94.6	10.0	9.0	8.2	6.8	5.1	T
FEDERATED NATIONAL INS CO	FL	C	500.7	138.8	241.4	-16.3	3.5	6.1	4.9	6.4	4.0	CRT
FEDERATED RURAL ELECTRIC INS EXCH	KS	B	531.4	179.2	120.3	10.5	8.8	7.0	9.1	6.8	4.1	RT
FEDERATED SERVICE INS CO	MN	B-	470.4	221.1	144.6	10.1	10.0	9.3	8.1	6.8	4.5	T
FFVA MUTUAL INS CO	FL	C	335.1	148.7	113.2	5.2	8.2	5.6	4.6	6.6	4.0	RT
FHM INS CO	FL	C-	83.9	37.2	28.0	0.5	7.6	4.6	1.8	6.5	3.1	FRT
FIDELITY & DEPOSIT CO OF MARYLAND	MD	C+	227.8	171.0	0.0	1.1	10.0	N/A	4.6	9.3	4.5	FRT
FIDELITY & GUARANTY INS	WI	C+	156.0	88.3	20.8	2.1	10.0	7.5	3.6	7.1	4.3	T
FIDELITY & GUARANTY INS CO	IA	C+	21.5	19.5	0.0	0.2	10.0	N/A	6.1	7.0	3.4	DGT

See Page 27 for explanation of footnotes and   64   www.weissratings.com
Page 28 for explanation of stability factors.
Arrows denote recent upgrades ▲ or downgrades ▼   (see Section VII for explanations)

RISK ADJ. RATIO #1	CAPITAL RATIO #2	PREMIUM TO SURPLUS (%)	RESV. TO SURPLUS (%)	RESV. DEVELOP. 1 YEAR (%)	2 YEAR (%)	LOSS RATIO (%)	EXP. RATIO (%)	COMB RATIO (%)	CASH FROM UNDER-WRITING (%)	NET PREMIUM GROWTH (%)	INVEST. IN AFFIL (%)	INSURANCE COMPANY NAME
4.0	3.0	45.7	8.7	-1.4	-1.0	51.7	36.7	88.4	116.9	1.2	8.3	FARMERS & MECHANICS MUTUAL IC OF
4.6	2.8	16.4	2.7	-0.7	0.3	29.9	48.3	78.2	122.7	0.7	0.0	FARMERS & MERCHANTS MUTUAL FIRE I
4.6	3.4	79.8	28.5	-4.2	-3.4	63.1	31.0	94.1	108.1	2.1	6.4	FARMERS ALLIANCE MUTUAL INS CO
1.0	0.7	119.1	2.6	7.4	0.1	83.8	65.9	149.7	55.5	67.3	0.0	FARMERS ALLIANCE MUTUAL INS CO
2.1	1.8	92.6	68.0	-0.3	-5.1	71.5	28.9	100.4	104.7	5.6	21.3 •	FARMERS AUTOMOBILE INS ASN
1.8	1.2	128.0	27.0	1.8	2.4	65.4	34.3	99.7	100.7	5.5	0.0	FARMERS FIRE INS CO
4.4	3.1	104.5	62.7	1.4	1.8	68.8	33.7	102.5	97.4	6.2	0.0	FARMERS INS CO
0.7	0.6	N/A	N/A	N/A	N/A	N/A	N/A	N/A	84.9	0.0	0.0	FARMERS INS CO OF AZ
1.8	1.0	89.3	80.5	-1.4	-8.0	51.7	37.5	89.2	107.8	2.2	0.0	FARMERS INS CO OF FLEMINGTON
3.1	2.2	155.0	89.3	1.6	1.8	68.4	33.6	102.0	104.5	6.2	0.0	FARMERS INS CO OF IDAHO
2.4	1.7	197.3	117.1	2.5	3.2	68.7	33.7	102.4	103.7	6.2	0.0 •	FARMERS INS CO OF OREGON
3.3	2.3	146.8	84.7	1.5	1.8	68.4	33.8	102.2	100.9	6.2	0.0 •	FARMERS INS CO OF WA
0.8	0.7	183.7	112.7	2.8	3.8	69.0	35.0	104.0	94.3	6.2	45.9 •	FARMERS INS EXCHANGE
8.6	8.3	N/A	1.3	-0.2	0.2	N/A	N/A	N/A	N/A	0.0	12.4	FARMERS INS HAWAII INC
3.2	2.3	146.5	84.4	1.5	1.8	68.4	33.7	102.1	104.2	6.2	0.0	FARMERS INS OF COLUMBUS INC
1.8	1.1	102.3	17.3	0.4	-3.1	47.6	37.6	85.2	117.6	8.5	0.0	FARMERS MUTUAL F I C OF
3.5	2.2	66.9	4.5	-1.7	0.3	50.8	42.8	93.6	102.0	-8.1	0.0	FARMERS MUTUAL F I C OF OKARCHE
4.2	2.7	57.6	60.5	-4.1	-7.5	58.0	33.8	91.8	119.5	4.7	0.1	FARMERS MUTUAL F I C OF SALEM CTY
3.2	2.0	45.2	12.1	-3.8	-6.2	48.3	33.6	81.9	109.6	1.2	0.0	FARMERS MUTUAL FIRE INS CO OF
1.6	1.2	98.3	39.7	-1.3	-2.0	77.9	20.4	98.3	103.5	-7.6	38.4 •	FARMERS MUTUAL HAIL INS CO OF IA
5.0	3.3	54.6	5.2	-0.4	-0.9	33.2	49.5	82.7	117.8	2.5	0.0	FARMERS MUTUAL INS CO
2.2	1.3	212.5	11.5	-2.9	6.1	56.0	32.2	88.2	113.5	7.0	9.1	FARMERS MUTUAL INS CO OF
4.2	3.0	103.6	26.8	-1.2	-1.9	65.8	25.7	91.5	121.9	17.9	0.0 •	FARMERS MUTUAL INS CO OF NE
2.5	1.7	80.9	18.7	-0.1	-0.8	62.7	36.7	99.4	108.0	7.5	0.3	FARMERS MUTUAL OF TENNESSEE
3.1	2.2	154.2	88.9	1.6	1.9	68.4	33.7	102.1	104.9	6.2	0.0	FARMERS NEW CENTURY INS CO
27.1	17.2	32.9	27.6	0.3	0.3	70.5	33.2	103.7	48.0	-57.5	0.0 •	FARMERS REINS CO
2.8	2.5	N/A	N/A	N/A	N/A	N/A	N/A	N/A	201.9	0.0	0.0	FARMERS SPECIALTY INS CO
5.3	4.7	N/A	N/A	N/A	N/A	N/A	N/A	N/A	266.2	0.0	0.0	FARMERS TEXAS COUNTY MUTUAL INS
4.2	2.7	59.0	21.6	-6.7	-10.6	49.9	35.4	85.3	115.5	12.9	3.6	FARMERS UNION MUTUAL INS CO
4.2	3.5	101.9	14.2	-2.7	-3.0	56.7	30.9	87.6	113.9	6.9	0.0	FARMERS UNION MUTUAL INS CO
1.2	0.9	83.3	4.2	-0.1	-7.6	51.1	37.9	89.0	105.7	-48.8	0.0	FARMERS UNION MUTUAL INS CO
2.5	1.6	105.6	181.1	-3.4	-8.2	58.7	30.3	89.0	110.3	2.9	0.1 •	FARMINGTON CASUALTY CO
4.1	2.5	17.3	1.4	-0.3	0.1	37.6	38.4	76.0	126.6	1.0	0.0	FARMINGTON MUTUAL INS CO
3.8	2.7	109.5	78.1	1.3	1.0	71.1	32.6	103.7	98.7	3.7	0.0	FARMLAND MUTUAL INS CO
N/A	N/A	N/A	N/A	N/A	N/A	N/A	N/A	N/A	N/A	0.0	0.0	FB INS CO
N/A	N/A	N/A	N/A	N/A	N/A	N/A	N/A	N/A	N/A	0.0	0.0	FBALLIANCE INS CO
N/A	N/A	N/A	N/A	N/A	N/A	N/A	N/A	N/A	N/A	0.0	0.0	FBALLIANCE INS INC
N/A	N/A	N/A	N/A	N/A	N/A	N/A	N/A	N/A	153.0	0.0	0.0	FCCI ADVANTAGE INS CO
430.6	215.4	N/A	N/A	N/A	N/A	N/A	N/A	N/A	104.3	0.0	0.0	FCCI COMMERCIAL INS CO
2.3	1.6	122.4	121.9	-3.3	-5.5	65.8	30.7	96.5	111.2	11.2	8.0 •	FCCI INS CO
4.5	3.1	116.9	201.6	-0.6	-13.8	80.1	33.2	113.3	88.3	5.6	0.0	FD INS CO
1.1	0.4	102.7	239.5	-6.2	-12.9	72.2	18.0	90.2	145.1	4.7	0.0	FDM PREFERRED INS CO
1.2	1.1	55.3	91.3	-2.4	-4.8	54.3	30.0	84.3	118.6	3.2	38.8 •	FEDERAL INS CO
3.8	3.1	45.5	48.1	-4.9	-10.0	66.8	25.3	92.1	112.1	9.9	14.4 •	FEDERATED MUTUAL INS CO
0.9	0.6	166.3	62.0	-2.8	-3.5	55.6	31.4	87.0	120.1	31.3	0.0	FEDERATED NATIONAL INS CO
3.1	2.2	67.9	140.7	-11.2	-22.2	71.6	14.5	86.1	133.6	7.2	0.0	FEDERATED RURAL ELECTRIC INS EXCH
6.2	3.9	68.5	72.4	-7.5	-15.2	66.8	25.5	92.3	110.5	9.9	0.0 •	FEDERATED SERVICE INS CO
2.5	1.9	78.8	87.3	-1.9	-6.1	63.3	26.6	89.9	114.2	6.1	0.0	FFVA MUTUAL INS CO
2.0	1.5	77.8	112.7	-9.0	3.4	67.2	32.6	99.8	74.1	-15.8	0.0	FHM INS CO
7.9	7.4	N/A	N/A	N/A	N/A	N/A	N/A	N/A	-61.3	0.0	13.5	FIDELITY & DEPOSIT CO OF MARYLAND
10.4	6.6	24.1	41.3	-0.7	-1.6	58.7	31.5	90.2	139.8	2.9	0.0	FIDELITY & GUARANTY INS
27.4	24.7	N/A	N/A	N/A	N/A	N/A	N/A	N/A	120.1	0.0	0.0	FIDELITY & GUARANTY INS CO

999 + Denotes number greater than 999.9%
999 - Denotes number less than -999.99%
• Bullets denote a more detailed analysis is available in Section II.

INSURANCE COMPANY NAME	DOM. STATE	RATING	TOTAL ASSETS ($MIL)	CAPITAL & SURPLUS ($MIL)	ANNUAL NET PREMIUM ($MIL)	NET INCOME ($MIL)	CAPITAL-IZATION INDEX (PTS)	RESERVE ADQ INDEX (PTS)	PROFIT-ABILITY INDEX (PTS)	LIQUIDITY INDEX (PTS)	STAB. INDEX (PTS)	STABILITY FACTORS
FIDELITY MOHAWK INS CO	NJ	C+ (2)	17.0	15.1	0.0	0.3	9.0	N/A	6.9	7.0	3.3	DT
FIDUCIARY INS CO OF AMERICA	NY	E- (3)	90.7	-32.8	57.8	-21.2	0.0	0.2	0.2	0.0	0.0	CDLR
FINANCIAL AMERICAN PROP & CAS INS CO	TX	C-	22.4	9.0	1.2	0.1	10.0	5.0	2.2	8.8	2.4	DFGR
FINANCIAL CASUALTY & SURETY INC	TX	C	24.0	16.2	13.9	1.1	7.0	5.8	8.4	7.3	2.7	DFGT
FINANCIAL GUARANTY INS CO	NY	E	2,419.3	66.4	11.9	24.1	0.0	0.9	0.2	3.0	0.0	CFGL
FINANCIAL INDEMNITY CO	IL	B-	90.7	24.6	0.0	0.0	10.0	N/A	3.7	10.0	3.8	DRT
FINANCIAL PACIFIC INS CO	CA	B	234.1	100.1	71.0	1.6	9.3	6.9	6.8	7.0	4.5	RT
FINGER LAKES FIRE & CASUALTY CO	NY	C+	38.5	26.1	9.4	0.9	9.5	6.2	8.3	7.0	3.2	DGRT
FINIAL REINS CO	CT	D+	1,226.1	840.1	99.4	19.6	10.0	6.6	8.3	10.0	2.5	RT
FIRE DISTRICTS INS CO	NY	C-	14.2	3.9	3.0	0.1	4.3	9.3	8.5	8.3	2.4	CDGT
FIRE DISTRICTS OF NY MUT INS CO INC	NY	C+	83.5	24.7	14.9	0.4	6.5	6.4	6.9	7.4	3.2	DRT
FIRE INS EXCHANGE	CA	C+	2,431.5	764.4	1,119.8	-17.2	5.3	5.9	3.9	4.3	4.8	FLRT
FIREMANS FUND INDEMNITY CORP	NJ	C+	16.2	15.0	0.0	0.0	10.0	N/A	4.6	6.8	3.3	DGT
FIREMANS FUND INS CO	CA	C	2,208.8	1,565.9	-1,189.5	371.4	6.1	5.0	2.1	6.6	3.6	FRT
FIREMANS FUND INS CO OF HI INC	HI	C+	13.0	9.1	0.0	0.0	10.0	N/A	6.3	6.5	3.4	DGRT
FIREMANS FUND INS CO OF OH	OH	C	53.3	50.5	0.0	0.5	10.0	3.6	6.9	7.0	4.0	DRT
FIREMENS INS CO OF WASHINGTON DC	DE	C	102.5	32.4	0.0	0.3	10.0	N/A	6.7	9.2	3.8	T
FIRST ACCEPTANCE INS CO	TX	C (1)	269.3	89.2	186.5	-6.5	7.5	6.1	2.9	4.3	4.0	LRT
FIRST ACCEPTANCE INS CO OF GEORGIA	GA	C (1)	90.4	22.1	73.5	-2.7	4.8	6.0	2.9	6.6	3.6	CRT
FIRST ACCEPTANCE INS CO OF TN INC	TN	C (1)	30.4	9.1	22.6	-0.8	6.0	6.1	2.9	5.6	2.9	DGRT
FIRST AMERICAN PROP & CAS INS CO	CA	C	99.5	42.1	59.5	-0.5	7.1	6.4	3.3	4.5	3.4	LRT
FIRST AMERICAN SPECIALTY INS CO	CA	C	115.7	53.5	67.1	3.7	6.8	4.5	6.1	3.7	3.6	LRT
FIRST BENEFITS INS MUTUAL INC	NC	D	43.3	8.3	18.0	0.3	1.6	9.8	8.0	7.0	1.7	CDT
FIRST CHICAGO INS CO	IL	D	72.7	13.2	40.1	-0.3	3.2	6.9	6.5	6.3	2.3	DRT
FIRST CHOICE CASUALTY INS CO	NV	D	17.6	5.2	7.3	0.0	3.7	3.6	3.2	0.4	2.3	CDFG
FIRST COLONIAL INS CO	FL	B+	370.3	157.1	76.8	-3.8	10.0	7.7	3.6	7.6	5.0	RT
FIRST COMMUNITY INS CO	FL	C	101.2	40.9	46.0	0.4	8.3	6.4	4.8	6.9	3.7	FRT
FIRST DAKOTA INDEMNITY CO	SD	C	43.9	14.0	15.5	0.9	5.8	5.8	8.7	6.4	3.0	DRT
FIRST F&C INS OF HI INC	HI	C	9.1	9.1	0.0	-0.5	10.0	N/A	2.9	7.0	2.9	DGRT
FIRST FINANCIAL INS CO	IL	C-	557.6	439.8	24.6	2.9	7.3	8.0	7.6	7.8	2.6	RT
FIRST FLORIDIAN AUTO & HOME INS CO	FL	B	275.9	201.7	59.8	3.8	10.0	6.2	6.3	6.9	4.0	T
FIRST FOUNDERS ASR CO	NJ	D+	5.1	4.3	0.4	0.2	10.0	6.0	8.4	9.0	2.0	DGT
FIRST GUARD INS CO	AZ	B-	27.5	24.4	16.7	2.2	10.0	7.3	9.0	7.9	3.5	DGT
FIRST INDEMNITY INS OF HI INC	HI	C	7.4	7.4	0.0	0.1	10.0	N/A	3.6	7.0	2.8	DGRT
FIRST INDEMNITY OF AMERICA INS CO	NJ	D	8.8	5.6	7.2	0.2	6.3	1.8	5.5	3.8	2.1	DFGL
FIRST INS CO OF HI LTD	HI	C	653.7	286.8	190.1	-0.6	10.0	9.4	5.8	6.8	4.2	RT
FIRST JERSEY CASUALTY INS CO INC	NJ	U (2)	5.9	5.2	0.0	0.3	N/A	2.8	3.0	9.3	3.3	FRT
FIRST LIBERTY INS CORP	IL	C+	22.8	22.3	0.0	0.1	10.0	3.6	4.1	7.0	3.5	ADGT
FIRST MEDICAL INS CO RRG	VT	C	92.2	51.4	10.0	4.6	9.3	9.4	4.8	7.0	3.5	DT
FIRST MERCURY INS CO	DE	C-	162.5	50.1	5.9	-0.4	10.0	3.5	3.5	2.0	3.3	AFLR
FIRST MUTUAL INS CO	NC	D+	6.2	4.8	1.6	0.0	10.0	7.4	6.5	9.3	2.1	DGRT
FIRST NATIONAL INS CO OF AMERICA	NH	B	57.5	55.9	0.0	0.5	10.0	3.8	6.8	7.0	4.1	ART
FIRST NET INS CO	GU	D	19.5	12.4	6.4	0.9	7.3	3.6	4.5	7.2	2.3	DGT
FIRST NONPROFIT INS CO	DE	C-	127.4	27.0	22.9	2.5	8.6	5.1	1.8	7.5	3.2	DRT
FIRST PROFESSIONALS INS CO INC	FL	C	270.6	167.1	-0.7	7.5	10.0	9.6	3.6	7.8	4.0	FRT
FIRST PROTECTIVE INS CO	FL	U	--	--	--	--	N/A	--	--	--	--	Z
FIRST SECURITY INS OF HI INC	HI	C	5.5	5.5	0.0	-0.1	10.0	N/A	3.6	7.0	2.6	DGRT
FIRST SPECIALTY INS CORP	MO	C	212.6	71.9	0.0	2.3	7.9	4.3	5.3	7.0	4.2	FGRT
FIRST STATE INS CO	CT	U	199.8	30.5	0.0	-0.2	N/A	0.3	2.4	5.0	0.5	ACFG
FIRST SURETY CORP	WV	C-	10.3	5.2	1.3	0.1	7.5	4.0	2.4	8.9	2.1	DFGR
FIRST WASHINGTON INS CO	DC	U	1.2	1.2	0.0	0.0	N/A	N/A	2.3	9.2	2.3	FGT
FIRSTCOMP INS CO	NE	B	296.0	128.2	45.5	4.2	8.1	4.9	6.9	8.2	4.6	RT

See Page 27 for explanation of footnotes and
Page 28 for explanation of stability factors.   66   www.weissratings.com
Arrows denote recent upgrades ▲ or downgrades ▼ (see Section VII for explanations)

RISK ADJ. RATIO #1	CAPITAL RATIO #2	PREMIUM TO SURPLUS (%)	RESV. TO SURPLUS (%)	RESV. DEVELOP. 1 YEAR (%)	2 YEAR (%)	LOSS RATIO (%)	EXP. RATIO (%)	COMB RATIO (%)	CASH FROM UNDER- WRITING (%)	NET PREMIUM GROWTH (%)	INVEST. IN AFFIL (%)	INSURANCE COMPANY NAME
3.9	2.3	N/A	N/A	N/A	N/A	N/A	N/A	N/A	N/A	0.0	0.0	FIDELITY MOHAWK INS CO
-0.4	-0.3	999 +	999 +	171.6	178.0	98.5	19.4	117.9	98.6	29.7	0.0	FIDUCIARY INS CO OF AMERICA
3.2	2.9	13.3	1.8	0.2	0.1	39.0	145.3	184.3	68.0	18.9	0.0	FINANCIAL AMERICAN PROP & CAS INS
1.3	1.1	92.2	17.4	-10.5	-13.2	17.4	76.1	93.5	110.7	-13.9	0.0	FINANCIAL CASUALTY & SURETY INC
0.2	0.1	18.0	999 +	-260.5	-144.3	161.4	81.0	242.4	4.4	-26.2	1.4	FINANCIAL GUARANTY INS CO
3.3	2.9	N/A	N/A	N/A	N/A	N/A	N/A	N/A	-27.6	0.0	0.0	FINANCIAL INDEMNITY CO
4.3	2.7	69.6	73.7	-1.9	-5.6	61.2	17.1	78.3	129.8	10.3	0.0	FINANCIAL PACIFIC INS CO
4.1	2.6	37.8	15.6	-3.1	-2.0	52.5	35.3	87.8	103.4	4.5	0.0	FINGER LAKES FIRE & CASUALTY CO
5.7	3.7	11.7	44.1	7.1	5.5	73.0	-2.4	70.6	719.2	N/A	0.0 ●	FINIAL REINS CO
1.2	0.4	92.9	216.6	-5.8	-11.8	72.2	15.0	87.2	134.6	4.7	0.0	FIRE DISTRICTS INS CO
1.5	1.0	62.8	193.9	-2.0	-0.6	77.2	15.3	92.5	148.1	4.7	7.1	FIRE DISTRICTS OF NY MUT INS CO INC
0.8	0.7	142.3	87.1	2.2	2.9	69.0	33.7	102.7	100.8	6.2	56.5 ●	FIRE INS EXCHANGE
30.5	27.4	N/A	N/A	N/A	N/A	N/A	N/A	N/A	202.5	0.0	0.0	FIREMANS FUND INDEMNITY CORP
1.9	1.8	-91.8	224.4	-105.5	-78.9	132.5	-25.2	107.3	-47.0	-148.3	21.5 ●	FIREMANS FUND INS CO
7.5	6.7	N/A	N/A	N/A	N/A	N/A	N/A	N/A	999 +	0.0	0.0	FIREMANS FUND INS CO OF HI INC
53.9	41.9	N/A	N/A	N/A	N/A	N/A	N/A	N/A	-1.0	0.0	0.0	FIREMANS FUND INS CO OF OH
4.2	3.8	N/A	N/A	N/A	N/A	N/A	N/A	N/A	93.2	0.0	0.0	FIREMENS INS CO OF WASHINGTON DC
1.3	1.1	188.8	81.2	0.4	-2.6	82.0	21.2	103.2	99.0	22.9	18.3	FIRST ACCEPTANCE INS CO
0.7	0.6	297.4	128.0	0.8	-4.5	82.0	21.2	103.2	98.3	22.9	0.0	FIRST ACCEPTANCE INS CO OF
0.8	0.7	228.4	98.3	0.5	-4.7	82.0	21.2	103.2	96.9	22.9	0.0	FIRST ACCEPTANCE INS CO OF TN INC
1.7	1.1	146.4	42.1	4.8	3.7	72.0	36.2	108.2	97.6	2.9	0.0	FIRST AMERICAN PROP & CAS INS CO
1.9	1.1	143.7	41.0	-0.2	7.5	61.5	33.1	94.6	106.8	1.9	0.0	FIRST AMERICAN SPECIALTY INS CO
0.5	0.4	211.9	258.2	-32.6	-32.7	60.7	23.6	84.3	132.6	3.8	0.0	FIRST BENEFITS INS MUTUAL INC
1.0	0.6	305.0	218.0	-2.7	4.2	66.3	28.0	94.3	126.5	31.3	4.6	FIRST CHICAGO INS CO
1.0	0.5	140.3	101.0	2.2	N/A	72.3	35.7	108.0	81.5	54.4	0.0	FIRST CHOICE CASUALTY INS CO
15.7	8.9	48.1	6.2	1.2	-0.4	69.9	31.4	101.3	125.9	16.8	0.0 ●	FIRST COLONIAL INS CO
3.0	2.3	113.6	37.5	-0.2	-2.9	46.2	56.5	102.7	92.7	24.1	0.0	FIRST COMMUNITY INS CO
1.1	0.9	117.3	152.6	-1.9	-5.5	69.0	23.5	92.5	119.0	12.1	0.0	FIRST DAKOTA INDEMNITY CO
101.5	50.7	N/A	N/A	N/A	N/A	N/A	N/A	N/A	N/A	0.0	0.0	FIRST F&C INS OF HI INC
1.2	1.2	5.8	15.6	-1.5	-2.0	35.1	54.4	89.5	90.3	-10.5	78.5 ●	FIRST FINANCIAL INS CO
13.0	9.9	30.2	21.9	-1.1	-3.2	62.0	24.2	86.2	106.2	-11.4	0.0 ●	FIRST FLORIDIAN AUTO & HOME INS CO
8.2	5.7	9.2	8.8	1.1	0.5	31.5	71.6	103.1	129.3	1.2	0.0	FIRST FOUNDERS ASR CO
9.3	4.9	75.1	8.5	-1.2	-0.8	62.5	17.4	79.9	141.6	55.4	0.0	FIRST GUARD INS CO
108.1	54.0	N/A	N/A	N/A	N/A	N/A	N/A	N/A	N/A	0.0	0.0	FIRST INDEMNITY INS OF HI INC
1.0	0.9	133.8	-4.7	-0.1	17.4	25.7	72.3	98.0	96.5	5.3	0.0	FIRST INDEMNITY OF AMERICA INS CO
5.2	3.7	69.1	82.3	-1.0	-4.5	67.2	31.0	98.2	109.7	5.0	3.9 ●	FIRST INS CO OF HI LTD
N/A	N/A	N/A	12.7	-8.8	-5.5	999 +	999 +	999 +	-0.1	-100.8	0.0	FIRST JERSEY CASUALTY INS CO INC
66.1	33.0	N/A	N/A	N/A	N/A	N/A	N/A	N/A	N/A	0.0	0.0	FIRST LIBERTY INS CORP
2.3	1.9	15.7	60.2	-7.7	-12.3	61.3	5.0	66.3	209.8	-4.2	0.0	FIRST MEDICAL INS CO RRG
5.5	4.6	11.8	N/A	N/A	N/A	N/A	17.1	N/A	3.3	0.0	0.0	FIRST MERCURY INS CO
9.0	6.8	32.3	1.7	-0.7	-0.7	31.2	30.1	61.3	152.9	23.9	0.0	FIRST MUTUAL INS CO
93.4	73.6	N/A	N/A	N/A	N/A	N/A	N/A	N/A	N/A	0.0	0.0	FIRST NATIONAL INS CO OF AMERICA
1.7	1.3	55.7	23.5	-2.8	14.0	42.4	45.3	87.7	114.4	18.9	0.0	FIRST NET INS CO
2.6	2.0	101.0	36.3	N/A	N/A	67.0	28.3	95.3	217.5	0.0	4.9	FIRST NONPROFIT INS CO
7.2	6.2	-0.4	66.8	-12.6	-29.4	999 +	-499.1	999 +	2.3	77.5	0.0	FIRST PROFESSIONALS INS CO INC
N/A	N/A	--	--	--	--	--	--	--	--	--	--	FIRST PROTECTIVE INS CO
140.6	70.2	N/A	N/A	N/A	N/A	N/A	N/A	N/A	N/A	0.0	0.0	FIRST SECURITY INS OF HI INC
7.1	4.2	N/A	50.9	5.9	4.9	999 +	999 +	999 +	6.5	-104.7	0.0	FIRST SPECIALTY INS CORP
N/A	N/A	N/A	777.3	29.6	57.2	999 +	999 +	999 +	N/A	-59.2	31.0	FIRST STATE INS CO
1.5	1.2	26.1	36.2	N/A	-21.6	100.5	107.1	207.6	128.7	51.9	0.0	FIRST SURETY CORP
N/A	N/A	N/A	N/A	N/A	N/A	N/A	N/A	N/A	N/A	0.0	0.0	FIRST WASHINGTON INS CO
2.8	1.8	38.3	104.5	-9.9	-15.1	35.1	29.3	64.4	168.5	0.7	0.0	FIRSTCOMP INS CO

999 + Denotes number greater than 999.9%
999 - Denotes number less than -999.99%
● Bullets denote a more detailed analysis is available in Section II.

INSURANCE COMPANY NAME	DOM. STATE	RATING	TOTAL ASSETS ($MIL)	CAPITAL & SURPLUS ($MIL)	ANNUAL NET PREMIUM ($MIL)	NET INCOME ($MIL)	CAPITAL-IZATION INDEX (PTS)	RESERVE ADQ INDEX (PTS)	PROFIT-ABILITY INDEX (PTS)	LIQUIDITY INDEX (PTS)	STAB. INDEX (PTS)	STABILITY FACTORS
FIRSTLINE NATIONAL INS CO	MD	C+	87.6	48.1	36.0	-0.2	8.5	7.0	5.9	6.8	3.7	T
FITCHBURG MUTUAL INS CO	MA	C+	119.3	55.2	36.6	-0.3	8.8	5.9	5.2	6.9	3.8	RT
FLAGSHIP CITY INS CO	PA	C+	54.2	12.3	0.0	0.1	8.8	N/A	7.4	7.0	3.1	DT
▲FLORIDA FAMILY INS CO	FL	B-	105.7	57.9	49.5	1.5	8.7	6.2	8.4	6.3	3.6	FT
FLORIDA FARM BU CASUALTY INS CO	FL	B-	559.1	292.4	238.6	0.9	9.9	7.7	8.5	6.6	4.5	T
FLORIDA FARM BUREAU GENERAL INS CO	FL	B	10.1	10.1	0.0	0.1	10.0	N/A	6.9	7.0	4.5	DGT
FLORIDA LAWYERS MUTUAL INS CO	FL	C+	82.3	43.5	12.5	0.3	9.2	9.4	8.2	7.8	3.4	DRT
FLORIDA PENINSULA INS CO	FL	C	346.1	136.9	115.4	7.6	7.2	4.3	9.0	6.9	4.0	FT
FLORIDA SELECT INS CO	FL	F (5)	0.0	0.0	-0.3	0.0	0.0	5.0	1.9	7.0	0.0	CDFT
FLORIDA SPECIALTY INS CO	FL	C	59.3	25.0	7.9	-1.4	9.7	7.4	4.3	7.8	3.1	FGRT
FLORISTS INS CO	IL	C	6.7	6.1	0.0	0.0	10.0	N/A	3.4	10.0	2.7	DFGR
FLORISTS MUTUAL INS CO	IL	C-	128.7	24.3	21.1	0.7	7.3	3.7	1.3	2.4	2.9	DFLT
FMH AG RISK INS CO	IA	B-	293.6	108.9	-6.8	0.9	10.0	7.0	3.8	2.7	4.1	FLRT
FMI INS CO	NJ	B- (2)	47.2	35.5	0.0	0.4	7.2	N/A	6.9	7.0	3.8	T
FOREMOST COUNTY MUTUAL INS CO	TX	C+	94.9	4.8	0.0	0.3	2.9	N/A	8.9	5.9	3.2	CDFT
FOREMOST INS CO	MI	B	2,292.9	1,112.9	0.0	18.6	10.0	6.2	7.8	9.4	4.9	RT
FOREMOST LLOYDS OF TEXAS	TX	C+	68.1	4.6	0.0	0.1	3.6	N/A	8.4	5.4	3.2	CDFT
FOREMOST P&C INS CO	MI	C+	66.4	18.1	0.0	0.1	9.3	N/A	6.4	9.0	3.3	DFT
FOREMOST SIGNATURE INS CO	MI	C+	69.8	20.0	0.0	0.1	9.4	N/A	5.9	10.0	3.4	DFT
FORESTRY MUTUAL INS CO	NC	C	59.5	19.5	23.0	-1.3	7.1	10.0	5.5	6.7	2.9	DRT
FORT WAYNE MEDICAL ASR CO RRG	AZ	D+	4.6	2.6	0.9	0.0	9.1	9.4	8.5	7.4	1.9	DFGT
FORTRESS INS CO	IL	B-	133.3	62.3	21.8	0.9	5.9	6.1	4.6	7.7	3.8	DT
FORTUITY INS CO	MI	B	41.4	17.5	17.3	1.0	8.9	9.3	6.6	6.6	4.9	DGRT
FOUNDERS INS CO (IL)	IL	C	155.2	70.1	41.1	1.0	8.6	3.8	3.3	6.7	4.0	RT
FOUNDERS INS CO (NJ)	NJ	C (2)	6.5	6.4	0.0	0.1	10.0	N/A	4.8	10.0	2.7	DT
FOUNDERS INS CO OF MI	MI	U	6.0	5.8	0.0	0.0	N/A	6.5	4.2	10.0	4.6	FGT
FRANDISCO P&C INS CO	GA	B-	104.2	77.1	39.1	6.9	10.0	7.3	8.7	7.0	3.8	T
▲FRANK WINSTON CRUM INS CO	FL	C-	69.8	19.5	17.2	0.4	2.6	4.9	3.3	7.5	2.5	CDGR
FRANKENMUTH MUTUAL INS CO	MI	B	1,242.1	541.9	450.8	26.1	9.1	9.2	6.3	6.5	4.9	T
FRANKLIN CASUALTY INS CO RRG	VT	D	10.7	4.0	3.2	-0.2	3.3	7.0	5.9	8.7	2.0	DFGR
FRANKLIN HOMEOWNERS ASSR CO	DE	U (2)	75.7	74.7	0.0	2.6	N/A	3.6	4.1	7.0	5.4	FT
FRANKLIN INS CO	PA	C	28.7	12.5	8.9	0.2	8.0	6.9	7.1	7.3	3.0	DGRT
FRANKLIN MUTUAL INS CO	NJ	B (2)	824.4	543.5	112.1	21.7	8.1	8.2	7.9	8.4	4.6	T
FREDERICK MUTUAL INS CO	MD	C-	46.1	21.6	21.1	0.2	7.4	4.4	1.8	6.4	2.9	DFT
FREDERICKSBURG PROFESSIONAL RISK	VT	D	20.3	12.3	2.0	0.2	8.1	9.6	5.4	9.3	1.6	DGRT
FREEDOM ADVANTAGE INS CO	PA	D+	11.0	3.8	4.1	-0.1	4.7	7.0	4.8	7.2	2.0	DFGR
FREEDOM SPECIALTY INS CO	OH	B	57.0	13.0	0.0	0.3	8.6	N/A	7.7	10.0	4.3	DFGT
FREMONT INS CO	MI	D	139.7	42.8	58.1	2.2	8.7	4.2	4.3	6.3	1.7	RT
FRIENDS COVE MUTUAL INS CO	PA	C-	5.5	2.9	2.9	0.5	7.3	5.9	2.4	6.0	1.9	DFGR
FRONTLINE INS UNLIMITED CO	IL	U	--	--	--	--	N/A	--	--	--	--	Z
FULMONT MUTUAL INS CO	NY	D	4.0	1.3	2.3	0.0	5.0	3.8	1.6	6.8	1.1	DFGR
GABLES RRG INC	VT	E	10.1	4.8	3.1	0.2	7.2	5.1	3.0	6.7	0.0	DGT
GALEN INS CO	MO	E	14.0	1.2	6.0	-0.9	1.1	5.1	0.3	7.2	0.1	CDGR
GARRISON P&C INS CO	TX	B	1,779.1	649.6	1,190.8	-17.6	8.3	6.9	5.5	3.2	4.9	LRT
GATEWAY INS CO	MO	D	62.4	20.1	28.2	1.3	1.9	3.8	2.9	6.5	2.3	DFRT
GEICO ADVANTAGE INS CO	NE	B-	1,177.8	537.2	476.5	-91.3	7.6	4.7	2.7	3.9	4.7	FGLT
GEICO CASUALTY CO	MD	C-	2,755.4	918.5	1,619.8	-5.9	7.4	9.6	2.7	2.4	3.3	GLT
GEICO CHOICE INS CO	NE	A-	647.0	266.3	315.1	-28.2	8.0	3.9	2.8	5.7	5.5	FGT
GEICO COUNTY MUTUAL INS CO	TX	C	88.9	5.0	0.0	0.0	3.8	N/A	4.9	0.0	2.8	CDGL
GEICO GENERAL INS CO	MD	B+	226.3	153.6	0.0	0.2	10.0	N/A	7.1	10.0	5.0	T
GEICO INDEMNITY CO	MD	B	7,092.5	3,906.9	2,397.8	82.5	7.8	9.6	8.4	6.4	5.1	GT
GEICO MARINE INS CO	MD	B-	134.9	43.6	23.9	-2.2	7.9	8.7	3.4	6.5	3.6	FRT

See Page 27 for explanation of footnotes and Page 28 for explanation of stability factors.

Arrows denote recent upgrades ▲ or downgrades ▼   (see Section VII for explanations)

68

www.weissratings.com

RISK ADJ. RATIO #1	CAPITAL RATIO #2	PREMIUM TO SURPLUS (%)	RESV. TO SURPLUS (%)	RESV. DEVELOP. 1 YEAR (%)	RESV. DEVELOP. 2 YEAR (%)	LOSS RATIO (%)	EXP. RATIO (%)	COMB RATIO (%)	CASH FROM UNDER-WRITING (%)	NET PREMIUM GROWTH (%)	INVEST. IN AFFIL (%)	INSURANCE COMPANY NAME
2.8	2.0	75.7	60.5	1.1	0.4	60.9	34.4	95.3	111.7	10.7	0.0	FIRSTLINE NATIONAL INS CO
3.3	2.3	68.2	43.1	N/A	2.9	74.3	35.4	109.7	96.1	4.1	5.3	FITCHBURG MUTUAL INS CO
2.1	1.8	N/A	N/A	N/A	N/A	N/A	N/A	N/A	999 +	0.0	0.0	FLAGSHIP CITY INS CO
2.6	2.4	87.9	16.5	0.1	2.0	57.6	43.0	100.6	94.8	-1.0	16.5	FLORIDA FAMILY INS CO
5.1	3.6	81.6	36.8	-3.8	-3.4	73.4	20.7	94.1	106.3	0.6	2.6 •	FLORIDA FARM BU CASUALTY INS CO
87.2	43.6	N/A	N/A	N/A	N/A	N/A	N/A	N/A	N/A	0.0	0.0	FLORIDA FARM BUREAU GENERAL INS
3.8	2.3	29.4	53.3	-9.7	-16.0	48.6	20.1	68.7	143.2	27.7	0.0	FLORIDA LAWYERS MUTUAL INS CO
2.5	2.0	90.2	74.2	-5.7	-9.5	44.4	33.9	78.3	95.8	-15.8	1.4	FLORIDA PENINSULA INS CO
-1.9	-1.7	2.3	-16.5	8.4	0.3	537.6	-780.2	-242.6	28.4	0.0	0.0	FLORIDA SELECT INS CO
4.6	3.3	30.3	7.7	-0.8	-1.9	40.2	93.8	134.0	84.3	-56.4	0.0	FLORIDA SPECIALTY INS CO
23.4	21.0	N/A	4.5	N/A	N/A	N/A	N/A	N/A	-224.8	0.0	0.0	FLORISTS INS CO
2.3	1.6	89.0	127.6	-2.0	-2.4	104.9	27.7	132.6	45.7	-60.8	6.3	FLORISTS MUTUAL INS CO
11.3	10.1	-6.2	N/A	2.8	-3.5	N/A	-108.6	N/A	6.9	-104.6	0.0	FMH AG RISK INS CO
1.9	1.1	N/A	N/A	N/A	N/A	N/A	N/A	N/A	N/A	0.0	0.0	FMI INS CO
0.5	0.5	N/A	N/A	N/A	N/A	N/A	N/A	N/A	67.0	0.0	0.0	FOREMOST COUNTY MUTUAL INS CO
9.5	6.8	N/A	0.8	-0.2	-0.3	N/A	N/A	N/A	999 +	0.0	6.6 •	FOREMOST INS CO
0.6	0.5	N/A	N/A	N/A	N/A	N/A	N/A	N/A	-73.5	0.0	0.0	FOREMOST LLOYDS OF TEXAS
2.7	2.4	N/A	N/A	N/A	N/A	N/A	N/A	N/A	-55.8	0.0	0.0	FOREMOST P&C INS CO
2.9	2.6	N/A	N/A	N/A	N/A	N/A	N/A	N/A	-179.6	0.0	0.0	FOREMOST SIGNATURE INS CO
1.3	1.0	108.7	87.8	-14.1	-31.7	46.7	29.9	76.6	123.0	15.3	4.4	FORESTRY MUTUAL INS CO
3.2	2.2	34.8	30.7	-1.5	-10.4	21.3	45.1	66.4	88.7	0.4	0.0	FORT WAYNE MEDICAL ASR CO RRG
1.2	0.8	35.7	86.8	0.5	0.1	76.9	30.0	106.9	87.0	-11.8	0.0	FORTRESS INS CO
3.4	2.5	105.2	72.6	-9.2	-12.2	62.1	30.8	92.9	109.6	5.3	0.0	FORTUITY INS CO
4.4	3.0	59.3	86.3	-1.3	-4.0	65.5	33.7	99.2	95.7	-36.7	4.6	FOUNDERS INS CO (IL)
92.0	45.6	N/A	N/A	N/A	N/A	N/A	N/A	N/A	310.0	0.0	0.0	FOUNDERS INS CO (NJ)
N/A	N/A	N/A	3.3	1.1	0.5	N/A	N/A	N/A	N/A	0.0	0.0	FOUNDERS INS CO OF MI
4.9	4.2	55.4	2.5	0.1	-0.5	14.0	65.6	79.6	126.5	15.1	0.0	FRANDISCO P&C INS CO
0.9	0.5	125.2	130.1	17.8	19.2	58.4	40.1	98.5	107.6	66.6	0.0	FRANK WINSTON CRUM INS CO
3.3	2.6	88.7	61.2	-7.8	-10.1	62.1	30.8	92.9	112.6	5.3	12.8 •	FRANKENMUTH MUTUAL INS CO
1.4	0.9	77.1	156.8	-8.4	-20.0	47.7	38.1	85.8	93.9	-3.6	0.0	FRANKLIN CASUALTY INS CO RRG
N/A	N/A	N/A	0.1	0.1	0.1	N/A	N/A	N/A	N/A	-100.0	0.0	FRANKLIN HOMEOWNERS ASSR CO
2.7	1.7	72.7	77.0	-1.9	-4.9	61.2	31.2	92.4	117.9	10.3	0.0	FRANKLIN INS CO
2.7	1.8	20.6	20.5	-1.3	-2.5	60.4	32.3	92.7	111.4	0.0	6.7	FRANKLIN MUTUAL INS CO
2.1	1.3	100.3	57.3	-3.6	10.3	70.5	44.3	114.8	82.3	-13.6	0.0	FREDERICK MUTUAL INS CO
4.5	3.2	16.3	47.4	-9.8	-28.4	30.5	12.5	43.0	355.0	-8.3	0.0	FREDERICKSBURG PROFESSIONAL RISK
1.2	0.8	114.9	167.2	-44.9	-51.5	50.2	32.6	82.8	91.0	2.9	0.0	FREEDOM ADVANTAGE INS CO
2.1	1.9	N/A	N/A	N/A	N/A	N/A	N/A	N/A	96.8	0.0	0.0	FREEDOM SPECIALTY INS CO
2.9	2.2	140.9	103.5	0.5	3.2	70.1	27.3	97.4	108.9	5.7	0.0	FREMONT INS CO
2.0	1.3	116.6	18.7	4.4	5.7	63.7	46.0	109.7	97.0	3.2	0.0	FRIENDS COVE MUTUAL INS CO
N/A	N/A	--	--	--	--	--	--	--	--	--	--	FRONTLINE INS UNLIMITED CO
1.2	0.8	204.2	152.5	0.5	11.4	109.0	9.9	118.9	85.0	-32.0	3.4	FULMONT MUTUAL INS CO
1.6	1.2	70.4	76.4	-25.8	-102.1	34.6	11.8	46.4	264.5	-0.7	0.0	GABLES RRG INC
0.1	0.1	238.2	341.4	19.4	N/A	90.8	67.0	157.8	91.8	4.8	0.0	GALEN INS CO
2.4	1.7	181.7	86.7	1.3	-2.6	85.9	12.9	98.8	110.8	13.6	0.0 •	GARRISON P&C INS CO
0.7	0.6	149.9	85.6	3.5	10.9	58.5	25.4	83.9	73.3	26.5	0.0	GATEWAY INS CO
1.6	1.2	89.4	32.8	-3.2	-5.9	100.5	33.7	134.2	80.7	147.4	0.0 •	GEICO ADVANTAGE INS CO
1.6	1.2	174.2	78.7	-3.1	-44.7	90.8	20.9	111.7	99.3	146.2	0.0 •	GEICO CASUALTY CO
1.9	1.3	106.5	35.9	-3.4	-9.6	93.2	22.9	116.1	94.2	134.3	0.0 •	GEICO CHOICE INS CO
0.6	0.5	N/A	N/A	N/A	N/A	N/A	N/A	N/A	112.7	0.0	0.0	GEICO COUNTY MUTUAL INS CO
19.7	17.7	N/A	N/A	N/A	N/A	N/A	N/A	N/A	N/A	0.0	0.0 •	GEICO GENERAL INS CO
2.1	1.6	58.8	32.0	-1.0	-33.3	80.3	13.5	93.8	110.7	351.6	16.4 •	GEICO INDEMNITY CO
2.9	1.9	49.3	11.8	-2.3	-7.1	84.3	32.5	116.8	75.7	33.3	0.0	GEICO MARINE INS CO

999 + Denotes number greater than 999.9%
999 - Denotes number less than -999.99%
• Bullets denote a more detailed analysis is available in Section II.

INSURANCE COMPANY NAME	DOM. STATE	RATING	TOTAL ASSETS ($MIL)	CAPITAL & SURPLUS ($MIL)	ANNUAL NET PREMIUM ($MIL)	NET INCOME ($MIL)	CAPITAL-IZATION INDEX (PTS)	RESERVE ADQ INDEX (PTS)	PROFIT-ABILITY INDEX (PTS)	LIQUIDITY INDEX (PTS)	STAB. INDEX (PTS)	STABILITY FACTORS
GEICO SECURE INS CO	NE	A-	436.8	259.4	147.3	-6.0	8.7	4.7	3.5	6.7	5.9	GT
GEISINGER INS CORP RRG	VT	D-	12.3	11.8	1.2	0.3	10.0	3.6	5.6	8.5	1.3	DGRT
GEM STATE INS CO	ID	C-	11.2	8.5	3.5	0.3	9.8	6.2	8.7	6.8	2.2	DGT
GEMINI INS CO	DE	C	128.7	56.4	0.0	0.6	10.0	N/A	6.3	7.0	4.0	RT
GENERAL AUTOMOBILE INS CO	OH	C	101.1	28.9	77.0	-2.5	6.1	4.1	3.6	2.0	3.6	LT
GENERAL CASUALTY CO OF WI	WI	C	1,086.9	316.1	180.2	10.3	7.6	4.7	3.1	5.6	4.2	FRT
GENERAL CASUALTY INS CO	WI	C-	13.6	7.3	22.2	0.2	6.5	3.9	1.8	6.3	3.1	DFRT
GENERAL INS CO OF AM	NH	C	108.3	106.3	0.0	0.5	10.0	3.9	2.9	7.0	4.1	ART
GENERAL REINS CORP	DE	C+	15,099.1	11,105.1	548.5	609.3	7.5	7.9	6.4	9.1	3.6	RT
GENERAL SECURITY IND CO OF AZ	AZ	D+	374.2	63.6	29.1	7.4	7.9	6.0	8.8	9.0	2.8	GRT
GENERAL SECURITY NATIONAL INS CO	NY	C-	344.5	133.0	89.3	8.0	7.3	6.8	3.9	6.9	3.2	RT
GENERAL STAR INDEMNITY CO	DE	C	749.0	523.8	66.8	4.8	9.8	8.8	3.8	9.7	4.0	RT
GENERAL STAR NATIONAL INS CO	DE	B-	212.1	162.8	9.8	2.1	10.0	9.0	3.7	10.0	3.5	DFRT
GENERALI - US BRANCH	NY	C-	63.9	27.1	21.9	-1.4	7.0	3.0	3.9	6.4	3.2	FRT
GENESEE PATRONS COOP INS	NY	D	8.9	5.2	3.8	0.1	8.0	6.5	8.1	6.8	2.1	DFGR
GENESIS INS CO	DE	C	176.7	119.0	10.4	1.7	10.0	9.2	3.6	10.0	2.7	DRT
GENEVA INS CO	IN	D+	4.2	1.5	4.4	0.0	3.1	3.7	1.8	2.2	1.4	CDGL
GENWORTH FINANCIAL ASR CORP	NC	U	7.5	7.4	0.0	0.2	N/A	6.4	1.6	7.0	2.8	FGT
GENWORTH MORTGAGE INS CORP	NC	C	2,817.4	1,162.9	621.1	174.8	6.7	3.2	3.6	6.6	4.0	RT
GENWORTH MORTGAGE REINS CORP	NC	B	14.5	11.3	1.3	0.5	10.0	4.6	2.7	9.5	4.0	ADGT
GENWORTH MTG INS CORP OF NC	NC	C	342.0	163.7	61.6	22.0	7.3	4.7	3.9	6.5	4.3	FT
GEORGIA CASUALTY & SURETY CO	GA	C	40.9	19.8	13.4	0.4	8.8	6.0	5.1	6.7	3.4	DT
GEORGIA DEALERS INS CO	GA	D-	12.6	2.7	4.2	-0.7	1.0	4.2	0.6	5.7	1.3	CDGT
GEORGIA FARM BUREAU CASUALTY INS CO	GA	B	3.5	3.5	0.0	0.0	10.0	N/A	3.3	10.0	4.6	DGT
▲GEORGIA FARM BUREAU MUTUAL INS CO	GA	B-	674.5	242.8	437.9	6.1	7.4	5.9	2.9	5.6	4.1	T
GEORGIA MUNICIPAL CAPTIVE INS CO	GA	D+	10.5	2.8	2.7	0.1	5.7	4.9	6.4	7.1	1.9	DGT
GEORGIA TRANSPORTATION CAPTIVE INS	GA	D (1)	2.9	1.5	0.7	0.1	7.6	9.6	8.1	9.0	1.2	DGT
GEOVERA INS CO	CA	D+	85.2	28.9	25.7	2.7	1.2	7.7	3.8	6.0	2.4	CRT
GEOVERA SPECIALTY INS CO	DE	C	108.1	21.4	12.0	1.9	3.2	7.5	4.2	6.9	2.6	CDRT
GERMAN AMERICAN FARM MUTUAL	TX	B-	4.3	3.1	0.7	-0.2	10.0	5.2	4.4	9.3	3.5	DGT
GERMAN MUTUAL INS CO	OH	D-	41.5	16.7	19.8	0.6	7.0	5.8	3.1	6.7	1.3	DGRT
GERMANIA FARM MUTUAL INS ASN	TX	C-	393.8	144.8	174.6	-25.7	6.8	5.9	2.9	3.8	3.3	FLRT
GERMANIA FIRE & CASUALTY CO	TX	C	30.6	13.4	18.6	-0.2	8.5	6.7	3.4	5.5	3.1	DGRT
GERMANIA INS CO	TX	C+	75.3	46.4	26.6	1.4	9.7	6.3	8.9	6.5	3.7	RT
GERMANIA SELECT INS CO	TX	B	209.0	73.3	141.3	-5.4	9.1	8.0	4.1	5.1	4.6	RT
GERMANTOWN INS CO	PA	C+	93.6	43.8	30.6	0.1	9.8	6.8	5.3	6.7	3.8	T
GERMANTOWN MUTUAL INS CO	WI	B-	104.8	54.2	45.7	3.8	10.0	8.6	8.3	6.1	3.5	RT
GLOBAL HAWK INS CO RRG	VT	D-	44.3	6.7	24.3	-1.7	0.7	2.5	2.9	7.6	1.3	CDRT
GLOBAL HAWK PROPERTY CAS INS CO	DE	U	6.5	6.5	0.0	0.0	N/A	N/A	4.9	7.0	3.5	GT
GLOBAL INS CO	GA	U (3)	3.5	3.5	0.0	0.0	N/A	6.1	6.0	7.0	4.2	GORT
GLOBAL LIBERTY INS CO OF NY	NY	D	67.7	22.7	36.9	1.9	5.5	4.1	5.7	6.6	2.3	DRT
GLOBAL REINS CORP OF AM	NY	D+	279.0	90.7	-0.3	-6.0	2.0	9.3	1.7	10.0	2.6	CFRT
GNY CUSTOM INS CO	AZ	B	58.5	52.5	2.7	0.6	10.0	4.6	6.6	9.1	4.5	DT
GOAUTO INS CO	LA	D	43.1	8.1	15.5	-0.5	1.6	4.7	2.8	7.2	2.2	CDGR
GOLDEN BEAR INS CO	CA	C	133.4	50.2	21.3	0.9	7.6	9.4	8.8	7.4	3.4	GRT
GOLDEN EAGLE INS CORP	NH	C	58.7	55.8	0.0	0.5	10.0	3.8	2.9	10.0	3.9	FRT
GOLDEN INS CO A RRG	NV	E+	12.8	3.5	5.0	0.2	1.2	1.3	6.7	8.6	0.8	CDGT
GOLDSTREET INS CO	NY	U	5.6	4.5	0.0	-0.1	N/A	9.3	3.9	10.0	4.5	FGRT
GOOD SHEPHERD RECIPROCAL RRG	SC	D-	9.1	5.7	2.3	-0.1	2.2	1.9	2.9	7.2	1.3	DGT
GOODVILLE MUTUAL CAS CO	PA	B	237.7	134.7	112.5	3.2	9.9	6.1	8.8	6.8	4.1	RT
GOTHAM INS CO	NY	C	223.9	75.8	75.7	-1.9	7.1	5.5	4.4	7.3	2.9	T
GOVERNMENT EMPLOYEES INS CO	MD	B	23,562.9	13,622.6	6,468.3	384.8	8.4	9.5	8.6	6.6	5.1	GT

See Page 27 for explanation of footnotes and Page 28 for explanation of stability factors.
Arrows denote recent upgrades ▲ or downgrades ▼ (see Section VII for explanations)

70

www.weissratings.com

RISK ADJ. RATIO #1	CAPITAL RATIO #2	PREMIUM TO SURPLUS (%)	RESV. TO SURPLUS (%)	RESV. DEVELOP. 1 YEAR (%)	RESV. DEVELOP. 2 YEAR (%)	LOSS RATIO (%)	EXP. RATIO (%)	COMB RATIO (%)	CASH FROM UNDER-WRITING (%)	NET PREMIUM GROWTH (%)	INVEST. IN AFFIL (%)	INSURANCE COMPANY NAME
3.2	2.2	54.7	18.4	-1.4	-4.5	86.7	22.7	109.4	101.5	122.0	0.0 ●	GEICO SECURE INS CO
10.7	6.4	10.5	4.4	N/A	N/A	42.6	59.9	102.5	104.7	1.0	0.0	GEISINGER INS CORP RRG
4.2	2.8	43.2	8.2	-0.4	0.5	65.4	31.3	96.7	109.0	11.9	0.0	GEM STATE INS CO
7.2	6.5	N/A	N/A	N/A	N/A	N/A	N/A	N/A	N/A	0.0	0.0	GEMINI INS CO
0.7	0.7	245.6	72.2	3.1	6.4	70.0	26.3	96.3	120.3	8.6	0.0	GENERAL AUTOMOBILE INS CO
1.6	1.3	56.7	63.7	0.7	1.4	63.9	38.2	102.1	80.4	-21.1	44.1 ●	GENERAL CASUALTY CO OF WI
2.3	1.7	122.9	138.2	1.4	2.7	63.9	37.5	101.4	80.5	-23.0	0.0	GENERAL CASUALTY INS CO
9.4	9.2	N/A	N/A	N/A	N/A	N/A	N/A	N/A	N/A	0.0	14.5	GENERAL INS CO OF AM
1.6	1.4	5.0	26.6	-1.4	-2.6	56.8	37.2	94.0	90.9	-7.6	45.3 ●	GENERAL REINS CORP
2.3	1.5	47.0	44.8	-10.1	-5.9	31.8	15.3	47.1	515.3	16.7	0.0	GENERAL SECURITY IND CO OF AZ
2.1	1.3	71.7	101.7	-0.5	-4.0	55.3	33.9	89.2	119.1	17.2	0.0	GENERAL SECURITY NATIONAL INS CO
5.1	3.2	12.3	26.5	-2.4	-4.5	60.3	47.4	107.7	103.5	-7.5	0.0 ●	GENERAL STAR INDEMNITY CO
8.0	5.5	5.9	26.4	-3.9	-5.3	56.6	53.9	110.5	81.0	-5.0	0.0	GENERAL STAR NATIONAL INS CO
4.5	3.1	79.6	67.6	-1.1	7.6	75.6	27.9	103.5	86.7	-31.0	0.3	GENERALI - US BRANCH
2.7	1.7	77.5	10.6	-4.9	-5.5	66.5	27.9	94.4	99.7	10.4	0.0	GENESEE PATRONS COOP INS
5.6	4.1	8.7	43.1	-3.7	-7.3	67.4	26.5	93.9	118.3	-17.5	0.0	GENESIS INS CO
0.5	0.4	286.0	89.0	11.6	7.0	71.5	32.2	103.7	100.1	53.6	0.0	GENEVA INS CO
N/A	N/A	N/A	N/A	-0.4	-0.4	999 +	N/A	N/A	N/A	0.0	0.0	GENWORTH FINANCIAL ASR CORP
1.5	1.3	57.9	68.8	-1.4	3.9	35.9	27.0	62.9	96.0	15.5	17.7 ●	GENWORTH MORTGAGE INS CORP
10.7	9.6	11.5	1.4	N/A	0.3	5.3	5.1	10.4	731.5	-14.5	0.0	GENWORTH MORTGAGE REINS CORP
2.2	1.7	41.4	73.0	-0.3	5.2	46.0	0.4	46.4	88.5	11.8	16.3	GENWORTH MTG INS CORP OF NC
3.5	2.5	69.3	57.2	-3.0	-4.4	64.4	31.5	95.9	98.8	8.6	0.0	GEORGIA CASUALTY & SURETY CO
0.2	0.1	126.8	199.3	19.8	12.1	156.7	20.5	177.2	113.6	12.7	0.0	GEORGIA DEALERS INS CO
144.1	67.7	N/A	N/A	N/A	N/A	N/A	N/A	N/A	N/A	0.0	0.0	GEORGIA FARM BUREAU CASUALTY INS
1.8	1.2	184.6	64.5	5.4	2.4	73.5	31.0	104.5	101.6	5.7	1.5 ●	GEORGIA FARM BUREAU MUTUAL INS
1.3	0.5	99.7	203.2	-9.4	-13.5	80.8	14.2	95.0	150.3	0.9	0.0	GEORGIA MUNICIPAL CAPTIVE INS CO
2.7	1.5	50.6	75.8	-1.4	-28.8	70.0	26.8	96.8	155.1	3.9	0.0	GEORGIA TRANSPORTATION CAPTIVE
0.4	0.2	95.3	20.0	-1.5	-2.5	27.9	34.4	62.3	149.8	-2.9	0.0	GEOVERA INS CO
0.7	0.4	55.9	11.7	-0.9	-1.5	27.9	34.4	62.3	164.5	-2.9	0.0	GEOVERA SPECIALTY INS CO
4.7	3.9	21.5	5.1	-3.1	-3.7	82.0	4.0	86.0	127.0	25.5	0.0	GERMAN AMERICAN FARM MUTUAL
2.1	1.4	136.9	44.2	1.5	1.1	59.5	27.9	87.4	124.0	4.4	0.0	GERMAN MUTUAL INS CO
0.9	0.8	101.1	23.5	0.9	1.6	80.1	24.7	104.8	100.6	-2.0	52.6	GERMANIA FARM MUTUAL INS ASN
2.2	1.9	137.6	48.5	1.1	0.9	83.1	24.4	107.5	98.4	1.7	0.0	GERMANIA FIRE & CASUALTY CO
4.1	3.3	59.0	29.0	N/A	0.5	58.7	22.5	81.2	103.7	-7.0	0.0	GERMANIA INS CO
2.5	2.1	180.5	53.0	-0.5	-1.9	77.3	25.9	103.2	100.5	8.7	1.5	GERMANIA SELECT INS CO
3.8	3.0	69.8	45.7	0.8	0.6	76.2	26.5	102.7	98.4	-1.2	0.0	GERMANTOWN INS CO
5.2	3.7	91.1	47.2	-5.7	-1.6	54.0	30.0	84.0	123.6	6.1	0.0	GERMANTOWN MUTUAL INS CO
0.3	0.2	312.6	284.8	29.9	10.8	89.4	18.8	108.2	126.9	10.9	0.0	GLOBAL HAWK INS CO RRG
N/A	N/A	N/A	N/A	N/A	N/A	N/A	N/A	N/A	N/A	0.0	0.0	GLOBAL HAWK PROPERTY CAS INS CO
N/A	N/A	N/A	N/A	N/A	-0.6	N/A	N/A	N/A	N/A	100.0	0.0	GLOBAL INS CO
2.1	1.3	180.1	90.6	0.9	20.7	63.3	28.6	91.9	108.6	25.5	0.0	GLOBAL LIBERTY INS CO OF NY
0.5	0.3	-0.3	186.4	-2.9	-1.8	-537.1	999 +	999 +	1.2	-156.4	0.0	GLOBAL REINS CORP OF AM
23.2	18.3	5.3	7.7	0.1	N/A	68.7	30.9	99.6	110.4	7.4	0.0	GNY CUSTOM INS CO
0.5	0.4	221.9	123.2	-2.5	-2.5	108.3	-3.6	104.7	135.2	25.5	0.0	GOAUTO INS CO
2.0	1.3	43.7	115.7	-17.9	-25.4	62.0	18.1	80.1	192.1	59.5	0.0	GOLDEN BEAR INS CO
66.7	60.0	N/A	N/A	N/A	N/A	N/A	N/A	N/A	N/A	0.0	0.0	GOLDEN EAGLE INS CORP
0.3	0.2	141.5	98.4	41.9	56.7	70.0	25.4	95.4	168.5	39.2	0.0	GOLDEN INS CO A RRG
N/A	N/A	N/A	22.7	N/A	-11.7	N/A	N/A	N/A	N/A	0.0	0.0	GOLDSTREET INS CO
0.7	0.5	39.9	39.5	-19.4	-17.3	23.2	8.9	32.1	173.8	2.9	0.0	GOOD SHEPHERD RECIPROCAL RRG
4.3	3.0	85.2	27.5	0.8	0.5	59.5	27.8	87.3	117.7	4.4	0.0	GOODVILLE MUTUAL CAS CO
1.6	1.0	99.5	126.4	6.4	4.3	69.9	33.8	103.7	125.6	17.3	0.0	GOTHAM INS CO
3.3	2.1	46.4	31.4	-1.1	-30.6	82.3	9.1	91.4	111.0	895.9	0.7 ●	GOVERNMENT EMPLOYEES INS CO

999 + Denotes number greater than 999.9%
999 - Denotes number less than -999.99%

● Bullets denote a more detailed analysis is available in Section II.

INSURANCE COMPANY NAME	DOM. STATE	RATING	TOTAL ASSETS ($MIL)	CAPITAL & SURPLUS ($MIL)	ANNUAL NET PREMIUM ($MIL)	NET INCOME ($MIL)	CAPITAL- IZATION INDEX (PTS)	RESERVE ADQ INDEX (PTS)	PROFIT- ABILITY INDEX (PTS)	LIQUIDITY INDEX (PTS)	STAB. INDEX (PTS)	STABILITY FACTORS
GOVERNMENT ENTITIES MUTUAL INC	DC	U (5)	74.0	30.0	8.0	0.0	N/A	5.8	6.7	7.9	4.1	DR
GOVERNMENTAL INTERINS	IL	B	67.4	46.8	7.9	-0.4	10.0	8.6	4.0	7.5	4.1	DFT
GOVT TECHNOLOGY INS CO RRG INC	NV	B-	1.5	0.7	0.7	0.1	6.8	N/A	4.8	7.1	3.5	DGT
GRACO RRG INC	SC	U	1.4	0.6	0.0	0.1	N/A	N/A	4.8	10.0	1.7	GT
GRAIN DEALERS MUTUAL INS CO	IN	C	9.8	7.5	0.0	0.7	10.0	3.6	6.3	10.0	2.9	DGRT
GRANADA INS CO	FL	E+	31.0	8.8	7.3	0.3	0.4	0.7	3.5	5.7	0.6	CDFG
GRANGE INDEMNITY INS CO	OH	C	106.0	53.3	48.9	2.9	9.4	6.2	8.6	6.5	3.5	T
GRANGE INS ASSN	WA	B-	282.4	143.8	145.0	2.9	9.1	6.0	4.7	6.0	4.0	FRT
GRANGE INS CO OF MI	OH	C	74.1	41.6	30.6	1.7	9.3	6.2	8.6	6.7	3.2	T
GRANGE MUTUAL CAS CO	OH	B	2,258.8	1,119.8	1,026.8	43.1	8.6	6.2	8.3	6.2	4.8	RT
GRANGE MUTUAL FIRE INS CO	PA	D+	4.4	3.4	1.0	0.0	9.3	7.4	8.0	7.2	2.0	DGRT
GRANGE P&C INS CO	OH	C+	69.8	40.3	24.4	2.6	10.0	6.2	8.7	6.8	3.2	T
GRANITE MUTUAL INS CO	VT	C+	4.5	4.5	0.0	0.1	10.0	N/A	6.2	7.0	3.4	DGRT
GRANITE RE INC	OK	C	47.0	23.1	24.6	2.9	4.8	10.0	8.5	6.9	2.9	DRT
GRANITE STATE INS CO	IL	C+	34.7	31.7	0.0	0.3	10.0	N/A	3.5	7.0	3.8	GT
GRANWEST P&C	WA	C	21.6	20.8	0.7	0.2	10.0	6.2	8.1	9.1	3.5	DFGR
GRAPHIC ARTS MUTUAL INS CO	NY	C+	144.5	55.9	41.1	0.7	9.6	6.1	5.1	6.7	4.0	T
GRAY CASUALTY & SURETY CO	LA	C	17.3	14.5	2.1	0.1	10.0	N/A	3.5	9.2	2.6	DGRT
GRAY INS CO	LA	C+	284.0	108.0	67.1	0.2	7.4	5.6	4.9	6.9	3.4	RT
GRAY INS CO OF LOUISIANA	LA	U	6.1	6.0	0.0	0.0	N/A	0.0	4.7	0.0	0.0	LT
GREAT AMERICAN ALLIANCE INS CO	OH	C	30.1	30.1	0.0	0.3	10.0	N/A	5.1	7.0	3.7	AGRT
GREAT AMERICAN ASR CO	OH	C+	19.6	19.6	0.0	0.1	10.0	N/A	6.3	7.0	3.4	ADGR
GREAT AMERICAN CASUALTY INS CO	OH	U	10.8	10.8	0.0	0.1	N/A	N/A	3.6	7.0	4.8	AGT
GREAT AMERICAN CONTEMPORARY INS CO	OH	U	10.5	10.5	0.0	0.1	N/A	N/A	4.2	7.0	4.9	AGRT
GREAT AMERICAN E & S INS CO	DE	C	47.1	46.6	0.0	0.4	10.0	N/A	6.5	7.0	3.9	ART
GREAT AMERICAN FIDELITY INS CO	DE	C	47.2	46.6	0.0	0.4	10.0	N/A	6.5	7.0	3.9	ADRT
GREAT AMERICAN INS CO	OH	B-	6,188.9	1,685.9	2,354.2	147.5	7.4	8.2	8.5	6.7	3.6	ART
GREAT AMERICAN INS CO OF NEW YORK	NY	C	47.7	47.7	0.0	0.5	10.0	N/A	6.8	7.0	3.9	ART
GREAT AMERICAN LLOYDS INS CO	TX	U	1.5	1.5	0.0	0.0	N/A	N/A	6.2	7.0	3.0	GRT
GREAT AMERICAN PROTECTION INS CO	OH	C	21.9	21.9	0.0	0.3	10.0	N/A	3.6	7.0	3.7	ADGR
GREAT AMERICAN SECURITY INS CO	OH	C	15.2	15.2	0.0	0.1	10.0	N/A	3.6	7.0	3.3	ADGR
GREAT AMERICAN SPIRIT INS CO	OH	C	16.8	16.7	0.0	0.1	10.0	N/A	3.6	7.0	3.3	ADGR
GREAT CENTRAL FIRE INS CO	LA	D+ (2)	3.9	3.0	3.0	0.0	6.6	6.1	6.8	6.8	2.1	DFT
GREAT DIVIDE INS CO	ND	C	246.2	67.6	0.0	0.8	10.0	3.7	6.6	7.5	4.1	RT
GREAT FALLS INS CO	ME	D	9.9	2.7	2.3	0.2	2.0	4.8	3.0	6.2	1.9	CDGT
GREAT LAKES CASUALTY INS CO	MI	C	17.4	17.3	0.0	0.2	10.0	N/A	7.0	7.0	2.7	DGT
▲GREAT LAKES MUTUAL INS CO	MI	C-	11.0	7.2	3.6	0.6	9.3	8.5	8.9	6.9	2.1	DGT
GREAT MIDWEST INS CO	TX	B	200.2	105.6	93.5	-2.1	7.8	5.3	4.4	6.9	4.2	T
GREAT NORTHERN INS CO	IN	B	1,666.2	459.6	391.3	49.3	8.2	8.9	6.5	6.8	4.3	T
GREAT NORTHWEST INS CO	MN	C-	19.8	7.1	0.0	0.3	8.7	3.3	5.1	9.9	2.7	DGRT
GREAT PLAINS CASUALTY INC	IA	C	18.2	16.6	6.0	0.7	10.0	8.2	8.0	7.0	2.8	DGT
GREAT WEST CASUALTY CO	NE	B	2,008.2	613.3	849.2	33.1	8.8	9.4	8.8	6.4	4.8	AT
GREATER NEW YORK MUTUAL INS CO	NY	B-	971.5	458.7	228.8	6.9	8.5	6.2	5.1	6.9	4.3	RT
GREEN HILLS INS CO A RRG	VT	D-	10.7	5.0	3.6	0.8	7.2	9.6	1.9	6.7	1.3	DGT
GREEN MOUNTAIN INS CO	VT	B	11.7	11.2	0.0	0.1	10.0	N/A	7.5	7.0	4.0	DGT
GREEN TREE PERPETUAL ASR CO	PA	U	0.2	0.2	0.0	0.0	N/A	4.8	2.0	7.0	0.6	FGT
GREENVILLE CASUALTY INS CO INC	SC	C-	10.6	5.9	5.2	-0.3	7.2	4.0	2.8	6.4	2.3	DFGT
GREENWICH INS CO	DE	C	1,118.6	352.2	159.3	21.1	7.6	7.5	3.5	7.7	3.8	ART
GRINNELL MUTUAL REINS CO	IA	B-	1,078.2	559.3	525.1	41.3	8.8	8.3	7.9	6.2	4.3	RT
GRINNELL SELECT INS CO	IA	C	38.4	24.4	0.0	0.2	10.0	N/A	2.9	10.0	3.7	DFGT
GROWERS AUTOMOBILE INS ASN	IN	D	6.3	5.0	0.1	0.1	7.4	4.6	3.9	9.9	2.1	DGT
GUARANTEE CO OF NORTH AMERICA USA	MI	B	209.3	172.1	41.2	4.6	10.0	6.1	8.0	8.9	4.1	RT

See Page 27 for explanation of footnotes and   72   www.weissratings.com
Page 28 for explanation of stability factors.
Arrows denote recent upgrades ▲ or downgrades ▼   (see Section VII for explanations)

RISK ADJ. RATIO #1	CAPITAL RATIO #2	PREMIUM TO SURPLUS (%)	RESV. TO SURPLUS (%)	RESV. DEVELOP. 1 YEAR (%)	RESV. DEVELOP. 2 YEAR (%)	LOSS RATIO (%)	EXP. RATIO (%)	COMB RATIO (%)	CASH FROM UNDER- WRITING (%)	NET PREMIUM GROWTH (%)	INVEST. IN AFFIL (%)	INSURANCE COMPANY NAME
N/A	N/A	28.3	141.5	-3.7	-8.6	65.0	21.6	86.6	177.6	4.6	0.0	GOVERNMENT ENTITIES MUTUAL INC
5.7	4.2	16.6	28.8	-2.4	-5.8	76.6	47.3	123.9	74.8	0.8	0.0	GOVERNMENTAL INTERINS
1.1	0.9	102.1	N/A	N/A	N/A	3.2	81.5	84.7	141.8	10.7	0.0	GOVT TECHNOLOGY INS CO RRG INC
N/A	N/A	N/A	N/A	N/A	N/A	N/A	N/A	N/A	-2.3	0.0	0.0	GRACO RRG INC
9.1	8.2	N/A	N/A	N/A	N/A	N/A	N/A	N/A	N/A	0.0	0.0	GRAIN DEALERS MUTUAL INS CO
0.2	0.1	86.2	133.4	28.4	66.5	98.6	6.9	105.5	45.8	-7.0	0.0	GRANADA INS CO
4.3	2.7	97.1	53.5	1.8	2.0	69.1	26.8	95.9	108.2	0.5	0.0	GRANGE INDEMNITY INS CO
3.2	2.4	105.4	42.4	2.9	3.0	80.5	26.8	107.3	92.8	4.1	8.8	GRANGE INS ASSN
4.2	2.6	76.6	42.2	1.4	1.5	69.1	27.1	96.2	102.7	0.5	0.0	GRANGE INS CO OF MI
2.8	2.0	96.1	53.0	1.7	1.8	69.1	30.3	99.4	107.3	0.5	11.8 ●	GRANGE MUTUAL CAS CO
4.0	2.4	31.1	2.5	-1.3	-1.2	34.9	45.5	80.4	120.5	12.3	0.0	GRANGE MUTUAL FIRE INS CO
5.7	3.6	64.9	35.8	1.2	1.5	69.1	11.6	80.7	108.6	0.5	0.0	GRANGE P&C INS CO
109.8	56.9	N/A	N/A	N/A	N/A	N/A	N/A	N/A	N/A	0.0	0.0	GRANITE MUTUAL INS CO
1.0	0.8	122.9	91.0	-33.3	-50.0	18.9	71.9	90.8	123.4	5.9	0.0	GRANITE RE INC
19.9	15.3	N/A	N/A	N/A	N/A	N/A	N/A	N/A	N/A	0.0	4.1	GRANITE STATE INS CO
55.4	37.9	3.5	4.4	-1.5	0.8	25.8	47.3	73.1	55.6	-75.7	0.0	GRANWEST P&C
4.0	2.7	74.4	108.2	-1.6	-3.9	65.5	33.7	99.2	95.6	12.7	2.5	GRAPHIC ARTS MUTUAL INS CO
7.4	5.4	14.5	13.3	N/A	N/A	73.2	53.6	126.8	117.2	5.6	0.0	GRAY CASUALTY & SURETY CO
1.7	1.2	63.8	157.1	N/A	-0.1	54.8	42.6	97.4	104.2	-7.0	12.8	GRAY INS CO
N/A	N/A	N/A	N/A	N/A	N/A	N/A	N/A	N/A	N/A	0.0	0.0	GRAY INS CO OF LOUISIANA
96.0	48.0	N/A	N/A	N/A	N/A	N/A	N/A	N/A	N/A	0.0	0.0	GREAT AMERICAN ALLIANCE INS CO
105.3	51.6	N/A	N/A	N/A	N/A	N/A	N/A	N/A	N/A	0.0	0.0	GREAT AMERICAN ASR CO
N/A	N/A	N/A	N/A	N/A	N/A	N/A	N/A	N/A	N/A	0.0	0.0	GREAT AMERICAN CASUALTY INS CO
N/A	N/A	N/A	N/A	N/A	N/A	N/A	N/A	N/A	N/A	0.0	0.0	GREAT AMERICAN CONTEMPORARY INS
81.8	41.8	N/A	N/A	N/A	N/A	N/A	N/A	N/A	N/A	0.0	0.0	GREAT AMERICAN E & S INS CO
78.2	40.0	N/A	N/A	N/A	N/A	N/A	N/A	N/A	N/A	0.0	0.0	GREAT AMERICAN FIDELITY INS CO
1.8	1.3	151.8	172.6	-3.9	-1.1	55.6	34.7	90.3	118.6	4.3	10.7 ●	GREAT AMERICAN INS CO
67.0	36.9	N/A	N/A	N/A	N/A	N/A	N/A	N/A	N/A	0.0	0.0	GREAT AMERICAN INS CO OF NEW
N/A	N/A	N/A	N/A	N/A	N/A	N/A	N/A	N/A	N/A	0.0	0.0	GREAT AMERICAN LLOYDS INS CO
69.4	35.6	N/A	N/A	N/A	N/A	N/A	N/A	N/A	N/A	0.0	0.0	GREAT AMERICAN PROTECTION INS CO
127.1	63.5	N/A	N/A	N/A	N/A	N/A	N/A	N/A	N/A	0.0	0.0	GREAT AMERICAN SECURITY INS CO
124.2	62.1	N/A	N/A	N/A	N/A	N/A	N/A	N/A	N/A	0.0	0.0	GREAT AMERICAN SPIRIT INS CO
1.2	1.0	97.7	7.7	0.4	1.4	24.6	76.5	101.1	98.5	-10.8	0.0	GREAT CENTRAL FIRE INS CO
6.9	6.2	N/A	N/A	N/A	N/A	N/A	N/A	N/A	128.4	0.0	0.0	GREAT DIVIDE INS CO
0.7	0.4	93.5	73.6	-0.1	4.3	80.5	22.8	103.3	160.3	31.1	0.0	GREAT FALLS INS CO
91.1	44.0	N/A	N/A	N/A	N/A	N/A	N/A	N/A	N/A	0.0	0.0	GREAT LAKES CASUALTY INS CO
5.3	3.2	54.2	17.5	-6.3	-4.7	32.2	34.0	66.2	148.6	-5.9	0.0	GREAT LAKES MUTUAL INS CO
3.1	1.9	86.9	60.5	1.0	8.2	63.8	31.7	95.5	117.9	31.3	0.4	GREAT MIDWEST INS CO
2.9	1.8	83.4	138.8	-3.5	-7.3	56.5	29.3	85.8	118.6	4.1	0.0 ●	GREAT NORTHERN INS CO
2.5	2.2	N/A	11.8	9.4	7.0	N/A	N/A	N/A	27.0	0.0	0.0	GREAT NORTHWEST INS CO
7.0	4.1	37.6	8.9	-6.6	-8.6	36.4	12.1	48.5	130.5	15.6	0.0	GREAT PLAINS CASUALTY INC
3.3	2.0	144.9	126.3	-2.9	-12.4	71.4	21.0	92.4	109.5	7.8	0.0 ●	GREAT WEST CASUALTY CO
2.3	1.9	51.5	75.4	0.7	0.1	68.7	30.9	99.6	110.4	7.4	16.4 ●	GREATER NEW YORK MUTUAL INS CO
1.6	1.0	68.4	93.4	-79.4	-26.6	13.9	23.0	36.9	355.7	609.8	0.0	GREEN HILLS INS CO A RRG
5.4	3.2	N/A	N/A	N/A	N/A	N/A	N/A	N/A	N/A	0.0	0.0	GREEN MOUNTAIN INS CO
N/A	N/A	N/A	N/A	N/A	-4.7	N/A	N/A	N/A	N/A	0.0	0.0	GREEN TREE PERPETUAL ASR CO
1.8	1.5	81.7	50.0	-11.8	17.1	33.8	47.8	81.6	83.1	-57.9	34.5	GREENVILLE CASUALTY INS CO INC
1.6	1.4	45.4	110.6	0.8	-1.8	71.2	35.0	106.2	94.2	4.8	25.1 ●	GREENWICH INS CO
3.6	2.4	101.6	47.2	-1.4	-2.0	53.2	27.9	81.1	124.7	8.6	3.3 ●	GRINNELL MUTUAL REINS CO
8.5	7.6	N/A	N/A	N/A	N/A	N/A	N/A	N/A	-61.7	0.0	0.0	GRINNELL SELECT INS CO
2.2	1.3	2.6	4.6	1.8	1.9	218.2	92.6	310.8	53.2	0.0	0.0	GROWERS AUTOMOBILE INS ASN
7.1	5.2	24.3	5.2	-0.9	-1.6	26.2	64.8	91.0	121.5	12.8	0.0	GUARANTEE CO OF NORTH AMERICA

999 + Denotes number greater than 999.9%
999 - Denotes number less than -999.99%

● Bullets denote a more detailed analysis is available in Section II.

INSURANCE COMPANY NAME	DOM. STATE	RATING	TOTAL ASSETS ($MIL)	CAPITAL & SURPLUS ($MIL)	ANNUAL NET PREMIUM ($MIL)	NET INCOME ($MIL)	CAPITAL-IZATION INDEX (PTS)	RESERVE ADQ INDEX (PTS)	PROFIT-ABILITY INDEX (PTS)	LIQUIDITY INDEX (PTS)	STAB. INDEX (PTS)	STABILITY FACTORS
GUARANTEE INS CO	FL	E+	367.6	52.9	64.8	-1.5	1.0	0.2	2.2	6.2	0.5	CFRT
GUARDIAN INDEMNITY INC	MT	E (2)	6.2	2.8	1.1	0.2	3.6	6.9	2.2	8.8	0.0	DT
GUARDIAN INS CO	VI	C	32.4	16.1	19.4	-0.3	7.8	6.1	3.3	6.0	2.9	DGT
GUIDEONE AMERICA INS CO	IA	C+	13.0	10.7	0.0	0.1	10.0	N/A	6.6	7.0	3.3	DGRT
GUIDEONE ELITE INS CO	IA	C+	32.4	24.8	0.0	0.2	10.0	N/A	7.4	7.0	3.7	GRT
GUIDEONE MUTUAL INS CO	IA	B	1,249.1	421.2	360.2	-68.2	7.5	9.0	3.6	6.8	4.5	RT
GUIDEONE NATIONAL INS CO	IA	C+	54.1	47.3	0.0	0.4	10.0	N/A	7.9	8.1	3.9	T
GUIDEONE P&C INS CO	IA	B	456.3	245.7	112.6	-3.6	8.8	8.2	4.5	6.9	4.5	RT
GUIDEONE SPECIALTY MUTUAL INS CO	IA	B	269.5	94.6	90.1	-3.9	8.2	9.3	4.6	7.0	4.4	RT
GUIDEONE TEXAS INS CO	TX	B- (3)	3.3	3.2	0.0	0.0	10.0	N/A	6.7	7.0	3.9	DFGR
GUILDERLAND REINS CO	NY	U	3.5	3.3	0.0	0.0	N/A	3.6	6.8	7.0	4.2	GT
GUILFORD INS CO	IL	C-	385.7	278.0	32.8	3.5	7.9	8.0	6.8	8.2	2.6	RT
GULF BUILDERS RRG INC	SC	F (5)	0.0	0.0	-0.1	0.0	3.0	4.6	0.8	10.0	0.0	FGT
GULF GUARANTY INS CO	MS	C	4.4	3.8	0.4	-0.1	10.0	6.2	2.9	8.6	2.3	DFGT
GULF UNDERWRITERS INS CO	CT	U	51.1	51.0	0.0	0.7	N/A	N/A	7.4	7.0	5.4	T
GULFSTREAM P&C INS CO	FL	C+	117.9	35.7	55.9	0.2	7.4	7.0	7.8	7.9	3.4	T
GUTHRIE RRG	SC	C-	47.2	15.7	7.3	0.3	7.6	9.6	3.6	7.2	2.7	DT
HALIFAX MUTUAL INS CO	NC	D-	7.9	3.9	3.4	0.2	7.1	8.6	2.9	7.2	1.3	DGRT
HALLMARK COUNTY MUTUAL INS CO	TX	C	5.9	5.5	0.0	0.0	10.0	N/A	4.9	6.9	2.4	DGRT
HALLMARK INS CO	AZ	D+	307.9	104.6	121.0	2.1	7.9	4.9	6.1	7.4	2.2	RT
HALLMARK NATIONAL INS CO	AZ	C	84.4	25.8	32.0	-0.3	7.6	4.7	6.0	7.1	2.7	RT
HALLMARK SPECIALTY INS CO	OK	B-	219.4	58.9	76.6	1.0	7.7	4.6	6.2	7.0	3.7	RT
HAMDEN ASR RRG INC	VT	U	89.4	1.8	0.0	0.0	N/A	N/A	8.2	10.0	0.8	CT
HAMILTON INS CO	DE	U	24.5	20.4	1.0	-4.5	N/A	4.9	1.4	7.4	2.6	DFGR
HAMILTON MUTUAL INS CO	IA	C	86.3	35.2	30.3	1.1	9.1	7.9	5.9	6.9	3.8	T
▼HAMILTON SPECIALTY INS CO	DE	B-	85.4	53.9	3.8	-10.3	8.5	4.6	2.7	7.0	3.5	DFGT
HANNAHSTOWN MUTUAL INS CO	PA	D+	4.2	2.6	1.5	0.2	8.1	6.5	6.4	7.3	1.9	DGRT
HANOVER AMERICAN INS CO	NH	C	30.2	30.2	0.0	0.4	10.0	N/A	7.3	7.0	3.7	GRT
HANOVER FIRE & CASUALTY INS CO	PA	D+	5.4	3.0	4.5	-0.1	6.0	6.2	5.5	6.8	2.0	DGRT
HANOVER INS CO	NH	B	6,972.7	2,147.8	3,046.3	69.2	7.3	4.2	6.3	6.1	5.1	AT
HANOVER LLOYDS INS CO	TX	C+	6.0	6.0	0.0	0.1	10.0	N/A	7.2	7.0	3.0	DGRT
HANOVER NATIONAL INS CO	NH	U	12.4	12.4	0.0	0.1	N/A	N/A	7.4	7.0	5.0	GOT
HANOVER NJ INS CO	NH	U	31.9	31.9	0.0	0.4	N/A	N/A	7.4	7.0	5.4	GRT
HARBOR INS CO	OK	D+	11.7	3.2	4.7	0.5	7.3	6.9	2.3	7.9	1.9	DFGT
HARCO NATIONAL INS CO	IL	B-	338.9	168.6	86.0	4.4	7.0	5.3	6.1	5.5	4.3	RT
HARFORD MUTUAL INS CO	MD	B-	404.4	194.3	114.1	0.4	8.3	6.9	7.5	7.0	4.1	RT
HARLEYSVILLE INS CO	PA	C	153.1	25.9	0.0	0.2	9.6	3.9	3.4	7.8	3.7	AFT
HARLEYSVILLE INS CO OF NEW YORK	PA	C	77.8	23.6	0.0	0.3	10.0	3.9	3.3	9.3	3.6	DFRT
HARLEYSVILLE INS CO OF NJ	NJ	C-	99.8	46.3	0.0	0.1	10.0	3.9	1.9	7.0	3.1	AFT
HARLEYSVILLE LAKE STATES INS CO	MI	C	62.7	36.6	0.0	0.2	10.0	3.9	2.9	7.0	3.6	AT
HARLEYSVILLE PREFERRED INS CO	PA	C-	136.2	46.8	0.0	0.3	10.0	3.9	1.9	7.0	3.1	AT
HARLEYSVILLE WORCESTER INS CO	PA	C-	206.9	55.9	0.0	0.1	10.0	3.9	1.9	7.0	3.1	AT
HARTFORD ACCIDENT & INDEMNITY CO	CT	B	11,729.7	3,218.0	3,444.7	122.3	7.8	5.8	6.5	6.7	4.5	AT
HARTFORD CASUALTY INS CO	IN	B	2,370.8	950.3	579.6	34.3	10.0	5.9	5.9	6.9	4.9	AT
HARTFORD FIRE INS CO	CT	B	25,602.1	13,094.5	4,373.1	328.5	7.7	4.9	5.8	6.9	5.1	AT
HARTFORD INS CO OF IL	IL	B	3,931.9	1,345.1	1,064.3	54.3	9.2	5.9	5.6	6.8	4.8	AT
HARTFORD INS CO OF THE MIDWEST	IN	B	633.3	482.3	52.7	9.1	10.0	5.0	8.2	7.9	4.7	AT
HARTFORD INS CO OF THE SOUTHEAST	CT	B	184.8	59.0	52.7	2.9	8.6	5.9	6.0	6.8	4.1	AT
HARTFORD LLOYDS INS CO	TX	B	73.1	70.2	1.1	1.2	10.0	3.6	7.9	10.0	4.2	AGT
HARTFORD SM BOIL INSPECTION & INS	CT	B	1,179.3	558.4	271.5	52.1	9.1	9.0	5.5	6.9	4.7	FT
HARTFORD SM BOIL INSPECTION IC OF CT	CT	B	74.4	36.7	11.1	5.0	10.0	8.0	3.8	8.2	4.2	DT
HARTFORD UNDERWRITERS INS CO	CT	B	1,651.2	632.4	421.5	25.0	9.8	5.9	5.7	6.8	4.8	AT

See Page 27 for explanation of footnotes and
Page 28 for explanation of stability factors.
Arrows denote recent upgrades ▲ or downgrades ▼   (see Section VII for explanations)

74

www.weissratings.com

RISK ADJ. CAPITAL RATIO #1	CAPITAL RATIO #2	PREMIUM TO SURPLUS (%)	RESV. TO SURPLUS (%)	RESV. DEVELOP. 1 YEAR (%)	2 YEAR (%)	LOSS RATIO (%)	EXP. RATIO (%)	COMB RATIO (%)	CASH FROM UNDER-WRITING (%)	NET PREMIUM GROWTH (%)	INVEST. IN AFFIL (%)	INSURANCE COMPANY NAME
0.6	0.3	138.5	203.1	68.9	100.7	73.8	25.8	99.6	57.8	-43.3	4.4	GUARANTEE INS CO
0.7	0.5	39.9	106.7	-15.2	1.7	68.4	18.9	87.3	114.2	0.6	0.0	GUARDIAN INDEMNITY INC
1.7	1.4	116.3	20.6	1.7	1.6	65.8	36.3	102.1	90.1	-9.5	20.1	GUARDIAN INS CO
13.5	12.1	N/A	N/A	N/A	N/A	N/A	N/A	N/A	-40.1	0.0	0.0	GUIDEONE AMERICA INS CO
12.4	11.2	N/A	N/A	N/A	N/A	N/A	N/A	N/A	-13.2	0.0	0.0	GUIDEONE ELITE INS CO
1.5	1.2	77.6	83.9	-2.4	-5.3	67.1	33.5	100.6	128.6	1.5	22.9 ●	GUIDEONE MUTUAL INS CO
25.6	18.9	N/A	N/A	N/A	N/A	N/A	N/A	N/A	307.2	0.0	0.0	GUIDEONE NATIONAL INS CO
2.5	2.1	45.3	48.9	-1.3	-3.2	67.1	34.2	101.3	145.0	1.5	20.8 ●	GUIDEONE P&C INS CO
2.4	1.7	91.8	99.2	-2.7	-6.5	67.1	34.2	101.3	201.8	1.5	7.9	GUIDEONE SPECIALTY MUTUAL INS CO
118.8	60.3	N/A	N/A	N/A	N/A	N/A	N/A	N/A	999 +	0.0	0.0	GUIDEONE TEXAS INS CO
N/A	N/A	N/A	N/A	N/A	N/A	N/A	N/A	N/A	80.7	0.0	0.0	GUILDERLAND REINS CO
1.6	1.6	11.9	32.1	-2.0	-2.9	44.4	51.7	96.1	92.6	-10.5	47.3 ●	GUILFORD INS CO
0.5	0.5	-52.9	20.2	-3.2	-0.7	27.2	-79.2	-52.0	1.0	-167.1	0.0	GULF BUILDERS RRG INC
7.3	5.7	9.6	1.7	-0.8	-1.2	35.0	122.4	157.4	42.7	-63.6	0.0	GULF GUARANTY INS CO
N/A	N/A	N/A	N/A	N/A	N/A	N/A	N/A	N/A	-27.7	0.0	0.0	GULF UNDERWRITERS INS CO
2.0	1.8	152.4	35.6	-7.0	-7.9	48.6	36.1	84.7	108.9	7.8	0.0	GULFSTREAM P&C INS CO
1.5	1.2	39.6	160.1	-7.2	-12.9	60.2	5.0	65.2	201.7	-1.9	0.0	GUTHRIE RRG
2.1	1.4	95.6	9.4	-7.4	-6.1	43.7	28.7	72.4	102.7	5.2	0.0	HALIFAX MUTUAL INS CO
30.5	27.5	N/A	N/A	N/A	N/A	N/A	N/A	N/A	N/A	0.0	0.0	HALLMARK COUNTY MUTUAL INS CO
2.4	1.8	118.1	108.0	-2.8	-2.4	65.6	25.5	91.1	128.1	36.6	12.5	HALLMARK INS CO
2.7	1.8	126.3	136.8	-3.0	-2.7	65.6	36.1	101.7	109.0	-21.8	0.0	HALLMARK NATIONAL INS CO
3.1	1.9	131.0	141.8	-3.0	-2.4	65.6	33.5	99.1	117.4	-22.0	0.0	HALLMARK SPECIALTY INS CO
N/A	N/A	N/A	N/A	N/A	N/A	N/A	N/A	N/A	N/A	0.0	0.0	HAMDEN ASR RRG INC
N/A	N/A	4.8	0.8	N/A	N/A	82.8	775.7	858.5	32.0	0.0	0.0	HAMILTON INS CO
3.7	2.5	89.3	91.4	-2.4	-2.0	65.5	31.4	96.9	112.6	4.8	0.0	HAMILTON MUTUAL INS CO
1.6	1.5	7.1	1.4	N/A	N/A	86.0	410.3	496.3	59.9	0.0	34.0	HAMILTON SPECIALTY INS CO
3.0	1.8	63.0	7.7	-1.6	-2.8	46.6	39.6	86.2	114.6	16.8	0.0	HANNAHSTOWN MUTUAL INS CO
87.6	42.1	N/A	N/A	N/A	N/A	N/A	N/A	N/A	N/A	0.0	0.0	HANOVER AMERICAN INS CO
0.9	0.8	149.0	12.7	-2.5	-0.7	17.0	71.2	88.2	111.6	21.2	0.0	HANOVER FIRE & CASUALTY INS CO
1.4	1.2	139.2	117.7	4.4	9.1	66.4	34.8	101.2	106.2	4.8	20.1 ●	HANOVER INS CO
77.2	34.8	N/A	N/A	N/A	N/A	N/A	N/A	N/A	N/A	0.0	0.0	HANOVER LLOYDS INS CO
N/A	N/A	N/A	N/A	N/A	N/A	N/A	N/A	N/A	N/A	0.0	0.0	HANOVER NATIONAL INS CO
N/A	N/A	N/A	N/A	N/A	N/A	N/A	N/A	N/A	N/A	0.0	0.0	HANOVER NJ INS CO
1.4	1.3	167.9	82.6	-3.8	0.1	78.0	31.1	109.1	82.1	-12.8	0.0	HARBOR INS CO
1.3	1.0	52.3	53.1	2.0	-1.8	61.7	31.2	92.9	108.8	20.8	13.6	HARCO NATIONAL INS CO
2.3	1.8	59.0	44.6	0.8	0.3	60.9	33.0	93.9	117.8	9.7	14.4 ●	HARFORD MUTUAL INS CO
2.9	2.6	N/A	N/A	N/A	N/A	N/A	N/A	N/A	40.4	0.0	0.0	HARLEYSVILLE INS CO
3.5	3.1	N/A	N/A	N/A	N/A	N/A	N/A	N/A	22.8	0.0	0.0	HARLEYSVILLE INS CO OF NEW YORK
7.9	7.1	N/A	N/A	N/A	N/A	N/A	N/A	N/A	999 +	0.0	0.0	HARLEYSVILLE INS CO OF NJ
9.6	8.6	N/A	N/A	N/A	N/A	N/A	N/A	N/A	39.1	0.0	0.0	HARLEYSVILLE LAKE STATES INS CO
6.4	5.8	N/A	N/A	N/A	N/A	N/A	N/A	N/A	119.2	0.0	0.0	HARLEYSVILLE PREFERRED INS CO
6.8	6.2	N/A	N/A	N/A	N/A	N/A	N/A	N/A	111.4	0.0	0.0	HARLEYSVILLE WORCESTER INS CO
2.0	1.4	105.1	181.8	1.2	2.7	66.1	29.7	95.8	108.2	2.9	9.2 ●	HARTFORD ACCIDENT & INDEMNITY CO
4.8	3.1	64.1	110.8	0.8	1.6	66.1	28.4	94.5	108.2	2.9	0.0 ●	HARTFORD CASUALTY INS CO
2.0	1.4	32.5	56.3	0.4	0.8	66.1	32.9	99.0	106.5	2.9	26.3 ●	HARTFORD FIRE INS CO
3.8	2.4	82.5	142.7	1.0	2.1	66.1	29.7	95.8	108.2	2.9	0.0 ●	HARTFORD INS CO OF IL
26.1	16.9	11.1	19.2	0.1	0.3	66.1	16.4	82.5	108.2	2.9	0.0 ●	HARTFORD INS CO OF THE MIDWEST
3.2	2.1	94.8	163.9	1.1	2.4	66.1	28.3	94.4	108.2	2.9	0.0	HARTFORD INS CO OF THE SOUTHEAST
72.1	44.1	1.5	2.6	N/A	N/A	66.1	-17.2	48.9	108.4	2.9	0.0	HARTFORD LLOYDS INS CO
2.9	2.5	42.7	23.5	-5.0	-5.9	27.3	64.7	92.0	98.8	-64.8	14.4 ●	HARTFORD SM BOIL INSPECTION & INS
5.8	5.0	25.1	13.1	-2.4	-2.8	28.9	-24.8	4.1	293.6	-66.2	1.8	HARTFORD SM BOIL INSPECTION IC OF
4.3	2.8	69.2	119.7	0.8	1.8	66.1	27.6	93.7	108.2	2.9	0.0 ●	HARTFORD UNDERWRITERS INS CO

999 + Denotes number greater than 999.9%
999 - Denotes number less than -999.99%
● Bullets denote a more detailed analysis is available in Section II.

INSURANCE COMPANY NAME	DOM. STATE	RATING	TOTAL ASSETS ($MIL)	CAPITAL & SURPLUS ($MIL)	ANNUAL NET PREMIUM ($MIL)	NET INCOME ($MIL)	CAPITAL-IZATION INDEX (PTS)	RESERVE ADQ INDEX (PTS)	PROFIT-ABILITY INDEX (PTS)	LIQUIDITY INDEX (PTS)	STAB. INDEX (PTS)	STABILITY FACTORS
HARTLAND MUTUAL INS CO	ND	C	13.1	8.2	5.7	0.2	9.1	6.4	8.6	8.2	2.2	DGT
HASTINGS MUTUAL INS CO	MI	B	862.9	409.1	388.6	18.2	10.0	5.8	8.1	6.7	4.7	T
HAULERS INS CO	TN	B-	73.4	38.7	35.8	0.9	9.6	6.5	5.5	6.5	3.8	T
HAWAII EMPLOYERS MUTUAL INS CO	HI	C	376.8	228.3	67.6	5.1	10.0	5.5	6.9	7.1	4.1	RT
HAWAIIAN INS & GUARANTY CO LTD	HI	C+	26.9	13.4	11.3	0.6	8.2	5.8	6.1	7.3	3.2	DGRT
HAWKEYE-SECURITY INS CO	WI	C	13.7	13.1	0.0	0.1	10.0	N/A	5.9	7.0	3.1	DGRT
HAY CREEK MUTUAL INS CO	MN	D	5.8	3.2	2.6	0.3	8.4	5.9	6.6	7.3	1.9	DGT
HCC SPECIALTY INS CO	OK	B-	20.6	16.5	0.0	0.0	10.0	N/A	6.8	7.0	3.5	DFGR
HDI GLOBAL INS CO	IL	C	329.9	127.4	8.4	5.4	10.0	8.3	7.0	7.0	3.5	FRT
HEALTH CARE CASUALTY RRG INC	DC	D	14.3	2.3	3.2	0.1	5.0	10.0	8.5	9.0	1.8	DGRT
HEALTH CARE INDEMNITY INC	CO	C	438.3	179.6	37.4	5.7	7.2	9.9	6.7	8.4	2.4	FRT
HEALTH CARE INDUSTRY LIAB RECIP INS	DC	D	47.0	17.2	4.0	0.3	8.0	4.9	8.3	8.1	2.3	DRT
▲HEALTH CARE INS RECPL	MN	C-	27.6	5.4	7.0	-0.7	3.9	9.5	2.4	6.7	2.1	CDGR
HEALTH CARE MUT CAPTIVE INS CO	GA	D-	13.0	3.7	3.3	0.0	3.6	6.0	2.9	6.4	1.3	DGRT
HEALTH PROVIDERS INS RECIPROCAL RRG	HI	B-	79.4	58.1	7.3	0.3	10.0	9.4	8.6	7.0	3.8	DRT
HEALTHCARE PROFESSIONAL INS CO INC	NY	D+	242.6	61.0	30.4	5.4	2.8	5.0	6.0	6.7	2.5	CFRT
HEALTHCARE PROVIDERS INS EXCH	PA	E+	55.1	19.5	25.1	2.5	0.9	0.5	1.4	6.9	0.8	CDFR
HEALTHCARE UNDERWRITERS GRP MUT	OH	C	91.2	47.3	17.1	0.2	9.3	9.3	4.0	8.0	3.4	DFGR
HEALTHCARE UNDERWRITING CO RRG	VT	D	166.0	22.1	43.7	-7.4	1.7	3.6	2.9	9.0	2.0	CDT
HEARTLAND HEALTHCARE RECIPROCAL	VT	D+	14.6	7.2	2.7	0.3	8.8	7.0	3.8	8.5	2.1	DGT
HEARTLAND MUTUAL INS CO	MN	D- (1)	7.0	4.2	4.0	0.4	10.0	6.7	8.6	7.1	1.0	DGT
HEREFORD INS CO	NY	C	199.4	25.7	64.7	2.0	5.4	4.0	5.6	7.1	3.1	DRT
HERITAGE CASUALTY INS CO	KS	U	65.3	63.0	0.0	-1.0	N/A	3.6	4.0	7.0	5.4	RT
HERITAGE INDEMNITY CO	CA	C+	158.0	49.9	57.9	12.8	10.0	5.0	1.9	7.1	3.9	RT
HERITAGE P&C INS CO	FL	C+	663.9	208.6	391.7	-8.8	4.8	4.6	5.7	6.9	3.9	CGT
HERMITAGE INS CO	NY	E+ (3)	167.6	10.7	-32.3	-1.3	5.2	0.9	0.1	2.3	0.5	DFLR
HIGH POINT P&C INS CO	NJ	B (2)	345.1	321.9	0.0	4.1	8.1	3.9	7.1	7.0	4.4	T
HIGH POINT PREFERRED INS CO	NJ	B- (2)	251.0	116.0	115.5	28.0	8.0	7.0	6.4	6.8	4.3	T
HIGH POINT SAFETY & INS CO	NJ	B- (2)	62.5	49.6	0.0	0.6	10.0	N/A	7.4	7.0	4.0	T
HIGHLANDS INS CO	TX	F (5)	0.0	0.0	40.8	0.0	0.0	0.7	0.0	1.9	0.0	CDFL
HIGHMARK CASUALTY INS CO	PA	C	452.5	169.8	282.9	-4.8	7.5	7.0	5.9	6.5	4.2	RT
HILLSTAR INS CO	IN	C	3.6	3.6	0.0	0.0	10.0	4.6	3.6	7.0	2.9	ADGT
HINGHAM MUTUAL FIRE INS CO	MA	C+	62.0	39.6	20.7	0.5	8.2	8.3	4.8	6.7	3.7	FRT
HISCOX INS CO	IL	B-	218.8	64.4	50.4	2.7	5.0	6.2	5.5	7.5	3.7	CRT
HLTHCR PROVIDERS INS CO	SC	C-	77.3	41.7	7.9	-0.3	9.0	9.4	6.6	9.0	3.3	DRT
HM CASUALTY INS CO	PA	B-	24.8	10.2	0.0	-0.5	10.0	N/A	5.9	10.0	3.5	DFGT
HOCHHEIM PRAIRIE CASUALTY INS CO	TX	C	73.8	33.7	40.3	-1.1	7.6	7.0	3.9	5.7	3.5	FRT
HOCHHEIM PRAIRIE FARM MUT INS ASN	TX	D-	117.9	45.4	79.6	-20.7	7.1	4.7	2.1	3.0	1.3	FLRT
HOLYOKE MUTUAL INS CO IN SALEM	MA	B+	217.0	102.4	101.2	2.8	9.9	7.6	5.9	6.4	5.0	T
HOME & FARM INS CO	IN	C	10.0	6.9	1.9	0.0	10.0	6.5	4.3	6.9	2.7	DGRT
HOME CONSTRUCTION INS CO RRG	NV	U (2)	5.3	2.3	0.0	0.1	N/A	3.0	4.4	10.0	3.0	FRT
HOME STATE COUNTY MUTUAL INS CO	TX	C	291.9	7.1	4.7	0.3	3.4	8.3	8.8	1.0	2.7	CLRT
HOME VALUE INS CO	OH	F (5)	0.0	0.0	0.0	0.0	8.4	N/A	0.9	10.0	0.0	DFGT
HOME-OWNERS INS CO	MI	A-	2,106.0	1,042.3	809.4	59.2	10.0	5.9	8.4	6.7	5.9	FT
HOMELAND INS CO OF DE	DE	B	52.0	51.7	0.0	0.4	10.0	N/A	4.9	7.0	4.3	DT
HOMELAND INS CO OF NY	NY	C	114.8	113.7	0.0	0.1	8.9	3.8	5.7	7.0	3.9	FRT
HOMEOWNERS CHOICE ASR CO INC	AL	U (1)	1.9	1.9	0.0	0.0	N/A	N/A	3.7	7.0	3.4	GT
HOMEOWNERS CHOICE PROP & CAS INS	FL	C-	396.2	172.9	215.8	-1.7	6.5	4.7	5.8	7.0	3.3	T
HOMEOWNERS OF AMERICA INS CO	TX	D	46.0	15.8	7.7	-1.8	9.7	6.3	5.0	7.2	2.3	DGRT
HOMESHIELD FIRE & CASUALTY INS CO	OK	U	1.1	1.1	0.0	0.0	N/A	N/A	3.8	7.0	2.6	FGT
HOMESITE INDEMNITY CO	KS	C	56.2	40.0	0.0	0.2	10.0	4.7	5.4	7.1	3.5	FRT
HOMESITE INS CO	CT	C	154.1	86.4	0.0	0.8	10.0	4.7	5.5	7.0	3.6	FRT

See Page 27 for explanation of footnotes and
Page 28 for explanation of stability factors.
Arrows denote recent upgrades ▲ or downgrades ▼   (see Section VII for explanations)

76

www.weissratings.com

RISK ADJ. CAPITAL RATIO #1	RATIO #2	PREMIUM TO SURPLUS (%)	RESV. TO SURPLUS (%)	RESV. DEVELOP. 1 YEAR (%)	2 YEAR (%)	LOSS RATIO (%)	EXP. RATIO (%)	COMB RATIO (%)	CASH FROM UNDER- WRITING (%)	NET PREMIUM GROWTH (%)	INVEST. IN AFFIL (%)	INSURANCE COMPANY NAME
5.5	3.2	72.8	7.9	-0.5	-2.6	59.7	32.2	91.9	103.7	0.5	1.8	HARTLAND MUTUAL INS CO
5.1	3.5	100.6	58.3	-2.4	-8.9	58.2	31.5	89.7	112.8	3.9	0.0 ●	HASTINGS MUTUAL INS CO
3.8	2.8	94.5	62.0	-5.8	-9.0	80.9	25.3	106.2	95.8	1.9	0.0	HAULERS INS CO
4.2	2.9	30.6	46.0	0.3	0.4	72.9	26.7	99.6	125.5	10.3	0.0 ●	HAWAII EMPLOYERS MUTUAL INS CO
3.0	2.4	88.6	36.6	-1.4	3.9	58.1	44.9	103.0	104.1	6.7	0.0	HAWAIIAN INS & GUARANTY CO LTD
43.3	38.9	N/A	N/A	N/A	N/A	N/A	N/A	N/A	N/A	0.0	0.0	HAWKEYE-SECURITY INS CO
2.6	2.0	90.9	8.5	-2.8	2.6	17.7	41.9	59.6	172.3	5.2	0.0	HAY CREEK MUTUAL INS CO
12.8	11.5	N/A	N/A	N/A	N/A	N/A	N/A	N/A	999 +	0.0	0.0	HCC SPECIALTY INS CO
6.0	4.0	6.4	29.8	0.1	-2.2	107.0	-140.2	-33.2	116.2	27.1	4.0	HDI GLOBAL INS CO
1.0	0.8	145.5	326.6	-20.3	-53.2	62.7	35.4	98.1	99.2	-2.7	0.0	HEALTH CARE CASUALTY RRG INC
1.8	1.6	21.4	169.3	-7.0	-59.7	48.9	-27.1	21.8	62.4	-42.7	0.0	HEALTH CARE INDEMNITY INC
2.8	2.2	23.9	56.1	-0.9	-4.5	74.2	3.9	78.1	144.0	6.6	0.0	HEALTH CARE INDUSTRY LIAB RECIP
0.6	0.4	113.1	270.8	-11.7	-19.7	66.6	23.5	90.1	122.6	9.7	0.0	HEALTH CARE INS RECPL
1.2	0.8	99.6	156.6	15.1	-2.8	71.5	42.3	113.8	108.0	-33.8	0.0	HEALTH CARE MUT CAPTIVE INS CO
6.4	4.1	12.7	27.3	-7.7	-13.7	34.0	30.9	64.9	101.5	5.2	0.0	HEALTH PROVIDERS INS RECIPROCAL
0.7	0.6	50.9	297.4	-7.9	-32.2	42.3	22.8	65.1	81.3	-12.7	0.0	HEALTHCARE PROFESSIONAL INS CO
0.3	0.2	140.5	265.0	33.4	73.8	81.6	39.1	120.7	86.0	-33.0	0.0	HEALTHCARE PROVIDERS INS EXCH
3.8	3.1	36.7	66.7	-10.1	-7.9	46.1	45.4	91.5	73.7	263.5	0.0	HEALTHCARE UNDERWRITERS GRP
0.4	0.3	143.7	300.6	-34.8	-8.4	75.3	5.1	80.4	162.3	5.2	0.0	HEALTHCARE UNDERWRITING CO RRG
2.5	1.8	34.9	73.6	-2.5	3.4	68.9	34.1	103.0	115.4	7.1	0.0	HEARTLAND HEALTHCARE RECIPROCAL
4.5	3.9	105.0	4.5	-1.8	-4.6	41.6	32.8	74.4	138.9	10.6	0.0	HEARTLAND MUTUAL INS CO
1.2	0.8	264.4	378.5	10.5	16.8	88.3	10.7	99.0	118.1	4.5	0.0	HEREFORD INS CO
N/A	N/A	N/A	N/A	N/A	N/A	N/A	N/A	N/A	N/A	0.0	0.0	HERITAGE CASUALTY INS CO
5.4	4.7	148.6	3.2	1.2	0.4	84.0	19.7	103.7	115.4	23.5	0.0	HERITAGE INDEMNITY CO
1.1	0.7	181.0	38.7	-2.8	-0.4	44.7	36.4	81.1	153.6	18.1	0.0 ●	HERITAGE P&C INS CO
1.2	1.1	-431.0	N/A	-101.2	69.8	108.5	-15.2	93.3	-35.1	-119.2	0.0	HERMITAGE INS CO
1.8	1.7	N/A	N/A	N/A	N/A	N/A	N/A	N/A	N/A	0.0	56.6	HIGH POINT P&C INS CO
2.4	1.9	99.6	47.6	-1.4	-8.2	48.7	20.2	68.9	159.9	16.9	5.3	HIGH POINT PREFERRED INS CO
5.3	3.1	N/A	N/A	N/A	N/A	N/A	N/A	N/A	N/A	0.0	0.0	HIGH POINT SAFETY & INS CO
-0.0	-0.0	196.4	999 +	74.9	99.7	109.3	70.8	180.1	41.8	-86.8	0.0	HIGHLANDS INS CO
2.4	1.7	163.4	127.9	-2.1	3.5	76.6	21.9	98.5	109.1	-5.2	0.0	HIGHMARK CASUALTY INS CO
250.8	125.4	N/A	N/A	N/A	N/A	N/A	N/A	N/A	N/A	-100.0	0.0	HILLSTAR INS CO
3.0	2.1	53.2	18.8	-0.5	-1.8	67.0	40.4	107.4	90.3	-5.0	14.0	HINGHAM MUTUAL FIRE INS CO
1.0	0.7	82.3	68.7	0.7	-0.2	60.8	16.5	77.3	161.0	34.6	11.4	HISCOX INS CO
3.3	2.1	17.3	46.2	-11.8	-17.6	24.8	38.7	63.5	181.5	-19.9	0.0	HLTHCR PROVIDERS INS CO
3.5	3.1	N/A	N/A	N/A	N/A	N/A	N/A	N/A	64.8	0.0	0.0	HM CASUALTY INS CO
2.6	1.8	117.8	54.9	-13.7	-28.1	72.0	23.0	95.0	94.8	-15.0	0.9	HOCHHEIM PRAIRIE CASUALTY INS CO
0.8	0.7	122.6	19.0	1.7	6.1	85.4	25.1	110.5	71.2	-11.3	38.4	HOCHHEIM PRAIRIE FARM MUT INS ASN
4.7	3.3	101.7	53.2	-1.2	-1.7	70.7	29.7	100.4	96.0	-1.5	0.7 ●	HOLYOKE MUTUAL INS CO IN SALEM
6.9	6.2	27.7	7.8	-0.4	-1.5	63.0	34.6	97.6	98.7	-4.7	0.1	HOME & FARM INS CO
N/A	N/A	N/A	123.8	5.5	22.3	N/A	N/A	N/A	N/A	-100.0	0.0	HOME CONSTRUCTION INS CO RRG
0.6	0.6	69.5	41.1	-7.7	-4.7	81.5	1.5	83.0	102.9	26.7	0.0	HOME STATE COUNTY MUTUAL INS CO
0.4	0.4	0.3	N/A	N/A	N/A	999 +	999 +	999 +	0.2	0.0	0.0	HOME VALUE INS CO
6.3	4.5	82.9	59.4	0.5	-0.2	66.8	25.9	92.7	99.2	-18.5	0.0 ●	HOME-OWNERS INS CO
79.1	35.1	N/A	N/A	N/A	N/A	N/A	N/A	N/A	N/A	0.0	0.0	HOMELAND INS CO OF DE
2.3	2.3	N/A	N/A	N/A	N/A	N/A	N/A	N/A	N/A	0.0	48.2	HOMELAND INS CO OF NY
N/A	N/A	N/A	N/A	N/A	N/A	N/A	N/A	N/A	N/A	0.0	0.0	HOMEOWNERS CHOICE ASR CO INC
2.5	1.5	110.7	26.3	4.7	4.9	37.0	44.7	81.7	114.6	-23.0	0.0 ●	HOMEOWNERS CHOICE PROP & CAS INS
3.4	2.9	50.7	14.6	2.6	1.6	96.9	-52.3	44.6	883.5	36.2	0.0	HOMEOWNERS OF AMERICA INS CO
N/A	N/A	N/A	N/A	N/A	N/A	N/A	N/A	N/A	N/A	0.0	0.0	HOMESHIELD FIRE & CASUALTY INS CO
13.0	11.7	N/A	N/A	N/A	N/A	N/A	N/A	N/A	-887.3	100.0	0.0	HOMESITE INDEMNITY CO
11.5	10.3	N/A	N/A	N/A	N/A	N/A	N/A	N/A	232.7	100.0	0.0	HOMESITE INS CO

999 + Denotes number greater than 999.9%
999 - Denotes number less than -999.99%
● Bullets denote a more detailed analysis is available in Section II.

INSURANCE COMPANY NAME	DOM. STATE	RATING	TOTAL ASSETS ($MIL)	CAPITAL & SURPLUS ($MIL)	ANNUAL NET PREMIUM ($MIL)	NET INCOME ($MIL)	CAPITAL-IZATION INDEX (PTS)	RESERVE ADQ INDEX (PTS)	PROFIT-ABILITY INDEX (PTS)	LIQUIDITY INDEX (PTS)	STAB. INDEX (PTS)	STABILITY FACTORS
HOMESITE INS CO OF CA	CA	C	51.7	36.9	0.0	0.2	10.0	4.6	5.0	7.0	3.5	FRT
HOMESITE INS CO OF FL	IL	C	13.5	11.0	0.0	0.0	10.0	4.7	4.1	10.0	2.9	DFGR
HOMESITE INS CO OF GA	GA	C	19.0	11.7	0.0	0.1	10.0	4.7	5.4	10.0	3.0	DGRT
HOMESITE INS CO OF IL	IL	C	12.9	9.3	0.0	0.1	10.0	4.7	5.5	10.0	2.9	DGRT
HOMESITE INS CO OF NY	NY	C	30.8	16.8	0.0	0.4	10.0	4.7	5.2	7.6	3.3	DFGR
HOMESITE INS CO OF THE MIDWEST	ND	C	426.6	101.4	0.0	0.7	10.0	7.1	5.3	7.0	3.7	RT
HOMESITE LLOYDS OF TEXAS	TX	C-	31.7	15.8	0.0	0.1	10.0	4.7	5.7	10.0	3.2	DFGR
HOMESTEAD INS CO	PA	U	4.5	3.2	0.7	0.0	N/A	6.4	2.0	9.9	3.1	DGRT
▲HOMESTEAD MUTUAL INS CO	WI	C-	8.9	7.0	2.1	0.3	7.6	3.6	6.4	7.0	2.1	DGT
HOOSIER INS CO	IN	C-	8.9	7.4	25.6	0.5	6.7	3.8	2.1	6.7	3.2	DFRT
HORACE MANN INS CO	IL	B	456.9	184.3	247.2	2.7	7.5	8.6	6.8	5.2	4.4	AT
HORACE MANN LLOYDS	TX	B-	5.8	2.9	0.0	0.0	10.0	N/A	7.1	10.0	3.6	DFGT
HORACE MANN P&C INS CO	IL	B	284.5	118.8	159.2	2.1	7.4	8.6	7.5	5.3	4.4	ART
HORIZON MIDWEST CASUALTY CO	KS	U	2.6	2.6	0.0	0.0	N/A	N/A	4.9	7.0	4.0	GT
HOSPITALITY INS CO	MA	C	12.2	10.6	0.0	0.0	10.0	N/A	7.0	7.0	2.9	DGT
HOSPITALITY MUT CAPT INS CO	GA	F (5)	0.0	0.0	2.5	0.0	0.0	5.8	2.5	0.0	0.0	CDFG
HOSPITALITY MUTUAL INS CO	MA	B-	60.8	28.7	14.6	-0.4	4.4	9.2	4.6	7.8	3.5	CDT
HOSPITALS INS CO	NY	C-	1,559.0	449.0	216.1	2.9	4.6	5.1	6.7	6.9	2.3	RT
HOUSING & REDEVELOPMENT INS EXCH	PA	C	47.6	15.0	24.1	-0.7	6.3	7.0	5.3	7.1	2.6	DRT
HOUSING AUTHORITY PROP A MUTUAL CO	VT	B	169.0	118.7	41.3	1.0	10.0	8.9	6.9	6.9	4.2	RT
HOUSING AUTHORITY RISK RET GROUP	VT	B-	307.2	189.8	30.9	-0.7	10.0	9.4	5.6	7.4	4.1	RT
HOUSING ENTERPRISE INS CO	VT	C+	73.2	32.1	21.7	-0.4	5.1	6.2	3.9	6.8	3.7	CT
HOUSING SPECIALTY INS CO	VT	C	17.3	15.3	1.1	-0.2	10.0	N/A	3.7	9.1	3.2	DGT
HOUSTON CASUALTY CO	TX	B-	3,769.6	2,058.8	808.3	17.2	8.0	7.6	7.3	8.1	4.6	GRT
HOUSTON GENERAL INS EXCH	TX	U	5.2	5.1	0.0	0.1	N/A	4.6	1.9	10.0	3.1	GRT
HOUSTON SPECIALTY INS CO	TX	B-	482.7	277.0	122.1	3.5	6.3	5.7	4.7	6.9	4.2	T
HOW INS CO A RRG	VA	U (5)	0.4	0.4	0.0	0.0	N/A	1.1	1.9	10.0	0.0	CT
HPIC RRG	SC	U	1.3	0.9	0.0	-0.1	N/A	N/A	2.5	7.0	3.0	GT
HSB SPECIALTY INS CO	CT	B	53.5	50.1	0.0	0.1	10.0	N/A	3.9	10.0	4.3	DFT
HUDSON EXCESS INS CO	DE	B	66.0	57.1	0.0	1.4	10.0	N/A	7.7	7.4	4.2	T
HUDSON INS CO	DE	C-	1,138.5	477.9	149.4	20.9	8.3	6.2	6.9	5.5	3.3	RT
HUDSON SPECIALTY INS CO	NY	D+	360.9	207.9	51.0	8.4	9.7	7.7	8.9	6.9	2.6	RT
HUTTERIAN BRETHREN MUTUAL INS CORP	IL	D	3.2	2.8	0.3	0.1	10.0	3.7	3.5	9.3	1.6	DFGT
HYUNDAI MARINE & FIRE INS CO LTD	CA	B-	97.6	53.1	24.7	1.4	10.0	8.8	4.2	8.6	3.9	GRT
ICI MUTUAL INS CO A RRG	VT	B	353.4	262.1	31.0	6.7	10.0	8.9	7.9	8.0	4.3	T
ID COUNTIES RISK MGMT PROGRAM UNDW	ID	C-	64.8	32.8	23.7	4.0	7.6	9.4	8.8	6.8	3.2	RT
IDS PROPERTY CASUALTY INS CO	WI	B-	1,765.1	736.4	1,068.2	-22.9	8.4	3.3	3.6	4.3	4.8	LRT
IFA INS CO	NJ	E	13.2	0.4	14.6	-2.0	0.0	0.6	0.2	0.0	0.0	CDFG
IL STATE BAR ASSOC MUTUAL INS CO	IL	C+	74.2	35.4	14.8	1.4	9.0	9.4	6.9	8.0	3.3	DRT
ILLINOIS CASUALTY CO	IL	C+	99.4	28.0	41.6	0.7	7.2	9.4	6.2	6.5	3.2	RT
ILLINOIS EMCASCO INS CO	IA	C+	356.7	104.5	151.5	3.8	7.9	8.5	6.6	6.6	4.5	T
ILLINOIS FARMERS INS CO	IL	C+	253.3	86.3	112.0	-2.4	7.3	6.0	3.8	6.4	4.4	RT
ILLINOIS INS CO	IA	C	46.5	30.9	19.1	2.1	7.8	8.8	9.3	8.6	3.7	DT
ILLINOIS NATIONAL INS CO	IL	C+	42.0	38.3	0.0	0.3	10.0	N/A	2.8	7.0	3.8	T
ILLINOIS UNION INS CO	IL	C	408.6	162.7	0.0	1.4	10.0	N/A	6.7	7.0	4.1	RT
IMPERIAL F&C INS CO	LA	C	100.2	48.5	0.0	0.4	10.0	4.5	4.5	7.0	3.9	FRT
IMPERIUM INS CO	TX	C-	380.7	181.7	116.7	2.2	4.6	1.6	3.8	6.5	2.9	RT
IMT INS CO	IA	B	344.8	148.4	199.8	12.7	9.2	6.1	7.4	6.2	4.1	RT
INDEMNITY CO OF CA	CA	C	21.2	15.5	2.7	-0.2	9.0	8.3	2.9	8.2	2.4	DGRT
INDEMNITY INS CO OF NORTH AMERICA	PA	C	462.8	124.5	95.2	3.8	8.3	7.8	8.4	7.6	3.9	RT
INDEMNITY NATIONAL INS CO	MS	C	23.1	12.3	1.8	0.6	8.3	9.3	5.7	9.5	2.7	DGRT
INDEPENDENCE AMERICAN INS CO	DE	C+	119.6	65.0	149.8	1.2	7.6	7.4	8.4	2.4	3.9	LRT

See Page 27 for explanation of footnotes and
Page 28 for explanation of stability factors.
Arrows denote recent upgrades ▲ or downgrades ▼   (see Section VII for explanations)

78

www.weissratings.com

RISK ADJ. RATIO #1	CAPITAL RATIO #2	PREMIUM TO SURPLUS (%)	RESV. TO SURPLUS (%)	RESV. DEVELOP. 1 YEAR (%)	2 YEAR (%)	LOSS RATIO (%)	EXP. RATIO (%)	COMB RATIO (%)	CASH FROM UNDER- WRITING (%)	NET PREMIUM GROWTH (%)	INVEST. IN AFFIL (%)	INSURANCE COMPANY NAME
12.5	11.3	N/A	N/A	N/A	N/A	N/A	N/A	N/A	-113.1	100.0	0.0	HOMESITE INS CO OF CA
13.0	11.7	N/A	N/A	N/A	N/A	N/A	N/A	N/A	999 +	100.0	0.0	HOMESITE INS CO OF FL
6.1	5.5	N/A	N/A	N/A	N/A	N/A	N/A	N/A	89.3	100.0	0.0	HOMESITE INS CO OF GA
8.1	7.3	N/A	N/A	N/A	N/A	N/A	N/A	N/A	-38.3	100.0	0.0	HOMESITE INS CO OF IL
5.9	5.3	N/A	N/A	N/A	N/A	N/A	N/A	N/A	416.2	100.0	0.0	HOMESITE INS CO OF NY
10.2	9.2	N/A	N/A	N/A	-60.9	N/A	N/A	N/A	119.4	100.0	0.0	HOMESITE INS CO OF THE MIDWEST
5.1	4.6	N/A	N/A	N/A	N/A	N/A	N/A	N/A	806.3	100.0	0.0	HOMESITE LLOYDS OF TEXAS
N/A	N/A	20.8	43.0	6.1	3.4	66.6	38.5	105.1	105.3	0.0	0.0	HOMESTEAD INS CO
2.6	1.6	33.3	2.7	0.7	N/A	34.0	41.5	75.5	139.9	0.0	0.3	HOMESTEAD MUTUAL INS CO
2.1	1.5	134.6	144.4	1.5	2.8	63.9	35.8	99.7	89.9	-17.6	0.0	HOOSIER INS CO
3.0	1.9	132.6	55.3	-2.3	-6.9	70.9	25.7	96.6	99.7	3.7	0.0 ●	HORACE MANN INS CO
2.9	2.6	N/A	N/A	N/A	N/A	N/A	N/A	N/A	-44.7	0.0	0.0	HORACE MANN LLOYDS
2.7	1.7	129.6	54.0	-2.3	-6.8	70.9	25.8	96.7	97.9	3.7	0.0	HORACE MANN P&C INS CO
N/A	N/A	N/A	N/A	N/A	N/A	N/A	N/A	N/A	N/A	0.0	0.0	HORIZON MIDWEST CASUALTY CO
17.4	9.6	N/A	N/A	N/A	N/A	N/A	N/A	N/A	-996.9	0.0	0.0	HOSPITALITY INS CO
0.1	0.1	408.3	213.6	77.4	0.4	85.4	54.4	139.8	89.5	84.7	0.0	HOSPITALITY MUT CAPT INS CO
1.0	0.7	51.8	77.0	-4.6	-3.6	50.0	39.6	89.6	135.5	9.2	19.5	HOSPITALITY MUTUAL INS CO
0.9	0.8	48.2	215.3	-2.8	-63.7	88.7	10.2	98.9	149.6	-5.7	0.0 ●	HOSPITALS INS CO
1.3	1.0	155.4	136.1	2.5	3.2	67.0	27.9	94.9	125.4	8.4	0.0	HOUSING & REDEVELOPMENT INS EXCH
3.7	3.3	34.6	18.9	-4.3	-4.3	51.6	37.8	89.4	96.1	7.7	17.2	HOUSING AUTHORITY PROP A MUTUAL
3.7	2.9	16.1	42.8	-3.8	-11.7	77.7	32.2	109.9	101.3	3.9	12.1 ●	HOUSING AUTHORITY RISK RET GROUP
0.9	0.5	66.8	74.8	-4.3	1.5	64.1	35.5	99.6	111.3	25.0	0.0	HOUSING ENTERPRISE INS CO
10.6	7.1	7.1	2.2	N/A	N/A	62.0	69.3	131.3	106.3	0.0	0.0	HOUSING SPECIALTY INS CO
1.9	1.7	41.7	35.1	-0.8	-1.2	66.4	26.2	92.6	81.1	140.1	39.5 ●	HOUSTON CASUALTY CO
N/A	N/A	N/A	N/A	N/A	N/A	539.1	999 +	999 +	0.4	0.0	0.0	HOUSTON GENERAL INS EXCH
1.0	0.9	45.4	24.2	1.7	5.2	63.5	35.1	98.6	135.6	64.2	44.5 ●	HOUSTON SPECIALTY INS CO
N/A	N/A	N/A	N/A	N/A	26.4	N/A	N/A	N/A	N/A	0.0	0.0	HOW INS CO A RRG
N/A	N/A	N/A	N/A	N/A	N/A	N/A	N/A	N/A	N/A	0.0	0.0	HPIC RRG
46.2	41.6	N/A	N/A	N/A	N/A	N/A	N/A	N/A	4.6	0.0	0.0	HSB SPECIALTY INS CO
25.5	23.0	N/A	0.8	N/A	N/A	N/A	N/A	N/A	-137.8	0.0	0.0	HUDSON EXCESS INS CO
2.1	1.9	32.6	36.0	-1.1	-3.4	76.0	30.5	106.5	87.6	-10.3	37.4 ●	HUDSON INS CO
3.3	2.9	25.3	43.6	-3.1	-3.3	46.8	25.1	71.9	88.8	-19.3	19.2 ●	HUDSON SPECIALTY INS CO
7.8	5.3	14.6	1.1	-7.4	-2.4	37.6	74.8	112.4	80.3	124.6	0.0	HUTTERIAN BRETHREN MUTUAL INS
5.5	3.5	47.9	32.8	-0.3	-5.3	57.3	38.5	95.8	126.7	22.8	0.0	HYUNDAI MARINE & FIRE INS CO LTD
11.4	7.0	12.4	23.7	-2.6	-7.4	59.5	37.0	96.5	150.4	3.0	-0.1 ●	ICI MUTUAL INS CO A RRG
1.8	1.5	82.9	95.2	3.5	-9.3	71.4	27.4	98.8	105.6	1.5	0.0	ID COUNTIES RISK MGMT PROGRAM
2.5	2.0	156.3	83.2	11.0	17.7	97.7	15.8	113.5	97.1	6.7	3.2 ●	IDS PROPERTY CASUALTY INS CO
-0.0	-0.0	500.5	814.8	19.4	63.4	83.8	48.1	131.9	51.8	-55.6	0.0	IFA INS CO
3.8	2.5	43.9	81.8	-13.8	-16.6	55.7	29.3	85.0	118.9	4.9	0.0	IL STATE BAR ASSOC MUTUAL INS CO
1.5	1.1	155.0	156.0	-7.6	-14.4	59.2	35.3	94.5	114.0	1.4	0.0	ILLINOIS CASUALTY CO
2.4	1.6	151.7	155.3	-4.1	-3.6	65.5	31.4	96.9	112.6	4.8	0.0	ILLINOIS EMCASCO INS CO
1.2	1.1	123.9	74.2	1.7	2.1	68.8	33.8	102.6	107.8	6.2	38.1	ILLINOIS FARMERS INS CO
2.2	1.8	66.4	46.3	-4.7	-4.3	24.6	28.1	52.7	215.0	18.6	0.0	ILLINOIS INS CO
20.4	16.4	N/A	N/A	N/A	N/A	N/A	N/A	N/A	N/A	0.0	6.2	ILLINOIS NATIONAL INS CO
15.7	9.5	N/A	19.1	N/A	N/A	N/A	N/A	N/A	21.8	0.0	0.0	ILLINOIS UNION INS CO
7.1	6.4	N/A	N/A	N/A	-10.7	N/A	N/A	N/A	458.1	-100.0	0.0	IMPERIAL F&C INS CO
1.1	0.8	65.6	93.2	9.6	29.7	74.0	32.4	106.4	89.2	-19.0	32.7	IMPERIUM INS CO
3.9	2.5	144.7	41.9	1.5	1.0	61.0	31.5	92.5	112.8	11.0	0.4	IMT INS CO
1.8	1.6	17.7	2.7	-0.2	-6.8	19.9	84.3	104.2	103.5	181.2	3.1	INDEMNITY CO OF CA
2.7	1.8	78.8	142.0	-1.4	-0.3	72.8	20.1	92.9	118.2	6.3	0.0	INDEMNITY INS CO OF NORTH AMERICA
3.3	1.9	15.2	30.8	-10.2	-16.5	-7.2	40.4	33.2	238.7	-3.3	0.0	INDEMNITY NATIONAL INS CO
3.0	1.7	236.3	71.6	0.7	-0.4	66.8	31.6	98.4	110.4	12.1	0.0	INDEPENDENCE AMERICAN INS CO

999 + Denotes number greater than 999.9%
999 - Denotes number less than -999.99%

● Bullets denote a more detailed analysis is available in Section II.

INSURANCE COMPANY NAME	DOM. STATE	RATING	TOTAL ASSETS ($MIL)	CAPITAL & SURPLUS ($MIL)	ANNUAL NET PREMIUM ($MIL)	NET INCOME ($MIL)	CAPITAL-IZATION INDEX (PTS)	RESERVE ADQ INDEX (PTS)	PROFIT-ABILITY INDEX (PTS)	LIQUIDITY INDEX (PTS)	STAB. INDEX (PTS)	STABILITY FACTORS
INDEPENDENCE CASUALTY INS CO	MA	D	4.6	4.6	0.0	0.1	10.0	N/A	7.8	7.0	2.3	DGRT
INDEPENDENT MUTUAL FIRE INS CO	IL	C+	44.6	38.5	3.6	0.1	7.7	4.6	6.7	7.2	3.4	DT
INDIAN HARBOR INS CO	DE	C-	161.3	46.4	26.5	0.0	8.4	7.6	3.5	6.2	3.0	AFRT
INDIANA FARMERS MUTUAL INS CO	IN	B	408.5	186.5	189.5	4.7	8.1	7.0	5.3	5.8	4.6	RT
INDIANA HEALTHCARE RECIPROCAL RRG	VT	C-	36.1	18.8	6.2	1.3	7.7	7.0	6.3	7.1	2.7	DGT
INDIANA INS CO	IN	C	69.8	65.1	0.0	0.0	10.0	3.9	3.1	10.0	4.1	RT
INDIANA LUMBERMENS MUTUAL INS CO	IN	C	57.4	15.4	15.6	0.2	6.9	7.0	1.7	6.9	3.0	DFRT
INDIANA OLD NATIONAL INS CO	VT	C	2,150.0	2,147.8	1.3	19.5	10.0	N/A	7.5	10.0	3.2	RT
INFINITY ASSURANCE INS CO	OH	B-	7.1	5.6	1.4	0.0	10.0	5.1	5.1	8.5	3.5	ADGT
INFINITY AUTO INS CO	OH	C	9.7	7.6	1.4	0.1	10.0	5.1	3.9	6.9	2.9	ADGT
INFINITY CASUALTY INS CO	OH	B-	7.5	6.1	1.4	0.0	10.0	5.1	4.4	6.9	3.5	ADGT
INFINITY COUNTY MUTUAL INS CO	TX	C	39.3	5.1	0.0	0.0	7.1	N/A	5.4	10.0	2.9	DFGT
INFINITY INDEMNITY INS CO	IN	C	6.0	4.6	1.4	0.0	10.0	5.1	3.3	7.0	2.9	ADGT
INFINITY INS CO	IN	B	2,018.9	652.9	1,360.9	24.6	7.9	6.5	6.1	4.4	4.5	ALRT
INFINITY PREFERRED INS CO	OH	C	4.9	3.5	1.4	0.0	10.0	6.1	3.8	7.6	2.9	ADGT
INFINITY SAFEGUARD INS CO	OH	C+	5.1	3.7	1.4	0.0	10.0	5.2	3.6	7.4	3.3	ADGT
INFINITY SECURITY INS CO	IN	C	6.0	4.6	1.4	0.0	10.0	5.2	3.7	7.0	2.9	AGT
INFINITY SELECT INS CO	IN	B-	6.7	5.3	1.4	0.0	10.0	5.1	4.9	8.0	3.5	ADGT
INFINITY STANDARD INS CO	IN	C	7.0	5.6	1.4	0.0	10.0	5.1	5.3	7.5	2.9	ADFG
INLAND INS CO	NE	C	250.8	191.3	0.5	2.8	8.2	4.6	6.7	10.0	2.6	DGRT
INLAND MUTUAL INS CO	WV	C-	6.7	6.3	0.4	0.1	9.9	7.9	6.3	8.9	2.1	DFGR
INNOVATIVE PHYSICIAN SOLUTIONS RRG	VT	E	6.2	1.3	1.5	-0.3	0.1	1.9	1.3	8.4	0.0	CDGT
INS CO OF GREATER NY	NY	C+	119.7	60.6	27.2	1.0	10.0	6.2	5.3	6.9	3.9	T
INS CO OF ILLINOIS	IL	B	20.9	20.7	0.0	0.1	10.0	N/A	3.3	7.0	4.1	ADGT
INS CO OF NORTH AMERICA	PA	C	898.7	242.2	237.9	8.5	7.6	7.9	7.7	6.9	3.7	RT
INS CO OF THE AMERICAS	FL	U	7.4	4.5	-1.0	0.0	N/A	10.0	1.2	7.1	2.4	FGRT
INS CO OF THE SOUTH	GA	D+	36.6	12.6	28.4	1.2	2.1	6.6	8.3	6.3	2.4	CDGT
INS CO OF THE STATE OF PA	PA	C	222.7	85.9	0.0	3.5	10.0	4.3	1.9	7.0	3.9	AT
INS CO OF THE WEST	CA	C	2,066.2	818.2	744.1	51.3	7.1	4.7	8.3	6.4	3.7	RT
INS PLACEMENT FACILITY OF PA	PA	E- (2)	8.8	-4.1	8.0	-1.3	0.0	7.0	0.0	7.3	0.0	CDFT
▼INSUREMAX INS CO	IN	E	5.0	1.3	7.0	-0.9	2.7	4.0	0.4	0.7	0.0	CDFG
INSURORS INDEMNITY CO	TX	D+	30.2	13.6	12.2	-1.0	7.9	9.3	6.2	7.1	2.0	DGT
INSURORS INDEMNITY LLOYDS	TX	C-	4.9	2.6	0.0	0.0	10.0	N/A	4.3	10.0	2.3	DGRT
INTEGON CASUALTY INS CO	NC	C	40.0	6.2	0.0	0.1	7.2	3.6	2.7	10.0	2.7	DFRT
INTEGON GENERAL INS CORP	NC	C	37.0	6.3	0.0	0.1	7.7	3.5	1.9	6.7	2.7	DFGR
INTEGON INDEMNITY CORP	NC	C	101.9	39.3	0.0	0.4	8.9	3.5	5.2	9.9	3.7	FGRT
INTEGON NATIONAL INS CO	NC	C	2,215.7	389.6	1,155.3	11.9	5.8	3.7	3.1	4.3	3.9	GLRT
INTEGON PREFERRED INS CO	NC	C	70.2	6.7	0.0	0.2	6.1	3.6	3.4	6.7	2.7	DFRT
INTEGRA INS INC	MN	D	1.9	1.9	2.8	0.0	4.7	N/A	7.4	6.6	1.7	DGT
INTEGRAND ASR CO	PR	C	118.0	62.7	38.9	2.2	9.6	5.9	2.6	7.3	3.5	FRT
INTEGRITY MUTUAL INS CO	WI	B-	94.5	46.6	40.3	1.6	7.9	6.2	8.1	6.4	3.8	T
INTEGRITY P&C INS CO	WI	D	22.9	12.9	8.6	0.8	9.7	6.2	8.7	6.5	1.9	DGT
INTERBORO INS CO	NY	D	78.4	38.0	52.5	8.0	7.6	9.3	5.9	6.5	2.3	RT
INTERINS EXCHANGE	CA	B+	9,074.7	5,674.9	3,017.0	-13.9	10.0	7.4	7.9	6.6	5.1	T
INTERNATIONAL FIDELITY INS CO	NJ	C+	205.8	85.5	101.4	1.2	7.4	8.8	3.4	6.8	3.0	RT
INTERSTATE BANKERS CASUALTY CO	IL	F (5)	0.0	0.0	11.3	0.0	0.6	3.2	0.7	2.2	0.0	CDFL
INTERSTATE FIRE & CAS CO	IL	C	109.2	68.0	0.0	0.9	10.0	3.5	4.3	7.0	4.2	FRT
INTREPID INS CO	MI	U	35.0	30.3	0.0	0.8	N/A	4.6	5.5	7.0	5.2	GT
IOWA AMERICAN INS CO	IA	B	25.3	9.7	7.2	0.1	9.3	7.9	6.7	6.9	4.7	DGT
IOWA MUTUAL INS CO	IA	B	99.7	35.3	21.5	0.5	7.8	7.8	5.4	6.8	4.1	T
IQS INS RRG INC	VT	D (1)	1.7	1.4	0.4	0.0	9.7	3.3	8.7	9.0	1.2	DFGT
IRONSHORE INDEMNITY INC	MN	B-	429.5	166.2	51.6	4.5	7.8	5.4	4.8	6.9	3.7	RT

See Page 27 for explanation of footnotes and
Page 28 for explanation of stability factors.
Arrows denote recent upgrades ▲ or downgrades ▼   (see Section VII for explanations)

80

www.weissratings.com

RISK ADJ. RATIO #1	CAPITAL RATIO #2	PREMIUM TO SURPLUS (%)	RESV. TO SURPLUS (%)	RESV. DEVELOP. 1 YEAR (%)	RESV. DEVELOP. 2 YEAR (%)	LOSS RATIO (%)	EXP. RATIO (%)	COMB RATIO (%)	CASH FROM UNDER-WRITING (%)	NET PREMIUM GROWTH (%)	INVEST. IN AFFIL (%)	INSURANCE COMPANY NAME
89.4	44.7	N/A	N/A	N/A	N/A	N/A	N/A	N/A	N/A	0.0	0.0	INDEPENDENCE CASUALTY INS CO
2.3	1.4	9.7	0.7	N/A	N/A	30.7	95.1	125.8	80.8	3.6	0.0	INDEPENDENT MUTUAL FIRE INS CO
2.9	1.8	58.6	142.7	1.2	-2.6	71.2	36.0	107.2	94.2	4.8	0.0	INDIAN HARBOR INS CO
3.0	1.8	105.3	50.0	-10.2	-14.7	59.1	30.7	89.8	115.4	5.3	0.0	INDIANA FARMERS MUTUAL INS CO
2.2	1.5	36.8	81.2	-9.4	-0.9	61.7	19.1	80.8	131.8	12.4	0.0	INDIANA HEALTHCARE RECIPROCAL
6.5	6.3	N/A	N/A	N/A	N/A	N/A	N/A	N/A	N/A	0.0	19.8	INDIANA INS CO
1.7	1.3	103.0	104.2	-3.1	5.2	68.3	32.7	101.0	81.9	10.6	26.1	INDIANA LUMBERMENS MUTUAL INS CO
59.2	22.2	0.1	N/A	N/A	N/A	4.6	41.6	46.2	221.4	-6.8	0.0 •	INDIANA OLD NATIONAL INS CO
10.0	9.0	24.5	11.7	-0.5	-0.5	77.1	18.4	95.5	101.2	1.9	0.0	INFINITY ASSURANCE INS CO
10.5	9.4	18.1	8.6	-0.3	-0.4	77.1	18.4	95.5	101.7	1.9	0.0	INFINITY AUTO INS CO
10.7	9.7	22.7	10.8	-0.4	-0.5	77.1	18.4	95.5	101.0	1.9	0.0	INFINITY CASUALTY INS CO
1.0	0.9	N/A	N/A	N/A	N/A	N/A	N/A	N/A	N/A	0.0	0.0	INFINITY COUNTY MUTUAL INS CO
8.1	7.3	30.0	14.3	-0.5	-0.5	77.1	18.4	95.5	101.2	1.9	0.0	INFINITY INDEMNITY INS CO
1.8	1.5	208.5	99.4	-3.9	-4.4	77.1	18.4	95.5	98.7	2.0	3.5 •	INFINITY INS CO
6.2	5.5	39.7	18.9	-0.7	-0.8	77.1	18.4	95.5	101.0	1.9	0.0	INFINITY PREFERRED INS CO
6.6	5.9	37.3	17.8	-0.7	-0.7	77.1	18.4	95.5	100.9	1.9	0.0	INFINITY SAFEGUARD INS CO
8.2	7.4	29.9	14.3	-0.6	-0.6	77.1	18.4	95.5	101.0	1.9	0.0	INFINITY SECURITY INS CO
9.3	8.4	26.0	12.4	-0.5	-0.6	77.1	18.4	95.5	101.4	1.9	0.0	INFINITY SELECT INS CO
3.3	3.2	24.8	11.8	-0.5	-0.5	77.1	18.4	95.5	81.1	1.9	26.6	INFINITY STANDARD INS CO
3.1	1.8	0.3	1.4	N/A	N/A	-1.8	122.5	120.7	66.5	-19.5	0.0	INLAND INS CO
5.4	3.2	7.0	3.2	-2.1	-5.1	54.5	53.2	107.7	84.1	-8.2	0.0	INLAND MUTUAL INS CO
0.1	0.1	127.8	218.3	13.0	25.6	80.5	40.9	121.4	99.1	5.3	0.0	INNOVATIVE PHYSICIAN SOLUTIONS
3.9	3.2	45.9	67.1	0.6	0.1	68.7	30.9	99.6	110.4	7.4	0.0	INS CO OF GREATER NY
186.1	93.0	N/A	N/A	N/A	N/A	N/A	N/A	N/A	N/A	0.0	0.0	INS CO OF ILLINOIS
2.0	1.3	101.9	183.5	-1.8	-0.5	72.8	27.7	100.5	109.4	6.3	0.0 •	INS CO OF NORTH AMERICA
N/A	N/A	-21.6	26.6	-12.9	-19.9	15.7	-50.6	-34.9	N/A	0.0	0.0	INS CO OF THE AMERICAS
0.5	0.4	251.7	24.1	-2.2	-6.0	37.9	40.5	78.4	160.7	237.4	0.0	INS CO OF THE SOUTH
6.4	5.8	N/A	N/A	N/A	N/A	N/A	N/A	N/A	N/A	100.0	0.0	INS CO OF THE STATE OF PA
1.5	1.0	98.8	123.5	-3.5	-1.1	63.0	22.9	85.9	159.1	19.7	9.6 •	INS CO OF THE WEST
-0.6	-0.5	-194.6	-30.1	14.9	-15.0	58.3	58.4	116.7	84.8	-0.6	0.0	INS PLACEMENT FACILITY OF PA
0.3	0.3	329.5	179.2	8.2	13.4	96.8	37.8	134.6	64.5	1.6	0.0	INSUREMAX INS CO
1.7	1.2	85.6	34.1	-9.8	-13.9	28.3	51.4	79.7	136.6	30.8	10.2	INSURORS INDEMNITY CO
3.2	2.9	N/A	N/A	N/A	N/A	N/A	N/A	N/A	87.8	0.0	0.0	INSURORS INDEMNITY LLOYDS
1.2	1.1	N/A	N/A	N/A	N/A	N/A	N/A	N/A	-248.3	0.0	0.0	INTEGON CASUALTY INS CO
1.4	1.2	N/A	N/A	N/A	N/A	N/A	N/A	N/A	39.2	0.0	0.0	INTEGON GENERAL INS CORP
2.3	2.0	N/A	N/A	N/A	N/A	N/A	N/A	N/A	-157.4	0.0	32.4	INTEGON INDEMNITY CORP
0.8	0.6	257.7	91.5	2.8	9.7	75.2	18.6	93.8	128.7	24.4	5.5 •	INTEGON NATIONAL INS CO
0.9	0.8	N/A	N/A	N/A	N/A	N/A	N/A	N/A	76.5	0.0	0.0	INTEGON PREFERRED INS CO
0.6	0.5	132.3	N/A	N/A	N/A	N/A	93.3	93.3	107.0	8.1	0.0	INTEGRA INS INC
6.3	4.0	65.1	36.1	-0.1	3.5	65.0	34.9	99.9	87.2	9.9	0.1	INTEGRAND ASR CO
2.0	1.6	88.4	48.8	1.5	1.7	69.1	29.8	98.9	105.0	0.5	25.1	INTEGRITY MUTUAL INS CO
4.6	2.9	70.4	38.8	1.3	1.5	69.1	18.3	87.4	105.8	0.5	0.0	INTEGRITY P&C INS CO
2.1	1.8	145.5	61.5	-4.4	-9.5	55.6	38.9	94.5	109.6	6.6	0.0	INTERBORO INS CO
4.9	3.0	53.6	18.4	-0.5	-1.0	71.9	21.8	93.7	107.3	5.3	0.8 •	INTERINS EXCHANGE
1.5	1.3	120.8	3.2	-9.4	-7.6	19.3	78.1	97.4	107.5	-5.8	14.5	INTERNATIONAL FIDELITY INS CO
0.2	0.1	419.9	488.2	70.8	45.7	92.2	36.2	128.4	90.7	-16.0	0.0	INTERSTATE BANKERS CASUALTY CO
11.8	10.6	N/A	N/A	N/A	N/A	N/A	N/A	N/A	14.2	0.0	0.0	INTERSTATE FIRE & CAS CO
N/A	N/A	N/A	N/A	N/A	N/A	N/A	N/A	N/A	N/A	0.0	0.0	INTREPID INS CO
3.2	2.5	75.4	54.7	-2.2	-4.0	64.4	36.7	101.1	100.2	-3.1	0.0	IOWA AMERICAN INS CO
2.2	1.6	62.0	45.0	-1.8	-3.4	64.4	36.7	101.1	94.0	4.1	16.9	IOWA MUTUAL INS CO
3.0	2.4	31.9	17.6	8.3	9.8	31.6	37.9	69.5	81.9	0.6	0.0	IQS INS RRG INC
2.6	1.7	33.5	55.5	2.3	7.3	77.5	36.9	114.4	119.0	-16.6	0.0	IRONSHORE INDEMNITY INC

999 + Denotes number greater than 999.9%
999 - Denotes number less than -999.99%
• Bullets denote a more detailed analysis is available in Section II.

INSURANCE COMPANY NAME	DOM. STATE	RATING	TOTAL ASSETS ($MIL)	CAPITAL & SURPLUS ($MIL)	ANNUAL NET PREMIUM ($MIL)	NET INCOME ($MIL)	CAPITAL-IZATION INDEX (PTS)	RESERVE ADQ INDEX (PTS)	PROFIT-ABILITY INDEX (PTS)	LIQUIDITY INDEX (PTS)	STAB. INDEX (PTS)	STABILITY FACTORS
IRONSHORE RRG (DC) INC	DC	D-	3.2	0.8	0.2	-0.1	4.4	4.7	1.7	8.1	0.5	DGT
IRONSHORE SPECIALTY INS CO	AZ	C	1,111.8	340.7	112.0	-1.2	7.7	6.0	7.9	6.9	3.7	RT
ISLAND HOME INS CO	GU	D-	26.7	14.7	27.9	1.9	7.9	2.2	7.7	2.7	1.3	DGLT
ISLAND INS CO LTD	HI	B-	340.6	134.2	97.0	5.3	8.9	9.3	7.6	7.0	3.8	RT
ISLAND PREMIER INS CO LTD	HI	C	10.3	5.6	0.0	0.1	10.0	N/A	6.8	10.0	2.7	DFGT
ISMIE INDEMNITY CO	IL	U	52.7	52.0	0.0	0.1	N/A	N/A	6.8	7.0	5.4	T
ISMIE MUTUAL INS CO	IL	B-	1,482.7	666.8	168.4	-5.0	10.0	9.6	6.3	7.6	4.5	FRT
IU HEALTH RRG INC	SC	D	14.7	2.7	0.0	0.0	10.0	N/A	1.9	7.0	1.9	DFGR
JAMES RIVER CASUALTY CO	VA	C+	32.2	16.7	4.5	0.1	8.8	5.9	6.9	7.0	3.3	DFGT
JAMES RIVER INS CO	OH	C	556.3	131.8	67.2	5.7	7.6	9.3	2.7	6.9	4.0	RT
JEFFERSON INS CO	NY	C	85.7	56.3	86.4	4.1	7.2	7.4	8.8	6.1	3.5	RT
JEWELERS MUTUAL INS CO	WI	B	380.0	235.9	165.9	5.5	10.0	6.4	8.6	6.7	4.4	T
JM WOODWORTH RRG INC	NV	E+	8.1	0.7	0.7	-1.4	0.1	0.5	0.0	6.1	0.0	CFGR
JUNIATA MUTUAL INS CO	PA	D+	8.5	5.2	4.8	0.3	8.2	7.7	5.5	6.9	2.1	DFGR
KAMMCO CASUALTY CO	KS	U	5.0	5.0	0.0	0.0	N/A	N/A	3.9	7.0	4.5	FGT
KANSAS MEDICAL MUTUAL INS CO	KS	B	153.3	108.7	19.9	-0.9	10.0	9.3	4.1	7.0	4.1	DRT
KANSAS MUTUAL INS CO	KS	C- (2)	13.5	7.7	6.8	0.5	9.5	6.8	7.2	6.8	2.2	DT
KEMPER FINANCIAL INDEMNITY CO	IL	U	20.3	20.3	0.0	0.2	N/A	N/A	7.4	7.0	5.4	GRT
KEMPER INDEPENDENCE INS CO	IL	B	91.1	9.2	0.0	0.2	6.7	3.6	5.4	7.0	4.1	DRT
KENSINGTON INS CO	NY	D	13.3	3.4	6.1	0.0	1.5	4.5	1.5	7.2	1.5	CDFG
KENTUCKIANA MEDICAL RRG & INS CO INC	KY	E	50.3	33.0	5.5	-0.3	7.7	7.0	5.3	7.4	0.0	GRT
KENTUCKY EMPLOYERS MUTUAL INS	KY	B-	917.8	208.5	141.1	6.7	6.9	6.8	5.5	6.9	4.0	RT
KENTUCKY FARM BUREAU MUTUAL INS CO	KY	B	2,373.1	1,254.3	877.8	27.8	10.0	6.5	6.3	6.1	4.8	T
KENTUCKY HOSPITAL INS CO RRG	KY	D	20.8	6.8	2.4	-0.4	7.0	9.4	2.1	6.8	2.2	DGRT
KENTUCKY NATIONAL INS CO	KY	D	30.9	10.1	26.2	0.2	2.1	4.7	2.9	0.7	2.3	DGLR
KESWICK GUARANTY INC	VI	B- (1)	4.9	4.8	0.4	-0.1	9.0	4.6	6.2	7.0	3.5	DGT
KEY INS CO	KS	D	30.8	7.0	42.9	-0.8	1.2	4.3	4.8	0.0	1.9	CGLT
KEY RISK INS CO	IA	C	50.5	30.4	0.0	0.4	10.0	N/A	6.8	7.0	3.7	RT
KEYSTONE MUTUAL INS CO	MO	E	2.6	0.2	1.8	0.0	0.0	2.0	0.9	7.0	0.0	CDFG
KEYSTONE NATIONAL INS CO	PA	C+	16.9	9.0	1.9	0.1	10.0	7.6	7.9	9.0	3.1	DGRT
KINGSTONE INS CO	NY	C	116.4	44.9	60.4	3.4	7.3	3.1	8.8	6.4	3.3	GRT
KINSALE INS CO	AR	B	442.4	136.8	84.0	8.0	7.0	6.3	6.5	7.6	4.1	T
KNIGHT SPECIALTY INS CO	DE	B	81.3	46.1	0.0	0.3	10.0	N/A	4.9	10.0	4.1	GT
KNIGHTBROOK INS CO	DE	D	221.1	63.2	11.9	-4.0	3.5	1.0	2.7	7.3	2.2	CFRT
KOOKMIN BEST INS CO LTD US BR	NY	E+	351.7	127.5	27.3	-12.3	1.6	0.3	0.7	6.9	0.5	CFGR
LACKAWANNA AMERICAN INS CO	PA	B-	85.7	40.4	22.5	1.0	8.7	8.5	8.9	7.0	3.7	RT
LACKAWANNA CASUALTY CO	PA	B-	227.0	87.5	78.7	2.5	7.1	8.7	3.6	6.2	3.9	RT
LACKAWANNA NATIONAL INS CO	PA	C+	36.8	14.7	11.2	0.5	7.2	8.5	8.9	7.0	3.2	DGRT
LAFAYETTE INS CO	LA	B-	198.8	87.0	62.2	1.6	9.1	8.6	8.1	6.8	4.3	T
LAKE STREET RRG INC	VT	D	2.1	1.0	0.2	0.0	8.3	7.1	2.4	10.0	1.0	DGT
LAKEVIEW INS CO	FL	C+	34.6	17.5	16.5	0.6	8.6	6.1	8.6	6.6	3.3	DGT
LAMMICO	LA	B	408.4	219.3	49.0	3.6	10.0	9.1	8.6	8.7	4.2	RT
LAMMICO RRG INC	DC	D+	5.8	5.6	0.0	0.1	10.0	4.7	4.7	10.0	1.4	DGT
LAMORAK INS CO	PA	C	26.0	23.5	0.0	0.0	10.0	3.8	1.9	7.0	3.5	DGRT
LANCER INDEMNITY CO	NY	C	28.0	10.3	8.9	0.4	4.1	4.2	3.3	7.0	2.9	CDGR
LANCER INS CO	IL	B	661.1	193.8	263.0	9.8	7.6	4.4	5.9	6.6	4.1	RT
LANCET IND RRG INC	NV	D	19.0	5.4	8.4	-0.1	2.5	3.3	3.5	7.6	2.1	DFGT
LANDCAR CASUALTY CO	UT	C	40.1	16.5	11.0	0.6	7.1	6.2	3.6	7.0	2.9	DGT
LANDMARK AMERICAN INS CO	OK	C	402.9	238.5	42.9	8.9	10.0	7.7	8.8	7.3	3.5	ART
LAUNDRY OWNERS MUTUAL LIAB INS ASN	PA	C-	16.5	7.5	4.2	0.5	6.3	5.0	4.1	7.0	2.2	DGRT
LAWYERS MUTUAL INS CO	CA	B-	318.3	218.1	36.4	7.9	10.0	9.4	8.9	7.9	4.0	RT
LAWYERS MUTUAL INS CO OF KENTUCKY	KY	C	24.0	10.7	4.3	0.2	7.7	9.7	6.8	7.0	2.3	DGRT

See Page 27 for explanation of footnotes and
Page 28 for explanation of stability factors.
Arrows denote recent upgrades ▲ or downgrades ▼   (see Section VII for explanations)

82

www.weissratings.com

RISK ADJ. RATIO #1	CAPITAL RATIO #2	PREMIUM TO SURPLUS (%)	RESV. TO SURPLUS (%)	RESV. DEVELOP. 1 YEAR (%)	RESV. DEVELOP. 2 YEAR (%)	LOSS RATIO (%)	EXP. RATIO (%)	COMB RATIO (%)	CASH FROM UNDER-WRITING (%)	NET PREMIUM GROWTH (%)	INVEST. IN AFFIL (%)	INSURANCE COMPANY NAME
0.9	0.8	19.4	33.2	-0.5	-3.9	100.4	111.6	212.0	-509.9	59.2	0.0	IRONSHORE RRG (DC) INC
2.3	1.4	33.5	75.7	-1.0	0.9	76.6	14.5	91.1	155.0	-11.9	0.0 ●	IRONSHORE SPECIALTY INS CO
2.8	1.6	194.8	30.2	-685.4	-597.9	69.7	20.6	90.3	110.3	-10.4	0.0	ISLAND HOME INS CO
4.0	2.6	76.3	103.7	-12.6	-20.0	56.6	35.6	92.2	114.6	0.8	4.7	ISLAND INS CO LTD
3.8	3.4	N/A	N/A	N/A	N/A	N/A	N/A	N/A	N/A	0.0	0.0	ISLAND PREMIER INS CO LTD
N/A	N/A	N/A	N/A	N/A	N/A	N/A	N/A	N/A	N/A	0.0	0.0	ISMIE INDEMNITY CO
4.1	3.4	25.1	97.4	-6.4	-17.5	57.9	29.8	87.7	81.1	-11.0	4.2 ●	ISMIE MUTUAL INS CO
1.0	0.9	N/A	N/A	N/A	N/A	N/A	N/A	N/A	N/A	0.0	0.0	IU HEALTH RRG INC
2.8	2.0	27.4	49.6	-2.6	-6.1	65.2	26.5	91.7	83.0	21.6	0.0	JAMES RIVER CASUALTY CO
2.2	1.4	56.1	101.8	-3.9	-8.8	65.2	24.0	89.2	94.1	21.6	6.0	JAMES RIVER INS CO
1.6	1.3	166.2	10.8	-1.6	-0.5	29.8	57.9	87.7	120.0	14.3	0.0	JEFFERSON INS CO
5.5	3.4	73.3	10.3	-1.0	-2.0	44.9	41.4	86.3	126.6	7.7	0.1 ●	JEWELERS MUTUAL INS CO
0.0	0.0	36.7	377.5	-3.2	89.0	37.9	52.4	90.3	56.0	-79.7	0.0	JM WOODWORTH RRG INC
2.6	1.9	102.3	5.9	1.9	-0.1	63.3	42.8	106.1	94.9	4.2	0.0	JUNIATA MUTUAL INS CO
N/A	N/A	N/A	N/A	N/A	N/A	N/A	N/A	N/A	N/A	0.0	0.0	KAMMCO CASUALTY CO
6.1	4.5	18.3	27.7	-1.0	-2.4	70.1	43.4	113.5	84.3	1.6	3.4	KANSAS MEDICAL MUTUAL INS CO
3.1	2.6	87.8	14.2	-3.7	-6.9	69.3	24.1	93.4	107.3	-1.8	0.0	KANSAS MUTUAL INS CO
N/A	N/A	N/A	N/A	N/A	N/A	N/A	N/A	N/A	N/A	0.0	0.0	KEMPER FINANCIAL INDEMNITY CO
1.1	1.0	N/A	N/A	N/A	N/A	N/A	N/A	N/A	-430.3	0.0	0.0	KEMPER INDEPENDENCE INS CO
0.5	0.3	178.1	184.5	5.8	50.0	70.5	58.7	129.2	78.4	-26.2	0.0	KENSINGTON INS CO
2.2	1.6	17.0	41.9	-23.8	-7.5	-31.5	12.2	-19.3	155.2	139.3	0.0	KENTUCKIANA MEDICAL RRG & INS CO
1.5	1.0	71.7	296.1	-2.0	-4.1	90.2	39.0	129.2	98.0	-10.6	0.0 ●	KENTUCKY EMPLOYERS MUTUAL INS
5.5	3.6	71.6	31.1	-1.5	-3.6	79.6	23.6	103.2	97.9	3.1	0.8 ●	KENTUCKY FARM BUREAU MUTUAL INS
1.2	1.0	33.4	137.9	-30.4	-25.9	57.5	34.7	92.2	141.6	-16.8	0.0	KENTUCKY HOSPITAL INS CO RRG
0.7	0.5	263.7	90.7	0.4	-12.5	70.6	30.3	100.9	99.5	2.4	15.3	KENTUCKY NATIONAL INS CO
4.5	2.5	8.0	1.8	N/A	N/A	69.1	12.8	81.9	122.1	11.4	0.0	KESWICK GUARANTY INC
0.2	0.2	545.6	216.4	25.4	19.8	76.1	23.0	99.1	105.1	9.1	0.0	KEY INS CO
8.6	7.7	N/A	N/A	N/A	N/A	N/A	N/A	N/A	99.7	0.0	0.0	KEY RISK INS CO
0.1	0.1	999 +	808.4	95.3	112.4	38.1	60.6	98.7	91.5	11.3	0.0	KEYSTONE MUTUAL INS CO
4.3	3.8	21.9	6.5	-0.1	-1.1	56.7	32.6	89.3	190.4	21.3	0.0	KEYSTONE NATIONAL INS CO
2.1	1.4	154.5	59.3	-2.5	2.2	47.7	29.0	76.7	154.5	39.5	2.0	KINGSTONE INS CO
1.8	1.0	65.8	97.2	-9.1	-6.6	56.8	3.5	60.3	417.8	36.6	0.0	KINSALE INS CO
3.4	2.0	N/A	N/A	N/A	N/A	N/A	N/A	N/A	14.2	0.0	0.0	KNIGHT SPECIALTY INS CO
1.0	0.6	25.6	98.8	25.0	62.0	173.6	38.1	211.7	30.5	-66.3	1.8	KNIGHTBROOK INS CO
0.5	0.3	19.4	159.6	336.3	999 +	500.5	128.3	628.8	29.2	-46.0	0.0	KOOKMIN BEST INS CO LTD US BR
2.8	2.2	57.4	63.5	-1.2	-3.5	73.8	16.8	90.6	119.1	10.9	0.0	LACKAWANNA AMERICAN INS CO
1.2	1.1	97.3	112.8	-1.8	-4.8	73.6	16.7	90.3	115.7	10.9	29.6	LACKAWANNA CASUALTY CO
1.7	1.4	80.0	85.3	-1.8	-5.1	73.8	16.7	90.5	119.5	10.9	0.0	LACKAWANNA NATIONAL INS CO
4.1	2.5	73.4	77.8	-1.9	-5.4	61.2	31.7	92.9	119.2	10.3	0.0	LAFAYETTE INS CO
2.3	2.1	22.0	90.0	-11.6	-44.6	83.3	66.5	149.8	130.0	-21.3	0.0	LAKE STREET RRG INC
2.6	2.4	96.8	18.2	0.1	2.2	57.6	43.0	100.6	94.7	-1.0	0.0	LAKEVIEW INS CO
5.4	4.1	22.8	72.9	-3.1	-8.1	64.3	26.4	90.7	104.4	-0.6	0.1 ●	LAMMICO
64.5	33.1	0.4	0.9	-0.1	-2.0	375.0	-203.8	171.2	-109.4	4.8	0.0	LAMMICO RRG INC
8.9	5.3	N/A	N/A	N/A	N/A	N/A	N/A	N/A	N/A	0.0	0.0	LAMORAK INS CO
0.8	0.5	90.3	93.3	13.3	19.9	82.0	29.1	111.1	200.5	5.6	0.0	LANCER INDEMNITY CO
2.1	1.4	143.7	172.5	15.7	12.0	81.8	28.1	109.9	116.5	8.4	0.0	LANCER INS CO
0.9	0.6	166.2	160.8	24.1	-18.5	94.2	19.8	114.0	58.9	31.0	-10.7	LANCET IND RRG INC
1.4	0.9	70.6	8.0	1.5	0.1	65.4	7.1	72.5	220.7	10.7	0.0	LANDCAR CASUALTY CO
15.7	9.7	18.7	28.0	-1.8	-3.2	33.6	28.3	61.9	140.0	-5.2	0.0 ●	LANDMARK AMERICAN INS CO
2.2	1.3	59.6	86.7	-14.0	-40.7	60.5	37.2	97.7	105.9	-14.3	0.0	LAUNDRY OWNERS MUTUAL LIAB INS
9.3	5.9	17.4	37.1	-7.8	-15.7	44.8	10.5	55.3	135.2	1.1	0.1 ●	LAWYERS MUTUAL INS CO
2.5	1.8	42.2	87.7	-33.6	-43.7	39.1	22.6	61.7	102.3	-15.9	0.0	LAWYERS MUTUAL INS CO OF

999 + Denotes number greater than 999.9%
999 - Denotes number less than -999.99%
● Bullets denote a more detailed analysis is available in Section II.

INSURANCE COMPANY NAME	DOM. STATE	RATING		TOTAL ASSETS ($MIL)	CAPITAL & SURPLUS ($MIL)	ANNUAL NET PREMIUM ($MIL)	NET INCOME ($MIL)	CAPITAL-IZATION INDEX (PTS)	RESERVE ADQ INDEX (PTS)	PROFIT-ABILITY INDEX (PTS)	LIQUIDITY INDEX (PTS)	STAB. INDEX (PTS)	STABILITY FACTORS
LAWYERS MUTUAL LIAB INS CO OF NC	NC	B-		101.6	72.2	14.4	1.9	10.0	9.4	8.9	8.0	3.7	DRT
LCTA CASUALTY INS CO	LA	U		77.5	30.9	0.0	-0.8	N/A	0.0	2.9	0.0	0.0	LT
LE MARS INS CO	IA	C+		63.9	24.0	29.3	-0.8	8.1	5.9	3.1	6.5	3.7	FRT
LEAGUE OF WI MUNICIPALITIES MUT INS	WI	C+		69.9	25.9	23.7	-3.0	7.8	9.8	4.3	6.9	3.3	RT
LEATHERSTOCKING COOP INS CO	NY	C		32.0	17.9	13.4	1.4	8.4	9.3	8.8	6.8	2.7	DGRT
LEBANON VALLEY INS CO	PA	C		25.2	11.1	8.1	0.2	8.5	9.3	2.9	6.8	2.9	DGRT
LEGAL MUTUAL LIAB INS SOCIETY OF MD	MD	U	(5)	0.5	0.0	0.0	0.0	N/A	6.1	0.0	7.2	0.0	FRT
LEMIC INS CO	LA	F	(5)	0.0	0.0	15.4	0.0	0.0	1.6	0.1	7.0	0.0	CDFR
LENDERS PROTECTION ASR CO RRG	NE	D+		2.5	2.4	0.0	0.1	10.0	N/A	4.1	10.0	1.9	DGT
LEON HIX INS CO	SC	U		3.4	3.3	0.0	0.0	N/A	N/A	5.7	7.0	3.6	FGT
▼LEXINGTON INS CO	DE	C		25,270.1	6,289.3	5,564.4	604.3	7.8	4.4	3.7	6.3	2.8	FRT
LEXINGTON NATIONAL INS CORP	FL	E+		58.7	17.9	11.5	1.0	7.8	6.2	4.5	7.3	0.7	DRT
LEXON INS CO	TX	C-		212.1	53.4	69.6	-6.0	7.0	1.4	3.7	7.5	2.4	RT
LIBERTY AMERICAN INS CO	FL	U		8.7	8.5	0.0	0.3	N/A	4.7	2.1	10.0	3.3	GT
LIBERTY AMERICAN SELECT INS CO	FL	U		8.3	8.3	0.0	0.1	N/A	4.7	2.2	10.0	3.4	FGT
LIBERTY COUNTY MUTUAL INS CO	TX	C-		7.1	5.3	0.0	-0.1	10.0	N/A	3.3	7.0	2.6	DGT
LIBERTY FIRST RRG INS CO	UT	F	(5)	0.0	0.0	2.5	0.0	0.2	0.5	1.9	8.5	0.0	CDGR
LIBERTY INS CORP	IL	C-		245.6	239.4	0.0	2.7	10.0	3.2	3.6	7.0	3.3	AT
LIBERTY INS UNDERWRITERS INC	IL	C		192.6	127.3	0.0	1.7	10.0	3.6	6.7	10.0	4.3	ART
LIBERTY LLOYDS OF TX INS CO	TX	B		6.6	6.5	0.0	0.0	10.0	N/A	6.4	7.0	4.3	DGT
LIBERTY MUTUAL FIRE INS CO	WI	B-		5,500.1	1,395.3	2,050.6	-12.2	7.4	4.4	5.4	6.1	3.6	AT
LIBERTY MUTUAL INS CO	MA	B		42,340.6	15,926.0	12,816.1	-162.7	7.6	5.8	5.4	6.4	4.3	ART
LIBERTY MUTUAL MID ATLANTIC INS CO	MA	C		20.1	19.3	0.0	0.1	10.0	N/A	7.5	7.0	3.4	DGT
LIBERTY MUTUAL PERSONAL INS CO	MA	B		6.9	6.9	0.0	0.0	10.0	N/A	6.2	7.0	4.0	DGT
LIBERTY NORTHWEST INS CORP	OR	C		54.6	54.5	0.0	0.5	10.0	N/A	3.0	10.0	4.0	FRT
LIBERTY PERSONAL INS CO	NH	C		16.8	15.9	0.0	0.2	10.0	N/A	2.9	10.0	3.2	DFGT
LIBERTY SURPLUS INS CORP	NH	C		164.9	104.0	0.0	0.0	10.0	N/A	7.2	4.6	4.3	ALT
LIGHTHOUSE CASUALTY CO	IL	D		24.7	4.5	11.3	0.2	1.6	3.6	3.8	6.3	2.3	CDGT
LIGHTHOUSE PROPERTY INS CORP	LA	C+		76.4	22.1	30.8	1.8	5.6	6.0	7.2	7.8	3.0	DT
LIGHTNING ROD MUTUAL INS CO	OH	B-		267.4	158.2	107.6	4.8	10.0	7.8	6.0	6.8	4.1	T
LINCOLN GENERAL INS CO	PA	F	(4)	65.6	-6.9	0.7	-8.7	0.0	4.1	0.0	9.0	0.0	CDFG
LION INS CO (FL)	FL	B		253.2	86.4	28.2	2.8	9.0	8.6	8.7	9.3	4.0	RT
LITITZ MUTUAL INS CO	PA	B-		253.2	160.5	74.7	8.6	7.5	6.4	4.8	6.1	4.0	ART
LITTLE BLACK MUTUAL INS CO	WI	D		6.1	3.2	2.4	0.4	5.7	6.2	3.0	6.3	1.9	DGRT
LIVINGSTON MUTUAL INS CO	PA	C		2.9	1.5	0.5	-0.1	9.0	6.1	3.5	7.4	2.3	DFGT
LM GENERAL INS CO	IL	B-		10.9	10.8	0.0	0.1	10.0	5.3	4.4	7.0	3.8	DGT
LM INS CORP	IL	C		118.5	116.5	0.0	1.3	10.0	3.7	5.3	7.0	4.3	AT
LM P&C INS CO	IN	U		67.5	36.0	0.0	0.2	N/A	5.7	4.2	7.0	5.8	GT
LOCUST MUTUAL FIRE INS CO	PA	U	(2)	1.2	1.2	0.0	0.0	N/A	3.6	2.6	8.2	1.8	DT
LONE STAR ALLIANCE INC A RRG	DC	D		9.0	2.0	0.2	0.2	8.8	3.6	3.9	10.0	1.5	DGT
LONE STAR NATIONAL INS CO	IN	D-		6.5	4.1	0.9	0.0	10.0	4.6	3.8	9.0	0.5	DGRT
LOUISIANA FARM BUREAU CAS INS CO	LA	B		10.9	10.8	0.0	0.1	10.0	N/A	7.6	10.0	4.3	DGT
LOUISIANA FARM BUREAU MUTUAL INS CO	LA	B		219.4	128.1	86.7	3.1	10.0	6.9	8.9	6.7	4.3	T
LOYA CASUALTY INS CO	CA	D+		119.5	40.5	145.3	-6.5	6.0	9.0	3.1	1.2	2.7	LT
LOYA INS CO	TX	D+		274.5	115.8	330.6	-14.7	6.8	4.0	2.6	1.1	2.6	LT
LR INS INC	DE	U		1.5	1.5	0.0	-0.1	N/A	N/A	1.9	10.0	3.1	FGT
LUBA CASUALTY INS CO	LA	B		226.1	81.5	74.8	3.3	7.9	8.7	7.7	6.9	4.3	RT
LUMBER MUTUAL INS CO	MA	F	(5)	0.0	0.0	0.0	0.0	0.3	2.4	1.8	9.1	0.0	CFGR
LUMBERMENS UNDERWRITING ALLIANCE	MO	F	(5)	354.2	-41.9	63.8	-18.6	0.0	4.1	0.1	7.0	0.0	CDFR
LUTHERAN MUTUAL FIRE INS CO	IL	C		10.5	10.3	0.3	0.0	10.0	5.2	6.3	7.2	2.3	DGT
LVHN RRG	SC	U		58.8	5.0	0.0	0.0	N/A	0.1	4.5	1.0	0.0	LT
LYNDON SOUTHERN INS CO	DE	B-		142.9	47.4	75.6	3.1	7.0	5.1	8.5	6.7	3.7	GRT

See Page 27 for explanation of footnotes and Page 28 for explanation of stability factors. 84 www.weissratings.com

Arrows denote recent upgrades ▲ or downgrades ▼ (see Section VII for explanations)

RISK ADJ. CAPITAL RATIO #1	CAPITAL RATIO #2	PREMIUM TO SURPLUS (%)	RESV. TO SURPLUS (%)	RESV. DEVELOP. 1 YEAR (%)	RESV. DEVELOP. 2 YEAR (%)	LOSS RATIO (%)	EXP. RATIO (%)	COMB RATIO (%)	CASH FROM UNDER-WRITING (%)	NET PREMIUM GROWTH (%)	INVEST. IN AFFIL (%)	INSURANCE COMPANY NAME
6.1	4.0	20.9	25.9	-4.4	-10.9	56.6	25.9	82.5	127.3	2.0	3.1	LAWYERS MUTUAL LIAB INS CO OF NC
N/A	N/A	N/A	N/A	N/A	N/A	N/A	N/A	N/A	N/A	0.0	0.0	LCTA CASUALTY INS CO
2.5	1.5	111.8	64.1	2.1	6.1	75.4	32.8	108.2	91.4	-1.5	0.0	LE MARS INS CO
1.9	1.4	81.6	89.9	-7.1	-27.1	67.6	17.3	84.9	132.8	7.7	5.4	LEAGUE OF WI MUNICIPALITIES MUT INS
2.7	1.9	82.0	29.1	-5.3	-7.0	47.7	29.3	77.0	155.0	27.2	0.0	LEATHERSTOCKING COOP INS CO
2.7	1.9	74.1	67.5	-5.6	-4.0	65.6	39.6	105.2	90.3	4.3	0.0	LEBANON VALLEY INS CO
N/A	N/A	-11.4	373.3	-16.7	-9.0	-823.1	-175.2	-998.3	-90.6	94.5	0.0	LEGAL MUTUAL LIAB INS SOCIETY OF
-0.0	-0.0	-739.3	999 +	53.8	50.0	121.0	52.5	173.5	71.1	-29.6	0.0	LEMIC INS CO
120.8	61.2	N/A	N/A	N/A	N/A	N/A	N/A	N/A	1.1	0.0	0.0	LENDERS PROTECTION ASR CO RRG
N/A	N/A	N/A	N/A	N/A	N/A	N/A	N/A	N/A	N/A	0.0	0.0	LEON HIX INS CO
2.1	1.4	84.4	195.0	13.9	13.9	88.8	30.2	119.0	84.4	-8.8	0.3 ●	LEXINGTON INS CO
1.9	1.5	68.1	1.5	-0.8	-3.2	3.5	72.7	76.2	120.5	-4.7	0.0	LEXINGTON NATIONAL INS CORP
1.1	0.9	132.5	43.6	3.8	13.0	23.9	71.3	95.2	99.8	12.3	1.4	LEXON INS CO
N/A	N/A	N/A	N/A	-0.3	-0.1	N/A	N/A	N/A	-0.3	0.0	0.0	LIBERTY AMERICAN INS CO
N/A	N/A	N/A	N/A	-0.3	-0.1	N/A	N/A	N/A	-0.1	0.0	0.0	LIBERTY AMERICAN SELECT INS CO
7.8	7.1	N/A	N/A	N/A	N/A	N/A	N/A	N/A	N/A	0.0	0.0	LIBERTY COUNTY MUTUAL INS CO
-0.3	-0.2	149.9	267.7	21.4	98.2	41.3	11.6	52.9	222.4	-50.3	0.0	LIBERTY FIRST RRG INS CO
124.3	63.2	N/A	N/A	N/A	N/A	N/A	N/A	N/A	N/A	0.0 ●	LIBERTY INS CORP
17.0	15.3	N/A	N/A	N/A	N/A	N/A	N/A	N/A	16.3	0.0	0.0	LIBERTY INS UNDERWRITERS INC
102.4	92.1	N/A	N/A	N/A	N/A	N/A	N/A	N/A	N/A	0.0	0.0	LIBERTY LLOYDS OF TX INS CO
2.0	1.4	146.6	193.5	-1.0	-1.3	68.4	30.2	98.6	103.1	1.0	4.6 ●	LIBERTY MUTUAL FIRE INS CO
1.6	1.4	81.0	107.0	-0.5	-0.6	68.4	30.6	99.0	102.1	1.0	27.1 ●	LIBERTY MUTUAL INS CO
55.7	22.6	N/A	N/A	N/A	N/A	N/A	N/A	N/A	N/A	0.0	0.0	LIBERTY MUTUAL MID ATLANTIC INS CO
240.3	120.2	N/A	N/A	N/A	N/A	N/A	N/A	N/A	N/A	0.0	0.0	LIBERTY MUTUAL PERSONAL INS CO
3.8	3.7	N/A	N/A	N/A	N/A	N/A	N/A	N/A	N/A	0.0	25.0	LIBERTY NORTHWEST INS CORP
37.3	33.5	N/A	N/A	N/A	N/A	N/A	N/A	N/A	N/A	0.0	0.0	LIBERTY PERSONAL INS CO
14.3	12.9	N/A	N/A	N/A	N/A	N/A	N/A	N/A	725.3	0.0	0.0	LIBERTY SURPLUS INS CORP
0.5	0.4	270.0	150.9	20.8	2.1	65.2	32.9	98.1	179.0	8.8	0.0	LIGHTHOUSE CASUALTY CO
2.1	1.3	148.8	31.6	-3.3	-0.6	38.9	40.2	79.1	144.1	7.7	0.0	LIGHTHOUSE PROPERTY INS CORP
4.9	3.1	71.0	28.1	-1.6	-3.4	62.4	30.9	93.3	110.6	1.5	0.1	LIGHTNING ROD MUTUAL INS CO
-0.1	-0.1	54.4	999 +	-273.1	999 +	-255.0	720.4	465.4	1.8	-28.5	0.0	LINCOLN GENERAL INS CO
4.0	2.3	33.8	56.1	0.3	-7.5	43.0	34.8	77.8	181.1	18.7	0.0	LION INS CO (FL)
2.3	1.4	49.1	13.2	-1.4	-2.1	57.8	41.1	98.9	105.7	6.5	0.0	LITITZ MUTUAL INS CO
1.6	1.0	103.2	12.9	0.4	-2.4	48.6	38.0	86.6	110.6	0.5	0.0	LITTLE BLACK MUTUAL INS CO
2.7	2.2	31.6	8.4	-4.2	-3.1	69.9	35.7	105.6	70.4	-3.7	0.0	LIVINGSTON MUTUAL INS CO
90.5	45.2	N/A	0.5	N/A	-4.7	N/A	N/A	N/A	N/A	0.0	0.0	LM GENERAL INS CO
143.2	66.9	N/A	N/A	N/A	N/A	N/A	N/A	N/A	N/A	0.0	0.0	LM INS CORP
N/A	N/A	N/A	56.2	2.6	5.5	999 +	29.4	999 +	N/A	-100.0	0.0	LM P&C INS CO
N/A	N/A	2.6	N/A	-2.5	N/A	-68.7	290.6	221.9	45.0	8.6	0.0	LOCUST MUTUAL FIRE INS CO
1.0	0.9	11.0	10.0	-2.1	N/A	126.3	-70.4	55.9	37.2	687.9	0.0	LONE STAR ALLIANCE INC A RRG
4.9	4.4	21.1	21.4	-0.7	1.5	68.3	31.4	99.7	97.4	10.6	0.0	LONE STAR NATIONAL INS CO
90.7	45.3	N/A	N/A	N/A	N/A	N/A	N/A	N/A	N/A	0.0	0.0	LOUISIANA FARM BUREAU CAS INS CO
5.2	4.7	67.6	11.3	-2.6	-5.8	54.0	22.4	76.4	126.1	3.6	4.1	LOUISIANA FARM BUREAU MUTUAL INS
1.0	0.9	390.9	151.3	-5.1	-2.9	68.9	36.2	105.1	103.5	14.9	0.0	LOYA CASUALTY INS CO
1.0	0.9	285.0	120.7	3.2	9.9	75.6	32.9	108.5	98.4	5.0	24.6	LOYA INS CO
N/A	N/A	N/A	N/A	N/A	N/A	N/A	999 +	999 +	1.1	0.0	0.0	LR INS INC
2.1	1.6	87.5	104.2	-9.4	-6.2	51.3	33.8	85.1	112.3	-0.5	0.0	LUBA CASUALTY INS CO
0.1	0.1	0.7	407.0	33.1	32.6	999 +	999 +	999 +	0.4	146.2	54.4	LUMBER MUTUAL INS CO
-0.3	-0.2	-283.3	-645.8	3.0	15.1	97.4	177.7	275.1	71.0	-23.8	0.0	LUMBERMENS UNDERWRITING
12.5	8.8	2.5	0.3	1.0	-0.5	89.9	102.0	191.9	56.5	0.3	0.0	LUTHERAN MUTUAL FIRE INS CO
N/A	N/A	N/A	N/A	114.6	240.6	N/A	N/A	N/A	93.7	0.0	0.0	LVHN RRG
2.1	1.3	177.5	18.8	-1.6	-0.9	37.9	45.0	82.9	111.2	39.6	0.0	LYNDON SOUTHERN INS CO

999 + Denotes number greater than 999.9%
999 - Denotes number less than -999.99%
● Bullets denote a more detailed analysis is available in Section II.

INSURANCE COMPANY NAME	DOM. STATE	RATING	TOTAL ASSETS ($MIL)	CAPITAL & SURPLUS ($MIL)	ANNUAL NET PREMIUM ($MIL)	NET INCOME ($MIL)	CAPITAL-IZATION INDEX (PTS)	RESERVE ADQ INDEX (PTS)	PROFIT-ABILITY INDEX (PTS)	LIQUIDITY INDEX (PTS)	STAB. INDEX (PTS)	STABILITY FACTORS
MA EMPLOYERS INS CO	MA	C	4.3	3.6	0.0	0.0	10.0	N/A	6.3	9.8	2.8	DGRT
MACHINERY INS INC	FL	D-	2.3	2.0	0.5	0.1	9.7	3.6	2.9	8.3	0.0	DGT
MADA INS EXCHANGE	MN	U	0.4	0.1	0.0	0.0	N/A	0.1	1.9	9.8	0.3	CFGR
MADISON MUTUAL INS CO	IL	C+	64.6	40.1	32.5	2.4	8.4	5.0	3.2	6.1	3.3	FRT
MADISON MUTUAL INS CO	NY	C+	13.5	9.2	3.6	0.3	10.0	7.6	5.9	6.8	3.0	DGRT
MAG MUTUAL INS CO	GA	B-	1,748.4	890.7	200.2	-0.9	9.3	9.4	8.4	7.3	4.7	RT
MAIDEN RE NORTH AMERICA INC	MO	B-	1,319.8	293.0	416.4	-8.5	5.5	6.0	4.6	6.5	4.1	CT
MAIDSTONE INS CO	NY	C-	64.5	8.3	28.4	-5.3	4.1	6.4	0.8	5.1	2.9	CDFG
MAIN STREET AMER PROTECTION INS CO	FL	U	15.7	15.5	0.0	0.3	N/A	N/A	7.8	7.0	5.2	DGT
MAIN STREET AMERICA ASR CO	FL	C	43.3	43.0	0.0	1.3	10.0	N/A	7.0	7.0	3.6	T
MAISON INS CO	LA	C	51.6	16.9	30.4	-0.2	5.6	4.7	3.8	7.1	3.3	DGT
MAKE TRANSPORTATION INS INC RRG	DE	D	5.2	2.0	1.3	0.0	8.8	9.4	6.1	7.7	1.6	DGRT
MANHATTAN RE-INS CO	DE	F (5)	0.0	0.0	0.0	0.0	5.6	9.8	0.8	9.2	2.0	FRT
MANUFACTURERS ALLIANCE INS CO	PA	C-	195.4	64.2	44.9	0.6	7.5	2.2	3.0	6.6	3.3	ART
MANUFACTURING TECHNOLOGY MUT INS	MI	C+	54.5	21.9	19.2	-2.2	5.3	9.7	5.0	6.9	3.2	CDRT
MAPFRE INS CO	NJ	C	79.5	22.2	51.5	0.0	5.3	3.7	3.8	2.6	3.4	DGLR
MAPFRE INS CO OF FLORIDA	FL	C	104.4	30.2	76.0	0.0	7.3	4.3	2.5	5.4	2.9	GT
MAPFRE INS CO OF NY	NY	C+	154.2	47.0	103.9	0.2	8.0	4.2	2.5	4.9	3.3	LT
MAPFRE PAN AMERICAN INS CO	PR	C	24.2	11.7	2.6	2.1	10.0	7.3	4.7	8.0	2.4	DGT
MAPFRE PRAICO INS CO	PR	C-	433.1	173.1	163.9	5.3	6.8	8.4	6.0	5.6	2.9	T
MAPLE VALLEY MUTUAL INS CO	WI	C	13.4	8.7	5.2	0.5	9.2	7.6	6.5	7.0	2.2	DGRT
MARATHON FINANCIAL INS INC RRG	DE	D+	8.1	2.4	-0.9	0.1	7.2	7.9	5.5	10.0	1.9	DFGR
MARKEL AMERICAN INS CO	VA	C	364.7	145.5	129.8	6.6	8.2	9.5	7.5	7.0	2.4	ART
MARKEL GLOBAL REINS CO	DE	B	1,649.7	753.1	211.7	-6.6	8.1	7.5	4.2	7.4	4.8	RT
MARKEL INS CO	IL	C	1,525.8	380.0	534.2	16.9	6.3	9.4	4.5	6.8	3.6	ART
MARYSVILLE MUTUAL INS CO	KS	C+	45.1	25.8	21.4	0.9	8.9	6.1	7.1	6.6	3.2	RT
MASSACHUSETTS BAY INS CO	NH	C+	65.0	65.0	0.0	0.8	10.0	N/A	7.6	7.0	4.1	RT
MASSACHUSETTS HOMELAND INS CO	MA	C (3)	8.9	8.3	0.0	-0.4	10.0	N/A	4.5	7.0	2.8	DFGR
MAXUM CASUALTY INS CO	DE	C	52.1	18.6	13.1	0.3	7.2	4.9	6.0	7.4	2.7	DRT
MAXUM INDEMNITY CO	DE	C	280.8	116.5	69.0	1.0	8.0	4.9	6.8	7.3	4.0	RT
MAYA ASR CO	NY	E+	17.2	3.2	7.3	0.0	0.6	0.1	3.8	2.2	0.8	CDFG
MBIA INS CORP	NY	D	752.7	489.7	87.0	-103.8	3.1	1.0	1.7	1.0	1.4	CDFL
MCIC VERMONT INC RRG	VT	U	1,772.1	530.5	230.2	0.0	N/A	0.0	4.4	7.0	0.0	CFT
MCMILLAN WARNER MUTUAL INS CO	WI	C	16.2	8.9	6.8	0.1	7.8	7.6	4.7	7.0	2.5	DGRT
MD RRG INC	MT	D	23.9	14.2	3.9	0.2	9.3	9.9	8.5	9.6	2.3	DFGR
MDADVANTAGE INS CO OF NJ	NJ	C	364.6	139.8	36.1	3.2	8.1	9.3	8.4	8.0	3.5	T
MDOW INS CO	TX	B-	18.9	12.5	0.0	1.1	10.0	N/A	8.8	7.0	3.5	DGT
MED MAL RRG INC	TN	D	3.6	1.4	0.4	0.0	7.5	3.8	2.2	7.0	1.3	DFGT
MEDCHOICE RRG INC	VT	U	2.9	2.0	0.0	0.0	N/A	N/A	3.0	10.0	3.6	DFGT
MEDICAL ALLIANCE INS CO	IL	D+	9.8	5.0	2.5	0.1	9.3	N/A	5.2	8.5	2.1	DGRT
MEDICAL INS EXCHANGE OF CALIFORNIA	CA	B	413.4	171.0	51.3	3.4	9.9	8.9	4.8	7.3	4.1	FRT
MEDICAL LIABILITY ALLIANCE	MO	B-	77.5	51.6	10.4	-1.3	10.0	9.3	6.1	7.9	3.9	DRT
MEDICAL LIABILITY MUTUAL INS CO	NY	D+	5,539.7	1,865.5	410.9	57.7	7.3	9.6	6.9	7.6	2.4	FRT
MEDICAL MUTUAL INS CO OF MAINE	ME	B	275.0	159.4	37.3	2.0	10.0	9.5	8.6	9.1	4.1	RT
MEDICAL MUTUAL INS CO OF NC	NC	B-	516.9	246.0	64.0	16.5	10.0	9.3	3.5	8.5	4.1	RT
MEDICAL MUTUAL LIAB INS SOC OF MD	MD	B-	811.1	393.9	108.1	4.6	10.0	9.5	7.7	7.5	4.3	FRT
MEDICAL PROFESSIONAL MUTUAL INS CO	MA	B-	2,998.9	1,552.1	241.3	17.9	8.2	9.4	8.5	7.1	4.5	RT
MEDICAL PROTECTIVE CO	IN	B	2,726.3	1,577.2	226.5	53.8	9.4	9.9	8.7	8.5	5.0	T
MEDICAL PROVIDERS MUTUAL INS CO RRG	DC	D+	7.1	3.6	1.5	0.0	9.5	9.8	6.9	9.3	2.0	FGRT
MEDICAL SECURITY INS CO	NC	C+	18.5	17.4	0.0	0.1	10.0	6.9	7.4	9.0	3.3	DFGR
MEDICUS INS CO	TX	B-	69.9	34.8	0.0	0.5	10.0	4.1	6.4	9.1	3.8	FRT
MEDMAL DIRECT INS CO	FL	B-	40.0	21.9	11.5	0.4	6.8	6.4	4.4	8.3	3.5	DGT

See Page 27 for explanation of footnotes and Page 28 for explanation of stability factors.

Arrows denote recent upgrades ▲ or downgrades ▼   (see Section VII for explanations)

86

www.weissratings.com

RISK ADJ. CAPITAL RATIO #1	RATIO #2	PREMIUM TO SURPLUS (%)	RESV. TO SURPLUS (%)	RESV. DEVELOP. 1 YEAR (%)	2 YEAR (%)	LOSS RATIO (%)	EXP. RATIO (%)	COMB RATIO (%)	CASH FROM UNDER-WRITING (%)	NET PREMIUM GROWTH (%)	INVEST. IN AFFIL (%)	INSURANCE COMPANY NAME
12.1	10.9	N/A	N/A	N/A	N/A	N/A	N/A	N/A	999 +	0.0	0.0	MA EMPLOYERS INS CO
6.0	4.4	29.0	1.9	1.5	N/A	-13.0	56.6	43.6	167.7	-1.0	0.0	MACHINERY INS INC
N/A	N/A	N/A	268.3	1.0	840.6	N/A	N/A	N/A	N/A	0.0	0.0	MADA INS EXCHANGE
2.9	1.9	80.5	27.9	0.6	8.2	83.7	26.7	110.4	84.5	-0.9	0.0	MADISON MUTUAL INS CO
5.6	3.4	41.1	15.8	-1.9	-2.4	67.6	37.3	104.9	90.4	13.2	0.0	MADISON MUTUAL INS CO
3.2	2.5	22.7	56.5	-6.1	-12.6	71.3	25.6	96.9	94.8	3.2	12.5 ●	MAG MUTUAL INS CO
1.2	0.7	141.5	154.1	3.5	0.9	69.9	33.8	103.7	96.1	-5.1	0.0 ●	MAIDEN RE NORTH AMERICA INC
0.3	0.2	205.9	164.4	-3.9	-11.3	93.5	33.5	127.0	83.4	106.4	0.0	MAIDSTONE INS CO
N/A	N/A	N/A	N/A	N/A	N/A	N/A	N/A	N/A	N/A	0.0	0.0	MAIN STREET AMER PROTECTION INS
43.9	21.8	N/A	N/A	N/A	N/A	N/A	N/A	N/A	N/A	0.0	0.0	MAIN STREET AMERICA ASR CO
1.2	0.8	184.2	12.1	1.2	-2.6	38.8	44.6	83.4	150.0	23.1	0.0	MAISON INS CO
1.9	1.7	69.0	73.6	-0.9	-21.5	69.2	18.3	87.5	127.1	-3.3	0.0	MAKE TRANSPORTATION INS INC RRG
2.4	0.9	-0.2	102.5	-76.7	-71.0	999 +	999 +	999 +	0.9	-120.0	0.0	MANHATTAN RE-INS CO
1.8	1.3	75.8	149.4	8.5	22.1	83.1	26.0	109.1	103.7	-9.9	5.7	MANUFACTURERS ALLIANCE INS CO
1.3	0.6	81.4	106.2	-18.7	-48.4	53.3	18.0	71.3	177.7	4.1	0.0	MANUFACTURING TECHNOLOGY MUT
1.0	0.8	235.3	97.9	3.4	11.8	84.1	21.8	105.9	100.5	57.5	0.0	MAPFRE INS CO
1.5	1.2	257.2	102.9	3.3	8.7	84.1	22.3	106.4	128.1	88.0	0.0	MAPFRE INS CO OF FLORIDA
2.0	1.7	226.2	97.3	3.4	8.6	84.1	23.1	107.2	110.9	38.5	0.0	MAPFRE INS CO OF NY
4.3	3.0	26.8	0.9	-0.4	-0.5	34.1	38.8	72.9	468.9	286.6	0.0	MAPFRE PAN AMERICAN INS CO
1.4	0.9	100.9	46.3	-3.2	-6.0	44.0	42.6	86.6	107.1	5.5	9.1	MAPFRE PRAICO INS CO
3.5	2.6	64.3	12.5	-1.6	-1.1	54.2	34.1	88.3	98.5	3.2	0.0	MAPLE VALLEY MUTUAL INS CO
1.4	1.3	-40.1	1.5	-1.1	-1.2	N/A	38.3	38.3	254.5	-186.0	0.0	MARATHON FINANCIAL INS INC RRG
3.0	1.9	95.1	79.2	-8.8	-10.5	52.3	38.9	91.2	116.8	-1.3	0.0	MARKEL AMERICAN INS CO
2.6	1.7	29.1	58.5	0.4	-0.9	71.7	34.5	106.2	111.0	-4.1	13.6 ●	MARKEL GLOBAL REINS CO
1.8	0.9	151.4	226.7	-1.9	-2.9	68.2	37.1	105.3	118.7	6.1	0.0 ●	MARKEL INS CO
2.9	2.5	86.4	5.8	-0.5	-0.7	50.9	27.9	78.8	125.6	5.4	0.0	MARYSVILLE MUTUAL INS CO
87.8	41.1	N/A	N/A	N/A	N/A	N/A	N/A	N/A	N/A	0.0	0.0	MASSACHUSETTS BAY INS CO
30.8	27.1	N/A	N/A	N/A	N/A	N/A	N/A	N/A	N/A	0.0	0.0	MASSACHUSETTS HOMELAND INS CO
1.8	1.2	72.2	107.2	4.1	12.2	63.1	33.7	96.8	110.1	3.4	0.0	MAXUM CASUALTY INS CO
2.6	1.8	60.2	89.4	3.3	9.8	63.1	34.0	97.1	108.4	3.4	7.4	MAXUM INDEMNITY CO
0.2	0.2	241.3	244.1	88.6	161.9	100.2	1.3	101.5	61.6	4.2	0.0	MAYA ASR CO
0.7	0.2	14.3	-54.4	25.9	38.4	81.8	-2.1	79.7	26.1	-16.8	50.5 ●	MBIA INS CORP
N/A	N/A	46.1	200.6	-7.9	999 +	107.2	25.4	132.6	89.8	5.2	0.0	MCIC VERMONT INC RRG
2.2	1.7	81.3	15.2	-3.0	-4.6	50.2	34.6	84.8	118.3	9.8	0.0	MCMILLAN WARNER MUTUAL INS CO
3.6	2.6	29.7	62.1	-21.6	-36.7	97.5	15.0	112.5	200.0	-10.1	0.0	MD RRG INC
2.1	1.9	26.5	118.4	-6.1	-10.4	64.8	26.8	91.6	128.3	-5.2	0.0	MDADVANTAGE INS CO OF NJ
7.0	6.3	N/A	N/A	N/A	N/A	N/A	N/A	N/A	7.2	0.0	0.0	MDOW INS CO
2.0	1.8	25.7	52.0	-7.5	-6.0	41.0	46.8	87.8	-168.0	-33.5	0.0	MED MAL RRG INC
N/A	N/A	0.4	N/A	N/A	N/A	60.1	105.3	165.4	12.7	0.0	0.0	MEDCHOICE RRG INC
2.7	2.4	51.2	N/A	N/A	N/A	17.1	74.7	91.8	174.6	2.2	0.0	MEDICAL ALLIANCE INS CO
3.6	2.6	29.5	75.5	-4.7	-5.4	82.4	17.6	100.0	106.8	-6.9	2.8	MEDICAL INS EXCHANGE OF
7.8	5.5	19.7	32.0	-6.7	-9.1	53.7	18.2	71.9	172.3	-2.9	0.0	MEDICAL LIABILITY ALLIANCE
1.7	1.4	22.5	180.3	-10.6	-25.2	77.6	11.8	89.4	75.3	-16.2	0.3 ●	MEDICAL LIABILITY MUTUAL INS CO
6.7	4.7	23.7	52.8	-7.0	-16.1	53.6	24.8	78.4	160.7	9.9	0.0	MEDICAL MUTUAL INS CO OF MAINE
4.0	2.9	27.9	67.2	-10.8	-10.6	57.2	11.6	68.8	139.0	-6.8	3.9 ●	MEDICAL MUTUAL INS CO OF NC
3.6	3.2	28.0	51.7	-7.5	-18.3	53.9	16.3	70.2	107.8	-5.6	13.3 ●	MEDICAL MUTUAL LIAB INS SOC OF MD
2.0	1.7	15.7	76.0	-7.2	-13.4	60.0	34.8	94.8	95.4	-8.5	23.6 ●	MEDICAL PROFESSIONAL MUTUAL INS
4.4	3.1	14.4	50.6	-4.0	-63.7	59.5	13.2	72.7	145.5	133.3	0.0 ●	MEDICAL PROTECTIVE CO
3.6	3.1	41.3	78.9	-15.4	-32.6	22.3	25.3	47.6	145.9	4.9	0.0	MEDICAL PROVIDERS MUTUAL INS CO
28.3	22.1	N/A	1.9	-2.1	-6.1	N/A	N/A	N/A	42.3	-100.0	0.0	MEDICAL SECURITY INS CO
7.3	6.5	N/A	36.5	N/A	N/A	N/A	N/A	N/A	400.7	0.0	0.0	MEDICUS INS CO
2.2	1.4	53.7	57.1	0.5	-3.0	60.0	42.0	102.0	125.6	-15.6	0.0	MEDMAL DIRECT INS CO

999 + Denotes number greater than 999.9%
999 - Denotes number less than -999.99%
● Bullets denote a more detailed analysis is available in Section II.

INSURANCE COMPANY NAME	DOM. STATE	RATING	TOTAL ASSETS ($MIL)	CAPITAL & SURPLUS ($MIL)	ANNUAL NET PREMIUM ($MIL)	NET INCOME ($MIL)	CAPITAL-IZATION INDEX (PTS)	RESERVE ADQ INDEX (PTS)	PROFIT-ABILITY INDEX (PTS)	LIQUIDITY INDEX (PTS)	STAB. INDEX (PTS)	STABILITY FACTORS
MEDMARC CASUALTY INS CO	VT	C	276.4	190.1	25.7	3.4	8.5	6.8	6.7	7.7	4.0	RT
MEDPRO RRG	DC	C-	84.3	7.3	-0.7	-0.2	6.2	9.2	4.3	8.9	2.1	CDGT
MEDSTAR LIABILITY LTD INS CO INC RRG	DC	U (5)	3.7	1.0	0.7	0.0	N/A	10.0	2.4	9.3	1.7	DFRT
MEEMIC INS CO	MI	C	249.2	78.4	96.8	3.7	9.1	4.1	4.8	6.3	4.1	T
MEMBERS INS CO	NC	D	29.0	12.8	15.8	-0.3	7.8	8.3	4.5	6.9	2.3	DGT
MEMBERSELECT INS CO	MI	B-	485.4	150.0	174.3	4.8	9.2	4.3	4.9	6.5	4.5	T
MEMIC CASUALTY CO	NH	C+	45.0	18.9	14.1	-0.1	5.7	4.7	3.9	7.5	3.4	DGT
MEMIC INDEMNITY CO	NH	C	425.5	126.8	142.2	-2.4	6.6	8.7	4.3	6.6	3.2	RT
MENDAKOTA CASUALTY CO	IL	U	36.5	23.1	12.1	-0.7	N/A	5.1	2.9	7.2	4.1	DGT
MENDAKOTA INS CO	MN	B	11.6	9.3	0.0	0.0	10.0	3.4	6.0	10.0	4.4	DFGR
MENDOTA INS CO	MN	D+	121.2	39.0	104.1	0.4	0.3	3.1	3.8	0.0	2.5	CFLR
MENNONITE MUTUAL INS CO	OH	C	26.2	14.0	12.6	0.7	8.7	6.6	8.5	7.0	2.6	DGT
MENTAL HEALTH RISK RETENTION GROUP	VT	C	28.2	16.0	4.0	0.8	9.0	9.7	8.9	8.4	2.7	DGT
MERASTAR INS CO	IL	B-	33.2	9.9	0.0	0.2	9.8	N/A	5.6	10.0	3.8	DGRT
MERCED PROPERTY & CASUALTY CO	CA	C+	22.3	17.2	4.4	0.3	9.6	7.7	5.5	7.0	3.4	DGRT
MERCER INS CO	PA	C	263.7	112.4	79.9	1.5	7.9	6.9	7.1	6.9	4.2	RT
MERCER INS CO OF NJ INC	NJ	C	88.4	32.7	26.6	0.5	7.8	7.0	6.0	6.9	3.8	RT
MERCHANTS BONDING CO (MUTUAL)	IA	B-	172.9	102.5	73.2	5.4	8.7	6.9	8.7	6.9	3.9	RT
MERCHANTS MUTUAL INS CO	NY	B-	505.7	180.9	147.2	5.6	8.8	5.6	6.4	6.7	4.1	RT
MERCHANTS NATIONAL BONDING INC	IA	C	29.0	13.1	10.0	0.7	7.7	5.9	8.7	6.8	3.0	DGRT
MERCHANTS NATIONAL INS CO	NH	B-	127.1	49.7	42.0	1.5	7.1	4.9	5.3	6.7	3.7	RT
MERCHANTS PREFERRED INS CO	NY	B-	70.9	28.0	21.0	0.8	8.0	5.6	6.3	6.7	3.8	RT
MERCHANTS PROPERTY INS CO OF IN	IN	U	76.5	58.3	0.0	0.6	N/A	N/A	6.9	7.0	5.4	T
MERCURY CASUALTY CO	CA	B	1,905.1	937.0	662.7	28.3	7.6	5.8	3.7	6.8	4.9	T
MERCURY COUNTY MUTUAL INS CO	TX	B	12.3	4.5	0.0	0.0	8.5	N/A	3.5	7.6	4.7	DFGT
MERCURY INDEMNITY CO OF AMERICA	FL	D	60.0	38.0	0.0	0.1	10.0	N/A	6.2	7.0	2.3	FT
MERCURY INDEMNITY CO OF GEORGIA	GA	B	15.5	10.6	0.0	0.1	10.0	N/A	6.4	7.0	4.9	DFGT
MERCURY INS CO	CA	B+	1,600.5	645.5	1,472.7	15.8	8.0	5.8	5.7	5.1	5.2	T
MERCURY INS CO OF FL	FL	C	44.6	41.3	0.0	0.4	10.0	N/A	6.5	10.0	3.9	T
MERCURY INS CO OF GA	GA	B	21.1	18.0	0.0	0.2	10.0	N/A	7.7	10.0	4.9	DGT
MERCURY INS CO OF IL	IL	B	36.1	34.0	0.0	0.2	8.3	N/A	6.9	10.0	4.6	DFGT
MERCURY NATIONAL INS CO	IL	B	16.5	15.7	0.0	0.1	10.0	3.6	6.8	10.0	4.9	DGT
MERIDIAN SECURITY INS CO	IN	C	123.3	71.3	0.0	0.6	10.0	N/A	7.3	10.0	3.5	RT
MERITPLAN INS CO	CA	C	14.6	13.2	0.0	0.1	10.0	6.0	1.9	7.0	3.1	DFGT
MERRIMACK MUTUAL FIRE INS CO	MA	B-	1,409.3	900.9	259.3	19.9	7.8	6.4	5.5	6.9	4.7	FT
MESA UNDERWRITERS SPECIALTY INS CO	NJ	C	320.0	80.4	103.5	5.0	7.6	9.2	7.2	6.9	3.5	RT
MET LLOYDS INS CO OF TX	TX	B	108.6	17.3	0.0	0.3	8.1	N/A	6.3	7.0	4.8	DFT
METROMILE INS CO	DE	U	14.9	14.3	0.0	-0.7	N/A	N/A	1.8	7.0	3.0	GRT
METROPOLITAN CASUALTY INS CO	RI	B	197.5	55.7	0.0	1.0	10.0	N/A	7.9	7.0	4.2	T
METROPOLITAN DIRECT PROP & CAS INS	RI	B	136.3	32.6	0.0	0.6	10.0	N/A	7.2	7.0	4.5	T
METROPOLITAN GENERAL INS CO	RI	B	43.0	38.0	0.0	0.7	10.0	N/A	7.9	10.0	4.4	DT
METROPOLITAN GROUP PROP & CAS INS	RI	B	673.2	404.6	0.0	23.0	10.0	4.5	6.8	9.7	4.9	FT
METROPOLITAN P&C INS CO	RI	B-	5,739.6	2,390.1	3,524.3	14.6	8.0	8.6	7.7	2.6	5.1	LT
MFS MUTUAL INS CO	IA	C-	3.9	2.6	1.1	-0.2	6.7	6.1	2.0	5.9	1.9	DGRT
MGA INS CO	TX	C	254.5	100.8	226.6	4.1	7.5	2.7	5.9	4.9	3.6	LRT
MGIC ASSURANCE CORP	WI	U	6.7	6.6	0.0	0.0	N/A	6.0	2.7	10.0	3.9	FGT
MGIC CREDIT ASR CORP	WI	U	8.4	8.0	0.1	0.2	N/A	7.7	1.9	7.0	3.1	GT
MGIC INDEMNITY CORP	WI	D+	139.1	92.0	16.3	0.3	10.0	3.6	1.9	8.2	2.4	ADT
MGIC MORTGAGE REINS CORP	WI	D+	5.1	5.1	0.1	0.4	9.0	4.8	2.6	9.1	2.4	DFGT
MGIC REINS CORP	WI	D+	5.8	5.8	23.3	20.5	2.4	9.5	1.9	7.8	2.4	CDFR
▲MGIC REINS CORP OF WI	WI	D-	543.4	134.9	96.5	4.2	1.4	6.1	1.9	5.9	1.2	FT
MGIC RESIDENTIAL REINSURANCE CORP	WI	D+	5.1	5.1	0.1	0.4	8.8	4.9	2.7	9.0	2.4	DFGT

RISK ADJ. CAPITAL RATIO #1	RATIO #2	PREMIUM TO SURPLUS (%)	RESV. TO SURPLUS (%)	RESV. DEVELOP. 1 YEAR (%)	2 YEAR (%)	LOSS RATIO (%)	EXP. RATIO (%)	COMB RATIO (%)	CASH FROM UNDER- WRITING (%)	NET PREMIUM GROWTH (%)	INVEST. IN AFFIL (%)	INSURANCE COMPANY NAME
2.3	1.9	14.0	31.0	-4.0	-6.9	47.5	37.2	84.7	112.5	26.4	26.7	MEDMARC CASUALTY INS CO
0.9	0.8	-9.8	51.1	-23.1	-30.4	-35.2	-78.3	-113.5	411.0	-125.9	0.0	MEDPRO RRG
N/A	N/A	58.5	194.5	6.5	-100.8	125.3	54.0	179.3	74.5	6.0	0.0	MEDSTAR LIABILITY LTD INS CO INC
3.1	2.4	126.9	93.3	0.4	3.1	70.1	27.5	97.6	101.2	5.7	0.0	MEEMIC INS CO
1.9	1.3	117.2	29.2	-5.0	-9.1	68.6	24.2	92.8	106.1	9.3	0.0	MEMBERS INS CO
3.2	2.5	120.0	98.8	-0.2	1.7	70.5	27.2	97.7	99.9	5.7	0.0	MEMBERSELECT INS CO
1.6	0.8	75.0	64.3	-5.3	-2.1	77.5	21.8	99.3	314.6	48.5	0.0	MEMIC CASUALTY CO
1.5	1.1	113.2	137.4	-2.3	-5.0	78.1	23.8	101.9	140.8	25.2	0.0	MEMIC INDEMNITY CO
N/A	N/A	51.3	19.0	-1.6	-27.9	52.2	29.1	81.3	103.4	N/A	1.9	MENDAKOTA CASUALTY CO
10.7	9.6	N/A	N/A	N/A	N/A	N/A	N/A	N/A	39.7	0.0	0.0	MENDAKOTA INS CO
0.1	0.1	268.9	115.1	8.8	6.9	77.0	26.5	103.5	91.6	-11.8	34.0	MENDOTA INS CO
3.0	2.1	94.1	14.3	-3.8	-4.1	42.3	41.2	83.5	117.7	10.3	0.0	MENNONITE MUTUAL INS CO
3.7	2.4	26.5	64.6	-17.9	-29.2	26.8	13.6	40.4	230.8	0.7	0.0	MENTAL HEALTH RISK RETENTION
2.5	2.3	N/A	N/A	N/A	N/A	N/A	N/A	N/A	N/A	0.0	0.0	MERASTAR INS CO
5.0	3.1	26.0	8.3	-2.6	-2.4	66.4	58.5	124.9	82.6	6.5	0.0	MERCED PROPERTY & CASUALTY CO
2.0	1.6	71.0	75.2	-1.9	-5.4	61.2	31.5	92.7	109.3	10.3	18.9	MERCER INS CO
2.7	1.7	83.6	88.6	-2.2	-6.3	61.2	32.0	93.2	119.8	10.3	0.0	MERCER INS CO OF NJ INC
2.6	2.0	75.5	20.0	-4.5	-5.9	8.8	67.1	75.9	137.5	46.3	5.1	MERCHANTS BONDING CO (MUTUAL)
2.8	2.2	84.9	120.0	-2.1	1.3	65.3	32.7	98.0	102.3	-1.1	10.0	MERCHANTS MUTUAL INS CO
1.7	1.4	81.2	21.5	-4.9	-3.8	8.8	67.1	75.9	128.5	46.3	0.0	MERCHANTS NATIONAL BONDING INC
1.7	1.3	104.2	128.8	-2.7	1.8	65.3	32.7	98.0	104.9	-1.1	27.5	MERCHANTS NATIONAL INS CO
3.2	1.6	77.6	95.9	-1.9	1.2	65.3	32.7	98.0	101.2	-1.1	0.0	MERCHANTS PREFERRED INS CO
N/A	N/A	N/A	N/A	N/A	N/A	N/A	N/A	N/A	N/A	0.0	0.0	MERCHANTS PROPERTY INS CO OF IN
1.4	1.3	67.8	38.1	2.4	3.4	77.5	26.3	103.8	88.7	-9.9	38.8 ●	MERCURY CASUALTY CO
2.2	1.9	N/A	N/A	N/A	N/A	N/A	N/A	N/A	109.0	0.0	0.0	MERCURY COUNTY MUTUAL INS CO
10.1	9.1	N/A	N/A	N/A	N/A	N/A	N/A	N/A	263.2	0.0	0.0	MERCURY INDEMNITY CO OF AMERICA
6.9	6.2	N/A	N/A	N/A	N/A	N/A	N/A	N/A	-172.2	0.0	0.0	MERCURY INDEMNITY CO OF GEORGIA
1.7	1.5	224.1	74.0	-1.2	-0.5	69.6	25.8	95.4	103.2	4.0	0.0 ●	MERCURY INS CO
38.5	34.7	N/A	N/A	N/A	N/A	N/A	N/A	N/A	-605.9	0.0	0.0	MERCURY INS CO OF FL
17.7	14.9	N/A	N/A	N/A	N/A	N/A	N/A	N/A	-189.5	0.0	0.0	MERCURY INS CO OF GA
2.0	1.8	N/A	N/A	N/A	N/A	N/A	N/A	N/A	-163.6	0.0	49.6	MERCURY INS CO OF IL
31.1	17.4	N/A	N/A	N/A	N/A	N/A	N/A	N/A	5.4	0.0	0.0	MERCURY NATIONAL INS CO
10.4	9.2	N/A	N/A	N/A	N/A	N/A	N/A	N/A	-277.4	0.0	0.0	MERIDIAN SECURITY INS CO
23.5	21.1	-0.2	1.4	0.4	0.1	-654.6	955.0	300.4	999 +	56.7	0.0	MERITPLAN INS CO
2.0	1.5	30.7	16.3	-1.4	-2.8	68.5	37.6	106.1	90.0	-1.0	23.8 ●	MERRIMACK MUTUAL FIRE INS CO
2.1	1.4	137.1	195.6	-4.8	-13.3	57.7	34.4	92.1	114.0	9.8	0.0	MESA UNDERWRITERS SPECIALTY INS
2.0	1.8	N/A	N/A	N/A	N/A	N/A	N/A	N/A	210.8	0.0	0.0	MET LLOYDS INS CO OF TX
N/A	N/A	N/A	N/A	N/A	N/A	N/A	N/A	N/A	-16.1	0.0	0.0	METROMILE INS CO
5.9	5.3	N/A	N/A	N/A	N/A	N/A	N/A	N/A	999 +	0.0	0.0	METROPOLITAN CASUALTY INS CO
3.6	3.2	N/A	N/A	N/A	N/A	N/A	N/A	N/A	999 +	0.0	0.0	METROPOLITAN DIRECT PROP & CAS
24.9	22.4	N/A	N/A	N/A	N/A	N/A	N/A	N/A	999 +	0.0	0.0	METROPOLITAN GENERAL INS CO
32.5	14.9	N/A	13.8	N/A	N/A	N/A	N/A	N/A	-12.4	0.0	0.0 ●	METROPOLITAN GROUP PROP & CAS
2.1	1.7	150.9	63.7	-3.0	-6.7	70.2	26.9	97.1	101.3	1.7	22.1 ●	METROPOLITAN P&C INS CO
1.3	0.9	41.0	4.6	0.1	1.0	64.9	48.1	113.0	87.3	5.8	0.0	MFS MUTUAL INS CO
1.3	1.2	225.4	87.2	-4.1	5.3	72.1	25.8	97.9	108.4	12.4	0.0	MGA INS CO
N/A	N/A	0.5	2.8	0.2	-0.5	62.3	387.6	449.9	17.2	-39.0	0.0	MGIC ASSURANCE CORP
N/A	N/A	1.0	2.8	-1.3	-2.4	-380.7	345.3	-35.4	-128.1	-42.3	0.0	MGIC CREDIT ASR CORP
4.6	4.3	17.9	2.3	-0.1	-0.1	3.9	89.9	93.8	444.2	-0.3	4.3	MGIC INDEMNITY CORP
20.8	16.6	2.3	28.5	-12.1	-23.7	-372.9	148.9	-224.0	7.9	-30.8	0.0	MGIC MORTGAGE REINS CORP
0.3	0.3	112.3	376.2	-10.7	-19.5	53.7	51.1	104.8	65.9	-19.9	0.0	MGIC REINS CORP
0.7	0.5	74.1	157.9	-123.0	-220.1	35.4	66.4	101.8	83.2	-2.9	0.0	MGIC REINS CORP OF WI
21.0	17.1	2.4	29.4	-13.1	-26.1	-372.9	148.9	-224.0	7.9	-30.8	0.0	MGIC RESIDENTIAL REINSURANCE

999 + Denotes number greater than 999.9%
999 - Denotes number less than -999.99%
● Bullets denote a more detailed analysis is available in Section II.

INSURANCE COMPANY NAME	DOM. STATE	RATING	TOTAL ASSETS ($MIL)	CAPITAL & SURPLUS ($MIL)	ANNUAL NET PREMIUM ($MIL)	NET INCOME ($MIL)	CAPITAL-IZATION INDEX (PTS)	RESERVE ADQ INDEX (PTS)	PROFIT-ABILITY INDEX (PTS)	LIQUIDITY INDEX (PTS)	STAB. INDEX (PTS)	STABILITY FACTORS
MHA INS CO	MI	C	561.1	277.2	73.2	6.8	10.0	4.8	5.6	7.4	2.3	DRT
MIAMI MUTUAL INS CO	OH	B	55.7	26.1	31.6	1.4	7.7	8.2	6.4	6.0	4.0	DRT
MIC GENERAL INS CORP	MI	C	42.1	19.0	0.0	0.1	10.0	3.5	6.0	6.0	3.4	DRT
MIC P&C INS CORP	MI	C	97.2	54.9	0.0	0.8	10.0	N/A	5.7	7.0	3.8	FRT
MIC REINS CORP	WI	C-	2.6	2.1	0.9	1.1	10.0	3.6	5.9	9.6	2.4	DGT
MIC REINS CORP OF WI	WI	C-	2.7	2.1	1.0	1.3	10.0	4.6	4.1	9.8	2.6	DGT
MICA RRG INC	DC	U	0.8	0.8	0.0	0.0	N/A	N/A	2.7	7.0	2.6	FGT
MICHIGAN AUTO INS PLACEMENT FACILITY	MI	U	--	--	--	--	N/A	--	--	--	--	Z
MICHIGAN COMMERCIAL INS MUTUAL	MI	C-	76.2	18.7	36.4	-0.6	4.1	4.4	1.6	5.8	2.9	DFRT
MICHIGAN INS CO	MI	C+	141.0	50.0	72.7	4.8	8.7	7.6	7.6	6.7	3.9	T
▲MICHIGAN MILLERS MUTUAL INS CO	MI	C-	173.3	53.7	52.1	3.5	7.8	4.4	1.5	5.3	3.0	FRT
MICHIGAN PROFESSIONAL INS EXCHANGE	MI	C+	100.3	50.6	12.0	2.2	9.3	9.5	6.7	7.7	3.4	DRT
MICO INS CO	OH	U	10.9	10.8	0.0	0.1	N/A	N/A	3.4	7.0	4.6	GT
MID AMERICAN FIRE & CAS CO	NH	B-	8.3	8.3	0.0	0.0	10.0	N/A	6.3	7.0	3.6	DGRT
MID-CENTURY INS CO	CA	B-	4,005.3	1,013.3	2,388.9	-16.6	7.5	6.6	5.4	4.9	4.9	LRT
MID-CENTURY INS CO OF TX	TX	B-	38.5	35.9	0.0	0.1	10.0	N/A	6.7	7.0	3.8	DGRT
MID-CONTINENT CAS CO	OH	C+	516.6	162.9	123.3	6.4	4.4	5.2	7.0	7.2	4.5	CRT
MID-CONTINENT EXCESS & SURPLUS INS	DE	C+	17.6	17.6	0.0	0.2	10.0	N/A	7.3	7.0	3.4	DGT
MID-CONTINENT INS CO	OH	C	20.4	19.9	3.9	0.9	8.1	6.3	3.7	8.1	3.4	DGRT
MID-HUDSON CO-OPERTIVE INS CO	NY	C	23.9	10.7	8.9	-0.6	7.6	8.0	4.8	7.0	2.6	DGRT
MIDDLE STATES INS CO	OK	C-	5.7	5.3	0.8	-0.1	10.0	5.2	3.9	7.8	2.1	DFGT
MIDDLESEX INS CO	WI	B	719.1	254.4	187.7	3.8	9.3	8.2	6.1	6.9	4.8	T
MIDDLESEX MUTUAL ASR CO	CT	B	193.6	90.7	74.8	1.8	10.0	7.5	3.9	6.5	4.6	FT
MIDROX INS CO	NY	D+	7.9	3.3	3.3	-0.1	7.7	8.9	5.7	6.5	2.0	DGRT
MIDSOUTH MUTUAL INS CO	TN	C	26.2	10.0	6.3	-0.5	5.3	7.0	3.3	7.6	2.3	CDGT
MIDSTATE MUTUAL INS CO	NY	C+	41.1	25.7	11.4	1.0	9.1	7.7	5.7	6.7	3.3	DRT
MIDSTATES REINS CORP	IL	U	82.5	34.1	0.0	-0.4	N/A	3.8	2.6	9.2	3.8	FRT
MIDVALE INDEMNITY CO	IL	D-	13.9	13.1	0.0	0.3	10.0	6.6	8.1	9.1	1.0	DFGR
MIDWEST BUILDERS CASUALTY MUTUAL	KS	B	83.1	45.2	24.6	1.3	7.6	6.9	7.4	7.0	4.0	T
MIDWEST EMPLOYERS CAS CO	DE	C+	155.7	104.2	0.0	1.6	10.0	3.6	4.3	6.4	4.3	RT
▲MIDWEST FAMILY MUTUAL INS CO	IA	B-	210.7	58.5	106.1	3.7	7.7	5.7	6.7	6.7	3.6	RT
MIDWEST INS CO	IL	C	88.7	32.3	23.7	0.8	6.5	2.8	7.5	7.1	3.3	RT
MIDWEST INS GROUP INC RRG	VT	D	6.5	1.8	1.5	-0.1	2.9	10.0	4.1	6.4	1.5	DFGR
MIDWESTERN EQUITY TITLE INS CO	IN	D+	3.5	2.9	0.1	0.0	8.0	3.6	8.0	10.0	2.0	DGRT
MIDWESTERN INDEMNITY CO	NH	C	27.7	27.4	0.0	0.1	10.0	N/A	6.0	7.0	3.7	DGRT
MILBANK INS CO	IA	C+	606.8	136.0	274.3	-6.6	7.1	4.9	4.1	5.7	4.3	ART
MILLERS CAPITAL INS CO	PA	B-	126.9	63.0	47.1	0.7	8.7	9.4	4.1	6.2	3.8	FRT
MILLERS CLASSIFIED INS CO	IL	F (5)	2.7	0.0	-0.4	0.0	2.4	7.0	0.1	5.1	0.0	CFRT
MILLERS FIRST INS CO	IL	F (5)	7.8	-4.0	0.0	0.0	0.0	4.8	0.1	7.0	0.0	CDRT
MILLVILLE INS CO OF NY	NY	C-	3.1	2.7	0.0	0.0	10.0	3.6	5.7	7.0	2.3	DGT
MILLVILLE MUTUAL INS CO	PA	C+	80.2	51.8	28.5	1.9	9.4	6.4	8.8	6.9	3.5	T
MILWAUKEE CASUALTY INS CO	WI	B	105.9	24.7	23.1	0.2	7.2	5.9	9.3	7.6	4.1	DGRT
MINNESOTA LAWYERS MUTUAL INS CO	MN	B	174.3	82.2	32.3	1.2	9.3	6.9	6.8	6.9	4.3	RT
MISSISSIPPI FARM BUREAU CAS INS CO	MS	B-	414.9	255.4	175.3	9.9	10.0	7.6	6.7	6.9	4.5	T
MISSOURI DOCTORS MUTUAL INS CO	MO	E	6.5	0.3	3.9	0.0	0.0	0.3	0.1	7.0	0.0	CDFG
MISSOURI HOSPITAL PLAN	MO	C+	180.6	132.3	21.2	-13.4	8.9	6.3	3.5	7.1	3.4	FRT
MISSOURI PHYSICIANS ASSOCIATES	MO	U	1.9	1.8	0.0	0.0	N/A	7.9	5.9	7.0	0.0	FGRT
MISSOURI PROFESSIONALS MUTUAL INS	MO	E	17.2	0.8	9.0	-0.3	0.0	1.2	0.0	7.0	0.0	CDFG
MISSOURI VALLEY MUTUAL INS CO	SD	D+	6.0	3.5	3.4	0.2	8.6	6.5	5.7	6.1	2.0	DGRT
MITSUI SUMITOMO INS CO OF AMER	NY	B+	925.8	331.5	174.4	7.8	9.5	9.3	6.8	6.9	5.1	T
MITSUI SUMITOMO INS USA INC	NY	C+	135.5	62.8	23.0	0.1	10.0	8.7	6.0	7.9	3.2	T
MMG INS CO	ME	B	252.2	94.5	156.0	0.9	9.2	6.0	6.8	6.1	4.0	RT

See Page 27 for explanation of footnotes and
Page 28 for explanation of stability factors.

www.weissratings.com

Arrows denote recent upgrades ▲ or downgrades ▼   (see Section VII for explanations)

RISK ADJ. CAPITAL		PREMIUM TO SURPLUS (%)	RESV. TO SURPLUS (%)	RESV. DEVELOP.		LOSS RATIO (%)	EXP. RATIO (%)	COMB RATIO (%)	CASH FROM UNDER-WRITING (%)	NET PREMIUM GROWTH (%)	INVEST. IN AFFIL (%)	INSURANCE COMPANY NAME
RATIO #1	RATIO #2			1 YEAR (%)	2 YEAR (%)							
5.0	3.7	27.0	73.7	12.0	12.7	79.6	32.3	111.9	96.4	0.6	0.0 ●	MHA INS CO
2.7	1.7	128.6	39.6	-3.3	-4.2	61.0	31.6	92.6	103.3	-1.0	0.0	MIAMI MUTUAL INS CO
4.9	4.4	N/A	N/A	N/A	N/A	N/A	N/A	N/A	999 +	0.0	0.0	MIC GENERAL INS CORP
9.2	8.3	N/A	N/A	N/A	N/A	N/A	N/A	N/A	218.9	0.0	0.0	MIC P&C INS CORP
4.1	3.6	25.1	2.8	-0.5	-0.4	4.2	76.5	80.7	390.5	-22.1	0.0	MIC REINS CORP
3.3	3.0	17.2	2.2	-0.3	-0.4	0.9	81.8	82.7	417.9	-34.2	0.0	MIC REINS CORP OF WI
N/A	N/A	N/A	N/A	N/A	N/A	N/A	N/A	N/A	N/A	0.0	0.0	MICA RRG INC
N/A	N/A	--	--	--	--	--	--	--	--	--	--	MICHIGAN AUTO INS PLACEMENT
0.7	0.6	181.7	219.7	5.1	3.5	72.0	39.3	111.3	88.0	1.0	0.0	MICHIGAN COMMERCIAL INS MUTUAL
3.3	2.2	157.5	89.5	-2.2	-2.2	58.9	29.8	88.7	132.6	37.2	0.0	MICHIGAN INS CO
2.3	1.5	103.0	104.9	-1.1	13.5	74.1	49.0	123.1	77.9	-50.7	0.0	MICHIGAN MILLERS MUTUAL INS CO
3.0	2.4	23.7	74.6	-6.0	-15.4	73.2	12.8	86.0	120.3	6.4	0.0	MICHIGAN PROFESSIONAL INS
N/A	N/A	N/A	N/A	N/A	N/A	N/A	N/A	N/A	-53.4	0.0	0.0	MICO INS CO
241.5	120.8	N/A	N/A	N/A	N/A	N/A	N/A	N/A	N/A	0.0	0.0	MID AMERICAN FIRE & CAS CO
1.8	1.3	233.4	143.6	2.1	1.4	68.3	33.8	102.1	103.0	6.2	8.2 ●	MID-CENTURY INS CO
40.5	36.5	N/A	N/A	N/A	N/A	N/A	N/A	N/A	-31.2	0.0	0.0	MID-CENTURY INS CO OF TX
0.9	0.6	80.3	176.6	9.3	11.4	65.2	43.8	109.0	93.0	-13.9	11.5	MID-CONTINENT CAS CO
77.7	36.3	N/A	N/A	N/A	N/A	N/A	N/A	N/A	N/A	0.0	0.0	MID-CONTINENT EXCESS & SURPLUS
31.0	20.7	20.4	44.6	1.5	1.8	62.3	43.7	106.0	94.3	-13.9	0.0	MID-CONTINENT INS CO
1.6	1.1	78.8	26.8	1.8	-5.7	55.9	38.5	94.4	123.9	22.0	0.0	MID-HUDSON CO-OPERTIVE INS CO
5.5	3.4	15.5	6.2	0.1	-0.3	68.6	30.1	98.7	85.7	-16.2	0.0	MIDDLE STATES INS CO
3.7	2.4	75.1	120.8	-2.8	-4.3	72.7	27.5	100.2	115.7	3.5	4.2 ●	MIDDLESEX INS CO
4.6	3.3	84.6	44.2	-1.0	-1.3	70.7	30.1	100.8	83.1	-1.5	4.3	MIDDLESEX MUTUAL ASR CO
2.0	1.3	96.4	34.0	-7.4	-4.2	61.9	30.9	92.8	103.7	2.5	0.1	MIDROX INS CO
1.2	0.6	61.3	50.7	-4.6	-12.4	73.4	28.6	102.0	179.9	265.7	0.0	MIDSOUTH MUTUAL INS CO
4.2	2.9	46.4	27.5	-1.4	-1.7	58.9	35.8	94.7	95.5	3.1	0.0	MIDSTATE MUTUAL INS CO
N/A	N/A	N/A	124.4	1.2	11.3	N/A	N/A	N/A	N/A	-100.0	0.0	MIDSTATES REINS CORP
36.7	33.0	N/A	N/A	-0.1	-0.1	N/A	N/A	N/A	999 +	0.0	0.0	MIDVALE INDEMNITY CO
2.1	1.7	55.6	69.8	-3.8	-13.7	64.9	27.8	92.7	123.4	11.4	10.6	MIDWEST BUILDERS CASUALTY MUTUAL
6.0	5.6	N/A	N/A	N/A	N/A	N/A	N/A	N/A	29.8	0.0	0.0	MIDWEST EMPLOYERS CAS CO
2.2	1.5	196.4	134.7	1.1	4.9	71.1	23.7	94.8	121.2	5.4	0.0	MIDWEST FAMILY MUTUAL INS CO
1.7	1.0	75.6	115.8	3.4	4.8	64.8	24.9	89.7	110.2	21.0	0.0	MIDWEST INS CO
0.9	0.6	84.1	160.3	-24.9	-57.9	46.2	45.5	91.7	86.2	-29.6	0.0	MIDWEST INS GROUP INC RRG
2.7	1.6	3.0	N/A	N/A	N/A	N/A	29.1	29.1	319.6	4.1	0.0	MIDWESTERN EQUITY TITLE INS CO
3.6	3.6	N/A	N/A	N/A	N/A	N/A	N/A	N/A	N/A	0.0	29.2	MIDWESTERN INDEMNITY CO
1.5	0.9	192.9	160.5	2.4	9.1	68.5	33.4	101.9	108.8	6.6	0.0	MILBANK INS CO
2.9	2.1	76.3	54.7	-19.0	-15.1	68.2	39.0	107.2	80.5	7.1	0.0	MILLERS CAPITAL INS CO
0.1	0.1	-78.8	746.7	-6.6	-14.0	357.3	-361.7	-4.4	-3.5	-106.7	0.0	MILLERS CLASSIFIED INS CO
-1.5	-1.3	N/A	N/A	N/A	N/A	N/A	N/A	N/A	N/A	-100.0	0.0	MILLERS FIRST INS CO
15.8	14.2	N/A	N/A	N/A	N/A	N/A	N/A	N/A	110.6	0.0	0.0	MILLVILLE INS CO OF NY
3.8	2.7	57.4	18.3	1.0	0.9	60.0	29.5	89.5	120.9	5.2	4.1	MILLVILLE MUTUAL INS CO
1.2	0.8	104.1	48.2	-0.2	0.2	58.5	-15.1	43.4	999 +	209.4	3.6	MILWAUKEE CASUALTY INS CO
3.9	2.5	40.7	74.8	-2.5	-2.4	71.4	24.1	95.5	118.7	4.0	0.0	MINNESOTA LAWYERS MUTUAL INS CO
5.4	4.9	68.6	14.7	-1.3	-1.8	59.4	22.5	81.9	128.7	3.0	0.0 ●	MISSISSIPPI FARM BUREAU CAS INS CO
0.0	0.0	999 +	999 +	45.6	96.4	9.5	59.9	69.4	83.6	4.0	0.0	MISSOURI DOCTORS MUTUAL INS CO
2.3	2.0	14.5	24.5	-3.8	-5.3	47.6	4.9	52.5	149.8	-7.0	26.6	MISSOURI HOSPITAL PLAN
N/A	N/A	N/A	4.2	-0.9	-1.7	N/A	N/A	N/A	N/A	0.0	0.0	MISSOURI PHYSICIANS ASSOCIATES
0.0	0.0	928.9	999 +	70.4	74.2	79.8	47.2	127.0	25.7	236.4	29.1	MISSOURI PROFESSIONALS MUTUAL INS
3.7	2.6	105.3	7.7	-3.0	0.7	50.3	37.5	87.8	103.3	0.6	0.0	MISSOURI VALLEY MUTUAL INS CO
3.9	2.4	52.0	121.5	-4.9	-11.6	71.2	28.8	100.0	100.7	-9.1	0.0 ●	MITSUI SUMITOMO INS CO OF AMER
6.3	4.2	36.9	81.7	-3.3	-7.6	71.2	27.3	98.5	132.0	8.0	0.0	MITSUI SUMITOMO INS USA INC
3.4	2.3	165.1	52.1	1.1	2.1	65.4	32.2	97.6	102.6	9.6	0.0	MMG INS CO

999 + Denotes number greater than 999.9%
999 - Denotes number less than -999.99%
● Bullets denote a more detailed analysis is available in Section II.

INSURANCE COMPANY NAME	DOM. STATE	RATING	TOTAL ASSETS ($MIL)	CAPITAL & SURPLUS ($MIL)	ANNUAL NET PREMIUM ($MIL)	NET INCOME ($MIL)	CAPITAL-IZATION INDEX (PTS)	RESERVE ADQ INDEX (PTS)	PROFIT-ABILITY INDEX (PTS)	LIQUIDITY INDEX (PTS)	STAB. INDEX (PTS)	STABILITY FACTORS
MMIC INS INC	MN	B	704.6	328.2	108.7	27.0	7.8	9.4	8.8	7.2	4.7	RT
MMIC RRG INC	DC	U	0.7	0.6	0.0	0.0	N/A	N/A	2.5	10.0	1.8	FGT
MO EMPLOYERS MUTUAL INS CO	MO	B-	637.0	252.7	202.6	11.6	7.9	9.3	7.1	6.7	4.1	RT
MODERN USA INS CO	FL	C+	45.1	14.5	25.6	-1.7	5.2	4.3	4.8	6.5	3.1	CDT
MONARCH NATIONAL INS CO	FL	U	35.6	30.9	2.1	0.0	N/A	N/A	3.8	10.0	4.7	DGT
MONROE GUARANTY INS CO	IN	C	51.6	52.6	0.0	0.6	10.0	N/A	6.4	10.0	3.5	RT
MONTEREY INS CO	CA	C+	82.8	34.7	39.3	0.7	7.3	6.0	6.7	6.4	3.7	FT
MONTGOMERY MUTUAL INS CO	MA	C	51.7	51.2	0.0	0.5	10.0	N/A	7.0	7.0	4.0	DRT
MONTOUR MUTUAL INS CO	PA	U	0.9	0.6	0.2	0.0	N/A	6.3	2.0	6.8	2.0	FGT
MORTGAGE GUARANTY INS CORP	WI	D+	4,375.5	1,476.6	905.5	9.6	5.2	3.1	2.7	6.3	2.4	ART
MOTOR CLUB INS CO	RI	B	46.8	45.6	1.5	0.0	9.5	4.6	5.5	8.2	4.1	DGT
MOTORISTS COMMERCIAL MUTUAL INS CO	OH	B	354.2	152.9	132.7	1.8	9.0	7.9	6.6	6.6	4.8	T
MOTORISTS MUTUAL INS CO	OH	B+	1,375.1	545.2	491.5	7.1	8.9	7.9	5.3	6.5	5.1	T
MOTORS INS CORP	MI	D	2,054.9	749.7	420.5	-15.0	10.0	7.8	2.6	7.1	0.9	RT
MOUND PRAIRIE MUTUAL INS CO	MN	D+	7.1	3.9	3.7	0.4	8.0	6.0	5.2	7.4	2.0	DGT
MOUNT BEACON INS CO	FL	C-	33.5	18.1	27.5	-5.8	5.3	3.6	2.5	9.1	2.8	GT
MOUNT CARROLL MUTUAL INS CO	IL	D+	6.7	4.8	2.6	0.4	7.8	8.0	8.3	6.6	2.1	DGRT
MOUNT VERNON FIRE INS CO	PA	C	555.8	385.0	67.7	5.7	7.8	9.0	8.0	8.5	4.3	RT
MOUNT VERNON SPECIALTY INS CO	NE	C+	33.6	33.3	0.0	-0.9	7.4	N/A	3.5	10.0	3.7	DFGT
MOUNTAIN LAKE RRG INC	VT	D	1.7	1.2	0.1	0.0	9.7	7.0	3.4	8.5	1.1	DGT
MOUNTAIN LAUREL ASR CO	OH	C	162.8	61.8	155.2	6.5	7.3	8.7	9.1	2.2	3.6	LRT
MOUNTAIN LAUREL RRG INC	VT	D-	18.5	9.3	4.7	0.4	4.3	9.9	5.4	7.0	1.0	DFGT
MOUNTAIN STATES COMM INS CO	NM	U	1.1	1.0	0.0	0.0	N/A	N/A	3.9	10.0	3.7	DFGT
MOUNTAIN STATES HEALTHCARE RECIP	MT	D	119.1	48.1	24.0	-0.6	8.2	7.0	5.3	6.8	2.3	FT
MOUNTAIN STATES INDEMNITY CO	NM	C	51.2	32.6	7.3	0.3	8.6	6.5	3.2	7.0	3.6	DFRT
MOUNTAIN STATES MUTUAL CAS CO	NM	B-	148.9	76.3	35.0	-3.4	8.1	6.0	2.9	7.0	3.9	FRT
MOUNTAIN VALLEY INDEMNITY CO	NY	D	41.9	20.3	10.0	1.0	8.5	6.5	5.2	6.7	1.7	DFGR
MOUNTAIN WEST FARM BU MUTUAL INS CO	WY	B-	391.0	155.4	168.8	-8.9	7.6	9.3	4.3	4.9	4.0	FLT
MOUNTAINPOINT INS CO	AZ	U	12.0	12.0	0.0	0.1	N/A	3.6	2.4	7.0	3.6	GRT
MOWER COUNTY FARMERS MUT INS CO	MN	D+	5.3	3.4	1.9	0.1	10.0	7.5	8.7	7.1	2.0	DGT
MPM INS CO OF KS	KS	D	4.2	3.6	0.5	0.1	10.0	3.8	2.1	0.7	2.0	DFGL
MSA INS CO	SC	B-	18.6	18.3	0.0	0.2	10.0	N/A	7.1	7.0	3.5	DGT
MT HAWLEY INS CO	IL	C	924.7	486.5	208.2	22.3	8.2	9.3	3.5	6.9	4.0	ART
MT MORRIS MUTUAL INS CO	WI	C-	34.1	16.4	18.0	1.7	7.2	6.7	8.1	5.8	2.5	DGRT
MT WASHINGTON ASR CORP	NH	C	6.7	3.6	0.0	0.1	10.0	N/A	5.7	9.8	2.4	DGRT
MULTINATIONAL INS CO	PR	D+	33.1	10.5	14.7	0.4	1.8	4.5	1.6	2.6	2.5	CDGL
MUNICH REINS AMERICA INC	DE	C+	17,460.2	4,833.9	3,120.4	188.2	7.9	9.2	6.3	6.9	3.4	FRT
MUNICIPAL ASR CORP	NY	A+	1,125.1	379.3	-4.8	69.3	10.0	N/A	5.1	10.0	6.5	GT
MUNICIPAL MUTUAL INS CO	WV	C+	34.4	23.3	12.3	-0.3	8.7	8.0	4.6	6.7	3.1	DGT
MUNICIPAL PROPERTY INS CO	WI	U	14.5	8.8	1.9	0.5	N/A	N/A	3.5	9.1	3.8	DGT
MUTUAL BENEFIT INS CO	PA	B-	215.0	88.7	87.4	1.6	8.9	9.3	6.9	6.5	3.9	RT
MUTUAL FIRE INS CO OF S BEND TOWNSHP	PA	D+(2)	3.5	3.4	0.1	0.1	10.0	5.0	6.5	10.0	2.0	DT
MUTUAL INS CO OF AZ	AZ	B	1,032.8	603.9	105.2	14.5	10.0	9.4	8.4	8.3	4.9	RT
MUTUAL INS CO OF LEHIGH CTY	PA	D	2.7	1.4	1.7	0.2	6.8	6.1	2.2	6.2	1.1	DFGR
MUTUAL OF ENUMCLAW INS CO	OR	B	738.6	319.4	376.1	3.1	9.2	6.9	4.6	6.4	4.7	RT
MUTUAL OF WAUSAU INS CORP	WI	C	23.7	15.4	9.1	0.7	7.7	6.4	6.4	6.7	2.7	DGT
MUTUAL RRG INC	HI	C+	117.7	45.4	19.4	2.4	10.0	9.6	8.9	7.8	3.4	RT
MUTUAL SAVINGS FIRE INS CO	AL	D	4.9	4.0	0.0	0.0	10.0	N/A	3.2	7.0	2.2	DGRT
MUTUALAID EXCHANGE	KS	C+	27.7	16.7	11.1	0.1	7.6	7.9	3.8	6.8	3.0	DGRT
MYCOMPASS INC	IA	U	5.0	5.0	0.0	0.0	N/A	N/A	4.9	7.0	0.0	CGT
NAMIC INS CO	IN	C+	55.3	26.7	5.0	0.4	9.0	9.3	6.0	9.0	3.2	DT
NARRAGANSETT BAY INS CO	RI	D	227.7	74.1	78.4	12.5	6.9	4.0	2.9	6.8	2.3	GRT

See Page 27 for explanation of footnotes and Page 28 for explanation of stability factors.
Arrows denote recent upgrades ▲ or downgrades ▼   (see Section VII for explanations)

92

www.weissratings.com

RISK ADJ. CAPITAL RATIO #1	RATIO #2	PREMIUM TO SURPLUS (%)	RESV. TO SURPLUS (%)	RESV. DEVELOP. 1 YEAR (%)	2 YEAR (%)	LOSS RATIO (%)	EXP. RATIO (%)	COMB RATIO (%)	CASH FROM UNDER-WRITING (%)	NET PREMIUM GROWTH (%)	INVEST. IN AFFIL (%)	INSURANCE COMPANY NAME
1.8	1.5	33.2	72.6	-7.0	-13.8	77.4	21.7	99.1	106.6	2.1	24.2 ●	MMIC INS INC
N/A	N/A	0.2	N/A	N/A	N/A	N/A	999 +	999 +	1.0	-34.9	0.0	MMIC RRG INC
2.1	1.6	85.2	104.5	-4.8	-9.6	62.1	27.5	89.6	119.0	6.9	0.1 ●	MO EMPLOYERS MUTUAL INS CO
1.0	0.6	159.7	41.0	2.0	6.4	56.3	41.4	97.7	113.2	3.3	0.0	MODERN USA INS CO
N/A	N/A	6.7	0.8	N/A	N/A	43.7	37.7	81.4	260.5	0.0	0.0	MONARCH NATIONAL INS CO
92.7	44.7	N/A	N/A	N/A	N/A	N/A	N/A	N/A	82.8	0.0	0.0	MONROE GUARANTY INS CO
2.0	1.3	115.5	78.8	1.3	1.7	69.9	33.5	103.4	96.9	-11.0	0.0	MONTEREY INS CO
100.3	50.4	N/A	N/A	N/A	N/A	N/A	N/A	N/A	N/A	0.0	0.0	MONTGOMERY MUTUAL INS CO
N/A	N/A	26.3	4.8	0.3	0.4	38.0	112.5	150.5	82.6	-1.1	0.0	MONTOUR MUTUAL INS CO
1.0	0.9	57.5	99.0	-5.6	-7.6	36.8	64.0	100.8	95.6	19.4	7.2 ●	MORTGAGE GUARANTY INS CORP
4.4	2.6	3.4	0.5	N/A	N/A	53.3	65.7	119.0	70.1	711.1	0.0	MOTOR CLUB INS CO
3.3	2.4	88.4	64.2	-2.6	-4.8	64.4	36.7	101.1	97.9	-3.1	6.8	MOTORISTS COMMERCIAL MUTUAL INS
2.9	2.1	88.7	64.4	-2.5	-4.4	64.4	37.0	101.4	99.4	-1.9	10.1 ●	MOTORISTS MUTUAL INS CO
4.3	2.9	56.3	16.2	-1.4	-3.4	54.7	40.7	95.4	97.4	-11.6	3.6 ●	MOTORS INS CORP
2.5	2.0	104.0	5.1	1.8	-0.9	22.8	38.5	61.3	160.6	0.6	0.0	MOUND PRAIRIE MUTUAL INS CO
1.0	0.7	107.7	26.7	0.1	N/A	85.8	7.8	93.6	130.8	227.3	0.0	MOUNT BEACON INS CO
3.4	2.1	58.7	8.6	-0.3	-2.6	48.4	34.6	83.0	106.0	-8.9	0.4	MOUNT CARROLL MUTUAL INS CO
2.1	1.6	16.9	24.0	-3.2	-6.2	37.8	41.0	78.8	118.2	0.5	22.6 ●	MOUNT VERNON FIRE INS CO
1.3	1.3	0.1	N/A	N/A	N/A	59.8	999 +	999 +	-2.5	0.0	89.0	MOUNT VERNON SPECIALTY INS CO
4.2	3.1	10.2	36.3	-4.4	-11.1	47.2	146.3	193.5	90.2	0.0	0.0	MOUNTAIN LAKE RRG INC
1.5	1.4	283.9	74.0	-2.1	-5.0	70.9	21.2	92.1	116.2	13.1	0.0	MOUNTAIN LAUREL ASR CO
1.0	0.7	53.8	86.4	-14.1	-39.5	14.6	64.0	78.6	89.9	-14.4	0.0	MOUNTAIN LAUREL RRG INC
N/A	N/A	N/A	N/A	N/A	N/A	N/A	N/A	N/A	-272.4	0.0	0.0	MOUNTAIN STATES COMM INS CO
2.5	1.7	50.9	118.3	3.6	1.6	101.1	11.7	112.8	99.7	-8.4	0.0	MOUNTAIN STATES HEALTHCARE RECIP
4.8	2.6	22.4	44.8	-3.1	-8.2	67.2	37.5	104.7	78.9	-6.4	2.1	MOUNTAIN STATES INDEMNITY CO
2.0	1.6	43.7	62.8	2.1	0.8	85.4	40.8	126.2	89.8	3.0	25.2	MOUNTAIN STATES MUTUAL CAS CO
3.7	2.6	50.9	34.1	0.6	1.1	72.6	5.4	78.0	48.0	-22.4	0.0	MOUNTAIN VALLEY INDEMNITY CO
1.9	1.3	104.5	59.4	-8.3	-17.0	76.5	25.4	101.9	94.5	5.3	7.3	MOUNTAIN WEST FARM BU MUTUAL INS
N/A	N/A	N/A	N/A	N/A	N/A	N/A	N/A	N/A	N/A	0.0	0.0	MOUNTAINPOINT INS CO
4.7	3.3	58.1	8.9	-0.3	-2.5	46.6	41.8	88.4	132.8	11.4	0.0	MOWER COUNTY FARMERS MUT INS CO
13.9	12.5	13.6	12.4	-1.6	-13.1	91.8	21.0	112.8	66.8	-94.6	0.0	MPM INS CO OF KS
86.8	42.1	N/A	N/A	N/A	N/A	N/A	N/A	N/A	N/A	0.0	0.0	MSA INS CO
2.4	1.8	46.5	66.1	-4.8	-9.1	37.4	39.2	76.6	142.6	-0.6	14.2 ●	MT HAWLEY INS CO
1.9	1.3	128.1	31.9	-1.8	1.8	50.6	31.7	82.3	124.0	3.4	0.0	MT MORRIS MUTUAL INS CO
3.4	3.0	N/A	N/A	N/A	N/A	N/A	N/A	N/A	37.6	0.0	0.0	MT WASHINGTON ASR CORP
0.9	0.5	212.9	99.2	13.4	10.5	55.9	53.7	109.6	118.0	-4.9	0.0	MULTINATIONAL INS CO
2.9	1.8	62.9	122.5	-3.3	-7.4	62.4	35.6	98.0	105.5	-3.9	0.0 ●	MUNICH REINS AMERICA INC
25.6	15.5	-0.7	N/A	N/A	N/A	N/A	-350.0	-350.0	-29.8	4.4	0.0 ●	MUNICIPAL ASR CORP
3.2	2.2	53.3	11.6	-4.8	-4.5	58.6	30.5	89.1	109.2	7.7	0.0	MUNICIPAL MUTUAL INS CO
N/A	N/A	22.7	2.7	N/A	N/A	103.0	37.2	140.2	371.8	0.0	0.0	MUNICIPAL PROPERTY INS CO
3.1	2.3	102.3	67.1	-9.1	-10.3	63.9	31.9	95.8	100.0	6.4	9.2	MUTUAL BENEFIT INS CO
87.9	73.5	2.8	0.1	-0.1	-0.1	14.6	53.6	68.2	156.0	-13.4	0.0	MUTUAL FIRE INS CO OF S BEND
7.1	5.0	17.9	48.3	-6.6	-14.7	53.7	19.2	72.9	136.6	-0.2	0.0 ●	MUTUAL INS CO OF AZ
2.0	1.2	145.4	16.3	8.6	5.2	70.8	39.8	110.6	81.2	-0.7	1.7	MUTUAL INS CO OF LEHIGH CTY
3.8	2.7	129.7	69.1	0.5	-3.8	77.5	30.9	108.4	98.0	7.4	3.9 ●	MUTUAL OF ENUMCLAW INS CO
2.7	1.6	64.0	7.7	-1.6	-1.7	39.3	45.7	85.0	117.8	-1.9	0.0	MUTUAL OF WAUSAU INS CORP
3.8	2.9	45.1	91.6	-18.9	-28.2	78.9	9.1	88.0	235.7	2.7	0.2	MUTUAL RRG INC
9.8	8.8	N/A	N/A	N/A	N/A	N/A	N/A	N/A	324.0	0.0	0.0	MUTUAL SAVINGS FIRE INS CO
1.5	1.4	69.7	15.9	-2.0	-3.1	62.6	27.8	90.4	107.4	2.4	37.9	MUTUALAID EXCHANGE
N/A	N/A	N/A	N/A	N/A	N/A	N/A	N/A	N/A	N/A	0.0	0.0	MYCOMPASS INC
4.2	2.5	19.1	25.2	-3.8	-8.8	50.8	39.7	90.5	157.2	3.9	0.0	NAMIC INS CO
2.5	2.1	132.2	37.2	-1.7	5.7	60.1	20.0	80.1	124.8	11.8	0.0	NARRAGANSETT BAY INS CO

999 + Denotes number greater than 999.9%
999 - Denotes number less than -999.99%
● Bullets denote a more detailed analysis is available in Section II.

INSURANCE COMPANY NAME	DOM. STATE	RATING	TOTAL ASSETS ($MIL)	CAPITAL & SURPLUS ($MIL)	ANNUAL NET PREMIUM ($MIL)	NET INCOME ($MIL)	CAPITAL-IZATION INDEX (PTS)	RESERVE ADQ INDEX (PTS)	PROFIT-ABILITY INDEX (PTS)	LIQUIDITY INDEX (PTS)	STAB. INDEX (PTS)	STABILITY FACTORS
NASW RRG INC	DC	D	7.8	5.0	0.4	0.1	10.0	4.6	4.3	10.0	2.1	DGT
NATIONAL AMERICAN INS CO	OK	C+	189.9	66.2	68.4	2.4	8.8	6.2	8.7	6.6	3.6	RT
NATIONAL AMERICAN INS CO OF CA	CA	U	32.1	14.1	0.0	-0.9	N/A	2.1	1.7	10.0	2.9	FGRT
NATIONAL ASSISTED LIVING RRG INC	DC	D+	8.2	4.0	1.6	-0.2	5.9	9.8	5.9	6.8	2.0	DFGT
NATIONAL BAIL & SURETY CO	FL	U	2.1	2.0	0.0	0.0	N/A	6.5	2.9	10.0	3.6	GT
NATIONAL BUILDERS & CONTRACTORS INS	NV	D	3.0	1.7	0.1	0.0	5.7	5.1	2.4	9.8	1.4	DFGR
NATIONAL BUILDERS INS CO	DE	B	84.6	27.0	19.8	0.4	7.3	9.3	8.8	6.8	4.1	RT
NATIONAL BUILDING MATERIAL ASR CO	IN	E+	6.3	4.1	0.9	0.0	9.4	4.7	3.9	7.1	0.6	DGRT
NATIONAL CASUALTY CO	WI	B+	402.1	136.6	0.0	1.6	10.0	N/A	7.7	7.8	5.0	FT
NATIONAL CATHOLIC RRG	VT	D-	63.5	14.3	10.8	0.3	1.1	2.6	1.6	5.9	1.2	CDFR
NATIONAL CONTINENTAL INS CO	NY	C	141.6	58.7	14.6	7.2	10.0	9.3	5.4	9.0	3.6	FT
NATIONAL DIRECT INS CO	NV	D	5.1	2.2	4.1	0.0	4.6	6.2	4.6	1.6	1.8	DGLT
NATIONAL FARMERS UNION PROP & CAS	WI	C	182.7	44.8	49.1	0.0	7.4	3.9	2.3	6.7	3.7	FRT
NATIONAL FIRE & CASUALTY CO	IL	C	7.9	4.3	2.8	-0.2	7.9	9.3	3.4	6.6	2.8	DGRT
NATIONAL FIRE & INDEMNITY EXCHANGE	MO	C-	11.1	5.7	3.1	0.1	8.6	5.7	3.4	6.9	2.1	DFGR
NATIONAL FIRE & MARINE INS CO	NE	C	8,533.9	4,980.3	822.2	234.2	8.0	6.1	7.4	8.3	3.9	GRT
NATIONAL FIRE INS CO OF HARTFORD	IL	C	115.8	114.6	0.0	2.1	10.0	N/A	7.2	9.5	3.8	ART
NATIONAL GENERAL ASR CO	MO	C	43.2	16.8	0.0	0.1	10.0	3.6	3.9	7.5	3.3	DRT
NATIONAL GENERAL INS CO	MO	C	57.2	26.6	0.0	0.4	10.0	3.7	3.4	10.0	3.7	RT
NATIONAL GENERAL INS ONLINE INC	MO	C	41.0	11.4	0.0	0.1	9.3	3.6	6.8	9.8	3.0	DFGR
NATIONAL GENL PREMIER INS CO	CA	C+	20.4	16.3	0.0	0.1	10.0	6.9	8.4	10.0	3.3	DFGR
NATIONAL GUARDIAN RRG INC	HI	C-	11.4	6.5	-3.0	-0.1	7.7	9.9	5.5	7.7	2.2	DFGR
NATIONAL HERITAGE INS CO	IL	D+	3.6	1.6	3.1	-0.3	7.7	4.9	1.5	7.4	1.6	DFGT
NATIONAL HOME INS CO RRG	CO	U	20.2	6.8	0.0	-0.7	N/A	0.5	1.9	9.2	0.8	FGRT
NATIONAL INDEMNITY CO	NE	B	163,246.0	90,361.0	18,456.6	2,805.1	7.8	5.9	6.8	6.7	4.1	T
NATIONAL INDEMNITY CO OF MID-AMERICA	IA	C	236.5	167.4	6.6	1.5	7.9	7.6	6.9	9.2	4.3	DRT
NATIONAL INDEMNITY CO OF THE SOUTH	FL	C+	353.8	181.9	102.8	6.2	7.9	6.2	7.9	8.7	4.3	GRT
NATIONAL INDEPENDENT TRUCKERS IC	SC	C-	14.0	7.7	3.3	0.2	7.8	6.0	5.4	6.9	2.2	DGRT
NATIONAL INS ASSN	IN	U	13.6	13.5	0.0	0.1	N/A	N/A	6.5	7.0	5.1	GT
NATIONAL INS CO	PR	F (5)	0.0	0.0	0.0	0.0	5.7	3.8	0.7	5.7	0.0	DT
NATIONAL INS CO OF WI	WI	C+	20.1	18.3	5.1	0.8	9.2	9.7	3.8	6.5	3.1	DFGT
NATIONAL INTERSTATE INS CO	OH	C+	1,237.9	315.1	295.3	6.3	7.3	4.4	6.5	6.7	4.6	RT
NATIONAL INTERSTATE INS CO OF HAWAII	OH	C-	54.8	12.8	8.4	0.2	8.4	4.7	6.9	8.0	3.1	DRT
NATIONAL LIABILITY & FIRE INS CO	CT	B-	2,341.1	935.9	762.1	37.6	8.2	8.5	5.1	8.6	4.9	GRT
NATIONAL LLOYDS INS CO	TX	B-	225.9	113.8	134.3	-3.6	9.9	5.0	5.7	7.0	4.0	RT
NATIONAL MEDICAL PROFESSIONAL RRG	SC	D+	3.6	2.9	0.0	-0.1	10.0	N/A	2.0	7.0	2.0	DFGR
NATIONAL MORTGAGE INS CORP	WI	A-	530.6	345.8	103.9	-21.1	10.0	N/A	0.2	7.0	5.7	GT
NATIONAL MORTGAGE RE INC ONE	WI	C	43.6	24.3	10.3	-0.6	10.0	N/A	3.2	8.6	3.7	DGT
NATIONAL MUTUAL INS CO	OH	C	75.4	31.0	35.8	1.8	7.7	8.2	6.5	6.1	3.5	RT
NATIONAL PUBLIC FINANCE GUAR CORP	NY	B	4,754.2	2,651.5	17.0	99.7	10.0	5.9	8.6	7.0	4.0	AFT
NATIONAL SECURITY FIRE & CAS CO	AL	B-	77.8	35.6	53.5	1.3	7.8	6.0	6.4	6.0	3.6	RT
NATIONAL SERVICE CONTRACT INS CO	DC	C	13.2	11.3	0.7	0.1	10.0	4.6	6.7	10.0	2.5	DGRT
NATIONAL SPECIALTY INS CO	TX	C+	78.0	47.5	25.0	1.3	10.0	6.1	8.4	7.0	3.8	RT
NATIONAL SURETY CORP	IL	C	133.6	70.9	0.0	0.9	10.0	3.4	4.5	6.4	4.2	FGRT
NATIONAL TRUST INS CO	IN	C	36.3	37.1	0.0	0.3	10.0	N/A	5.9	9.2	3.4	GRT
NATIONAL UNION FIRE INS CO OF PITTSB	PA	C	27,169.5	6,639.7	5,564.4	631.5	7.8	3.7	3.7	6.4	2.8	AFRT
NATIONAL UNITY INS CO	TX	D	50.3	9.8	43.0	-3.0	1.2	5.3	1.2	0.3	1.5	CDFL
NATIONS INS CO	CA	C-	35.5	10.0	25.4	0.2	4.4	4.3	2.3	7.0	2.3	DGT
NATIONWIDE AFFINITY INS CO OF AMER	OH	B	419.2	12.7	0.0	0.2	6.8	N/A	4.2	7.3	4.4	FT
NATIONWIDE AGRIBUSINESS INS CO	IA	B-	567.3	71.7	0.0	0.7	10.0	N/A	8.2	6.9	4.2	AFT
NATIONWIDE ASR CO	WI	B-	144.8	61.5	0.0	0.9	10.0	N/A	6.3	10.0	4.1	AT
NATIONWIDE GENERAL INS CO	OH	B-	415.0	23.3	0.0	0.5	8.3	N/A	6.5	0.9	3.9	AGLT

See Page 27 for explanation of footnotes and
Page 28 for explanation of stability factors.
Arrows denote recent upgrades ▲ or downgrades ▼   (see Section VII for explanations)

94

www.weissratings.com

RISK ADJ. CAPITAL RATIO #1	CAPITAL RATIO #2	PREMIUM TO SURPLUS (%)	RESV. TO SURPLUS (%)	RESV. DEVELOP. 1 YEAR (%)	RESV. DEVELOP. 2 YEAR (%)	LOSS RATIO (%)	EXP. RATIO (%)	COMB RATIO (%)	CASH FROM UNDER-WRITING (%)	NET PREMIUM GROWTH (%)	INVEST. IN AFFIL (%)	INSURANCE COMPANY NAME
5.1	4.0	9.1	3.8	1.1	-1.3	47.5	12.7	60.2	169.7	58.2	0.0	NASW RRG INC
3.5	2.3	104.4	114.2	-5.8	-3.8	55.6	40.0	95.6	133.9	-4.0	0.0	NATIONAL AMERICAN INS CO
N/A	N/A	0.3	123.8	-1.9	0.4	-911.5	999 +	999 +	1.5	-90.0	16.3	NATIONAL AMERICAN INS CO OF CA
1.5	0.9	38.9	68.4	-18.9	-43.3	47.7	56.9	104.6	82.1	-16.4	0.0	NATIONAL ASSISTED LIVING RRG INC
N/A	N/A	1.3	2.5	-2.0	-3.1	N/A	-10.7	-10.7	119.4	-62.6	0.0	NATIONAL BAIL & SURETY CO
2.2	1.6	6.2	87.7	0.2	-189.8	46.7	147.1	193.8	22.3	-73.4	0.0	NATIONAL BUILDERS & CONTRACTORS
2.2	1.6	75.2	105.7	-11.1	-13.0	54.9	24.8	79.7	134.7	5.9	0.0	NATIONAL BUILDERS INS CO
4.5	3.5	21.2	21.4	-0.7	1.5	68.3	32.7	101.0	109.0	10.6	0.0	NATIONAL BUILDING MATERIAL ASR CO
13.0	11.7	N/A	N/A	N/A	N/A	N/A	N/A	N/A	33.6	0.0	0.0 •	NATIONAL CASUALTY CO
0.4	0.2	82.7	330.0	24.4	14.9	123.9	30.5	154.4	86.2	-5.6	0.0	NATIONAL CATHOLIC RRG
7.4	6.6	28.2	83.2	-14.4	-15.8	48.9	-79.4	-30.5	30.9	-13.7	0.0	NATIONAL CONTINENTAL INS CO
0.8	0.7	185.2	92.8	2.0	-4.8	74.7	23.6	98.3	89.7	-7.1	0.0	NATIONAL DIRECT INS CO
2.1	1.3	113.5	127.1	1.5	2.8	63.9	37.4	101.3	81.3	-22.3	0.0	NATIONAL FARMERS UNION PROP &
2.3	1.4	66.3	29.2	-11.2	-13.7	58.3	35.8	94.1	111.2	113.8	0.0	NATIONAL FIRE & CASUALTY CO
2.4	2.1	56.1	52.7	-2.0	-1.1	66.2	55.1	121.3	88.8	9.6	0.0	NATIONAL FIRE & INDEMNITY
2.3	1.5	14.4	18.4	-1.3	-1.4	44.7	27.4	72.1	220.1	15.7	6.5 •	NATIONAL FIRE & MARINE INS CO
82.8	35.2	N/A	N/A	N/A	N/A	N/A	N/A	N/A	N/A	0.0	0.0	NATIONAL FIRE INS CO OF HARTFORD
4.0	3.6	N/A	N/A	N/A	N/A	N/A	N/A	N/A	195.6	0.0	0.0	NATIONAL GENERAL ASR CO
5.7	5.1	N/A	N/A	N/A	N/A	N/A	N/A	N/A	-85.1	0.0	0.0	NATIONAL GENERAL INS CO
2.5	2.2	N/A	N/A	N/A	N/A	N/A	N/A	N/A	-6.3	0.0	0.0	NATIONAL GENERAL INS ONLINE INC
12.9	11.6	N/A	N/A	N/A	-4.2	N/A	N/A	N/A	-141.6	100.0	0.0	NATIONAL GENL PREMIER INS CO
3.4	3.0	-44.7	55.9	-75.9	-79.8	129.8	-28.9	100.9	26.2	-219.1	0.0	NATIONAL GUARDIAN RRG INC
1.4	1.1	166.1	9.8	-0.3	-1.3	65.8	41.3	107.1	93.4	7.0	0.0	NATIONAL HERITAGE INS CO
N/A	N/A	N/A	59.6	-6.4	28.2	95.6	999 +	999 +	N/A	100.0	0.0	NATIONAL HOME INS CO RRG
1.8	1.5	20.5	26.1	-1.3	4.4	75.1	21.6	96.7	116.9	-30.8	22.2 •	NATIONAL INDEMNITY CO
2.7	1.6	3.9	8.4	-0.1	-0.3	92.6	36.5	129.1	134.3	-7.7	0.0	NATIONAL INDEMNITY CO OF
2.5	1.6	57.4	46.7	0.8	4.5	72.8	22.7	95.5	170.0	22.1	0.0	NATIONAL INDEMNITY CO OF THE
2.1	1.5	44.9	33.8	1.1	5.3	34.8	46.2	81.0	132.1	1.3	0.0	NATIONAL INDEPENDENT TRUCKERS IC
N/A	N/A	N/A	N/A	N/A	N/A	N/A	N/A	N/A	N/A	0.0	0.0	NATIONAL INS ASSN
1.7	0.8	N/A	N/A	N/A	N/A	N/A	N/A	N/A	N/A	-100.0	0.0	NATIONAL INS CO
15.3	8.7	29.5	19.1	-25.0	-33.6	77.3	35.9	113.2	19.7	-50.7	0.0	NATIONAL INS CO OF WI
1.5	1.2	99.9	136.4	5.1	13.2	75.1	29.0	104.1	113.0	1.4	17.6 •	NATIONAL INTERSTATE INS CO
2.1	1.9	66.4	90.6	3.4	9.5	75.1	30.4	105.5	91.1	1.4	0.0	NATIONAL INTERSTATE INS CO OF
2.7	1.7	79.6	82.0	-2.1	-3.9	68.9	26.9	95.8	132.7	20.6	0.0 •	NATIONAL LIABILITY & FIRE INS CO
3.5	2.9	110.3	22.4	3.1	8.2	61.1	31.2	92.3	105.7	-3.5	0.0	NATIONAL LLOYDS INS CO
8.9	8.0	N/A	N/A	N/A	N/A	N/A	N/A	N/A	178.9	0.0	0.0	NATIONAL MEDICAL PROFESSIONAL
2.9	2.5	28.3	0.2	N/A	N/A	1.4	93.0	94.4	107.0	232.5	0.0 •	NATIONAL MORTGAGE INS CORP
4.0	2.8	41.4	0.3	N/A	N/A	2.0	42.1	44.1	229.8	271.4	0.0	NATIONAL MORTGAGE RE INC ONE
2.8	1.7	122.8	37.8	-3.1	-4.1	61.0	31.6	92.6	104.6	-1.0	0.0	NATIONAL MUTUAL INS CO
28.9	19.0	0.7	-1.2	3.2	1.9	-2.8	359.2	356.4	26.3	25.6	0.3 •	NATIONAL PUBLIC FINANCE GUAR CORP
2.3	1.6	155.2	23.8	-2.7	-0.7	58.5	35.8	94.3	107.4	3.3	12.6	NATIONAL SECURITY FIRE & CAS CO
16.7	12.3	5.7	N/A	N/A	N/A	N/A	92.3	92.3	123.2	-13.5	0.0	NATIONAL SERVICE CONTRACT INS CO
6.0	3.9	54.3	5.5	0.8	0.7	49.1	37.7	86.8	136.3	7.7	0.0	NATIONAL SPECIALTY INS CO
9.7	8.7	N/A	N/A	N/A	N/A	N/A	N/A	N/A	64.3	0.0	0.0	NATIONAL SURETY CORP
146.9	73.4	N/A	N/A	N/A	N/A	N/A	N/A	N/A	-870.2	0.0	0.0	NATIONAL TRUST INS CO
2.4	1.6	83.3	192.4	13.5	17.2	88.8	30.1	118.9	84.4	-0.9	1.0 •	NATIONAL UNION FIRE INS CO OF
0.3	0.2	323.0	151.7	42.7	20.7	82.3	39.1	121.4	75.2	-22.9	3.0	NATIONAL UNITY INS CO
0.7	0.6	264.0	84.7	6.8	6.0	83.4	22.8	106.2	95.5	56.6	0.0	NATIONS INS CO
1.0	0.9	N/A	N/A	N/A	N/A	N/A	N/A	N/A	-0.3	0.0	0.0	NATIONWIDE AFFINITY INS CO OF AMER
5.7	4.5	N/A	N/A	N/A	N/A	N/A	N/A	N/A	62.0	0.0	0.0	NATIONWIDE AGRIBUSINESS INS CO
7.4	6.7	N/A	N/A	N/A	N/A	N/A	N/A	N/A	-60.1	0.0	0.0	NATIONWIDE ASR CO
2.0	1.6	N/A	N/A	N/A	N/A	N/A	N/A	N/A	187.8	0.0	0.0	NATIONWIDE GENERAL INS CO

999 + Denotes number greater than 999.9%
999 - Denotes number less than -999.99%
• Bullets denote a more detailed analysis is available in Section II.

INSURANCE COMPANY NAME	DOM. STATE	RATING	TOTAL ASSETS ($MIL)	CAPITAL & SURPLUS ($MIL)	ANNUAL NET PREMIUM ($MIL)	NET INCOME ($MIL)	CAPITAL-IZATION INDEX (PTS)	RESERVE ADQ INDEX (PTS)	PROFIT-ABILITY INDEX (PTS)	LIQUIDITY INDEX (PTS)	STAB. INDEX (PTS)	STABILITY FACTORS
NATIONWIDE INDEMNITY CO	OH	C+	3,004.2	1,061.9	0.4	48.8	6.1	2.3	3.8	9.7	4.5	FGT
NATIONWIDE INS CO OF AM	WI	B-	453.4	153.1	0.0	1.6	10.0	N/A	7.3	7.0	4.5	T
NATIONWIDE INS CO OF FL	OH	C+	316.9	305.8	34.9	5.2	10.0	5.2	7.7	8.7	3.1	T
NATIONWIDE LLOYDS	TX	B	44.9	28.5	0.0	0.2	10.0	N/A	6.1	7.0	4.3	FT
NATIONWIDE MUTUAL FIRE INS CO	OH	B+	6,045.9	2,623.6	2,242.5	-13.2	10.0	6.2	4.3	6.5	5.1	AT
NATIONWIDE MUTUAL INS CO	OH	B	36,667.7	12,353.5	15,510.8	-272.9	7.4	5.3	4.5	5.1	5.1	AT
NATIONWIDE P&C INS CO	OH	B-	688.5	47.6	0.0	0.0	9.8	N/A	3.4	10.0	3.9	AFT
NAU COUNTRY INS CO	MN	C	1,291.9	356.1	343.9	-0.9	7.4	3.7	3.9	7.5	4.3	FRT
NAUTILUS INS CO	AZ	C	264.0	160.8	0.0	2.0	10.0	3.9	3.1	10.0	3.8	RT
NAVIGATORS INS CO	NY	B	2,764.8	997.0	757.1	36.2	8.2	6.8	7.5	6.8	4.6	RT
NAVIGATORS SPECIALTY INS CO	NY	B-	178.2	137.5	0.0	1.6	10.0	N/A	7.0	7.0	4.4	T
NAZARETH MUTUAL INS CO	PA	C-	13.7	6.9	6.0	0.5	7.6	7.8	7.5	6.6	2.1	DGRT
NCMIC INS CO	IA	B	731.1	274.4	145.6	9.9	7.8	9.6	8.9	7.4	4.2	RT
NCMIC RRG INC	VT	C-	6.7	4.1	0.8	0.0	9.7	3.7	4.5	9.4	2.5	DGT
NEIGHBORHOOD SPIRIT PROP & CAS CO	CA	C+	283.2	117.8	149.3	-2.3	9.4	6.1	6.1	6.6	4.5	RT
NETHERLANDS INS CO	NH	C	92.0	87.6	0.0	1.0	10.0	3.8	3.6	7.0	4.3	RT
NEVADA CAPITAL INS CO	NV	B-	105.5	53.2	42.9	0.4	8.5	6.0	6.7	6.0	3.9	T
NEVADA DOCS MEDICAL RRG INC	NV	U (3)	2.6	1.0	0.0	0.1	N/A	4.0	0.8	2.5	0.0	LRT
▼NEVADA GENERAL INS CO	NV	D+	16.2	6.3	13.9	-1.5	7.8	6.2	1.4	6.0	2.6	DFGT
NEVADA MUTUAL INS CO	NV	D+	31.0	9.4	4.2	-0.2	3.5	4.0	3.9	5.2	2.5	DFGR
NEW CENTURY INS CO	TX	C	9.2	5.1	3.0	-0.6	10.0	6.3	3.8	6.8	2.6	DGRT
NEW ENGLAND GUARANTY INS CO INC	VT	U	44.3	41.1	0.0	0.4	N/A	N/A	7.8	7.0	5.4	T
NEW ENGLAND INS CO	CT	U	37.6	35.7	0.0	0.5	N/A	6.0	3.0	10.0	4.4	AGT
NEW ENGLAND MUTUAL INS CO	MA	B-	45.3	40.6	-2.2	0.4	10.0	4.7	4.1	6.2	3.9	DFT
NEW ENGLAND REINS CORP	CT	U	38.6	36.6	0.0	0.4	N/A	6.0	3.3	10.0	5.0	AGT
NEW HAMPSHIRE EMPLOYERS INS CO	NH	B-	4.0	3.4	0.0	0.0	10.0	N/A	6.3	7.0	3.5	DFGT
NEW HAMPSHIRE INS CO	IL	C	213.0	89.7	0.0	4.9	10.0	3.5	1.9	7.0	4.1	AT
NEW HOME WARRANTY INS CO RRG	DC	B-	19.9	6.3	3.2	0.0	7.7	4.9	4.7	8.0	3.5	DGT
NEW JERSEY CASUALTY INS CO	NJ	C+(2)	560.1	239.0	79.5	20.3	8.4	5.8	8.7	7.1	4.5	T
NEW JERSEY INDEMNITY INS CO	NJ	C+(2)	78.6	66.2	6.1	2.7	10.0	7.0	7.8	9.1	4.1	DFT
NEW JERSEY PHYS UNITED RECIP EXCH	NJ	D+	30.9	11.7	5.2	-1.5	2.6	2.9	1.8	7.0	2.5	DFGT
NEW JERSEY RE-INS CO	NJ	B	548.6	409.8	21.5	7.1	9.0	6.9	8.0	8.6	4.7	FT
NEW JERSEY SKYLANDS INS ASSN	NJ	D+(2)	71.9	12.9	17.1	-3.1	3.2	3.7	1.3	0.4	2.5	DFLT
NEW JERSEY SKYLANDS INS CO	NJ	C- (2)	53.0	11.5	9.2	-1.9	7.0	3.9	2.0	5.6	3.1	DGT
NEW LONDON COUNTY MUTUAL INS CO	CT	B-	114.5	64.4	35.7	1.8	8.5	8.4	5.0	6.7	3.8	FRT
NEW MEXICO ASR CO	NM	C-	5.9	1.7	0.0	0.0	5.9	N/A	3.4	8.1	2.0	DGT
NEW MEXICO EMPLOYERS ASR CO	NM	B-	6.2	1.9	0.0	-0.1	6.0	N/A	3.6	6.8	3.5	DGT
NEW MEXICO FOUNDATION INS CO	NM	C	23.4	17.3	0.0	0.1	10.0	3.6	7.4	10.0	3.3	DGRT
NEW MEXICO MUTUAL CASUALTY CO	NM	C+	366.2	144.6	100.8	6.9	7.2	6.1	8.3	6.9	4.0	T
NEW MEXICO PREMIER INS CO	NM	C+	3.7	1.4	0.0	0.0	7.8	N/A	5.6	9.0	3.2	DGT
NEW MEXICO PROPERTY & CASUALTY CO	NM	U (1)	1.7	1.0	0.0	0.0	N/A	10.0	2.9	6.8	2.9	FGRT
NEW MEXICO SAFETY CASUALTY CO	NM	D+	5.2	1.9	0.0	0.1	8.0	N/A	6.9	9.2	2.1	DGT
NEW MEXICO SECURITY INS CO	NM	D+	3.6	1.6	0.0	0.0	9.2	N/A	6.3	9.0	2.0	DGT
NEW MEXICO SOUTHWEST CASUALTY CO	NM	C-	17.9	11.4	0.0	0.1	9.2	N/A	4.2	9.7	3.0	DGRT
NEW SOUTH INS CO	NC	C	52.8	7.6	0.0	0.1	7.2	3.5	2.4	9.4	2.8	DFRT
NEW YORK CENTRAL MUTUAL FIRE INS CO	NY	B- (1)	1,054.2	494.5	422.4	1.7	9.9	6.2	5.4	6.6	4.3	RT
NEW YORK HEALTHCARE INS CO INC RRG	DC	E+	26.1	4.9	6.3	0.1	0.1	0.3	4.4	8.3	0.4	CDGR
NEW YORK MARINE & GENERAL INS CO	NY	B-	1,274.9	374.9	401.2	-10.3	6.7	6.8	3.8	6.9	4.3	RT
▲NEW YORK MUNICIPAL INS RECIPROCAL	NY	B-	156.2	56.3	49.2	-0.9	7.8	6.9	3.9	6.6	3.6	RT
NEW YORK SCHOOLS INS RECIPROCAL	NY	B	257.6	163.5	61.9	2.1	10.0	8.3	8.6	6.9	4.5	RT
NEW YORK TRANSPORTATION INS CORP	NY	U (5)	0.0	0.0	0.0	0.0	N/A	4.1	1.9	10.0	1.8	FT
NEWPORT BONDING & SURETY CO	PR	U	4.3	2.4	0.0	0.1	N/A	1.3	3.4	4.2	0.0	LT

See Page 27 for explanation of footnotes and
Page 28 for explanation of stability factors.
Arrows denote recent upgrades ▲ or downgrades ▼   (see Section VII for explanations)

96

www.weissratings.com

RISK ADJ. CAPITAL RATIO #1	CAPITAL RATIO #2	PREMIUM TO SURPLUS (%)	RESV. TO SURPLUS (%)	RESV. DEVELOP. 1 YEAR (%)	2 YEAR (%)	LOSS RATIO (%)	EXP. RATIO (%)	COMB RATIO (%)	CASH FROM UNDER-WRITING (%)	NET PREMIUM GROWTH (%)	INVEST. IN AFFIL (%)	INSURANCE COMPANY NAME
1.8	0.8	N/A	193.3	8.7	21.3	999 +	999 +	999 +	N/A	203.7	0.0 ●	NATIONWIDE INDEMNITY CO
14.1	12.7	N/A	N/A	N/A	N/A	N/A	N/A	N/A	421.8	0.0	0.0	NATIONWIDE INS CO OF AM
53.4	38.7	11.6	4.9	0.3	-0.1	54.1	30.2	84.3	102.6	-7.2	0.0 ●	NATIONWIDE INS CO OF FL
9.1	8.2	N/A	N/A	N/A	N/A	N/A	N/A	N/A	999 +	0.0	0.0	NATIONWIDE LLOYDS
4.7	3.4	86.1	61.4	1.0	0.8	71.1	32.5	103.6	101.8	3.7	4.6 ●	NATIONWIDE MUTUAL FIRE INS CO
1.4	1.2	125.9	89.7	1.5	1.2	71.1	32.5	103.6	101.7	3.7	29.0 ●	NATIONWIDE MUTUAL INS CO
3.4	2.0	N/A	N/A	N/A	N/A	N/A	N/A	N/A	999 +	0.0	0.0	NATIONWIDE P&C INS CO
2.2	1.4	111.2	120.4	1.6	2.7	63.9	36.2	100.1	87.9	-17.2	0.0 ●	NAU COUNTRY INS CO
6.6	5.6	N/A	N/A	N/A	N/A	N/A	N/A	N/A	999 +	0.0	0.0	NAUTILUS INS CO
2.3	1.8	79.7	112.4	-6.5	-7.0	62.4	33.5	95.9	123.4	0.6	5.9 ●	NAVIGATORS INS CO
23.9	21.5	N/A	N/A	N/A	N/A	N/A	N/A	N/A	N/A	0.0	0.0	NAVIGATORS SPECIALTY INS CO
2.2	1.5	93.1	15.1	1.8	-0.6	47.9	47.1	95.0	105.2	4.3	0.0	NAZARETH MUTUAL INS CO
2.1	1.4	55.6	105.2	-7.1	-23.6	58.1	29.5	87.6	128.4	-1.0	1.4 ●	NCMIC INS CO
3.4	2.5	19.2	30.4	-2.4	-3.7	58.9	-64.5	-5.6	-317.1	-21.5	0.0	NCMIC RRG INC
3.8	2.7	124.5	71.8	1.3	1.6	68.5	33.7	102.2	103.6	6.2	0.0	NEIGHBORHOOD SPIRIT PROP & CAS CO
68.2	61.4	N/A	N/A	N/A	N/A	N/A	N/A	N/A	N/A	0.0	0.0	NETHERLANDS INS CO
3.2	2.0	81.8	55.8	0.9	1.2	69.9	33.5	103.4	96.9	-11.0	1.3	NEVADA CAPITAL INS CO
N/A	N/A	N/A	N/A	N/A	N/A	N/A	N/A	N/A	N/A	-100.0	0.0	NEVADA DOCS MEDICAL RRG INC
0.7	0.7	110.4	44.8	4.8	3.6	74.6	45.9	120.5	84.1	15.3	0.0	NEVADA GENERAL INS CO
0.9	0.7	43.9	111.5	-29.7	-56.4	-5.9	43.9	38.0	33.7	-48.1	33.4	NEVADA MUTUAL INS CO
3.1	2.8	54.9	8.5	-0.8	0.5	64.8	32.4	97.2	99.2	2.9	0.0	NEW CENTURY INS CO
N/A	N/A	N/A	N/A	N/A	N/A	N/A	N/A	N/A	N/A	0.0	0.0	NEW ENGLAND GUARANTY INS CO INC
N/A	N/A	N/A	6.7	0.3	0.4	999 +	999 +	999 +	N/A	-59.2	0.0	NEW ENGLAND INS CO
28.0	25.2	-5.6	N/A	-2.9	-2.3	107.2	24.8	132.0	8.2	-105.4	0.0	NEW ENGLAND MUTUAL INS CO
N/A	N/A	N/A	6.5	0.3	0.4	999 +	999 +	999 +	N/A	-59.2	0.0	NEW ENGLAND REINS CORP
14.1	12.7	N/A	N/A	N/A	N/A	N/A	N/A	N/A	N/A	0.0	0.0	NEW HAMPSHIRE EMPLOYERS INS CO
6.8	6.2	N/A	N/A	N/A	N/A	N/A	N/A	N/A	N/A	100.0	0.0	NEW HAMPSHIRE INS CO
1.6	1.4	51.3	7.8	-0.5	1.8	41.8	17.0	58.8	292.6	21.3	0.0	NEW HOME WARRANTY INS CO RRG
3.5	2.3	33.3	118.6	-1.0	-14.6	60.7	20.1	80.8	148.3	-10.2	0.0	NEW JERSEY CASUALTY INS CO
18.7	16.7	9.2	12.0	-5.4	-11.2	38.9	22.0	60.9	73.6	-0.5	0.0	NEW JERSEY INDEMNITY INS CO
1.0	0.9	40.3	98.1	-1.6	6.4	63.2	50.3	113.5	69.6	-1.5	0.0	NEW JERSEY PHYS UNITED RECIP EXCH
4.3	2.5	5.4	34.4	0.5	-4.3	95.1	34.6	129.7	61.0	-36.0	0.0 ●	NEW JERSEY RE-INS CO
0.6	0.5	132.4	131.7	28.0	22.5	118.7	10.1	128.8	76.8	-31.7	26.5	NEW JERSEY SKYLANDS INS ASSN
1.4	1.0	79.9	80.0	20.1	17.9	111.9	9.5	121.4	174.5	-31.7	0.0	NEW JERSEY SKYLANDS INS CO
2.8	2.2	55.3	19.6	-0.5	-1.8	67.0	39.7	106.7	92.4	-5.0	19.3	NEW LONDON COUNTY MUTUAL INS CO
1.3	0.8	N/A	121.4	N/A	N/A	N/A	N/A	N/A	-0.3	0.0	0.0	NEW MEXICO ASR CO
1.3	0.7	N/A	120.2	N/A	N/A	N/A	N/A	N/A	999 +	0.0	0.0	NEW MEXICO EMPLOYERS ASR CO
10.1	4.0	N/A	25.2	N/A	N/A	N/A	N/A	N/A	6.5	0.0	0.0	NEW MEXICO FOUNDATION INS CO
1.6	1.2	72.4	141.6	-8.0	-3.9	44.4	34.5	78.9	128.6	2.9	11.0	NEW MEXICO MUTUAL CASUALTY CO
1.6	1.4	N/A	56.3	N/A	N/A	N/A	N/A	N/A	13.8	0.0	0.0	NEW MEXICO PREMIER INS CO
N/A	N/A	-0.8	85.0	-17.5	-25.1	999 +	999 +	-53.4	18.1	92.4	0.0	NEW MEXICO PROPERTY & CASUALTY
1.7	1.4	N/A	56.5	N/A	N/A	N/A	N/A	N/A	47.7	0.0	0.0	NEW MEXICO SAFETY CASUALTY CO
2.2	2.0	N/A	27.9	N/A	N/A	N/A	N/A	N/A	58.3	0.0	0.0	NEW MEXICO SECURITY INS CO
6.3	2.4	N/A	42.7	N/A	N/A	N/A	N/A	N/A	343.4	0.0	0.0	NEW MEXICO SOUTHWEST CASUALTY
1.2	1.1	N/A	N/A	N/A	N/A	N/A	N/A	N/A	-317.3	0.0	0.0	NEW SOUTH INS CO
4.0	2.9	85.9	57.3	-1.4	0.1	66.9	30.7	97.6	102.7	0.4	4.5	NEW YORK CENTRAL MUTUAL FIRE INS
0.1	0.1	136.4	379.9	28.8	66.3	73.8	40.5	114.3	143.9	-31.7	0.0	NEW YORK HEALTHCARE INS CO INC
1.3	0.9	105.8	139.4	7.3	0.8	70.3	35.3	105.6	108.3	15.6	14.7 ●	NEW YORK MARINE & GENERAL INS CO
1.9	1.4	88.4	121.0	-5.0	-0.4	68.6	30.1	98.7	104.1	11.7	0.0	NEW YORK MUNICIPAL INS RECIPROCAL
4.8	3.4	38.9	53.8	-3.9	-6.3	65.9	19.1	85.0	120.0	8.7	0.0	NEW YORK SCHOOLS INS RECIPROCAL
N/A	N/A	N/A	42.3	N/A	N/A	N/A	N/A	N/A	N/A	0.0	0.0	NEW YORK TRANSPORTATION INS
N/A	N/A	N/A	N/A	N/A	N/A	N/A	N/A	N/A	N/A	0.0	0.0	NEWPORT BONDING & SURETY CO

999 + Denotes number greater than 999.9%
999 - Denotes number less than -999.99%
● Bullets denote a more detailed analysis is available in Section II.

INSURANCE COMPANY NAME	DOM. STATE	RATING	TOTAL ASSETS ($MIL)	CAPITAL & SURPLUS ($MIL)	ANNUAL NET PREMIUM ($MIL)	NET INCOME ($MIL)	CAPITAL-IZATION INDEX (PTS)	RESERVE ADQ INDEX (PTS)	PROFIT-ABILITY INDEX (PTS)	LIQUIDITY INDEX (PTS)	STAB. INDEX (PTS)	STABILITY FACTORS
NEWPORT INS CO	AZ	U	12.0	11.5	0.0	0.0	N/A	6.0	1.9	7.0	3.1	FGT
NGM INS CO	FL	B-	2,412.3	1,033.2	967.6	8.9	8.8	5.9	6.7	6.4	4.6	RT
NHRMA MUTUAL INS CO	IL	C-	32.8	12.6	13.7	1.6	3.7	6.1	3.2	6.5	2.4	DGRT
NJ MANUFACTURERS INS CO	NJ	B	6,882.1	2,580.6	1,629.6	20.4	8.2	6.6	4.6	6.8	5.1	T
NLC MUTUAL INS CO	VT	B	326.2	129.1	14.0	4.4	7.0	4.2	6.6	8.6	4.1	RT
NODAK MUTUAL INS CO	ND	B-	256.4	139.8	124.9	2.5	9.1	8.8	6.8	6.2	4.0	T
NOETIC SPECIALTY INS CO	VT	C	123.0	71.4	11.6	2.8	9.4	9.4	8.6	8.4	3.5	DRT
NORCAL MUTUAL INS CO	CA	B-	1,623.1	670.3	314.1	-4.9	7.7	9.3	5.3	7.0	4.6	FGRT
NORCAL SPECIALTY INS CO	PA	B-	264.8	245.4	-35.7	8.0	10.0	4.9	6.8	6.8	4.4	T
NORFOLK & DEDHAM MUTUAL FIRE INS CO	MA	C+	383.8	179.6	128.9	0.8	9.3	4.8	5.9	6.9	4.1	RT
NORGUARD INS CO	PA	D	716.4	176.5	188.3	4.1	1.5	9.5	8.7	1.6	2.0	CGLR
NORMANDY INS CO	FL	D+	40.3	11.0	23.3	0.2	2.0	7.0	4.8	6.0	2.4	CDGT
NORTH AMERICAN CAPACITY INS CO	NH	C	99.2	46.8	0.0	1.0	10.0	3.6	3.8	7.8	3.5	FRT
NORTH AMERICAN ELITE INS CO	NH	C	124.2	36.8	0.0	1.3	10.0	N/A	5.6	6.1	3.7	FGRT
NORTH AMERICAN SPECIALTY INS CO	NH	C	462.5	305.8	2.8	7.8	10.0	6.4	7.0	10.0	3.6	FRT
NORTH CAROLINA FARM BU MUTUAL INS	NC	B	1,860.2	1,106.8	716.6	15.4	10.0	8.7	4.3	6.6	4.7	T
NORTH CAROLINA GRANGE MUTUAL INS	NC	D	29.7	15.5	17.2	1.2	6.8	7.0	2.9	5.8	2.3	DGT
NORTH COUNTRY INS CO	NY	C	27.1	17.8	7.2	1.0	10.0	8.0	8.8	7.0	2.7	DGT
NORTH EAST INS CO	ME	D (3)	35.9	15.7	-6.2	0.5	7.4	1.6	1.3	7.7	1.6	DFRT
NORTH LIGHT SPECIALTY INS CO	IL	B-	90.3	49.5	0.0	-1.0	10.0	N/A	4.3	7.0	3.9	T
NORTH PACIFIC INS CO	OR	C	7.9	7.8	0.0	0.1	10.0	N/A	6.3	7.0	2.8	DGRT
NORTH POINTE INS CO	PA	C-	39.6	26.8	36.8	1.1	7.0	3.9	3.9	6.8	3.3	RT
NORTH RIVER INS CO	NJ	C-	1,050.7	288.0	365.6	6.4	6.7	5.7	6.0	7.3	3.3	ART
NORTH STAR GENERAL INS CO	MN	U	4.3	4.3	0.0	0.0	N/A	N/A	3.7	7.0	4.3	GT
NORTH STAR MUTUAL INS CO	MN	B-	684.9	392.1	338.6	30.3	10.0	7.5	8.6	6.8	4.2	RT
NORTHERN MUTUAL INS CO	MI	C	33.6	22.1	15.1	2.0	8.8	6.9	6.4	6.8	2.9	DGRT
NORTHERN SECURITY INS CO	VT	C	8.5	8.3	0.0	0.1	10.0	N/A	6.1	7.0	2.8	DGRT
NORTHFIELD INS CO	IA	C+	395.1	133.9	108.1	6.1	7.9	8.5	6.8	6.9	4.5	T
NORTHLAND CASUALTY CO	CT	B	109.4	38.6	29.1	1.7	8.2	8.4	8.4	6.7	4.4	T
NORTHLAND INS CO	CT	B	1,211.3	569.1	253.5	16.5	9.1	7.9	6.5	6.9	4.7	T
NORTHSTONE INS CO	PA	C	57.5	11.1	5.2	0.1	5.5	6.1	4.7	7.5	3.0	DT
NORTHWEST DENTISTS INS CO	WA	C	21.3	11.6	6.3	0.1	8.2	7.0	8.7	7.3	2.8	DGT
NORTHWEST GF MUTUAL INS CO	SD	D-	18.2	8.8	11.1	1.4	7.6	8.5	6.2	6.7	1.3	DGT
NORTHWESTERN NATL INS CO SEG ACCNT	WI	E+	26.0	2.6	0.4	-0.2	0.4	N/A	0.5	7.3	0.5	CDFG
NORTHWESTERN NTL INS CO MILWAUKEE	WI	F	26.3	2.6	0.0	0.0	3.5	N/A	1.9	7.0	0.0	DFGR
NOVA CASUALTY CO	NY	C+	95.2	92.6	0.0	0.2	8.7	N/A	5.8	7.0	4.3	FRT
NOVANT HEALTH RRG INC	SC	E	9.8	6.2	2.6	0.1	6.3	4.7	7.0	9.4	0.0	DFGR
NUCLEAR ELECTRIC INS LTD	DE	U (2)	4,761.0	3,796.2	204.3	22.6	N/A	3.5	4.3	6.9	5.3	F
▲NUTMEG INS CO	CT	C-	770.2	578.5	73.8	13.5	10.0	4.9	8.2	8.4	2.9	AGT
OAK RIVER INS CO	NE	C	606.1	199.1	110.9	2.0	5.8	9.2	6.2	8.0	4.1	RT
OAKWOOD INS CO	TN	U	66.9	30.9	0.0	-1.3	N/A	5.9	2.4	9.7	3.8	FGT
OASIS RECIPROCAL RRG	VT	B-	13.5	4.2	3.4	0.6	5.6	4.0	8.3	7.9	3.5	CDGT
OBI AMERICA INS CO	PA	U	15.9	15.2	0.0	0.1	N/A	N/A	4.9	7.0	5.2	GT
OBI NATIONAL INS CO	PA	C+	13.1	13.1	0.0	0.0	10.0	N/A	4.0	7.0	3.2	DGT
OBSTETRICIANS & GYNECOLOGISTS RRG	MT	U (3)	0.5	0.1	0.0	-0.3	N/A	3.2	0.1	9.6	1.1	GRT
OCCIDENTAL FIRE & CAS CO OF NC	NC	C-	554.7	150.9	123.4	3.4	6.4	4.4	5.7	5.3	2.7	RT
OCEAN HARBOR CASUALTY INS CO	FL	B-	231.7	55.7	165.1	3.2	6.0	9.7	6.9	2.9	3.7	FLRT
OCEAN MARINE INDEMNITY INS CO	LA	C-	11.9	7.3	0.6	0.1	10.0	4.0	2.6	7.3	2.2	DFGR
OCEANUS INS CO A RRG	SC	D-	54.2	9.3	23.4	-1.1	0.9	1.3	0.8	5.2	1.2	CDFR
ODYSSEY REINS CO	CT	C	7,394.0	3,265.6	1,575.5	131.7	7.3	9.4	5.8	6.6	2.7	ART
OGLESBY REINS CO	IL	A+	4,277.3	3,181.2	1,206.2	40.8	10.0	N/A	7.9	7.3	8.4	GT
OHA INS SOLUTIONS INC	OH	E	40.6	28.7	-0.4	0.4	10.0	9.3	6.0	9.4	0.0	DFGR

See Page 27 for explanation of footnotes and   98   www.weissratings.com
Page 28 for explanation of stability factors.
Arrows denote recent upgrades ▲ or downgrades ▼   (see Section VII for explanations)

RISK ADJ. RATIO #1	CAPITAL RATIO #2	PREMIUM TO SURPLUS (%)	RESV. TO SURPLUS (%)	RESV. DEVELOP. 1 YEAR (%)	2 YEAR (%)	LOSS RATIO (%)	EXP. RATIO (%)	COMB RATIO (%)	CASH FROM UNDER- WRITING (%)	NET PREMIUM GROWTH (%)	INVEST. IN AFFIL (%)	INSURANCE COMPANY NAME
N/A	N/A	-0.2	1.6	1.3	0.1	-654.6	955.0	300.4	223.4	56.7	0.0	NEWPORT INS CO
2.9	2.2	94.8	74.0	1.9	5.3	68.0	31.5	99.5	99.8	-0.1	11.6 ●	NGM INS CO
1.2	0.8	125.0	175.5	-23.3	-45.3	76.4	10.1	86.5	116.1	-6.8	10.8	NHRMA MUTUAL INS CO
2.4	1.8	66.6	126.6	-2.3	-5.2	78.6	14.0	92.6	105.6	-1.8	11.8 ●	NJ MANUFACTURERS INS CO
1.6	1.1	11.2	147.0	-2.0	-0.9	81.2	18.7	99.9	98.7	4.4	0.0	NLC MUTUAL INS CO
3.6	2.5	92.0	24.7	-7.0	-10.1	57.3	25.7	83.0	117.9	-1.4	10.6	NODAK MUTUAL INS CO
3.5	2.6	16.8	56.7	-8.6	-14.2	32.8	39.3	72.1	114.1	3.5	0.0	NOETIC SPECIALTY INS CO
1.6	1.4	46.9	91.0	-7.4	-11.8	80.3	18.5	98.8	90.1	51.1	27.4 ●	NORCAL MUTUAL INS CO
16.3	9.3	-15.1	3.3	N/A	N/A	999 +	-64.6	999 +	89.6	-146.4	0.0 ●	NORCAL SPECIALTY INS CO
3.6	2.4	72.7	46.5	0.6	3.0	75.3	34.6	109.9	97.0	4.1	2.8	NORFOLK & DEDHAM MUTUAL FIRE INS
0.3	0.2	113.3	123.7	0.1	-0.9	59.9	20.0	79.9	181.7	55.3	0.0	NORGUARD INS CO
0.6	0.3	207.9	102.8	11.3	-7.2	61.0	31.7	92.7	106.1	10.5	0.0	NORMANDY INS CO
6.8	6.1	N/A	2.7	N/A	N/A	N/A	N/A	N/A	-153.0	0.0	0.0	NORTH AMERICAN CAPACITY INS CO
4.3	3.9	N/A	3.1	N/A	N/A	999 +	999 +	999 +	-25.8	-94.6	0.0	NORTH AMERICAN ELITE INS CO
4.1	3.8	0.7	8.0	0.1	0.2	16.6	-7.4	9.2	-181.9	-80.3	15.3 ●	NORTH AMERICAN SPECIALTY INS CO
6.0	4.0	66.5	28.2	-5.2	-7.7	68.5	24.5	93.0	105.9	6.1	0.6 ●	NORTH CAROLINA FARM BU MUTUAL INS
1.7	1.2	125.4	23.8	-3.4	-7.5	54.3	29.2	83.5	121.5	4.7	0.0	NORTH CAROLINA GRANGE MUTUAL INS
5.6	4.3	43.3	24.4	-1.7	-2.6	35.4	42.6	78.0	123.2	2.2	3.8	NORTH COUNTRY INS CO
3.8	3.4	-42.0	N/A	10.6	46.4	108.5	-15.2	93.3	-35.1	-125.3	0.0	NORTH EAST INS CO
8.6	7.7	N/A	N/A	N/A	N/A	N/A	N/A	N/A	999 +	0.0	0.0	NORTH LIGHT SPECIALTY INS CO
216.7	108.4	N/A	N/A	N/A	N/A	N/A	N/A	N/A	N/A	0.0	0.0	NORTH PACIFIC INS CO
5.3	3.8	147.5	140.1	1.5	2.8	63.9	31.7	95.6	129.5	40.9	0.0	NORTH POINTE INS CO
1.1	0.9	119.4	174.4	-0.8	-1.2	64.1	34.2	98.3	108.7	23.2	21.0 ●	NORTH RIVER INS CO
N/A	N/A	N/A	N/A	N/A	N/A	N/A	N/A	N/A	N/A	0.0	0.0	NORTH STAR GENERAL INS CO
6.0	4.2	93.5	27.2	-1.0	-2.2	49.2	28.6	77.8	132.7	6.7	0.8 ●	NORTH STAR MUTUAL INS CO
3.7	2.4	74.9	14.7	-8.3	-10.3	54.2	34.1	88.3	112.7	1.5	0.0	NORTHERN MUTUAL INS CO
116.5	56.4	N/A	N/A	N/A	N/A	N/A	N/A	N/A	N/A	0.0	0.0	NORTHERN SECURITY INS CO
2.6	1.6	84.6	145.1	-2.7	-6.6	58.7	30.2	88.9	114.5	2.9	0.0	NORTHFIELD INS CO
2.9	1.9	78.5	134.7	-2.6	-6.5	58.7	30.2	88.9	104.0	2.9	0.0	NORTHLAND CASUALTY CO
3.0	2.4	46.6	79.9	-1.5	-3.6	58.7	30.2	88.9	112.2	2.9	15.6 ●	NORTHLAND INS CO
1.5	1.0	46.8	196.2	-13.6	-26.1	69.2	31.9	101.1	109.8	-15.6	0.0	NORTHSTONE INS CO
3.4	2.4	54.6	47.5	-16.6	-21.7	29.8	35.0	64.8	103.0	-0.7	0.0	NORTHWEST DENTISTS INS CO
2.6	2.2	152.5	24.3	-5.8	-6.7	49.6	35.0	84.6	119.0	0.4	0.2	NORTHWEST GF MUTUAL INS CO
0.2	0.1	16.9	577.4	N/A	N/A	337.6	342.5	680.1	8.0	-10.8	40.7	NORTHWESTERN NATL INS CO SEG
0.6	0.6	N/A	N/A	N/A	N/A	N/A	N/A	N/A	N/A	0.0	0.0	NORTHWESTERN NTL INS CO
2.1	2.1	N/A	N/A	N/A	N/A	N/A	N/A	N/A	N/A	0.0	53.1	NOVA CASUALTY CO
1.3	1.0	42.1	45.6	-2.7	-12.4	49.3	30.2	79.5	64.2	4.3	0.0	NOVANT HEALTH RRG INC
N/A	N/A	5.4	8.5	4.3	9.8	124.5	18.1	142.6	42.2	0.0	2.8	NUCLEAR ELECTRIC INS LTD
58.8	52.9	13.9	24.0	0.3	0.7	66.1	29.8	95.9	108.2	2.9	43.4 ●	NUTMEG INS CO
1.7	1.1	55.3	157.9	-9.3	-13.3	60.5	23.1	83.6	138.0	2.7	0.0 ●	OAK RIVER INS CO
N/A	N/A	N/A	122.1	N/A	3.3	N/A	999 +	999 +	N/A	0.0	0.0	OAKWOOD INS CO
1.2	0.7	74.1	129.6	-9.2	-37.2	36.9	25.6	62.5	281.8	116.1	0.0	OASIS RECIPROCAL RRG
N/A	N/A	N/A	N/A	N/A	N/A	N/A	N/A	N/A	N/A	0.0	0.0	OBI AMERICA INS CO
130.3	59.0	N/A	N/A	N/A	N/A	N/A	N/A	N/A	N/A	0.0	0.0	OBI NATIONAL INS CO
N/A	N/A	1.9	83.3	-10.8	-13.1	-551.4	999 +	999 +	-955.5	102.7	0.0	OBSTETRICIANS & GYNECOLOGISTS
1.1	0.9	84.8	80.0	7.6	11.1	70.4	28.5	98.9	118.7	-20.4	30.0	OCCIDENTAL FIRE & CAS CO OF NC
1.2	0.9	328.7	142.2	-57.7	-65.9	54.4	41.3	95.7	98.0	21.2	13.3	OCEAN HARBOR CASUALTY INS CO
4.7	3.0	8.6	57.7	0.8	-0.5	107.4	59.3	166.7	49.2	-42.1	0.0	OCEAN MARINE INDEMNITY INS CO
0.3	0.2	240.1	431.4	40.9	49.9	71.5	59.3	130.8	63.6	-5.0	0.0	OCEANUS INS CO A RRG
1.5	1.2	47.9	89.4	-5.7	-10.0	52.2	32.2	84.4	111.3	-12.5	29.4 ●	ODYSSEY REINS CO
10.6	7.8	38.7	13.4	N/A	N/A	72.0	19.1	91.1	209.2	580.7	0.0 ●	OGLESBY REINS CO
8.7	6.7	-1.5	38.4	-1.7	-11.8	33.5	-21.3	12.2	42.4	-105.7	0.0	OHA INS SOLUTIONS INC

999 + Denotes number greater than 999.9%
999 - Denotes number less than -999.99%
● Bullets denote a more detailed analysis is available in Section II.

INSURANCE COMPANY NAME	DOM. STATE	RATING	TOTAL ASSETS ($MIL)	CAPITAL & SURPLUS ($MIL)	ANNUAL NET PREMIUM ($MIL)	NET INCOME ($MIL)	CAPITAL-IZATION INDEX (PTS)	RESERVE ADQ INDEX (PTS)	PROFIT-ABILITY INDEX (PTS)	LIQUIDITY INDEX (PTS)	STAB. INDEX (PTS)	STABILITY FACTORS
OHIC INS CO	OH	U	95.0	57.2	0.0	1.4	N/A	3.1	3.9	9.4	2.9	CFRT
OHIO BAR LIABILITY INS CO	OH	B-	38.6	27.9	5.9	0.2	10.0	7.8	7.4	7.6	3.9	DGT
OHIO CASUALTY INS CO	NH	C	5,600.3	1,645.1	2,050.6	2.0	8.0	5.9	6.5	6.2	3.7	ART
OHIO FARMERS INS CO	OH	B-	2,815.4	2,114.4	336.1	50.3	7.3	7.5	4.7	6.9	4.6	T
OHIO INDEMNITY CO	OH	C	151.0	49.7	67.6	5.0	8.4	9.3	6.1	6.6	2.9	T
OHIO MUTUAL INS CO	OH	B-	268.7	210.3	53.5	1.8	7.5	7.7	7.8	6.9	4.1	T
OHIO SECURITY INS CO	NH	C-	15.8	15.7	0.0	0.2	10.0	N/A	6.4	7.0	3.1	ADGR
OKLAHOMA ATTORNEYS MUTUAL INS CO	OK	B	55.0	37.3	6.5	0.4	10.0	6.9	4.7	9.3	4.1	DRT
OKLAHOMA FARM BUREAU MUTUAL INS CO	OK	B-	299.7	104.2	123.9	-9.7	7.8	9.3	4.9	6.8	4.0	T
OKLAHOMA P&C INS CO	OK	U	3.4	2.9	0.0	0.0	N/A	9.8	5.1	10.0	3.1	FGT
OKLAHOMA SPECIALTY INS CO	OK	C+	20.3	18.7	0.0	0.5	10.0	N/A	8.1	7.4	3.4	DFGT
OKLAHOMA SURETY CO	OH	C	16.5	16.0	3.9	0.8	7.6	6.3	3.7	8.4	3.2	DGRT
OLD AMERICAN CTY MUTUAL FIRE INS CO	TX	E+	83.3	5.0	36.8	0.0	0.0	7.3	5.1	0.0	0.7	CDFL
OLD AMERICAN INDEMNITY CO	KY	B-	16.1	9.6	1.0	-0.1	10.0	4.8	4.2	9.7	3.5	DFGR
OLD DOMINION INS CO	FL	B-	35.3	35.1	0.0	0.6	10.0	N/A	7.9	7.0	3.8	GT
OLD ELIZABETH MUTUAL FIRE INS CO	PA	U (2)	0.6	0.5	0.1	0.0	N/A	4.6	2.4	7.7	1.7	FT
OLD GLORY INS CO	TX	C-	22.9	9.8	8.5	-0.9	7.1	6.5	4.5	6.4	2.3	DGRT
OLD GUARD INS CO	OH	C+	435.1	196.4	159.2	5.4	8.9	9.1	6.6	6.5	4.3	T
OLD RELIABLE CAS CO	MO	C-	6.0	4.9	0.0	-0.1	10.0	N/A	2.3	7.0	2.5	DGRT
OLD REPUB INS CO	PA	B	2,868.4	1,078.1	420.9	48.9	9.2	5.5	8.8	7.4	4.8	ART
OLD REPUB UNION INS CO	IL	B	59.4	52.1	0.0	0.5	8.7	6.0	6.7	10.0	4.3	DFGR
OLD REPUBLIC GENERAL INS CORP	IL	B	1,992.7	538.9	311.4	25.4	7.2	6.9	8.9	7.0	4.8	T
OLD REPUBLIC LLOYDS OF TX	TX	B	2.2	0.8	0.7	0.0	7.5	9.3	3.9	8.1	4.9	DGT
OLD REPUBLIC SECURITY ASR CO	IL	U	1,067.4	200.8	329.9	8.4	N/A	0.3	1.5	4.3	0.6	CGLR
OLD REPUBLIC SURETY CO	WI	B	118.5	60.8	47.0	2.6	8.0	9.5	8.6	6.9	4.3	RT
OLD UNITED CAS CO	KS	C	566.2	191.1	141.7	11.1	10.0	7.4	2.9	7.7	3.7	RT
OLYMPUS INS CO	FL	C-	91.0	30.5	-23.6	0.0	7.8	2.6	3.6	8.4	3.2	FRT
OMAHA INDEMNITY CO	WI	U	14.4	12.3	0.0	0.0	N/A	6.8	3.9	10.0	5.0	GT
OMEGA INS CO	FL	C-	42.8	15.7	15.4	1.3	7.7	4.5	5.9	7.5	3.2	DGRT
OMEGA ONE INS CO	AL	C	12.4	11.1	0.6	0.3	10.0	7.0	4.6	9.3	2.9	DGRT
OMNI INDEMNITY CO	IL	B	76.6	22.2	22.5	-1.7	7.6	2.1	2.1	5.7	4.0	DFRT
OMNI INS CO	IL	B-	149.2	66.1	66.3	0.7	7.4	2.2	2.1	3.5	3.8	FLRT
OMS NATIONAL INS CO RRG	IL	B-	391.4	222.7	63.8	1.5	8.5	9.2	8.6	8.3	4.1	RT
ONE ALLIANCE INS CORP	PR	U	12.3	9.8	0.6	-1.1	N/A	N/A	2.5	7.7	3.7	DFGT
ONECIS INS CO	IL	U	23.6	21.4	0.0	0.3	N/A	N/A	7.8	10.0	4.9	GT
ONTARIO INS CO	NY	C	17.1	11.9	3.8	0.2	10.0	7.9	8.0	7.7	2.4	DGRT
ONTARIO REINS CO LTD	GA	C-	26.5	20.8	0.5	0.2	7.8	5.3	6.6	9.6	2.9	DGT
ONYX INS CO INC A RRG	TN	D-	26.0	6.8	11.5	0.0	0.9	3.6	2.6	8.2	1.2	CDGT
OOIDA RISK RETENTION GROUP INC	VT	C	96.4	20.2	18.8	0.2	5.2	9.4	3.1	7.4	2.9	DFRT
OPHTHALMIC MUTUAL INS CO RRG	VT	B	274.6	202.4	39.8	8.9	10.0	9.3	8.9	7.8	4.2	RT
ORANGE COUNTY MEDICAL RECIP INS RRG	AZ	D	5.9	5.0	0.7	0.2	10.0	9.6	6.6	9.6	2.1	DGT
ORDINARY MUTUAL A RRG CORP	VT	U	2.6	1.2	0.0	0.0	N/A	7.0	1.9	9.1	1.8	FGRT
OREGON AUTOMOBILE INS CO	OR	C	7.8	7.8	0.0	0.0	10.0	N/A	6.0	7.0	2.8	DGRT
OREGON MUTUAL INS CO	OR	C-	221.1	70.0	126.7	3.1	7.7	6.7	1.9	5.5	3.3	FRT
ORISKA INS CO	NY	E	34.8	11.4	10.2	0.9	0.1	0.4	2.9	0.0	0.2	CDGL
ORTHOFORUM INS CO	SC	D-	19.7	3.3	6.4	-0.7	0.7	1.6	2.7	7.4	1.2	CDGT
OSWEGO COUNTY MUTUAL INS CO	NY	C	25.4	15.1	6.6	0.8	8.7	9.3	8.7	6.9	2.6	DGT
OTSEGO COUNTY PATRONS CO-OP F R	NY	D	1.9	0.6	0.4	0.1	7.1	8.3	2.5	6.8	1.0	DFGR
OTSEGO MUTUAL FIRE INS CO	NY	B	117.2	101.5	4.4	1.6	10.0	7.4	8.8	9.1	4.4	DT
OWNERS INS CO	OH	A-	3,891.6	1,660.9	1,705.9	94.6	9.3	8.6	8.4	6.7	5.6	T
P&C INS CO OF HARTFORD	IN	B	240.0	113.3	52.7	5.6	10.0	5.9	6.6	7.4	4.5	AT
P&S INS RRG INC	SC	U	0.9	0.5	0.0	-0.1	N/A	N/A	3.5	9.5	1.7	GT

See Page 27 for explanation of footnotes and Page 28 for explanation of stability factors.
Arrows denote recent upgrades ▲ or downgrades ▼   (see Section VII for explanations)

100

www.weissratings.com

RISK ADJ. RATIO #1	CAPITAL RATIO #2	PREMIUM TO SURPLUS (%)	RESV. TO SURPLUS (%)	RESV. DEVELOP. 1 YEAR (%)	RESV. DEVELOP. 2 YEAR (%)	LOSS RATIO (%)	EXP. RATIO (%)	COMB RATIO (%)	CASH FROM UNDER-WRITING (%)	NET PREMIUM GROWTH (%)	INVEST. IN AFFIL (%)	INSURANCE COMPANY NAME
N/A	N/A	N/A	67.4	-22.3	-28.7	N/A	N/A	N/A	35.2	-100.0	0.0	OHIC INS CO
4.4	3.1	21.4	23.0	-2.8	-3.7	53.5	35.8	89.3	120.5	4.4	6.7	OHIO BAR LIABILITY INS CO
2.8	1.8	125.2	165.3	-0.9	-1.1	68.4	30.2	98.6	102.9	1.0	2.1 ●	OHIO CASUALTY INS CO
1.2	1.2	16.8	14.7	-0.6	-1.3	62.7	33.9	96.6	108.8	2.1	69.2 ●	OHIO FARMERS INS CO
2.7	1.9	148.6	31.5	-9.8	-14.0	42.9	43.4	86.3	116.4	12.4	0.0	OHIO INDEMNITY CO
1.3	1.3	26.6	13.0	-1.0	-1.8	61.6	32.9	94.5	110.8	3.1	66.6 ●	OHIO MUTUAL INS CO
153.7	74.3	N/A	N/A	N/A	N/A	N/A	N/A	N/A	N/A	0.0	0.0	OHIO SECURITY INS CO
5.2	3.4	17.9	26.5	-3.0	-5.6	70.2	23.9	94.1	116.2	0.6	0.0	OKLAHOMA ATTORNEYS MUTUAL INS
2.1	1.6	100.4	42.5	-10.7	-15.0	70.5	15.6	86.1	110.4	-9.2	12.8	OKLAHOMA FARM BUREAU MUTUAL INS
N/A	N/A	N/A	18.2	-6.1	-12.2	N/A	N/A	N/A	N/A	0.0	0.0	OKLAHOMA P&C INS CO
30.7	27.6	N/A	N/A	N/A	N/A	N/A	N/A	N/A	156.3	0.0	0.0	OKLAHOMA SPECIALTY INS CO
25.8	17.9	25.4	55.4	1.8	2.2	62.3	43.6	105.9	94.3	-13.9	0.0	OKLAHOMA SURETY CO
0.1	0.1	736.3	N/A	-0.6	-0.6	-0.1	99.0	98.9	98.3	-14.2	0.0	OLD AMERICAN CTY MUTUAL FIRE INS
5.3	4.7	10.3	6.3	0.9	1.2	56.5	58.6	115.1	47.3	-25.6	0.0	OLD AMERICAN INDEMNITY CO
54.1	25.8	N/A	N/A	N/A	N/A	N/A	N/A	N/A	N/A	0.0	0.0	OLD DOMINION INS CO
N/A	N/A	9.9	0.4	N/A	N/A	7.5	143.2	150.7	60.5	-17.6	0.0	OLD ELIZABETH MUTUAL FIRE INS CO
1.4	1.1	89.4	91.0	-8.9	-14.2	50.4	47.0	97.4	103.1	9.2	0.0	OLD GLORY INS CO
3.7	2.4	85.8	75.0	-2.8	-6.6	62.7	34.0	96.7	108.4	2.1	0.0 ●	OLD GUARD INS CO
10.6	9.6	N/A	N/A	N/A	N/A	N/A	N/A	N/A	30.6	0.0	0.0	OLD RELIABLE CAS CO
4.0	2.4	40.7	97.8	-0.9	1.2	53.5	31.0	84.5	130.4	5.1	0.6 ●	OLD REPUB INS CO
3.4	2.0	N/A	8.1	-1.5	-2.0	999 +	999 +	-507.3	-141.1	-51.7	0.0	OLD REPUB UNION INS CO
2.6	1.2	62.3	221.7	-3.8	-8.4	81.7	5.7	87.4	152.1	2.7	0.0 ●	OLD REPUBLIC GENERAL INS CORP
1.5	1.3	88.1	129.0	-3.7	-10.6	63.7	41.8	105.5	108.0	2.9	0.0	OLD REPUBLIC LLOYDS OF TX
N/A	N/A	179.1	388.1	87.7	127.5	106.4	21.0	127.4	99.0	0.0	0.0	OLD REPUBLIC SECURITY ASR CO
2.1	1.6	80.6	34.9	-13.1	-23.4	10.7	70.4	81.1	123.1	6.8	0.2	OLD REPUBLIC SURETY CO
7.3	4.0	77.0	4.5	-0.3	-0.7	43.4	27.8	71.2	154.9	12.0	0.0	OLD UNITED CAS CO
2.3	1.9	-77.9	44.6	-1.9	1.2	-304.1	136.8	-167.3	116.6	N/A	0.0	OLYMPUS INS CO
N/A	N/A	N/A	15.9	0.1	0.8	N/A	N/A	N/A	N/A	0.0	0.0	OMAHA INDEMNITY CO
1.9	1.6	102.6	29.4	10.5	13.1	71.3	32.5	103.8	116.5	35.4	0.0	OMEGA INS CO
10.2	6.0	5.7	0.6	-2.5	-6.2	-38.3	11.2	-27.1	579.4	0.0	0.0	OMEGA ONE INS CO
1.4	1.2	94.8	74.4	20.8	36.8	84.3	23.6	107.9	54.4	-33.5	0.0	OMNI INDEMNITY CO
1.4	1.3	100.6	78.9	21.8	34.0	84.3	23.7	108.0	65.3	-33.5	30.5	OMNI INS CO
2.4	1.9	29.4	54.4	-2.0	-1.2	68.0	27.6	95.6	121.5	-2.9	17.1 ●	OMS NATIONAL INS CO RRG
N/A	N/A	5.4	0.6	N/A	N/A	57.0	445.0	502.0	22.8	0.0	0.0	ONE ALLIANCE INS CORP
N/A	N/A	N/A	N/A	N/A	N/A	N/A	999 +	999 +	666.7	-89.5	0.0	ONECIS INS CO
5.5	3.4	32.9	15.6	-1.6	-2.8	68.3	32.4	100.7	100.5	3.2	0.0	ONTARIO INS CO
3.0	1.7	2.4	3.3	N/A	0.4	57.1	49.0	106.1	73.0	-6.3	0.0	ONTARIO REINS CO LTD
0.5	0.3	250.8	161.0	23.6	4.5	71.7	40.5	112.2	134.2	-7.8	0.0	ONYX INS CO INC A RRG
1.0	0.8	94.8	177.0	-12.0	-8.5	78.5	18.3	96.8	81.9	4.6	0.0	OOIDA RISK RETENTION GROUP INC
12.6	7.9	20.7	20.5	-2.2	-10.8	39.9	25.3	65.2	139.6	-3.1	0.0 ●	OPHTHALMIC MUTUAL INS CO RRG
10.0	6.2	15.0	14.9	-12.3	-12.8	-31.4	21.6	-9.8	131.0	-4.3	0.0	ORANGE COUNTY MEDICAL RECIP INS
N/A	N/A	N/A	113.8	1.3	3.7	N/A	N/A	N/A	N/A	0.0	0.0	ORDINARY MUTUAL A RRG CORP
241.9	121.0	N/A	N/A	N/A	N/A	N/A	N/A	N/A	N/A	0.0	0.0	OREGON AUTOMOBILE INS CO
2.2	1.5	185.6	127.1	11.4	2.4	87.2	33.7	120.9	88.6	-9.8	4.6	OREGON MUTUAL INS CO
0.1	0.1	96.1	146.2	5.7	48.3	64.4	33.1	97.5	124.0	-26.2	0.0	ORISKA INS CO
0.2	0.1	181.5	313.6	39.3	29.1	89.2	21.4	110.6	145.6	12.7	0.0	ORTHOFORUM INS CO
3.2	2.1	47.5	36.1	-3.3	-6.2	58.5	34.8	93.3	119.1	5.8	0.0	OSWEGO COUNTY MUTUAL INS CO
1.2	1.1	74.4	15.9	-1.2	-5.2	89.3	19.6	108.9	91.9	9.5	0.0	OTSEGO COUNTY PATRONS CO-OP F R
7.8	4.6	4.5	2.7	-0.4	-0.7	51.8	1.7	53.5	255.0	-1.0	0.0	OTSEGO MUTUAL FIRE INS CO
4.5	3.0	109.5	75.5	-2.7	-5.4	61.6	29.8	91.4	109.5	0.9	0.0 ●	OWNERS INS CO
6.2	4.0	48.9	84.5	0.6	1.3	66.1	17.7	83.8	108.2	2.9	0.0	P&C INS CO OF HARTFORD
N/A	N/A	N/A	N/A	N/A	N/A	N/A	N/A	N/A	42.9	0.0	0.0	P&S INS RRG INC

999 + Denotes number greater than 999.9%
999 - Denotes number less than -999.99%
● Bullets denote a more detailed analysis is available in Section II.

INSURANCE COMPANY NAME	DOM. STATE	RATING	TOTAL ASSETS ($MIL)	CAPITAL & SURPLUS ($MIL)	ANNUAL NET PREMIUM ($MIL)	NET INCOME ($MIL)	CAPITAL-IZATION INDEX (PTS)	RESERVE ADQ INDEX (PTS)	PROFIT-ABILITY INDEX (PTS)	LIQUIDITY INDEX (PTS)	STAB. INDEX (PTS)	STABILITY FACTORS
PACE RRG INC	VT	D	5.8	3.3	0.1	0.0	3.5	4.0	5.9	7.0	2.0	DFGR
PACIFIC COMPENSATION INS CO	CA	C-	324.8	87.8	101.8	0.7	3.0	3.8	1.7	5.8	2.9	CGRT
PACIFIC EMPLOYERS INS CO	PA	B-	3,697.7	1,278.3	846.9	35.9	8.8	7.7	8.4	7.0	3.9	RT
PACIFIC INDEMNITY CO	WI	B	6,797.0	2,868.6	1,691.9	255.0	9.6	8.5	8.6	6.8	4.3	T
PACIFIC INDEMNITY INS CO	GU	C	33.1	20.8	8.9	1.1	9.1	8.7	8.7	8.3	2.9	DGRT
PACIFIC INS CO LTD	CT	B	661.0	232.8	179.1	10.2	9.1	5.9	6.0	6.8	4.6	AT
PACIFIC PIONEER INS CO	CA	D	26.6	7.6	6.6	0.3	4.0	3.5	1.3	5.7	2.0	DFGR
PACIFIC PROPERTY & CASUALTY CO	CA	B	82.0	44.9	39.3	1.7	7.8	8.3	8.8	5.9	4.6	RT
PACIFIC SPECIALTY INS CO	CA	C+	328.2	137.7	180.4	8.6	7.2	5.8	3.2	5.8	4.0	RT
PACIFIC SPECIALTY PROPERTY & CAS CO	TX	E	5.1	4.6	0.4	0.0	10.0	6.1	4.5	9.5	0.0	DGRT
PACIFIC STAR INS CO	WI	C	13.1	10.5	1.6	0.2	10.0	5.3	5.0	9.3	2.8	DGRT
PACO ASR CO INC	IL	C	73.5	34.1	10.0	0.6	5.0	9.3	7.2	7.6	3.6	DRT
PAFCO GENERAL INS CO	IN	F (5)	0.0	0.0	6.3	0.0	1.5	4.9	0.3	2.9	0.0	CDFL
PALADIN REINS CORP	NY	U	1.3	0.6	-0.1	-0.1	N/A	5.1	2.5	7.0	2.1	FGT
PALISADES INS CO	NJ	D+(2)	29.0	12.3	0.0	0.1	10.0	N/A	5.2	7.0	2.5	DT
PALISADES P&C INS CO	NJ	D (2)	14.2	11.9	0.0	0.2	10.0	N/A	2.9	7.0	1.5	DT
PALISADES SAFETY & INS ASSOC	NJ	C (2)	1,159.7	366.8	575.4	-8.9	3.7	6.8	3.6	2.9	3.5	CFLT
PALLADIUM RRG INC	VT	D+	79.4	9.1	26.2	0.7	0.6	N/A	2.3	8.5	1.3	CDGT
PALMETTO CASUALTY INS CO	SC	C+	7.0	6.9	0.0	0.1	10.0	N/A	7.1	7.0	3.0	DGT
PALMETTO SURETY CORP	SC	C	11.2	3.5	6.2	0.6	2.0	9.3	3.7	4.3	2.7	CDFG
▼PALOMAR SPECIALTY INS CO	OR	C-	114.5	67.3	40.8	-2.4	2.6	N/A	3.6	6.3	2.3	CGT
PANHANDLE FARMERS MUT INS CO OF WV	WV	C-	4.8	2.5	2.7	0.0	7.6	4.7	3.9	6.7	1.9	DGRT
PARAMOUNT INS CO	MD	D	7.5	1.8	4.5	-0.7	5.4	3.0	1.3	6.1	1.5	DFGR
PARAMOUNT INS CO	NY	E	38.0	4.2	11.1	-2.8	0.3	1.7	0.7	4.4	0.1	CDLR
PARATRANSIT INS CO A MUTUAL RRG	TN	C-	23.7	12.9	3.8	0.3	8.3	9.5	8.1	7.9	2.5	DGRT
PARK INS CO	NY	E	26.8	3.0	8.6	-0.8	0.0	0.1	1.6	0.0	0.1	CDFG
PARTNER REINSURANCE CO OF THE US	NY	C	5,025.4	1,422.8	1,201.8	24.0	7.3	9.6	8.1	6.8	4.3	FRT
PARTNERRE AMERICA INS CO	DE	C+	398.9	129.8	32.2	1.4	10.0	6.0	7.9	8.7	4.4	RT
PARTNERRE INS CO OF NY	NY	C	126.5	110.4	0.2	1.0	8.4	6.2	4.3	9.4	4.0	DGRT
PARTNERS MUTUAL INS CO	WI	C-	44.2	11.6	13.5	0.5	7.2	5.0	4.2	6.6	2.3	DRT
PASSPORT INS CO	ND	U (2)	2.0	1.6	0.0	0.0	N/A	N/A	4.2	7.0	2.1	T
PATRIOT GENERAL INS CO	WI	B	26.1	25.3	0.0	0.3	10.0	N/A	5.5	10.0	4.9	DGT
PATRIOT INS CO	ME	C	112.0	35.9	46.2	2.5	8.5	9.4	6.8	6.4	2.9	T
PATRONS MUTUAL FIRE INS CO OF IN PA	PA	D+(2)	2.8	2.6	0.4	0.1	10.0	7.9	4.9	10.0	1.9	DT
PATRONS MUTUAL INS CO OF CT	CT	C	53.6	21.5	9.8	-0.1	9.7	6.0	4.8	6.7	3.5	DFRT
PATRONS OXFORD INS CO	ME	C	21.6	9.7	0.0	0.1	9.6	4.6	4.6	7.0	2.8	DFGT
PAWTUCKET INS CO	RI	U	7.0	2.1	0.0	0.2	N/A	0.1	1.9	7.0	0.4	GRT
PCH MUTUAL INS CO INC RRG	DC	D	7.4	2.6	2.3	0.0	2.0	9.9	1.7	9.1	1.9	CDFG
PEACE CHURCH RRG INC	VT	D	22.5	15.6	2.9	0.9	10.0	9.5	8.5	8.3	2.3	DGRT
PEACHTREE CASUALTY INS CO	FL	D	22.6	5.0	13.6	-2.3	1.7	2.8	0.8	0.0	1.5	CDFG
PEAK P&C INS CORP	WI	B	45.7	39.5	0.0	0.5	10.0	N/A	8.3	9.2	4.0	RT
PEERLESS INDEMNITY INS CO	IL	C+	189.3	186.1	0.0	2.4	10.0	3.8	5.4	10.0	4.3	RT
PEERLESS INS CO	NH	B-	13,004.0	3,347.6	5,126.4	-7.4	7.5	4.7	6.4	6.1	3.9	RT
PEKIN INS CO	IL	B+	312.8	124.7	120.2	-1.1	10.0	8.9	5.4	6.5	5.0	T
PELEUS INS CO	VA	U	125.3	49.7	0.0	0.4	N/A	N/A	5.7	7.0	5.4	DGRT
PELICAN INS RRG	VT	D	17.2	11.7	0.9	-0.1	7.6	6.7	3.0	6.8	2.3	DGRT
PEMCO MUTUAL INS CO	WA	B-	721.3	276.7	396.6	19.6	8.8	6.2	5.9	5.9	4.1	RT
PENINSULA INDEMNITY CO	MD	C	11.5	9.8	0.0	0.2	10.0	N/A	5.3	7.0	2.9	DFGR
PENINSULA INS CO	MD	C+	89.4	42.2	46.3	0.0	9.2	5.9	5.3	6.7	3.9	T
PENN CHARTER MUTL INS CO	PA	C	14.1	11.3	0.0	0.1	7.3	7.2	6.9	10.0	2.9	DGT
PENN MILLERS INS CO	PA	C	118.5	68.1	0.0	1.7	10.0	6.9	3.6	7.0	3.7	FRT
PENN NATIONAL SECURITY INS CO	PA	B-	950.7	309.7	330.9	10.6	9.0	5.9	5.8	6.4	4.4	T

RISK ADJ. CAPITAL RATIO #1	RATIO #2	PREMIUM TO SURPLUS (%)	RESV. TO SURPLUS (%)	RESV. DEVELOP. 1 YEAR (%)	2 YEAR (%)	LOSS RATIO (%)	EXP. RATIO (%)	COMB RATIO (%)	CASH FROM UNDER-WRITING (%)	NET PREMIUM GROWTH (%)	INVEST. IN AFFIL (%)	INSURANCE COMPANY NAME
2.3	1.8	3.5	30.0	-17.5	-39.3	-497.4	512.1	14.7	-5.7	11.9	0.0	PACE RRG INC
0.6	0.3	116.9	196.4	N/A	-0.9	76.6	36.4	113.0	131.2	46.5	0.0	PACIFIC COMPENSATION INS CO
3.0	2.1	68.3	123.0	-1.2	-0.3	72.8	23.7	96.5	115.7	6.3	5.7 •	PACIFIC EMPLOYERS INS CO
4.6	2.9	57.7	96.7	-2.4	-5.4	56.7	28.9	85.6	118.9	4.1	0.1 •	PACIFIC INDEMNITY CO
4.5	2.7	44.7	18.5	-1.0	-9.9	35.8	40.2	76.0	123.3	3.3	0.0	PACIFIC INDEMNITY INS CO
3.7	2.4	80.6	139.3	0.9	2.1	66.1	29.7	95.8	108.2	2.9	0.0 •	PACIFIC INS CO LTD
0.9	0.6	92.3	100.7	0.2	22.7	78.6	34.7	113.3	58.8	-3.4	0.0	PACIFIC PIONEER INS CO
2.8	1.7	91.0	46.7	-1.8	-5.0	76.1	23.5	99.6	103.3	8.2	0.0	PACIFIC PROPERTY & CASUALTY CO
1.9	1.5	135.7	49.8	-3.0	0.7	55.5	40.9	96.4	102.8	0.4	1.6	PACIFIC SPECIALTY INS CO
11.5	7.8	9.2	2.0	-0.2	-0.6	34.8	59.0	93.8	95.8	44.5	0.0	PACIFIC SPECIALTY PROPERTY & CAS
7.9	6.2	15.6	11.3	-2.9	-0.7	52.9	36.6	89.5	98.8	-17.4	0.0	PACIFIC STAR INS CO
1.2	0.8	29.7	85.6	-1.9	-5.3	69.4	26.4	95.8	99.1	-5.9	0.0	PACO ASR CO INC
0.4	0.3	196.2	297.0	7.1	-17.7	95.7	39.4	135.1	51.3	-17.6	0.0	PAFCO GENERAL INS CO
N/A	N/A	-15.7	39.9	-80.5	-101.0	410.2	-198.0	212.2	81.2	N/A	0.0	PALADIN REINS CORP
3.8	3.5	N/A	N/A	N/A	N/A	N/A	N/A	N/A	N/A	0.0	0.0	PALISADES INS CO
15.1	12.1	N/A	N/A	N/A	N/A	N/A	N/A	N/A	N/A	0.0	0.5	PALISADES P&C INS CO
0.7	0.6	156.8	146.0	-5.1	-7.3	75.9	30.9	106.8	93.7	4.0	32.1	PALISADES SAFETY & INS ASSOC
0.3	0.2	344.4	320.1	N/A	N/A	93.8	9.0	102.8	999 +	N/A	0.0	PALLADIUM RRG INC
90.9	45.4	N/A	N/A	N/A	N/A	N/A	N/A	N/A	N/A	0.0	0.0	PALMETTO CASUALTY INS CO
0.4	0.4	202.7	26.3	-9.3	-13.3	13.3	82.3	95.6	90.1	40.0	0.0	PALMETTO SURETY CORP
0.4	0.3	58.6	2.2	N/A	N/A	12.8	54.1	66.9	150.4	224.3	0.0	PALOMAR SPECIALTY INS CO
2.3	1.7	104.3	11.5	-17.3	-2.6	47.6	40.5	88.1	114.0	2.4	0.0	PANHANDLE FARMERS MUT INS CO OF
0.8	0.7	248.1	109.2	-9.6	4.2	70.2	48.1	118.3	86.2	-5.2	0.0	PARAMOUNT INS CO
0.1	0.0	157.4	491.0	40.2	45.5	115.3	34.8	150.1	96.4	-28.9	0.0	PARAMOUNT INS CO
2.8	1.9	29.8	58.7	-0.2	-0.7	51.3	28.9	80.2	171.4	3.8	0.0	PARATRANSIT INS CO A MUTUAL RRG
0.1	0.0	281.8	511.1	253.9	371.6	128.1	-13.7	114.4	49.4	10.8	0.0	PARK INS CO
1.9	1.2	85.5	169.9	-17.4	-28.5	61.8	29.6	91.4	93.5	-0.2	2.9 •	PARTNER REINSURANCE CO OF THE US
11.3	6.8	25.1	17.9	-2.1	0.4	90.3	-6.7	83.6	114.9	25.4	0.0	PARTNERRE AMERICA INS CO
4.9	2.0	0.2	56.4	-2.1	-3.7	-599.9	190.2	-409.7	91.7	N/A	0.0	PARTNERRE INS CO OF NY
2.1	1.4	143.8	143.4	-3.0	-6.5	65.0	35.2	100.2	120.0	1.4	0.0	PARTNERS MUTUAL INS CO
N/A	N/A	N/A	N/A	N/A	N/A	N/A	N/A	N/A	N/A	0.0	0.0	PASSPORT INS CO
77.1	50.3	N/A	N/A	N/A	N/A	N/A	N/A	N/A	277.3	0.0	0.0	PATRIOT GENERAL INS CO
3.1	2.3	137.8	95.1	-12.2	-16.4	62.1	30.8	92.9	106.2	5.3	0.0	PATRIOT INS CO
11.4	7.9	14.3	6.3	-4.2	-2.9	27.4	47.2	74.6	127.1	-0.9	0.0	PATRONS MUTUAL FIRE INS CO OF IN
4.4	2.7	45.4	37.7	0.5	2.1	68.5	33.4	101.9	86.0	6.6	0.0	PATRONS MUTUAL INS CO OF CT
3.6	3.3	N/A	N/A	N/A	N/A	N/A	N/A	N/A	60.0	0.0	0.0	PATRONS OXFORD INS CO
N/A	N/A	N/A	13.7	179.9	114.3	N/A	N/A	N/A	N/A	0.0	0.0	PAWTUCKET INS CO
0.4	0.3	87.8	95.0	-1.4	-43.3	55.2	46.1	101.3	4.8	90.6	0.0	PCH MUTUAL INS CO INC RRG
5.4	3.5	19.4	28.6	-2.9	-10.5	51.4	20.8	72.2	104.4	-1.3	0.0	PEACE CHURCH RRG INC
0.4	0.3	188.6	106.9	6.2	N/A	97.5	56.4	153.9	59.5	-41.3	0.0	PEACHTREE CASUALTY INS CO
22.5	20.3	N/A	N/A	N/A	N/A	N/A	N/A	N/A	53.0	0.0	0.0	PEAK P&C INS CORP
100.2	46.8	N/A	N/A	N/A	N/A	N/A	N/A	N/A	N/A	0.0	0.0	PEERLESS INDEMNITY INS CO
2.0	1.4	154.6	204.0	-1.1	-1.4	68.4	30.3	98.7	103.1	1.0	6.0 •	PEERLESS INS CO
4.4	3.0	95.7	70.2	-0.3	-5.4	71.5	28.9	100.4	107.1	5.6	3.4 •	PEKIN INS CO
N/A	N/A	N/A	N/A	N/A	N/A	N/A	N/A	N/A	-37.9	0.0	0.0	PELEUS INS CO
1.9	1.3	7.1	24.9	1.6	4.5	142.5	152.6	295.1	95.5	-62.2	0.0	PELICAN INS RRG
2.9	2.3	153.1	72.8	0.8	0.1	77.0	27.9	104.9	96.9	7.1	0.4 •	PEMCO MUTUAL INS CO
15.1	13.5	N/A	N/A	N/A	N/A	N/A	N/A	N/A	62.2	0.0	0.0	PENINSULA INDEMNITY CO
3.1	2.4	110.6	48.0	0.3	0.4	69.2	27.9	97.1	114.9	10.3	13.7	PENINSULA INS CO
2.0	1.2	0.4	0.4	0.4	-0.2	237.5	46.9	284.4	43.9	4.0	0.0	PENN CHARTER MUTL INS CO
10.3	9.2	N/A	40.7	-1.8	0.7	N/A	N/A	N/A	-40.0	-100.0	0.0	PENN MILLERS INS CO
3.5	2.4	110.4	110.1	-2.2	-5.1	65.0	36.3	101.3	102.8	1.4	0.0 •	PENN NATIONAL SECURITY INS CO

999 + Denotes number greater than 999.9%
999 - Denotes number less than -999.99%
• Bullets denote a more detailed analysis is available in Section II.

INSURANCE COMPANY NAME	DOM. STATE	RATING	TOTAL ASSETS ($MIL)	CAPITAL & SURPLUS ($MIL)	ANNUAL NET PREMIUM ($MIL)	NET INCOME ($MIL)	CAPITAL-IZATION INDEX (PTS)	RESERVE ADQ INDEX (PTS)	PROFIT-ABILITY INDEX (PTS)	LIQUIDITY INDEX (PTS)	STAB. INDEX (PTS)	STABILITY FACTORS
PENN RESERVE INS CO LTD	PA	D	1.9	1.7	0.1	0.0	10.0	N/A	4.7	10.0	1.5	DGT
PENN-AMERICA INS CO	PA	C	148.6	81.6	21.2	-0.8	7.2	6.1	3.3	6.9	4.1	FRT
PENN-PATRIOT INS CO	VA	C	21.6	21.2	-2.4	0.1	10.0	4.6	4.6	6.9	3.5	FGRT
PENN-STAR INS CO	PA	C	132.5	46.6	48.5	-1.2	8.1	6.1	3.6	8.9	3.9	GRT
PENNSYLVANIA INS CO	IA	C	58.8	43.4	19.1	2.0	9.3	8.2	7.0	9.2	3.9	DRT
PENNSYLVANIA LUMBERMENS MUTUAL INS	PA	B	467.2	117.2	155.8	8.8	7.3	4.5	3.0	6.2	4.2	RT
PENNSYLVANIA MANUFACTURERS ASN INS	PA	C	876.8	263.6	134.7	2.8	8.2	2.4	6.2	6.6	3.7	ART
PENNSYLVANIA MANUFACTURERS IND CO	PA	C	205.3	72.8	44.9	0.7	8.0	2.5	3.1	6.7	3.8	ART
PENNSYLVANIA NTL MUTUAL CAS INS CO	PA	B-	1,268.3	592.1	330.9	12.8	7.8	5.9	5.3	6.5	4.5	FRT
PENNSYLVANIA PHYSICIANS RECIP INS	PA	U	8.2	1.3	0.0	-0.2	N/A	3.3	0.9	7.3	0.0	CFGR
PEOPLES TRUST INS CO	FL	C-	255.5	75.0	131.4	-12.8	3.3	2.7	3.7	2.8	2.9	CFLT
PERMANENT GEN ASR CORP OF OHIO	OH	C	200.4	75.2	113.2	-4.0	8.0	5.2	4.1	6.3	3.4	FRT
PERMANENT GENERAL ASR CORP	OH	C-	351.0	104.8	262.6	-8.1	7.6	4.6	3.9	5.0	3.1	RT
PERSONAL SERVICE INS CO	PA	C+	39.2	9.3	10.6	-0.4	7.3	1.8	2.2	4.2	3.1	DFGL
PETROLEUM CAS CO	TX	C	37.8	24.3	5.6	1.6	5.2	5.8	4.8	9.7	3.0	DGT
PETROLEUM MARKETERS MGMT INS CO	IA	C-	32.0	23.7	3.6	0.9	7.8	6.5	6.2	7.2	3.1	DGT
PHARMACISTS MUTUAL INS CO	IA	B	278.4	110.6	92.1	3.9	9.2	6.7	6.4	6.7	4.2	RT
PHENIX MUTUAL FIRE INS CO	NH	B-	65.8	24.3	21.5	0.6	8.0	8.0	6.6	6.7	3.9	DT
PHILADELPHIA CBSP FOR INS OF HOUSES	PA	B-	312.6	233.7	36.6	-1.6	7.2	6.2	4.4	6.7	4.1	FRT
PHILADELPHIA CONTRIBUTIONSHIP INS CO	PA	B-	205.7	112.3	55.0	-0.8	8.6	6.6	5.1	6.6	4.1	RT
PHILADELPHIA INDEMNITY INS CO	PA	B-	7,811.8	2,225.1	2,696.2	160.0	8.1	7.9	5.5	6.6	4.6	RT
PHILADELPHIA REINS CORP	PA	U	6.8	6.6	-62.6	-0.2	N/A	7.0	1.9	8.8	3.1	FGRT
PHOEBE RECIPROCAL RRG	SC	E (1)	6.2	4.5	0.4	0.0	9.0	9.3	8.6	9.9	0.0	DGT
PHOENIX FUND INC	NC	F (5)	0.0	0.0	25.2	0.0	0.0	0.3	5.2	5.9	0.0	CDT
PHOENIX INS CO	CT	B	4,300.2	1,840.2	1,039.8	52.5	7.6	8.2	8.4	6.9	5.0	T
PHYSICIANS CASUALTY RRG INC	NV	D+	12.1	3.2	5.4	0.6	1.7	6.1	6.4	8.5	1.9	CDGT
PHYSICIANS IND RRG INC	NV	D	5.4	1.2	1.5	-0.1	1.7	10.0	0.8	9.0	1.3	CDGT
PHYSICIANS INS A MUTL CO	WA	B-	499.8	228.1	76.3	8.0	10.0	9.4	6.9	7.5	4.1	RT
PHYSICIANS INS CO	FL	D+	12.8	6.9	4.3	-0.6	6.4	4.1	1.9	6.9	2.7	DGRT
PHYSICIANS INS EXCHANGE RESOURCE	VT	D-	2.9	1.1	1.1	-0.4	1.3	4.1	1.2	6.8	1.0	CDFG
PHYSICIANS INS MUTUAL	MO	E	3.7	0.7	0.9	-0.4	5.7	10.0	2.1	7.1	0.1	DGT
PHYSICIANS INS PROGRAM	PA	C-	27.0	11.2	4.7	-0.3	4.8	6.6	3.7	7.3	2.4	DFGR
PHYSICIANS PROACTIVE PROTECTION INC	SC	D+	90.9	28.7	9.1	0.9	3.1	6.0	5.7	7.9	2.1	CDRT
PHYSICIANS PROFESSIONAL LIABILTY RRG	VT	C	36.4	18.9	4.1	0.3	9.3	9.6	4.7	7.0	2.9	DFGR
PHYSICIANS RECIPROCAL INSURERS	NY	E-	1,301.4	-164.7	285.3	-12.8	0.0	10.0	0.9	7.0	0.0	CFRT
PHYSICIANS REIMBURSEMENT FUND RRG	VT	C-	31.5	10.9	2.5	-0.4	4.1	10.0	3.9	7.0	2.4	DGRT
PHYSICIANS SPECIALTY LTD RRG	SC	D	12.7	5.8	0.2	-0.1	6.4	9.6	4.4	7.0	2.1	DFGR
PIA PROFESSIONAL LIABILITY INS RRG	MT	D	2.1	1.0	0.6	-0.3	4.4	5.7	1.7	8.4	1.2	DGT
PIEDMONT MUTUAL INS CO	NC	D+	4.5	3.0	1.8	0.2	7.2	8.2	2.9	6.9	1.9	DGRT
PIH INS CO A RECIP RRG	HI	B-	17.6	10.9	4.2	0.3	8.0	9.5	9.4	7.8	3.5	DGT
PILGRIM INS CO	MA	C	79.9	17.3	29.5	0.4	6.3	5.9	6.6	6.1	3.2	DT
PINE TREE INS RECIPROCAL RRG	VT	D- (5)	10.6	3.3	0.7	0.0	0.9	4.7	1.0	9.0	1.0	CDFG
PINNACLEPOINT INS CO	WV	C	60.9	11.1	5.2	0.3	5.6	4.0	6.4	7.9	2.9	DT
PIONEER SPECIALTY INS CO	MN	C-	66.3	26.5	27.3	0.8	8.8	8.3	8.7	6.7	3.1	RT
PIONEER STATE MUTUAL INS CO	MI	B	526.4	309.7	183.3	15.0	10.0	8.7	8.7	6.9	4.7	T
PLANS LIABILITY INS CO	OH	C	76.1	33.1	4.0	-0.5	2.1	4.6	1.5	7.7	2.4	CDFG
PLATEAU CASUALTY INS CO	TN	C+	42.2	20.7	16.7	0.2	7.4	5.5	8.0	7.0	3.1	DFRT
PLATINUM TRANSPORT INS RRG INC	HI	U	2.9	0.8	-0.4	-0.4	N/A	N/A	0.9	9.1	0.0	DGT
PLATTE RIVER INS CO	NE	C	136.4	42.3	33.0	0.7	8.3	3.9	4.8	7.5	3.5	RT
PLAZA INS CO	IA	C+	72.2	26.9	0.0	0.2	10.0	N/A	7.2	6.9	3.7	FRT
PLICO INC	OK	C-	94.5	71.0	-40.6	1.9	10.0	9.9	8.1	7.9	3.3	FRT
PLYMOUTH ROCK ASR CORP	MA	B-	571.3	174.7	339.1	3.6	7.3	5.9	6.2	2.8	4.0	LRT

See Page 27 for explanation of footnotes and Page 28 for explanation of stability factors.

104

www.weissratings.com

Arrows denote recent upgrades ▲ or downgrades ▼   (see Section VII for explanations)

RISK ADJ. CAPITAL RATIO #1	CAPITAL RATIO #2	PREMIUM TO SURPLUS (%)	RESV. TO SURPLUS (%)	RESV. DEVELOP. 1 YEAR (%)	RESV. DEVELOP. 2 YEAR (%)	LOSS RATIO (%)	EXP. RATIO (%)	COMB RATIO (%)	CASH FROM UNDER-WRITING (%)	NET PREMIUM GROWTH (%)	INVEST. IN AFFIL (%)	INSURANCE COMPANY NAME
19.5	12.7	8.1	6.8	N/A	N/A	43.8	N/A	43.8	275.7	0.0	0.0	PENN RESERVE INS CO LTD
1.1	1.1	25.5	34.7	-2.2	0.1	60.5	30.8	91.3	32.6	-15.9	55.4	PENN-AMERICA INS CO
126.3	52.7	-11.6	N/A	N/A	N/A	N/A	N/A	N/A	-9.7	-148.4	0.0	PENN-PATRIOT INS CO
2.4	1.6	101.9	97.0	-6.0	0.7	60.5	21.5	82.0	961.8	381.5	0.0	PENN-STAR INS CO
3.3	2.7	46.3	32.3	-3.0	-5.8	24.6	28.1	52.7	214.9	18.6	0.0	PENNSYLVANIA INS CO
2.3	1.3	146.6	148.3	-4.2	8.6	68.3	32.8	101.1	102.8	10.6	0.0	PENNSYLVANIA LUMBERMENS MUTUAL
2.5	1.7	53.5	105.4	5.9	19.7	83.1	26.2	109.3	100.8	-9.9	0.0 ●	PENNSYLVANIA MANUFACTURERS ASN
2.2	1.5	64.6	127.2	7.3	19.1	83.1	26.0	109.1	99.6	-9.9	0.0	PENNSYLVANIA MANUFACTURERS IND
1.7	1.5	57.9	57.7	-1.1	-2.6	65.0	35.5	100.5	89.6	1.4	33.5 ●	PENNSYLVANIA NTL MUTUAL CAS INS
N/A	N/A	N/A	358.0	65.5	40.8	190.1	N/A	N/A	2.8	100.0	0.0	PENNSYLVANIA PHYSICIANS RECIP INS
0.8	0.5	149.4	84.0	-16.5	-3.6	73.6	31.8	105.4	81.9	-26.7	0.0	PEOPLES TRUST INS CO
1.5	1.4	141.0	41.5	1.8	2.8	70.0	26.4	96.4	77.6	41.0	24.5	PERMANENT GEN ASR CORP OF OHIO
1.1	1.0	233.0	68.5	3.0	4.8	70.0	26.3	96.3	99.4	27.4	0.7	PERMANENT GENERAL ASR CORP
1.3	1.1	109.6	86.0	23.8	43.1	84.3	16.7	101.0	72.1	-33.5	0.0	PERSONAL SERVICE INS CO
1.1	0.7	24.7	42.5	2.9	3.9	65.8	29.0	94.8	177.4	84.2	0.0	PETROLEUM CAS CO
2.3	1.4	15.3	19.3	-0.4	0.1	40.9	41.3	82.2	134.5	10.1	5.8	PETROLEUM MARKETERS MGMT INS CO
3.9	2.7	87.0	90.0	-6.9	-10.4	59.0	33.5	92.5	110.4	3.8	4.5	PHARMACISTS MUTUAL INS CO
2.7	1.8	90.6	65.8	-2.6	-5.0	64.4	36.6	101.0	99.6	4.1	0.0	PHENIX MUTUAL FIRE INS CO
1.3	1.1	15.7	10.8	-0.6	-0.5	75.1	34.0	109.1	94.5	-1.4	50.4 ●	PHILADELPHIA CBSP FOR INS OF
3.2	2.0	49.7	32.5	0.5	0.4	76.2	26.1	102.3	101.7	-1.2	0.0	PHILADELPHIA CONTRIBUTIONSHIP INS
2.3	1.7	131.7	171.6	-0.5	-2.3	60.4	29.2	89.6	131.1	5.6	0.0 ●	PHILADELPHIA INDEMNITY INS CO
N/A	N/A	-932.4	N/A	-40.9	-46.2	101.3	-0.1	101.2	999 +	0.0	0.0	PHILADELPHIA REINS CORP
3.6	2.2	8.6	30.1	-3.5	-9.9	30.7	35.8	66.5	189.4	-8.2	0.0	PHOEBE RECIPROCAL RRG
0.1	0.1	378.0	273.0	49.1	32.3	71.3	27.2	98.5	133.5	0.0	0.0	PHOENIX FUND INC
1.8	1.6	59.6	102.1	-1.9	-5.0	58.7	30.2	88.9	108.0	3.0	26.6 ●	PHOENIX INS CO
0.6	0.4	212.9	150.0	-28.8	-47.4	38.3	39.3	77.6	241.3	16.7	0.0	PHYSICIANS CASUALTY RRG INC
0.5	0.4	166.1	280.5	-2.2	-66.0	61.4	90.5	151.9	100.3	-29.7	0.0	PHYSICIANS IND RRG INC
4.0	3.1	34.7	90.4	-10.6	-18.9	84.4	18.6	103.0	99.0	-0.5	3.0 ●	PHYSICIANS INS A MUTL CO
0.6	0.5	58.1	21.4	-6.7	14.0	24.2	44.4	68.6	165.1	N/A	0.0	PHYSICIANS INS CO
0.5	0.3	100.6	122.4	6.3	-161.3	88.7	63.5	152.2	68.2	6.0	0.0	PHYSICIANS INS EXCHANGE RESOURCE
0.7	0.6	75.5	248.3	-40.0	-85.8	86.0	16.6	102.6	255.4	2.7	0.0	PHYSICIANS INS MUTUAL
1.0	0.7	43.3	136.2	0.7	9.6	70.3	33.8	104.1	72.9	-5.7	0.0	PHYSICIANS INS PROGRAM
0.6	0.5	34.7	137.4	-15.8	17.9	22.1	21.8	43.9	111.9	-14.0	0.0	PHYSICIANS PROACTIVE PROTECTION
3.1	2.7	21.9	52.0	-11.2	-24.3	38.6	81.2	119.8	77.0	-0.2	0.0	PHYSICIANS PROFESSIONAL LIABILTY
-0.2	-0.2	-206.1	999 +	-50.2	-75.1	84.7	34.8	119.5	83.2	-23.8	0.0	PHYSICIANS RECIPROCAL INSURERS
0.7	0.6	23.1	164.9	-28.1	-73.0	31.7	69.0	100.7	112.1	-7.9	0.0	PHYSICIANS REIMBURSEMENT FUND
1.7	1.2	3.8	87.9	-23.4	-46.0	-332.1	68.3	-263.8	128.6	-85.6	0.0	PHYSICIANS SPECIALTY LTD RRG
0.7	0.4	43.4	52.1	-15.8	-12.7	84.5	69.2	153.7	118.4	24.0	0.0	PIA PROFESSIONAL LIABILITY INS RRG
1.9	1.3	64.0	8.6	-2.5	-3.9	33.6	56.5	90.1	124.9	9.4	0.0	PIEDMONT MUTUAL INS CO
2.6	1.5	39.8	37.0	-25.6	-20.4	19.8	13.9	33.7	203.5	-1.3	0.0	PIH INS CO A RECIP RRG
1.3	0.9	185.1	86.8	-1.4	4.0	77.8	23.8	101.6	116.0	7.4	0.0	PILGRIM INS CO
0.2	0.2	19.9	184.0	-2.6	40.1	149.7	47.1	196.8	35.4	-56.4	0.0	PINE TREE INS RECIPROCAL RRG
1.5	1.0	47.8	200.0	-14.6	-29.3	69.2	31.7	100.9	101.5	-15.6	0.0	PINNACLEPOINT INS CO
3.0	2.2	105.8	76.6	-5.7	-5.5	65.2	25.3	90.5	112.8	19.5	0.0	PIONEER SPECIALTY INS CO
5.1	3.2	62.7	29.8	-5.5	-7.5	60.6	28.2	88.8	120.0	5.1	0.0 ●	PIONEER STATE MUTUAL INS CO
0.5	0.4	11.8	106.2	5.7	2.7	186.8	72.7	259.5	49.7	59.2	0.0	PLANS LIABILITY INS CO
1.6	1.4	82.2	7.7	-0.7	-1.2	46.5	46.0	92.5	94.9	3.2	31.2	PLATEAU CASUALTY INS CO
N/A	N/A	-38.7	3.1	N/A	N/A	-21.2	-48.2	-69.4	140.7	0.0	0.0	PLATINUM TRANSPORT INS RRG INC
3.0	1.7	78.3	69.7	1.4	1.5	54.8	45.0	99.8	106.3	14.5	0.0	PLATTE RIVER INS CO
4.3	3.8	N/A	N/A	N/A	N/A	N/A	N/A	N/A	-20.8	0.0	0.0	PLAZA INS CO
17.3	12.8	-58.4	21.1	-70.1	-57.9	106.7	-10.8	95.9	-282.1	-252.8	0.6	PLICO INC
1.7	1.2	210.3	98.7	-1.6	4.4	77.8	23.3	101.1	108.1	7.4	0.0	PLYMOUTH ROCK ASR CORP

999 + Denotes number greater than 999.9%
999 - Denotes number less than -999.99%
● Bullets denote a more detailed analysis is available in Section II.

INSURANCE COMPANY NAME	DOM. STATE	RATING	TOTAL ASSETS ($MIL)	CAPITAL & SURPLUS ($MIL)	ANNUAL NET PREMIUM ($MIL)	NET INCOME ($MIL)	CAPITAL-IZATION INDEX (PTS)	RESERVE ADQ INDEX (PTS)	PROFIT-ABILITY INDEX (PTS)	LIQUIDITY INDEX (PTS)	STAB. INDEX (PTS)	STABILITY FACTORS
PMI INS CO	AZ	F	109.7	60.7	16.2	2.3	8.4	3.7	2.9	6.9	0.0	DFGR
PMI MORTGAGE INS CO	AZ	F	918.5	-1,466.1	202.4	61.2	0.0	3.3	0.9	7.0	0.0	CFGR
PODIATRY INS CO OF AM	IL	C+	303.0	129.1	46.6	5.1	8.0	9.3	8.1	7.0	4.4	AFT
POINT GUARD INS CO	PR	C-	63.5	14.0	46.3	0.7	4.0	3.7	4.6	3.5	2.6	CDGL
POLICYHOLDERS MUTUAL INS CO	WI	U	0.3	0.3	0.0	0.0	N/A	N/A	8.4	10.0	0.8	GRT
PONCE DE LEON LTC RRG INC	FL	D	7.5	3.5	1.1	-0.8	8.0	5.8	1.4	6.9	2.0	DFGR
POSITIVE PHYSICIANS INS	PA	C	53.7	15.7	12.2	0.5	3.8	9.7	8.7	8.1	2.6	DRT
POTOMAC INS CO	PA	U	10.7	9.2	0.0	-0.3	N/A	1.9	1.5	0.0	0.0	CFGL
PRAETORIAN INS CO	PA	C	658.9	218.7	300.7	1.7	7.5	3.8	2.4	2.7	4.1	FLRT
PRE-PAID LEGAL CAS INC	OK	C	19.9	16.8	44.5	2.7	5.5	7.2	3.7	1.7	2.8	DGLT
PREFERRED AUTO INS CO	TN	D	8.3	3.4	2.5	0.3	8.7	9.3	5.9	9.0	2.0	DGRT
PREFERRED CONTRACTORS INS CO RRG	MT	E	102.6	10.8	29.5	-0.7	0.0	0.4	2.7	5.8	0.1	CDGR
PREFERRED EMPLOYERS INS CO	CA	C	102.1	45.6	0.0	0.5	10.0	3.8	7.4	9.9	3.9	RT
PREFERRED MUTUAL INS CO	NY	B	526.3	225.4	204.4	10.6	9.4	9.1	6.1	6.7	4.3	RT
PREFERRED PHYSICIANS MEDICAL RRG	MO	B	214.6	125.5	27.9	3.8	10.0	9.3	8.9	8.3	4.1	RT
PREFERRED PROFESSIONAL INS CO	NE	B	307.3	158.2	36.4	2.8	10.0	9.4	3.8	7.2	4.3	FRT
PREFERRED PROFESSIONAL RRG	DC	U	1.0	0.6	0.0	0.0	N/A	3.6	1.9	9.9	0.6	GT
PREMIER GROUP INS CO	TN	C	62.9	35.8	14.7	1.7	9.3	8.6	8.9	8.0	3.3	DRT
PREMIER INS CO OF MA	CT	B	280.7	243.1	73.8	11.0	10.0	4.7	7.0	6.8	4.6	FT
PREMIER INS EXCHANGE RRG	VT	U (5)	7.8	7.4	0.0	0.0	N/A	6.3	3.2	7.0	3.7	FT
PREMIER PHYSICIANS INS CO INC A RRG	NV	E	10.8	0.7	4.0	-1.8	1.2	4.2	0.1	4.7	0.1	CDFG
PREPARED INS CO	FL	C-	69.4	19.5	42.4	0.2	3.1	4.2	3.5	6.8	2.9	CDT
PREVISOR INS CO	CO	U	8.6	8.0	0.0	-0.2	N/A	N/A	3.5	10.0	3.7	DGT
PRIME INS CO	IL	C	79.0	41.5	27.8	2.6	7.3	6.0	8.9	7.3	3.4	RT
PRIME P&C INS INC	IL	C	19.9	12.6	3.9	0.2	9.8	3.7	6.2	7.4	2.9	DGT
PRIMEONE INS CO	MI	D	15.7	7.6	4.0	-0.4	5.3	5.2	1.2	8.6	2.2	DGT
PRIMERO INS CO	NV	C-	15.8	8.5	11.3	-0.5	7.4	8.5	3.6	6.5	2.8	DGRT
PRINCETON EXCESS & SURPLUS LINES INS	DE	C	147.6	62.0	0.0	4.1	10.0	N/A	8.4	7.0	3.6	RT
PRINCETON INS CO	NJ	C	667.4	464.1	31.0	10.4	10.0	9.6	8.4	9.7	3.8	RT
PRIORITY ONE INS CO	TX	C	20.0	9.5	7.6	-1.5	7.9	6.2	1.7	6.4	2.9	DFGR
PRIVILEGE UNDERWRITERS RECIP EXCH	FL	B-	376.8	114.1	138.0	-1.7	6.9	5.8	2.7	6.7	3.5	FGT
PROAIR RRG INC	NV	F (5)	0.5	0.0	0.2	0.0	7.1	6.5	0.1	2.6	0.0	LT
PROASSURANCE AMER MUTL A RRG	DC	U	10.5	10.1	0.0	0.1	N/A	N/A	4.9	10.0	4.9	DGT
PROASSURANCE CASUALTY CO	MI	B-	1,074.4	373.6	151.1	16.2	9.4	9.7	3.4	7.4	4.6	ART
PROASSURANCE INDEMNTIY CO INC	AL	C+	1,394.4	596.4	197.4	38.2	9.8	9.6	3.0	7.3	4.4	ART
PROASSURANCE SPECIALTY INS CO INC	AL	C	48.6	30.1	0.0	2.7	10.0	N/A	3.9	7.2	3.7	GT
PROBUILDERS SPECIALTY INS CO RRG	DC	U	13.5	12.5	0.0	0.6	N/A	6.0	2.2	2.9	3.4	FGLR
PROCENTURY INS CO	MI	C-	170.0	46.2	56.1	3.4	7.4	2.2	4.1	6.6	3.3	FRT
PRODUCERS AGRICULTURE INS CO	TX	C	734.5	76.9	0.0	14.8	10.0	5.8	6.4	0.0	3.9	GLRT
PRODUCERS LLOYDS INS CO	TX	C	6.4	6.0	0.0	-0.1	10.0	N/A	3.9	10.0	2.7	DGRT
PROFESSIONAL CASUALTY ASSN	PA	C-	46.0	13.6	12.5	0.7	5.2	7.0	3.6	6.8	2.4	DFRT
PROFESSIONAL EXCHANGE ASR CO (A	HI	D	10.6	2.8	1.7	0.0	2.0	4.1	4.2	8.8	1.4	CDGT
PROFESSIONAL INS EXCHANGE MUTUAL	UT	D+	8.1	5.0	1.3	0.0	7.2	4.9	3.9	7.6	2.1	DGT
PROFESSIONAL QUALITY LIABILITY INS	VT	U	2.1	2.0	0.0	0.0	N/A	5.8	2.6	7.0	2.6	FGRT
PROFESSIONAL SECURITY INS CO	AZ	C+	85.6	67.7	0.5	0.9	10.0	3.6	3.9	10.0	4.1	DFGT
▲PROFESSIONAL SOLUTIONS INS CO	IA	C-	23.1	8.3	3.4	-0.1	4.8	8.7	2.4	6.8	2.8	DGRT
PROFESSIONALS ADVOCATE INS CO	MD	B-	133.4	105.7	5.5	0.9	10.0	8.9	8.4	9.6	4.1	DT
PROFESSIONALS RRG INC	MT	D	4.1	1.1	0.2	-0.1	7.9	6.9	2.0	7.7	1.2	DFGT
PROGRESSIVE ADVANCED INS CO	OH	C	462.3	172.3	285.0	3.7	8.4	7.5	8.8	2.7	3.7	LRT
PROGRESSIVE AMERICAN INS CO	OH	C	472.8	185.8	206.1	2.3	10.0	6.1	8.6	7.0	3.8	RT
PROGRESSIVE BAYSIDE INS CO	OH	C	152.2	37.0	103.1	2.6	7.3	6.2	9.1	6.8	3.5	RT
PROGRESSIVE CASUALTY INS CO	OH	B-	7,375.3	1,792.4	5,050.3	78.7	5.4	6.2	8.9	1.3	4.5	LRT

See Page 27 for explanation of footnotes and Page 28 for explanation of stability factors.

Arrows denote recent upgrades ▲ or downgrades ▼   (see Section VII for explanations)

106

www.weissratings.com

RISK ADJ. RATIO #1	CAPITAL RATIO #2	PREMIUM TO SURPLUS (%)	RESV. TO SURPLUS (%)	RESV. DEVELOP. 1 YEAR (%)	RESV. DEVELOP. 2 YEAR (%)	LOSS RATIO (%)	EXP. RATIO (%)	COMB RATIO (%)	CASH FROM UNDER-WRITING (%)	NET PREMIUM GROWTH (%)	INVEST. IN AFFIL (%)	INSURANCE COMPANY NAME
1.7	1.4	25.6	37.7	4.7	7.2	48.7	28.6	77.3	48.2	99.4	0.0	PMI INS CO
-1.1	-0.8	-13.7	-158.6	-2.6	-3.8	130.0	-3.6	126.4	38.3	65.7	6.5	PMI MORTGAGE INS CO
3.3	2.3	37.5	111.0	-6.1	-12.6	70.3	20.2	90.5	71.4	-3.9	0.0	PODIATRY INS CO OF AM
0.3	0.3	244.7	24.3	21.3	-3.7	92.8	-2.5	90.3	143.5	94.7	0.0	POINT GUARD INS CO
N/A	N/A	8.3	N/A	N/A	N/A	N/A	52.2	52.2	145.8	50.5	0.0	POLICYHOLDERS MUTUAL INS CO
1.7	1.4	23.9	77.8	-4.0	-19.0	122.5	15.2	137.7	45.5	82.2	0.0	PONCE DE LEON LTC RRG INC
0.8	0.6	80.7	197.6	-17.7	-37.5	52.3	35.6	87.9	136.3	26.6	0.0	POSITIVE PHYSICIANS INS
N/A	N/A	N/A	999 +	N/A	-0.1	133.5	-800.4	-666.9	N/A	-537.5	0.0	POTOMAC INS CO
3.3	2.2	123.3	138.3	1.4	2.9	63.9	39.8	103.7	80.4	-27.6	0.0 ●	PRAETORIAN INS CO
1.0	0.8	284.0	0.5	-0.1	-0.3	38.4	51.0	89.4	111.9	4.2	0.0	PRE-PAID LEGAL CAS INC
2.4	2.1	81.1	52.0	-18.3	-15.1	85.1	12.7	97.8	99.9	10.4	0.0	PREFERRED AUTO INS CO
0.0	0.0	436.6	831.9	27.6	89.4	68.1	20.5	88.6	128.1	N/A	0.0	PREFERRED CONTRACTORS INS CO
6.5	5.8	N/A	N/A	N/A	N/A	N/A	N/A	N/A	-128.2	0.0	0.0	PREFERRED EMPLOYERS INS CO
4.7	3.0	96.1	70.4	-2.5	-6.7	67.8	27.9	95.7	98.1	2.3	0.0 ●	PREFERRED MUTUAL INS CO
4.4	3.5	22.5	53.4	-3.7	-6.5	49.7	26.8	76.5	172.2	-1.1	0.0	PREFERRED PHYSICIANS MEDICAL RRG
5.2	3.9	23.2	63.3	-6.2	-12.2	77.7	13.9	91.6	63.5	-13.9	0.4	PREFERRED PROFESSIONAL INS CO
N/A	N/A	7.1	8.6	-1.1	-0.4	69.9	161.5	231.4	127.3	116.4	0.0	PREFERRED PROFESSIONAL RRG
3.2	2.6	42.1	46.5	-5.4	-7.8	54.1	27.0	81.1	132.1	-5.4	0.0	PREMIER GROUP INS CO
16.9	13.7	31.5	17.7	-2.3	-0.5	59.7	34.1	93.8	82.9	-34.3	0.0 ●	PREMIER INS CO OF MA
N/A	N/A	N/A	4.7	N/A	0.1	N/A	N/A	N/A	N/A	0.0	0.0	PREMIER INS EXCHANGE RRG
0.1	0.0	223.5	218.6	28.8	27.4	90.1	60.0	150.1	61.4	-8.0	0.0	PREMIER PHYSICIANS INS CO INC A
0.7	0.5	211.8	67.5	1.5	7.1	66.6	38.4	105.0	114.6	32.3	0.0	PREPARED INS CO
N/A	N/A	0.3	0.5	N/A	N/A	999 +	999 +	999 +	14.3	0.0	0.0	PREVISOR INS CO
1.7	1.2	70.8	46.4	-2.7	-1.8	45.1	21.7	66.8	170.2	12.9	18.9	PRIME INS CO
4.7	2.8	31.5	35.9	6.7	-1.4	65.4	33.9	99.3	119.6	-40.4	0.0	PRIME P&C INS INC
1.1	0.7	52.9	66.1	-9.4	4.5	28.5	53.5	82.0	85.9	177.1	0.0	PRIMEONE INS CO
1.6	1.4	127.7	64.3	-2.7	-10.0	87.5	12.2	99.7	94.6	16.8	0.0	PRIMERO INS CO
7.4	6.6	N/A	N/A	N/A	N/A	N/A	N/A	N/A	57.9	0.0	0.0	PRINCETON EXCESS & SURPLUS LINES
7.1	5.4	6.7	30.0	-1.2	-2.5	79.3	24.5	103.8	90.1	-6.3	0.0 ●	PRINCETON INS CO
2.0	1.3	72.1	36.5	11.5	1.1	89.0	35.5	124.5	89.7	2.3	9.0	PRIORITY ONE INS CO
2.1	1.3	140.0	28.1	-3.0	4.2	60.6	45.4	106.0	95.5	43.1	1.6	PRIVILEGE UNDERWRITERS RECIP
0.0	0.0	44.4	12.2	-1.6	-3.5	64.5	81.9	146.4	101.6	70.3	0.0	PROAIR RRG INC
N/A	N/A	0.1	N/A	N/A	N/A	75.3	141.8	217.1	52.9	0.0	0.0	PROASSURANCE AMER MUTL A RRG
2.9	2.2	34.1	129.4	-9.3	-23.7	59.9	24.7	84.6	89.5	-4.4	0.0 ●	PROASSURANCE CASUALTY CO
4.0	3.0	35.5	119.7	-10.3	-19.9	52.2	18.0	70.2	110.1	-7.6	0.7 ●	PROASSURANCE INDEMNTIY CO INC
9.0	8.1	N/A	11.9	N/A	N/A	N/A	N/A	N/A	-146.5	0.0	0.0	PROASSURANCE SPECIALTY INS CO INC
N/A	N/A	N/A	0.3	-461.5	-391.8	N/A	N/A	N/A	-0.1	0.0	0.0	PROBUILDERS SPECIALTY INS CO RRG
2.0	1.3	129.7	234.7	15.2	23.6	77.1	37.1	114.2	65.8	0.7	0.0	PROCENTURY INS CO
4.7	2.6	N/A	N/A	N/A	3.4	N/A	999 +	999 +	278.0	-53.8	48.7	PRODUCERS AGRICULTURE INS CO
32.3	29.1	N/A	N/A	N/A	N/A	N/A	N/A	N/A	19.6	0.0	0.0	PRODUCERS LLOYDS INS CO
1.3	1.0	107.8	221.8	-9.1	3.9	58.7	36.3	95.0	92.6	-1.8	0.0	PROFESSIONAL CASUALTY ASSN
0.4	0.2	58.2	107.5	-27.4	-46.9	71.3	40.1	111.4	254.7	-20.8	0.0	PROFESSIONAL EXCHANGE ASR CO (A
1.6	1.1	25.8	46.5	-2.6	-4.6	63.7	45.9	109.6	106.8	-0.3	0.0	PROFESSIONAL INS EXCHANGE MUTUAL
N/A	N/A	N/A	6.6	2.4	4.0	999 +	N/A	N/A	N/A	100.0	0.0	PROFESSIONAL QUALITY LIABILITY INS
11.0	6.5	0.7	1.7	-0.3	0.3	118.2	-106.2	12.0	833.2	70.3	0.0	PROFESSIONAL SECURITY INS CO
0.8	0.6	40.8	90.6	1.5	-3.8	109.5	33.1	142.6	113.9	4.6	0.0	PROFESSIONAL SOLUTIONS INS CO
10.4	6.4	5.4	11.3	-0.8	-4.9	51.3	57.2	108.5	766.4	3.2	0.0	PROFESSIONALS ADVOCATE INS CO
1.1	1.0	19.0	43.7	-2.1	2.6	98.7	133.4	232.1	76.9	-37.8	0.0	PROFESSIONALS RRG INC
2.1	1.9	170.2	65.3	-2.3	-0.5	74.5	19.1	93.6	102.5	11.2	0.0	PROGRESSIVE ADVANCED INS CO
3.6	3.2	112.8	46.3	-1.5	-0.6	71.6	19.9	91.5	107.6	3.2	0.0	PROGRESSIVE AMERICAN INS CO
1.5	1.3	302.2	124.2	-4.1	-1.5	71.6	20.3	91.9	113.9	3.2	0.0	PROGRESSIVE BAYSIDE INS CO
1.0	0.8	313.7	128.9	-4.0	-1.5	71.6	20.5	92.1	111.4	3.2	17.7 ●	PROGRESSIVE CASUALTY INS CO

999 + Denotes number greater than 999.9%
999 - Denotes number less than -999.99%
● Bullets denote a more detailed analysis is available in Section II.

INSURANCE COMPANY NAME	DOM. STATE	RATING	TOTAL ASSETS ($MIL)	CAPITAL & SURPLUS ($MIL)	ANNUAL NET PREMIUM ($MIL)	NET INCOME ($MIL)	CAPITAL-IZATION INDEX (PTS)	RESERVE ADQ INDEX (PTS)	PROFIT-ABILITY INDEX (PTS)	LIQUIDITY INDEX (PTS)	STAB. INDEX (PTS)	STABILITY FACTORS
PROGRESSIVE CHOICE INS CO	OH	U	7.9	5.5	0.0	0.0	N/A	4.6	1.9	7.0	3.1	GRT
PROGRESSIVE CLASSIC INS CO	WI	C	401.7	104.5	309.2	3.9	7.3	6.2	8.9	7.2	3.8	RT
PROGRESSIVE COMMERCIAL CASUALTY	OH	U	8.2	8.2	0.0	0.1	N/A	N/A	3.8	7.0	4.8	GOT
PROGRESSIVE COUNTY MUTUAL INS CO	TX	C	551.8	5.0	0.0	0.0	2.4	N/A	3.9	7.0	2.5	CFRT
PROGRESSIVE DIRECT INS CO	OH	C	6,529.2	1,922.0	5,521.8	106.7	7.2	7.7	8.9	1.3	4.3	LRT
PROGRESSIVE EXPRESS INS CO	OH	C	237.6	52.6	40.0	0.5	10.0	6.5	8.5	6.3	3.6	FRT
PROGRESSIVE FREEDOM INS CO	NJ	C	4.0	2.5	0.4	0.1	10.0	6.6	5.3	7.7	2.3	DGRT
PROGRESSIVE GARDEN STATE INS CO	NJ	B-	354.8	59.4	51.0	1.9	9.7	6.1	8.2	7.4	4.1	RT
PROGRESSIVE GULF INS CO	OH	C	269.4	75.8	206.1	4.5	7.5	6.1	2.6	5.1	3.5	RT
PROGRESSIVE HAWAII INS CORP	OH	C	197.7	62.4	164.6	5.7	7.6	9.4	9.6	5.0	3.6	RT
PROGRESSIVE MARATHON INS CO	MI	C	510.9	159.7	427.5	10.4	7.3	7.7	8.9	2.3	3.7	LRT
PROGRESSIVE MAX INS CO	OH	C	482.5	148.1	427.5	8.3	7.2	7.7	8.9	4.4	3.7	LRT
PROGRESSIVE MICHIGAN INS CO	MI	C	528.2	154.6	412.3	7.4	7.5	6.1	8.9	5.8	3.8	RT
PROGRESSIVE MOUNTAIN INS CO	OH	C	294.5	74.5	103.1	2.8	9.2	6.1	8.4	6.2	3.6	RT
PROGRESSIVE NORTHERN INS CO	WI	C+	1,556.6	425.8	1,236.8	23.4	7.2	6.2	9.4	2.3	4.3	LRT
PROGRESSIVE NORTHWESTERN INS CO	OH	C+	1,516.9	421.5	1,236.8	20.8	7.2	6.2	9.3	4.3	4.4	LRT
PROGRESSIVE PALOVERDE INS CO	IN	C	150.6	45.7	35.6	0.8	9.7	7.3	8.6	6.5	3.5	FRT
PROGRESSIVE PREFERRED INS CO	OH	C	774.8	211.0	618.4	10.0	7.3	6.2	9.3	3.0	3.9	LRT
PROGRESSIVE PREMIER INS CO OF IL	OH	C	270.8	61.9	142.5	1.9	7.6	7.7	8.9	5.4	4.0	RT
PROGRESSIVE SECURITY INS CO	LA	C	286.3	54.9	38.0	0.4	10.0	6.1	8.5	7.4	3.6	RT
PROGRESSIVE SELECT INS CO	OH	C	642.7	172.5	135.9	2.3	10.0	6.2	8.1	4.9	3.8	FLRT
PROGRESSIVE SOUTHEASTERN INS CO	IN	C	178.0	63.4	103.1	2.1	7.9	6.1	8.9	6.3	4.0	RT
PROGRESSIVE SPECIALTY INS CO	OH	C	979.7	310.4	721.5	15.6	7.4	6.1	2.5	2.3	3.9	LRT
PROGRESSIVE UNIVERSAL INS CO	WI	C	375.6	123.0	285.0	8.3	7.6	7.6	8.9	1.1	4.0	LRT
PROGRESSIVE WEST INS CO	OH	C	134.2	35.2	30.1	0.7	9.9	5.9	6.3	6.9	3.6	RT
PROPERTY-OWNERS INS CO	IN	B+	257.1	121.9	78.9	4.6	8.5	4.8	8.2	6.7	5.1	T
PROSELECT INS CO	MA	C	95.8	24.0	0.0	0.4	10.0	N/A	5.6	7.0	3.7	DRT
PROSELECT NATIONAL INS CO INC	AZ	U	13.8	13.1	0.0	0.1	N/A	N/A	6.0	7.0	5.1	GT
PROTECTION MUTUAL INS CO	PA	U	0.6	0.5	0.0	0.0	N/A	7.4	2.3	9.6	1.4	FGRT
PROTECTIVE INS CO	IN	B	763.4	397.9	233.2	24.1	7.1	8.7	6.5	6.7	4.9	RT
PROTECTIVE P&C INS CO	MO	B-	375.3	164.9	65.1	9.4	10.0	6.1	5.3	6.9	4.3	RT
PROTECTIVE SPECIALTY INS CO	IN	B	67.3	59.7	1.0	0.1	9.6	4.2	5.8	10.0	4.8	DFT
PROVIDENCE MUTUAL FIRE INS CO	RI	B-	189.2	90.0	73.4	-1.9	8.5	7.6	2.4	6.4	3.9	FRT
PROVIDENCE PLANTATIONS INS CO	RI	U	1.2	1.2	0.0	0.0	N/A	N/A	3.6	7.0	0.0	CGT
PROVIDENCE WASHINGTON INS CO	RI	U	213.9	75.8	0.3	0.3	N/A	10.0	3.6	10.0	6.1	GT
PUBLIC SERVICE INS CO	IL	E	295.8	32.2	100.1	-25.5	0.5	1.6	0.5	7.0	0.1	CDFR
PUBLIC UTILITY MUTUAL INS CO RRG	VT	E	7.1	5.7	0.9	0.0	10.0	9.3	8.5	8.2	0.3	DGRT
PUERTO RICO MED DEFENSE MUT INS CO	PR	D	17.0	3.9	6.4	0.7	2.0	3.3	8.0	7.1	2.0	CDGT
PURE INS CO	FL	B-	279.0	153.5	138.0	-0.2	7.7	5.7	3.5	7.6	3.8	T
PYMATUNING MUTUAL FIRE INS CO	PA	D+(2)	3.3	3.3	0.0	-0.1	10.0	N/A	3.3	10.0	2.0	DGT
QBE INS CORP	PA	B-	2,608.9	721.7	597.0	-2.3	7.9	3.8	3.6	4.5	4.8	FLRT
QBE REINS CORP	PA	B	1,212.7	830.0	186.6	-1.4	7.5	5.9	3.8	6.4	4.9	RT
QBE SEGUROS	PR	D	74.1	16.6	33.4	-0.7	0.9	3.8	2.2	7.0	1.5	CDRT
QBE SPECIALTY INS CO	ND	C-	447.4	108.0	288.6	3.2	7.4	3.7	2.7	5.5	3.3	RT
QUALITAS INS CO	CA	C	42.8	15.0	16.8	-1.5	7.2	3.6	2.8	7.7	2.7	DGRT
QUALITY CASUALTY INS CO	AL	D	1.5	0.8	0.0	0.0	9.2	6.2	3.6	10.0	1.5	DFGR
QUANTA INDEMNITY CO	CO	U	39.4	19.3	0.0	-0.7	N/A	9.5	1.9	7.0	2.1	CRT
QUEEN CITY ASR INC	VT	U	2,480.4	2,256.5	171.0	86.1	N/A	N/A	8.9	6.8	3.8	T
QUINCY MUTUAL FIRE INS CO	MA	B	1,536.0	1,007.8	313.3	16.5	9.1	7.8	5.7	6.9	4.7	RT
R&Q REINS CO	PA	U	165.7	21.7	0.1	3.3	N/A	0.2	1.2	9.5	0.0	CFGR
RADIAN GUARANTY INC	PA	D+	3,805.1	1,387.9	845.7	240.0	6.8	3.4	3.9	6.8	2.4	ART
RADIAN GUARANTY REINS INC	PA	D	6.9	3.1	35.8	-1.8	0.7	5.1	1.9	0.0	2.2	CDFG

See Page 27 for explanation of footnotes and
Page 28 for explanation of stability factors.
Arrows denote recent upgrades ▲ or downgrades ▼   (see Section VII for explanations)

www.weissratings.com

RISK ADJ. CAPITAL RATIO #1	CAPITAL RATIO #2	PREMIUM TO SURPLUS (%)	RESV. TO SURPLUS (%)	RESV. DEVELOP. 1 YEAR (%)	RESV. DEVELOP. 2 YEAR (%)	LOSS RATIO (%)	EXP. RATIO (%)	COMB. RATIO (%)	CASH FROM UNDER-WRITING (%)	NET PREMIUM GROWTH (%)	INVEST. IN AFFIL (%)	INSURANCE COMPANY NAME
N/A	N/A	N/A	N/A	N/A	N/A	N/A	N/A	N/A	N/A	0.0	0.0	PROGRESSIVE CHOICE INS CO
1.4	1.2	310.9	127.8	-4.0	-1.5	71.6	20.0	91.6	114.6	3.2	0.0	PROGRESSIVE CLASSIC INS CO
N/A	N/A	N/A	N/A	N/A	N/A	N/A	N/A	N/A	N/A	0.0	0.0	PROGRESSIVE COMMERCIAL CASUALTY
0.4	0.2	N/A	N/A	N/A	N/A	N/A	N/A	N/A	-252.0	0.0	0.0	PROGRESSIVE COUNTY MUTUAL INS CO
1.3	1.1	309.7	118.7	-4.2	-0.8	74.5	19.5	94.0	114.0	11.2	0.0 ●	PROGRESSIVE DIRECT INS CO
5.7	3.6	76.9	52.5	-0.7	-1.9	70.0	18.0	88.0	88.5	7.2	0.0	PROGRESSIVE EXPRESS INS CO
4.1	3.7	14.9	17.6	1.2	-3.0	68.8	14.9	83.7	147.5	-29.4	0.0	PROGRESSIVE FREEDOM INS CO
3.1	2.7	89.2	57.6	-0.1	-1.3	83.0	16.3	99.3	117.4	11.0	0.0	PROGRESSIVE GARDEN STATE INS CO
1.5	1.3	292.1	120.0	-3.5	-1.0	71.6	19.5	91.1	113.7	3.2	0.0	PROGRESSIVE GULF INS CO
1.7	1.4	294.0	103.9	-9.0	-17.7	69.5	18.8	88.3	119.9	11.9	0.0	PROGRESSIVE HAWAII INS CORP
1.3	1.2	289.4	111.0	-3.9	-0.7	74.5	19.2	93.7	110.0	11.2	0.0	PROGRESSIVE MARATHON INS CO
1.2	1.1	308.7	118.3	-4.1	-0.8	74.5	19.5	94.0	117.8	11.2	0.0	PROGRESSIVE MAX INS CO
1.5	1.3	282.7	116.2	-3.8	-1.4	71.6	20.0	91.6	110.9	3.2	0.0	PROGRESSIVE MICHIGAN INS CO
2.9	2.5	144.9	59.6	-2.1	-0.8	71.6	18.9	90.5	116.7	3.2	0.0	PROGRESSIVE MOUNTAIN INS CO
1.4	1.2	311.6	128.1	-4.1	-1.5	71.6	19.5	91.1	112.7	3.2	0.0 ●	PROGRESSIVE NORTHERN INS CO
1.3	1.1	312.2	128.3	-4.1	-1.5	71.6	20.1	91.7	115.0	3.2	0.0 ●	PROGRESSIVE NORTHWESTERN INS CO
3.1	2.7	80.0	30.7	-1.1	-0.2	74.5	18.4	92.9	67.5	11.2	0.0	PROGRESSIVE PALOVERDE INS CO
1.4	1.2	311.2	127.9	-4.0	-1.5	71.6	19.5	91.1	111.4	3.2	0.0 ●	PROGRESSIVE PREFERRED INS CO
1.5	1.3	239.4	91.8	-3.3	-0.6	74.5	20.1	94.6	99.1	11.2	0.0	PROGRESSIVE PREMIER INS CO OF IL
5.3	4.4	70.3	24.5	-1.5	-2.1	74.6	17.8	92.4	124.1	-3.3	0.0	PROGRESSIVE SECURITY INS CO
3.9	3.5	80.1	30.9	-0.9	-0.4	77.5	17.8	95.3	88.4	15.7	0.0	PROGRESSIVE SELECT INS CO
1.7	1.5	169.3	69.6	-2.3	-0.9	71.6	17.1	88.7	111.6	3.2	0.0	PROGRESSIVE SOUTHEASTERN INS CO
1.7	1.4	270.8	111.3	-2.9	-0.8	71.6	19.3	90.9	111.4	3.2	0.0 ●	PROGRESSIVE SPECIALTY INS CO
1.5	1.3	251.3	96.4	-3.2	-0.6	74.5	17.7	92.2	108.3	11.2	0.0	PROGRESSIVE UNIVERSAL INS CO
3.4	2.9	87.8	35.9	0.5	2.2	79.9	19.8	99.7	96.4	-0.9	0.0	PROGRESSIVE WEST INS CO
3.4	1.9	68.2	43.6	2.8	N/A	60.6	34.0	94.6	125.6	9.0	0.0 ●	PROPERTY-OWNERS INS CO
3.1	2.8	N/A	N/A	N/A	N/A	N/A	N/A	N/A	97.9	0.0	0.0	PROSELECT INS CO
N/A	N/A	N/A	N/A	N/A	N/A	N/A	N/A	N/A	N/A	0.0	0.0	PROSELECT NATIONAL INS CO INC
N/A	N/A	9.6	2.8	-1.8	-2.0	94.8	111.4	206.2	23.3	78.8	0.0	PROTECTION MUTUAL INS CO
1.5	1.1	59.9	72.5	-3.0	-8.8	57.4	32.6	90.0	118.2	-0.9	26.7 ●	PROTECTIVE INS CO
9.1	5.9	42.0	9.1	-2.8	-1.8	60.5	29.4	89.9	101.6	1.6	0.0	PROTECTIVE P&C INS CO
4.3	3.1	1.7	11.3	1.1	8.5	67.4	54.2	121.6	4.8	-54.4	0.0	PROTECTIVE SPECIALTY INS CO
3.0	1.9	81.2	53.6	-2.5	-2.4	81.2	38.6	119.8	88.6	4.7	0.7	PROVIDENCE MUTUAL FIRE INS CO
N/A	N/A	N/A	N/A	N/A	N/A	N/A	N/A	N/A	N/A	0.0	0.0	PROVIDENCE PLANTATIONS INS CO
N/A	N/A	0.4	86.3	-2.6	-78.0	999 +	-982.1	999 +	N/A	143.6	0.0	PROVIDENCE WASHINGTON INS CO
0.1	0.0	172.8	580.2	36.1	45.4	118.1	39.1	157.2	64.4	-28.9	0.0	PUBLIC SERVICE INS CO
7.5	4.9	15.9	11.9	-7.7	-10.8	6.1	54.7	60.8	153.4	11.3	0.0	PUBLIC UTILITY MUTUAL INS CO RRG
0.9	0.5	189.0	234.1	-0.1	42.0	61.2	34.0	95.2	143.1	-3.0	0.0	PUERTO RICO MED DEFENSE MUT INS
2.8	1.7	90.1	18.1	-1.5	2.7	60.3	45.4	105.7	104.6	43.1	1.8	PURE INS CO
47.4	45.4	0.4	N/A	N/A	N/A	264.1	288.5	552.6	198.8	-10.0	0.0	PYMATUNING MUTUAL FIRE INS CO
2.1	1.5	81.1	88.0	1.1	2.0	63.9	37.1	101.0	87.2	-19.6	16.5 ●	QBE INS CORP
1.3	1.3	22.9	23.4	0.3	0.5	63.9	33.2	97.1	101.7	10.9	73.9 ●	QBE REINS CORP
0.4	0.2	251.9	119.3	2.1	14.4	55.6	43.6	99.2	98.9	16.2	0.0	QBE SEGUROS
1.7	1.1	156.8	160.2	1.7	2.9	63.9	34.1	98.0	101.2	-2.2	0.0	QBE SPECIALTY INS CO
1.4	1.0	105.0	17.4	0.5	N/A	60.0	38.2	98.2	181.4	N/A	0.0	QUALITAS INS CO
2.4	2.2	N/A	N/A	-0.4	0.5	N/A	N/A	N/A	23.9	0.0	0.0	QUALITY CASUALTY INS CO
N/A	N/A	0.2	81.9	-19.6	-33.5	999 +	999 +	999 +	-8.8	932.5	0.0	QUANTA INDEMNITY CO
N/A	N/A	7.9	N/A	N/A	N/A	N/A	0.3	0.3	999 +	0.5	0.0	QUEEN CITY ASR INC
3.9	2.4	32.1	20.8	-2.7	-5.2	78.5	34.9	113.4	96.2	16.4	3.4 ●	QUINCY MUTUAL FIRE INS CO
N/A	N/A	0.4	757.8	148.0	200.4	999 +	999 +	999 +	0.4	-43.2	0.0	R&Q REINS CO
1.7	1.5	50.1	49.8	-7.8	-6.0	22.2	27.1	49.3	92.2	6.0	0.8 ●	RADIAN GUARANTY INC
0.3	0.3	730.2	N/A	-106.6	-126.1	27.3	10.4	37.7	31.3	-61.9	0.5	RADIAN GUARANTY REINS INC

999 + Denotes number greater than 999.9%
999 - Denotes number less than -999.99%
● Bullets denote a more detailed analysis is available in Section II.

INSURANCE COMPANY NAME	DOM. STATE	RATING	TOTAL ASSETS ($MIL)	CAPITAL & SURPLUS ($MIL)	ANNUAL NET PREMIUM ($MIL)	NET INCOME ($MIL)	CAPITAL-IZATION INDEX (PTS)	RESERVE ADQ INDEX (PTS)	PROFIT-ABILITY INDEX (PTS)	LIQUIDITY INDEX (PTS)	STAB. INDEX (PTS)	STABILITY FACTORS
RADIAN INS INC	PA	D+	22.6	18.8	15.3	-0.3	9.9	9.3	1.9	7.1	2.4	DGT
RADIAN INVESTOR SURETY INC	PA	U	5.0	4.9	0.0	0.0	N/A	N/A	1.9	7.0	3.1	FGT
RADIAN MORTGAGE ASR INC	PA	U	8.7	8.6	0.0	-0.1	N/A	N/A	2.1	7.0	3.3	AFGT
RADIAN MORTGAGE GUARANTY INC	PA	U	19.9	19.8	0.0	-0.2	N/A	N/A	3.8	7.0	5.0	FGT
RADIAN MORTGAGE INS INC	PA	D+	2.8	2.8	7.6	-0.1	2.4	5.1	1.9	0.0	2.3	CDFG
RADIAN REINS INC	PA	U	467.9	143.0	63.9	28.3	N/A	N/A	5.9	7.0	5.4	T
RADNOR SPECIALTY INS CO	NE	U	26.1	26.1	0.0	0.0	N/A	N/A	4.9	7.0	5.4	GT
RAINIER INS CO	AZ	C+	25.6	21.0	2.4	0.1	10.0	6.5	5.8	10.0	3.3	DGT
RAM MUTUAL INS CO	MN	B-	105.5	62.5	47.1	4.9	8.5	9.0	8.5	7.1	3.6	RT
RAMPART INS CO	NY	U	31.2	11.0	0.0	-0.4	N/A	4.8	1.9	9.2	3.1	CFGT
RANCHERS & FARMERS MUTUAL INS CO	TX	D+	35.3	3.4	1.0	0.7	4.0	5.8	5.6	6.8	1.9	CDGR
REAL LEGACY ASR CO INC	PR	D	143.5	48.6	55.8	1.7	7.0	8.9	3.2	6.6	0.7	DRT
REAMSTOWN MUTUAL INS CO	PA	D+	8.1	3.0	6.3	0.0	6.7	6.1	4.7	6.3	2.0	DGRT
RECREATION RRG INC	VT	U	3.1	2.7	0.0	-0.1	N/A	0.0	2.7	0.0	0.0	LT
RED CLAY RRG INC	SC	B-	8.3	4.3	1.4	-0.1	9.2	9.8	7.1	9.3	3.5	DFGT
RED ROCK RISK RETENTION GROUP INC	AZ	D	6.4	3.9	1.2	0.2	4.4	1.9	1.2	6.4	2.0	DFGT
RED SHIELD INS CO	WA	B	38.6	21.5	12.9	0.1	8.3	6.6	6.1	8.4	4.0	DGRT
REDPOINT COUNTY MUTUAL INS CO	TX	C-	13.4	5.0	0.0	0.0	10.0	N/A	8.0	7.0	2.1	DGRT
REDWOOD FIRE & CAS INS CO	NE	C	1,512.1	574.0	401.2	13.6	3.2	7.9	8.0	7.3	3.6	CT
REGENT INS CO	WI	C	90.8	30.9	36.2	0.5	7.3	3.8	2.3	7.0	3.4	FGRT
REGIS INS CO	PA	F (4)	0.6	-0.2	-0.6	-0.5	0.2	3.7	0.0	0.0	0.0	CFGL
RELIABLE LLOYDS INS CO	TX	C	17.8	12.8	0.0	0.9	10.0	N/A	8.9	7.0	3.0	DGRT
RELIAMAX INS CO	SD	D	15.5	5.0	6.2	0.5	2.7	4.2	2.1	6.4	2.3	DGRT
RELIAMAX SURETY CO	SD	C	52.3	21.5	16.7	-0.8	8.8	7.7	6.0	7.5	3.0	DT
RENAISSANCE RE US INC	MD	B-	1,600.5	546.1	323.7	20.7	7.9	9.5	4.6	6.8	3.6	FRT
REPUB MORTGAGE INS CO	NC	F	695.3	43.0	157.2	52.6	0.0	3.9	1.9	0.9	0.0	CFLR
REPUBLIC CREDIT INDEMNITY CO	IL	D+	65.3	7.6	17.9	-0.5	1.2	4.1	2.3	7.7	2.4	CDT
REPUBLIC FIRE & CASUALTY INS CO	OK	C	9.1	8.1	0.0	0.1	10.0	N/A	5.2	9.0	2.8	DGRT
REPUBLIC INDEMNITY CO OF AMERICA	CA	B-	2,274.5	504.1	793.3	29.2	5.6	9.2	7.0	6.5	4.7	ACRT
REPUBLIC INDEMNITY OF CA	CA	C	32.0	31.8	0.0	0.2	10.0	4.6	6.0	7.0	3.8	GRT
REPUBLIC LLOYDS	TX	C	12.2	12.3	0.0	0.0	10.0	N/A	3.9	10.0	2.1	DGRT
REPUBLIC MORTGAGE INS CO OF FLORIDA	FL	C	24.1	8.7	2.7	0.8	4.6	3.8	2.9	7.6	2.8	DFGT
REPUBLIC MORTGAGE INS CO OF NC	NC	D	169.5	17.8	28.6	8.8	1.0	4.0	1.9	5.1	1.9	CDFR
REPUBLIC RRG	SC	U (2)	1.7	1.7	0.0	0.0	N/A	4.6	3.0	10.0	2.3	FT
▼REPUBLIC UNDERWRITERS INS CO	TX	C	712.4	158.9	285.9	-72.8	8.2	3.7	2.8	6.6	4.1	RT
REPUBLIC-FRANKLIN INS CO	OH	C+	104.5	51.8	24.6	1.3	10.0	6.1	6.7	6.9	4.0	T
REPUBLIC-VANGUARD INS CO	AZ	B-	24.6	24.4	0.0	0.2	10.0	N/A	6.1	10.0	3.7	DGRT
REPWEST INS CO	AZ	D	316.9	169.7	39.8	11.3	1.5	3.4	3.0	6.9	1.9	CRT
RESIDENCE MUTUAL INS CO	CA	C-	122.8	82.4	41.4	0.1	7.6	8.1	8.1	6.6	2.7	RT
RESPONSE INDEMNITY CO OF CA	CA	C-	7.3	4.9	2.7	0.1	9.5	4.6	6.3	7.6	1.5	DFGR
RESPONSE INS CO	IL	C-	38.1	35.6	0.0	0.1	7.4	N/A	7.3	10.0	2.9	DGRT
RESPONSE WORLDWIDE DIRECT AUTO INS	IL	U	6.9	6.9	0.0	0.1	N/A	N/A	6.7	10.0	4.7	GRT
RESPONSE WORLDWIDE INS CO	IL	U	11.3	11.2	0.0	0.1	N/A	N/A	8.0	7.0	4.9	GRT
RESPONSIVE AUTO INS CO	FL	C-	27.0	8.2	21.1	-1.0	3.5	3.1	3.6	6.2	2.3	CDGT
RESTORATION RRG INC	VT	C	77.2	27.2	13.6	-0.3	5.3	9.6	7.5	7.3	3.1	DRT
RETAILERS CASUALTY INS CO	LA	C	79.8	37.6	22.9	1.0	7.8	5.9	7.1	6.8	3.3	DRT
RETAILERS INS CO	MI	D	21.4	9.7	8.2	0.1	7.0	9.4	4.1	6.9	2.3	DGRT
RETAILFIRST INS CO	FL	B	295.4	141.4	100.0	3.0	8.5	6.6	6.8	6.6	4.6	T
RIDER INS CO	NJ	D+	41.4	10.4	10.5	-1.3	5.6	4.5	1.4	2.8	2.4	DFGL
RIVERPORT INS CO	IA	B	115.6	36.8	0.0	0.3	10.0	3.9	6.1	7.9	4.1	RT
RLI INS CO	IL	B	1,808.7	924.0	450.9	38.5	7.2	8.2	8.7	6.9	4.7	ART
ROCHDALE INS CO	NY	C-	390.6	94.9	144.7	5.0	4.9	3.4	8.5	6.0	3.0	GRT

RISK ADJ. CAPITAL RATIO #1	CAPITAL RATIO #2	PREMIUM TO SURPLUS (%)	RESV. TO SURPLUS (%)	RESV. DEVELOP. 1 YEAR (%)	RESV. DEVELOP. 2 YEAR (%)	LOSS RATIO (%)	EXP. RATIO (%)	COMB RATIO (%)	CASH FROM UNDER-WRITING (%)	NET PREMIUM GROWTH (%)	INVEST. IN AFFIL (%)	INSURANCE COMPANY NAME
7.5	6.2	80.2	4.5	-5.7	-10.5	-49.1	25.7	-23.4	87.2	-31.4	0.0	RADIAN INS INC
N/A	N/A	N/A	N/A	N/A	N/A	N/A	N/A	N/A	N/A	0.0	0.0	RADIAN INVESTOR SURETY INC
N/A	N/A	N/A	N/A	N/A	N/A	N/A	N/A	N/A	N/A	0.0	0.0	RADIAN MORTGAGE ASR INC
N/A	N/A	N/A	N/A	N/A	N/A	N/A	N/A	N/A	N/A	0.0	0.0	RADIAN MORTGAGE GUARANTY INC
1.1	1.0	269.1	N/A	-6.5	-15.8	-12.5	25.0	12.5	62.1	-31.9	0.0	RADIAN MORTGAGE INS INC
N/A	N/A	46.1	92.1	N/A	N/A	34.9	N/A	34.9	-66.4	0.0	0.0	RADIAN REINS INC
N/A	N/A	N/A	N/A	N/A	N/A	N/A	N/A	N/A	N/A	0.0	0.0	RADNOR SPECIALTY INS CO
5.3	3.2	11.6	17.5	2.0	0.1	42.6	49.9	92.5	97.6	12.3	0.0	RAINIER INS CO
4.3	2.8	82.7	34.0	-6.7	-6.2	44.1	29.6	73.7	141.0	3.6	0.0	RAM MUTUAL INS CO
N/A	N/A	N/A	174.7	-8.3	-7.4	999 +	999 +	999 +	2.0	-96.4	0.0	RAMPART INS CO
0.7	0.6	36.3	12.0	2.0	3.2	137.2	-68.3	68.9	188.2	340.2	0.0	RANCHERS & FARMERS MUTUAL INS CO
1.4	0.9	115.4	42.9	1.6	-1.5	53.3	44.8	98.1	103.1	14.3	-10.2	REAL LEGACY ASR CO INC
1.3	0.9	210.8	31.2	-3.4	-0.6	56.3	39.6	95.9	103.3	13.7	0.0	REAMSTOWN MUTUAL INS CO
N/A	N/A	N/A	N/A	N/A	N/A	N/A	N/A	N/A	N/A	0.0	0.0	RECREATION RRG INC
3.4	2.1	34.4	54.9	-26.5	-48.1	25.9	18.4	44.3	136.5	-1.3	0.0	RED CLAY RRG INC
1.2	1.0	41.3	63.2	21.9	35.6	129.8	31.7	161.5	28.1	207.6	0.0	RED ROCK RISK RETENTION GROUP INC
2.8	1.8	61.2	35.2	N/A	-1.7	42.9	52.2	95.1	104.5	7.4	0.0	RED SHIELD INS CO
2.3	2.1	N/A	N/A	N/A	N/A	N/A	N/A	N/A	-51.2	0.0	0.0	REDPOINT COUNTY MUTUAL INS CO
0.7	0.4	72.6	118.3	-3.6	-3.7	70.2	21.7	91.9	190.4	6.4	0.0 •	REDWOOD FIRE & CAS INS CO
4.2	3.7	126.7	139.9	1.5	2.7	63.9	36.9	100.8	83.9	-23.7	0.0	REGENT INS CO
-0.4	-0.3	-185.8	421.4	26.9	26.7	221.2	-180.7	40.5	-10.9	-121.5	0.0	REGIS INS CO
8.3	7.5	N/A	N/A	N/A	N/A	N/A	N/A	N/A	18.1	0.0	0.0	RELIABLE LLOYDS INS CO
0.7	0.4	140.1	148.8	-19.8	-0.5	48.3	24.0	72.3	194.8	1.1	0.0	RELIAMAX INS CO
3.5	2.5	74.1	7.2	-8.8	-3.3	36.7	44.6	81.3	128.9	-10.1	0.0	RELIAMAX SURETY CO
2.9	1.8	62.1	155.5	-9.1	-20.0	51.6	37.0	88.6	93.6	-4.6	0.0 •	RENAISSANCE RE US INC
0.2	0.1	672.8	999 +	-297.4	-42.5	59.0	7.8	66.8	65.8	-13.8	0.1	REPUB MORTGAGE INS CO
0.3	0.2	222.0	592.9	-192.1	-214.8	102.2	12.3	114.5	111.2	-29.4	0.0	REPUBLIC CREDIT INDEMNITY CO
17.8	16.0	N/A	N/A	N/A	N/A	N/A	N/A	N/A	-382.6	0.0	0.0	REPUBLIC FIRE & CASUALTY INS CO
1.0	0.7	147.7	303.4	-4.6	-15.5	65.0	24.8	89.8	115.0	19.1	1.5 •	REPUBLIC INDEMNITY CO OF AMERICA
78.8	39.5	N/A	N/A	N/A	N/A	N/A	N/A	N/A	N/A	-100.0	0.0	REPUBLIC INDEMNITY OF CA
128.7	62.0	N/A	N/A	N/A	N/A	N/A	N/A	N/A	156.5	0.0	0.0	REPUBLIC LLOYDS
1.5	1.1	35.4	103.3	-20.8	-33.4	59.0	17.1	76.1	57.1	-13.8	0.0	REPUBLIC MORTGAGE INS CO OF
0.4	0.3	201.8	764.5	-153.1	-54.8	49.2	14.4	63.6	43.0	-16.7	0.0	REPUBLIC MORTGAGE INS CO OF NC
N/A	N/A	N/A	N/A	-1.8	-0.7	N/A	N/A	N/A	N/A	0.0	0.0	REPUBLIC RRG
1.4	1.1	111.8	72.7	3.0	11.0	57.8	41.1	98.9	103.1	17.2	14.4 •	REPUBLIC UNDERWRITERS INS CO
6.0	3.9	48.8	71.1	-1.1	-2.6	65.5	33.7	99.2	95.5	12.7	0.0	REPUBLIC-FRANKLIN INS CO
74.8	34.7	N/A	N/A	N/A	N/A	N/A	N/A	N/A	N/A	0.0	0.0	REPUBLIC-VANGUARD INS CO
0.4	0.4	25.1	86.2	-0.3	0.2	20.9	59.0	79.9	97.9	11.3	0.0	REPWEST INS CO
2.4	1.5	51.4	15.1	-2.2	-4.9	70.4	22.6	93.0	103.6	9.2	8.6	RESIDENCE MUTUAL INS CO
5.4	3.3	57.2	5.4	0.9	-0.1	37.9	39.8	77.7	5.3	26.0	0.0	RESPONSE INDEMNITY CO OF CA
1.2	1.2	N/A	N/A	N/A	N/A	N/A	N/A	N/A	11.7	0.0	88.9	RESPONSE INS CO
N/A	N/A	N/A	N/A	N/A	N/A	N/A	N/A	N/A	0.1	0.0	0.0	RESPONSE WORLDWIDE DIRECT AUTO
N/A	N/A	N/A	N/A	N/A	N/A	N/A	N/A	N/A	50.3	0.0	0.0	RESPONSE WORLDWIDE INS CO
0.6	0.5	227.3	71.4	-6.4	-5.4	62.6	35.6	98.2	102.6	-4.1	0.0	RESPONSIVE AUTO INS CO
1.2	0.9	53.8	138.1	-21.1	-22.4	51.7	13.9	65.6	212.8	4.7	0.0	RESTORATION RRG INC
2.3	1.7	63.7	83.6	-16.0	-22.1	42.2	35.6	77.8	113.0	1.9	0.0	RETAILERS CASUALTY INS CO
1.4	1.1	84.8	80.4	-1.2	-12.8	62.2	38.6	100.8	105.7	16.3	0.0	RETAILERS INS CO
2.5	1.9	73.0	90.5	-2.4	-4.0	68.0	30.8	98.8	103.0	0.1	0.0	RETAILFIRST INS CO
1.2	0.8	91.9	68.7	4.2	19.5	69.7	57.5	127.2	65.3	-62.1	0.0	RIDER INS CO
4.9	4.4	N/A	N/A	N/A	N/A	N/A	N/A	N/A	407.9	0.0	0.0	RIVERPORT INS CO
1.4	1.2	52.1	53.8	-3.6	-2.7	47.4	41.1	88.5	118.5	3.0	36.5 •	RLI INS CO
0.9	0.6	166.8	159.6	9.7	19.8	67.0	25.3	92.3	151.8	44.8	0.0	ROCHDALE INS CO

999 + Denotes number greater than 999.9%
999 - Denotes number less than -999.99%
• Bullets denote a more detailed analysis is available in Section II.

INSURANCE COMPANY NAME	DOM. STATE	RATING	TOTAL ASSETS ($MIL)	CAPITAL & SURPLUS ($MIL)	ANNUAL NET PREMIUM ($MIL)	NET INCOME ($MIL)	CAPITAL-IZATION INDEX (PTS)	RESERVE ADQ INDEX (PTS)	PROFIT-ABILITY INDEX (PTS)	LIQUIDITY INDEX (PTS)	STAB. INDEX (PTS)	STABILITY FACTORS
ROCHE SURETY & CASUALTY INC	FL	C	24.2	9.4	2.9	0.5	9.5	N/A	8.4	8.8	2.3	DGT
ROCKFORD MUTUAL INS CO	IL	C+	77.3	36.4	45.5	1.2	6.0	5.7	5.3	5.4	3.4	RT
ROCKHILL INS CO	AZ	C	171.0	98.2	0.0	0.6	10.0	N/A	5.7	8.1	4.0	FRT
ROCKINGHAM CASUALTY CO	VA	C	30.7	28.9	0.0	0.2	10.0	4.1	7.0	10.0	3.5	DFGR
ROCKINGHAM INS CO	VA	B-	125.4	65.9	44.0	1.7	6.2	6.9	5.2	5.9	3.9	RT
ROCKWOOD CASUALTY INS CO	PA	C-	250.3	95.5	43.8	5.3	7.7	9.5	8.1	7.2	3.2	RT
ROMULUS INS RRG INC	SC	U	2.6	1.9	0.6	0.1	N/A	N/A	5.9	8.4	2.4	DGT
ROOT INS CO	OH	U	4.0	3.9	0.0	0.0	N/A	7.3	1.9	9.2	3.1	FGT
RPX RRG INC	HI	U	4.9	4.3	0.0	-0.1	N/A	4.9	4.2	10.0	0.0	FGT
RSUI INDEMNITY CO	NH	C+	3,423.5	1,476.8	720.4	83.9	8.0	8.0	7.7	6.9	4.3	ART
RURAL COMMUNITY INS CO	MN	B (1)	3,260.3	246.8	362.9	-2.1	10.0	7.8	5.4	6.2	4.7	RT
RURAL MUTUAL INS CO	WI	B-	448.9	223.8	162.6	9.8	10.0	8.7	8.9	6.7	4.1	RT
RURAL TRUST INS CO	TX	C- (1)	20.1	12.8	4.4	0.0	7.9	6.1	3.7	9.1	2.5	DGRT
RUTGERS CASUALTY INS CO	NJ	C-	21.4	7.9	4.3	-0.1	7.9	6.4	1.9	8.0	2.8	DFGR
RUTGERS ENHANCED INS CO	NJ	D+(2)	11.6	4.5	2.9	-0.5	8.0	5.8	2.9	7.4	2.5	DFT
RVI AMERICA INS CO	CT	C	106.2	74.0	4.3	0.9	10.0	4.7	7.7	10.0	3.3	DRT
RVOS FARM MUTUAL INS CO	TX	D	79.1	23.4	60.5	-4.6	5.5	5.6	2.9	1.5	2.3	LRT
SAFE AUTO INS CO	OH	B-	400.0	160.8	315.8	1.2	7.6	9.3	4.8	2.4	4.0	LT
SAFE HARBOR INS CO	FL	C	83.5	25.6	50.0	2.1	5.0	3.4	9.3	6.5	3.5	DT
SAFE INS CO	WV	D	10.9	8.9	2.8	0.4	10.0	8.0	8.7	7.9	2.3	DGRT
SAFECARD SERVICES INS CO	ND	D	1.9	1.8	0.2	0.0	10.0	3.6	3.8	10.0	1.5	DGT
SAFECO INS CO OF AMERICA	NH	B-	4,349.5	1,417.2	1,537.9	-2.6	7.9	5.9	6.6	6.3	3.9	ART
SAFECO INS CO OF IL	IL	B	186.2	182.2	0.0	1.1	10.0	3.8	5.3	7.0	4.6	ART
SAFECO INS CO OF INDIANA	IN	B	15.1	15.1	0.0	0.1	10.0	N/A	6.3	7.0	4.0	DGRT
SAFECO INS CO OF OREGON	OR	B	13.9	13.6	0.0	0.1	10.0	N/A	7.5	7.0	4.1	DGRT
SAFECO LLOYDS INS CO	TX	B-	13.1	13.0	0.0	0.1	10.0	N/A	6.4	7.0	3.9	DGRT
SAFECO NATIONAL INS CO	NH	B-	15.5	14.7	0.0	0.2	10.0	N/A	3.0	7.0	3.9	ADGR
SAFECO SURPLUS LINES INS CO	NH	U	42.2	41.5	0.0	0.4	N/A	N/A	6.9	7.0	5.4	RT
SAFEPOINT INS CO	FL	B-	117.8	40.3	41.7	0.4	8.4	3.6	8.0	7.2	3.6	GT
SAFETY FIRST INS CO	IL	C	71.9	66.3	1.4	1.3	10.0	7.6	6.9	10.0	4.0	DGRT
SAFETY INDEMNITY INS CO	MA	C+	122.0	56.2	52.2	1.7	10.0	8.7	5.0	6.7	3.5	T
SAFETY INS CO	MA	B-	1,455.7	583.9	671.6	28.1	8.8	8.8	3.6	5.9	4.4	FRT
SAFETY NATIONAL CASUALTY CORP	MO	C	6,043.9	1,653.4	728.9	85.6	7.1	1.9	6.3	7.4	3.4	RT
SAFETY P&C INS CO	MA	C	45.1	18.1	22.4	0.6	8.1	9.2	4.5	6.6	2.3	DT
SAFETY SPECIALTY INS CO	MO	C-	70.2	65.6	0.9	1.6	10.0	2.4	2.9	6.5	3.2	DFT
SAFEWAY INS CO	IL	B-	464.8	286.0	204.4	-3.9	7.7	5.1	5.6	6.6	4.2	RT
SAFEWAY INS CO OF AL	IL	C	60.1	30.1	38.3	-1.1	8.2	5.2	3.6	6.3	3.7	FRT
SAFEWAY INS CO OF GA	GA	C	60.8	31.0	37.5	-1.3	8.3	6.1	3.4	6.0	3.7	FRT
SAFEWAY INS CO OF LA	LA	C+	120.8	60.8	75.8	-2.4	9.6	6.1	3.9	5.8	3.9	FRT
SAGAMORE INS CO	IN	B-	156.4	126.9	18.9	1.9	10.0	6.1	5.5	9.0	4.2	DT
SAGE RRG INC	NV	D	2.6	1.1	1.5	0.1	5.6	N/A	7.6	8.2	0.9	DGT
SAINT LUKES HEALTH SYSTEM RRG	SC	D+	15.2	8.3	1.9	0.5	5.5	4.9	1.9	6.5	2.2	DFGR
SALEM COUNTY MUTUAL FIRE INS CO	NJ	U (5)	0.0	0.0	0.0	0.0	N/A	N/A	0.7	7.0	1.9	FT
SAMARITAN RRG INC	SC	C-	31.8	18.2	8.9	1.4	7.9	6.9	7.7	7.6	2.7	DGT
▼SAMSUNG FIRE & MARINE INS CO LTD US	NY	C-	190.8	41.7	58.2	-8.8	5.3	4.8	1.7	6.2	2.9	RT
SAN ANTONIO INDEMNITY CO	TX	F (5)	0.0	0.0	4.2	0.0	0.3	5.5	1.1	0.0	0.0	CDGL
SAN DIEGO INS CO	CA	U	68.0	64.2	0.0	0.7	N/A	N/A	6.5	7.0	5.4	T
SAN FRANCISCO REINS CO	CA	C+	3,220.1	649.3	2,282.7	14.4	3.3	1.0	3.9	6.4	4.4	CGRT
SAUCON MUTUAL INS CO	PA	U (2)	19.0	15.9	-0.1	0.2	N/A	7.2	4.8	10.0	4.7	FT
SAUQUOIT VALLEY INS CO	NY	C-	4.6	3.8	0.6	0.0	7.4	7.4	3.6	7.1	2.0	DFGR
SAVERS P&C INS CO	MO	C-	223.9	56.4	77.5	4.6	7.2	2.0	4.7	6.5	3.0	FRT
SAWGRASS MUTUAL INS CO	FL	D	39.2	20.1	2.8	-1.4	6.9	1.7	2.9	6.9	2.3	DFGT

See Page 27 for explanation of footnotes and
Page 28 for explanation of stability factors.

112

www.weissratings.com

Arrows denote recent upgrades ▲ or downgrades ▼   (see Section VII for explanations)

RISK ADJ. CAPITAL RATIO #1	CAPITAL RATIO #2	PREMIUM TO SURPLUS (%)	RESV. TO SURPLUS (%)	RESV. DEVELOP. 1 YEAR (%)	RESV. DEVELOP. 2 YEAR (%)	LOSS RATIO (%)	EXP. RATIO (%)	COMB RATIO (%)	CASH FROM UNDER-WRITING (%)	NET PREMIUM GROWTH (%)	INVEST. IN AFFIL (%)	INSURANCE COMPANY NAME
3.2	2.7	30.6	N/A	N/A	N/A	N/A	72.3	72.3	130.7	-3.9	0.0	ROCHE SURETY & CASUALTY INC
1.5	1.0	130.0	50.1	-9.4	-6.4	55.1	36.8	91.9	102.3	-3.0	0.0	ROCKFORD MUTUAL INS CO
3.1	3.0	N/A	N/A	N/A	N/A	N/A	N/A	N/A	36.9	0.0	33.4	ROCKHILL INS CO
43.7	39.3	N/A	N/A	N/A	N/A	N/A	N/A	N/A	792.7	0.0	0.0	ROCKINGHAM CASUALTY CO
1.1	1.0	69.1	28.2	-4.9	-8.6	62.3	34.5	96.8	116.8	9.9	25.3	ROCKINGHAM INS CO
2.0	1.6	49.3	109.9	-4.3	-12.4	49.6	35.9	85.5	128.4	-8.7	17.9	ROCKWOOD CASUALTY INS CO
N/A	N/A	30.0	6.1	N/A	N/A	35.0	18.0	53.0	547.4	0.0	0.0	ROMULUS INS RRG INC
N/A	N/A	0.2	0.4	-0.1	-0.4	26.4	999 +	999 +	23.7	-99.3	0.0	ROOT INS CO
N/A	N/A	-0.4	1.9	-8.9	-13.3	-189.6	999 +	999 +	10.4	-102.0	0.0	RPX RRG INC
2.3	1.7	48.6	89.3	-0.3	-3.8	53.8	28.4	82.2	144.4	-5.7	9.1 •	RSUI INDEMNITY CO
4.9	2.5	52.3	3.6	-0.3	-3.1	79.1	-9.6	69.5	173.8	-4.5	0.0	RURAL COMMUNITY INS CO
6.0	4.1	76.1	46.9	-1.2	-5.3	59.9	24.4	84.3	127.7	6.3	0.0 •	RURAL MUTUAL INS CO
2.3	1.4	35.1	8.5	-0.4	0.1	62.0	35.7	97.7	91.3	302.2	0.0	RURAL TRUST INS CO
2.7	1.8	54.0	101.7	-0.9	-2.8	84.6	38.8	123.4	87.2	-2.3	0.0	RUTGERS CASUALTY INS CO
2.3	1.6	64.7	122.0	-1.6	-4.6	84.6	38.8	123.4	90.1	-2.3	0.0	RUTGERS ENHANCED INS CO
15.4	13.9	5.9	2.8	-2.9	-2.9	2.7	70.0	72.7	999 +	-3.7	0.0	RVI AMERICA INS CO
0.9	0.7	222.9	27.2	3.6	7.2	62.9	29.2	92.1	106.0	13.6	27.0	RVOS FARM MUTUAL INS CO
1.7	1.5	201.3	83.7	N/A	-13.9	74.5	23.5	98.0	92.7	2.3	0.0	SAFE AUTO INS CO
1.3	1.1	216.1	58.6	-2.2	9.2	49.1	35.7	84.8	130.3	2.1	0.0	SAFE HARBOR INS CO
5.2	3.3	34.4	10.4	-1.6	-2.9	36.5	44.8	81.3	124.9	-3.5	0.0	SAFE INS CO
19.5	17.6	9.0	0.6	N/A	N/A	6.3	11.2	17.5	893.5	0.0	0.0	SAFECARD SERVICES INS CO
2.5	1.8	110.4	145.7	-0.8	-1.0	68.4	30.2	98.6	103.1	1.0	6.8 •	SAFECO INS CO OF AMERICA
3.6	3.6	N/A	N/A	N/A	N/A	N/A	N/A	N/A	N/A	0.0	30.1	SAFECO INS CO OF IL
127.2	63.6	N/A	N/A	N/A	N/A	N/A	N/A	N/A	N/A	0.0	0.0	SAFECO INS CO OF INDIANA
78.7	45.5	N/A	N/A	N/A	N/A	N/A	N/A	N/A	N/A	0.0	0.0	SAFECO INS CO OF OREGON
201.5	100.8	N/A	N/A	N/A	N/A	N/A	N/A	N/A	N/A	0.0	0.0	SAFECO LLOYDS INS CO
37.4	33.7	N/A	N/A	N/A	N/A	N/A	N/A	N/A	N/A	0.0	0.0	SAFECO NATIONAL INS CO
N/A	N/A	N/A	N/A	N/A	N/A	N/A	N/A	N/A	N/A	0.0	0.0	SAFECO SURPLUS LINES INS CO
2.8	2.0	99.9	58.9	15.4	N/A	67.9	23.1	91.0	126.8	-53.7	0.0	SAFEPOINT INS CO
38.2	19.5	2.2	4.4	-1.7	-4.1	73.5	42.2	115.7	108.5	1.3	0.0	SAFETY FIRST INS CO
4.9	3.4	94.8	61.7	-3.3	-7.5	83.0	26.6	109.6	95.3	1.5	0.0	SAFETY INDEMNITY INS CO
3.1	2.2	117.6	76.6	-3.8	-8.3	83.0	26.2	109.2	91.6	1.5	6.4 •	SAFETY INS CO
1.5	1.1	47.7	218.4	3.6	10.0	86.1	20.2	106.3	235.1	8.6	4.4 •	SAFETY NATIONAL CASUALTY CORP
2.5	1.7	127.4	82.9	-4.3	-9.9	83.0	28.4	111.4	96.0	1.5	0.0	SAFETY P&C INS CO
43.6	27.1	1.5	N/A	N/A	0.2	235.7	171.9	407.6	-2.0	-71.5	0.0	SAFETY SPECIALTY INS CO
1.6	1.4	67.7	27.1	1.4	0.7	82.2	21.6	103.8	101.1	22.0	41.1 •	SAFEWAY INS CO
1.8	1.7	123.4	51.8	2.5	1.5	82.2	22.4	104.6	88.3	-2.2	0.0	SAFEWAY INS CO OF AL
1.9	1.7	116.6	50.0	2.4	1.5	82.2	24.6	106.8	85.9	-13.5	0.0	SAFEWAY INS CO OF GA
2.8	2.5	120.3	51.0	2.5	1.5	82.2	23.9	106.1	88.0	-9.0	0.0	SAFEWAY INS CO OF LA
15.4	8.5	15.1	9.0	0.9	1.0	69.1	36.2	105.3	106.6	-18.3	0.0	SAGAMORE INS CO
1.4	0.8	146.4	27.9	N/A	N/A	55.0	11.8	66.8	345.8	0.0	0.0	SAGE RRG INC
1.1	0.8	23.8	62.1	9.7	16.7	144.5	53.8	198.3	45.6	-46.2	0.0	SAINT LUKES HEALTH SYSTEM RRG
N/A	N/A	-0.1	N/A	N/A	N/A	N/A	999 +	999 +	-0.5	0.0	0.0	SALEM COUNTY MUTUAL FIRE INS CO
2.6	1.6	51.5	42.8	4.8	-6.7	77.9	13.0	90.9	150.1	2.7	0.0	SAMARITAN RRG INC
1.0	0.5	119.3	178.3	17.3	16.3	86.5	32.5	119.0	101.0	-27.4	0.0	SAMSUNG FIRE & MARINE INS CO LTD
0.2	0.1	394.1	58.1	-14.1	1.3	76.0	26.0	102.0	99.2	75.3	0.0	SAN ANTONIO INDEMNITY CO
N/A	N/A	N/A	N/A	N/A	N/A	N/A	N/A	N/A	N/A	0.0	0.0	SAN DIEGO INS CO
1.8	1.2	348.0	339.6	999 +	999 +	100.0	0.6	100.6	999 +	0.0	0.0 •	SAN FRANCISCO REINS CO
N/A	N/A	-0.5	0.3	-0.3	-0.3	-74.6	999 +	999 +	-8.1	-0.1	0.0	SAUCON MUTUAL INS CO
2.2	1.3	16.8	4.8	-2.3	-0.3	67.2	34.0	101.2	84.0	0.7	0.0	SAUQUOIT VALLEY INS CO
1.6	1.0	131.3	237.6	16.2	25.9	77.1	37.2	114.3	73.7	0.7	0.0	SAVERS P&C INS CO
1.4	1.1	13.9	49.0	-0.2	48.1	114.3	-51.6	62.7	46.8	-40.9	0.0	SAWGRASS MUTUAL INS CO

999 + Denotes number greater than 999.9%
999 - Denotes number less than -999.99%
• Bullets denote a more detailed analysis is available in Section II.

INSURANCE COMPANY NAME	DOM. STATE	RATING	TOTAL ASSETS ($MIL)	CAPITAL & SURPLUS ($MIL)	ANNUAL NET PREMIUM ($MIL)	NET INCOME ($MIL)	CAPITAL-IZATION INDEX (PTS)	RESERVE ADQ INDEX (PTS)	PROFIT-ABILITY INDEX (PTS)	LIQUIDITY INDEX (PTS)	STAB. INDEX (PTS)	STABILITY FACTORS
SCOR REINS CO	NY	C-	2,929.1	1,086.2	846.9	24.6	6.8	6.3	6.0	6.7	3.3	RT
SCOTTSDALE INDEMNITY CO	OH	B	93.0	38.6	0.0	0.5	10.0	N/A	6.5	8.5	4.2	RT
SCOTTSDALE INS CO	OH	B-	2,561.9	768.6	747.5	-4.0	8.4	6.2	4.2	6.4	4.9	AT
SCOTTSDALE SURPLUS LINES INS CO	AZ	B	50.1	47.4	0.0	0.5	10.0	N/A	8.1	10.0	4.7	DRT
SCRUBS MUTUAL ASR CO RRG	NV	C-	16.4	3.9	6.6	0.0	5.1	4.4	4.7	6.6	2.0	DGRT
SEABRIGHT INS CO	TX	D-	31.2	25.7	-295.9	0.1	10.0	6.0	1.5	7.0	1.1	FRT
SEAVIEW INS CO	CA	C	23.1	12.0	9.7	1.4	8.5	6.1	7.4	7.6	2.6	DGT
SEAWAY MUTUAL INS CO	PA	U (2)	2.1	2.1	0.0	0.0	N/A	N/A	6.8	10.0	2.6	FT
SECURA INS A MUTUAL CO	WI	B-	1,066.5	375.3	462.5	9.1	8.1	9.3	8.3	6.5	4.2	RT
SECURA SUPREME INS CO	WI	C+	134.9	58.1	51.4	1.8	10.0	8.7	8.6	6.7	3.9	T
SECURIAN CASUALTY CO	MN	B	228.6	118.4	180.8	5.3	8.1	6.3	8.8	5.9	4.9	RT
SECURITY AMERICA RRG INC	VT	D+	5.2	2.9	2.1	0.0	4.6	4.4	4.5	7.9	1.9	DFGR
SECURITY FIRST INS CO	FL	B-	226.7	52.3	141.6	-3.1	7.2	4.0	3.5	6.0	3.7	RT
SECURITY MUTUAL INS CO	NY	C+	102.0	52.9	35.8	1.2	9.6	6.5	8.1	6.7	3.4	RT
SECURITY NATIONAL INS CO	DE	B	1,174.9	178.4	143.4	7.9	7.3	5.6	9.7	7.6	4.6	GRT
SECURITY NATIONAL INS CO	FL	D+	121.2	35.9	0.0	0.6	10.0	3.8	4.0	9.1	2.5	RT
SECURITY PLAN FIRE INS CO	LA	D	7.8	6.8	5.2	0.3	8.2	7.8	7.8	7.0	1.8	DGRT
SELECT INS CO	TX	U	78.0	77.0	0.0	1.1	N/A	N/A	7.8	10.0	5.4	T
SELECT MARKETS INS CO	IL	U	15.8	15.8	0.0	0.1	N/A	N/A	6.2	7.0	5.2	GT
SELECT MD RRG INC	MT	D	2.7	0.9	0.2	-0.2	8.2	5.0	2.9	7.4	1.4	DGT
SELECT RISK INS CO	PA	C	41.9	15.8	15.4	0.3	8.3	9.3	7.0	6.6	3.2	DGT
SELECTIVE AUTO INS CO OF NJ	NJ	B	356.3	82.7	124.2	5.3	7.6	9.3	7.6	6.8	4.4	AT
SELECTIVE CASUALTY INS CO	NJ	B (2)	413.4	92.3	144.9	12.1	7.7	5.0	8.5	6.8	4.9	T
SELECTIVE F&C INS CO	NJ	B (2)	180.5	39.4	62.1	5.3	7.7	5.0	8.5	6.7	4.1	T
SELECTIVE INS CO OF AM	NJ	B	2,216.9	546.6	662.4	33.9	8.0	9.1	7.1	6.8	4.6	AT
SELECTIVE INS CO OF NEW ENGLAND	NJ	C-	182.6	41.4	62.1	2.7	7.8	9.4	8.3	6.8	3.3	AT
SELECTIVE INS CO OF NY	NY	B	413.5	97.5	144.9	6.2	7.7	9.3	7.8	6.9	4.3	AT
SELECTIVE INS CO OF SC	IN	B	614.0	134.7	186.3	8.3	7.8	9.3	7.7	6.8	4.5	AT
SELECTIVE INS CO OF THE SOUTHEAST	IN	B	474.9	102.3	144.9	6.2	7.7	9.3	7.6	6.8	4.4	AT
SELECTIVE WAY INS CO	NJ	B	1,264.9	291.8	434.7	17.3	7.6	9.3	7.7	6.9	4.6	AT
SENECA INS CO	NY	D+	202.3	139.8	0.0	-4.0	10.0	4.9	5.5	7.0	2.8	FRT
SENECA SPECIALTY INS CO	DE	C+	49.3	49.3	0.0	0.8	10.0	3.6	7.5	10.0	3.9	RT
SENIOR AMERICAN INS CO	PA	E-	13.9	-1.1	2.4	-1.1	0.0	0.5	0.5	0.0	0.0	CDFG
SENTINEL ASR RRG INC	HI	E	17.0	9.5	4.0	-1.1	7.2	5.9	3.9	7.7	0.0	DGRT
SENTINEL INS CO LTD	CT	B	250.6	175.5	31.6	7.2	10.0	4.9	8.9	7.3	4.6	AT
SENTRUITY CASUALTY CO	TX	B-	188.3	45.8	7.8	0.2	10.0	5.0	8.7	9.0	3.7	RT
SENTRY CASUALTY CO	WI	B	287.5	73.6	46.9	1.5	10.0	8.1	5.6	7.2	4.5	T
SENTRY INS A MUTUAL CO	WI	A	7,458.5	4,520.1	1,014.2	57.1	8.5	7.5	6.8	7.0	6.1	T
SENTRY LLOYDS OF TX	TX	B	7.0	7.0	0.0	0.1	10.0	N/A	7.7	10.0	4.9	DGT
SENTRY SELECT INS CO	WI	B+	706.8	237.0	187.7	4.1	9.2	8.3	6.0	6.7	5.1	T
SEQUOIA INDEMNITY CO	NV	C+	14.2	10.2	0.6	0.1	10.0	7.0	6.3	7.0	3.1	DGRT
SEQUOIA INS CO	CA	C	197.0	72.1	22.9	0.5	10.0	6.0	2.8	8.3	3.5	FGRT
SERVICE INS CO (FL)	FL	B	49.9	40.4	14.0	3.0	9.4	6.0	6.5	6.9	4.1	RT
SERVICE INS CO (NJ)	NJ	D	13.7	7.6	1.9	0.5	10.0	9.3	8.3	9.1	2.2	DGRT
SERVICE LLOYDS INS CO	TX	B-	306.0	115.7	81.2	0.3	9.2	8.4	7.3	6.8	4.0	RT
SEVEN SEAS INS CO	FL	C	19.1	17.2	17.9	3.9	8.9	7.4	3.6	7.9	2.9	DGRT
SFM MUTUAL INS CO	MN	B	547.6	128.4	148.9	4.7	6.3	6.5	8.5	6.6	4.1	CT
SFM SAFE INS CO	MN	U	3.2	3.0	0.0	0.0	N/A	N/A	4.9	7.0	4.2	DGT
SFM SELECT INS CO	MN	D	4.0	3.5	0.0	0.0	10.0	4.6	5.7	10.0	2.3	DFGR
SHEBOYGAN FALLS INS CO	WI	C+	33.6	12.8	18.8	0.3	7.5	4.3	5.2	6.7	3.2	DGRT
SHELBY INS CO	TX	F (5)	0.0	0.0	0.0	0.0	10.0	N/A	2.6	7.0	0.0	
SHELTER GENERAL INS CO	MO	C+	131.4	69.5	35.8	3.8	9.3	8.2	3.1	6.4	3.7	RT

See Page 27 for explanation of footnotes and
Page 28 for explanation of stability factors.
Arrows denote recent upgrades ▲ or downgrades ▼   (see Section VII for explanations)

114

www.weissratings.com

RISK ADJ. CAPITAL RATIO #1	RATIO #2	PREMIUM TO SURPLUS (%)	RESV. TO SURPLUS (%)	RESV. DEVELOP. 1 YEAR (%)	2 YEAR (%)	LOSS RATIO (%)	EXP. RATIO (%)	COMB RATIO (%)	CASH FROM UNDER-WRITING (%)	NET PREMIUM GROWTH (%)	INVEST. IN AFFIL (%)	INSURANCE COMPANY NAME
2.1	1.3	88.0	116.8	-9.2	-5.6	48.6	37.9	86.5	109.6	6.1	0.0 ●	SCOR REINS CO
5.5	5.0	N/A	N/A	N/A	N/A	N/A	N/A	N/A	-292.9	0.0	0.0	SCOTTSDALE INDEMNITY CO
2.2	1.8	97.6	69.5	1.1	1.0	71.1	32.5	103.6	99.4	3.7	19.0 ●	SCOTTSDALE INS CO
52.6	47.3	N/A	N/A	N/A	N/A	N/A	N/A	N/A	-262.4	0.0	0.0	SCOTTSDALE SURPLUS LINES INS CO
1.0	0.6	166.3	148.5	18.9	9.6	67.0	34.0	101.0	101.3	26.8	0.0	SCRUBS MUTUAL ASR CO RRG
15.7	14.1	999 +	N/A	-230.3	-103.5	100.0	-3.9	96.1	-708.4	N/A	0.0	SEABRIGHT INS CO
2.7	2.1	71.2	4.2	-3.2	-4.4	0.5	54.6	55.1	169.0	5.2	0.3	SEAVIEW INS CO
N/A	N/A	0.6	N/A	N/A	N/A	N/A	472.3	472.3	21.2	-12.6	0.0	SEAWAY MUTUAL INS CO
2.4	1.8	131.0	101.7	-5.2	-6.9	60.1	30.6	90.7	116.1	9.0	6.8 ●	SECURA INS A MUTUAL CO
4.9	3.7	91.7	71.1	-3.7	-5.2	60.1	30.0	90.1	121.2	9.0	0.0	SECURA SUPREME INS CO
2.4	1.8	160.2	20.4	-2.3	-2.3	49.4	40.8	90.2	117.3	20.5	0.0	SECURIAN CASUALTY CO
1.0	0.7	76.0	60.1	-12.1	4.5	22.8	65.9	88.7	82.0	1.9	0.0	SECURITY AMERICA RRG INC
1.1	1.0	256.0	59.2	6.1	4.9	66.0	29.2	95.2	118.9	42.6	0.0	SECURITY FIRST INS CO
4.1	3.2	70.4	48.8	-3.0	-2.8	53.0	37.7	90.7	106.4	2.5	0.0	SECURITY MUTUAL INS CO
1.6	1.0	95.9	68.0	2.3	5.7	63.5	-9.7	53.8	-652.0	126.5	3.2	SECURITY NATIONAL INS CO
4.2	3.8	N/A	3.2	2.4	3.5	N/A	N/A	N/A	235.0	0.0	0.0	SECURITY NATIONAL INS CO
2.5	2.1	80.5	7.3	-1.4	-3.7	32.5	59.4	91.9	110.1	1.4	0.0	SECURITY PLAN FIRE INS CO
N/A	N/A	N/A	N/A	N/A	N/A	N/A	N/A	N/A	1.6	0.0	0.0	SELECT INS CO
N/A	N/A	N/A	N/A	N/A	N/A	N/A	N/A	N/A	999 +	0.0	0.0	SELECT MARKETS INS CO
1.3	1.2	16.1	34.3	-39.0	-25.6	-153.6	136.0	-17.6	112.3	-40.4	0.0	SELECT MD RRG INC
3.0	1.9	101.1	66.4	-9.0	-10.4	63.9	31.9	95.8	103.3	6.4	0.0	SELECT RISK INS CO
2.2	1.5	160.2	228.5	-5.5	-14.6	57.7	34.4	92.1	113.5	9.8	0.0	SELECTIVE AUTO INS CO OF NJ
2.3	1.5	157.0	223.9	-5.5	-14.4	57.7	34.4	92.1	111.7	9.8	0.0	SELECTIVE CASUALTY INS CO
2.2	1.5	157.6	224.7	-5.4	-14.2	57.7	34.4	92.1	112.9	9.8	0.0	SELECTIVE F&C INS CO
2.7	1.8	127.2	181.4	-4.2	-11.5	57.7	34.4	92.1	114.7	9.8	0.0 ●	SELECTIVE INS CO OF AM
2.2	1.5	157.7	224.9	-5.5	-14.3	57.7	34.4	92.1	113.8	9.8	0.0	SELECTIVE INS CO OF NEW ENGLAND
2.2	1.5	155.8	222.1	-5.5	-14.7	57.7	34.4	92.1	113.8	9.8	0.0	SELECTIVE INS CO OF NY
2.4	1.6	145.7	207.8	-5.0	-13.3	57.7	34.3	92.0	111.2	9.8	0.0	SELECTIVE INS CO OF SC
2.3	1.6	150.5	214.7	-5.3	-14.2	57.7	34.3	92.0	112.0	9.8	0.0	SELECTIVE INS CO OF THE SOUTHEAST
2.2	1.5	159.4	227.4	-5.4	-13.9	57.7	34.4	92.1	115.6	9.8	0.0 ●	SELECTIVE WAY INS CO
3.2	3.0	N/A	N/A	N/A	N/A	N/A	N/A	N/A	153.1	0.0	37.0	SENECA INS CO
37.5	14.6	N/A	N/A	N/A	N/A	N/A	N/A	N/A	N/A	0.0	0.0	SENECA SPECIALTY INS CO
-0.2	-0.1	999 +	999 +	999 +	999 +	155.6	-3.8	151.8	41.7	-6.2	0.0	SENIOR AMERICAN INS CO
1.5	1.2	38.9	43.6	-36.3	-25.7	-15.8	23.1	7.3	166.6	8.1	0.0	SENTINEL ASR RRG INC
16.0	10.4	18.8	32.5	0.2	0.6	66.1	-16.0	50.1	108.2	2.9	0.0	SENTINEL INS CO LTD
4.8	4.0	17.1	1.3	0.2	0.4	46.5	43.6	90.1	329.8	29.2	0.0	SENTRUITY CASUALTY CO
4.5	2.8	65.3	105.0	-2.4	-3.6	72.7	27.5	100.2	126.1	3.5	0.0	SENTRY CASUALTY CO
2.5	2.1	23.0	37.0	-0.9	-1.4	72.7	27.4	100.1	113.5	1.7	23.4 ●	SENTRY INS A MUTUAL CO
244.5	122.3	N/A	N/A	N/A	N/A	N/A	N/A	N/A	205.6	0.0	0.0	SENTRY LLOYDS OF TX
3.7	2.3	80.9	130.1	-3.0	-4.6	72.7	27.5	100.2	108.2	3.5	0.0 ●	SENTRY SELECT INS CO
7.9	5.6	6.6	2.3	0.1	2.0	66.0	79.7	145.7	4.5	58.5	5.8	SEQUOIA INDEMNITY CO
3.3	2.8	32.3	19.3	-0.3	0.2	49.8	51.6	101.4	76.5	436.1	10.9	SEQUOIA INS CO
5.3	3.2	37.5	7.7	-0.5	2.0	42.0	31.2	73.2	138.1	-6.1	0.0	SERVICE INS CO (FL)
4.5	3.9	26.5	7.9	-5.3	-11.5	1.7	48.2	49.9	188.7	13.3	0.0	SERVICE INS CO (NJ)
3.8	2.7	66.5	57.4	-7.4	-9.4	40.8	47.9	88.7	99.9	-0.4	0.0	SERVICE LLOYDS INS CO
2.4	2.3	110.3	4.2	0.2	-1.3	18.7	15.4	34.1	305.1	-0.3	1.7	SEVEN SEAS INS CO
1.2	0.9	122.6	250.6	N/A	-0.1	74.3	20.8	95.1	120.0	-1.4	1.8	SFM MUTUAL INS CO
N/A	N/A	N/A	N/A	N/A	N/A	N/A	N/A	N/A	N/A	0.0	0.0	SFM SAFE INS CO
16.8	15.1	N/A	N/A	-0.6	-0.2	N/A	N/A	N/A	N/A	0.0	0.0	SFM SELECT INS CO
1.7	1.2	142.2	52.6	-1.7	5.3	58.0	28.9	86.9	117.2	9.7	0.0	SHEBOYGAN FALLS INS CO
19.5	17.2	N/A	N/A	N/A	N/A	N/A	N/A	N/A	1.9	0.0	0.0	SHELBY INS CO
2.9	2.5	52.6	69.9	-4.6	-1.9	83.4	25.4	108.8	81.4	3.1	10.4	SHELTER GENERAL INS CO

999 + Denotes number greater than 999.9%
999 - Denotes number less than -999.99%
● Bullets denote a more detailed analysis is available in Section II.

INSURANCE COMPANY NAME	DOM. STATE	RATING	TOTAL ASSETS ($MIL)	CAPITAL & SURPLUS ($MIL)	ANNUAL NET PREMIUM ($MIL)	NET INCOME ($MIL)	CAPITAL-IZATION INDEX (PTS)	RESERVE ADQ INDEX (PTS)	PROFIT-ABILITY INDEX (PTS)	LIQUIDITY INDEX (PTS)	STAB. INDEX (PTS)	STABILITY FACTORS
SHELTER MUTUAL INS CO	MO	B	3,210.5	1,831.5	1,379.7	10.3	8.0	7.5	5.4	5.8	5.0	T
SHELTER REINS CO	MO	B-	437.6	316.1	103.5	20.0	8.7	7.0	4.8	6.7	3.7	RT
SIGMA RRG INC	DC	B-	16.7	6.8	2.5	0.1	7.4	9.3	8.7	9.8	3.5	DGT
SILVER OAK CASUALTY INC	NE	B-	249.0	101.6	55.1	7.1	8.4	9.3	8.9	7.0	4.1	RT
SIMED	PR	C	159.8	99.0	19.3	8.8	10.0	8.8	8.0	7.2	3.8	DRT
SIRIUS AMERICA INS CO	NY	C+	1,444.0	534.5	283.9	59.5	6.0	6.3	4.3	7.2	3.1	FRT
SLAVONIC INS CO OF TEXAS	TX	U	4.7	4.7	0.0	0.1	N/A	7.2	6.8	10.0	4.5	GRT
SLAVONIC MUTUAL FIRE INS ASN	TX	C+	29.5	29.0	0.8	0.3	10.0	4.6	6.9	9.1	3.3	DGRT
SOCIETY INS A MUTUAL CO	WI	B	398.5	135.8	153.0	3.3	8.4	6.4	7.4	6.5	4.1	T
SOMERSET CASUALTY INS CO	PA	D	39.1	22.6	7.8	0.4	10.0	9.2	8.9	7.1	2.2	DGRT
SOMPO JAPAN CANOPIUS RE AG	DE	U	25.2	25.2	0.0	0.0	N/A	0.0	4.9	0.0	0.0	LT
SOMPO JAPAN FIRE & MAR INS CO AMER	NY	C+	77.6	74.4	0.1	0.4	10.0	3.6	6.0	10.0	4.1	DGT
SOMPO JAPAN INS CO OF AM	NY	B	1,236.8	548.6	183.0	13.8	9.1	9.0	3.6	7.2	4.6	RT
SOMPO JAPAN NIPPONKOA INS INC	GU	D (2)	7.0	1.4	3.6	0.4	0.9	6.5	8.0	8.6	0.6	CDGT
SONNENBERG MUTUAL INS CO	OH	C	24.6	14.7	9.8	0.5	8.6	7.8	6.2	6.8	2.9	DGT
SOUTH CAROLINA FARM BU MUTUAL INS	SC	C	107.9	50.1	52.2	-1.9	8.4	6.5	2.9	6.4	3.5	T
SOUTH CAROLINA FARM BUREAU INS	SC	D	3.4	3.1	0.0	0.0	10.0	N/A	5.8	7.0	2.3	DGT
SOUTHERN COUNTY MUTUAL INS CO	TX	C	34.3	30.0	0.0	1.2	10.0	N/A	4.5	10.0	3.7	GRT
SOUTHERN FARM BUREAU CAS INS CO	MS	B-	2,152.0	1,311.0	838.3	-16.1	8.5	7.8	4.7	6.4	4.8	T
SOUTHERN FARM BUREAU PROPERTY	MS	U	58.0	55.7	0.0	0.4	N/A	N/A	5.9	7.0	5.4	RT
SOUTHERN FIDELITY INS CO	FL	B	207.3	87.3	106.9	2.8	8.4	6.9	8.2	6.4	4.0	RT
SOUTHERN FIDELITY P&C INC	FL	C+	109.5	30.5	63.3	1.0	5.3	4.8	8.5	6.6	3.3	CT
SOUTHERN FIRE & CASUALTY CO	WI	C	7.7	6.7	8.0	0.2	7.2	4.1	5.1	7.9	2.7	DGRT
SOUTHERN GENERAL INS CO	GA	D	44.7	12.2	37.6	-1.8	5.0	5.8	1.5	0.3	2.3	DFLR
SOUTHERN GUARANTY INS CO	WI	C-	14.5	9.2	30.3	0.3	6.8	3.9	1.8	7.0	3.1	DFRT
SOUTHERN INS CO	TX	C	38.5	25.7	0.4	-7.3	7.2	4.2	2.9	7.4	3.5	FGRT
SOUTHERN INS CO OF VA	VA	C+	143.5	63.6	68.6	1.5	9.9	5.9	4.2	6.6	4.0	RT
SOUTHERN MUTUAL CHURCH INS CO	SC	C+	60.5	31.5	24.9	4.1	7.7	8.0	3.6	6.7	3.1	RT
SOUTHERN MUTUAL INS CO	GA	C+	17.0	13.7	0.1	0.1	10.0	5.0	7.7	9.9	3.2	DFGR
SOUTHERN OAK INS CO	FL	C	130.3	53.4	68.1	3.4	7.5	4.6	7.0	6.7	2.9	T
SOUTHERN PILOT INS CO	WI	C	12.4	6.9	12.7	0.3	6.3	4.0	2.6	6.8	2.8	DGRT
SOUTHERN PIONEER PROP & CAS INS CO	AR	C	44.3	18.5	24.8	-1.7	6.4	6.0	3.9	6.9	2.9	DRT
SOUTHERN STATES INS EXCHANGE	VA	C+	48.4	17.9	14.4	0.1	7.9	9.4	7.0	6.8	3.0	DRT
SOUTHERN TRUST INS CO	GA	B-	44.8	19.5	29.0	-0.4	7.9	6.0	4.9	6.5	3.7	DRT
SOUTHERN UNDERWRITERS INS CO	OK	C	5.4	5.1	0.0	0.1	10.0	N/A	4.2	9.1	2.5	DGRT
SOUTHERN VANGUARD INS CO	TX	C	24.5	10.6	6.8	-0.5	9.9	3.5	5.2	7.0	2.5	DGRT
SOUTHERN-OWNERS INS CO	MI	B+	695.8	228.5	266.1	6.3	8.5	9.0	7.5	6.8	5.2	T
SOUTHLAND LLOYDS INS CO	TX	U (5)	0.0	0.0	0.0	0.0	N/A	6.4	1.3	9.9	2.5	FT
SOUTHWEST GENERAL INS CO	NM	D	2.5	1.4	0.8	-0.1	8.8	9.3	2.1	7.6	1.6	DFGT
SOUTHWEST MARINE & GEN INS CO	AZ	C+	119.3	62.4	28.9	-0.9	7.5	3.2	4.1	6.7	3.0	FT
SOUTHWEST PHYSICIANS RRG INC	SC	U	65.9	27.4	0.0	7.7	N/A	4.8	6.6	9.5	2.4	CFRT
SPARTA AMERICAN INS CO	CA	C (3)	33.0	11.1	1.4	-0.7	5.2	2.2	1.2	7.6	3.0	CDFG
SPARTA INS CO	CT	D+	319.8	97.2	4.3	-25.3	6.8	1.9	0.9	9.5	2.5	FRT
SPARTAN INS CO	TX	D+	6.9	5.8	3.1	0.1	9.3	6.0	7.3	7.6	2.1	DGRT
SPARTAN PROPERTY INS CO	SC	C	28.6	22.3	10.0	2.7	7.4	5.1	3.5	7.8	3.1	DFGT
SPECIALTY RISK OF AMERICA	IL	D+	14.2	5.4	6.1	0.0	3.5	5.5	3.7	6.8	2.1	DGT
SPECIALTY SURPLUS INS CO	IL	U	17.2	16.8	0.0	0.2	N/A	5.5	3.5	7.0	4.7	GT
SPINNAKER INS CO	IL	U	35.4	31.5	0.3	-1.8	N/A	6.0	3.5	10.0	5.0	FGRT
SPIRIT COMMERCIAL AUTO RRG INC	NV	E (1)	70.7	13.6	34.0	0.2	0.0	0.2	2.0	6.4	0.2	CDT
SPIRIT MOUNTAIN INS CO RRG INC	DC	D	6.1	3.7	2.0	0.2	8.3	10.0	8.8	9.3	2.0	DGRT
SPRING VALLEY MUTUAL INS CO	MN	D	4.3	4.3	0.0	0.2	10.0	5.0	3.9	10.0	1.5	DGRT
SPRINGFIELD INS CO	CA	D+	93.1	30.3	18.0	2.5	5.6	1.6	1.9	6.8	2.5	DFT

See Page 27 for explanation of footnotes and Page 28 for explanation of stability factors.
Arrows denote recent upgrades ▲ or downgrades ▼ (see Section VII for explanations)

116

www.weissratings.com

RISK ADJ. RATIO #1	CAPITAL RATIO #2	PREMIUM TO SURPLUS (%)	RESV. TO SURPLUS (%)	RESV. DEVELOP. 1 YEAR (%)	RESV. DEVELOP. 2 YEAR (%)	LOSS RATIO (%)	EXP. RATIO (%)	COMB RATIO (%)	CASH FROM UNDER-WRITING (%)	NET PREMIUM GROWTH (%)	INVEST. IN AFFIL (%)	INSURANCE COMPANY NAME
2.2	1.7	77.2	27.5	-1.7	-1.3	69.4	28.7	98.1	105.2	4.2	24.2 ●	SHELTER MUTUAL INS CO
4.3	2.8	34.9	33.9	-8.2	-12.3	46.6	29.0	75.6	122.8	0.0	0.0 ●	SHELTER REINS CO
2.0	1.3	36.7	120.3	-8.5	-9.6	75.1	11.9	87.0	231.3	-8.7	0.0	SIGMA RRG INC
3.1	2.3	58.3	102.9	-8.1	-16.9	56.8	22.7	79.5	136.5	-1.6	0.0	SILVER OAK CASUALTY INC
6.6	4.6	21.4	64.7	-4.9	-5.7	70.3	27.5	97.8	82.9	-7.0	0.0	SIMED
1.4	0.9	54.9	129.6	-2.4	-5.3	53.7	36.5	90.2	86.7	6.3	0.0 ●	SIRIUS AMERICA INS CO
N/A	N/A	0.3	0.1	-0.1	-0.2	33.3	421.9	455.2	21.1	-8.3	0.0	SLAVONIC INS CO OF TEXAS
6.5	6.1	2.9	N/A	N/A	N/A	42.5	68.1	110.6	115.6	-9.0	16.0	SLAVONIC MUTUAL FIRE INS ASN
2.6	1.9	116.1	114.3	-2.4	1.3	62.4	28.7	91.1	117.5	0.9	0.0	SOCIETY INS A MUTUAL CO
3.8	3.0	35.3	38.5	-0.4	-7.0	52.8	21.2	74.0	198.6	25.1	0.0	SOMERSET CASUALTY INS CO
N/A	N/A	N/A	N/A	N/A	N/A	N/A	N/A	N/A	N/A	0.0	0.0	SOMPO JAPAN CANOPIUS RE AG
71.8	62.9	0.1	0.4	0.1	0.1	499.7	999 +	-624.2	264.9	717.6	0.0	SOMPO JAPAN FIRE & MAR INS CO
4.5	2.8	37.5	86.8	-3.1	-7.4	64.8	34.5	99.3	105.2	-4.4	1.4 ●	SOMPO JAPAN INS CO OF AM
0.3	0.2	263.7	25.1	-5.5	-7.4	28.2	33.1	61.3	150.4	69.8	0.0	SOMPO JAPAN NIPPONKOA INS INC
3.2	2.0	69.3	27.4	-1.6	-3.4	62.4	30.9	93.3	110.5	1.5	0.0	SONNENBERG MUTUAL INS CO
2.4	2.1	100.3	21.2	-2.6	-4.6	65.9	29.1	95.0	100.2	-1.0	8.2	SOUTH CAROLINA FARM BU MUTUAL INS
18.8	16.9	N/A	N/A	N/A	N/A	N/A	N/A	N/A	N/A	0.0	0.0	SOUTH CAROLINA FARM BUREAU INS
22.4	20.2	N/A	N/A	N/A	N/A	N/A	N/A	N/A	21.3	0.0	0.0	SOUTHERN COUNTY MUTUAL INS CO
2.1	1.9	63.6	29.1	-2.0	-2.7	83.9	19.9	103.8	95.0	-0.4	31.8 ●	SOUTHERN FARM BUREAU CAS INS CO
N/A	N/A	N/A	N/A	N/A	N/A	N/A	N/A	N/A	N/A	0.0	0.0	SOUTHERN FARM BUREAU PROPERTY
3.2	2.6	123.1	29.2	0.4	1.4	46.7	47.4	94.1	106.1	-5.8	0.0	SOUTHERN FIDELITY INS CO
1.5	0.9	209.1	71.4	N/A	-4.9	54.1	42.3	96.4	102.4	-7.5	0.0	SOUTHERN FIDELITY P&C INC
7.0	4.9	126.5	117.8	1.5	2.8	63.9	31.1	95.0	139.0	47.6	0.0	SOUTHERN FIRE & CASUALTY CO
0.7	0.6	265.6	74.9	0.3	-0.6	73.4	27.4	100.8	86.7	-10.4	0.0	SOUTHERN GENERAL INS CO
2.2	1.5	133.0	142.7	1.5	2.9	63.9	35.8	99.7	89.9	-5.8	0.0	SOUTHERN GUARANTY INS CO
1.4	0.8	1.4	29.6	-0.2	1.0	-21.9	-92.3	-114.2	26.9	-45.7	0.0	SOUTHERN INS CO
4.3	2.9	111.1	57.2	-0.6	-0.8	67.7	31.4	99.1	106.3	3.8	0.0	SOUTHERN INS CO OF VA
2.5	1.8	94.6	28.1	-3.4	-4.2	56.1	36.9	93.0	110.3	8.2	0.0	SOUTHERN MUTUAL CHURCH INS CO
13.0	11.7	0.8	0.4	0.2	0.1	35.1	-477.5	-442.4	-181.6	-16.7	0.0	SOUTHERN MUTUAL INS CO
2.8	2.2	136.7	38.8	-6.3	N/A	53.2	30.8	84.0	111.8	-8.8	0.0	SOUTHERN OAK INS CO
4.1	3.1	151.6	149.0	1.6	3.0	63.9	32.8	96.7	115.0	16.5	0.0	SOUTHERN PILOT INS CO
1.5	1.0	127.8	41.5	-3.0	1.4	59.5	32.5	92.0	106.7	9.4	0.0	SOUTHERN PIONEER PROP & CAS INS
2.4	1.5	82.4	75.5	-2.7	-12.5	57.9	23.7	81.6	102.5	1.0	0.0	SOUTHERN STATES INS EXCHANGE
1.9	1.3	128.2	24.1	1.0	3.3	53.6	42.9	96.5	105.7	8.1	0.0	SOUTHERN TRUST INS CO
45.2	34.2	N/A	N/A	N/A	N/A	N/A	N/A	N/A	295.1	0.0	0.0	SOUTHERN UNDERWRITERS INS CO
3.6	3.0	60.7	11.2	6.0	6.8	72.7	18.3	91.0	152.3	-32.9	0.0	SOUTHERN VANGUARD INS CO
2.8	2.0	121.2	124.5	-6.5	-5.1	65.1	27.1	92.2	112.5	7.7	0.0 ●	SOUTHERN-OWNERS INS CO
N/A	N/A	N/A	3.2	5.6	2.8	N/A	N/A	N/A	N/A	0.0	0.0	SOUTHLAND LLOYDS INS CO
2.7	2.1	52.1	15.3	-7.0	-11.2	37.6	77.3	114.9	76.2	-11.4	0.0	SOUTHWEST GENERAL INS CO
3.0	1.7	46.8	51.6	14.1	17.1	76.1	34.0	110.1	28.6	-9.2	0.0	SOUTHWEST MARINE & GEN INS CO
N/A	N/A	N/A	185.8	-36.6	-13.7	N/A	N/A	N/A	N/A	-100.0	0.0	SOUTHWEST PHYSICIANS RRG INC
1.5	0.8	11.5	201.8	26.4	43.0	134.1	153.5	287.6	22.8	-92.2	0.0	SPARTA AMERICAN INS CO
1.3	0.7	3.5	171.3	17.2	40.5	440.6	182.3	622.9	7.7	-66.3	3.3	SPARTA INS CO
3.0	2.6	54.4	2.0	-0.4	-0.5	3.3	71.8	75.1	127.6	1.7	0.0	SPARTAN INS CO
2.6	1.7	51.4	1.7	-1.5	-0.3	3.8	62.5	66.3	108.6	-24.1	0.0	SPARTAN PROPERTY INS CO
0.7	0.5	117.8	77.3	-5.4	-12.9	63.8	45.1	108.9	91.4	19.2	0.0	SPECIALTY RISK OF AMERICA
N/A	N/A	N/A	0.2	N/A	-0.2	N/A	N/A	N/A	N/A	0.0	0.0	SPECIALTY SURPLUS INS CO
N/A	N/A	0.9	N/A	N/A	0.1	141.1	370.7	511.8	9.6	0.0	0.0	SPINNAKER INS CO
0.1	0.1	278.0	297.6	122.8	136.3	97.1	-1.2	95.9	128.1	-18.5	0.0	SPIRIT COMMERCIAL AUTO RRG INC
2.9	2.4	56.7	37.8	-35.5	-45.6	-11.9	61.7	49.8	172.8	-8.2	0.0	SPIRIT MOUNTAIN INS CO RRG INC
85.2	41.8	N/A	N/A	N/A	N/A	N/A	N/A	N/A	N/A	0.0	0.0	SPRING VALLEY MUTUAL INS CO
2.2	1.1	64.5	216.6	15.7	42.1	92.6	29.5	122.1	73.8	-15.1	0.0	SPRINGFIELD INS CO

999 + Denotes number greater than 999.9%
999 - Denotes number less than -999.99%
● Bullets denote a more detailed analysis is available in Section II.

INSURANCE COMPANY NAME	DOM. STATE	RATING	TOTAL ASSETS ($MIL)	CAPITAL & SURPLUS ($MIL)	ANNUAL NET PREMIUM ($MIL)	NET INCOME ($MIL)	CAPITAL-IZATION INDEX (PTS)	RESERVE ADQ INDEX (PTS)	PROFIT-ABILITY INDEX (PTS)	LIQUIDITY INDEX (PTS)	STAB. INDEX (PTS)	STABILITY FACTORS
ST CHARLES INS CO RRG	SC	E	15.0	12.9	1.5	0.5	10.0	10.0	8.7	9.1	0.3	DGT
ST CLAIR INS CO	NY	U	1.3	1.3	0.0	0.0	N/A	N/A	2.9	7.0	1.8	FGT
▲ST JOHNS INS CO	FL	C-	133.5	49.7	34.1	-0.1	2.8	5.6	4.9	3.0	2.9	CFLT
ST LUKES HEALTH NETWORK INS CO RRG	VT	E	64.7	17.9	14.5	2.1	1.6	2.6	5.1	6.7	0.1	CDT
ST PAUL FIRE & MARINE INS CO	CT	B	18,479.2	5,641.7	5,252.1	275.2	7.5	8.6	4.0	6.8	5.1	T
ST PAUL GUARDIAN INS CO	CT	C+	76.0	26.3	20.8	1.1	7.7	8.3	5.2	6.5	3.7	DFT
ST PAUL MERCURY INS CO	CT	B-	328.3	130.6	83.1	5.7	9.2	8.1	4.5	6.7	4.5	T
ST PAUL PROTECTIVE INS CO	CT	B-	520.9	235.2	120.6	7.9	10.0	7.9	6.1	6.8	4.6	T
ST PAUL SURPLUS LINES INS CO	DE	C	641.4	207.9	182.9	11.2	5.0	8.6	7.0	6.6	4.0	CT
STANDARD CASUALTY CO	TX	C+	38.0	15.4	25.7	-3.8	7.3	4.9	2.9	6.8	3.1	DGT
STANDARD FIRE INS CO	CT	B	3,665.0	1,205.9	1,005.7	51.6	7.7	8.4	6.7	6.8	5.0	T
STANDARD GUARANTY INS CO	DE	B-	342.2	140.6	219.2	15.2	7.3	5.7	6.3	5.6	4.5	FRT
STANDARD MUTUAL INS CO	IL	C	53.1	18.9	43.5	-0.8	7.5	9.3	1.8	5.6	2.9	DFRT
STAR & SHIELD INS EXCHANGE	FL	D-	14.3	4.5	10.1	-0.5	1.5	1.5	0.5	1.0	0.9	CDFG
STAR CASUALTY INS CO	FL	D+	12.5	5.4	8.6	-2.3	7.0	1.6	2.1	7.0	2.2	DFGT
STAR INS CO	MI	C	862.8	312.3	213.0	26.3	8.0	3.3	5.7	6.7	3.6	RT
STARNET INS CO	DE	C	236.0	114.4	0.0	1.2	10.0	N/A	4.6	10.0	4.3	FRT
STARR INDEMNITY & LIABILITY CO	TX	B	4,391.4	2,017.5	1,078.1	32.4	7.2	4.9	7.7	6.8	4.5	RT
STARR SURPLUS LINES INS CO	IL	B-	372.4	105.3	46.3	5.8	6.5	3.6	6.6	5.9	3.6	T
STARSTONE NATIONAL INS CO	DE	C	274.7	96.4	78.4	3.3	8.4	6.9	6.1	7.4	3.5	GT
STARSTONE SPECIALTY INS CO	DE	C-	180.8	117.5	24.1	0.8	6.6	2.9	3.9	7.0	3.2	FRT
STATE AUTO INS CO OF OH	OH	C-	34.0	16.8	0.0	0.2	10.0	N/A	6.9	7.0	3.3	ADGR
STATE AUTO INS CO OF WI	WI	B-	18.3	12.0	0.0	0.1	10.0	N/A	5.7	7.0	3.6	ADGR
STATE AUTO P&C INS CO	IA	C	2,404.1	636.0	999.2	-16.3	7.4	5.8	4.6	6.2	4.3	ART
STATE AUTOMOBILE MUTUAL INS CO	OH	C+	2,449.7	775.9	675.9	-16.6	7.1	5.9	3.7	6.3	4.3	AT
STATE FARM CTY MUTUAL INS CO OF TX	TX	C+	214.2	22.6	34.6	-7.4	8.8	6.5	1.7	6.3	3.7	FT
STATE FARM FIRE & CAS CO	IL	B	37,184.7	15,447.6	15,914.0	1,089.0	7.4	8.0	5.2	5.5	5.1	T
STATE FARM FLORIDA INS CO	FL	B-	2,073.8	1,103.0	584.0	68.5	8.6	6.5	9.1	6.8	4.9	T
STATE FARM GENERAL INS CO	IL	B	7,064.0	4,108.0	1,904.2	106.1	10.0	6.5	8.8	6.7	5.0	T
STATE FARM GUARANTY INS CO	IL	C	36.8	13.5	0.0	0.0	10.0	N/A	6.1	10.0	3.1	DGRT
STATE FARM INDEMNITY CO	IL	B	2,231.1	1,209.0	621.0	17.7	10.0	9.3	6.7	6.7	5.0	T
STATE FARM LLOYDS	TX	B	3,331.5	1,185.5	1,572.6	42.3	8.2	6.9	6.2	5.9	5.0	FT
STATE FARM MUTUAL AUTOMOBILE INS CO	IL	B+	143,802.0	86,467.6	37,511.4	-439.3	8.1	7.7	4.6	6.5	5.3	T
STATE INS FUND	NY	U	--	--	--	--	N/A	--	--	--	--	Z
STATE INS FUND DISABILITY BENEFITS	NY	U	--	--	--	--	N/A	--	--	--	--	Z
STATE MUTUAL INS CO (ME)	ME	C	2.5	2.3	0.0	0.0	9.1	N/A	8.0	7.0	2.2	DGT
STATE NATIONAL FIRE INS CO	LA	C	2.4	1.5	0.8	0.0	7.2	7.4	1.8	6.9	2.5	DGT
STATE NATIONAL INS CO	TX	B-	321.6	236.8	56.2	2.7	8.2	5.1	7.6	7.0	4.1	RT
STATE VOLUNTEER MUTUAL INS CO	TN	B	1,203.2	537.1	113.4	-3.7	10.0	9.4	6.2	8.7	4.9	RT
STATES SELF-INSURERS RISK RET GROUP	VT	D-	24.0	9.4	2.6	0.1	0.9	3.4	3.9	6.9	1.3	CDGR
STEADFAST INS CO	DE	C+	674.1	503.7	0.0	2.3	9.1	N/A	7.4	6.9	4.5	FRT
STEADPOINT INS CO	TN	C-	24.9	8.8	9.1	0.6	5.2	7.0	8.7	7.0	2.3	DGRT
STERLING CASUALTY INS CO	CA	D-	14.4	3.1	6.1	-0.5	3.6	2.7	1.2	0.3	1.3	DFGL
STERLING INS CO	NY	B-	169.1	104.6	57.8	5.5	10.0	9.3	8.8	6.9	3.9	RT
STERLING INS COOP INC	NY	U	0.5	0.4	0.0	-0.1	N/A	0.0	1.6	0.0	0.0	LT
STICO MUTUAL INS CO RRG	VT	D	23.7	12.0	3.4	0.2	6.3	9.2	6.8	7.9	1.8	DGRT
STILLWATER INS CO	CA	B-	336.8	168.7	186.9	-2.7	6.1	8.1	5.9	1.9	4.0	LRT
STILLWATER P&C INS CO	NY	C+	121.7	114.3	2.3	2.2	10.0	4.6	6.2	10.0	4.1	T
STONE VALLEY MUTUAL FIRE INS CO	PA	U (2)	0.8	0.8	0.1	0.0	N/A	5.0	7.3	10.0	2.3	T
STONEGATE INS CO	IL	D	17.6	4.9	14.2	0.0	1.4	1.0	2.9	6.0	1.5	CDGT
STONETRUST COMMERCIAL INS CO	LA	C	147.3	46.2	57.5	-1.0	6.6	4.5	4.3	6.6	3.4	RT
STONEWOOD INS CO	NC	C+	84.1	25.6	5.4	0.6	9.4	8.2	3.1	7.0	3.6	RT

See Page 27 for explanation of footnotes and Page 28 for explanation of stability factors.

Arrows denote recent upgrades ▲ or downgrades ▼   (see Section VII for explanations)

118

www.weissratings.com

RISK ADJ. CAPITAL RATIO #1	RATIO #2	PREMIUM TO SURPLUS (%)	RESV. TO SURPLUS (%)	RESV. DEVELOP. 1 YEAR (%)	2 YEAR (%)	LOSS RATIO (%)	EXP. RATIO (%)	COMB RATIO (%)	CASH FROM UNDER-WRITING (%)	NET PREMIUM GROWTH (%)	INVEST. IN AFFIL (%)	INSURANCE COMPANY NAME
6.1	3.5	12.6	10.7	-16.5	-64.0	-33.0	35.7	2.7	256.1	5.7	0.0	ST CHARLES INS CO RRG
N/A	N/A	N/A	N/A	N/A	N/A	N/A	N/A	N/A	N/A	0.0	0.0	ST CLAIR INS CO
0.5	0.5	67.9	28.6	4.7	6.3	95.9	1.4	97.3	93.1	-3.4	0.0	ST JOHNS INS CO
0.5	0.4	100.4	303.6	-16.6	-20.6	90.6	6.7	97.3	117.4	3.2	0.0	ST LUKES HEALTH NETWORK INS CO
1.8	1.4	94.4	164.7	-2.9	-7.0	58.8	30.3	89.1	108.2	2.5	14.7 ●	ST PAUL FIRE & MARINE INS CO
2.4	1.5	82.4	141.4	-2.5	-6.1	58.7	30.2	88.9	90.6	2.9	0.0	ST PAUL GUARDIAN INS CO
3.9	2.5	66.5	114.1	-2.0	-4.9	58.7	30.3	89.0	97.0	2.9	0.0	ST PAUL MERCURY INS CO
4.9	3.1	53.1	91.0	-1.7	-4.0	58.7	30.2	88.9	109.4	3.0	0.0 ●	ST PAUL PROTECTIVE INS CO
1.0	0.6	93.0	159.4	-3.0	-7.2	58.7	30.3	88.9	108.5	2.9	0.0 ●	ST PAUL SURPLUS LINES INS CO
1.4	0.9	149.4	19.7	5.0	8.2	62.2	40.9	103.1	106.3	12.9	0.0	STANDARD CASUALTY CO
1.8	1.4	84.8	145.5	-2.6	-6.2	58.7	30.3	89.0	109.2	2.9	17.3 ●	STANDARD FIRE INS CO
1.9	1.5	173.6	45.0	-8.0	7.1	42.2	55.7	97.9	66.4	-21.3	0.0	STANDARD GUARANTY INS CO
1.6	1.3	216.2	58.2	-10.9	-17.5	68.6	35.4	104.0	95.9	1.9	0.0	STANDARD MUTUAL INS CO
0.3	0.3	202.1	113.6	-40.9	2.6	94.6	41.4	136.0	52.0	72.7	0.0	STAR & SHIELD INS EXCHANGE
1.0	0.8	111.5	31.7	19.0	25.2	92.6	28.8	121.4	86.8	-9.4	0.0	STAR CASUALTY INS CO
2.1	1.7	67.8	122.7	8.6	13.3	77.1	36.9	114.0	108.2	0.7	16.8 ●	STAR INS CO
12.4	11.1	N/A	N/A	N/A	N/A	N/A	N/A	N/A	999 +	0.0	0.0	STARNET INS CO
1.4	1.1	58.3	73.1	1.4	2.3	75.0	19.1	94.1	166.4	6.1	35.9 ●	STARR INDEMNITY & LIABILITY CO
1.5	0.9	46.8	80.2	4.1	8.9	75.9	12.3	88.2	349.8	-31.3	0.0	STARR SURPLUS LINES INS CO
3.1	1.6	84.5	73.7	-6.1	-22.3	64.5	8.7	73.2	219.5	67.2	0.0	STARSTONE NATIONAL INS CO
1.2	1.1	21.3	55.2	12.8	29.0	122.4	-31.0	91.4	68.8	84.0	62.8	STARSTONE SPECIALTY INS CO
5.2	4.7	N/A	N/A	N/A	N/A	N/A	N/A	N/A	15.3	0.0	0.0	STATE AUTO INS CO OF OH
6.8	6.1	N/A	N/A	N/A	N/A	N/A	N/A	N/A	52.8	0.0	0.0	STATE AUTO INS CO OF WI
1.9	1.2	152.5	126.8	1.9	7.1	68.5	33.4	101.9	106.7	6.6	0.0 ●	STATE AUTO P&C INS CO
1.1	1.0	82.0	68.2	1.0	3.4	68.5	33.9	102.4	111.5	6.6	47.3 ●	STATE AUTOMOBILE MUTUAL INS CO
1.9	1.4	115.1	48.4	3.7	0.9	103.5	25.2	128.7	81.1	10.3	0.0	STATE FARM CTY MUTUAL INS CO OF TX
2.5	1.6	112.1	49.5	0.7	-1.9	60.8	27.3	88.1	117.9	0.0	0.0 ●	STATE FARM FIRE & CAS CO
4.9	3.5	56.5	28.6	0.9	-1.5	42.1	26.4	68.5	134.6	-0.8	0.0 ●	STATE FARM FLORIDA INS CO
6.7	4.5	47.7	31.4	-1.1	-2.7	71.5	28.1	99.6	102.7	0.6	0.0 ●	STATE FARM GENERAL INS CO
3.4	3.1	N/A	N/A	N/A	N/A	N/A	N/A	N/A	-45.3	0.0	0.0	STATE FARM GUARANTY INS CO
5.8	5.0	52.0	59.9	-3.2	-4.6	82.5	23.2	105.7	91.8	1.8	0.7 ●	STATE FARM INDEMNITY CO
2.5	2.3	129.6	33.2	1.2	-0.2	63.0	9.9	72.9	103.7	-12.6	0.0 ●	STATE FARM LLOYDS
2.0	1.7	45.4	32.5	-0.5	-1.0	84.5	27.5	112.0	95.6	1.6	27.3 ●	STATE FARM MUTUAL AUTOMOBILE INS
N/A	N/A	--	--	--	--	--	--	--	--	--	--	STATE INS FUND
N/A	N/A	--	--	--	--	--	--	--	--	--	--	STATE INS FUND DISABILITY BENEFITS
4.0	2.3	N/A	N/A	N/A	N/A	N/A	N/A	N/A	N/A	0.0	0.0	STATE MUTUAL INS CO (ME)
1.1	1.0	59.5	1.7	-2.3	-1.7	17.6	86.7	104.3	89.5	122.0	0.0	STATE NATIONAL FIRE INS CO
1.9	1.8	24.4	2.5	0.4	0.3	49.1	37.7	86.8	138.6	7.7	45.5 ●	STATE NATIONAL INS CO
4.3	3.3	21.1	94.4	-7.6	-13.4	79.5	19.6	99.1	92.0	-1.0	0.0 ●	STATE VOLUNTEER MUTUAL INS CO
0.3	0.2	28.1	124.4	8.9	13.2	128.7	-4.0	124.7	90.3	52.0	0.0	STATES SELF-INSURERS RISK RET
2.4	2.3	N/A	N/A	N/A	N/A	N/A	N/A	N/A	42.3	0.0	45.3 ●	STEADFAST INS CO
1.2	1.0	110.5	115.1	-3.2	-8.5	45.8	29.4	75.2	148.3	6.1	0.0	STEADPOINT INS CO
0.9	0.7	240.9	146.1	29.6	30.0	106.7	37.0	143.7	78.0	-28.8	0.0	STERLING CASUALTY INS CO
6.4	4.8	58.7	23.4	-3.3	-6.2	48.0	34.2	82.2	122.3	5.7	0.2	STERLING INS CO
N/A	N/A	N/A	N/A	N/A	N/A	N/A	N/A	N/A	N/A	0.0	0.0	STERLING INS COOP INC
2.1	1.3	29.1	43.1	-13.0	-8.2	-9.7	66.8	57.1	131.3	-12.8	0.0	STICO MUTUAL INS CO RRG
1.1	0.8	115.3	31.6	-0.9	-4.8	62.1	33.6	95.7	107.8	8.8	40.5	STILLWATER INS CO
10.3	5.4	2.1	N/A	N/A	N/A	N/A	58.9	58.9	382.7	7.8	0.0	STILLWATER P&C INS CO
N/A	N/A	7.5	0.1	-0.1	-0.1	2.0	59.3	61.3	147.2	-1.5	0.0	STONE VALLEY MUTUAL FIRE INS CO
0.6	0.3	301.7	107.5	17.2	65.0	51.3	36.6	87.9	121.3	10.5	0.0	STONEGATE INS CO
1.4	1.0	117.6	128.8	9.8	15.7	73.9	34.5	108.4	115.3	-6.5	0.0	STONETRUST COMMERCIAL INS CO
3.6	2.4	21.6	39.2	-1.4	-3.3	65.2	27.3	92.5	130.8	21.6	0.0	STONEWOOD INS CO

999 + Denotes number greater than 999.9%
999 - Denotes number less than -999.99%
● Bullets denote a more detailed analysis is available in Section II.

INSURANCE COMPANY NAME	DOM. STATE	RATING	TOTAL ASSETS ($MIL)	CAPITAL & SURPLUS ($MIL)	ANNUAL NET PREMIUM ($MIL)	NET INCOME ($MIL)	CAPITAL-IZATION INDEX (PTS)	RESERVE ADQ INDEX (PTS)	PROFIT-ABILITY INDEX (PTS)	LIQUIDITY INDEX (PTS)	STAB. INDEX (PTS)	STABILITY FACTORS
STONINGTON INS CO	PA	E+	34.2	17.6	61.4	0.4	1.0	4.4	1.9	6.8	0.7	T
STRATFORD INS CO	NH	B-	146.1	83.5	12.1	0.6	10.0	9.4	7.9	8.0	4.1	RT
STRATHMORE INS CO	NY	C	54.8	25.2	13.6	0.4	8.2	6.2	5.3	6.9	3.7	T
SU INS CO	WI	C	16.1	12.6	13.7	0.6	10.0	6.1	7.0	6.9	2.4	DFGT
SUBLIMITY INS CO	OR	C+	38.2	16.3	25.7	0.2	8.0	6.0	6.8	5.7	3.3	DGRT
SUBURBAN HEALTH ORG RRG LLC	SC	U	0.9	0.8	0.0	0.1	N/A	N/A	3.6	7.0	2.0	FGT
SUECIA INS CO	NY	U	46.0	20.8	0.0	0.3	N/A	5.3	5.0	10.0	4.9	RT
SUMMITPOINT INS CO	WV	C	42.5	11.2	5.2	0.4	5.6	4.0	6.1	7.6	2.9	DFT
SUN SURETY INS CO	SD	C-	19.6	9.7	3.1	0.5	8.5	N/A	8.6	7.0	2.3	DGT
SUNAPEE MUTL FIRE INS CO	NH	B	4.2	3.8	0.0	0.0	8.9	N/A	8.4	7.0	4.0	DGT
SUNDERLAND MARINE INS CO LTD	AK	D	10.2	6.1	2.2	0.2	7.4	7.0	1.4	8.5	2.0	DFGR
SUNLAND RRG INC	TN	B-	7.0	1.1	0.6	0.2	7.5	5.8	7.5	1.2	3.5	DFGL
SUNZ INS CO	FL	E	88.0	15.6	24.9	3.6	0.2	1.0	2.8	1.9	0.3	CDFL
SURETEC INDEMNITY CO	CA	C+	21.7	11.7	7.8	0.4	8.1	3.7	5.8	7.7	3.1	DGT
SURETEC INS CO	TX	B-	225.5	87.4	59.3	6.7	9.5	8.7	8.6	8.1	3.9	RT
SURETY BONDING CO OF AMERICA	SD	C+	7.6	7.5	0.0	0.0	10.0	3.6	6.6	10.0	3.0	DGRT
SUSSEX INS CO	SC	C	758.6	142.7	-181.0	-1.2	5.0	2.9	1.3	8.7	4.2	CFT
SUTTER INS CO	CA	C	37.8	21.1	14.0	1.1	9.2	6.2	3.0	6.5	2.9	DFRT
▼SWISS REINS AMERICA CORP	NY	C+	13,573.0	3,124.8	1,987.4	92.5	5.3	9.3	3.1	7.0	3.2	CRT
SYNCORA CAPITAL ASR INC	NY	E	444.1	203.6	11.7	-9.6	8.8	0.5	3.5	10.0	0.0	DFT
SYNCORA GUARANTEE INC	NY	E-	1,282.2	1,150.7	12.8	49.7	10.0	0.8	5.0	10.0	0.0	FT
SYNERGY COMP INS CO	PA	D	32.8	10.9	12.1	0.5	4.7	9.7	8.7	6.9	2.3	DGRT
SYNERGY INS CO	NC	D+	62.6	19.9	17.9	2.9	2.6	7.0	5.5	7.2	2.7	CDRT
TANK OWNER MEMBERS INS CO	TX	C	27.4	13.9	5.9	1.0	7.7	9.0	8.0	8.0	2.5	DGRT
TDC NATIONAL ASR CO	OR	C	304.0	74.0	18.9	5.3	7.8	6.0	4.8	7.7	4.1	GT
TDC SPECIALTY INS CO	DC	C	67.1	46.3	0.5	0.6	10.0	7.5	4.7	10.0	3.8	DFT
TEACHERS AUTO INS CO	NJ	C+(2)	22.5	11.4	0.0	0.4	10.0	6.1	8.0	7.0	3.1	DT
TEACHERS INS CO	IL	B	342.6	146.3	196.6	3.2	7.5	8.5	7.5	5.2	4.4	AT
TECHNOLOGY INS CO	NH	C	2,351.4	527.8	985.0	30.8	5.2	3.0	8.6	6.7	3.6	GRT
TENNESSEE FARMERS ASR CO	TN	B+	1,408.6	935.8	586.1	57.0	9.3	8.0	4.2	6.3	5.1	T
TENNESSEE FARMERS MUTUAL INS CO	TN	B+	2,804.7	2,192.3	589.2	62.1	8.1	7.5	5.9	6.6	5.1	T
TERRA INS CO (A RRG)	VT	C+	35.2	19.0	7.2	1.1	9.4	6.0	8.7	8.1	3.2	DGRT
TERRAFIRMA RRG LLC	VT	D+	7.0	4.8	1.2	0.1	10.0	3.5	6.3	7.3	2.1	DGT
TEXAS BUILDERS INS CO	TX	U	12.1	10.0	0.0	0.4	N/A	9.6	5.0	7.0	4.9	FGRT
TEXAS FAIR PLAN ASSN	TX	E-	80.8	-22.1	88.3	-27.7	0.0	1.7	0.3	0.0	0.0	CDLT
TEXAS FARM BUREAU CASUALTY INS CO	TX	B+	1,179.5	629.4	644.4	-21.2	10.0	6.2	4.0	5.7	5.2	T
TEXAS FARM BUREAU MUTUAL INS CO	TX	C-	713.0	271.9	407.5	-61.3	9.1	6.1	3.9	5.8	3.3	T
TEXAS FARM BUREAU UNDERWRITERS	TX	C	57.2	19.8	0.0	0.0	10.0	N/A	5.3	7.0	3.4	DT
TEXAS FARMERS INS CO	TX	C+	357.3	86.1	149.3	-1.6	8.5	6.0	4.3	6.3	4.4	FRT
TEXAS HERITAGE INS CO	TX	C	22.1	16.4	4.3	-0.8	10.0	6.0	2.9	6.4	3.2	DFGR
TEXAS HOSPITAL INS EXCHANGE	TX	D+	35.3	20.4	7.6	0.8	8.4	10.0	8.4	7.1	2.5	DGRT
TEXAS INS CO	TX	C	28.6	13.1	31.2	2.0	2.8	7.0	9.2	7.3	2.9	CDGT
TEXAS LAWYERS INS EXCHANGE	TX	C	87.6	61.9	16.1	3.2	10.0	9.6	8.9	7.1	3.5	DFRT
TEXAS MEDICAL INS CO	TX	D	48.9	30.8	8.0	0.2	8.9	9.3	8.9	8.4	2.3	DRT
TEXAS PACIFIC INDEMNITY CO	TX	B	7.7	7.4	0.0	0.0	10.0	N/A	6.9	7.0	4.5	DGT
THAMES INS CO	CT	C	28.3	16.0	10.7	0.3	8.2	8.7	5.0	6.7	3.2	DFGT
THE INS CO	LA	C+	211.8	66.0	64.2	-1.3	7.6	9.4	6.8	6.8	3.6	RT
THIRD COAST INS CO	IL	U	18.9	18.9	0.0	0.4	N/A	4.7	8.0	7.0	5.3	GT
TIG INS CO	CA	U	1,868.9	498.9	0.0	34.4	N/A	4.6	2.7	7.3	3.7	CFRT
TITAN INDEMNITY CO	TX	B-	239.2	158.6	0.0	0.8	8.1	N/A	3.8	10.0	4.5	T
TITAN INS CO	MI	B-	108.9	100.3	0.0	1.1	10.0	N/A	3.8	7.0	4.5	DT
TITAN INS CO INC A RRG	SC	C-	58.5	43.4	6.5	2.9	10.0	N/A	9.2	9.3	3.3	RT

See Page 27 for explanation of footnotes and
Page 28 for explanation of stability factors.
Arrows denote recent upgrades ▲ or downgrades ▼   (see Section VII for explanations)

120

www.weissratings.com

RISK ADJ. RATIO #1	CAPITAL RATIO #2	PREMIUM TO SURPLUS (%)	RESV. TO SURPLUS (%)	RESV. DEVELOP. 1 YEAR (%)	2 YEAR (%)	LOSS RATIO (%)	EXP. RATIO (%)	COMB RATIO (%)	CASH FROM UNDER-WRITING (%)	NET PREMIUM GROWTH (%)	INVEST. IN AFFIL (%)	INSURANCE COMPANY NAME
2.3	1.6	175.4	178.4	1.7	2.8	63.9	33.8	97.7	103.7	0.6	0.0	STONINGTON INS CO
8.2	5.6	14.6	57.1	-1.4	-24.4	72.3	40.8	113.1	122.4	-59.7	0.0	STRATFORD INS CO
2.2	1.8	55.3	80.9	0.8	0.1	68.7	30.9	99.6	110.4	7.4	0.0	STRATHMORE INS CO
4.6	2.8	111.0	10.2	-1.6	-0.4	65.1	33.8	98.9	96.7	-7.4	0.0	SU INS CO
2.0	1.6	157.8	38.0	5.3	3.6	65.4	31.1	96.5	108.1	1.7	0.0	SUBLIMITY INS CO
N/A	N/A	N/A	N/A	N/A	N/A	N/A	N/A	N/A	-1.6	0.0	0.0	SUBURBAN HEALTH ORG RRG LLC
N/A	N/A	N/A	84.3	-0.3	-0.8	N/A	N/A	N/A	N/A	0.0	0.0	SUECIA INS CO
1.6	1.0	47.6	199.3	-14.6	-29.3	69.2	32.1	101.3	64.1	-15.6	0.0	SUMMITPOINT INS CO
2.3	1.8	35.0	N/A	N/A	N/A	9.3	76.2	85.5	115.4	-5.5	23.7	SUN SURETY INS CO
3.7	2.2	N/A	N/A	N/A	N/A	N/A	N/A	N/A	N/A	0.0	0.0	SUNAPEE MUTL FIRE INS CO
4.8	4.3	72.5	34.0	-3.1	-20.8	70.2	76.4	146.6	64.2	-25.7	0.0	SUNDERLAND MARINE INS CO LTD
0.7	0.6	42.9	33.3	-7.8	-10.8	53.2	15.6	68.8	14.8	9.4	0.0	SUNLAND RRG INC
0.2	0.1	176.8	105.4	15.1	24.5	38.2	58.9	97.1	86.7	13.6	0.0	SUNZ INS CO
2.1	1.7	68.9	24.4	-1.3	-1.6	33.2	58.5	91.7	122.0	-4.0	0.0	SURETEC INDEMNITY CO
3.1	2.4	68.5	11.2	-3.0	-9.5	12.5	57.0	69.5	141.6	9.0	5.4	SURETEC INS CO
86.8	41.2	N/A	N/A	N/A	N/A	N/A	N/A	N/A	N/A	0.0	0.0	SURETY BONDING CO OF AMERICA
1.3	0.6	-122.5	298.7	-66.6	-1.2	80.2	-27.9	52.3	-77.6	-182.5	0.0	SUSSEX INS CO
3.8	3.0	68.4	43.1	5.9	3.3	76.3	36.9	113.2	69.4	-38.5	0.0	SUTTER INS CO
0.9	0.6	55.5	122.7	-1.7	-7.8	50.4	36.7	87.1	131.7	5.6	0.0 ●	SWISS REINS AMERICA CORP
3.8	2.3	6.1	21.0	24.9	17.1	55.2	187.0	242.2	31.0	-23.6	0.0 ●	SYNCORA CAPITAL ASR INC
24.5	13.2	1.2	-4.2	-19.8	96.8	-325.2	278.7	-46.5	29.5	-33.3	0.0 ●	SYNCORA GUARANTEE INC
1.0	0.8	119.6	126.3	-12.1	-40.0	58.6	29.1	87.7	137.7	5.7	0.0	SYNERGY COMP INS CO
1.0	0.5	104.5	111.0	-0.4	-22.6	57.7	22.1	79.8	138.1	10.6	0.0	SYNERGY INS CO
2.6	1.7	46.4	67.7	-4.1	-9.5	34.9	12.1	47.0	217.5	-4.6	2.9	TANK OWNER MEMBERS INS CO
2.4	1.5	27.9	59.4	-12.7	-6.3	68.8	10.3	79.1	232.9	-3.8	0.0	TDC NATIONAL ASR CO
8.7	5.5	1.2	11.9	-0.1	-1.5	172.9	142.4	315.3	-38.9	N/A	0.0	TDC SPECIALTY INS CO
4.4	4.0	N/A	1.0	-0.5	-0.9	N/A	N/A	N/A	N/A	0.0	0.0	TEACHERS AUTO INS CO
3.0	1.9	132.7	55.3	-2.3	-6.9	70.9	25.7	96.6	100.9	3.7	0.0	TEACHERS INS CO
1.0	0.7	205.8	176.1	5.1	23.3	71.0	23.7	94.7	137.0	41.4	3.9 ●	TECHNOLOGY INS CO
4.9	3.3	67.0	19.4	-3.8	-5.3	66.4	14.6	81.0	126.4	2.7	2.6 ●	TENNESSEE FARMERS ASR CO
1.9	1.7	28.4	11.1	-1.8	-2.2	65.8	14.5	80.3	128.5	2.6	48.8 ●	TENNESSEE FARMERS MUTUAL INS CO
3.6	2.5	38.5	10.1	0.5	1.9	9.3	55.9	65.2	162.0	6.5	0.0	TERRA INS CO (A RRG)
4.9	3.2	26.3	24.4	4.1	5.3	67.3	34.4	101.7	149.4	8.4	0.0	TERRAFIRMA RRG LLC
N/A	N/A	-0.1	24.6	-6.4	-22.6	999 +	999 +	999 +	-0.7	82.2	0.9	TEXAS BUILDERS INS CO
-0.3	-0.2	999 +	548.0	-57.8	66.2	75.4	27.4	102.8	100.0	-4.1	0.0	TEXAS FAIR PLAN ASSN
4.2	3.3	99.5	36.1	0.5	0.2	88.2	17.7	105.9	98.5	3.8	0.0 ●	TEXAS FARM BUREAU CASUALTY INS
2.2	2.0	124.7	24.5	-1.8	0.7	76.5	20.2	96.7	101.0	4.7	1.3 ●	TEXAS FARM BUREAU MUTUAL INS CO
3.6	3.3	N/A	N/A	N/A	N/A	N/A	N/A	N/A	N/A	0.0	0.0	TEXAS FARM BUREAU UNDERWRITERS
2.7	1.9	169.9	102.7	2.4	3.1	68.8	32.4	101.2	96.5	6.2	0.0	TEXAS FARMERS INS CO
2.9	2.6	25.2	1.7	-0.1	0.7	138.7	36.0	174.7	53.6	7.6	0.0	TEXAS HERITAGE INS CO
5.0	3.1	38.3	53.7	-58.1	-63.1	-34.3	43.3	9.0	116.1	-5.7	0.0	TEXAS HOSPITAL INS EXCHANGE
0.9	0.7	283.2	120.6	-19.8	-18.9	53.6	17.2	70.8	197.7	N/A	0.0	TEXAS INS CO
11.6	7.6	27.4	28.0	-20.8	-30.4	32.3	4.1	36.4	145.8	6.0	0.1	TEXAS LAWYERS INS EXCHANGE
2.2	1.5	26.5	20.5	-10.7	-11.5	4.5	27.7	32.2	265.2	57.6	0.0	TEXAS MEDICAL INS CO
51.6	46.5	N/A	N/A	N/A	N/A	N/A	N/A	N/A	N/A	0.0	0.0	TEXAS PACIFIC INDEMNITY CO
3.3	2.2	68.4	24.2	-0.6	-2.3	67.0	40.4	107.4	89.9	-5.0	0.0	THAMES INS CO
1.7	1.3	95.7	143.7	-13.7	-15.5	53.1	32.3	85.4	103.2	2.5	0.0	THE INS CO
N/A	N/A	N/A	N/A	N/A	N/A	N/A	N/A	N/A	N/A	0.0	0.0	THIRD COAST INS CO
N/A	N/A	N/A	227.4	1.1	3.1	999 +	999 +	999 +	0.4	-192.4	18.5	TIG INS CO
1.7	1.7	N/A	N/A	N/A	N/A	N/A	N/A	N/A	17.0	0.0	62.7	TITAN INDEMNITY CO
46.2	25.0	N/A	N/A	N/A	N/A	N/A	N/A	N/A	7.7	0.0	0.0	TITAN INS CO
8.0	6.4	16.3	N/A	N/A	N/A	N/A	-43.0	-43.0	877.4	28.3	0.0	TITAN INS CO INC A RRG

999 + Denotes number greater than 999.9%
999 - Denotes number less than -999.99%

● Bullets denote a more detailed analysis is available in Section II.

INSURANCE COMPANY NAME	DOM. STATE	RATING	TOTAL ASSETS ($MIL)	CAPITAL & SURPLUS ($MIL)	ANNUAL NET PREMIUM ($MIL)	NET INCOME ($MIL)	CAPITAL-IZATION INDEX (PTS)	RESERVE ADQ INDEX (PTS)	PROFIT-ABILITY INDEX (PTS)	LIQUIDITY INDEX (PTS)	STAB. INDEX (PTS)	STABILITY FACTORS
TITLE INDUSTRY ASR CO RRG	VT	D+	7.2	4.8	0.6	0.2	10.0	7.0	8.9	9.0	2.1	DFGR
TM SPECIALTY INS CO	AZ	U	39.5	39.3	0.0	0.3	N/A	N/A	6.8	10.0	5.4	GT
TNUS INS CO	NY	B	62.8	56.0	0.0	0.8	10.0	4.6	6.3	10.0	4.1	DT
TOA REINS CO OF AMERICA	DE	B+	1,747.5	640.9	363.9	9.0	7.9	7.9	6.7	6.9	5.1	T
TOKIO MARINE AMERICA INS CO	NY	A	1,410.7	512.7	308.5	0.4	8.1	6.8	4.8	6.7	6.0	T
TOKIO MARINE PACIFIC INS LTD	GU	C	117.4	73.4	135.2	5.8	8.6	8.0	8.7	1.8	3.4	LT
TOKIO MARINE SPECIALTY INS CO	DE	C	563.1	207.8	141.9	9.7	9.4	7.7	8.9	6.8	3.9	T
TOKIO MILLENNIUM RE AG (US BRANCH)	NY	C+	931.4	247.8	647.4	29.6	6.8	3.6	2.0	6.9	3.3	GT
TOPA INS CO	CA	B-	175.8	80.8	65.3	2.3	8.9	7.9	3.9	6.5	3.8	RT
TOWER BONDING & SURETY CO	PR	D	3.7	2.6	1.8	-0.1	6.6	6.0	3.7	6.3	1.9	DFGT
TOWER HILL PREFERRED INS CO	FL	D	106.0	51.6	29.8	0.9	9.6	5.6	8.7	7.3	2.1	FRT
TOWER HILL PRIME INS CO	FL	D	191.9	94.6	40.8	7.0	10.0	3.3	6.1	7.6	1.6	FRT
TOWER HILL SELECT INS CO	FL	C	75.6	30.8	23.6	1.5	5.2	3.8	3.7	6.7	3.6	FRT
TOWER HILL SIGNATURE INS CO	FL	C-	120.1	53.4	42.9	2.7	5.9	3.8	5.1	6.5	3.3	T
TOYOTA MOTOR INS CO	IA	C+	505.3	241.0	91.8	11.4	10.0	5.2	8.9	7.3	4.0	RT
TRADERS INS CO	MO	D+	67.7	21.6	51.8	2.0	2.6	6.9	9.4	6.0	2.4	CDGR
TRADEWIND INS CO LTD	HI	C	12.5	8.0	0.0	0.1	10.0	N/A	6.0	10.0	2.8	DGT
TRANS CITY CASUALTY INS CO	AZ	C	18.0	12.3	3.1	0.5	10.0	9.4	7.9	9.5	2.8	DGRT
TRANS PACIFIC INS CO	NY	B	68.7	51.7	0.0	0.3	10.0	6.2	4.6	7.0	4.5	GT
TRANSAMERICA CASUALTY INS CO	OH	B-	378.1	171.5	318.0	4.1	8.4	5.3	8.5	4.9	4.5	LRT
TRANSATLANTIC REINS CO	NY	B	14,151.9	4,831.3	2,967.9	173.1	7.6	8.5	7.9	6.7	4.8	AFRT
TRANSGUARD INS CO OF AMERICA INC	IL	B	250.0	129.7	65.4	5.0	8.5	9.3	7.7	6.9	4.6	RT
TRANSIT GENERAL INS CO	IL	D	27.1	6.6	10.9	0.5	1.8	9.4	7.7	5.8	2.0	CDFG
TRANSIT MUTUAL INS CORP OF WI	WI	D-	14.9	9.7	2.4	0.4	10.0	9.6	8.7	8.1	0.6	DGT
TRANSPORT INS CO	OH	U	39.5	17.9	0.0	-0.7	N/A	1.4	2.7	7.0	2.1	FGRT
TRANSPORTATION INS CO	IL	C	80.1	76.5	0.0	1.1	10.0	N/A	6.1	10.0	3.8	ART
TRANSPORTATION INS SVCS RRG	SC	U	0.9	0.5	0.3	0.0	N/A	N/A	3.2	7.0	0.0	DFGT
TRAVCO INS CO	CT	B	229.5	73.6	56.1	2.9	8.6	8.3	6.8	6.7	4.4	T
TRAVEL AIR INS CO (KS)	KS	U	5.0	4.7	0.0	0.1	N/A	6.1	5.8	10.0	3.4	GT
TRAVELERS CASUALTY & SURETY CO	CT	A-	16,398.0	6,375.5	4,230.7	188.3	7.7	8.2	7.9	6.9	5.5	T
TRAVELERS CASUALTY & SURETY CO OF	CT	C+	4,564.3	2,398.7	1,372.9	229.9	10.0	9.6	9.4	7.0	3.0	RT
TRAVELERS CASUALTY CO	CT	C+	208.7	67.2	60.3	3.2	8.1	8.6	7.2	6.8	4.1	T
TRAVELERS CASUALTY CO OF	CT	B	327.5	98.2	97.7	5.1	7.9	8.7	6.4	6.7	4.5	T
TRAVELERS CASUALTY INS CO OF	CT	B	1,984.9	617.8	567.3	40.0	8.0	8.7	8.4	6.8	4.8	T
TRAVELERS COMMERCIAL CASUALTY CO	CT	B	337.5	103.0	97.7	5.8	8.0	8.7	7.1	6.7	4.5	T
TRAVELERS COMMERCIAL INS CO	CT	B	362.9	102.2	97.7	4.4	7.9	8.7	8.0	6.9	4.5	T
TRAVELERS CONSTITUTION STATE INS CO	CT	C+	208.2	67.0	60.3	3.1	8.1	8.6	6.9	6.7	4.1	T
TRAVELERS EXCESS & SURPLUS LINES CO	CT	B	214.8	69.1	56.1	3.0	8.4	8.5	6.9	6.9	4.4	T
TRAVELERS HOME & MARINE INS CO	CT	B	401.7	117.3	56.1	3.5	10.0	7.9	4.0	6.9	4.5	T
TRAVELERS INDEMNITY CO	CT	B+	21,495.2	6,856.9	4,840.0	354.8	7.7	8.2	6.0	6.9	5.1	LT
TRAVELERS INDEMNITY CO OF AMERICA	CT	B	631.1	200.2	160.0	9.0	8.5	8.5	6.3	6.8	4.6	T
TRAVELERS INDEMNITY CO OF CT	CT	B	1,098.3	368.9	284.7	17.8	8.6	8.3	5.7	6.8	4.7	T
TRAVELERS LLOYDS INS CO	TX	B	27.8	13.1	0.0	0.6	10.0	N/A	2.7	7.0	4.3	DGT
TRAVELERS LLOYDS OF TEXAS INS CO	TX	B	24.1	14.6	0.0	0.6	10.0	N/A	5.4	9.0	4.2	DFGT
TRAVELERS PERSONAL INS CO	CT	B	210.0	68.4	56.1	2.8	8.4	8.5	6.9	6.7	4.4	T
TRAVELERS PERSONAL SECURITY INS CO	CT	B	213.7	71.2	56.1	3.1	8.5	8.4	7.0	6.9	4.4	T
TRAVELERS PROPERTY CAS OF AMERICA	CT	B	840.3	451.4	74.8	7.3	10.0	7.5	4.2	7.6	4.7	FT
TRAVELERS PROPERTY CASUALTY INS CO	CT	B	256.6	76.0	62.3	3.0	8.4	8.5	7.4	6.8	4.4	T
TRENWICK AMERICA REINSURANCE CORP	CT	U	61.4	34.9	0.0	-0.7	N/A	9.6	5.0	10.0	3.3	T
TRI-CENTURY INS CO	PA	C	30.9	10.2	2.2	0.0	7.3	6.8	6.2	9.1	2.9	DRT
TRI-STATE CONSUMER INS CO	NY	B	98.0	37.9	28.6	-0.5	7.5	9.4	3.9	6.5	4.1	FRT
TRI-STATE INS CO OF MN	IA	C	48.7	32.5	0.0	0.3	10.0	N/A	6.3	7.0	3.8	T

See Page 27 for explanation of footnotes and
Page 28 for explanation of stability factors.
Arrows denote recent upgrades ▲ or downgrades ▼   (see Section VII for explanations)

122

www.weissratings.com

RISK ADJ. CAPITAL RATIO #1	CAPITAL RATIO #2	PREMIUM TO SURPLUS (%)	RESV. TO SURPLUS (%)	RESV. DEVELOP. 1 YEAR (%)	RESV. DEVELOP. 2 YEAR (%)	LOSS RATIO (%)	EXP. RATIO (%)	COMB RATIO (%)	CASH FROM UNDER-WRITING (%)	NET PREMIUM GROWTH (%)	INVEST. IN AFFIL (%)	INSURANCE COMPANY NAME
6.0	4.9	13.6	27.1	-3.1	-9.6	41.3	-75.6	-34.3	104.9	-7.0	0.0	TITLE INDUSTRY ASR CO RRG
N/A	N/A	N/A	N/A	N/A	N/A	N/A	N/A	N/A	742.0	0.0	0.0	TM SPECIALTY INS CO
30.1	27.1	N/A	2.1	N/A	N/A	N/A	N/A	N/A	-154.7	0.0	0.0	TNUS INS CO
2.4	1.6	54.1	120.3	-1.9	-3.0	64.1	27.2	91.3	102.1	3.5	0.0 ●	TOA REINS CO OF AMERICA
2.2	1.6	60.4	146.3	-0.7	0.7	78.0	28.4	106.4	85.7	24.4	14.0 ●	TOKIO MARINE AMERICA INS CO
4.5	2.4	201.9	35.8	-7.6	-1.4	81.1	15.7	96.8	103.0	11.0	0.0	TOKIO MARINE PACIFIC INS LTD
3.7	2.8	71.8	93.5	-0.4	-1.7	60.4	29.2	89.6	118.0	5.6	0.0 ●	TOKIO MARINE SPECIALTY INS CO
1.5	0.9	297.1	64.8	0.2	N/A	60.0	38.8	98.8	188.2	431.1	0.0 ●	TOKIO MILLENNIUM RE AG (US BRANCH)
3.4	2.4	84.7	76.6	0.4	-2.2	68.1	35.4	103.5	90.6	-6.3	7.6	TOPA INS CO
1.3	1.2	69.0	13.5	-9.8	-31.2	-14.5	102.4	87.9	85.1	-6.2	0.0	TOWER BONDING & SURETY CO
4.7	4.1	58.4	21.1	9.3	10.3	65.1	28.7	93.8	97.8	7.2	0.0	TOWER HILL PREFERRED INS CO
6.7	4.4	51.2	21.4	8.9	13.7	80.5	40.6	121.1	94.7	0.6	0.0	TOWER HILL PRIME INS CO
1.1	0.8	79.5	35.0	16.3	17.9	85.4	39.5	124.9	78.9	6.8	0.0	TOWER HILL SELECT INS CO
1.1	0.8	81.7	27.9	8.5	9.1	63.0	30.8	93.8	115.1	25.7	0.0	TOWER HILL SIGNATURE INS CO
6.8	5.5	40.1	4.3	0.6	0.2	48.8	25.5	74.3	174.2	15.1	0.0 ●	TOYOTA MOTOR INS CO
0.7	0.6	268.1	125.2	3.5	-2.7	78.8	13.3	92.1	123.8	26.8	0.0	TRADERS INS CO
5.8	5.2	N/A	N/A	N/A	N/A	N/A	N/A	N/A	N/A	0.0	6.0	TRADEWIND INS CO LTD
5.3	4.1	26.0	38.4	-7.4	-13.1	29.9	33.9	63.8	141.4	-1.9	1.9	TRANS CITY CASUALTY INS CO
16.2	8.9	N/A	17.6	-0.5	-0.6	999 +	999 +	999 +	-44.0	-172.3	0.0	TRANS PACIFIC INS CO
3.3	2.1	190.9	44.8	-1.7	-3.8	59.7	36.7	96.4	103.6	15.6	0.0	TRANSAMERICA CASUALTY INS CO
2.1	1.4	61.6	152.3	-4.2	-7.1	53.3	35.5	88.8	88.0	-0.6	8.9 ●	TRANSATLANTIC REINS CO
4.0	2.3	52.6	58.8	-4.8	-8.9	45.7	31.2	76.9	116.7	3.3	0.0	TRANSGUARD INS CO OF AMERICA INC
0.8	0.4	180.8	214.9	20.2	-16.3	79.1	10.0	89.1	112.5	-14.2	0.0	TRANSIT GENERAL INS CO
6.6	5.9	24.7	36.7	-5.3	-15.8	40.2	17.8	58.0	156.5	-3.4	0.0	TRANSIT MUTUAL INS CORP OF WI
N/A	N/A	N/A	176.3	N/A	0.2	N/A	N/A	N/A	N/A	0.0	57.4	TRANSPORT INS CO
66.2	28.2	N/A	N/A	N/A	N/A	N/A	N/A	N/A	N/A	0.0	0.0	TRANSPORTATION INS CO
N/A	N/A	78.3	35.9	N/A	N/A	91.8	30.5	122.3	N/A	0.0	0.0	TRANSPORTATION INS SVCS RRG
3.3	2.1	79.4	136.1	-2.6	-6.2	58.7	30.7	89.4	110.7	2.9	0.0	TRAVCO INS CO
N/A	N/A	N/A	0.5	0.1	0.2	N/A	N/A	N/A	N/A	0.0	0.0	TRAVEL AIR INS CO (KS)
1.6	1.3	66.4	113.8	-2.1	-4.9	58.7	30.5	89.2	108.4	2.9	26.8 ●	TRAVELERS CASUALTY & SURETY CO
5.5	3.9	65.3	48.2	-9.2	-28.8	20.9	39.7	60.6	161.5	-2.5	6.4 ●	TRAVELERS CASUALTY & SURETY CO
2.8	1.8	94.2	161.6	-3.0	-7.4	58.7	30.2	88.9	108.7	2.9	0.0	TRAVELERS CASUALTY CO
2.5	1.6	105.0	180.1	-3.4	-7.9	58.7	30.2	88.9	109.8	2.9	0.0	TRAVELERS CASUALTY CO OF
2.8	1.7	96.8	166.0	-3.2	-7.9	58.7	30.3	89.0	109.0	2.9	0.0 ●	TRAVELERS CASUALTY INS CO OF
2.6	1.7	100.5	172.4	-3.2	-7.9	58.7	30.2	88.9	110.0	2.9	0.0	TRAVELERS COMMERCIAL CASUALTY
2.6	1.6	99.9	171.3	-3.3	-8.0	58.7	30.6	89.3	110.9	2.9	0.0	TRAVELERS COMMERCIAL INS CO
2.8	1.8	94.4	162.0	-3.0	-7.3	58.7	30.2	88.9	109.0	2.9	0.0	TRAVELERS CONSTITUTION STATE INS
3.1	1.9	85.0	145.7	-2.7	-6.6	58.7	30.5	89.2	104.5	2.9	0.0	TRAVELERS EXCESS & SURPLUS LINES
5.0	3.1	49.3	84.6	-1.3	-3.3	58.7	33.1	91.8	99.3	2.9	0.0	TRAVELERS HOME & MARINE INS CO
1.7	1.4	70.7	121.4	-2.3	-5.6	58.7	29.8	88.5	107.9	2.9	21.4 ●	TRAVELERS INDEMNITY CO
3.1	2.0	83.9	143.9	-2.5	-6.3	58.7	31.0	89.7	105.9	2.9	0.0 ●	TRAVELERS INDEMNITY CO OF AMERICA
3.2	2.0	80.3	137.8	-2.4	-6.0	58.7	30.6	89.3	104.7	2.9	0.0 ●	TRAVELERS INDEMNITY CO OF CT
4.4	3.9	N/A	N/A	N/A	N/A	N/A	N/A	N/A	13.6	0.0	0.0	TRAVELERS LLOYDS INS CO
6.1	5.5	N/A	N/A	N/A	N/A	N/A	N/A	N/A	879.3	0.0	0.0	TRAVELERS LLOYDS OF TEXAS INS CO
3.0	1.9	85.6	146.8	-2.8	-6.7	58.7	30.3	89.0	108.5	2.9	0.0	TRAVELERS PERSONAL INS CO
3.2	2.0	82.3	141.2	-2.7	-6.4	58.7	29.9	88.6	109.3	2.9	0.0	TRAVELERS PERSONAL SECURITY INS
14.2	9.0	16.9	28.9	-0.5	-1.2	58.7	35.2	93.9	51.5	2.9	0.0 ●	TRAVELERS PROPERTY CAS OF
3.0	1.9	85.4	146.4	-2.8	-6.8	58.7	30.6	89.3	111.2	2.9	0.0	TRAVELERS PROPERTY CASUALTY INS
N/A	N/A	-0.1	63.4	-4.8	-40.5	999 +	999 +	999 +	-2.4	99.4	0.0	TRENWICK AMERICA REINSURANCE
1.5	1.3	21.5	86.5	-3.8	-2.9	89.1	-52.7	36.4	117.9	-0.8	0.0	TRI-CENTURY INS CO
1.7	1.2	72.5	104.8	-12.5	-17.9	52.6	38.3	90.9	93.9	-5.6	0.0	TRI-STATE CONSUMER INS CO
10.4	9.4	N/A	N/A	N/A	N/A	N/A	N/A	N/A	118.2	0.0	0.0	TRI-STATE INS CO OF MN

999 + Denotes number greater than 999.9%
999 - Denotes number less than -999.99%
● Bullets denote a more detailed analysis is available in Section II.

INSURANCE COMPANY NAME	DOM. STATE	RATING	TOTAL ASSETS ($MIL)	CAPITAL & SURPLUS ($MIL)	ANNUAL NET PREMIUM ($MIL)	NET INCOME ($MIL)	CAPITAL-IZATION INDEX (PTS)	RESERVE ADQ INDEX (PTS)	PROFIT-ABILITY INDEX (PTS)	LIQUIDITY INDEX (PTS)	STAB. INDEX (PTS)	STABILITY FACTORS
TRIAD GUARANTY ASR CORP	IL	F (5)	0.0	0.0	2.5	0.0	6.1	7.1	2.5	6.9	0.0	DFGT
TRIAD GUARANTY INS CORP	IL	F (5)	0.0	0.0	156.7	0.0	3.0	3.5	0.9	6.5	0.0	FT
TRIANGLE INS CO	OK	C+	90.9	28.5	36.6	0.5	6.4	9.2	8.8	6.7	3.3	RT
TRINITY RISK SOLUTIONS RECIP INS RRG	DC	E	8.4	4.0	0.6	0.0	4.0	4.8	1.9	6.5	0.0	DFGR
TRINITY UNIVERSAL INS CO	TX	B	1,921.2	772.8	1,210.9	18.5	7.9	9.1	3.8	2.8	4.7	AFLR
TRIPLE S PROPIEDAD INC	PR	B-	288.8	142.7	85.7	5.9	8.1	6.0	7.1	6.5	4.0	RT
TRITON INS CO	TX	B-	418.3	136.4	117.8	8.4	10.0	7.5	3.4	7.2	4.2	RT
TRIUMPHE CASUALTY CO	OH	C	61.9	19.7	8.4	0.4	10.0	5.8	8.4	9.1	3.4	DFGR
TRUCK INS EXCHANGE	CA	C+	2,206.8	606.2	1,157.1	-23.9	5.4	5.9	3.6	2.9	4.8	LRT
TRUMBULL INS CO	CT	B	230.3	103.5	52.7	6.7	10.0	5.9	7.1	7.1	4.5	AT
TRUSTGARD INS CO	OH	B-	116.2	67.4	42.8	3.3	10.0	6.2	8.7	6.7	3.7	T
TRUSTSTAR INS CO	MD	U (2)	0.6	0.6	0.0	-0.2	N/A	4.5	1.3	10.0	2.4	FT
TUDOR INS CO	NH	C	262.5	182.1	12.1	1.7	10.0	9.3	8.4	8.3	4.0	RT
TUSCARORA WAYNE INS CO	PA	B-	100.0	59.8	38.4	1.6	9.6	8.0	8.6	6.9	3.6	RT
TWIN CITY FIRE INS CO	IN	B	690.2	297.8	158.1	10.9	10.0	5.9	5.6	6.9	4.6	AT
TWIN LIGHTS INS CO	NJ	D (2)	8.5	8.1	0.0	0.1	10.0	N/A	6.3	7.0	2.2	DT
TYPTAP INS CO	FL	U	25.5	24.9	0.0	-0.1	N/A	0.0	3.8	0.0	0.0	LT
UFB CASUALTY INS CO	IN	B	8.7	8.7	0.0	0.1	10.0	N/A	6.5	7.4	4.8	DGT
UFG SPECIALTY INS CO	IA	U	42.9	17.1	12.6	0.4	N/A	8.6	5.1	9.2	5.3	DGRT
UMIA INS INC	OR	B	245.6	102.1	41.6	4.3	8.7	9.5	7.6	7.1	4.2	RT
UMIALIK INS CO	AK	B-	59.9	24.3	22.7	1.0	9.0	8.2	8.7	6.7	3.8	DRT
UNDERWRITERS AT LLOYDS	KY	D	185.9	33.4	42.2	1.8	1.7	5.8	5.9	8.3	1.9	CT
UNDERWRITERS AT LLOYDS (IL)	IL	D	322.9	173.5	67.5	24.5	8.2	6.9	3.3	7.9	2.3	FRT
UNDERWRITERS AT LLOYDS (VI)	VI	U	73.3	25.0	57.0	8.0	N/A	0.0	4.9	0.0	0.0	CLT
UNIGARD INDEMNITY CO	WI	C	10.6	7.4	16.3	0.0	6.2	3.9	2.1	7.2	3.0	DFRT
UNIGARD INS CO	WI	C	494.9	123.6	126.6	-1.6	7.8	4.0	2.8	6.5	4.0	FRT
UNION INS CO	IA	C	133.0	35.1	0.0	0.4	10.0	N/A	6.4	9.0	3.7	T
UNION INS CO OF PROVIDENCE	IA	C	88.6	62.2	37.9	4.8	10.0	7.7	7.4	7.2	4.0	T
UNION MUTUAL FIRE INS CO	VT	B-	202.3	81.3	95.8	2.4	7.5	8.5	5.5	6.0	3.9	FT
UNION MUTUAL INS CO	OK	F	3.6	0.1	3.0	-0.1	0.1	3.9	0.2	7.3	0.0	CDFG
UNION NATIONAL FIRE INS CO	LA	B	10.1	6.8	0.0	0.1	10.0	N/A	7.2	7.0	4.1	DGRT
UNION STANDARD LLOYDS	TX	C	2.7	0.9	0.0	0.0	7.6	N/A	6.7	7.0	2.8	DGT
UNIQUE INS CO	IL	D	96.3	18.1	42.6	1.1	1.2	1.9	6.0	5.6	1.5	CDT
UNITED AMERICAS INS CO	NY	U	5.8	5.4	0.0	0.0	N/A	3.7	2.3	9.2	3.4	CFGR
▼UNITED AUTOMOBILE INS CO	FL	E	339.0	42.3	182.8	-25.4	4.0	0.4	1.5	5.4	0.1	FRT
UNITED BUS INS CO	GA	D-	10.3	2.2	5.3	-0.2	1.9	1.8	2.9	6.6	1.3	DGRT
UNITED CASUALTY & SURETY CO INC	MA	D+	8.2	5.0	2.7	0.2	8.7	7.7	8.2	9.2	2.1	DGRT
UNITED CASUALTY INS CO OF AMERICA	IL	B	11.7	8.7	0.0	0.1	10.0	N/A	6.2	10.0	4.1	DGRT
UNITED CENTRAL PA RRG	VT	E	20.8	10.0	4.1	0.4	5.0	4.4	5.4	6.9	0.0	DFGT
UNITED EDUCATORS INS A RECIP RRG	VT	B-	866.1	309.0	144.6	15.1	7.5	9.3	8.6	7.4	3.8	RT
UNITED EQUITABLE INS CO	IL	D+	22.3	4.5	15.0	-0.3	3.7	7.0	3.7	6.5	2.1	DGT
UNITED FARM FAMILY INS CO	NY	B	42.7	12.7	8.3	0.2	9.7	8.7	6.7	7.0	4.6	DFGT
UNITED FARM FAMILY MUTUAL INS CO	IN	B	1,037.9	424.8	536.4	8.1	8.6	8.1	4.8	5.7	4.5	T
UNITED FINANCIAL CASUALTY CO	OH	B-	2,805.0	614.3	1,742.6	48.5	7.6	6.6	9.5	5.3	4.5	T
UNITED FIRE & CAS CO	IA	B	1,863.5	736.0	564.5	10.6	7.1	8.7	7.7	6.8	4.7	RT
UNITED FIRE & INDEMNITY CO	TX	C+	52.5	19.3	17.8	0.2	7.4	9.0	7.3	7.1	3.4	DT
UNITED FIRE LLOYDS	TX	C+	30.6	8.6	8.9	0.1	7.1	9.3	5.5	7.2	3.1	DGT
UNITED FRONTIER MUTUAL INS CO	NY	C	15.9	10.6	4.1	0.3	8.9	8.0	7.3	6.8	2.3	DGRT
UNITED GROUP CAPTIVE INS CO	GA	D (1)	1.3	0.6	0.6	0.0	6.4	6.6	1.7	8.0	0.9	DFGT
UNITED GUAR RESIDENTIAL INS CO OF NC	NC	C+	407.8	386.8	38.3	88.9	7.5	5.8	5.7	7.1	4.5	T
UNITED GUARANTY COML INS CO OF NC	NC	U	69.0	57.6	0.0	1.7	N/A	5.1	4.8	7.0	6.0	T
UNITED GUARANTY CREDIT INS CO	NC	B-	25.3	22.5	0.2	-0.5	10.0	6.6	5.0	10.0	3.8	DGT

See Page 27 for explanation of footnotes and Page 28 for explanation of stability factors.

124

www.weissratings.com

Arrows denote recent upgrades ▲ or downgrades ▼ (see Section VII for explanations)

RISK ADJ. CAPITAL RATIO #1	RATIO #2	PREMIUM TO SURPLUS (%)	RESV. TO SURPLUS (%)	RESV. DEVELOP. 1 YEAR (%)	2 YEAR (%)	LOSS RATIO (%)	EXP. RATIO (%)	COMB RATIO (%)	CASH FROM UNDER-WRITING (%)	NET PREMIUM GROWTH (%)	INVEST. IN AFFIL (%)	INSURANCE COMPANY NAME
1.6	1.3	29.6	92.6	-5.4	-76.8	122.9	39.9	162.8	47.9	-19.1	0.0	TRIAD GUARANTY ASR CORP
0.9	0.7	66.9	208.6	72.1	117.6	223.0	11.0	234.0	51.4	-20.7	1.1	TRIAD GUARANTY INS CORP
1.3	0.9	133.9	94.3	-10.3	-13.9	61.3	28.6	89.9	131.8	12.9	0.0	TRIANGLE INS CO
0.6	0.5	14.9	81.6	6.9	5.7	270.9	79.9	350.8	75.5	-74.9	0.0	TRINITY RISK SOLUTIONS RECIP INS
2.0	1.5	148.1	74.9	-3.0	-8.9	68.3	31.4	99.7	94.2	-5.4	15.6 ●	TRINITY UNIVERSAL INS CO
2.7	1.8	63.6	54.3	-2.0	-1.1	53.1	44.3	97.4	106.4	-3.8	0.0	TRIPLE S PROPIEDAD INC
6.8	3.9	65.2	14.9	-1.9	-1.5	39.7	33.5	73.2	123.8	2.4	0.0	TRITON INS CO
3.3	2.9	44.2	60.4	2.3	5.4	75.2	24.9	100.1	-9.0	1.4	0.0	TRIUMPHE CASUALTY CO
0.8	0.7	185.4	113.6	2.8	3.9	69.0	33.6	102.6	102.9	6.2	42.6 ●	TRUCK INS EXCHANGE
5.6	3.7	54.4	94.0	0.7	1.5	66.1	11.2	77.3	108.2	2.9	0.0	TRUMBULL INS CO
7.0	4.5	66.8	36.8	1.2	1.4	69.1	21.3	90.4	107.7	0.5	0.0	TRUSTGARD INS CO
N/A	N/A	-1.3	N/A	N/A	N/A	115.4	999 +	999 +	-3.4	-102.5	0.0	TRUSTSTAR INS CO
15.2	10.0	6.7	27.9	-0.7	-20.7	72.3	40.9	113.2	67.0	-59.8	0.0	TUDOR INS CO
3.7	2.7	66.7	24.1	-3.4	-4.6	54.3	38.3	92.6	108.0	6.7	9.5	TUSCARORA WAYNE INS CO
5.4	3.6	55.1	95.3	0.7	1.4	66.1	25.6	91.7	108.2	2.9	0.0 ●	TWIN CITY FIRE INS CO
17.8	10.1	N/A	N/A	N/A	N/A	N/A	N/A	N/A	N/A	0.0	0.0	TWIN LIGHTS INS CO
N/A	N/A	N/A	N/A	N/A	N/A	N/A	N/A	N/A	N/A	0.0	0.0	TYPTAP INS CO
97.6	48.8	N/A	N/A	N/A	N/A	N/A	N/A	N/A	N/A	0.0	0.0	UFB CASUALTY INS CO
N/A	N/A	75.4	81.6	-1.4	-6.9	61.1	22.8	83.9	-552.2	0.0	0.0	UFG SPECIALTY INS CO
3.2	2.2	35.6	95.3	-20.9	-16.9	35.8	18.3	54.1	93.3	-35.9	0.0	UMIA INS INC
3.3	2.4	97.8	70.9	-5.3	-5.2	65.2	25.2	90.4	109.5	19.5	0.0	UMIALIK INS CO
0.7	0.4	126.6	433.2	-1.7	11.5	53.7	25.2	78.9	129.1	-35.9	0.0	UNDERWRITERS AT LLOYDS
2.8	2.0	42.8	87.8	-11.3	-3.7	20.1	30.0	50.1	84.9	2.5	0.0	UNDERWRITERS AT LLOYDS (IL)
N/A	N/A	228.2	122.6	70.8	22.1	32.5	30.8	63.3	174.4	0.0	0.0	UNDERWRITERS AT LLOYDS (VI)
3.4	2.5	138.5	148.6	1.5	2.8	63.9	35.8	99.7	89.9	-9.3	0.0	UNIGARD INDEMNITY CO
2.1	1.4	110.5	115.5	1.3	2.5	63.9	34.9	98.8	96.1	-0.7	5.9	UNIGARD INS CO
3.9	3.5	N/A	N/A	N/A	N/A	N/A	N/A	N/A	89.6	0.0	0.0	UNION INS CO
14.9	13.0	65.3	66.9	-1.8	-1.5	65.5	31.4	96.9	112.6	4.8	0.0	UNION INS CO OF PROVIDENCE
1.7	1.4	122.7	47.9	-7.9	-7.5	63.5	33.1	96.6	94.6	-2.3	27.4	UNION MUTUAL FIRE INS CO
0.1	0.0	999 +	282.4	-26.9	6.6	65.0	37.0	102.0	51.5	0.0	0.0	UNION MUTUAL INS CO
6.2	5.6	N/A	N/A	N/A	N/A	N/A	N/A	N/A	19.9	0.0	0.0	UNION NATIONAL FIRE INS CO
1.2	1.1	N/A	N/A	N/A	N/A	N/A	N/A	N/A	108.0	0.0	0.0	UNION STANDARD LLOYDS
0.4	0.3	265.1	214.4	27.7	48.7	68.4	31.0	99.4	117.2	-16.4	10.2	UNIQUE INS CO
N/A	N/A	N/A	198.8	-15.7	-22.9	999 +	999 +	999 +	N/A	-133.3	0.0	UNITED AMERICAS INS CO
0.3	0.3	265.9	189.5	36.8	65.5	90.9	15.8	106.7	77.4	-15.2	1.5	UNITED AUTOMOBILE INS CO
0.5	0.3	241.3	99.8	-44.7	38.6	42.4	31.2	73.6	124.2	13.4	0.0	UNITED BUS INS CO
2.6	2.3	54.4	2.2	-2.0	-2.0	0.3	75.9	76.2	133.5	9.8	0.0	UNITED CASUALTY & SURETY CO INC
8.6	7.7	N/A	N/A	N/A	N/A	N/A	N/A	N/A	-47.1	0.0	0.0	UNITED CASUALTY INS CO OF AMERICA
1.0	0.7	44.9	86.2	-5.1	-18.1	75.4	9.6	85.0	83.3	-2.3	0.0	UNITED CENTRAL PA RRG
1.7	1.3	50.8	159.4	N/A	-10.1	78.2	20.8	99.0	152.2	4.0	0.0 ●	UNITED EDUCATORS INS A RECIP RRG
0.6	0.5	306.2	250.4	-12.8	-13.3	56.4	41.6	98.0	111.5	6.4	0.0	UNITED EQUITABLE INS CO
2.8	2.5	66.7	77.9	-4.2	-4.6	71.0	30.3	101.3	83.5	3.8	0.0	UNITED FARM FAMILY INS CO
3.4	2.2	129.4	60.7	-3.6	-2.4	65.9	25.7	91.6	109.1	5.2	3.4 ●	UNITED FARM FAMILY MUTUAL INS CO
2.0	1.4	314.1	189.6	-5.1	-5.4	70.0	19.1	89.1	123.4	7.6	0.0 ●	UNITED FINANCIAL CASUALTY CO
1.3	1.1	78.1	83.3	-1.9	-5.5	61.2	33.0	94.2	112.6	7.9	37.2 ●	UNITED FIRE & CAS CO
2.2	1.3	93.4	98.9	-2.4	-7.8	61.2	31.7	92.9	126.1	10.3	0.0	UNITED FIRE & INDEMNITY CO
1.9	1.2	104.9	111.1	-2.7	-14.1	61.2	31.7	92.9	182.4	10.3	0.0	UNITED FIRE LLOYDS
3.7	2.3	39.8	22.6	-2.2	-4.2	59.2	36.0	95.2	108.2	18.9	0.0	UNITED FRONTIER MUTUAL INS CO
1.2	0.9	114.9	119.8	21.3	3.5	100.8	25.1	125.9	82.5	-2.4	0.0	UNITED GROUP CAPTIVE INS CO
1.3	1.3	8.5	4.2	-4.8	-13.4	-21.2	9.8	-11.4	999 +	-49.4	68.3 ●	UNITED GUAR RESIDENTIAL INS CO OF
N/A	N/A	N/A	14.1	-16.6	-57.8	-154.3	N/A	N/A	N/A	0.0	0.0	UNITED GUARANTY COML INS CO OF NC
13.2	9.4	1.0	6.8	-2.9	-3.9	-33.6	24.5	-9.1	986.2	-1.6	0.0	UNITED GUARANTY CREDIT INS CO

999 + Denotes number greater than 999.9%
999 - Denotes number less than -999.99%
● Bullets denote a more detailed analysis is available in Section II.

INSURANCE COMPANY NAME	DOM. STATE	RATING	TOTAL ASSETS ($MIL)	CAPITAL & SURPLUS ($MIL)	ANNUAL NET PREMIUM ($MIL)	NET INCOME ($MIL)	CAPITAL-IZATION INDEX (PTS)	RESERVE ADQ INDEX (PTS)	PROFIT-ABILITY INDEX (PTS)	LIQUIDITY INDEX (PTS)	STAB. INDEX (PTS)	STABILITY FACTORS
UNITED GUARANTY INS CO	NC	C+	124.0	51.1	9.7	5.7	7.9	4.1	3.3	7.0	4.0	DFT
UNITED GUARANTY MORTGAGE INDEM CO	NC	C+	431.1	290.9	29.4	11.4	8.6	3.9	4.7	6.9	4.6	FGRT
UNITED GUARANTY MORTGAGE INS CO	NC	C+	122.4	49.6	9.7	5.7	7.9	4.1	3.2	6.9	3.9	DFT
UNITED GUARANTY MTG INS CO OF NC	NC	C+	124.8	51.9	9.7	5.7	7.9	4.1	3.3	6.9	4.0	DFT
UNITED GUARANTY RESIDENTIAL INS CO	NC	C	3,161.8	1,060.6	564.8	141.6	8.5	3.8	6.1	6.6	4.3	RT
UNITED HERITAGE PROP & CAS CO	ID	D+	40.8	16.5	26.8	0.8	7.4	6.9	6.1	5.1	1.4	DFT
UNITED HOME INS CO	AR	D	34.0	12.2	28.5	1.2	2.0	4.6	4.4	2.9	2.2	CDGL
UNITED HOME INS CO A RRG	VT	U	1.5	1.1	0.0	0.0	N/A	N/A	3.2	7.0	0.0	FGT
UNITED INS CO	UT	C-	35.9	10.4	28.2	0.6	3.6	7.0	8.5	1.0	2.3	CDGL
UNITED INTERNATIONAL INS CO	NY	U	4.8	4.7	0.0	0.0	N/A	5.0	3.9	7.0	4.5	GT
UNITED NATIONAL INS CO	PA	C	461.8	171.6	80.5	-1.5	7.3	6.1	3.0	8.0	4.1	GRT
UNITED NATIONAL SPECIALTY INS CO	WI	C+	55.6	20.2	20.9	-0.6	5.8	6.1	3.7	8.1	3.4	DGRT
UNITED OHIO INS CO	OH	B-	308.6	154.8	128.9	6.3	10.0	8.9	8.2	6.7	4.1	T
UNITED P&C INS CO	FL	C+	575.3	130.5	369.9	-9.3	4.4	4.7	4.9	5.9	4.0	CGT
UNITED SECURITY HEALTH & CASUALTY	IL	U	2.8	1.7	0.4	-0.3	N/A	N/A	0.8	7.7	2.0	DFGT
UNITED SERVICES AUTOMOBILE ASN	TX	B+	32,870.8	24,702.0	6,812.7	-211.1	7.6	7.4	5.0	6.8	5.2	T
UNITED SPECIALTY INS CO	DE	B	143.7	82.5	43.7	2.4	10.0	6.1	8.5	7.0	4.1	T
UNITED STATES FIDELITY & GUARANTY CO	CT	C	3,700.2	1,473.5	916.4	62.5	9.5	7.7	2.4	7.0	3.6	T
UNITED STATES SURETY CO	MD	C+	67.6	45.2	22.7	2.4	9.0	9.3	8.6	7.0	3.1	DRT
UNITED SURETY & INDEMNITY CO	PR	B	99.4	56.7	25.9	5.3	7.1	8.8	3.7	6.8	4.2	RT
UNITED WISCONSIN INS CO	WI	C+	395.1	110.8	100.9	6.4	7.6	3.6	6.2	6.4	4.4	GRT
UNITRIN ADVANTAGE INS CO	NY	D	3.3	2.6	0.0	0.0	10.0	N/A	7.8	10.0	2.3	DGRT
UNITRIN AUTO & HOME INS CO	NY	D+	81.8	36.9	0.0	0.8	10.0	3.6	8.4	7.0	2.5	RT
UNITRIN COUNTY MUTUAL INS CO	TX	B	31.8	4.5	0.0	0.0	6.3	N/A	5.7	10.0	4.1	CDGR
UNITRIN DIRECT INS CO	IL	B	12.5	8.4	0.0	0.1	10.0	N/A	5.4	7.0	4.1	DGRT
UNITRIN DIRECT PROPERTY & CAS CO	IL	B	15.1	10.2	0.0	0.2	10.0	N/A	6.9	7.0	4.1	DGRT
UNITRIN PREFERRED INS CO	NY	D+	24.0	10.4	0.0	0.2	10.0	N/A	7.9	7.0	2.4	DGRT
UNITRIN SAFEGUARD INS CO	WI	B	27.0	7.4	0.0	0.1	8.4	N/A	7.8	7.0	4.1	DGRT
UNIVERSAL FIRE & CASUALTY INS CO	IN	C-	15.3	7.2	2.6	0.4	8.6	N/A	6.5	8.2	2.2	DGT
UNIVERSAL INS CO	NC	D	34.5	9.8	20.6	-0.4	7.2	3.7	2.9	2.9	2.3	DFGL
UNIVERSAL INS CO (PR)	PR	B-	851.6	257.5	194.4	7.5	7.7	6.2	6.1	6.7	4.2	RT
UNIVERSAL INS CO OF NORTH AMERICA	FL	C+	118.9	34.1	52.8	-4.6	7.6	4.7	2.7	6.1	3.8	FOT
UNIVERSAL INS EXCHANGE	TX	F (5)	0.0	0.0	6.1	0.0	4.7	4.6	5.5	7.7	3.1	DRT
UNIVERSAL NORTH AMERICA INS CO	TX	C	200.3	75.5	114.1	1.7	3.5	6.0	5.6	2.3	3.8	CLRT
UNIVERSAL P&C INS CO	FL	D	967.3	294.2	623.0	34.5	5.2	5.8	4.3	6.8	1.8	GRT
UNIVERSAL SURETY CO	NE	C	184.9	136.0	3.0	2.1	8.1	7.4	8.2	9.9	2.6	DRT
UNIVERSAL SURETY OF AMERICA	SD	C	14.6	14.5	0.0	0.1	10.0	3.9	5.6	10.0	3.2	DGRT
UNIVERSAL UNDERWRITERS INS CO	IL	C+	404.7	345.6	0.0	2.7	10.0	N/A	6.0	10.0	4.5	RT
UNIVERSAL UNDERWRITERS OF TX	IL	C+	12.0	9.4	0.0	0.1	10.0	N/A	4.6	6.7	3.2	DFGR
UPLAND MUTUAL INS INC	KS	C	27.7	12.7	16.3	0.5	7.8	6.3	5.1	5.6	2.5	DGRT
UPMC HEALTH BENEFITS INC	PA	D+	151.5	65.9	91.2	1.8	2.0	5.0	4.6	5.8	2.6	CGT
UPMC WORK ALLIANCE INC	PA	D	4.9	1.7	2.3	0.1	1.7	3.8	2.8	7.4	2.1	CDGT
UPPER HUDSON NATIONAL INS CO	NY	D-	2.8	1.8	0.0	0.0	8.3	1.6	0.7	10.0	1.3	DFGT
URGENT CARE ASR CO RRG INC	NV	D	5.1	1.6	1.6	0.2	2.4	2.6	3.3	9.0	1.3	CDGR
URGENT MD RRG INC	VT	U	7.6	2.6	0.0	0.1	N/A	0.0	4.9	0.0	0.0	LT
US COASTAL INS CO	NY	D	27.4	9.2	12.0	2.1	1.6	3.6	2.1	6.9	2.1	DGT
US COASTAL P&C INS CO	FL	U	26.9	23.6	0.0	-1.3	N/A	0.0	2.6	0.0	0.0	LT
US FIRE INS CO	DE	C	3,914.8	1,202.5	1,262.9	85.3	7.1	5.6	5.2	7.0	3.7	ART
US INS CO OF AMERICA	IL	D	6.1	2.5	1.0	0.2	2.2	7.0	5.9	6.8	1.9	DGRT
US LEGAL SERVICES INC	TN	D	2.9	2.4	2.5	0.3	5.4	4.7	8.5	7.5	1.8	DGT
US LIABILITY INS CO	PA	C	886.0	539.2	187.2	5.4	7.3	8.8	7.7	7.6	4.3	RT
US LLOYDS INS CO	TX	C-	27.2	7.2	19.5	-2.3	7.2	6.5	2.9	6.8	2.3	DGRT

See Page 27 for explanation of footnotes and
Page 28 for explanation of stability factors.
Arrows denote recent upgrades ▲ or downgrades ▼   (see Section VII for explanations)

126

www.weissratings.com

RISK ADJ. RATIO #1	CAPITAL RATIO #2	PREMIUM TO SURPLUS (%)	RESV. TO SURPLUS (%)	RESV. DEVELOP. 1 YEAR (%)	RESV. DEVELOP. 2 YEAR (%)	LOSS RATIO (%)	EXP. RATIO (%)	COMB RATIO (%)	CASH FROM UNDER- WRITING (%)	NET PREMIUM GROWTH (%)	INVEST. IN AFFIL (%)	INSURANCE COMPANY NAME
3.7	2.8	19.4	59.3	-4.7	-5.2	24.4	36.7	61.1	55.2	-71.4	0.0	UNITED GUARANTY INS CO
6.8	5.1	10.3	36.7	-12.7	-25.1	47.6	22.4	70.0	70.6	-22.1	0.0 •	UNITED GUARANTY MORTGAGE INDEM
3.6	2.7	19.9	61.0	-4.8	-5.3	24.4	36.7	61.1	55.2	-71.4	0.0	UNITED GUARANTY MORTGAGE INS CO
3.8	2.8	19.1	58.4	-4.6	-5.1	24.4	36.7	61.1	55.2	-71.4	0.0	UNITED GUARANTY MTG INS CO OF NC
2.2	1.7	41.8	36.4	-0.4	-0.9	20.7	27.7	48.4	159.9	-28.6	7.6 •	UNITED GUARANTY RESIDENTIAL INS
1.8	1.4	169.3	47.7	4.7	5.8	81.9	29.9	111.8	90.3	3.2	0.0	UNITED HERITAGE PROP & CAS CO
0.6	0.5	256.5	65.9	0.2	6.4	70.2	22.0	92.2	109.8	-0.6	0.0	UNITED HOME INS CO
N/A	N/A	N/A	N/A	N/A	N/A	N/A	N/A	N/A	N/A	0.0	0.0	UNITED HOME INS CO A RRG
0.5	0.5	290.8	136.4	-12.2	-7.7	76.9	20.5	97.4	115.8	40.2	0.0	UNITED INS CO
N/A	N/A	N/A	1.6	1.6	1.6	N/A	N/A	N/A	N/A	0.0	0.0	UNITED INTERNATIONAL INS CO
1.4	1.1	46.5	50.0	-2.8	0.2	60.5	24.8	85.3	103.8	100.0	24.1	UNITED NATIONAL INS CO
1.2	0.8	104.7	101.1	-6.7	0.7	60.5	21.8	82.3	534.6	315.3	0.0	UNITED NATIONAL SPECIALTY INS CO
7.1	5.0	86.9	42.5	-3.1	-5.9	61.6	33.1	94.7	112.6	3.1	0.0	UNITED OHIO INS CO
0.9	0.7	273.4	54.2	0.9	-1.9	56.2	35.9	92.1	130.1	37.6	0.0	UNITED P&C INS CO
N/A	N/A	18.2	44.3	N/A	N/A	104.6	195.3	299.9	27.1	0.0	0.0	UNITED SECURITY HEALTH & CASUALTY
1.4	1.4	28.0	13.4	-0.1	-0.4	79.3	13.0	92.3	114.1	2.6	58.1 •	UNITED SERVICES AUTOMOBILE ASN
8.0	5.2	54.7	5.6	0.8	0.7	49.1	37.7	86.8	132.0	7.7	0.0	UNITED SPECIALTY INS CO
4.1	2.7	65.0	111.6	-1.2	-2.8	58.7	30.2	88.9	112.4	2.9	3.3 •	UNITED STATES FIDELITY & GUARANTY
3.4	2.7	53.5	15.5	-8.4	-18.8	11.8	54.0	65.8	157.8	3.9	0.0	UNITED STATES SURETY CO
1.7	1.1	47.8	20.1	-7.9	-8.2	-10.1	60.2	50.1	151.6	5.7	0.0	UNITED SURETY & INDEMNITY CO
1.7	1.3	97.3	108.7	-0.9	10.6	61.2	19.9	81.1	138.4	13.2	0.0	UNITED WISCONSIN INS CO
8.0	7.2	N/A	N/A	N/A	N/A	N/A	N/A	N/A	N/A	0.0	0.0	UNITRIN ADVANTAGE INS CO
5.9	5.3	N/A	N/A	N/A	N/A	N/A	N/A	N/A	-32.4	0.0	0.0	UNITRIN AUTO & HOME INS CO
1.0	0.9	N/A	N/A	N/A	N/A	N/A	N/A	N/A	-144.7	0.0	0.0	UNITRIN COUNTY MUTUAL INS CO
6.5	5.8	N/A	N/A	N/A	N/A	N/A	N/A	N/A	-14.3	0.0	0.0	UNITRIN DIRECT INS CO
6.8	6.1	N/A	N/A	N/A	N/A	N/A	N/A	N/A	119.0	0.0	0.0	UNITRIN DIRECT PROPERTY & CAS CO
3.6	3.3	N/A	N/A	N/A	N/A	N/A	N/A	N/A	-8.4	0.0	0.0	UNITRIN PREFERRED INS CO
2.1	1.9	N/A	N/A	N/A	N/A	N/A	N/A	N/A	2.5	0.0	0.0	UNITRIN SAFEGUARD INS CO
2.3	1.9	37.7	N/A	N/A	N/A	N/A	95.0	95.0	104.0	-1.5	0.0	UNIVERSAL FIRE & CASUALTY INS CO
1.9	1.1	200.1	70.5	-2.8	7.6	91.0	16.7	107.7	80.5	66.8	0.0	UNIVERSAL INS CO
1.9	1.4	74.8	23.6	-0.1	0.1	64.9	33.1	98.0	98.0	-1.0	16.6 •	UNIVERSAL INS CO (PR)
1.5	1.3	142.6	73.9	-12.1	-26.9	76.6	31.0	107.6	87.8	24.1	0.0	UNIVERSAL INS CO OF NORTH AMERICA
1.3	0.9	177.4	116.2	-13.0	26.8	55.0	37.7	92.7	111.4	9.9	0.3	UNIVERSAL INS EXCHANGE
0.8	0.5	154.7	37.6	-1.4	-1.9	67.3	29.7	97.0	103.0	9.1	0.0	UNIVERSAL NORTH AMERICA INS CO
1.3	1.2	242.4	32.9	0.1	-4.5	40.9	33.7	74.6	154.1	61.7	0.0 •	UNIVERSAL P&C INS CO
3.1	1.8	2.2	4.7	-0.7	-1.0	-16.6	58.9	42.3	142.5	-14.1	0.0	UNIVERSAL SURETY CO
84.3	40.5	N/A	N/A	N/A	N/A	N/A	N/A	N/A	N/A	0.0	0.0	UNIVERSAL SURETY OF AMERICA
10.1	9.2	N/A	N/A	N/A	N/A	N/A	N/A	N/A	-360.0	0.0	10.6 •	UNIVERSAL UNDERWRITERS INS CO
10.8	9.7	N/A	N/A	N/A	N/A	N/A	N/A	N/A	24.4	0.0	0.0	UNIVERSAL UNDERWRITERS OF TX
2.1	1.7	134.6	17.6	-4.0	-4.5	59.2	28.9	88.1	109.6	1.8	0.0	UPLAND MUTUAL INS INC
0.8	0.5	142.3	72.6	-21.0	-84.3	76.9	19.1	96.0	119.5	2.9	0.0	UPMC HEALTH BENEFITS INC
0.5	0.3	137.7	137.7	49.0	-3.9	108.9	23.7	132.6	169.9	57.8	0.0	UPMC WORK ALLIANCE INC
1.9	1.8	0.4	-10.0	63.2	74.2	-313.9	999 +	999 +	9.1	-98.1	0.0	UPPER HUDSON NATIONAL INS CO
0.5	0.4	115.4	127.3	-9.3	42.4	39.6	30.6	70.2	175.6	85.2	0.0	URGENT CARE ASR CO RRG INC
N/A	N/A	N/A	N/A	N/A	N/A	N/A	N/A	N/A	N/A	0.0	0.0	URGENT MD RRG INC
0.7	0.5	219.9	65.7	3.2	N/A	72.0	29.0	101.0	222.5	197.2	0.0	US COASTAL INS CO
N/A	N/A	N/A	N/A	N/A	N/A	N/A	N/A	N/A	N/A	0.0	0.0	US COASTAL P&C INS CO
1.4	1.1	107.2	156.6	-0.8	-1.3	64.1	35.0	99.1	113.8	23.2	19.2 •	US FIRE INS CO
1.1	0.6	44.8	120.0	-30.2	-29.5	57.9	46.8	104.7	137.4	-6.6	0.0	US INS CO OF AMERICA
1.0	0.8	116.8	9.2	N/A	-0.3	14.6	64.7	79.3	141.8	77.2	0.0	US LEGAL SERVICES INC
1.2	1.1	33.5	33.4	-6.4	-6.6	37.7	42.8	80.5	131.7	10.3	48.3 •	US LIABILITY INS CO
1.1	0.9	207.9	55.2	6.1	9.4	62.1	35.7	97.8	103.1	-4.4	0.0	US LLOYDS INS CO

999 + Denotes number greater than 999.9%
999 - Denotes number less than -999.99%
• Bullets denote a more detailed analysis is available in Section II.

INSURANCE COMPANY NAME	DOM. STATE	RATING	TOTAL ASSETS ($MIL)	CAPITAL & SURPLUS ($MIL)	ANNUAL NET PREMIUM ($MIL)	NET INCOME ($MIL)	CAPITAL-IZATION INDEX (PTS)	RESERVE ADQ INDEX (PTS)	PROFIT-ABILITY INDEX (PTS)	LIQUIDITY INDEX (PTS)	STAB. INDEX (PTS)	STABILITY FACTORS
US SPECIALTY INS CO	TX	B-	1,844.9	569.1	436.2	38.9	7.9	6.9	4.0	6.9	3.5	RT
US UNDERWRITERS INS CO	ND	C	165.7	122.8	13.0	0.1	10.0	9.1	8.4	10.0	4.0	FRT
USA INS CO	MS	D	15.0	6.6	10.7	0.4	7.6	7.0	2.4	6.6	2.1	DFGR
USA UNDERWRITERS	MI	C-	9.6	6.7	4.3	0.6	5.6	5.7	5.2	7.0	2.1	DGT
USAA CASUALTY INS CO	TX	A-	9,860.1	4,477.7	5,679.1	-46.3	8.9	7.9	5.9	5.6	5.7	T
USAA COUNTY MUTUAL INS CO	TX	U	5.7	5.7	0.0	0.1	N/A	N/A	3.9	7.0	4.6	GT
USAA GENERAL INDEMNITY CO	TX	B+	3,644.1	1,295.5	2,289.9	-27.7	8.1	9.3	6.2	3.6	5.0	LT
USAA TEXAS LLOYDS CO	TX	B	372.7	288.0	159.5	4.7	9.7	7.7	8.9	6.3	4.8	FRT
USPLATE GLASS INS CO	IL	C+	27.7	21.1	9.6	0.2	7.6	5.0	6.6	7.3	3.1	DGRT
UTAH BUSINESS INS CO	UT	D- (1)	19.4	4.0	14.2	-0.3	1.2	6.0	2.8	5.9	1.3	DGRT
UTICA FIRST INS CO	NY	B-	268.9	122.8	79.5	0.6	9.5	8.7	6.9	6.8	3.9	RT
UTICA LLOYDS OF TX	TX	B	7.5	7.3	0.0	0.3	10.0	N/A	8.5	10.0	4.0	DGT
UTICA MUTUAL INS CO	NY	B-	2,292.1	827.8	689.9	11.2	8.1	6.0	5.1	6.7	4.6	RT
UTICA NATIONAL ASR CO	NY	C	63.7	29.7	16.4	0.8	9.6	6.1	5.3	6.8	3.7	T
UTICA NATIONAL INS CO OF OHIO	OH	C+	15.3	13.6	0.0	1.0	10.0	N/A	7.6	7.2	3.2	DGT
UTICA NATIONAL INS CO OF TX	TX	C	34.4	16.0	8.2	0.4	9.9	6.1	6.6	6.9	3.2	DGT
UTICA SPECIALTY RISK INS CO	TX	U	32.1	31.8	0.0	0.6	N/A	N/A	7.1	10.0	5.4	GT
UV INS RRG INC	HI	D	1.3	1.0	0.4	0.0	8.1	5.9	6.7	8.5	1.4	DGT
VA FARM BUREAU TOWN & COUNTRY INS	VA	C+	69.0	24.5	26.5	1.0	8.4	9.3	7.1	6.6	3.6	DRT
VALLEY FORGE INS CO	PA	C	71.6	69.4	0.0	1.4	10.0	N/A	6.9	8.4	3.8	ART
VALLEY P&C INS CO	OR	B	12.3	7.6	0.0	0.1	10.0	N/A	6.6	7.0	4.1	DGRT
VANLINER INS CO	MO	B	385.6	134.6	109.7	1.8	9.3	4.5	8.1	6.6	4.8	RT
VANTAGE CASUALTY INS CO	IN	U	81.0	41.7	0.0	0.4	N/A	4.6	3.9	10.0	5.1	FT
VANTAPRO SPECIALTY INS CO	AR	U	23.8	23.2	0.0	0.0	N/A	N/A	6.8	7.0	5.4	GRT
VASA SPRING GARDEN MUTUAL INS CO	MN	D	5.0	2.7	2.2	0.1	8.8	5.9	4.4	7.1	1.9	DGT
VEHICULAR SERVICE INS CO RRG	OK	U	2.6	2.6	0.0	0.0	N/A	4.0	7.2	10.0	3.0	FGT
VELOCITY INS CO A RRG	SC	U	1.5	1.5	0.0	0.0	N/A	0.0	4.9	0.0	0.0	LT
VERLAN FIRE INS CO	NH	B-	26.2	26.2	0.0	0.3	10.0	N/A	6.9	10.0	3.7	GRT
VERMONT ACCIDENT INS CO	VT	B	8.5	7.8	0.0	0.1	9.2	N/A	7.6	7.0	4.3	DGT
VERMONT MUTUAL INS CO	VT	B-	794.0	396.0	358.5	17.8	9.8	9.1	8.5	6.5	4.2	FRT
VERSANT CASUALTY INS CO	MS	C	39.5	14.2	8.5	0.5	9.1	7.3	8.9	7.0	3.1	DGT
VERTERRA INS CO	TX	C-	69.0	48.1	13.4	2.2	9.0	6.0	8.4	8.3	3.0	DGRT
VESTA INS CORP	TX	F (5)	0.0	0.0	0.0	0.0	10.0	N/A	3.9	8.1	0.0	DGT
VETERINARY PET INS CO	OH	B-	139.9	103.1	277.0	0.6	8.9	5.8	6.6	2.3	4.5	LT
VFH CAPTIVE INS CO	GA	E	5.5	0.8	3.9	-0.1	0.1	5.9	0.5	0.0	0.0	CDFG
VICTORIA AUTOMOBILE INS CO	OH	B-	31.6	10.9	0.0	0.1	9.4	N/A	7.2	8.7	3.7	DFGT
VICTORIA FIRE & CASUALTY CO	OH	C	133.7	42.0	0.0	0.3	7.9	N/A	2.8	10.0	3.9	FT
VICTORIA NATIONAL INS CO	OH	U	3.5	3.5	0.0	0.0	N/A	N/A	6.1	10.0	4.2	FGT
VICTORIA SELECT INS CO	OH	B-	25.3	8.5	0.0	0.1	8.9	N/A	6.7	7.0	3.8	DFGT
VICTORIA SPECIALTY INSURANCE CO	OH	C-	20.2	3.5	0.0	0.0	6.8	N/A	3.9	7.0	2.4	DFGT
VICTORY INS CO	MT	E+	10.9	3.5	6.5	-0.3	0.5	1.3	0.9	3.7	0.8	CDFG
VIGILANT INS CO	NY	B	519.2	311.5	48.9	7.9	10.0	7.6	8.7	7.2	4.7	T
VIKING INS CO OF WI	WI	C	413.6	183.4	93.9	2.8	10.0	7.9	5.7	7.0	3.5	T
VIRGINIA FARM BUREAU FIRE & CAS INS	VA	C	58.6	21.7	29.1	0.9	8.0	9.4	6.2	6.5	3.5	DRT
VIRGINIA FARM BUREAU MUTUAL INS CO	VA	B-	392.4	180.2	196.1	5.9	7.8	9.3	3.9	6.5	4.0	RT
VIRGINIA PHYSICIANS RRG INC	MT	D	2.2	1.0	0.2	0.0	7.9	6.0	3.8	9.8	1.4	DGT
VIRGINIA SURETY CO INC	IL	B	1,231.9	382.0	299.6	21.5	9.8	8.0	8.4	6.7	4.3	RT
VISION INS CO	TX	D-	31.5	12.3	44.9	-4.9	2.2	5.2	1.8	0.3	1.3	DFGL
VOYAGER INDEMNITY INS CO	GA	C+	123.6	79.7	139.6	15.2	8.0	6.3	8.9	6.7	4.1	GRT
WADENA INS CO	IA	C	5.4	5.4	0.0	0.0	10.0	N/A	2.3	7.0	2.6	DGT
WALL ROSE MUTUAL INS CO	PA	U	0.9	0.4	0.3	0.0	N/A	4.9	1.4	1.4	1.1	FGLT
WARNER INS CO	IL	U	12.1	12.0	0.0	0.1	N/A	N/A	6.1	7.0	5.0	GT

See Page 27 for explanation of footnotes and Page 28 for explanation of stability factors.

Arrows denote recent upgrades ▲ or downgrades ▼ (see Section VII for explanations)

128

www.weissratings.com

RISK ADJ. RATIO #1	CAPITAL RATIO #2	PREMIUM TO SURPLUS (%)	RESV. TO SURPLUS (%)	RESV. DEVELOP. 1 YEAR (%)	RESV. DEVELOP. 2 YEAR (%)	LOSS RATIO (%)	EXP. RATIO (%)	COMB RATIO (%)	CASH FROM UNDER-WRITING (%)	NET PREMIUM GROWTH (%)	INVEST. IN AFFIL (%)	INSURANCE COMPANY NAME
2.6	1.7	83.0	168.6	1.6	-6.2	55.7	32.6	88.3	95.8	3.8	0.0 •	US SPECIALTY INS CO
6.5	4.8	10.5	29.5	-0.6	-4.1	50.2	39.5	89.7	110.6	-5.3	0.0	US UNDERWRITERS INS CO
1.7	1.4	171.5	82.0	5.6	1.4	80.8	26.7	107.5	87.4	0.2	0.9	USA INS CO
0.8	0.7	71.4	12.3	0.4	3.1	31.3	22.2	53.5	158.2	702.9	0.0	USA UNDERWRITERS
2.9	2.2	127.6	60.9	0.8	-1.5	85.9	12.5	98.4	113.4	17.4	7.9 •	USAA CASUALTY INS CO
N/A	N/A	N/A	N/A	N/A	N/A	N/A	N/A	N/A	1.4	0.0	0.0	USAA COUNTY MUTUAL INS CO
2.6	1.9	175.7	83.8	1.3	-3.2	85.9	12.2	98.1	104.2	5.2	0.0 •	USAA GENERAL INDEMNITY CO
8.5	6.9	56.2	26.8	-0.9	-2.3	85.6	27.0	112.6	67.2	-53.8	0.0 •	USAA TEXAS LLOYDS CO
2.0	1.4	47.8	0.4	-0.3	-0.1	4.6	75.8	80.4	120.8	3.4	0.0	USPLATE GLASS INS CO
0.4	0.3	328.6	300.6	-31.0	-25.7	57.1	39.2	96.3	112.1	-3.5	0.0	UTAH BUSINESS INS CO
3.2	2.5	66.0	70.3	-2.5	-7.1	71.7	26.5	98.2	105.1	7.7	0.0	UTICA FIRST INS CO
97.5	46.5	N/A	N/A	N/A	N/A	N/A	N/A	N/A	N/A	0.0	0.0	UTICA LLOYDS OF TX
2.3	1.7	85.0	123.6	-1.8	-4.4	65.5	33.8	99.3	96.0	9.9	11.5 •	UTICA MUTUAL INS CO
4.1	2.7	56.8	82.6	-1.3	-3.0	65.5	33.7	99.2	95.6	12.7	0.0	UTICA NATIONAL ASR CO
21.7	19.5	N/A	N/A	N/A	N/A	N/A	N/A	N/A	N/A	0.0	0.0	UTICA NATIONAL INS CO OF OHIO
4.2	2.8	52.7	76.7	-1.2	-2.8	65.5	33.7	99.2	95.7	12.7	0.0	UTICA NATIONAL INS CO OF TX
N/A	N/A	N/A	N/A	N/A	N/A	N/A	N/A	N/A	N/A	0.0	0.0	UTICA SPECIALTY RISK INS CO
4.2	3.4	43.0	15.1	-33.2	-21.6	-41.8	61.5	19.7	134.2	0.0	0.0	UV INS RRG INC
2.8	2.3	113.7	60.7	-6.9	-16.4	68.6	27.8	96.4	104.1	0.5	0.0	VA FARM BUREAU TOWN & COUNTRY
60.9	25.9	N/A	N/A	N/A	N/A	N/A	N/A	N/A	N/A	0.0	0.0	VALLEY FORGE INS CO
5.3	4.8	N/A	N/A	N/A	N/A	N/A	N/A	N/A	-51.0	0.0	0.0	VALLEY P&C INS CO
3.8	2.5	83.9	114.5	4.4	11.4	75.1	27.1	102.2	98.8	1.4	0.0	VANLINER INS CO
N/A	N/A	N/A	97.1	N/A	N/A	N/A	N/A	N/A	N/A	0.0	0.0	VANTAGE CASUALTY INS CO
N/A	N/A	N/A	N/A	N/A	N/A	N/A	N/A	N/A	N/A	0.0	0.0	VANTAPRO SPECIALTY INS CO
3.4	3.0	85.4	4.5	-2.7	2.5	25.4	34.1	59.5	160.2	-6.9	0.0	VASA SPRING GARDEN MUTUAL INS CO
N/A	N/A	0.7	N/A	N/A	N/A	N/A	248.1	248.1	39.4	-86.4	0.0	VEHICULAR SERVICE INS CO RRG
N/A	N/A	N/A	N/A	N/A	N/A	N/A	N/A	N/A	N/A	0.0	0.0	VELOCITY INS CO A RRG
71.8	32.2	N/A	N/A	N/A	N/A	N/A	N/A	N/A	N/A	0.0	0.0	VERLAN FIRE INS CO
4.1	2.4	N/A	N/A	N/A	N/A	N/A	N/A	N/A	N/A	0.0	0.0	VERMONT ACCIDENT INS CO
4.6	3.1	95.2	36.2	-4.2	-9.2	64.7	33.7	98.4	96.1	4.4	1.3 •	VERMONT MUTUAL INS CO
3.1	2.5	61.6	3.8	0.1	-0.6	43.4	20.7	64.1	244.6	6.1	10.3	VERSANT CASUALTY INS CO
3.4	2.2	28.8	36.0	-1.4	-0.4	63.0	22.9	85.9	163.5	19.7	0.0	VERTERRA INS CO
4.8	4.3	N/A	N/A	N/A	N/A	N/A	N/A	N/A	159.8	0.0	0.0	VESTA INS CORP
11.3	5.6	278.1	29.6	3.5	1.8	70.4	28.1	98.5	99.2	9.5	0.4	VETERINARY PET INS CO
0.1	0.1	651.1	631.4	43.3	23.3	88.6	35.6	124.2	91.6	-7.0	32.3	VFH CAPTIVE INS CO
3.0	2.7	N/A	N/A	N/A	N/A	N/A	N/A	N/A	96.4	0.0	0.0	VICTORIA AUTOMOBILE INS CO
1.6	1.5	N/A	N/A	N/A	N/A	N/A	N/A	N/A	-136.1	0.0	34.5	VICTORIA FIRE & CASUALTY CO
N/A	N/A	N/A	N/A	N/A	N/A	N/A	N/A	N/A	38.8	0.0	0.0	VICTORIA NATIONAL INS CO
2.7	2.4	N/A	N/A	N/A	N/A	N/A	N/A	N/A	200.1	0.0	0.0	VICTORIA SELECT INS CO
1.1	1.0	N/A	N/A	N/A	N/A	N/A	N/A	N/A	999 +	0.0	0.0	VICTORIA SPECIALTY INSURANCE CO
0.5	0.3	269.4	165.7	67.9	49.4	101.5	31.0	132.5	80.8	-34.2	0.0	VICTORY INS CO
8.7	6.4	16.0	26.6	-0.7	-1.6	56.5	29.0	85.5	118.4	4.1	6.8 •	VIGILANT INS CO
4.3	3.1	52.2	84.0	-1.9	-2.9	72.7	27.5	100.2	105.9	3.5	8.2	VIKING INS CO OF WI
2.2	1.9	141.4	68.9	-7.5	-18.2	68.6	26.4	95.0	107.9	4.0	0.0	VIRGINIA FARM BUREAU FIRE & CAS INS
2.0	1.7	115.4	50.2	-3.6	-12.5	56.7	31.8	88.5	116.2	2.7	21.6	VIRGINIA FARM BUREAU MUTUAL INS CO
1.6	1.4	24.8	26.0	-13.4	-16.3	39.2	65.1	104.3	999 +	-30.5	0.0	VIRGINIA PHYSICIANS RRG INC
4.0	3.5	82.4	15.5	-1.8	-1.0	62.7	27.0	89.7	137.5	-9.1	1.7 •	VIRGINIA SURETY CO INC
0.6	0.4	367.3	136.7	5.4	6.0	86.5	29.1	115.6	92.9	44.1	0.0	VISION INS CO
3.3	2.2	189.9	35.9	-0.7	0.1	37.5	37.6	75.1	151.9	29.1	0.0	VOYAGER INDEMNITY INS CO
95.6	44.4	N/A	N/A	N/A	N/A	N/A	N/A	N/A	-45.2	0.0	0.0	WADENA INS CO
N/A	N/A	92.9	16.3	2.4	6.6	92.8	41.1	133.9	55.3	1.2	0.0	WALL ROSE MUTUAL INS CO
N/A	N/A	N/A	N/A	N/A	N/A	N/A	N/A	N/A	-6.5	0.0	57.8	WARNER INS CO

999 + Denotes number greater than 999.9%
999 - Denotes number less than -999.99%
• Bullets denote a more detailed analysis is available in Section II.

INSURANCE COMPANY NAME	DOM. STATE	RATING	TOTAL ASSETS ($MIL)	CAPITAL & SURPLUS ($MIL)	ANNUAL NET PREMIUM ($MIL)	NET INCOME ($MIL)	CAPITAL-IZATION INDEX (PTS)	RESERVE ADQ INDEX (PTS)	PROFIT-ABILITY INDEX (PTS)	LIQUIDITY INDEX (PTS)	STAB. INDEX (PTS)	STABILITY FACTORS
WARRANTY UNDERWRITERS INS CO	TX	C-	34.4	16.4	1.9	0.8	7.2	10.0	2.9	7.4	3.0	DFGR
WASHINGTON CASUALTY CO	WA	E	28.7	21.3	0.0	0.3	10.0	4.1	6.8	10.0	0.0	DFGR
WASHINGTON COUNTY CO-OPERATIVE INS	NY	D	8.0	5.8	1.5	0.4	10.0	7.4	7.3	7.1	2.1	DGT
WASHINGTON INTL INS CO	NH	C	104.3	78.7	0.6	1.4	10.0	7.6	7.9	10.0	3.5	DRT
WATFORD INS CO	NJ	U	23.0	23.0	0.0	0.2	N/A	N/A	7.3	10.0	5.4	GRT
WATFORD SPECIALTY INS CO	NJ	U	62.1	59.1	0.0	-0.2	N/A	N/A	3.8	7.0	5.4	FT
WAUSAU BUSINESS INS CO	WI	C	35.4	28.8	0.0	0.3	10.0	3.5	3.4	7.0	3.7	ADGR
WAUSAU GENERAL INS CO	WI	U	15.1	12.3	0.0	0.1	N/A	N/A	3.3	7.0	4.5	AGRT
WAUSAU UNDERWRITERS INS CO	WI	C	109.0	67.6	0.0	1.1	10.0	3.6	3.6	7.0	4.1	ADRT
WAWANESA GENERAL INS CO	CA	C+	605.1	202.3	365.9	6.8	7.8	4.5	2.5	5.6	4.0	RT
WAYNE COOPERATIVE INS CO	NY	C	29.9	15.6	13.9	0.6	8.8	9.1	7.8	6.5	2.7	DGRT
WAYNE MUTUAL INS CO	OH	C+	69.4	34.8	43.0	2.4	8.4	8.6	8.8	6.3	3.3	T
WEA P&C INS CO	WI	C	17.0	4.8	11.3	0.0	7.2	7.0	2.5	6.3	2.5	DGT
WELLINGTON INS CO	TX	C	41.7	18.2	7.2	0.0	9.8	4.6	8.5	8.0	2.9	DGRT
▲WELLSPAN RRG	VT	D-	31.1	8.3	8.7	1.9	7.3	9.9	3.8	6.9	0.9	DGT
WESCAP INS CO	CO	U	3.8	1.0	0.0	-0.1	N/A	6.0	1.5	9.4	0.0	T
WESCO INS CO	DE	B-	1,794.7	334.5	416.8	-13.7	7.4	4.9	5.9	7.3	4.6	GRT
WEST AMERICAN INS CO	IN	C-	46.4	45.3	0.0	-0.1	10.0	N/A	2.5	7.0	3.1	AFRT
WEST BEND MUTUAL INS CO	WI	B+	2,456.0	911.6	960.5	20.1	8.8	7.0	8.5	6.4	5.1	T
WEST BRANCH MUTL INS CO	PA	C+	1.1	0.8	0.3	0.0	7.6	7.3	2.9	7.3	3.0	DGT
WEST VIRGINIA FARMERS MUT INS ASSOC	WV	C-	7.4	5.4	1.8	0.1	9.4	5.0	7.9	6.9	2.6	DGRT
WEST VIRGINIA INS CO	WV	C-	51.5	42.0	11.4	0.4	10.0	6.3	8.1	6.8	3.3	DT
WEST VIRGINIA MUTUAL INS CO	WV	D	166.7	97.0	18.4	-1.8	10.0	9.4	3.3	7.2	2.3	DRT
WEST VIRGINIA NATIONAL AUTO INS CO	WV	D+	6.7	3.6	4.5	0.1	7.4	6.9	1.7	2.9	2.0	DFGL
WESTCHESTER FIRE INS CO	PA	C+	1,753.9	674.1	374.1	6.4	9.4	8.2	3.3	6.9	4.5	RT
WESTCHESTER SURPLUS LINES INS CO	GA	C	354.8	113.4	42.4	5.0	10.0	8.0	6.3	6.9	2.8	FRT
WESTERN AGRICULTURAL INS CO	IA	B+	206.5	92.8	105.1	3.3	10.0	8.1	8.7	5.8	5.1	T
WESTERN CATHOLIC INS CO RRG	VT	E	4.5	1.1	1.3	-0.3	0.0	0.4	2.5	7.8	0.0	CDFG
WESTERN COMMUNITY INS CO	ID	B-	40.1	31.3	0.0	0.7	10.0	3.6	8.3	10.0	3.8	GT
WESTERN GENERAL INS CO	CA	D+	72.1	20.9	54.6	1.1	4.0	4.5	1.9	2.2	2.7	DFLR
WESTERN HERITAGE INS CO	AZ	B	137.4	110.8	0.0	0.9	10.0	N/A	6.9	10.0	4.5	FRT
WESTERN HOME INS CO	MN	C	71.7	29.7	27.3	1.0	9.2	8.2	8.8	6.8	3.4	RT
WESTERN MUTL INS CO (CA)	CA	C-	82.8	54.9	27.3	-0.1	7.1	8.1	8.2	6.6	2.7	RT
WESTERN MUTUAL FIRE INS CO	MN	B-	7.6	5.1	2.5	0.3	10.0	4.6	8.6	7.1	3.5	DGT
WESTERN NATIONAL ASR CO	MN	C	65.7	26.6	27.3	0.9	8.9	8.3	8.8	6.5	3.7	RT
WESTERN NATIONAL MUTUAL INS CO	MN	B-	929.6	408.1	340.6	12.0	8.5	8.2	8.7	6.7	4.3	RT
WESTERN PACIFIC MUT INS CO RISK RET	CO	B-	137.6	111.5	3.2	-0.1	10.0	9.3	7.3	9.9	3.6	DFRT
WESTERN PROFESSIONAL INS CO	WA	U	13.7	13.7	0.0	0.1	N/A	N/A	5.2	7.0	5.1	GT
WESTERN PROTECTORS INS CO	OR	C	9.7	8.9	-0.1	0.3	10.0	3.6	5.4	7.0	2.9	DGRT
WESTERN RESERVE MUTUAL CAS CO	OH	B-	187.1	109.5	78.2	3.5	9.9	7.8	6.0	6.4	4.0	T
WESTERN SELECT INS CO	IL	C	17.4	16.0	0.2	0.3	10.0	5.0	7.0	9.3	3.2	DGT
WESTERN SURETY CO	SD	C	1,962.4	1,369.0	295.8	46.6	10.0	9.3	8.0	6.9	2.9	RT
WESTERN WORLD INS CO	NH	C	905.5	426.6	96.7	1.7	7.5	9.6	6.8	7.0	4.1	FRT
WESTFIELD INS CO	OH	B-	2,634.5	1,113.3	955.3	40.2	9.5	9.1	7.7	6.6	4.6	T
WESTFIELD NATIONAL INS CO	OH	B-	634.5	288.0	230.0	8.6	9.3	9.0	7.5	6.6	4.6	T
WESTGUARD INS CO	PA	C+	884.7	452.0	19.0	2.4	6.3	9.4	7.9	10.0	3.3	FGRT
WESTMINSTER AMERICAN INS CO	MD	C	27.7	16.0	14.8	1.4	7.9	7.9	9.1	7.7	2.7	DGRT
WESTON INS CO	FL	C	81.5	47.1	0.7	0.5	10.0	3.6	4.2	10.0	2.2	DGT
WESTPORT INS CORP	MO	B-	4,890.9	1,507.8	281.6	136.4	6.3	6.9	3.5	7.0	4.2	FRT
WHITE PINE INS CO	MI	C	41.5	18.3	21.9	0.8	5.6	9.7	7.5	7.0	3.2	DGRT
WHITECAP SURETY CO	MN	D-	1.5	1.3	3.5	0.1	1.3	N/A	6.0	1.6	1.1	CDGL
WI LAWYERS MUTUAL INS CO	WI	C+	31.8	22.3	3.8	0.3	10.0	7.8	5.9	7.6	3.1	DGRT

See Page 27 for explanation of footnotes and Page 28 for explanation of stability factors.
Arrows denote recent upgrades ▲ or downgrades ▼ (see Section VII for explanations)

130

www.weissratings.com

RISK ADJ. RATIO #1	CAPITAL RATIO #2	PREMIUM TO SURPLUS (%)	RESV. TO SURPLUS (%)	RESV. DEVELOP. 1 YEAR (%)	2 YEAR (%)	LOSS RATIO (%)	EXP. RATIO (%)	COMB RATIO (%)	CASH FROM UNDER- WRITING (%)	NET PREMIUM GROWTH (%)	INVEST. IN AFFIL (%)	INSURANCE COMPANY NAME
2.4	1.8	12.7	59.2	-27.0	-48.2	34.8	73.9	108.7	38.0	-12.8	3.9	WARRANTY UNDERWRITERS INS CO
10.8	9.8	N/A	N/A	N/A	N/A	N/A	N/A	N/A	-86.7	0.0	0.0	WASHINGTON CASUALTY CO
5.5	3.9	28.7	7.0	-0.8	-0.5	58.7	30.2	88.9	104.1	14.8	0.0	WASHINGTON COUNTY CO-OPERATIVE
19.1	17.2	0.8	4.8	-1.7	-1.2	-46.2	151.0	104.8	337.1	-81.9	0.0	WASHINGTON INTL INS CO
N/A	N/A	N/A	N/A	N/A	N/A	N/A	N/A	N/A	N/A	0.0	0.0	WATFORD INS CO
N/A	N/A	N/A	N/A	N/A	N/A	N/A	N/A	N/A	N/A	0.0	0.0	WATFORD SPECIALTY INS CO
14.7	13.2	N/A	N/A	N/A	N/A	N/A	N/A	N/A	3.2	0.0	0.0	WAUSAU BUSINESS INS CO
N/A	N/A	N/A	N/A	N/A	N/A	N/A	N/A	N/A	N/A	0.0	0.0	WAUSAU GENERAL INS CO
11.2	10.1	N/A	N/A	N/A	N/A	N/A	N/A	N/A	5.1	0.0	0.0	WAUSAU UNDERWRITERS INS CO
1.9	1.5	187.1	90.3	5.0	5.5	102.5	10.7	113.2	97.2	6.5	0.0 ●	WAWANESA GENERAL INS CO
3.1	2.4	94.4	32.0	-7.5	-5.7	62.0	30.2	92.2	102.0	4.9	0.0	WAYNE COOPERATIVE INS CO
3.4	2.3	133.4	25.6	-4.4	-4.2	49.8	32.6	82.4	123.0	9.8	0.0	WAYNE MUTUAL INS CO
1.4	1.0	222.9	84.8	-15.0	-17.9	63.3	34.2	97.5	118.4	10.1	0.0	WEA P&C INS CO
4.6	3.7	40.1	28.1	-1.9	2.0	73.5	23.9	97.4	120.6	-50.6	0.0	WELLINGTON INS CO
1.5	1.2	117.9	228.3	-28.3	-34.7	76.4	5.3	81.7	129.7	13.4	0.0	WELLSPAN RRG
N/A	N/A	N/A	N/A	N/A	N/A	N/A	N/A	N/A	N/A	0.0	0.0	WESCAP INS CO
1.5	0.9	125.0	51.2	0.6	7.8	64.1	17.5	81.6	182.2	128.3	6.0 ●	WESCO INS CO
94.0	51.8	N/A	N/A	N/A	N/A	N/A	N/A	N/A	N/A	0.0	0.0	WEST AMERICAN INS CO
3.1	2.1	109.4	92.7	-4.7	-7.1	59.3	31.7	91.0	119.4	7.3	0.0 ●	WEST BEND MUTUAL INS CO
2.2	1.3	44.2	0.8	-0.5	-0.7	14.9	76.4	91.3	114.8	-8.0	0.0	WEST BRANCH MUTL INS CO
3.6	2.6	34.8	2.8	-0.9	-0.1	42.0	49.4	91.4	108.5	-1.1	0.0	WEST VIRGINIA FARMERS MUT INS
10.6	9.2	27.3	4.6	-1.2	-0.8	62.7	19.7	82.4	119.2	1.8	0.0	WEST VIRGINIA INS CO
4.9	3.8	18.7	45.7	-7.7	-10.4	86.1	38.2	124.3	68.6	-11.0	0.0	WEST VIRGINIA MUTUAL INS CO
1.8	1.6	128.2	79.4	8.5	-5.5	103.4	24.8	128.2	75.9	-28.7	0.0	WEST VIRGINIA NATIONAL AUTO INS CO
3.6	2.3	51.1	116.0	-0.9	-3.6	60.1	34.7	94.8	87.9	9.2	0.0 ●	WESTCHESTER FIRE INS CO
5.3	3.3	23.8	31.5	1.1	-2.9	55.3	23.4	78.7	85.1	0.1	0.0	WESTCHESTER SURPLUS LINES INS CO
4.4	3.4	118.3	48.3	-3.1	-5.2	62.3	26.4	88.7	121.4	3.6	2.0 ●	WESTERN AGRICULTURAL INS CO
0.1	0.0	95.9	201.6	41.1	103.8	47.2	43.7	90.9	68.4	-36.2	0.0	WESTERN CATHOLIC INS CO RRG
14.1	12.6	N/A	N/A	N/A	N/A	N/A	N/A	N/A	-9.9	0.0	0.0	WESTERN COMMUNITY INS CO
0.8	0.6	284.6	75.0	13.1	10.5	59.2	43.0	102.2	95.8	14.1	0.0	WESTERN GENERAL INS CO
26.2	23.6	N/A	N/A	N/A	N/A	N/A	N/A	N/A	-220.9	0.0	0.0	WESTERN HERITAGE INS CO
3.7	2.6	95.1	68.9	-5.2	-5.0	65.2	26.2	91.4	125.4	19.5	0.0	WESTERN HOME INS CO
1.8	1.1	51.9	15.2	-2.3	-5.1	70.4	22.8	93.2	103.6	9.2	13.3	WESTERN MUTL INS CO (CA)
6.0	5.4	52.8	9.4	0.5	2.2	61.6	23.8	85.4	128.6	-2.2	0.0	WESTERN MUTUAL FIRE INS CO
3.0	2.2	106.6	77.3	-5.6	-5.4	65.2	25.4	90.6	105.2	19.5	0.0	WESTERN NATIONAL ASR CO
2.4	2.0	87.2	63.2	-4.8	-4.8	65.2	25.2	90.4	123.1	19.5	18.9 ●	WESTERN NATIONAL MUTUAL INS CO
7.8	4.8	3.0	8.8	-2.2	-5.3	62.9	114.2	177.1	42.1	-2.7	0.0	WESTERN PACIFIC MUT INS CO RISK
N/A	N/A	N/A	N/A	N/A	N/A	N/A	N/A	N/A	N/A	0.0	0.0	WESTERN PROFESSIONAL INS CO
23.2	20.9	-1.0	N/A	N/A	N/A	N/A	39.9	N/A	373.3	-15.0	0.0	WESTERN PROTECTORS INS CO
4.6	2.9	73.4	29.0	-1.6	-3.4	62.4	30.9	93.3	108.7	1.5	0.2	WESTERN RESERVE MUTUAL CAS CO
30.0	24.3	1.4	1.1	0.1	0.1	82.5	-21.0	61.5	155.1	-1.2	0.0	WESTERN SELECT INS CO
6.9	5.3	22.4	20.5	-2.5	-9.9	21.8	61.0	82.8	87.9	-31.8	1.4 ●	WESTERN SURETY CO
1.6	1.5	23.0	90.6	-2.4	-37.2	72.3	39.7	112.0	45.0	-59.7	31.4 ●	WESTERN WORLD INS CO
4.2	2.8	87.4	76.4	-2.9	-6.5	62.7	34.1	96.8	108.4	2.1	0.0 ●	WESTFIELD INS CO
4.0	2.7	84.3	73.7	-2.8	-6.4	62.7	33.6	96.3	108.4	2.1	0.0 ●	WESTFIELD NATIONAL INS CO
1.3	1.2	4.4	4.6	N/A	-0.6	60.0	7.8	67.8	999 +	59.4	63.5 ●	WESTGUARD INS CO
1.7	1.6	98.9	10.9	-0.9	-0.3	25.4	30.9	56.3	170.2	21.0	0.0	WESTMINSTER AMERICAN INS CO
9.2	8.3	1.6	1.2	0.3	0.3	116.1	-500.7	-384.6	-807.7	129.6	0.0	WESTON INS CO
1.5	1.0	18.7	82.7	-2.8	-3.8	61.5	34.7	96.2	49.8	107.2	13.4 ●	WESTPORT INS CORP
1.2	0.9	125.7	42.2	-3.3	-6.1	47.7	38.4	86.1	118.0	49.1	0.0	WHITE PINE INS CO
0.3	0.3	304.8	N/A	N/A	N/A	N/A	96.1	96.1	103.9	12.2	0.0	WHITECAP SURETY CO
4.3	3.0	17.2	29.5	-3.0	-3.1	65.3	36.0	101.3	90.6	3.4	0.0	WI LAWYERS MUTUAL INS CO

999 + Denotes number greater than 999.9%
999 - Denotes number less than -999.99%
● Bullets denote a more detailed analysis is available in Section II.

INSURANCE COMPANY NAME	DOM. STATE	RATING	TOTAL ASSETS ($MIL)	CAPITAL & SURPLUS ($MIL)	ANNUAL NET PREMIUM ($MIL)	NET INCOME ($MIL)	CAPITAL-IZATION INDEX (PTS)	RESERVE ADQ INDEX (PTS)	PROFIT-ABILITY INDEX (PTS)	LIQUIDITY INDEX (PTS)	STAB. INDEX (PTS)	STABILITY FACTORS
WILLIAMSBURG NATIONAL INS CO	MI	C-	118.1	31.0	40.0	2.5	7.4	2.1	4.7	6.6	3.0	FRT
WILMINGTON INS CO	DE	D+	5.5	3.2	1.1	0.2	9.3	6.3	5.6	9.0	2.0	DGT
WILSHIRE INS CO	NC	C-	244.7	95.2	92.1	3.4	7.1	4.6	3.9	5.7	2.7	RT
WILSON MUTUAL INS CO	WI	B	93.2	25.0	21.5	0.2	7.9	8.0	4.8	6.4	4.1	T
WINDHAVEN INS CO	FL	E+	184.4	39.5	96.8	0.1	0.6	0.4	8.2	0.6	0.6	CGLR
WINDHAVEN NATIONAL INS CO	TX	C-	6.7	5.2	0.1	-1.2	2.4	4.5	1.2	5.2	2.1	CDFG
WINDSOR MOUNT JOY MUTUAL INS CO	PA	C+	74.5	46.8	28.7	1.3	10.0	8.4	8.7	7.2	3.4	RT
WINTHROP PHYSICIANS RECIP RRG	VT	B-	3.0	2.4	0.2	-0.1	10.0	4.6	3.9	10.0	3.5	DFGT
WISCONSIN COUNTY MUTUAL INS CORP	WI	C+	86.1	31.6	23.0	-1.8	7.6	9.1	3.8	7.0	3.4	RT
WISCONSIN MUNICIPAL MUTUAL INS CO	WI	C	54.4	38.0	3.2	0.3	10.0	8.8	4.2	8.1	3.3	DFRT
WISCONSIN MUTUAL INS CO	WI	B-	146.9	80.5	70.5	4.7	10.0	5.7	7.1	6.6	3.9	RT
WISCONSIN REINS CORP	WI	C	91.1	57.0	41.3	5.7	7.1	7.0	5.1	6.6	3.5	RT
WOLVERINE MUTUAL INS CO	MI	C	56.2	22.0	36.2	1.2	7.7	8.5	6.1	6.0	2.9	DT
WOODLANDS INS CO	TX	C-	12.5	10.8	0.3	0.0	10.0	N/A	4.8	10.0	2.3	DGT
WORK FIRST CASUALTY CO	DE	D	40.1	11.0	12.7	0.3	2.1	4.6	2.9	6.3	2.3	DFGR
WORKERS COMPENSATION EXCHANGE	ID	E	7.4	0.5	2.1	0.0	0.1	4.0	3.3	2.6	0.3	CDFG
WORKMENS AUTO INS CO	CA	D	41.0	19.1	19.7	-1.2	4.1	0.3	2.2	5.3	1.7	DFRT
WORTH CASUALTY CO	TX	C	18.4	8.5	0.0	0.2	10.0	5.3	4.6	7.1	2.8	DGRT
WRIGHT NATIONAL FLOOD INS CO	TX	C	32.3	20.7	0.0	5.5	10.0	4.6	5.2	7.5	2.7	DGT
WRM AMERICA INDEMNITY CO	NY	D+	15.5	15.4	-3.2	-0.1	10.0	6.1	1.8	10.0	2.6	DFGT
XL INS AMERICA INC	DE	C	742.2	189.7	132.7	4.4	7.4	7.6	3.6	6.7	3.6	FRT
XL INS CO OF NY INC	NY	C-	213.2	75.0	39.8	-0.4	8.8	7.6	3.7	7.1	3.1	ART
XL REINS AMERICA INC	NY	C	5,935.1	2,025.4	862.6	6.5	8.8	7.5	3.8	7.1	3.8	ART
XL SELECT INS CO	DE	D	135.6	42.0	26.5	-0.2	0.0	7.6	3.0	6.9	1.8	CRT
XL SPECIALTY INS CO	DE	C	846.2	255.5	79.6	-3.3	7.9	7.6	3.1	8.7	3.4	ART
YEL CO INS	FL	C	16.8	11.6	1.2	0.5	10.0	9.2	8.8	10.0	2.4	DGT
YELLOWSTONE INS EXCHANGE	VT	D	18.8	7.9	3.8	-0.2	7.8	10.0	5.2	9.6	2.2	DFGR
YORK INS CO OF MAINE	ME	C (3)	47.0	46.3	0.0	0.4	10.0	N/A	7.5	7.0	3.9	RT
YOSEMITE INS CO	IN	C	156.4	54.5	36.3	3.6	10.0	6.2	1.9	9.1	4.0	T
YOUNG AMERICA INS CO	TX	C-	55.2	17.2	67.2	-4.1	2.7	4.7	2.0	0.7	3.0	CDLR
ZALE INDEMNITY CO	TX	C+	51.0	16.6	19.9	-0.3	7.4	8.6	7.4	6.8	3.0	DRT
ZENITH INS CO	CA	C+	1,902.7	592.0	754.9	59.5	7.0	7.0	4.2	7.0	4.4	ART
ZEPHYR INS CO	HI	C-	114.7	75.4	41.0	8.2	10.0	3.6	9.5	8.4	2.9	GRT
ZNAT INS CO	CA	C	68.6	24.7	15.4	1.0	8.3	6.9	4.9	9.4	3.4	ART
ZURICH AMERICAN INS CO	NY	B-	30,823.4	7,465.3	4,540.4	505.3	8.1	6.1	6.5	6.9	3.5	RT
ZURICH AMERICAN INS CO OF IL	IL	C+	47.5	34.8	0.0	0.3	10.0	N/A	5.7	10.0	3.8	FRT

See Page 27 for explanation of footnotes and
Page 28 for explanation of stability factors.
Arrows denote recent upgrades ▲ or downgrades ▼   (see Section VII for explanations)

132

www.weissratings.com

RISK ADJ. CAPITAL RATIO #1	CAPITAL RATIO #2	PREMIUM TO SURPLUS (%)	RESV. TO SURPLUS (%)	RESV. DEVELOP. 1 YEAR (%)	RESV. DEVELOP. 2 YEAR (%)	LOSS RATIO (%)	EXP. RATIO (%)	COMB RATIO (%)	CASH FROM UNDER-WRITING (%)	NET PREMIUM GROWTH (%)	INVEST. IN AFFIL (%)	INSURANCE COMPANY NAME
1.9	1.2	123.8	224.0	15.5	24.7	77.1	37.2	114.3	78.3	0.7	0.0	WILLIAMSBURG NATIONAL INS CO
4.0	2.7	32.5	14.8	-0.7	-1.1	55.0	29.3	84.3	207.9	57.2	0.0	WILMINGTON INS CO
1.7	1.0	100.0	86.5	13.4	9.7	86.3	31.2	117.5	102.0	29.8	0.0	WILSHIRE INS CO
2.6	1.6	87.4	63.4	-2.5	-4.9	64.4	36.7	101.1	104.6	-3.1	0.0	WILSON MUTUAL INS CO
0.3	0.2	284.8	127.5	2.5	47.5	76.0	18.4	94.4	120.1	28.6	0.0	WINDHAVEN INS CO
1.2	0.9	3.0	63.3	39.0	6.3	118.6	999 +	999 +	58.5	-94.5	0.0	WINDHAVEN NATIONAL INS CO
5.0	4.2	63.4	11.6	-1.9	-4.5	39.1	42.1	81.2	133.8	1.8	0.0	WINDSOR MOUNT JOY MUTUAL INS CO
6.3	5.2	8.7	5.4	-1.7	-1.7	0.2	108.8	109.0	89.1	-32.6	0.0	WINTHROP PHYSICIANS RECIP RRG
1.8	1.3	69.9	102.1	-1.6	-7.4	73.9	28.8	102.7	113.5	9.2	7.6	WISCONSIN COUNTY MUTUAL INS CORP
8.0	5.6	8.4	15.1	0.9	-3.5	82.9	34.3	117.2	116.8	-7.3	6.2	WISCONSIN MUNICIPAL MUTUAL INS CO
5.6	3.9	93.6	41.8	-5.3	-8.2	57.8	24.4	82.2	120.4	2.8	0.0	WISCONSIN MUTUAL INS CO
1.9	1.5	79.3	54.2	-10.5	-15.8	46.9	21.3	68.2	127.4	3.4	14.7	WISCONSIN REINS CORP
2.2	1.7	176.2	58.1	-2.8	-4.4	61.8	31.6	93.4	108.0	-1.1	0.0	WOLVERINE MUTUAL INS CO
5.4	3.2	2.5	0.6	N/A	N/A	80.7	28.2	108.9	514.7	0.0	0.0	WOODLANDS INS CO
0.8	0.5	122.4	254.1	-24.7	-17.3	58.1	36.8	94.9	86.6	-0.6	0.0	WORK FIRST CASUALTY CO
0.1	0.1	406.1	999 +	-23.8	114.1	80.2	26.9	107.1	75.4	-8.9	0.0	WORKERS COMPENSATION EXCHANGE
1.3	1.0	100.7	79.4	4.9	79.4	92.0	36.9	128.9	65.5	-26.0	0.0	WORKMENS AUTO INS CO
3.5	3.1	N/A	N/A	N/A	-0.7	N/A	N/A	N/A	240.6	0.0	0.0	WORTH CASUALTY CO
7.9	7.1	0.1	N/A	0.1	-0.4	999 +	999 +	999 +	-6.5	104.1	0.0	WRIGHT NATIONAL FLOOD INS CO
15.8	9.1	-20.8	17.2	-3.6	-0.3	N/A	13.2	N/A	-39.0	-146.0	0.0	WRM AMERICA INDEMNITY CO
1.3	1.1	62.9	153.0	1.2	-2.5	71.2	33.9	105.1	94.2	4.8	21.1 ●	XL INS AMERICA INC
3.2	2.0	51.8	126.0	1.0	-2.4	71.2	35.3	106.5	94.2	4.8	0.0	XL INS CO OF NY INC
2.7	1.9	42.7	103.9	0.8	-1.8	71.2	35.2	106.4	101.3	4.8	11.2 ●	XL REINS AMERICA INC
0.0	0.0	57.0	138.7	1.0	-2.2	71.2	35.4	106.6	94.2	4.8	0.0	XL SELECT INS CO
3.8	2.8	60.0	146.0	1.1	-2.3	71.2	39.2	110.4	94.2	4.8	11.2	XL SPECIALTY INS CO
7.6	6.8	10.8	41.7	-3.5	-7.9	20.5	3.1	23.6	716.0	0.0	0.0	YEL CO INS
2.0	1.6	47.0	62.9	-41.1	-38.2	-4.4	64.8	60.4	-31.6	100.1	0.0	YELLOWSTONE INS EXCHANGE
60.4	34.5	N/A	N/A	N/A	N/A	N/A	N/A	N/A	N/A	-100.0	0.0	YORK INS CO OF MAINE
5.5	2.8	47.8	28.9	-4.2	-1.7	12.4	39.8	52.2	171.1	-28.9	0.0	YOSEMITE INS CO
0.5	0.4	412.2	214.6	16.2	8.5	83.8	38.5	122.3	93.7	24.3	0.0	YOUNG AMERICA INS CO
1.5	1.3	119.8	9.1	-5.9	-6.6	12.1	49.3	61.4	149.9	-12.6	37.9	ZALE INDEMNITY CO
1.3	1.0	121.4	185.0	-16.4	-26.3	46.6	32.4	79.0	131.8	7.3	6.2 ●	ZENITH INS CO
5.2	5.1	60.8	0.1	0.1	N/A	0.1	28.5	28.6	245.7	59.1	0.0	ZEPHYR INS CO
2.2	1.7	58.7	89.4	-7.0	-10.9	46.6	32.5	79.1	134.1	7.3	0.0	ZNAT INS CO
2.3	1.5	58.5	182.5	1.0	1.4	81.4	21.2	102.6	102.4	-4.2	5.9 ●	ZURICH AMERICAN INS CO
12.7	11.4	N/A	N/A	N/A	N/A	N/A	N/A	N/A	-182.7	0.0	0.0	ZURICH AMERICAN INS CO OF IL

999 + Denotes number greater than 999.9%
999 - Denotes number less than -999.99%
● Bullets denote a more detailed analysis is available in Section II.

Section II

Analysis of Largest Companies

A summary analysis of Weiss Recommended

U.S. Property and Casualty Insurers,

along with the largest companies based on capital and surplus.

Companies are listed in alphabetical order.

Section II Contents

This section contains rating factors, historical data and general information on each of the 450 largest property and casualty insurers in the U.S. that have the most recent quarterly financial information available.

1. Safety Rating
The current rating appears to the right of the company name. Our ratings are designed to distinguish levels of insolvency risk and are measured on a scale from A (Excellent) to F (Failed). Highly-rated companies are, in our opinion, less likely to experience financial difficulties than lower-rated firms. See *About Weiss Safety Ratings* for more information.

2. Major Rating Factors
A synopsis of the key indexes and sub-factors that have most influenced the rating of a particular insurer. Items are presented in the approximate order of their importance to the rating. There may be additional factors which have influenced the rating but do not appear due to space limitations or confidentiality agreements with insurers.

3. Other Rating Factors
A summary of those Weiss Ratings indexes that were not included as Major Rating Factors, but nevertheless, may have had some impact on the final grade.

4. Principal Business
The major types of policies written by an insurer along with the percentages for each line in relation to the entire book of business. Lines of business written by property and casualty insurers include personal and commercial insurance lines such as homeowners', auto, workers' compensation, commercial multiple peril, medical malpractice and product liability, among others.

5. Principal Investments
The major investments in an insurer's portfolio. These include cash, investment grade bonds, non investment grade bonds, common and preferred stock, and real estate.

6. Investments in Affiliates
The percentage of bonds, common and preferred stocks and other financial instruments an insurer has invested with affiliated companies.

7. Group Affiliation
The name of the group of companies to which a particular insurer belongs.

8. Licensed in
List of the states in which an insurer is licensed to conduct business.

9. Commenced Business
The month and year the company started its operations.

10. Address
The address of an insurer's corporate headquarters. This location may differ from the company's state of domicile.

11. Phone
The telephone number of an insurer's corporate headquarters.

12. Domicile State   The state that has primary regulatory responsibility for this company. You do not have to live in the domicile state to do business with this firm, provided it is registered to do business in your state.

13. NAIC Code   The identification number assigned to an insurer by the National Association of Insurance Commissioners (NAIC).

14. Historical Data   Five years of background data for Weiss Safety Rating, risk-adjusted capital ratios (moderate and severe loss scenarios), total assets, capital, net premium, and net income. See the following page for more details on how to read the historical data table.

**15. Customized   A graph or table depicting one of the company's major strengths or
    Graph (or Table)**   weaknesses.

How to Read the Historical Data Table

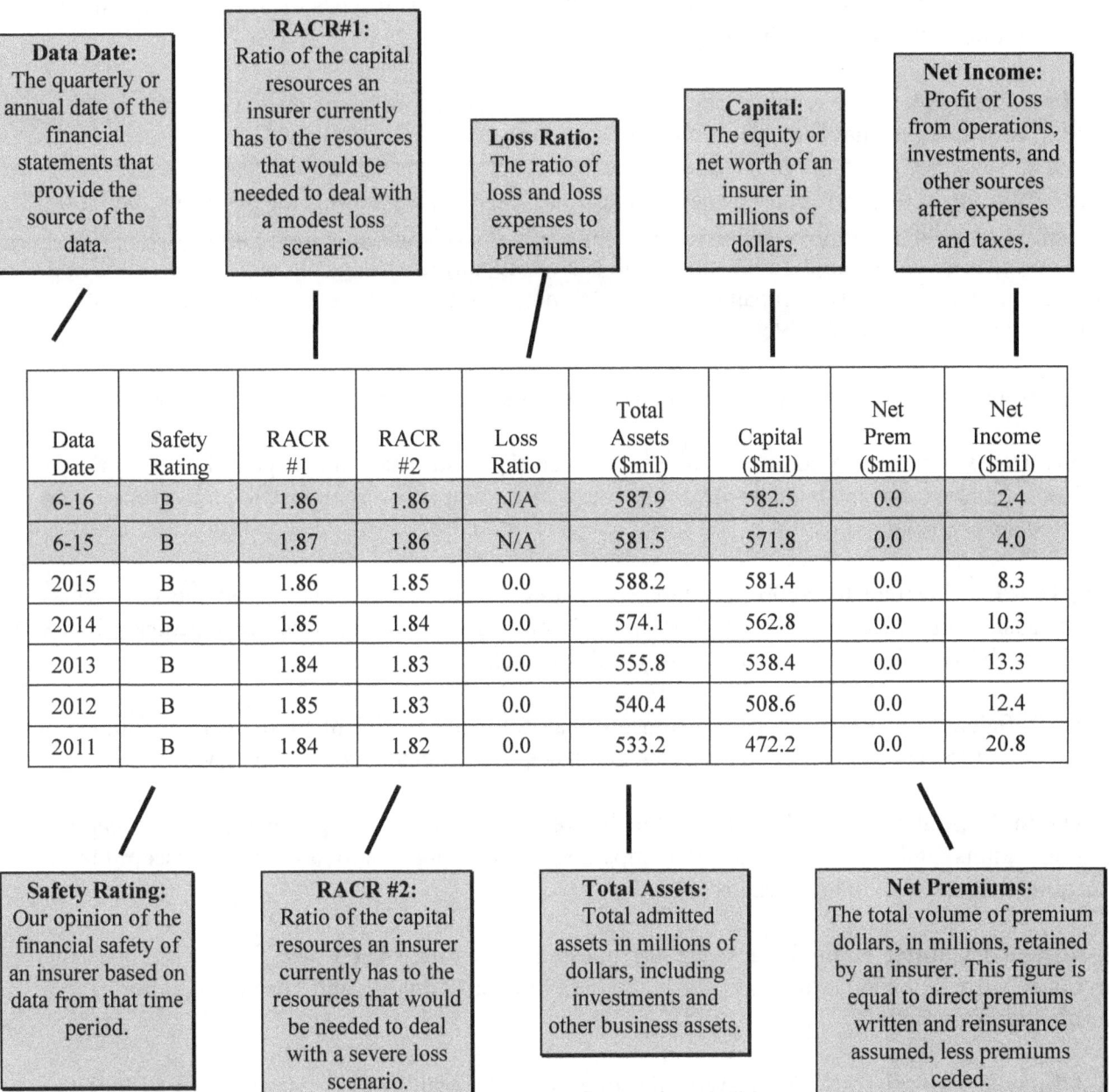

Data Date	Safety Rating	RACR #1	RACR #2	Loss Ratio	Total Assets ($mil)	Capital ($mil)	Net Prem ($mil)	Net Income ($mil)
6-16	B	1.86	1.86	N/A	587.9	582.5	0.0	2.4
6-15	B	1.87	1.86	N/A	581.5	571.8	0.0	4.0
2015	B	1.86	1.85	0.0	588.2	581.4	0.0	8.3
2014	B	1.85	1.84	0.0	574.1	562.8	0.0	10.3
2013	B	1.84	1.83	0.0	555.8	538.4	0.0	13.3
2012	B	1.85	1.83	0.0	540.4	508.6	0.0	12.4
2011	B	1.84	1.82	0.0	533.2	472.2	0.0	20.8

Data Date: The quarterly or annual date of the financial statements that provide the source of the data.

RACR#1: Ratio of the capital resources an insurer currently has to the resources that would be needed to deal with a modest loss scenario.

Loss Ratio: The ratio of loss and loss expenses to premiums.

Capital: The equity or net worth of an insurer in millions of dollars.

Net Income: Profit or loss from operations, investments, and other sources after expenses and taxes.

Safety Rating: Our opinion of the financial safety of an insurer based on data from that time period.

RACR #2: Ratio of the capital resources an insurer currently has to the resources that would be needed to deal with a severe loss scenario.

Total Assets: Total admitted assets in millions of dollars, including investments and other business assets.

Net Premiums: The total volume of premium dollars, in millions, retained by an insurer. This figure is equal to direct premiums written and reinsurance assumed, less premiums ceded.

Row Descriptions:

Row 1 contains the most recent quarterly data as filed with state regulators and is presented on a year-to-date basis. For example, the figure for year-end premiums includes premiums received through the year-end. **Row 2** consists of data from the same quarter of the prior year so that you can compare current quarterly results to those of a year ago.

Row 3 contains data from the most recent annual statutory filing. **Rows 4-7** include data from year-end statements going back four years from the most recent annual filing so that you can compare current year-end results to those of the previous four years. With the exception of Total Assets and Capital, quarterly data are not comparable with annual data.

Customized Graphs

In the lower right-hand corner of each company section, a customized graph or text block highlights a key factor affecting that company's financial strength. One of eleven types of information is found, identified by one of the following headings:

Capital plots the company's reported capital in millions of dollars over the last five years. Volatile changes in capital levels may indicate unstable operations.

Group Affiliation shows the group name, a composite Weiss Safety Rating for the group, and a list of the largest members with their ratings. The composite Safety Rating is made up of the weighted average, by assets, of the individual ratings of each company in the group (including life/health companies, property/casualty companies or HMOs) plus a factor for the financial strength of the holding company, where applicable.

Income Trends shows underwriting and net income results over the last five years.

Liquidity Index evaluates a company's ability to raise the cash necessary to pay claims. Various cash flow scenarios are modeled to determine how the company might fare in the event of an unexpected spike in claims costs.

Rating Indexes illustrate the score and range -- strong, good, fair or weak -- on the five Weiss indexes: Risk-Adjusted Capital Index #2 (Cap2), Stability Index (Stab.), Reserve Adequacy Index (Res.), Profitability Index (Prof.), and Liquidity Index (Liq.).

Reserve Deficiency shows whether the company has set aside sufficient funds to pay claims. A positive number indicates insufficient reserving and a negative number adequate reserving.

Reserves to Capital analyzes the relationship between loss and loss expense reserves to capital. Operating results and capital levels for companies with a high ratio are more susceptible to fluctuations than those with lower ratios.

Risk-Adjusted Capital Ratio #1 answers the question: In each of the past five years, does the insurer have sufficient capital to cover potential losses in its investments and business operations in a *moderate* loss scenario?

Risk-Adjusted Capital Ratio #2 answers the question: In each of the past five years, does the insurer have sufficient capital to cover potential losses in its investments and business operations in a *severe* loss scenario?

21ST CENTURY CENTENNIAL INS CO
B   **Good**

Major Rating Factors: History of adequate reserve strength (6.0 on a scale of 0 to 10) as reserves have been consistently at an acceptable level. Good overall profitability index (6.9). Fair expense controls. Return on equity has been low, averaging 2.4% over the past five years.

Other Rating Factors: Fair overall results on stability tests (4.8) including weak results on operational trends. Affiliation with Farmers Insurance Group of Companies is a strength. Strong long-term capitalization index (8.3) based on excellent current risk adjusted capital (severe and moderate loss scenarios). Moreover, capital levels have been consistent in recent years. Excellent liquidity (8.9) with ample operational cash flow and liquid investments.

Principal Business: Auto liability (69%) and auto physical damage (31%).

Principal Investments: Misc. investments (59%), investment grade bonds (40%), and cash (1%).

Investments in Affiliates: 60%

Group Affiliation: Farmers Insurance Group of Companies

Licensed in: All states except PR

Commenced Business: November 1977

Address: 500 Virginia Drive, Ft. Washington, PA 19034

Phone: (302) 252-2000   **Domicile State:** PA   **NAIC Code:** 34789

Data Date	Rating	RACR #1	RACR #2	Loss Ratio %	Total Assets ($mil)	Capital ($mil)	Net Premium ($mil)	Net Income ($mil)
6-16	B	1.86	1.86	N/A	587.9	582.5	0.0	2.4
6-15	B	1.87	1.86	N/A	581.5	571.8	0.0	4.0
2015	B	1.86	1.85	0.0	588.2	581.4	0.0	8.3
2014	B	1.85	1.84	0.0	574.1	562.8	0.0	10.3
2013	B	1.84	1.83	0.0	555.8	538.4	0.0	13.3
2012	B	1.85	1.83	0.0	540.4	508.6	0.0	12.4
2011	B	1.84	1.82	0.0	533.2	472.2	0.0	20.8

Reserve Deficiency (as % of capital)

* Adequate & redundant reserves show as negatives   ■ 1 Yr Dev □ 2 Yr Dev

21ST CENTURY INS CO
B   **Good**

Major Rating Factors: History of adequate reserve strength (5.0 on a scale of 0 to 10) as reserves have been consistently at an acceptable level. Good overall profitability index (6.0). Fair expense controls. Return on equity has been low, averaging 2.4% over the past five years.

Other Rating Factors: Fair overall results on stability tests (4.9) including weak results on operational trends. Affiliation with Farmers Insurance Group of Companies is a strength. Strong long-term capitalization index (10.0) based on excellent current risk adjusted capital (severe and moderate loss scenarios), despite some fluctuation in capital levels. Superior liquidity (10.0) with ample operational cash flow and liquid investments.

Principal Business: Auto liability (56%) and auto physical damage (44%).

Principal Investments: Investment grade bonds (92%), misc. investments (4%), and cash (4%).

Investments in Affiliates: None

Group Affiliation: Farmers Insurance Group of Companies

Licensed in: All states except HI, LA, MA, NH, NM, RI, WY, PR

Commenced Business: December 1968

Address: 6301 Owensmouth Ave, Woodland Hills, CA 91367

Phone: (302) 252-2000   **Domicile State:** CA   **NAIC Code:** 12963

Data Date	Rating	RACR #1	RACR #2	Loss Ratio %	Total Assets ($mil)	Capital ($mil)	Net Premium ($mil)	Net Income ($mil)
6-16	B	101.40	46.02	N/A	940.0	921.9	0.0	19.0
6-15	B	101.45	48.08	N/A	918.8	893.7	0.0	11.6
2015	B	100.94	45.85	0.0	912.6	902.6	0.0	24.3
2014	B	101.87	48.43	0.0	895.4	880.6	0.0	21.1
2013	B	55.30	36.29	0.0	880.8	861.7	0.0	15.0
2012	B	33.35	26.04	0.0	931.9	897.4	0.0	13.1
2011	B	60.71	27.86	0.0	944.6	877.1	0.0	25.5

Reserve Deficiency (as % of capital)

* Adequate & redundant reserves show as negatives   ■ 1 Yr Dev □ 2 Yr Dev

21ST CENTURY NORTH AMERICA INS
B   **Good**

Major Rating Factors: History of adequate reserve strength (6.0 on a scale of 0 to 10) as reserves have been consistently at an acceptable level. Good overall profitability index (6.7). Fair expense controls. Return on equity has been low, averaging 2.6% over the past five years.

Other Rating Factors: Fair overall results on stability tests (4.7) including weak results on operational trends. Affiliation with Farmers Insurance Group of Companies is a strength. Strong long-term capitalization index (10.0) based on excellent current risk adjusted capital (severe and moderate loss scenarios), despite some fluctuation in capital levels. Superior liquidity (10.0) with ample operational cash flow and liquid investments.

Principal Business: Auto liability (64%) and auto physical damage (36%).

Principal Investments: Investment grade bonds (80%), misc. investments (17%), and cash (3%).

Investments in Affiliates: 18%

Group Affiliation: Farmers Insurance Group of Companies

Licensed in: All states except PR

Commenced Business: May 1975

Address: 505 Carr Rd, Wilmington, DE 19809

Phone: (302) 252-2000   **Domicile State:** NY   **NAIC Code:** 32220

Data Date	Rating	RACR #1	RACR #2	Loss Ratio %	Total Assets ($mil)	Capital ($mil)	Net Premium ($mil)	Net Income ($mil)
6-16	B	5.92	5.70	N/A	577.2	560.4	0.0	3.5
6-15	B	5.93	5.75	N/A	579.5	549.8	0.0	4.5
2015	B	5.89	5.67	0.0	583.0	556.5	0.0	7.5
2014	B	5.90	5.73	0.0	577.6	545.0	0.0	6.0
2013	B	5.76	5.47	0.0	572.0	532.6	0.0	15.2
2012	B	5.74	5.45	0.0	569.0	517.3	0.0	17.1
2011	B	5.57	5.24	0.0	617.4	489.3	0.0	25.3

Reserve Deficiency (as % of capital)

* Adequate & redundant reserves show as negatives   ■ 1 Yr Dev □ 2 Yr Dev

21ST CENTURY PREMIER INS CO   B-   Good

Major Rating Factors: Fair overall results on stability tests (4.6 on a scale of 0 to 10) including weak results on operational trends. History of adequate reserve strength (6.0) as reserves have been consistently at an acceptable level.

Other Rating Factors: Good overall profitability index (6.9). Weak expense controls. Return on equity has been low, averaging 4.0% over the past five years. Strong long-term capitalization index (10.0) based on excellent current risk adjusted capital (severe and moderate loss scenarios). Moreover, capital levels have been consistent in recent years. Superior liquidity (10.0) with ample operational cash flow and liquid investments.

Principal Business: Auto liability (64%), auto physical damage (32%), homeowners multiple peril (3%), and group accident & health (1%).

Principal Investments: Investment grade bonds (75%), misc. investments (24%), and cash (1%).

Investments in Affiliates: 24%

Group Affiliation: Farmers Insurance Group of Companies

Licensed in: All states except PR

Commenced Business: April 1866

Address: 500 Virginia Drive, Ft. Washington, PA 19034

Phone: (302) 252-2000   **Domicile State:** PA   **NAIC Code:** 20796

Data Date	Rating	RACR #1	RACR #2	Loss Ratio %	Total Assets ($mil)	Capital ($mil)	Net Premium ($mil)	Net Income ($mil)
6-16	B-	4.56	4.49	N/A	281.7	279.8	0.0	2.2
6-15	B-	4.58	4.46	N/A	278.6	274.9	0.0	2.9
2015	B-	4.55	4.49	0.0	282.2	279.5	0.0	6.1
2014	B-	4.53	4.43	0.0	275.7	270.6	0.0	8.9
2013	B-	4.58	4.46	0.0	264.5	257.9	0.0	11.3
2012	B-	4.74	4.60	0.0	256.4	240.6	0.0	10.9
2011	C+	4.94	4.75	0.0	252.1	221.5	0.0	15.4

Farmers Insurance Group of Companies
Composite Group Rating: C

Largest Group Members	Assets ($mil)	Rating
FARMERS INS EXCHANGE	15567	C
MID-CENTURY INS CO	3905	B-
FIRE INS EXCHANGE	2335	C+
FOREMOST INS CO	2172	B
TRUCK INS EXCHANGE	2165	C+

21ST CENTURY SECURITY INS CO   B   Good

Major Rating Factors: History of adequate reserve strength (6.0 on a scale of 0 to 10) as reserves have been consistently at an acceptable level. Good overall profitability index (6.3). Fair expense controls. Return on equity has been low, averaging 2.4% over the past five years.

Other Rating Factors: Fair overall results on stability tests (4.6) including weak results on operational trends. Affiliation with Farmers Insurance Group of Companies is a strength. Strong long-term capitalization index (10.0) based on excellent current risk adjusted capital (severe and moderate loss scenarios), despite some fluctuation in capital levels. Superior liquidity (10.0) with ample operational cash flow and liquid investments.

Principal Business: Auto liability (75%) and auto physical damage (25%).

Principal Investments: Investment grade bonds (87%), misc. investments (12%), and cash (1%).

Investments in Affiliates: 12%

Group Affiliation: Farmers Insurance Group of Companies

Licensed in: AK, AR, CO, DC, DE, FL, ID, IN, IA, LA, ME, MD, MI, MN, MS, NE, NH, NY, ND, OK, OR, PA, SC, SD, TX, UT, VT, VA, WA, WV, WI

Commenced Business: January 1952

Address: 4501 Northpoint Pkwy, Ste 500, Alpharetta, GA 30022

Phone: (302) 252-2000   **Domicile State:** PA   **NAIC Code:** 23833

Data Date	Rating	RACR #1	RACR #2	Loss Ratio %	Total Assets ($mil)	Capital ($mil)	Net Premium ($mil)	Net Income ($mil)
6-16	B	8.78	8.53	N/A	198.7	196.5	0.0	0.8
6-15	B	8.61	8.19	N/A	198.1	194.1	0.0	2.1
2015	B	8.75	8.51	0.0	198.3	195.7	0.0	3.6
2014	B	8.54	8.13	0.0	196.4	191.9	0.0	3.2
2013	B	8.39	7.89	0.0	195.3	188.5	0.0	4.0
2012	B	8.25	7.73	0.0	196.9	184.2	0.0	4.6
2011	B	8.23	7.64	0.0	202.8	178.6	0.0	8.6

Reserve Deficiency (as % of capital)

2011   2012   2013   2014   2015

■ 1 Yr Dev   □ 2 Yr Dev

* Adequate & redundant reserves show as negatives

ACCIDENT FUND INS CO OF AMERICA   B-   Good

Major Rating Factors: Fair overall results on stability tests (4.6 on a scale of 0 to 10) including potential drain of affiliation with Blue Cross Blue Shield of Michigan and weak results on operational trends. Fair reserve development (3.7) as reserves have generally been sufficient to cover claims. In 2011, the two year reserve development was 18% deficient.

Other Rating Factors: Good liquidity (6.9) with sufficient resources (cash flows and marketable investments) to handle a spike in claims. Strong long-term capitalization index (7.0) based on excellent current risk adjusted capital (severe and moderate loss scenarios). Moreover, capital levels have been consistent in recent years. Excellent profitability (7.2).

Principal Business: Workers compensation (99%).

Principal Investments: Investment grade bonds (57%), misc. investments (39%), and non investment grade bonds (4%).

Investments in Affiliates: 18%

Group Affiliation: Blue Cross Blue Shield of Michigan

Licensed in: All states except PR

Commenced Business: December 1994

Address: 232 S Capitol Ave, Lansing, MI 48933

Phone: (517) 342-4200   **Domicile State:** MI   **NAIC Code:** 10166

Data Date	Rating	RACR #1	RACR #2	Loss Ratio %	Total Assets ($mil)	Capital ($mil)	Net Premium ($mil)	Net Income ($mil)
6-16	B-	1.29	1.02	N/A	3,099.4	872.7	423.0	42.8
6-15	B-	1.32	1.06	N/A	2,665.2	783.0	371.6	55.9
2015	B-	1.26	1.01	64.5	2,780.5	813.8	812.6	107.0
2014	B-	1.31	1.07	72.5	2,387.0	750.9	717.4	62.6
2013	C+	1.46	1.18	65.9	2,257.7	684.1	546.7	30.5
2012	C+	1.40	1.12	73.2	2,300.3	633.6	489.0	37.5
2011	C+	1.31	1.03	87.6	2,126.6	578.9	480.5	-26.6

Rating Indexes

Ranges   Cap. 2   Stab.   Res.   Prof.   Liq.

■ Weak   ▨ Fair   ▤ Good   □ Strong

ACE AMERICAN INS CO　　　　　　　　　　　　　B-　　　Good

Major Rating Factors: Fair overall results on stability tests (4.0 on a scale of 0 to 10) including potential drain of affiliation with Chubb Limited and weak results on operational trends. The largest net exposure for one risk is conservative at 2.0% of capital. Good overall profitability index (6.6). Good expense controls. Return on equity has been good over the last five years, averaging 12.4%.

Other Rating Factors: Good liquidity (6.7) with sufficient resources (cash flows and marketable investments) to handle a spike in claims. Strong long-term capitalization index (7.2) based on excellent current risk adjusted capital (severe and moderate loss scenarios), despite some fluctuation in capital levels. Ample reserve history (7.7) that can protect against increases in claims costs.

Principal Business: Other liability (32%), workers compensation (17%), group accident & health (12%), commercial multiple peril (10%), auto liability (6%), fire (4%), and other lines (18%).

Principal Investments: Investment grade bonds (55%), misc. investments (29%), non investment grade bonds (15%), and real estate (1%).

Investments in Affiliates: 20%

Group Affiliation: Chubb Limited

Licensed in: All states, the District of Columbia and Puerto Rico

Commenced Business: January 1946

Address: 436 Walnut St, Philadelphia, PA 19106

Phone: (215) 640-1000　**Domicile State:** PA　**NAIC Code:** 22667

Data Date	Rating	RACR #1	RACR #2	Loss Ratio %	Total Assets ($mil)	Capital ($mil)	Net Premium ($mil)	Net Income ($mil)
6-16	B-	1.42	1.13	N/A	12,643.3	2,758.5	800.3	82.8
6-15	B-	1.39	1.13	N/A	12,421.2	2,722.3	756.2	53.5
2015	B-	1.36	1.09	72.8	12,074.0	2,578.8	1,760.5	214.0
2014	B-	1.57	1.29	77.6	12,150.7	2,992.9	1,656.5	251.2
2013	B-	1.39	1.16	72.2	11,697.3	2,677.0	1,610.8	412.3
2012	B-	1.20	1.05	89.9	11,040.6	2,425.8	1,658.0	58.9
2011	B-	1.07	0.94	80.7	10,093.3	2,000.2	1,572.3	616.3

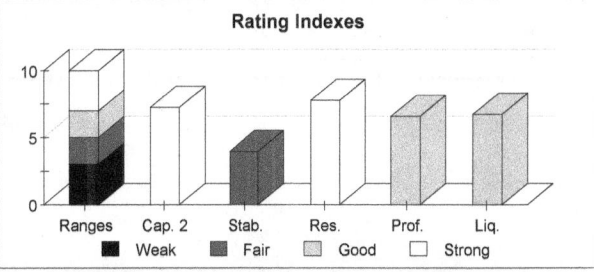

Rating Indexes

Ranges　Cap. 2　Stab.　Res.　Prof.　Liq.
■ Weak　■ Fair　□ Good　□ Strong

ACE P&C INS CO　　　　　　　　　　　　　　　B-　　　Good

Major Rating Factors: Fair overall results on stability tests (3.8 on a scale of 0 to 10) including potential drain of affiliation with Chubb Limited and weak results on operational trends. The largest net exposure for one risk is acceptable at 2.5% of capital. Good liquidity (6.9) with sufficient resources (cash flows and marketable investments) to handle a spike in claims.

Other Rating Factors: Strong long-term capitalization index (8.2) based on excellent current risk adjusted capital (severe and moderate loss scenarios), despite some fluctuation in capital levels. Ample reserve history (7.8) that can protect against increases in claims costs. Excellent profitability (7.8) with operating gains in each of the last five years.

Principal Business: Allied lines (76%), other liability (19%), and auto liability (3%).

Principal Investments: Investment grade bonds (76%), misc. investments (19%), and non investment grade bonds (6%).

Investments in Affiliates: 3%

Group Affiliation: Chubb Limited

Licensed in: All states, the District of Columbia and Puerto Rico

Commenced Business: August 1819

Address: 436 Walnut St, Philadelphia, PA 19106

Phone: (215) 640-1000　**Domicile State:** PA　**NAIC Code:** 20699

Data Date	Rating	RACR #1	RACR #2	Loss Ratio %	Total Assets ($mil)	Capital ($mil)	Net Premium ($mil)	Net Income ($mil)
6-16	B-	2.62	1.76	N/A	8,959.9	2,051.1	757.0	84.6
6-15	C	2.96	2.00	N/A	7,371.6	2,124.2	715.3	49.4
2015	C+	2.67	1.81	72.8	7,748.8	1,995.9	1,665.3	136.2
2014	C	3.02	2.05	77.6	7,360.7	2,064.4	1,567.0	115.6
2013	C	2.95	2.01	72.2	7,214.1	1,920.5	1,523.8	165.6
2012	C	2.93	1.96	89.9	7,925.9	1,802.5	1,568.4	68.6
2011	C	2.74	1.82	80.7	6,425.0	1,620.8	1,489.5	128.9

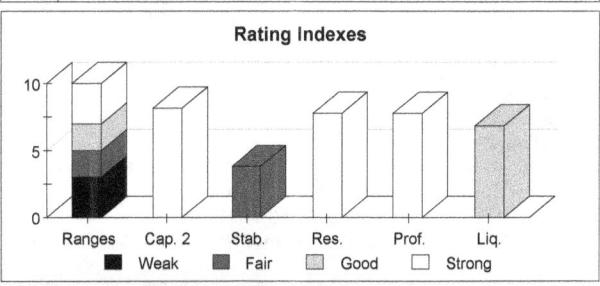

Rating Indexes

Ranges　Cap. 2　Stab.　Res.　Prof.　Liq.
■ Weak　■ Fair　□ Good　□ Strong

ACUITY A MUTUAL INS CO *　　　　　　　　　B+　　　Good

Major Rating Factors: Good liquidity (6.7 on a scale of 0 to 10) with sufficient resources (cash flows and marketable investments) to handle a spike in claims. Good overall results on stability tests (5.1) despite weak results on operational trends.

Other Rating Factors: Strong long-term capitalization index (9.4) based on excellent current risk adjusted capital (severe and moderate loss scenarios). Moreover, capital levels have been consistent in recent years. Ample reserve history (9.3) that helps to protect the company against sharp claims increases. Excellent profitability (8.9) with operating gains in each of the last five years.

Principal Business: Workers compensation (24%), auto liability (22%), auto physical damage (14%), commercial multiple peril (11%), homeowners multiple peril (10%), other liability (10%), and other lines (9%).

Principal Investments: Investment grade bonds (62%), misc. investments (29%), real estate (7%), and non investment grade bonds (3%).

Investments in Affiliates: None

Group Affiliation: None

Licensed in: AL, AZ, AR, CO, DE, GA, ID, IL, IN, IA, KS, KY, ME, MI, MN, MS, MO, MT, NE, NV, NM, ND, OH, OK, OR, PA, SD, TN, TX, UT, VT, VA, WA, WV, WI, WY

Commenced Business: September 1925

Address: 2800 S Taylor Dr, Sheboygan, WI 53081-8470

Phone: (920) 458-9131　**Domicile State:** WI　**NAIC Code:** 14184

Data Date	Rating	RACR #1	RACR #2	Loss Ratio %	Total Assets ($mil)	Capital ($mil)	Net Premium ($mil)	Net Income ($mil)
6-16	B+	4.40	2.65	N/A	3,483.6	1,521.1	635.6	81.1
6-15	B	3.92	2.39	N/A	3,257.0	1,427.4	602.4	82.9
2015	B+	4.33	2.64	61.9	3,349.5	1,429.9	1,269.9	142.0
2014	B	3.83	2.36	65.1	3,101.0	1,323.4	1,189.2	113.2
2013	B	3.77	2.33	62.0	2,826.4	1,202.3	1,074.0	111.1
2012	B	3.85	2.40	63.2	2,475.2	994.3	937.8	95.4
2011	B	4.10	2.61	67.9	2,231.7	870.4	799.0	50.5

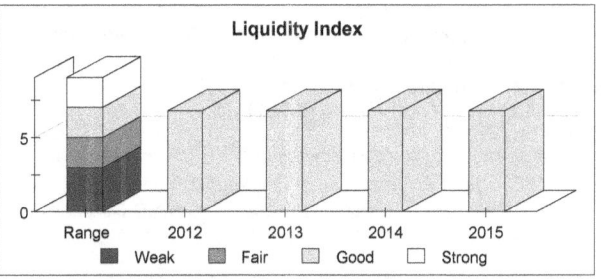

Liquidity Index

Range　2012　2013　2014　2015
■ Weak　■ Fair　□ Good　□ Strong

ADMIRAL INS CO   C   Fair

Major Rating Factors: Fair profitability index (3.4). Fair expense controls. Return on equity has been fair, averaging 29.5% over the past five years.
Other Rating Factors: Fair overall results on stability tests (3.9) including weak results on operational trends. Strong long-term capitalization index (7.8) based on excellent current risk adjusted capital (severe and moderate loss scenarios), despite some fluctuation in capital levels. Superior liquidity (10.0) with ample operational cash flow and liquid investments.
Principal Business: (Not applicable due to unusual reinsurance transactions.)
Principal Investments: Misc. investments (51%) and investment grade bonds (49%).
Investments in Affiliates: 50%
Group Affiliation: W R Berkley Corp
Licensed in: All states, the District of Columbia and Puerto Rico
Commenced Business: November 1952
Address: 1255 Orange Street, Wilmington, DE 19801
Phone: (856) 429-9200   **Domicile State:** DE   **NAIC Code:** 24856

Data Date	Rating	RACR #1	RACR #2	Loss Ratio %	Total Assets ($mil)	Capital ($mil)	Net Premium ($mil)	Net Income ($mil)
6-16	C	1.66	1.65	N/A	732.7	641.9	0.0	4.1
6-15	C-	1.68	1.67	N/A	713.0	623.2	0.0	3.8
2015	C	1.81	1.92	0.0	710.2	634.0	0.0	8.4
2014	C-	1.82	1.94	0.0	688.5	615.6	0.0	11.2
2013	C-	1.91	2.07	0.0	667.4	597.6	-255.7	826.2
2012	C	1.50	1.39	62.2	3,142.1	1,688.4	520.3	150.7
2011	C	1.35	1.24	59.6	3,018.2	1,481.0	499.0	170.1

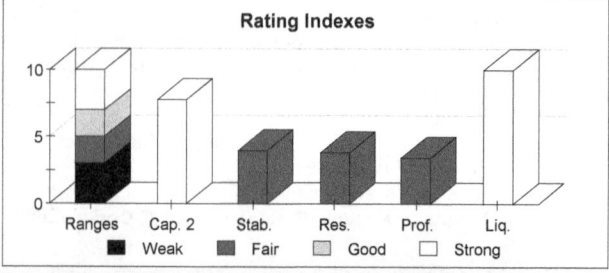

Rating Indexes

AFFILIATED FM INS CO   C   Fair

Major Rating Factors: Weak overall results on stability tests (2.6 on a scale of 0 to 10) including weak results on operational trends. The largest net exposure for one risk is excessive at 9.2% of capital. History of adequate reserve strength (6.5) as reserves have been consistently at an acceptable level.
Other Rating Factors: Good overall profitability index (6.5) despite operating losses during 2011. Return on equity has been fair, averaging 6.2% over the past five years. Good liquidity (6.9) with sufficient resources (cash flows and marketable investments) to handle a spike in claims. Strong long-term capitalization index (9.3) based on excellent current risk adjusted capital (severe and moderate loss scenarios). Moreover, capital levels have been consistent in recent years.
Principal Business: Fire (33%), inland marine (28%), allied lines (19%), commercial multiple peril (10%), boiler & machinery (7%), and ocean marine (3%).
Principal Investments: Investment grade bonds (56%), misc. investments (41%), and cash (3%).
Investments in Affiliates: None
Group Affiliation: Factory Mutual Ins
Licensed in: All states, the District of Columbia and Puerto Rico
Commenced Business: June 1950
Address: 270 Central Ave, Johnston, RI 02919-4949
Phone: (401) 275-3000   **Domicile State:** RI   **NAIC Code:** 10014

Data Date	Rating	RACR #1	RACR #2	Loss Ratio %	Total Assets ($mil)	Capital ($mil)	Net Premium ($mil)	Net Income ($mil)
6-16	C	3.98	2.44	N/A	2,889.7	1,520.6	208.0	26.2
6-15	C	4.17	2.58	N/A	2,614.2	1,439.0	194.4	51.7
2015	C	4.39	2.71	58.8	2,589.3	1,479.6	420.5	121.6
2014	C	4.35	2.70	52.5	2,528.7	1,397.6	386.6	119.1
2013	C	3.60	2.27	50.6	2,327.1	1,262.1	387.6	124.4
2012	C	2.70	1.77	59.7	2,302.2	1,034.1	444.2	86.0
2011	C	4.08	2.47	95.2	1,874.6	905.6	389.2	-23.7

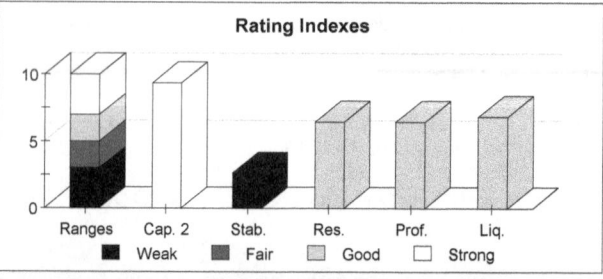

Rating Indexes

AGRINATIONAL INS CO   D   Weak

Major Rating Factors: Weak overall results on stability tests (1.3 on a scale of 0 to 10) including weak results on operational trends and negative cash flow from operations for 2015. The largest net exposure for one risk is excessive at 18.5% of capital. Good long-term capitalization index (5.4) based on good current risk adjusted capital (severe and moderate loss scenarios). Over the last several years, capital levels have remained relatively consistent.
Other Rating Factors: Good overall profitability index (5.7) despite operating losses during 2012. Return on equity has been low, averaging 2.6% over the past five years. Good liquidity (5.4) with sufficient resources (cash flows and marketable investments) to handle a spike in claims. Ample reserve history (9.6) that helps to protect the company against sharp claims increases.
Principal Business: Credit (77%), ocean marine (20%), other liability (2%), and commercial multiple peril (1%).
Principal Investments: Misc. investments (56%), investment grade bonds (29%), and cash (15%).
Investments in Affiliates: 53%
Group Affiliation: Archer Daniels Midland Co
Licensed in: AZ, CO, FL, VT
Commenced Business: September 1987
Address: 76 St Paul St Suite 500, Burlington, VT 05401-4477
Phone: (802) 862-4400   **Domicile State:** VT   **NAIC Code:** 10541

Data Date	Rating	RACR #1	RACR #2	Loss Ratio %	Total Assets ($mil)	Capital ($mil)	Net Premium ($mil)	Net Income ($mil)
6-16	D	0.96	0.78	N/A	658.6	248.1	138.6	25.0
6-15	E+	1.06	0.89	N/A	641.4	253.0	112.4	16.6
2015	D	1.00	0.81	72.3	973.5	254.2	287.3	20.2
2014	E+	0.90	0.73	73.6	974.9	243.1	212.1	23.1
2013	E	0.52	0.40	90.2	822.6	165.8	229.9	0.1
2012	E	0.48	0.37	106.5	790.5	164.8	192.9	-21.9
2011	E	0.66	0.54	87.9	705.9	181.5	162.7	0.2

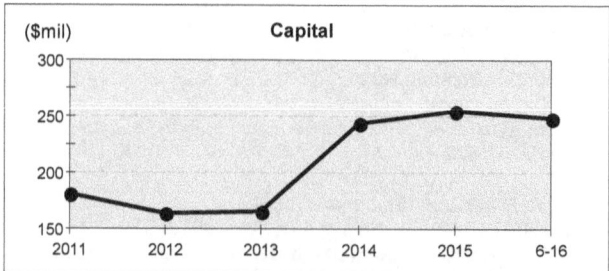

Capital

AIG PROPERTY CASUALTY CO   C   Fair

Major Rating Factors: Fair reserve development (3.8 on a scale of 0 to 10) as reserves have generally been sufficient to cover claims. In 2011, the two year reserve development was 17% deficient. Fair profitability index (4.5). Fair expense controls. ROE has been fair, averaging 26.8% over the past five years.

Other Rating Factors: Weak overall results on stability tests (2.8) including weak results on operational trends and negative cash flow from operations for 2015. The largest net exposure for one risk is excessive at 11.7% of capital. Strengths include potentially strong support from affiliation with American International Group. Good liquidity (6.3) with sufficient resources (cash flows and marketable investments) to handle a spike in claims. Strong long-term capitalization index (7.7) based on excellent current risk adjusted capital (severe and moderate loss scenarios), despite some fluctuation in capital levels.

Principal Business: Homeowners multiple peril (51%), inland marine (12%), other liability (9%), auto physical damage (8%), auto liability (7%), earthquake (5%), and other lines (9%).

Principal Investments: Investment grade bonds (68%), misc. investments (27%), non investment grade bonds (4%), and cash (1%).

Investments in Affiliates: 0%

Group Affiliation: American International Group

Licensed in: All states except HI, PR

Commenced Business: August 1871

Address: 2595 Interstate Dr Suite 103, Harrisburg, PA 17110

Phone: (212) 770-7000   **Domicile State:** PA   **NAIC Code:** 19402

Data Date	Rating	RACR #1	RACR #2	Loss Ratio %	Total Assets ($mil)	Capital ($mil)	Net Premium ($mil)	Net Income ($mil)
6-16	C	2.27	1.53	N/A	4,187.6	1,103.1	440.0	487.9
6-15	C+	2.12	1.33	N/A	5,140.5	1,591.1	445.6	57.4
2015	C	2.16	1.36	88.8	4,730.2	1,312.8	927.5	246.8
2014	C+	2.27	1.45	76.5	5,026.5	1,587.1	1,034.9	158.0
2013	C+	2.30	1.46	76.6	3,656.5	1,166.3	713.5	124.6
2012	C+	2.27	1.47	87.1	3,475.7	1,080.2	615.3	668.0
2011	C+	1.77	1.42	83.9	4,068.2	1,700.5	626.7	27.8

Reserve Deficiency (as % of capital)

* Adequate & redundant reserves show as negatives

■ 1 Yr Dev   □ 2 Yr Dev

ALAMANCE INS CO   C-   Fair

Major Rating Factors: Weak overall results on stability tests (2.6 on a scale of 0 to 10) including potential drain of affiliation with IFG Companies and weak results on operational trends. Strong long-term capitalization index (7.7) based on excellent current risk adjusted capital (severe and moderate loss scenarios), despite some fluctuation in capital levels.

Other Rating Factors: Ample reserve history (7.8) that can protect against increases in claims costs. Excellent profitability (7.4) with operating gains in each of the last five years. Excellent liquidity (8.1) with ample operational cash flow and liquid investments.

Principal Business: (This company is a reinsurer.)

Principal Investments: Misc. investments (60%) and investment grade bonds (40%).

Investments in Affiliates: 58%

Group Affiliation: IFG Companies

Licensed in: All states except CA, PR

Commenced Business: December 1998

Address: 238 International Road, Burlington, NC 27215

Phone: (336) 586-2500   **Domicile State:** IL   **NAIC Code:** 10957

Data Date	Rating	RACR #1	RACR #2	Loss Ratio %	Total Assets ($mil)	Capital ($mil)	Net Premium ($mil)	Net Income ($mil)
6-16	C-	1.49	1.46	N/A	485.5	378.9	14.6	4.3
6-15	C-	1.50	1.46	N/A	497.3	382.8	18.2	5.3
2015	C-	1.48	1.45	44.4	485.3	373.8	32.8	11.0
2014	C-	1.46	1.43	56.5	488.1	369.5	36.6	8.4
2013	C-	1.45	1.42	50.6	480.6	358.1	40.7	14.7
2012	C-	1.46	1.43	60.2	460.9	334.1	43.1	9.6
2011	C-	1.45	1.43	58.9	450.2	326.6	35.9	7.2

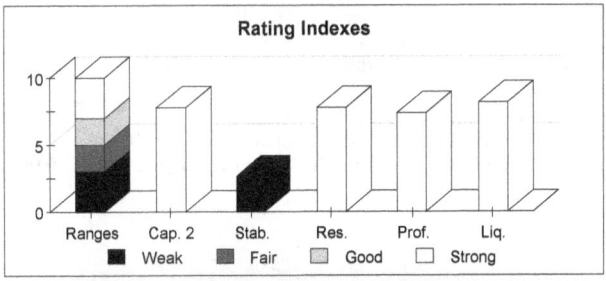

Rating Indexes

Ranges   Cap. 2   Stab.   Res.   Prof.   Liq.

■ Weak   ■ Fair   ▨ Good   □ Strong

ALASKA NATIONAL INS CO   B   Good

Major Rating Factors: Fair overall results on stability tests (4.7 on a scale of 0 to 10) including weak results on operational trends. Strong long-term capitalization index (9.2) based on excellent current risk adjusted capital (severe and moderate loss scenarios), despite some fluctuation in capital levels.

Other Rating Factors: Ample reserve history (9.4) that helps to protect the company against sharp claims increases. Excellent profitability (8.7) with operating gains in each of the last five years. Return on equity has been good over the last five years, averaging 10.9%. Excellent liquidity (7.4) with ample operational cash flow and liquid investments.

Principal Business: Workers compensation (78%), commercial multiple peril (6%), other liability (6%), auto liability (5%), inland marine (2%), auto physical damage (1%), and other lines (2%).

Principal Investments: Investment grade bonds (74%), misc. investments (25%), and cash (1%).

Investments in Affiliates: None

Group Affiliation: Alaska National Corp

Licensed in: AL, AK, AZ, CA, CO, FL, HI, ID, IL, IA, KS, LA, MN, MS, MO, MT, NV, NM, ND, OK, OR, SD, TX, UT, WA, WY

Commenced Business: October 1980

Address: 7001 Jewell Lake Rd, Anchorage, AK 99502-2800

Phone: (907) 248-2642   **Domicile State:** AK   **NAIC Code:** 38733

Data Date	Rating	RACR #1	RACR #2	Loss Ratio %	Total Assets ($mil)	Capital ($mil)	Net Premium ($mil)	Net Income ($mil)
6-16	B	3.46	2.42	N/A	916.1	410.9	106.7	18.8
6-15	B	3.03	2.11	N/A	883.8	379.1	106.1	20.6
2015	B	3.48	2.47	56.3	889.0	387.8	228.5	36.4
2014	B	3.10	2.13	55.7	879.8	380.5	212.3	50.5
2013	B	3.18	2.20	51.3	830.4	352.2	200.6	50.3
2012	B	3.45	2.42	69.2	753.4	293.6	183.9	20.9
2011	B	4.67	3.19	55.8	691.5	303.6	135.2	33.9

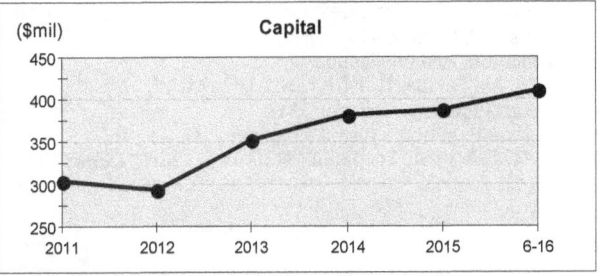

Capital

ALFA MUTUAL FIRE INS CO

B   Good

Major Rating Factors: Good overall profitability index (5.1 on a scale of 0 to 10) despite operating losses during 2011. Good liquidity (6.3) with sufficient resources (cash flows and marketable investments) to handle a spike in claims.
Other Rating Factors: Fair overall results on stability tests (4.9) including weak results on operational trends. Strong long-term capitalization index (8.4) based on excellent current risk adjusted capital (severe and moderate loss scenarios), despite some fluctuation in capital levels. Ample reserve history (7.7) that can protect against increases in claims costs.
Principal Business: Fire (48%), allied lines (44%), and inland marine (8%).
Principal Investments: Investment grade bonds (55%), misc. investments (42%), cash (1%), non investment grade bonds (1%), and real estate (1%).
Investments in Affiliates: 28%
Group Affiliation: Alfa Ins Group
Licensed in: AL, VA
Commenced Business: August 1946
Address: 2108 East South Blvd, Montgomery, AL 36116
Phone: (334) 288-3900   **Domicile State:** AL   **NAIC Code:** 19143

Data Date	Rating	RACR #1	RACR #2	Loss Ratio %	Total Assets ($mil)	Capital ($mil)	Net Premium ($mil)	Net Income ($mil)
6-16	B	2.41	1.90	N/A	715.5	408.4	176.0	2.7
6-15	B	2.28	1.73	N/A	720.3	430.1	168.3	6.4
2015	B	2.43	1.93	70.6	699.0	409.8	341.5	16.2
2014	B	2.23	1.71	70.2	697.1	419.8	336.0	8.0
2013	B	1.96	1.48	68.6	659.5	399.3	327.1	25.7
2012	B	1.65	1.23	68.5	608.2	362.6	311.3	12.3
2011	B	1.50	1.12	90.5	604.8	339.0	311.6	-30.1

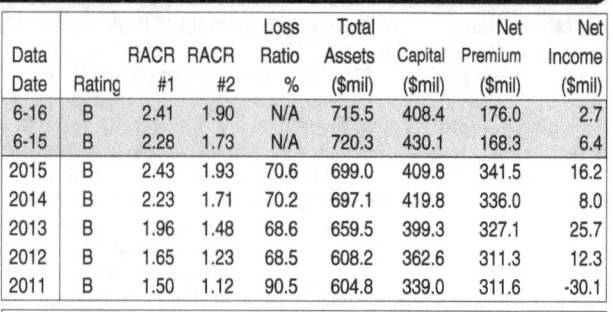

ALFA MUTUAL GENERAL INS CO *

B+   Good

Major Rating Factors: Good overall profitability index (5.6 on a scale of 0 to 10) despite operating losses during 2011. Good liquidity (6.6) with sufficient resources (cash flows and marketable investments) to handle a spike in claims.
Other Rating Factors: Good overall results on stability tests (5.0) despite weak results on operational trends. The largest net exposure for one risk is conservative at 1.3% of capital. Strong long-term capitalization index (8.5) based on excellent current risk adjusted capital (severe and moderate loss scenarios), despite some fluctuation in capital levels. Ample reserve history (7.5) that can protect against increases in claims costs.
Principal Business: Homeowners multiple peril (52%), auto liability (26%), auto physical damage (21%), and other liability (1%).
Principal Investments: Investment grade bonds (56%), misc. investments (38%), cash (5%), and non investment grade bonds (1%).
Investments in Affiliates: 1%
Group Affiliation: Alfa Ins Group
Licensed in: AL, GA, MS
Commenced Business: October 1955
Address: 2108 East South Blvd, Montgomery, AL 36116
Phone: (334) 288-3900   **Domicile State:** AL   **NAIC Code:** 19151

Data Date	Rating	RACR #1	RACR #2	Loss Ratio %	Total Assets ($mil)	Capital ($mil)	Net Premium ($mil)	Net Income ($mil)
6-16	B+	3.16	2.04	N/A	103.4	56.3	23.5	0.5
6-15	B+	2.77	1.82	N/A	106.1	59.5	22.4	4.3
2015	B+	3.12	2.04	70.7	100.9	56.9	45.5	5.8
2014	B+	2.40	1.57	70.3	99.0	57.9	44.8	3.4
2013	B+	2.35	1.58	68.8	94.8	54.3	43.6	4.1
2012	B	1.89	1.28	69.0	86.8	48.3	41.5	3.2
2011	B	1.61	1.09	91.1	81.8	43.4	41.6	-5.9

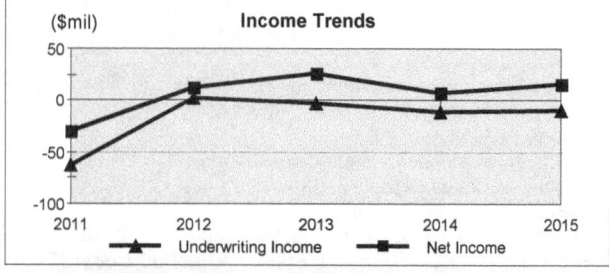

ALFA MUTUAL INS CO

B   Good

Major Rating Factors: History of adequate reserve strength (6.5 on a scale of 0 to 10) as reserves have been consistently at an acceptable level. Fair liquidity (3.6) as cash resources may not be adequate to cover a spike in claims.
Other Rating Factors: Fair overall results on stability tests (4.6) including weak results on operational trends. Strong long-term capitalization index (7.2) based on excellent current risk adjusted capital (severe and moderate loss scenarios), despite some fluctuation in capital levels. Weak profitability index (2.9) with operating losses during 2011.
Principal Business: Homeowners multiple peril (30%), auto physical damage (29%), auto liability (28%), farmowners multiple peril (8%), commercial multiple peril (3%), and inland marine (1%).
Principal Investments: Misc. investments (57%), investment grade bonds (35%), real estate (5%), non investment grade bonds (2%), and cash (1%).
Investments in Affiliates: 41%
Group Affiliation: Alfa Ins Group
Licensed in: AL, FL, GA, IL, IN, KY, NC, OH, PA, VA
Commenced Business: October 1947
Address: 2108 East South Blvd, Montgomery, AL 36116
Phone: (334) 288-3900   **Domicile State:** AL   **NAIC Code:** 19135

Data Date	Rating	RACR #1	RACR #2	Loss Ratio %	Total Assets ($mil)	Capital ($mil)	Net Premium ($mil)	Net Income ($mil)
6-16	B	1.31	1.08	N/A	1,251.2	487.1	305.1	2.3
6-15	B	1.33	1.07	N/A	1,261.6	523.9	291.8	9.5
2015	B	1.35	1.13	70.5	1,239.6	497.9	592.0	24.9
2014	B	1.38	1.11	70.2	1,275.0	537.8	582.4	12.4
2013	B	1.59	1.25	68.7	1,231.2	580.4	566.7	48.5
2012	B	1.40	1.09	69.5	1,150.4	525.1	539.4	11.8
2011	B	1.29	1.00	91.4	1,125.1	482.4	539.8	-84.9

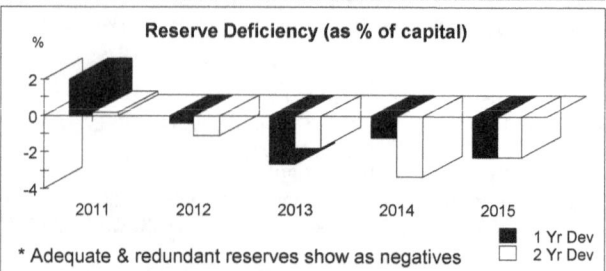

* Adequate & redundant reserves show as negatives

ALL AMERICA INS CO *   B+   Good

Major Rating Factors: Good liquidity (6.8 on a scale of 0 to 10) with sufficient resources (cash flows and marketable investments) to handle a spike in claims. Good overall results on stability tests (5.0) despite weak results on operational trends.

Other Rating Factors: Strong long-term capitalization index (10.0) based on excellent current risk adjusted capital (severe and moderate loss scenarios). Moreover, capital levels have been consistent in recent years. Ample reserve history (9.3) that helps to protect the company against sharp claims increases. Excellent profitability (7.6) with operating gains in each of the last five years.

Principal Business: Commercial multiple peril (58%), auto liability (20%), workers compensation (8%), auto physical damage (8%), and products liability (5%).

Principal Investments: Investment grade bonds (97%) and misc. investments (3%).

Investments in Affiliates: 0%

Group Affiliation: Central Mutual Ins Group

Licensed in: AZ, AR, CA, CO, CT, GA, ID, IL, IN, IA, KY, ME, MD, MA, MI, MS, NV, NJ, NY, NC, OH, OK, SC, TN, TX, VT, VA, WI

Commenced Business: August 1961

Address: 800 S Washington St, Van Wert, OH 45891

Phone: (419) 238-1010   **Domicile State:** OH   **NAIC Code:** 20222

Data Date	Rating	RACR #1	RACR #2	Loss Ratio %	Total Assets ($mil)	Capital ($mil)	Net Premium ($mil)	Net Income ($mil)
6-16	B+	6.03	4.12	N/A	280.0	147.0	47.3	0.8
6-15	B+	5.77	3.92	N/A	267.6	137.9	43.6	2.9
2015	B+	6.26	4.32	57.9	275.8	146.0	93.0	11.2
2014	B+	5.95	4.08	59.8	258.8	134.7	85.3	10.3
2013	B+	5.49	3.68	58.4	247.7	124.7	76.6	11.5
2012	B	5.05	3.35	70.7	240.3	113.5	70.4	5.0
2011	B	4.43	2.92	79.3	239.7	107.3	71.6	0.7

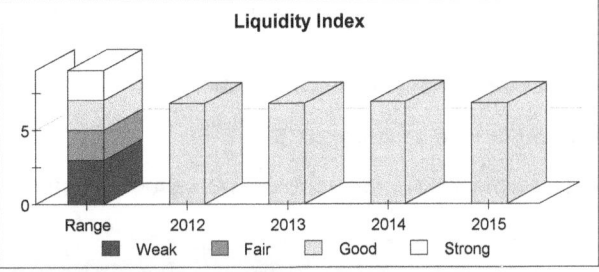

Liquidity Index

ALLIANZ GLOBAL RISKS US INS CO   C   Fair

Major Rating Factors: Fair profitability index (3.2 on a scale of 0 to 10) with operating losses during 2012 and the first six months of 2016. Average return on equity over the last five years has been poor at -1.3%. Fair overall results on stability tests (3.5) including weak results on operational trends, negative cash flow from operations for 2015 and excessive premium growth. The largest net exposure for one risk is high at 3.6% of capital.

Other Rating Factors: Good long-term capitalization index (5.7) based on fair current risk adjusted capital (severe and moderate loss scenarios), although results have slipped from the excellent range during the last year. Good liquidity (6.9) with sufficient resources (cash flows and marketable investments) to handle a spike in claims. Ample reserve history (8.4) that helps to protect the company against sharp claims increases.

Principal Business: Fire (28%), aircraft (21%), products liability (13%), inland marine (10%), other liability (10%), allied lines (8%), and other lines (11%).

Principal Investments: Misc. investments (66%), investment grade bonds (32%), cash (1%), and non investment grade bonds (1%).

Investments in Affiliates: 39%

Group Affiliation: Allianz Ins Group

Licensed in: All states, the District of Columbia and Puerto Rico

Commenced Business: December 1977

Address: 225 W Washington St Suite 1800, Chicago, IL 60606-3484

Phone: (888) 466-7883   **Domicile State:** IL   **NAIC Code:** 35300

Data Date	Rating	RACR #1	RACR #2	Loss Ratio %	Total Assets ($mil)	Capital ($mil)	Net Premium ($mil)	Net Income ($mil)
6-16	C	0.84	0.62	N/A	8,012.3	1,767.9	754.4	-193.7
6-15	C	2.29	1.46	N/A	5,229.1	2,772.3	549.9	60.9
2015	C	1.22	1.06	72.0	4,345.4	1,862.2	1,093.4	32.8
2014	C	0.80	0.51	73.1	3,322.7	759.1	1,236.6	44.4
2013	C-	0.74	0.52	79.5	3,176.9	867.3	868.2	10.0
2012	C-	0.75	0.54	82.8	3,099.8	866.9	916.0	-86.7
2011	C+	1.19	1.11	61.8	5,922.9	3,816.3	914.3	202.9

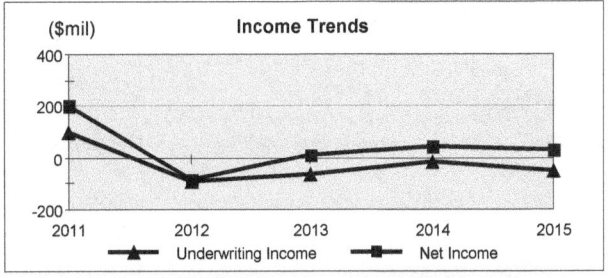

Income Trends

ALLIED WORLD INS CO   C   Fair

Major Rating Factors: Fair overall results on stability tests (3.4 on a scale of 0 to 10) including potential drain of affiliation with Allied World Asr Holding Group and weak results on operational trends. Strong long-term capitalization index (7.8) based on excellent current risk adjusted capital (severe and moderate loss scenarios), despite some fluctuation in capital levels.

Other Rating Factors: Ample reserve history (7.4) that can protect against increases in claims costs. Excellent profitability (7.3) despite modest operating losses during 2012. Excellent liquidity (7.0) with ample operational cash flow and liquid investments.

Principal Business: Other liability (86%), surety (7%), auto liability (2%), inland marine (1%), allied lines (1%), commercial multiple peril (1%), and fire (1%).

Principal Investments: Misc. investments (62%), investment grade bonds (31%), and non investment grade bonds (7%).

Investments in Affiliates: 47%

Group Affiliation: Allied World Asr Holding Group

Licensed in: All states, the District of Columbia and Puerto Rico

Commenced Business: October 1986

Address: 14 Centre St, Concord, NH 03301

Phone: (646) 794-0500   **Domicile State:** NH   **NAIC Code:** 22730

Data Date	Rating	RACR #1	RACR #2	Loss Ratio %	Total Assets ($mil)	Capital ($mil)	Net Premium ($mil)	Net Income ($mil)
6-16	C	1.71	1.59	N/A	1,802.4	1,038.1	103.2	7.8
6-15	C	1.55	1.39	N/A	1,747.6	1,083.2	100.9	14.2
2015	C	1.68	1.52	69.1	1,749.6	1,082.3	214.6	15.3
2014	C	1.56	1.40	69.9	1,727.2	1,092.9	198.3	24.7
2013	C	1.57	1.44	67.8	1,687.3	1,044.5	177.2	13.6
2012	C	1.72	1.68	74.2	1,435.6	868.5	168.2	-4.2
2011	C	1.74	1.76	73.4	1,034.9	829.0	73.5	21.3

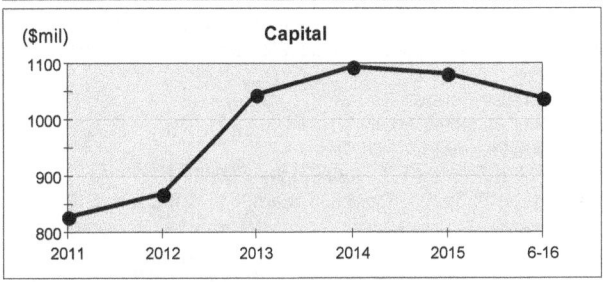

Capital

ALLIED WORLD SPECIALTY INS CO
B   Good

Major Rating Factors: Good liquidity (6.9 on a scale of 0 to 10) with sufficient resources (cash flows and marketable investments) to handle a spike in claims. Fair overall results on stability tests (4.7) including weak results on operational trends.

Other Rating Factors: Strong long-term capitalization index (9.6) based on excellent current risk adjusted capital (severe and moderate loss scenarios), despite some fluctuation in capital levels. Ample reserve history (7.6) that can protect against increases in claims costs. Excellent profitability (7.9) with operating gains in each of the last five years.

Principal Business: Other liability (49%), inland marine (17%), medical malpractice (11%), surety (6%), fire (5%), commercial multiple peril (4%), and other lines (8%).

Principal Investments: Investment grade bonds (74%), misc. investments (24%), and cash (2%).

Investments in Affiliates: 21%

Group Affiliation: Allied World Asr Holding Group

Licensed in: All states, the District of Columbia and Puerto Rico

Commenced Business: January 1972

Address: 10 Exchange Place, Jersey City, NJ 07302-3905

Phone: (860) 284-1300   **Domicile State:** DE   **NAIC Code:** 16624

Data Date	Rating	RACR #1	RACR #2	Loss Ratio %	Total Assets ($mil)	Capital ($mil)	Net Premium ($mil)	Net Income ($mil)
6-16	B	3.16	2.68	N/A	837.0	412.5	57.3	5.6
6-15	B-	2.49	2.00	N/A	815.2	394.6	56.1	7.3
2015	B	3.18	2.74	69.1	786.7	405.7	119.2	12.2
2014	B-	2.49	2.00	69.9	752.0	397.4	110.2	13.3
2013	B-	2.98	2.36	67.8	689.3	364.0	98.5	11.0
2012	B-	3.74	2.86	74.2	737.0	368.4	98.7	15.7
2011	C+	3.91	2.62	44.1	667.8	343.2	57.0	30.6

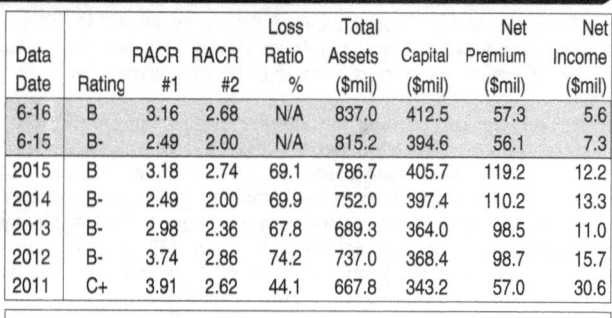

Liquidity Index

Range   2012   2013   2014   2015

■ Weak ■ Fair ▢ Good ▢ Strong

ALLSTATE F&C INS CO
C+   Fair

Major Rating Factors: Fair overall results on stability tests (4.3 on a scale of 0 to 10) including weak results on operational trends.

Other Rating Factors: Strong long-term capitalization index (10.0) based on excellent current risk adjusted capital (severe and moderate loss scenarios). Moreover, capital levels have been consistent in recent years. Excellent profitability (7.3) with operating gains in each of the last five years. Excellent expense controls. Superior liquidity (9.4) with ample operational cash flow and liquid investments.

Principal Business: Auto liability (55%), auto physical damage (41%), and homeowners multiple peril (4%).

Principal Investments: Investment grade bonds (97%) and misc. investments (3%).

Investments in Affiliates: None

Group Affiliation: Allstate Group

Licensed in: All states except CA, PR

Commenced Business: May 1973

Address: 2775 Sanders Rd, Northbrook, IL 60062-6127

Phone: (847) 402-5000   **Domicile State:** IL   **NAIC Code:** 29688

Data Date	Rating	RACR #1	RACR #2	Loss Ratio %	Total Assets ($mil)	Capital ($mil)	Net Premium ($mil)	Net Income ($mil)
6-16	C+	79.52	56.11	N/A	224.6	212.4	0.0	1.2
6-15	C	116.48	51.79	N/A	178.4	174.9	0.0	1.0
2015	C+	129.99	57.65	0.0	215.7	211.2	0.0	2.1
2014	C	136.54	60.77	0.0	175.3	173.9	0.0	1.6
2013	C	130.27	57.28	0.0	148.7	147.5	0.0	2.3
2012	C	171.45	77.79	0.0	141.7	140.1	0.0	2.1
2011	C	184.99	88.29	0.0	114.1	113.2	0.0	2.6

Allstate Group Composite Group Rating: B Largest Group Members	Assets ($mil)	Rating
ALLSTATE INS CO	43271	B
ALLSTATE LIFE INS CO	32348	B
ALLSTATE LIFE INS CO OF NEW YORK	6410	C+
ALLSTATE NJ INS CO	2445	B
AMERICAN HERITAGE LIFE INS CO	1831	B

ALLSTATE INS CO
B   Good

Major Rating Factors: History of adequate reserve strength (6.3 on a scale of 0 to 10) as reserves have been consistently at an acceptable level. Good overall results on stability tests (5.1) despite weak results on operational trends.

Other Rating Factors: Fair profitability index (3.9). Fair expense controls. Return on equity has been fair, averaging 10.0% over the past five years. Fair liquidity (4.4) as cash resources may not be adequate to cover a spike in claims. Strong long-term capitalization index (7.7) based on excellent current risk adjusted capital (severe and moderate loss scenarios), despite some fluctuation in capital levels.

Principal Business: Homeowners multiple peril (34%), auto liability (31%), auto physical damage (25%), commercial multiple peril (4%), allied lines (4%), other liability (1%), and inland marine (1%).

Principal Investments: Investment grade bonds (53%), misc. investments (32%), non investment grade bonds (16%), and real estate (1%).

Investments in Affiliates: 13%

Group Affiliation: Allstate Group

Licensed in: All states except NJ

Commenced Business: April 1931

Address: 2775 Sanders Rd, Northbrook, IL 60062-6127

Phone: (847) 402-5000   **Domicile State:** IL   **NAIC Code:** 19232

Data Date	Rating	RACR #1	RACR #2	Loss Ratio %	Total Assets ($mil)	Capital ($mil)	Net Premium ($mil)	Net Income ($mil)
6-16	B	1.89	1.45	N/A	43,881.3	14,856.0	14,080.8	271.8
6-15	B+	2.00	1.54	N/A	42,833.2	15,292.6	13,534.9	644.2
2015	B	1.97	1.52	70.1	43,271.2	15,318.3	27,774.3	1,705.4
2014	B+	2.15	1.68	68.0	43,246.3	16,265.6	26,453.4	2,313.8
2013	A-	2.21	1.72	66.4	43,733.3	17,254.7	25,108.5	2,465.5
2012	B+	2.07	1.62	69.4	42,133.1	16,260.9	24,193.4	1,950.4
2011	B+	1.78	1.42	78.4	41,023.0	15,126.7	23,547.7	223.0

Reserve Deficiency (as % of capital)

2011   2012   2013   2014   2015

* Adequate & redundant reserves show as negatives

■ 1 Yr Dev ▢ 2 Yr Dev

ALLSTATE NJ INS CO   B   Good

Major Rating Factors: History of adequate reserve strength (6.7 on a scale of 0 to 10) as reserves have been consistently at an acceptable level. Good liquidity (6.3) with sufficient resources (cash flows and marketable investments) to handle a spike in claims.

Other Rating Factors: Fair profitability index (3.9) with operating losses during 2011 and 2012. Return on equity has been fair, averaging 7.7% over the past five years. Fair overall results on stability tests (4.9) including weak results on operational trends. Strong long-term capitalization index (8.2) based on excellent current risk adjusted capital (severe and moderate loss scenarios), despite some fluctuation in capital levels.

Principal Business: Auto liability (43%), homeowners multiple peril (30%), auto physical damage (22%), allied lines (2%), other liability (2%), commercial multiple peril (1%), and inland marine (1%).

Principal Investments: Investment grade bonds (92%) and misc. investments (9%).

Investments in Affiliates: 5%
Group Affiliation: Allstate Group
Licensed in: IL, NJ, PA
Commenced Business: November 1997
Address: 2775 Sanders Rd, Northbrook, IL 60062-6127
Phone: (908) 252-5000   **Domicile State:** IL   **NAIC Code:** 10852

Data Date	Rating	RACR #1	RACR #2	Loss Ratio %	Total Assets ($mil)	Capital ($mil)	Net Premium ($mil)	Net Income ($mil)
6-16	B	2.41	1.86	N/A	2,550.9	822.0	580.4	45.1
6-15	B	2.42	1.80	N/A	2,516.7	829.9	575.1	27.1
2015	B	2.18	1.78	70.2	2,444.8	774.9	1,157.5	87.6
2014	B	2.22	1.75	63.4	2,478.3	802.8	1,163.9	134.9
2013	B	2.45	1.93	62.4	2,680.7	930.9	1,190.1	162.7
2012	B	1.97	1.53	91.5	2,647.6	767.5	1,199.4	-52.0
2011	B	2.23	1.85	86.9	2,658.2	813.4	1,158.3	-16.6

Reserve Deficiency (as % of capital)

* Adequate & redundant reserves show as negatives
■ 1 Yr Dev   □ 2 Yr Dev

ALLSTATE P&C INS CO   B   Good

Major Rating Factors: Fair overall results on stability tests (4.7 on a scale of 0 to 10) including weak results on operational trends and negative cash flow from operations for 2015. Strengths include potentially strong support from affiliation with Allstate Group. Strong long-term capitalization index (10.0) based on excellent current risk adjusted capital (severe and moderate loss scenarios). Moreover, capital levels have been consistent in recent years.

Other Rating Factors: Excellent profitability (7.4) with operating gains in each of the last five years. Excellent expense controls. Superior liquidity (10.0) with ample operational cash flow and liquid investments.

Principal Business: Auto liability (42%), auto physical damage (32%), homeowners multiple peril (24%), and inland marine (1%).

Principal Investments: Investment grade bonds (99%) and misc. investments (1%).

Investments in Affiliates: None
Group Affiliation: Allstate Group
Licensed in: All states except HI, MA, NJ, PR
Commenced Business: April 1985
Address: 2775 Sanders Rd, Northbrook, IL 60062-6127
Phone: (847) 402-5000   **Domicile State:** IL   **NAIC Code:** 17230

Data Date	Rating	RACR #1	RACR #2	Loss Ratio %	Total Assets ($mil)	Capital ($mil)	Net Premium ($mil)	Net Income ($mil)
6-16	B	66.58	56.47	N/A	249.7	230.2	0.0	1.3
6-15	B	69.35	62.42	N/A	233.8	217.3	0.0	1.1
2015	B	73.27	57.90	0.0	245.3	228.8	0.0	2.5
2014	B	87.44	62.79	0.0	215.5	206.0	0.0	2.2
2013	B	87.25	59.92	0.0	213.7	204.2	0.0	5.5
2012	B	109.24	64.02	0.0	204.4	197.8	0.0	4.6
2011	B	124.05	86.30	0.0	199.6	194.4	0.0	6.0

Allstate Group
Composite Group Rating: B

Largest Group Members	Assets ($mil)	Rating
ALLSTATE INS CO	43271	B
ALLSTATE LIFE INS CO	32348	B
ALLSTATE LIFE INS CO OF NEW YORK	6410	C+
ALLSTATE NJ INS CO	2445	B
AMERICAN HERITAGE LIFE INS CO	1831	B

AMBAC ASSURANCE CORP   E   Very Weak

Major Rating Factors: Poor long-term capitalization index (1.0 on a scale of 0 to 10) based on weak current risk adjusted capital (severe and moderate loss scenarios). A history of deficient reserves (2.5). Underreserving can have an adverse impact on capital and profits. In 2012, the two year reserve development was 53% deficient.

Other Rating Factors: Weak profitability index (1.9) with operating losses during 2011 and 2013. Return on equity has been fair, averaging 233.8% over the past five years. overall results on stability tests (-0.5) including weak risk adjusted capital in prior years, weak results on operational trends and negative cash flow from operations for 2015. The largest net exposure for one risk is excessive at 549.9% of capital. Superior liquidity (9.2) with ample operational cash flow and liquid investments.

Principal Business: Financial guaranty (100%).

Principal Investments: Misc. investments (50%), investment grade bonds (44%), and non investment grade bonds (6%).

Investments in Affiliates: 9%
Group Affiliation: AMBAC Financial Group Inc
Licensed in: All states except TN, WY
Commenced Business: March 1970
Address: 2 E Mifflin St Suite 600, Madison, WI 53703
Phone: (212) 668-0340   **Domicile State:** WI   **NAIC Code:** 18708

Data Date	Rating	RACR #1	RACR #2	Loss Ratio %	Total Assets ($mil)	Capital ($mil)	Net Premium ($mil)	Net Income ($mil)
6-16	E	0.79	0.38	N/A	5,367.0	754.6	100.8	136.7
6-15	E	0.42	0.18	N/A	4,560.8	235.2	135.9	234.6
2015	E	0.77	0.34	N/A	4,813.4	624.8	53.2	772.3
2014	E	0.36	0.16	N/A	4,451.6	100.0	63.6	724.8
2013	E	0.60	0.30	145.2	5,793.6	840.3	90.3	-235.6
2012	E	0.30	0.14	157.6	5,216.2	100.0	104.0	616.1
2011	E	0.48	0.24	251.8	5,905.0	495.3	138.9	-835.8

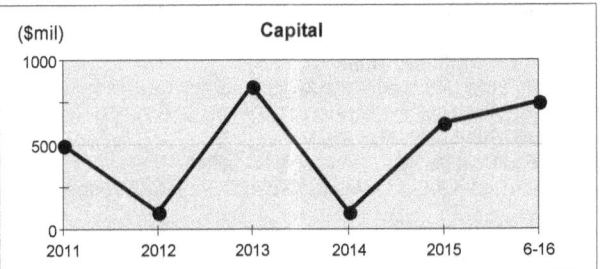

Capital

AMCO INS CO   C+   Fair

Major Rating Factors: Fair overall results on stability tests (4.5 on a scale of 0 to 10) including weak results on operational trends and negative cash flow from operations for 2015. Strengths include potentially strong support from affiliation with Nationwide Corp.

Other Rating Factors: Weak profitability index (2.5). Good expense controls. Return on equity has been fair, averaging 5.1% over the past five years. Strong long-term capitalization index (10.0) based on excellent current risk adjusted capital (severe and moderate loss scenarios), despite some fluctuation in capital levels. Excellent liquidity (7.7) with ample operational cash flow and liquid investments.

Principal Business: Auto liability (24%), commercial multiple peril (23%), homeowners multiple peril (18%), auto physical damage (17%), other liability (7%), fire (3%), and other lines (8%).

Principal Investments: Investment grade bonds (116%) and misc. investments (30%).

Investments in Affiliates: 16%

Group Affiliation: Nationwide Corp

Licensed in: All states except AK, HI, LA, MA, NH, NJ, OK, PR

Commenced Business: April 1959

Address: 1100 Locust St Dept 2007, Des Moines, IA 50391-2007

Phone: (515) 508-4211   **Domicile State:** IA   **NAIC Code:** 19100

Data Date	Rating	RACR #1	RACR #2	Loss Ratio %	Total Assets ($mil)	Capital ($mil)	Net Premium ($mil)	Net Income ($mil)
6-16	C+	5.26	4.51	N/A	940.5	201.7	0.0	1.8
6-15	C+	4.33	3.81	N/A	963.5	203.7	0.0	2.7
2015	C+	5.63	5.01	0.0	947.9	206.3	0.0	4.1
2014	C+	4.59	4.17	0.0	1,001.0	208.0	0.0	33.6
2013	B	8.61	7.54	0.0	1,067.8	363.8	0.0	7.8
2012	B	8.97	7.99	0.0	1,057.5	429.2	0.0	15.6
2011	B	8.21	6.79	0.0	1,873.9	463.4	0.0	15.6

Nationwide Corp
Composite Group Rating: B-
Largest Group Members

	Assets ($mil)	Rating
NATIONWIDE LIFE INS CO	126861	B-
NATIONWIDE MUTUAL INS CO	35924	B
NATIONWIDE LIFE ANNUITY INS CO	10758	C
NATIONWIDE MUTUAL FIRE INS CO	5938	B+
NATIONWIDE INDEMNITY CO	2995	C+

AMERICAN AGRICULTURAL INS CO   B   Good

Major Rating Factors: Good overall profitability index (5.1 on a scale of 0 to 10) despite operating losses during 2011. Return on equity has been low, averaging 2.3% over the past five years. Good liquidity (6.9) with sufficient resources (cash flows and marketable investments) to handle a spike in claims.

Other Rating Factors: Fair overall results on stability tests (4.4) including weak results on operational trends. Strong long-term capitalization index (7.7) based on excellent current risk adjusted capital (severe and moderate loss scenarios). Moreover, capital levels have been consistent in recent years. Ample reserve history (7.0) that can protect against increases in claims costs.

Principal Business: Allied lines (100%).

Principal Investments: Investment grade bonds (77%), misc. investments (16%), and cash (7%).

Investments in Affiliates: 0%

Group Affiliation: None

Licensed in: All states except AK, CA, HI, NV

Commenced Business: May 1948

Address: 225 South East sT, Indianapolis, IN 46202

Phone: (847) 969-2900   **Domicile State:** IN   **NAIC Code:** 10103

Data Date	Rating	RACR #1	RACR #2	Loss Ratio %	Total Assets ($mil)	Capital ($mil)	Net Premium ($mil)	Net Income ($mil)
6-16	B	2.20	1.58	N/A	1,247.8	554.6	149.7	8.8
6-15	C+	2.12	1.54	N/A	1,166.0	529.1	144.0	9.7
2015	B	2.22	1.61	71.4	1,152.6	541.2	304.9	38.5
2014	C+	2.16	1.59	65.8	1,105.1	525.7	295.4	56.1
2013	C+	1.86	1.38	73.3	1,093.1	489.3	342.2	55.3
2012	C	1.74	1.35	86.3	1,041.0	440.1	283.6	10.0
2011	C	1.68	1.25	115.8	1,089.7	430.2	356.1	-86.5

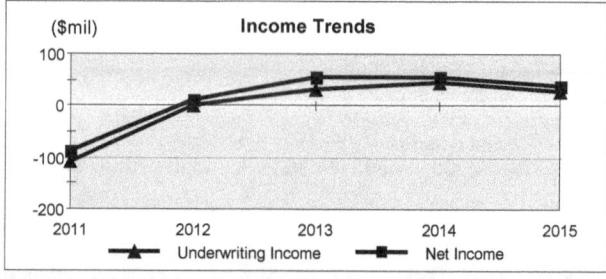

Income Trends

AMERICAN ALTERNATIVE INS CORP   C   Fair

Major Rating Factors: Fair overall results on stability tests (3.7 on a scale of 0 to 10) including potential drain of affiliation with Münchener Rückversicherungs-Gesellsc and weak results on operational trends.

Other Rating Factors: Strong long-term capitalization index (10.0) based on excellent current risk adjusted capital (severe and moderate loss scenarios), despite some fluctuation in capital levels. Excellent profitability (8.4) with operating gains in each of the last five years. Excellent expense controls. Return on equity has been excellent over the last five years averaging 16.3%. Superior liquidity (10.0) with ample operational cash flow and liquid investments.

Principal Business: Commercial multiple peril (24%), auto liability (17%), other liability (16%), other accident & health (14%), auto physical damage (9%), allied lines (7%), and other lines (15%).

Principal Investments: Investment grade bonds (112%) and non investment grade bonds (4%).

Investments in Affiliates: None

Group Affiliation: Münchener Rückversicherungs-Gesellsc

Licensed in: All states, the District of Columbia and Puerto Rico

Commenced Business: May 1923

Address: 555 College Rd E, Princeton, NJ 08543

Phone: (609) 243-4200   **Domicile State:** DE   **NAIC Code:** 19720

Data Date	Rating	RACR #1	RACR #2	Loss Ratio %	Total Assets ($mil)	Capital ($mil)	Net Premium ($mil)	Net Income ($mil)
6-16	C	16.51	12.33	N/A	518.5	183.5	0.0	13.4
6-15	C	16.44	12.99	N/A	535.7	185.1	0.0	16.6
2015	C	17.71	13.80	0.0	550.8	199.5	0.0	30.7
2014	C	14.93	13.43	0.0	526.4	168.9	0.0	30.8
2013	C	15.10	13.59	0.0	452.2	161.7	0.0	28.6
2012	C	14.37	12.94	0.0	464.7	156.2	0.0	23.1
2011	C	14.53	13.07	0.0	434.6	156.2	0.0	25.0

Münchener Rückversicherungs-Gesellsc
Composite Group Rating: C+
Largest Group Members

	Assets ($mil)	Rating
MUNICH REINS AMERICA INC	17498	C+
MUNICH AMERICAN REASSURANCE CO	7627	C
HARTFORD SM BOIL INSPECTION INS	1293	B
AMERICAN MODERN HOME INS CO	1277	C+
MUNICH AMERICAN LIFE REINS CO	1214	C+

AMERICAN BANKERS INS CO OF FL   B   Good

Major Rating Factors: History of adequate reserve strength (6.7 on a scale of 0 to 10) as reserves have been consistently at an acceptable level. Good liquidity (6.1) with sufficient resources (cash flows and marketable investments) to handle a spike in claims.

Other Rating Factors: Fair profitability index (4.8). Weak expense controls. Return on equity has been fair, averaging 18.2% over the past five years. Fair overall results on stability tests (4.7) including weak results on operational trends.

 Strong long-term capitalization index (7.4) based on excellent current risk adjusted capital (severe and moderate loss scenarios), despite some fluctuation in capital levels.

Principal Business: Other liability (48%), homeowners multiple peril (15%), inland marine (11%), allied lines (11%), credit (5%), credit accident & health (4%), and other lines (6%).

Principal Investments: Investment grade bonds (71%), misc. investments (22%), and non investment grade bonds (7%).

Investments in Affiliates: 1%

Group Affiliation: Assurant Inc

Licensed in: All states, the District of Columbia and Puerto Rico

Commenced Business: October 1947

Address: 11222 Quail Roost Dr, Miami, FL 33157

Phone: (305) 253-2244   **Domicile State:** FL   **NAIC Code:** 10111

Data Date	Rating	RACR #1	RACR #2	Loss Ratio %	Total Assets ($mil)	Capital ($mil)	Net Premium ($mil)	Net Income ($mil)
6-16	B	2.15	1.27	N/A	1,972.7	526.5	433.7	90.4
6-15	B	2.64	1.55	N/A	1,932.0	569.8	413.6	80.9
2015	B	2.06	1.20	39.9	1,877.6	483.2	867.5	142.3
2014	B	2.68	1.55	40.8	1,967.5	563.9	870.1	146.5
2013	B	2.62	1.49	40.1	1,844.9	542.1	884.0	96.5
2012	B	2.76	1.56	44.7	1,707.5	506.5	817.8	33.4
2011	B-	2.34	1.29	54.2	1,378.7	404.7	655.9	12.2

Reserve Deficiency (as % of capital)

* Adequate & redundant reserves show as negatives

■ 1 Yr Dev   □ 2 Yr Dev

AMERICAN EXCESS INS EXCHANGE RRG   C-   Fair

Major Rating Factors: Weak overall results on stability tests (2.2 on a scale of 0 to 10) including weak results on operational trends. The largest net exposure for one risk is excessive at 12.2% of capital. Fair profitability index (3.3) with operating losses during the first six months of 2016.

Other Rating Factors: Strong long-term capitalization index (8.2) based on excellent current risk adjusted capital (severe and moderate loss scenarios), despite some fluctuation in capital levels. Ample reserve history (9.2) that helps to protect the company against sharp claims increases. Excellent liquidity (7.6) with ample operational cash flow and liquid investments.

Principal Business: Medical malpractice (95%) and other liability (5%).

Principal Investments: Investment grade bonds (74%), misc. investments (20%), and cash (6%).

Investments in Affiliates: None

Group Affiliation: None

Licensed in: AK, AZ, CA, CO, FL, HI, ID, IL, IN, IA, KS, KY, ME, MD, MA, MI, MN, MO, MT, NE, NV, NM, NY, ND, OH, OK, OR, PA, RI, SC, SD, TN, TX, VT, VA, WA, WV, WI

Commenced Business: April 1998

Address: 150 Dorset St #238, S Burlinton, VT 05403

Phone: (858) 481-2727   **Domicile State:** VT   **NAIC Code:** 10903

Data Date	Rating	RACR #1	RACR #2	Loss Ratio %	Total Assets ($mil)	Capital ($mil)	Net Premium ($mil)	Net Income ($mil)
6-16	C-	2.39	1.72	N/A	325.9	162.6	11.1	-2.1
6-15	D	5.14	3.33	N/A	380.3	219.9	11.2	9.8
2015	D+	2.64	1.90	139.9	345.9	187.1	22.2	-1.6
2014	D	5.59	3.62	11.4	389.5	242.3	23.2	38.1
2013	D	4.44	2.94	25.0	410.8	243.9	23.6	33.7
2012	D	6.09	3.91	4.1	406.9	237.9	23.4	39.1
2011	D	5.10	3.42	16.1	399.3	211.9	27.3	39.9

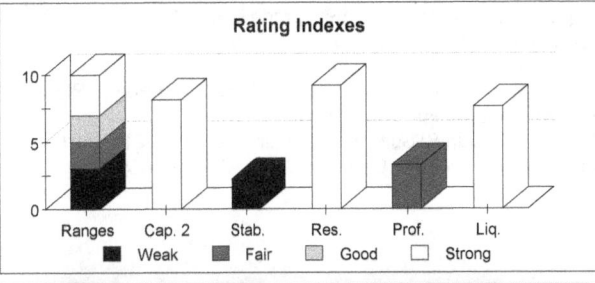

Rating Indexes

Ranges   Cap. 2   Stab.   Res.   Prof.   Liq.

■ Weak   ▨ Fair   ▥ Good   □ Strong

AMERICAN FAMILY MUT INS CO *   B+   Good

Major Rating Factors: Good overall profitability index (6.9 on a scale of 0 to 10). Fair expense controls. Good liquidity (6.3) with sufficient resources (cash flows and marketable investments) to handle a spike in claims.

Other Rating Factors: Good overall results on stability tests (5.2) despite weak results on operational trends. Strong long-term capitalization index (8.0) based on excellent current risk adjusted capital (severe and moderate loss scenarios). Moreover, capital levels have been consistent in recent years. Ample reserve history (8.2) that helps to protect the company against sharp claims increases.

Principal Business: Homeowners multiple peril (32%), auto liability (29%), auto physical damage (23%), commercial multiple peril (8%), other liability (3%), farmowners multiple peril (2%), and other lines (3%).

Principal Investments: Investment grade bonds (54%), misc. investments (41%), non investment grade bonds (3%), and real estate (2%).

Investments in Affiliates: 17%

Group Affiliation: American Family Ins Group

Licensed in: AZ, CO, FL, GA, ID, IL, IN, IA, KS, MN, MO, MT, NE, NV, NM, NC, ND, OH, OR, SC, SD, TN, TX, UT, VA, WA, WI, WY

Commenced Business: October 1927

Address: 6000 American Pkwy, Madison, WI 53783-0001

Phone: (608) 249-2111   **Domicile State:** WI   **NAIC Code:** 19275

Data Date	Rating	RACR #1	RACR #2	Loss Ratio %	Total Assets ($mil)	Capital ($mil)	Net Premium ($mil)	Net Income ($mil)
6-16	B+	2.17	1.67	N/A	16,216.1	6,554.3	3,459.1	108.9
6-15	B+	2.18	1.70	N/A	15,208.2	6,360.4	3,267.1	364.9
2015	B+	2.20	1.71	63.5	15,343.9	6,503.1	6,854.8	570.5
2014	B+	2.10	1.66	70.8	14,500.5	6,030.1	6,656.3	659.2
2013	B+	2.17	1.73	72.6	13,229.6	5,791.7	5,595.6	281.2
2012	B	2.56	1.94	73.0	12,038.9	5,165.0	5,435.1	323.7
2011	B	2.59	1.88	76.0	11,634.3	4,658.9	5,166.2	218.1

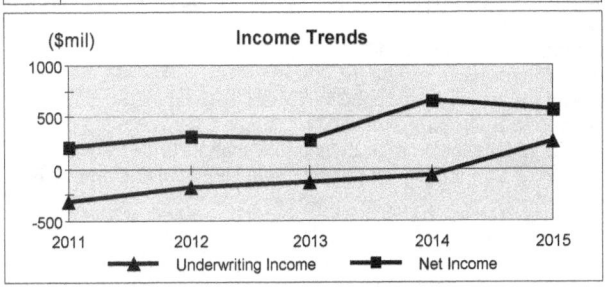

Income Trends

—▲— Underwriting Income   —■— Net Income

AMERICAN HOME ASR CO

C   **Fair**

Major Rating Factors: Fair reserve development (3.3 on a scale of 0 to 10) as the level of reserves has at times been insufficient to cover claims. In 2015 and 2011 the two year reserve development was 18% and 33% deficient respectively. Weak overall results on stability tests (2.8) including weak results on operational trends and negative cash flow from operations for 2015. The largest net exposure for one risk is excessive at 10.6% of capital.

Other Rating Factors: Good overall profitability index (5.1) despite operating losses during 2015. Return on equity has been fair, averaging 8.5% over the past five years. Good liquidity (6.5) with sufficient resources (cash flows and marketable investments) to handle a spike in claims. Strong long-term capitalization index (7.9) based on excellent current risk adjusted capital (severe and moderate loss scenarios), despite some fluctuation in capital levels.

Principal Business: Fire (42%), workers compensation (11%), products liability (8%), allied lines (7%), inland marine (6%), boiler & machinery (5%), and other lines (22%).

Principal Investments: Investment grade bonds (60%), misc. investments (37%), and non investment grade bonds (3%).

Investments in Affiliates: 1%

Group Affiliation: American International Group

Licensed in: All states except PR

Commenced Business: February 1899

Address: 175 Water St 18th Floor, New York, NY 10038

Phone: (212) 770-7000   **Domicile State:** NY   **NAIC Code:** 19380

Data Date	Rating	RACR #1	RACR #2	Loss Ratio %	Total Assets ($mil)	Capital ($mil)	Net Premium ($mil)	Net Income ($mil)
6-16	C	2.37	1.60	N/A	29,633.5	7,317.2	3,131.8	685.2
6-15	C+	2.30	1.55	N/A	26,244.7	6,762.2	2,739.5	448.1
2015	C	2.39	1.63	90.5	26,103.9	6,640.8	5,708.9	-75.2
2014	C+	2.48	1.69	74.2	26,408.3	7,247.9	5,499.4	808.2
2013	C	1.77	1.17	70.0	23,671.1	5,091.7	5,852.4	703.0
2012	C	2.16	1.46	79.5	24,302.3	6,004.3	5,204.4	285.5
2011	C	2.02	1.37	80.0	23,900.3	5,667.3	5,308.9	494.6

Reserve Deficiency (as % of capital)

* Adequate & redundant reserves show as negatives

■ 1 Yr Dev
□ 2 Yr Dev

AMERICAN INS CO

C-   **Fair**

Major Rating Factors: Weak profitability index (1.9 on a scale of 0 to 10). Good expense controls. Return on equity has been fair, averaging 5.3% over the past five years.

Other Rating Factors: Fair overall results on stability tests (3.1) including weak results on operational trends and negative cash flow from operations for 2015. Good liquidity (6.7) with sufficient resources (cash flows and marketable investments) to handle a spike in claims. Strong long-term capitalization index (10.0) based on excellent current risk adjusted capital (severe and moderate loss scenarios), despite some fluctuation in capital levels.

Principal Business: Commercial multiple peril (31%), homeowners multiple peril (19%), other liability (18%), workers compensation (9%), inland marine (9%), farmowners multiple peril (7%), and other lines (7%).

Principal Investments: Investment grade bonds (294%).

Investments in Affiliates: None

Group Affiliation: Allianz Ins Group

Licensed in: All states, the District of Columbia and Puerto Rico

Commenced Business: April 1846

Address: 41 S High St Suite 1700, Columbus, OH 43215-6101

Phone: (888) 466-7883   **Domicile State:** OH   **NAIC Code:** 21857

Data Date	Rating	RACR #1	RACR #2	Loss Ratio %	Total Assets ($mil)	Capital ($mil)	Net Premium ($mil)	Net Income ($mil)
6-16	C-	8.14	7.32	N/A	140.2	63.4	0.0	0.0
6-15	C-	75.46	63.09	N/A	345.5	319.2	0.0	4.0
2015	C	26.33	23.70	0.0	310.9	222.2	0.0	35.5
2014	C-	57.01	51.31	0.0	323.7	289.7	0.0	9.0
2013	C-	47.36	42.62	0.0	325.5	283.5	0.0	4.8
2012	D+	43.16	38.84	0.0	370.1	312.3	-144.8	20.7
2011	C	1.14	0.78	88.2	1,308.3	314.0	407.4	4.7

Rating Indexes

■ Weak   ▨ Fair   ▦ Good   □ Strong

AMERICAN INTERSTATE INS CO

B-   **Good**

Major Rating Factors: Fair overall results on stability tests (4.3 on a scale of 0 to 10) including potential drain of affiliation with Amerisafe Inc and weak results on operational trends. Strong long-term capitalization index (7.7) based on excellent current risk adjusted capital (severe and moderate loss scenarios), despite some fluctuation in capital levels.

Other Rating Factors: Ample reserve history (9.3) that helps to protect the company against sharp claims increases. Excellent profitability (8.5) with operating gains in each of the last five years. Return on equity has been good over the last five years, averaging 11.3%. Excellent liquidity (7.2) with ample operational cash flow and liquid investments.

Principal Business: Workers compensation (100%).

Principal Investments: Investment grade bonds (82%), misc. investments (17%), and cash (1%).

Investments in Affiliates: 13%

Group Affiliation: Amerisafe Inc

Licensed in: All states except CT, NJ, OH, PR

Commenced Business: April 1974

Address: 13321 California St Suite 310, Omaha, NE 68154

Phone: (800) 256-9052   **Domicile State:** NE   **NAIC Code:** 31895

Data Date	Rating	RACR #1	RACR #2	Loss Ratio %	Total Assets ($mil)	Capital ($mil)	Net Premium ($mil)	Net Income ($mil)
6-16	B-	1.94	1.55	N/A	1,291.5	409.4	150.2	33.9
6-15	B-	1.78	1.41	N/A	1,258.7	404.9	153.2	22.0
2015	B-	1.81	1.46	57.1	1,207.7	371.4	301.8	66.9
2014	B-	1.73	1.38	65.2	1,185.6	377.7	305.3	40.3
2013	B-	1.74	1.35	69.4	1,093.7	354.3	284.8	35.3
2012	B-	2.02	1.60	75.7	1,001.8	323.9	251.2	25.4
2011	B-	2.23	1.75	75.6	922.6	314.4	206.5	22.3

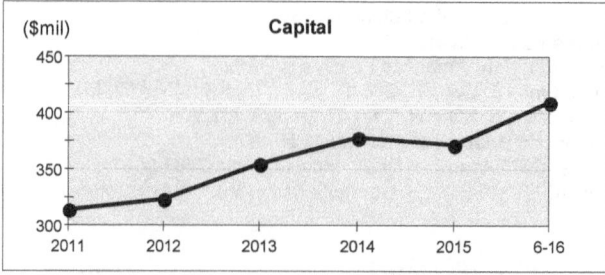

Capital ($mil)

AMERICAN MODERN HOME INS CO — C+ — Fair

Major Rating Factors: Fair overall results on stability tests (4.3 on a scale of 0 to 10) including fair financial strength of affiliated Münchener Rückversicherungs-Gesellsc, weak results on operational trends and negative cash flow from operations for 2015. Vulnerable liquidity (2.3) as a spike in claims may stretch capacity.

Other Rating Factors: Strong long-term capitalization index (7.5) based on excellent current risk adjusted capital (severe and moderate loss scenarios), despite some fluctuation in capital levels. Ample reserve history (7.8) that can protect against increases in claims costs. Excellent profitability (7.4) with operating gains in each of the last five years.

Principal Business: Homeowners multiple peril (35%), fire (25%), allied lines (17%), inland marine (8%), auto physical damage (5%), commercial multiple peril (3%), and other lines (7%).

Principal Investments: Investment grade bonds (60%), misc. investments (31%), real estate (11%), and non investment grade bonds (3%).

Investments in Affiliates: 35%

Group Affiliation: Münchener Rückversicherungs-Gesellsc

Licensed in: All states, the District of Columbia and Puerto Rico

Commenced Business: September 1965

Address: 7000 Midland Blvd, Amelia, OH 45102-2607

Phone: (800) 543-2644   **Domicile State:** OH   **NAIC Code:** 23469

Data Date	Rating	RACR #1	RACR #2	Loss Ratio %	Total Assets ($mil)	Capital ($mil)	Net Premium ($mil)	Net Income ($mil)
6-16	C+	2.04	1.62	N/A	1,295.2	419.9	179.2	9.0
6-15	C+	2.02	1.52	N/A	1,332.2	403.0	237.5	22.5
2015	C+	2.09	1.62	48.2	1,277.2	436.1	370.2	54.2
2014	C+	1.99	1.51	48.3	1,286.2	380.5	496.5	8.0
2013	C+	2.17	1.66	43.8	1,256.4	373.6	431.7	5.8
2012	C+	2.52	1.95	50.3	1,156.6	389.8	361.7	5.6
2011	C+	2.51	2.06	56.5	1,097.1	357.6	323.6	11.3

Münchener Rückversicherungs-Gesellsc
Composite Group Rating: C+

Largest Group Members	Assets ($mil)	Rating
MUNICH REINS AMERICA INC	17498	C+
MUNICH AMERICAN REASSURANCE CO	7627	C
HARTFORD SM BOIL INSPECTION INS	1293	B
AMERICAN MODERN HOME INS CO	1277	C+
MUNICH AMERICAN LIFE REINS CO	1214	C+

AMERICAN MUTUAL SHARE INS CORP — C- — Fair

Major Rating Factors: Weak overall results on stability tests (1.5 on a scale of 0 to 10) including weak results on operational trends and negative cash flow from operations for 2015. The largest net exposure for one risk is excessive at 448.9% of capital. Strengths include potentially strong support from affiliation with American Mutual Share Group. Fair profitability index (4.7) with operating losses during the first six months of 2016.

Other Rating Factors: History of adequate reserve strength (6.9) as reserves have been consistently at an acceptable level. Strong long-term capitalization index (10.0) based on excellent current risk adjusted capital (severe and moderate loss scenarios). Moreover, capital levels have been consistent in recent years. Superior liquidity (10.0) with ample operational cash flow and liquid investments.

Principal Business: Aggregate write-ins for other lines of business (100%).

Principal Investments: Investment grade bonds (71%), cash (22%), and misc. investments (7%).

Investments in Affiliates: 9%

Group Affiliation: American Mutual Share Group

Licensed in: AL, AZ, CA, ID, IL, IN, ME, NV, NH, OH, TX

Commenced Business: June 1974

Address: 5656 Frantz Rd, Dublin, OH 43017

Phone: (614) 764-1900   **Domicile State:** OH   **NAIC Code:** 12700

Data Date	Rating	RACR #1	RACR #2	Loss Ratio %	Total Assets ($mil)	Capital ($mil)	Net Premium ($mil)	Net Income ($mil)
6-16	C-	9.05	7.98	N/A	255.4	221.8	0.1	-1.9
6-15	C-	8.39	7.34	N/A	234.7	203.4	0.1	1.7
2015	C-	8.87	7.79	N/A	249.2	219.4	0.2	5.4
2014	C-	8.36	7.32	N/A	230.4	202.3	0.2	11.0
2013	C-	7.89	6.66	N/A	230.2	188.1	0.2	1.6
2012	C-	7.73	6.53	N/A	223.0	183.3	0.2	1.4
2011	C-	7.89	6.93	N/A	219.4	173.4	0.3	0.0

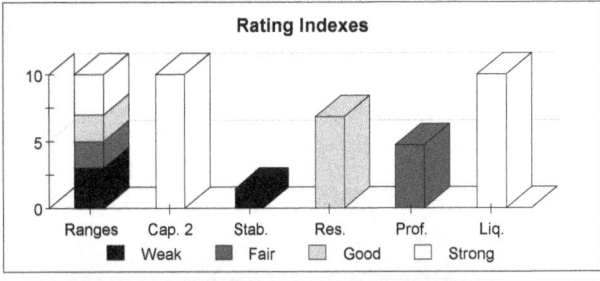

Rating Indexes — Ranges, Cap. 2, Stab., Res., Prof., Liq. — Weak, Fair, Good, Strong

AMERICAN NATIONAL PROPERTY & CAS CO — B — Good

Major Rating Factors: Good overall profitability index (6.8 on a scale of 0 to 10) despite modest operating losses during the first six months of 2016. Return on equity has been low, averaging 4.3% over the past five years. Good liquidity (6.2) with sufficient resources (cash flows and marketable investments) to handle a spike in claims.

Other Rating Factors: Fair overall results on stability tests (4.9) including weak results on operational trends. Strong long-term capitalization index (8.0) based on excellent current risk adjusted capital (severe and moderate loss scenarios), despite some fluctuation in capital levels. Ample reserve history (8.4) that helps to protect the company against sharp claims increases.

Principal Business: Auto liability (27%), homeowners multiple peril (27%), auto physical damage (16%), credit (13%), allied lines (7%), other liability (5%), and other lines (5%).

Principal Investments: Investment grade bonds (61%), misc. investments (38%), and real estate (1%).

Investments in Affiliates: 22%

Group Affiliation: American National Group Inc

Licensed in: All states except CT, MA, NY

Commenced Business: January 1974

Address: 1949 E Sunshine, Springfield, MO 65899-0001

Phone: (417) 887-4990   **Domicile State:** MO   **NAIC Code:** 28401

Data Date	Rating	RACR #1	RACR #2	Loss Ratio %	Total Assets ($mil)	Capital ($mil)	Net Premium ($mil)	Net Income ($mil)
6-16	B	2.12	1.75	N/A	1,292.6	628.9	251.4	-1.0
6-15	B	2.17	1.77	N/A	1,250.9	617.3	236.9	12.3
2015	B	2.15	1.79	70.4	1,275.6	635.9	496.5	33.1
2014	B	2.12	1.75	71.1	1,218.5	596.9	481.3	40.0
2013	B	2.02	1.65	75.2	1,155.6	537.5	468.0	25.4
2012	B	1.95	1.57	79.7	1,105.8	495.5	467.6	17.6
2011	B	1.67	1.27	82.4	1,019.2	383.6	485.0	14.0

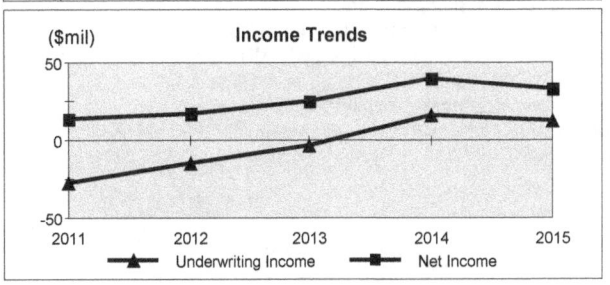

Income Trends ($mil) — Underwriting Income, Net Income — 2011, 2012, 2013, 2014, 2015

AMERICAN ROAD INS CO

C+   **Fair**

Major Rating Factors: Fair overall results on stability tests (3.0 on a scale of 0 to 10) including weak results on operational trends. The largest net exposure for one risk is excessive at 8.3% of capital. Good overall profitability index (5.6) despite operating losses during the first six months of 2016. Return on equity has been fair, averaging 7.7% over the past five years.

Other Rating Factors: Strong long-term capitalization index (10.0) based on excellent current risk adjusted capital (severe and moderate loss scenarios), despite some fluctuation in capital levels. Ample reserve history (7.4) that can protect against increases in claims costs. Superior liquidity (9.1) with ample operational cash flow and liquid investments.

Principal Business: (Not applicable due to unusual reinsurance transactions.)

Principal Investments: Investment grade bonds (98%), misc. investments (1%), and cash (1%).

Investments in Affiliates: None

Group Affiliation: Ford Motor Co

Licensed in: All states except PR

Commenced Business: December 1959

Address: The American Rd, Dearborn, MI 48121-6027

Phone: (313) 337-1102   **Domicile State:** MI   **NAIC Code:** 19631

Data Date	Rating	RACR #1	RACR #2	Loss Ratio %	Total Assets ($mil)	Capital ($mil)	Net Premium ($mil)	Net Income ($mil)
6-16	C+	10.44	6.23	N/A	663.4	237.2	81.3	-15.2
6-15	C+	22.31	11.54	N/A	621.0	255.8	65.0	11.0
2015	C+	21.55	11.34	65.0	642.2	251.1	134.6	30.3
2014	C+	22.71	12.29	97.5	556.9	246.6	125.8	3.3
2013	C+	21.22	11.60	64.2	564.2	276.0	118.1	48.6
2012	C	4.82	4.11	77.5	482.8	214.0	99.5	19.9
2011	C	5.05	4.39	84.0	460.7	205.1	89.7	17.7

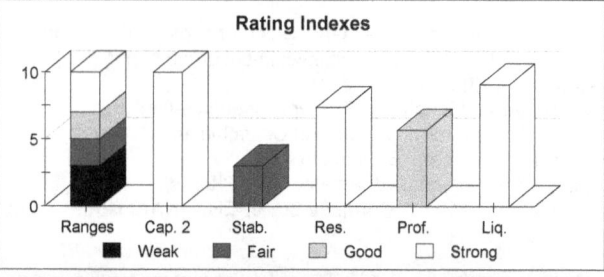

Rating Indexes — Ranges, Cap. 2, Stab., Res., Prof., Liq. (Weak, Fair, Good, Strong)

AMERICAN SECURITY INS CO

B-   **Good**

Major Rating Factors: Fair profitability index (3.3 on a scale of 0 to 10). Weak expense controls. Return on equity has been fair, averaging 41.8% over the past five years. Fair overall results on stability tests (4.7) including weak results on operational trends.

Other Rating Factors: History of adequate reserve strength (6.1) as reserves have been consistently at an acceptable level. Good liquidity (6.5) with sufficient resources (cash flows and marketable investments) to handle a spike in claims. Strong long-term capitalization index (7.6) based on excellent current risk adjusted capital (severe and moderate loss scenarios), despite some fluctuation in capital levels.

Principal Business: Allied lines (52%), fire (31%), inland marine (9%), other liability (4%), homeowners multiple peril (3%), and credit (1%).

Principal Investments: Investment grade bonds (72%), misc. investments (23%), non investment grade bonds (7%), and real estate (2%).

Investments in Affiliates: 10%

Group Affiliation: Assurant Inc

Licensed in: All states except NH

Commenced Business: September 1938

Address: 260 Interstate N Circle NW, Atlanta, GA 30339-2111

Phone: (770) 763-1000   **Domicile State:** DE   **NAIC Code:** 42978

Data Date	Rating	RACR #1	RACR #2	Loss Ratio %	Total Assets ($mil)	Capital ($mil)	Net Premium ($mil)	Net Income ($mil)
6-16	B-	2.10	1.57	N/A	1,506.1	553.3	504.4	78.2
6-15	B	1.71	1.33	N/A	1,778.1	699.1	633.5	113.4
2015	B-	2.02	1.51	36.6	1,584.9	558.8	1,047.3	298.5
2014	B	1.53	1.20	38.0	1,915.8	661.5	1,369.2	251.2
2013	B	2.55	1.82	33.6	2,078.0	740.8	1,601.9	294.2
2012	B	3.84	2.39	43.1	1,949.3	703.1	1,496.0	279.8
2011	B	3.25	2.19	36.2	1,730.4	634.6	1,280.6	284.4

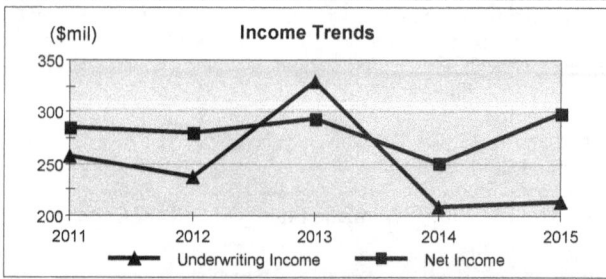

($mil) Income Trends — Underwriting Income, Net Income (2011–2015)

AMERICAN STANDARD INS CO OF WI *

B+   **Good**

Major Rating Factors: Good overall results on stability tests (5.0 on a scale of 0 to 10) despite weak results on operational trends. Strengths include potential support from affiliation with American Family Ins Group. Strong long-term capitalization index (10.0) based on excellent current risk adjusted capital (severe and moderate loss scenarios), despite some fluctuation in capital levels.

Other Rating Factors: Excellent profitability (7.7) with operating gains in each of the last five years. Excellent expense controls. Excellent liquidity (8.7) with ample operational cash flow and liquid investments.

Principal Business: Auto liability (66%) and auto physical damage (34%).

Principal Investments: Investment grade bonds (88%), misc. investments (8%), and cash (4%).

Investments in Affiliates: None

Group Affiliation: American Family Ins Group

Licensed in: AZ, CO, ID, IL, IN, IA, KS, MN, MO, MT, NE, NV, NM, NC, ND, OH, OR, SC, SD, UT, WA, WI, WY

Commenced Business: September 1961

Address: 6000 American Parkway, Madison, WI 53783-0001

Phone: (608) 249-2111   **Domicile State:** WI   **NAIC Code:** 19283

Data Date	Rating	RACR #1	RACR #2	Loss Ratio %	Total Assets ($mil)	Capital ($mil)	Net Premium ($mil)	Net Income ($mil)
6-16	B+	39.58	35.62	N/A	433.2	341.5	0.0	3.1
6-15	B+	34.91	31.42	N/A	507.3	336.4	0.0	7.1
2015	B+	37.42	33.68	0.0	443.0	338.3	0.0	9.1
2014	B+	39.45	35.50	0.0	414.8	329.3	0.0	10.3
2013	B+	40.40	36.36	0.0	393.9	318.6	0.0	8.0
2012	B+	39.71	35.74	0.0	384.6	310.7	0.0	11.7
2011	B+	41.26	37.14	0.0	360.0	299.0	0.0	10.8

American Family Ins Group Composite Group Rating: B+ Largest Group Members	Assets ($mil)	Rating
AMERICAN FAMILY MUT INS CO	15344	B+
AMERICAN FAMILY LIFE INS CO	5332	A+
AMERICAN STANDARD INS CO OF WI	443	B+
HOMESITE INS CO OF THE MIDWEST	340	C
PERMANENT GENERAL ASR CORP	313	C-

AMERICAN STRATEGIC INS CO   C   Fair

Major Rating Factors: Fair overall results on stability tests (3.9 on a scale of 0 to 10) including potential drain of affiliation with Progressive Corp and weak results on operational trends. Good overall profitability index (5.7) despite operating losses during 2012 and the first six months of 2016. Return on equity has been low, averaging 2.9% over the past five years.

Other Rating Factors: Good liquidity (6.6) with sufficient resources (cash flows and marketable investments) to handle a spike in claims. Strong long-term capitalization index (8.7) based on excellent current risk adjusted capital (severe and moderate loss scenarios), despite some fluctuation in capital levels. Ample reserve history (9.3) that helps to protect the company against sharp claims increases.

Principal Business: Homeowners multiple peril (71%), allied lines (21%), fire (5%), and other liability (2%).

Principal Investments: Investment grade bonds (91%), misc. investments (5%), and real estate (5%).

Investments in Affiliates: 1%

Group Affiliation: Progressive Corp

Licensed in: AL, AZ, CO, CT, DC, DE, FL, GA, IL, IA, KS, KY, ME, MD, MA, MI, MN, MS, MO, MT, NE, NV, NJ, NM, NC, ND, OH, OK, OR, PA, SC, TN, TX, UT, VT, VA, WA, WI

Commenced Business: December 1997

Address: 805 Executive Cir Dr W #300, St Petersburg, FL 33702

Phone: (727) 821-8765   **Domicile State:** FL   **NAIC Code:** 10872

Data Date	Rating	RACR #1	RACR #2	Loss Ratio %	Total Assets ($mil)	Capital ($mil)	Net Premium ($mil)	Net Income ($mil)
6-16	C	2.48	2.17	N/A	999.2	432.6	274.8	-7.1
6-15	C	2.19	1.88	N/A	945.7	381.7	254.5	13.9
2015	C	2.68	2.22	57.9	981.8	441.8	576.1	51.5
2014	C	2.34	1.89	63.7	885.3	375.4	500.6	11.3
2013	B-	2.34	1.88	54.1	736.4	307.4	409.5	30.1
2012	B-	1.95	1.56	69.3	603.9	227.7	343.9	-15.9
2011	B	2.16	1.71	67.9	438.0	165.3	215.9	0.3

Progressive Corp
Composite Group Rating: C+
Largest Group Members

	Assets ($mil)	Rating
PROGRESSIVE CASUALTY INS CO	6246	B-
PROGRESSIVE DIRECT INS CO	5835	C
UNITED FINANCIAL CASUALTY CO	2508	B-
PROGRESSIVE NORTHERN INS CO	1408	C+
PROGRESSIVE NORTHWESTERN INS CO	1372	C+

AMERICAN ZURICH INS CO   C+   Fair

Major Rating Factors: Fair overall results on stability tests (4.5 on a scale of 0 to 10) including weak results on operational trends and negative cash flow from operations for 2015.

Other Rating Factors: Strong long-term capitalization index (10.0) based on excellent current risk adjusted capital (severe and moderate loss scenarios). Moreover, capital levels have been consistent in recent years. Excellent profitability (7.6) with operating gains in each of the last five years. Superior liquidity (10.0) with ample operational cash flow and liquid investments.

Principal Business: Workers compensation (72%), inland marine (18%), commercial multiple peril (5%), other liability (2%), auto liability (2%), and auto physical damage (1%).

Principal Investments: Investment grade bonds (79%) and misc. investments (21%).

Investments in Affiliates: 15%

Group Affiliation: Zurich Financial Services Group

Licensed in: All states except PR

Commenced Business: September 1981

Address: 1400 American Ln Zurich Towers, Schaumburg, IL 60196-1056

Phone: (847) 605-6000   **Domicile State:** IL   **NAIC Code:** 40142

Data Date	Rating	RACR #1	RACR #2	Loss Ratio %	Total Assets ($mil)	Capital ($mil)	Net Premium ($mil)	Net Income ($mil)
6-16	C+	6.94	6.57	N/A	348.7	228.1	0.0	1.5
6-15	C	4.75	4.50	N/A	302.8	158.8	0.0	0.9
2015	C+	7.00	6.72	0.0	314.3	226.3	0.0	4.7
2014	C	4.79	4.61	0.0	264.5	157.5	0.0	2.9
2013	C	4.86	4.71	0.0	234.2	153.3	0.0	3.3
2012	C	4.68	4.53	0.0	212.7	151.0	0.0	8.3
2011	C	4.37	4.24	0.0	177.1	142.7	0.0	8.4

Zurich Financial Services Group
Composite Group Rating: C+
Largest Group Members

	Assets ($mil)	Rating
ZURICH AMERICAN INS CO	30471	B-
ZURICH AMERICAN LIFE INS CO	12271	C
FARMERS NEW WORLD LIFE INS CO	7049	B-
RURAL COMMUNITY INS CO	3680	B
CENTRE LIFE INS CO	1884	B-

AMERISURE INS CO   B-   Good

Major Rating Factors: Fair overall results on stability tests (4.4 on a scale of 0 to 10) including potential drain of affiliation with Amerisure Companies and weak results on operational trends. History of adequate reserve strength (6.4) as reserves have been consistently at an acceptable level.

Other Rating Factors: Good overall profitability index (6.8) despite modest operating losses during the first six months of 2016. Return on equity has been low, averaging 2.9% over the past five years. Good liquidity (6.8) with sufficient resources (cash flows and marketable investments) to handle a spike in claims. Strong long-term capitalization index (8.3) based on excellent current risk adjusted capital (severe and moderate loss scenarios), despite some fluctuation in capital levels.

Principal Business: Workers compensation (54%), commercial multiple peril (19%), auto liability (15%), other liability (7%), auto physical damage (3%), and products liability (2%).

Principal Investments: Investment grade bonds (103%), non investment grade bonds (1%), and cash (1%).

Investments in Affiliates: None

Group Affiliation: Amerisure Companies

Licensed in: All states except CA

Commenced Business: September 1968

Address: 26777 Halsted Road, Farmington Hills, MI 48331-3586

Phone: (248) 615-9000   **Domicile State:** MI   **NAIC Code:** 19488

Data Date	Rating	RACR #1	RACR #2	Loss Ratio %	Total Assets ($mil)	Capital ($mil)	Net Premium ($mil)	Net Income ($mil)
6-16	B-	2.58	1.83	N/A	821.3	237.2	117.9	-0.3
6-15	B-	2.57	1.81	N/A	783.3	228.9	113.1	5.8
2015	B-	2.70	1.93	64.5	785.9	238.7	232.8	14.2
2014	B-	2.65	1.87	67.2	752.2	224.5	215.4	8.1
2013	B-	2.57	1.75	73.1	721.6	215.7	199.3	3.4
2012	B-	2.83	1.93	71.1	690.5	212.3	173.2	4.5
2011	B-	3.16	2.14	74.5	670.3	207.0	151.4	5.5

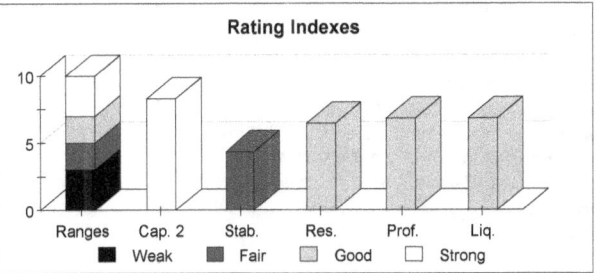

Rating Indexes

Ranges   Cap. 2   Stab.   Res.   Prof.   Liq.
■ Weak   ■ Fair   □ Good   □ Strong

AMERISURE MUTUAL INS CO   B-   Good

Major Rating Factors: Fair overall results on stability tests (4.7 on a scale of 0 to 10) including potential drain of affiliation with Amerisure Companies and weak results on operational trends. History of adequate reserve strength (6.3) as reserves have been consistently at an acceptable level.

Other Rating Factors: Good overall profitability index (6.8). Fair expense controls. Return on equity has been fair, averaging 5.3% over the past five years. Good liquidity (6.9) with sufficient resources (cash flows and marketable investments) to handle a spike in claims. Strong long-term capitalization index (8.2) based on excellent current risk adjusted capital (severe and moderate loss scenarios). Moreover, capital levels have been consistent in recent years.

Principal Business: Workers compensation (55%), commercial multiple peril (16%), other liability (13%), auto liability (9%), auto physical damage (2%), products liability (2%), and other lines (3%).

Principal Investments: Investment grade bonds (58%), misc. investments (39%), cash (1%), non investment grade bonds (1%), and real estate (1%).

Investments in Affiliates: 15%

Group Affiliation: Amerisure Companies

Licensed in: All states, the District of Columbia and Puerto Rico

Commenced Business: September 1912

Address: 26777 Halsted Rd, Farmington Hills, MI 48331-3586

Phone: (248) 615-9000   **Domicile State:** MI   **NAIC Code:** 23396

Data Date	Rating	RACR #1	RACR #2	Loss Ratio %	Total Assets ($mil)	Capital ($mil)	Net Premium ($mil)	Net Income ($mil)
6-16	B-	2.25	1.78	N/A	2,192.8	882.9	263.2	6.4
6-15	B-	2.27	1.77	N/A	2,111.3	860.5	252.6	25.1
2015	B-	2.26	1.80	64.5	2,124.5	875.2	519.9	71.2
2014	B-	2.25	1.77	67.2	2,069.7	843.0	481.1	48.1
2013	B-	2.16	1.69	73.1	1,981.8	803.8	445.2	41.0
2012	B-	2.15	1.69	71.1	1,843.4	732.9	386.7	36.1
2011	B-	2.07	1.63	74.5	1,751.7	673.0	338.2	31.9

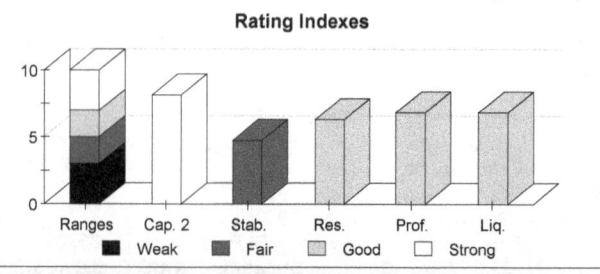

Rating Indexes

AMICA MUTUAL INS CO *   B+   Good

Major Rating Factors: Good overall profitability index (6.0 on a scale of 0 to 10). Good expense controls. Good liquidity (5.8) with sufficient resources (cash flows and marketable investments) to handle a spike in claims.

Other Rating Factors: Good overall results on stability tests (5.4) despite weak results on operational trends and negative cash flow from operations for 2015. Strong long-term capitalization index (8.2) based on excellent current risk adjusted capital (severe and moderate loss scenarios), despite some fluctuation in capital levels. Ample reserve history (8.1) that helps to protect the company against sharp claims increases.

Principal Business: Homeowners multiple peril (37%), auto liability (34%), auto physical damage (23%), other liability (3%), earthquake (1%), allied lines (1%), and inland marine (1%).

Principal Investments: Investment grade bonds (53%), misc. investments (48%), and real estate (1%).

Investments in Affiliates: 9%

Group Affiliation: Amica Mutual Group

Licensed in: All states except PR

Commenced Business: April 1907

Address: 100 Amica Way, Lincoln, RI 02865

Phone: (800) 652-6422   **Domicile State:** RI   **NAIC Code:** 19976

Data Date	Rating	RACR #1	RACR #2	Loss Ratio %	Total Assets ($mil)	Capital ($mil)	Net Premium ($mil)	Net Income ($mil)
6-16	B+	2.68	1.80	N/A	4,974.1	2,549.3	977.3	18.5
6-15	B+	2.98	1.97	N/A	4,959.1	2,692.3	922.2	23.4
2015	B+	2.72	1.84	80.9	4,961.9	2,611.3	1,942.8	56.2
2014	B+	2.97	1.97	66.3	5,061.7	2,759.8	1,841.5	185.5
2013	B+	2.97	1.95	69.9	4,855.2	2,649.7	1,746.7	145.2
2012	B+	2.94	1.92	76.5	4,391.2	2,377.5	1,633.4	69.9
2011	B+	2.91	1.90	83.0	4,126.7	2,260.4	1,539.3	61.3

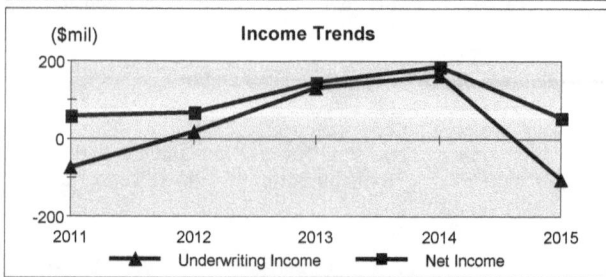

Income Trends

APPALACHIAN INS CO   C   Fair

Major Rating Factors: A history of deficient reserves (2.6 on a scale of 0 to 10) that places pressure on both capital and profits. In 2013 and 2014 the two year reserve development was 20% and 25% deficient respectively. Weak overall results on stability tests (2.4) including weak results on operational trends. The largest net exposure for one risk is excessive at 9.8% of capital.

Other Rating Factors: Good overall profitability index (6.1) despite operating losses during 2011. Return on equity has been low, averaging 4.9% over the past five years. Strong long-term capitalization index (9.0) based on excellent current risk adjusted capital (severe and moderate loss scenarios). Moreover, capital levels have been consistent in recent years. Excellent liquidity (8.1) with ample operational cash flow and liquid investments.

Principal Business: Inland marine (47%), allied lines (23%), ocean marine (17%), and fire (13%).

Principal Investments: Investment grade bonds (86%), cash (12%), and misc. investments (2%).

Investments in Affiliates: None

Group Affiliation: Factory Mutual Ins

Licensed in: All states, the District of Columbia and Puerto Rico

Commenced Business: January 1942

Address: 1301 Atwood Avenue, Johnston, RI 02919-4908

Phone: (401) 275-3000   **Domicile State:** RI   **NAIC Code:** 10316

Data Date	Rating	RACR #1	RACR #2	Loss Ratio %	Total Assets ($mil)	Capital ($mil)	Net Premium ($mil)	Net Income ($mil)
6-16	C	4.25	2.56	N/A	320.8	208.9	32.4	3.0
6-15	C	4.45	2.73	N/A	304.1	201.4	31.2	4.3
2015	C	4.19	2.50	58.1	324.1	205.9	65.2	9.2
2014	C	4.37	2.67	50.5	287.6	197.0	63.6	14.0
2013	C	4.26	2.68	50.6	290.5	182.9	64.5	13.0
2012	C	5.38	4.46	59.8	233.6	169.7	66.1	14.4
2011	C	4.61	3.11	95.3	237.5	155.0	58.8	-2.6

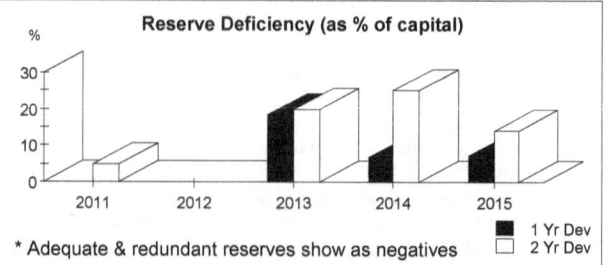

Reserve Deficiency (as % of capital)

* Adequate & redundant reserves show as negatives

ARBELLA MUTUAL INS CO   C+   Fair

Major Rating Factors: Fair overall results on stability tests (4.3 on a scale of 0 to 10) including potential drain of affiliation with Arbella Ins Group and weak results on operational trends. Fair profitability index (4.0) with operating losses during 2011 and 2015.
Other Rating Factors: Good liquidity (6.0) with sufficient resources (cash flows and marketable investments) to handle a spike in claims. Strong long-term capitalization index (8.2) based on excellent current risk adjusted capital (severe and moderate loss scenarios), despite some fluctuation in capital levels. Ample reserve history (7.8) that can protect against increases in claims costs.
Principal Business: Auto liability (40%), auto physical damage (31%), homeowners multiple peril (26%), fire (1%), other liability (1%), inland marine (1%), and allied lines (1%).
Principal Investments: Investment grade bonds (66%), misc. investments (32%), and cash (2%).
Investments in Affiliates: 14%
Group Affiliation: Arbella Ins Group
Licensed in: MA
Commenced Business: October 1988
Address: 1100 Crown Colony Dr, Quincy, MA 02269
Phone: (617) 328-2800   **Domicile State:** MA   **NAIC Code:** 17000

Data Date	Rating	RACR #1	RACR #2	Loss Ratio %	Total Assets ($mil)	Capital ($mil)	Net Premium ($mil)	Net Income ($mil)
6-16	C+	2.40	1.82	N/A	1,399.1	530.4	310.5	20.5
6-15	C+	2.36	1.88	N/A	1,288.6	503.8	285.1	-46.7
2015	C+	2.38	1.83	82.2	1,334.2	510.5	609.1	-45.0
2014	C+	2.65	2.13	62.9	1,285.7	561.2	577.0	28.6
2013	C+	2.69	2.06	64.5	1,177.8	523.9	496.4	22.8
2012	C+	2.71	2.09	64.1	1,139.1	480.9	464.9	35.2
2011	C+	2.58	1.93	86.5	1,237.8	408.0	437.5	-58.3

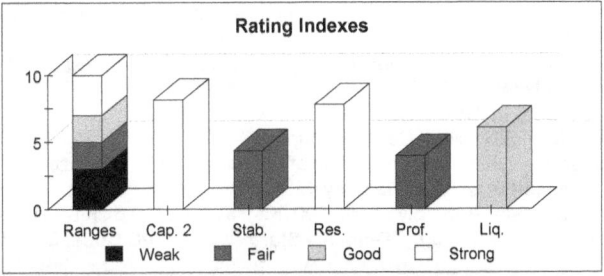

Rating Indexes

ARCH INS CO   C   Fair

Major Rating Factors: Fair overall results on stability tests (3.4 on a scale of 0 to 10) including potential drain of affiliation with Arch Capital Group Ltd and weak results on operational trends. Good overall profitability index (6.7) despite operating losses during 2011 and 2012. Return on equity has been low, averaging 1.9% over the past five years.
Other Rating Factors: Good liquidity (6.8) with sufficient resources (cash flows and marketable investments) to handle a spike in claims. Strong long-term capitalization index (7.3) based on excellent current risk adjusted capital (severe and moderate loss scenarios), despite some fluctuation in capital levels. Ample reserve history (7.5) that can protect against increases in claims costs.
Principal Business: Other liability (31%), workers compensation (23%), auto liability (11%), commercial multiple peril (8%), credit (5%), surety (5%), and other lines (17%).
Principal Investments: Investment grade bonds (78%), misc. investments (21%), and cash (1%).
Investments in Affiliates: 15%
Group Affiliation: Arch Capital Group Ltd
Licensed in: All states, the District of Columbia and Puerto Rico
Commenced Business: June 1980
Address: 3100 Broadway Suite 1000, Kansas City, MO 64111
Phone: (201) 743-4000   **Domicile State:** MO   **NAIC Code:** 11150

Data Date	Rating	RACR #1	RACR #2	Loss Ratio %	Total Assets ($mil)	Capital ($mil)	Net Premium ($mil)	Net Income ($mil)
6-16	C	1.61	1.27	N/A	3,619.7	875.3	393.6	38.5
6-15	C	1.39	1.06	N/A	3,498.3	807.3	381.7	7.2
2015	C	1.56	1.25	68.5	3,545.4	826.5	772.9	52.8
2014	C	1.39	1.07	67.3	3,200.9	778.4	785.5	37.6
2013	C	1.38	1.06	68.2	2,840.9	736.6	659.6	28.7
2012	C	1.21	0.88	75.6	2,696.9	563.5	750.0	-23.0
2011	C	0.70	0.54	73.8	2,318.1	569.7	618.5	-28.2

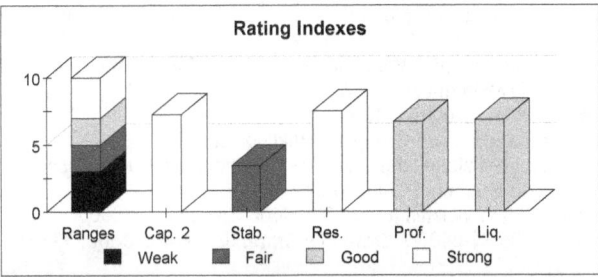

Rating Indexes

ARCH REINS CO   C-   Fair

Major Rating Factors: Weak overall results on stability tests (2.7 on a scale of 0 to 10) including potential drain of affiliation with Arch Capital Group Ltd and weak results on operational trends. The largest net exposure for one risk is conservative at 1.1% of capital. Strong long-term capitalization index (7.6) based on excellent current risk adjusted capital (severe and moderate loss scenarios). Moreover, capital levels have been consistent in recent years.
Other Rating Factors: Ample reserve history (8.1) that helps to protect the company against sharp claims increases. Excellent profitability (7.6) despite modest operating losses during 2011. Excellent liquidity (7.2) with ample operational cash flow and liquid investments.
Principal Business: (This company is a reinsurer.)
Principal Investments: Misc. investments (52%), investment grade bonds (44%), and cash (4%).
Investments in Affiliates: 49%
Group Affiliation: Arch Capital Group Ltd
Licensed in: All states except PR
Commenced Business: July 1995
Address: 1209 Orange St, Wilmington, DE 19801
Phone: (973) 898-9575   **Domicile State:** DE   **NAIC Code:** 10348

Data Date	Rating	RACR #1	RACR #2	Loss Ratio %	Total Assets ($mil)	Capital ($mil)	Net Premium ($mil)	Net Income ($mil)
6-16	C-	1.63	1.57	N/A	1,963.4	1,249.9	112.6	17.2
6-15	C-	1.60	1.56	N/A	1,797.9	1,111.0	114.1	14.9
2015	C-	1.59	1.56	49.2	1,904.9	1,201.4	219.0	32.7
2014	C-	1.61	1.57	52.1	1,736.9	1,104.0	245.5	33.3
2013	C-	1.61	1.58	46.8	1,547.9	1,013.2	204.0	33.0
2012	C-	1.71	1.67	65.1	1,315.9	822.6	190.0	7.2
2011	C-	1.69	1.66	74.0	1,223.5	822.9	145.3	-3.1

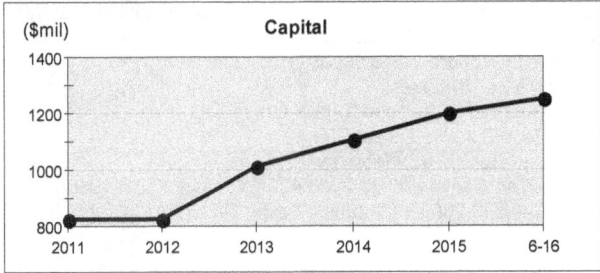

Capital

ARCH SPECIALTY INS CO   B   Good

Major Rating Factors: History of adequate reserve strength (6.0 on a scale of 0 to 10) as reserves have been consistently at an acceptable level. Good overall profitability index (5.5) despite operating losses during 2011, 2012 and the first six months of 2016. Return on equity has been low, averaging 0.9% over the past five years.

Other Rating Factors: Fair overall results on stability tests (4.7) including weak results on operational trends and negative cash flow from operations for 2015. Strong long-term capitalization index (10.0) based on excellent current risk adjusted capital (severe and moderate loss scenarios), despite some fluctuation in capital levels. Superior liquidity (9.3) with ample operational cash flow and liquid investments.

Principal Business: Other liability (43%), fire (24%), medical malpractice (11%), commercial multiple peril (7%), earthquake (6%), allied lines (4%), and other lines (5%).

Principal Investments: Investment grade bonds (89%), cash (7%), and misc. investments (4%).

Investments in Affiliates: None

Group Affiliation: Arch Capital Group Ltd

Licensed in: All states, the District of Columbia and Puerto Rico

Commenced Business: January 1965

Address: 2345 Grand Blvd Suite 900, Kansas City, MO 64108

Phone: (201) 743-4000   **Domicile State:** MO   **NAIC Code:** 21199

Data Date	Rating	RACR #1	RACR #2	Loss Ratio %	Total Assets ($mil)	Capital ($mil)	Net Premium ($mil)	Net Income ($mil)
6-16	B	5.59	4.45	N/A	515.4	300.0	0.1	-8.0
6-15	B	5.79	4.57	N/A	524.6	303.2	0.4	16.4
2015	B	5.76	4.62	N/A	503.0	305.9	0.3	23.3
2014	B	5.61	4.47	N/A	470.6	292.4	0.9	7.7
2013	B	21.66	13.74	N/A	473.5	283.5	0.0	5.6
2012	B	18.93	12.13	N/A	437.8	271.8	0.0	-6.8
2011	A-	16.52	9.72	N/A	462.5	315.1	0.0	-6.6

Reserve Deficiency (as % of capital)

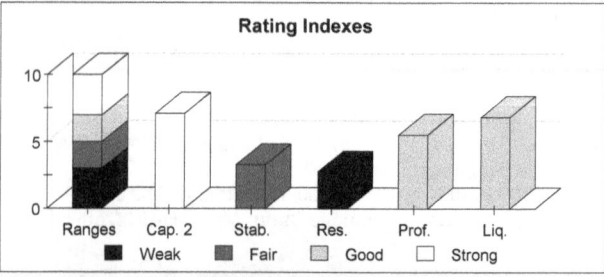

* Adequate & redundant reserves show as negatives

■ 1 Yr Dev   □ 2 Yr Dev

ARGONAUT INS CO   C   Fair

Major Rating Factors: Fair overall results on stability tests (3.3 on a scale of 0 to 10) including weak results on operational trends and negative cash flow from operations for 2015. A history of deficient reserves (2.8). Underreserving can have an adverse impact on capital and profits. In four of the last five years reserves (two year development) were between 16% and 20% deficient.

Other Rating Factors: Good overall profitability index (5.5) despite operating losses during 2012. Return on equity has been fair, averaging 5.5% over the past five years. Good liquidity (6.9) with sufficient resources (cash flows and marketable investments) to handle a spike in claims. Strong long-term capitalization index (7.1) based on excellent current risk adjusted capital (severe and moderate loss scenarios), despite some fluctuation in capital levels.

Principal Business: Other liability (34%), workers compensation (25%), surety (16%), commercial multiple peril (11%), auto liability (7%), aggregate write-ins for other lines of business (2%), and other lines (4%).

Principal Investments: Misc. investments (52%), investment grade bonds (40%), non investment grade bonds (6%), and cash (2%).

Investments in Affiliates: 12%

Group Affiliation: Argo Group Intl Holdings Ltd

Licensed in: All states, the District of Columbia and Puerto Rico

Commenced Business: May 1957

Address: 225 W Washington St 6th Floor, Chicago, IL 60606

Phone: (210) 321-8400   **Domicile State:** IL   **NAIC Code:** 19801

Data Date	Rating	RACR #1	RACR #2	Loss Ratio %	Total Assets ($mil)	Capital ($mil)	Net Premium ($mil)	Net Income ($mil)
6-16	C	2.40	1.58	N/A	1,616.4	795.7	94.2	28.5
6-15	C	1.50	0.99	N/A	1,250.5	404.4	90.1	25.6
2015	C	1.72	1.14	70.4	1,268.9	416.1	192.2	38.5
2014	C	1.43	0.94	88.6	1,280.4	390.8	185.2	13.4
2013	C	1.86	1.21	82.8	1,308.9	409.4	196.9	49.8
2012	C	1.66	1.05	93.0	1,337.3	380.5	217.8	-13.8
2011	C	1.70	1.09	93.1	1,328.1	373.0	229.0	20.5

Rating Indexes

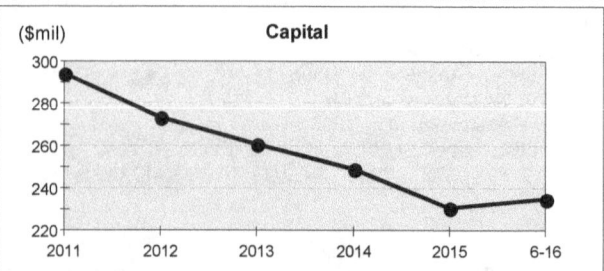

Ranges   Cap. 2   Stab.   Res.   Prof.   Liq.

■ Weak   ■ Fair   ▨ Good   □ Strong

ARROWOOD INDEMNITY CO   D+   Weak

Major Rating Factors: Weak overall results on stability tests (2.4 on a scale of 0 to 10) including weak risk adjusted capital in prior years, weak results on operational trends and negative cash flow from operations for 2015. Strengths include potentially strong support from affiliation with Arrowpoint Capital Group. The largest net exposure for one risk is acceptable at 2.1% of capital. Poor long-term capitalization index (0.7) based on weak current risk adjusted capital (severe and moderate loss scenarios).

Other Rating Factors: Weak profitability index (1.8) with operating losses during each of the last five years and the first six months of 2016. Average return on equity over the last five years has been poor at -8.0%. Fair reserve development (4.6) as reserves have generally been sufficient to cover claims. Superior liquidity (9.1) with ample operational cash flow and liquid investments.

Principal Business: (Not applicable due to unusual reinsurance transactions.)

Principal Investments: Investment grade bonds (69%), misc. investments (17%), non investment grade bonds (13%), and cash (1%).

Investments in Affiliates: 7%

Group Affiliation: Arrowpoint Capital Group

Licensed in: All states except PR

Commenced Business: February 1911

Address: 2711 Centerville Rd Suite 400, Wilmington, DE 19808

Phone: (704) 522-2000   **Domicile State:** DE   **NAIC Code:** 24678

Data Date	Rating	RACR #1	RACR #2	Loss Ratio %	Total Assets ($mil)	Capital ($mil)	Net Premium ($mil)	Net Income ($mil)
6-16	D+	0.39	0.23	N/A	1,294.8	235.0	0.3	-6.1
6-15	U	0.32	0.19	N/A	1,422.4	249.8	-2.2	-1.3
2015	D+	0.37	0.21	N/A	1,354.0	230.8	-1.8	-16.2
2014	U	0.28	0.17	N/A	1,473.7	249.0	-1.9	-38.1
2013	U	0.31	0.19	673.6	1,540.0	260.5	1.5	-3.2
2012	D	0.33	0.20	N/A	1,554.9	273.4	-2.6	-18.3
2011	D	0.51	0.30	N/A	1,727.4	294.4	0.5	-32.5

Capital

(Line chart, $mil, from 2011 to 6-16, showing a decline from about 293 to about 234)

ASPEN AMERICAN INS CO   B-   Good

Major Rating Factors: Fair overall results on stability tests (4.2 on a scale of 0 to 10) including potential drain of affiliation with Aspen Insurance Holdings Ltd, excessive premium growth and weak results on operational trends. Fair profitability index (3.6) with operating losses during each of the last five years. However, profits have turned positive in the first six months of 2016. Average return on equity over the last five years has been poor at -10.2%.

Other Rating Factors: History of adequate reserve strength (6.9) as reserves have been consistently at an acceptable level. Strong long-term capitalization index (10.0) based on excellent current risk adjusted capital (severe and moderate loss scenarios). Moreover, capital levels have been consistent in recent years. Excellent liquidity (8.3) with ample operational cash flow and liquid investments.

Principal Business: Commercial multiple peril (37%), other liability (32%), surety (10%), inland marine (8%), ocean marine (4%), fire (3%), and other lines (6%).

Principal Investments: Investment grade bonds (76%), cash (21%), and misc. investments (3%).

Investments in Affiliates: None

Group Affiliation: Aspen Insurance Holdings Ltd

Licensed in: All states, the District of Columbia and Puerto Rico

Commenced Business: December 1990

Address: 350 N St Paul St, Dallas, TX 75201

Phone: (860) 258-3500   **Domicile State:** TX   **NAIC Code:** 43460

Data Date	Rating	RACR #1	RACR #2	Loss Ratio %	Total Assets ($mil)	Capital ($mil)	Net Premium ($mil)	Net Income ($mil)
6-16	B-	4.17	2.69	N/A	606.7	278.4	44.8	8.8
6-15	C	3.06	2.00	N/A	526.8	253.5	29.6	-12.5
2015	C+	4.99	3.26	83.5	504.9	268.5	69.4	-14.8
2014	C	3.85	2.55	66.9	502.3	262.8	64.0	-24.1
2013	C	6.46	4.35	102.9	443.7	257.5	26.8	-27.4
2012	C	4.93	3.35	98.3	277.9	172.0	21.0	-34.6
2011	C-	8.75	6.60	275.0	143.2	103.0	5.5	-14.1

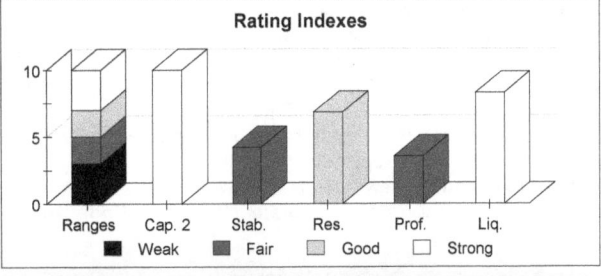

Rating Indexes

ASSOCIATED INDUSTRIES OF MA MUT INS   C+   Fair

Major Rating Factors: Fair overall results on stability tests (4.0 on a scale of 0 to 10) including potential drain of affiliation with AIM Mutual Group and weak results on operational trends. Good liquidity (6.8) with sufficient resources (cash flows and marketable investments) to handle a spike in claims.

Other Rating Factors: Strong long-term capitalization index (8.1) based on excellent current risk adjusted capital (severe and moderate loss scenarios). Moreover, capital levels have been consistent in recent years. Ample reserve history (9.4) that helps to protect the company against sharp claims increases. Excellent profitability (8.4) with operating gains in each of the last five years.

Principal Business: Workers compensation (100%).

Principal Investments: Investment grade bonds (86%), misc. investments (13%), and cash (1%).

Investments in Affiliates: 2%

Group Affiliation: AIM Mutual Group

Licensed in: CT, MA, NH

Commenced Business: January 1989

Address: 54 Third Ave, Burlington, MA 01803

Phone: (781) 221-1600   **Domicile State:** MA   **NAIC Code:** 33758

Data Date	Rating	RACR #1	RACR #2	Loss Ratio %	Total Assets ($mil)	Capital ($mil)	Net Premium ($mil)	Net Income ($mil)
6-16	C+	2.35	1.75	N/A	583.3	199.1	65.6	4.6
6-15	C	2.19	1.64	N/A	552.6	181.9	66.0	2.8
2015	C+	2.39	1.79	71.7	560.3	193.8	132.8	14.7
2014	C	2.31	1.73	74.6	530.9	180.6	129.2	11.6
2013	C	1.99	1.47	76.7	492.9	178.2	126.1	8.0
2012	C	2.12	1.57	75.7	448.4	164.4	113.0	10.0
2011	C	2.42	1.82	76.5	413.1	154.8	103.1	3.9

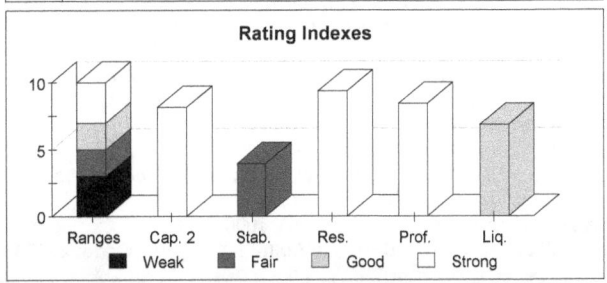

Rating Indexes

ASSURED GUARANTY CORP   C-   Fair

Major Rating Factors: A history of deficient reserves (2.2 on a scale of 0 to 10) that places pressure on both capital and profits. In 2015, the two year reserve development was 116% deficient. Weak overall results on stability tests (2.1) including weak results on operational trends and negative cash flow from operations for 2015. The largest net exposure for one risk is excessive at 12.8% of capital.

Other Rating Factors: Good overall profitability index (5.3) despite operating losses during 2015. Return on equity has been good over the last five years, averaging 11.6%. Strong long-term capitalization index (9.1) based on excellent current risk adjusted capital (severe and moderate loss scenarios), despite some fluctuation in capital levels. Excellent liquidity (7.0) with ample operational cash flow and liquid investments.

Principal Business: Financial guaranty (100%).

Principal Investments: Investment grade bonds (96%), non investment grade bonds (6%), cash (6%), and real estate (1%).

Investments in Affiliates: 13%

Group Affiliation: Assured Guaranty/Financial Sec Asr

Licensed in: All states, the District of Columbia and Puerto Rico

Commenced Business: January 1988

Address: 1325 Ave Of The Americas 18 Fl, New York, NY 10019

Phone: (212) 974-0100   **Domicile State:** MD   **NAIC Code:** 30180

Data Date	Rating	RACR #1	RACR #2	Loss Ratio %	Total Assets ($mil)	Capital ($mil)	Net Premium ($mil)	Net Income ($mil)
6-16	C-	3.04	2.59	N/A	3,022.8	1,435.1	72.2	67.1
6-15	C-	3.53	2.84	N/A	3,256.2	1,392.8	71.1	15.3
2015	C-	2.81	2.35	93.2	3,066.9	1,365.3	45.2	-91.6
2014	D+	2.98	2.46	N/A	3,888.9	1,421.9	58.6	129.3
2013	D+	2.15	1.82	N/A	2,504.4	692.6	-186.7	211.2
2012	D+	3.61	2.97	46.2	2,963.0	905.4	88.1	31.3
2011	C	3.81	3.13	N/A	3,010.4	1,021.5	92.7	229.9

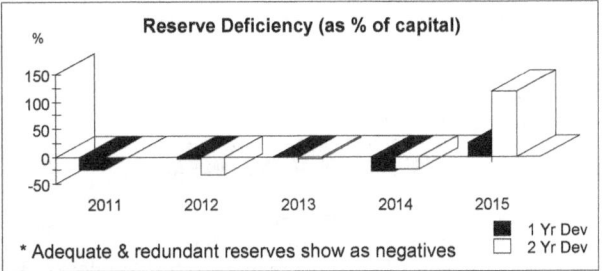

Reserve Deficiency (as % of capital)

* Adequate & redundant reserves show as negatives

ASSURED GUARANTY MUNICIPAL CORP | D+ | Weak

Major Rating Factors: Weak overall results on stability tests (1.9 on a scale of 0 to 10) including weak results on operational trends. The largest net exposure for one risk is excessive at 16.7% of capital. Strengths include potentially strong support from affiliation with Assured Guaranty/Financial Sec Asr. Strong long-term capitalization index (8.1) based on excellent current risk adjusted capital (severe and moderate loss scenarios), despite some fluctuation in capital levels.

Other Rating Factors: Fair reserve development (4.4) as reserves have generally been sufficient to cover claims. Excellent profitability (8.6) with operating gains in each of the last five years. Return on equity has been excellent over the last five years averaging 16.6%. Superior liquidity (9.5) with ample operational cash flow and liquid investments.

Principal Business: Financial guaranty (100%).

Principal Investments: Investment grade bonds (80%), misc. investments (17%), and non investment grade bonds (3%).

Investments in Affiliates: 12%

Group Affiliation: Assured Guaranty/Financial Sec Asr

Licensed in: All states, the District of Columbia and Puerto Rico

Commenced Business: September 1985

Address: 31 W 52nd St, New York, NY 10019

Phone: (212) 826-0100   **Domicile State:** NY   **NAIC Code:** 18287

Data Date	Rating	RACR #1	RACR #2	Loss Ratio %	Total Assets ($mil)	Capital ($mil)	Net Premium ($mil)	Net Income ($mil)
6-16	D+	2.82	1.72	N/A	5,665.6	2,440.8	134.4	122.1
6-15	D+	2.57	1.56	N/A	5,853.3	2,181.4	104.9	88.4
2015	D+	2.85	1.80	59.6	5,788.5	2,440.8	141.8	216.7
2014	D+	2.75	1.69	N/A	5,961.2	2,266.9	173.9	303.9
2013	D+	2.49	1.48	N/A	5,712.1	1,733.1	-191.3	339.6
2012	D+	2.07	1.42	65.6	4,498.5	1,780.1	196.1	203.3
2011	D+	1.61	0.98	N/A	4,385.6	1,209.3	150.8	398.5

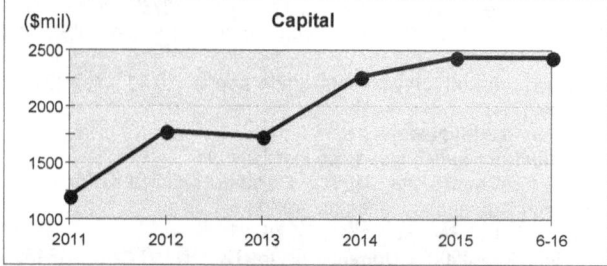

ATLANTIC SPECIALTY INS CO | B- | Good

Major Rating Factors: Fair overall results on stability tests (4.7 on a scale of 0 to 10) including potential drain of affiliation with White Mountains Group, weak results on operational trends and negative cash flow from operations for 2015. Fair profitability index (4.4) with operating losses during 2012 and 2014. Return on equity has been low, averaging 2.7% over the past five years.

Other Rating Factors: History of adequate reserve strength (5.7) as reserves have been consistently at an acceptable level. Good liquidity (6.8) with sufficient resources (cash flows and marketable investments) to handle a spike in claims. Strong long-term capitalization index (7.1) based on excellent current risk adjusted capital (severe and moderate loss scenarios), despite some fluctuation in capital levels.

Principal Business: Other liability (21%), ocean marine (12%), group accident & health (12%), commercial multiple peril (10%), auto liability (9%), inland marine (8%), and other lines (30%).

Principal Investments: Investment grade bonds (72%), misc. investments (27%), and cash (1%).

Investments in Affiliates: 12%

Group Affiliation: White Mountains Group

Licensed in: All states, the District of Columbia and Puerto Rico

Commenced Business: December 1986

Address: 140 Broadway, New York, NY 10005-1101

Phone: (781) 332-7000   **Domicile State:** NY   **NAIC Code:** 27154

Data Date	Rating	RACR #1	RACR #2	Loss Ratio %	Total Assets ($mil)	Capital ($mil)	Net Premium ($mil)	Net Income ($mil)
6-16	B-	1.75	1.34	N/A	2,256.9	603.6	276.1	7.8
6-15	C	1.35	0.97	N/A	2,538.9	688.9	314.7	15.5
2015	C+	1.79	1.37	65.9	2,340.3	622.3	590.1	45.0
2014	C	1.03	0.72	72.2	2,550.9	721.5	1,109.0	-14.1
2013	C	1.33	0.96	54.6	2,258.8	665.8	969.2	116.3
2012	C	1.87	1.31	68.7	2,248.4	716.7	850.5	-72.8
2011	C	33.25	21.46	59.1	105.2	93.4	6.5	1.1

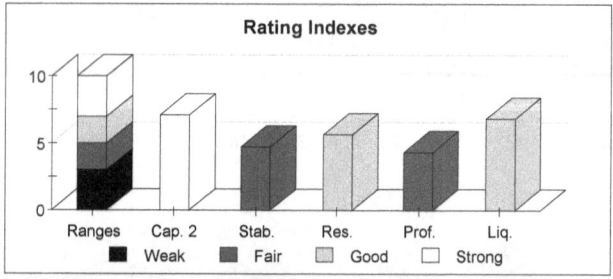

ATLANTIC STATES INS CO | B- | Good

Major Rating Factors: Fair overall results on stability tests (4.2 on a scale of 0 to 10) including potential drain of affiliation with Donegal Mutual Insurance Company and weak results on operational trends. History of adequate reserve strength (5.8) as reserves have been consistently at an acceptable level.

Other Rating Factors: Good overall profitability index (6.1) despite operating losses during 2011. Return on equity has been low, averaging 4.1% over the past five years. Good liquidity (6.3) with sufficient resources (cash flows and marketable investments) to handle a spike in claims. Strong long-term capitalization index (8.6) based on excellent current risk adjusted capital (severe and moderate loss scenarios). Moreover, capital levels have been consistent in recent years.

Principal Business: Auto liability (34%), auto physical damage (21%), commercial multiple peril (17%), homeowners multiple peril (14%), and workers compensation (12%).

Principal Investments: Investment grade bonds (85%), misc. investments (14%), and cash (1%).

Investments in Affiliates: None

Group Affiliation: Donegal Mutual Insurance Company

Licensed in: CT, DC, DE, GA, IN, IA, ME, MD, MI, NE, NH, NY, NC, OH, PA, SC, SD, TN, VT, VA, WV

Commenced Business: October 1986

Address: 1195 River Rd, Marietta, PA 17547-0302

Phone: (717) 426-1931   **Domicile State:** PA   **NAIC Code:** 22586

Data Date	Rating	RACR #1	RACR #2	Loss Ratio %	Total Assets ($mil)	Capital ($mil)	Net Premium ($mil)	Net Income ($mil)
6-16	B-	2.90	2.11	N/A	740.8	220.1	202.2	8.7
6-15	B-	2.75	2.01	N/A	672.0	197.2	189.2	3.6
2015	B-	2.85	2.08	66.0	705.5	207.6	393.1	13.4
2014	B-	2.82	2.06	68.4	636.4	191.2	371.3	6.1
2013	B-	2.83	2.01	64.7	595.4	186.6	346.9	12.6
2012	B-	3.35	2.47	67.6	538.8	180.5	303.3	12.5
2011	B-	3.55	2.60	77.7	509.2	173.5	274.5	-7.7

ATTORNEYS LIAB ASR SOCIETY INC RRG — D Weak

Major Rating Factors: Poor long-term capitalization index (1.0 on a scale of 0 to 10) based on weak current risk adjusted capital (severe and moderate loss scenarios). A history of deficient reserves (1.1). Underreserving can have an adverse impact on capital and profits. In 2014 and 2015 the two year reserve development was 53% and 70% deficient respectively.

Other Rating Factors: Weak overall results on stability tests (1.5) including weak risk adjusted capital in prior years and weak results on operational trends. The largest net exposure for one risk is high at 4.3% of capital. Fair profitability index (4.3) with operating losses during 2013 and 2014. Return on equity has been low, averaging 2.3% over the past five years. Excellent liquidity (7.0) with ample operational cash flow and liquid investments.

Principal Business: Other liability (100%).

Principal Investments: Misc. investments (52%), investment grade bonds (47%), and cash (1%).

Investments in Affiliates: 32%

Group Affiliation: Attorneys Liability Asr Soc Bermuda

Licensed in: All states except PR

Commenced Business: December 1987

Address: 148 College St Suite 204, Burlington, VT 05401

Phone: (312) 697-6900   **Domicile State:** VT   **NAIC Code:** 10639

Data Date	Rating	RACR #1	RACR #2	Loss Ratio %	Total Assets ($mil)	Capital ($mil)	Net Premium ($mil)	Net Income ($mil)
6-16	D	0.32	0.25	N/A	2,096.8	568.8	101.9	3.9
6-15	D	0.43	0.34	N/A	2,084.0	582.5	107.0	-18.0
2015	D	0.32	0.26	115.2	1,944.7	557.2	222.9	20.4
2014	D	0.45	0.36	111.6	2,036.0	594.1	243.3	-33.4
2013	C-	4.53	3.11	102.4	239.1	80.3	25.9	-3.2
2012	C-	3.66	2.62	85.9	153.7	59.2	23.2	5.3
2011	C-	3.92	2.80	72.1	137.1	56.7	23.3	5.0

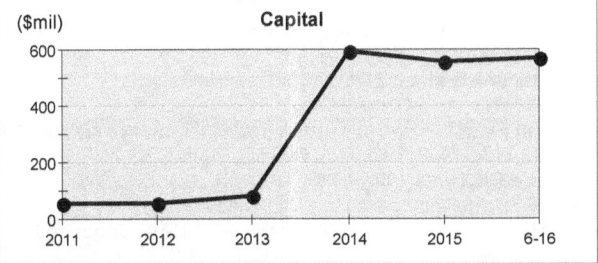

Capital

AUTO CLUB INDEMNITY CO * — B+ Good

Major Rating Factors: Good overall profitability index (6.4 on a scale of 0 to 10). Excellent expense controls. Return on equity has been low, averaging 0.8% over the past five years. Good liquidity (6.7) with sufficient resources (cash flows and marketable investments) to handle a spike in claims.

Other Rating Factors: Good overall results on stability tests (5.0) despite weak results on operational trends. Strong long-term capitalization index (7.6) based on excellent current risk adjusted capital (severe and moderate loss scenarios), despite some fluctuation in capital levels.

Principal Business: Homeowners multiple peril (99%) and other liability (1%).

Principal Investments: Investment grade bonds (87%), cash (12%), and misc. investments (1%).

Investments in Affiliates: None

Group Affiliation: Auto Club Enterprises Ins Group

Licensed in: TX

Commenced Business: December 1999

Address: 3333 Fairview Road, Costa Mesa, CA 92626-1698

Phone: (714) 850-5111   **Domicile State:** TX   **NAIC Code:** 11008

Data Date	Rating	RACR #1	RACR #2	Loss Ratio %	Total Assets ($mil)	Capital ($mil)	Net Premium ($mil)	Net Income ($mil)
6-16	B+	1.46	1.31	N/A	27.2	5.4	0.0	0.0
6-15	B+	1.61	1.45	N/A	23.5	5.3	0.0	0.0
2015	B+	1.73	1.55	0.0	21.6	5.4	0.0	0.0
2014	B+	1.80	1.62	0.0	20.0	5.3	0.0	0.0
2013	B+	1.92	1.72	0.0	18.0	5.2	0.0	0.0
2012	B+	2.00	1.80	0.0	16.7	5.2	0.0	0.0
2011	B+	2.36	2.13	0.0	13.7	5.1	0.0	0.0

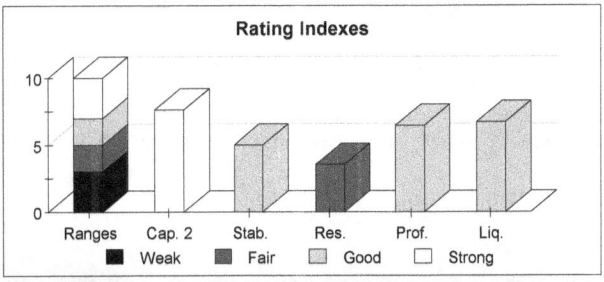

Rating Indexes

AUTO CLUB INS ASSN — B Good

Major Rating Factors: Good liquidity (6.3 on a scale of 0 to 10) with sufficient resources (cash flows and marketable investments) to handle a spike in claims. Fair overall results on stability tests (4.9) including potential drain of affiliation with Automobile Club of Michigan Group and weak results on operational trends.

Other Rating Factors: Fair reserve development (4.5) as reserves have generally been sufficient to cover claims. Fair profitability index (4.6) with operating losses during 2011. Strong long-term capitalization index (7.8) based on excellent current risk adjusted capital (severe and moderate loss scenarios), despite some fluctuation in capital levels.

Principal Business: Auto liability (39%), homeowners multiple peril (34%), auto physical damage (26%), and other liability (1%).

Principal Investments: Investment grade bonds (48%), misc. investments (46%), non investment grade bonds (6%), and real estate (1%).

Investments in Affiliates: 20%

Group Affiliation: Automobile Club of Michigan Group

Licensed in: IL, MI, MN, NE, NY, ND, PA, WI

Commenced Business: March 1922

Address: One Auto Club Dr, Dearborn, MI 48126

Phone: (313) 336-1234   **Domicile State:** MI   **NAIC Code:** 21202

Data Date	Rating	RACR #1	RACR #2	Loss Ratio %	Total Assets ($mil)	Capital ($mil)	Net Premium ($mil)	Net Income ($mil)
6-16	B	1.92	1.53	N/A	3,921.9	1,690.0	722.4	46.4
6-15	B	1.86	1.47	N/A	3,767.2	1,570.0	684.5	72.3
2015	B	1.84	1.49	70.5	3,783.3	1,592.8	1,432.8	127.5
2014	B	1.82	1.46	77.5	3,673.6	1,524.8	1,355.0	51.3
2013	B	1.89	1.53	74.0	3,650.4	1,575.8	1,351.3	48.5
2012	B	1.89	1.57	86.3	3,350.4	1,526.3	1,229.1	18.2
2011	B	1.92	1.61	81.8	3,572.6	1,591.4	1,487.9	-24.5

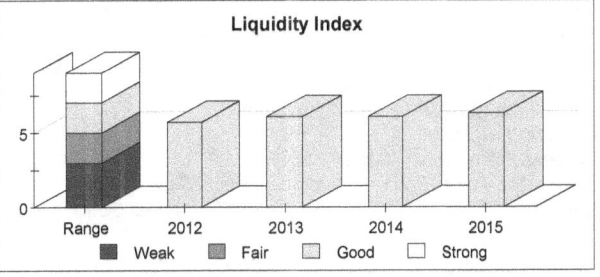

Liquidity Index

AUTO-OWNERS INS CO *   A-   Excellent

Major Rating Factors: Strong long-term capitalization index (8.7 on a scale of 0 to 10) based on excellent current risk adjusted capital (severe and moderate loss scenarios). Furthermore, this high level of risk adjusted capital has been consistently maintained in previous years. Excellent profitability (8.1) with operating gains in each of the last five years.

Other Rating Factors: History of adequate reserve strength (6.0) as reserves have been consistently at an acceptable level. Good liquidity (6.9) with sufficient resources (cash flows and marketable investments) to handle a spike in claims. Good overall results on stability tests (5.7) despite weak results on operational trends.

Principal Business: Homeowners multiple peril (29%), auto liability (18%), commercial multiple peril (11%), fire (11%), auto physical damage (10%), workers compensation (8%), and other lines (14%).

Principal Investments: Investment grade bonds (50%), misc. investments (49%), and real estate (1%).

Investments in Affiliates: 27%

Group Affiliation: Auto-Owners Group

Licensed in: AL, AZ, AR, CO, FL, GA, ID, IL, IN, IA, KS, KY, MI, MN, MS, MO, NE, NV, NM, NC, ND, OH, OR, PA, SC, SD, TN, UT, VA, WA, WI

Commenced Business: July 1916

Address: 6101 Anacapri Blvd, Lansing, MI 48917

Phone: (517) 323-1200   **Domicile State:** MI   **NAIC Code:** 18988

Data Date	Rating	RACR #1	RACR #2	Loss Ratio %	Total Assets ($mil)	Capital ($mil)	Net Premium ($mil)	Net Income ($mil)
6-16	A-	2.49	2.12	N/A	13,712.2	9,342.7	1,457.9	279.5
6-15	A-	2.51	2.16	N/A	12,728.9	8,394.4	1,308.3	263.8
2015	A-	2.44	2.12	51.7	13,117.6	8,777.0	2,873.1	476.6
2014	A-	2.42	2.10	63.1	12,207.7	7,969.1	2,541.0	344.2
2013	A	2.42	2.08	60.9	11,392.8	7,510.8	2,325.4	340.3
2012	A	2.43	2.08	67.0	10,308.1	6,591.0	2,230.3	260.7
2011	A	2.47	2.11	89.9	9,767.0	6,062.2	2,173.7	14.7

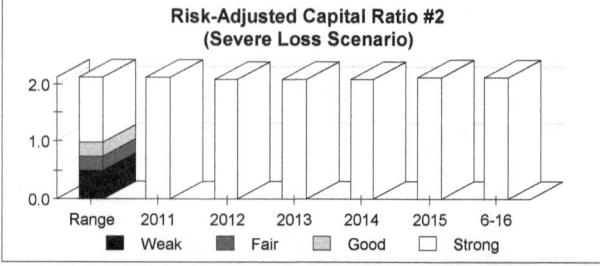

Risk-Adjusted Capital Ratio #2
(Severe Loss Scenario)

AUTOMOBILE CLUB INTERINSURANCE EXCH   C   Fair

Major Rating Factors: Fair profitability index (4.6 on a scale of 0 to 10) with operating losses during 2013 and the first six months of 2016. Fair overall results on stability tests (4.2) including fair financial strength of affiliated Auto Club Enterprises Ins Group and weak results on operational trends.

Other Rating Factors: Good liquidity (6.4) with sufficient resources (cash flows and marketable investments) to handle a spike in claims. Strong long-term capitalization index (8.6) based on excellent current risk adjusted capital (severe and moderate loss scenarios), despite some fluctuation in capital levels. Ample reserve history (7.4) that can protect against increases in claims costs.

Principal Business: Auto liability (53%) and auto physical damage (47%).

Principal Investments: Investment grade bonds (53%), misc. investments (49%), non investment grade bonds (4%), and real estate (1%).

Investments in Affiliates: 14%

Group Affiliation: Auto Club Enterprises Ins Group

Licensed in: AL, AR, CA, IL, IN, KS, LA, MS, MO, OH

Commenced Business: April 1927

Address: 12901 North Forty Dr, St Louis, MO 63141

Phone: (314) 523-7350   **Domicile State:** MO   **NAIC Code:** 15512

Data Date	Rating	RACR #1	RACR #2	Loss Ratio %	Total Assets ($mil)	Capital ($mil)	Net Premium ($mil)	Net Income ($mil)
6-16	C	2.73	2.05	N/A	419.5	209.8	64.4	-1.6
6-15	C	2.76	2.07	N/A	403.8	208.0	60.4	1.6
2015	C	2.79	2.12	71.9	406.3	209.9	127.0	5.1
2014	C	2.78	2.10	71.6	402.1	205.7	120.6	9.4
2013	C	2.71	2.03	71.1	415.9	198.0	115.9	-5.3
2012	C	3.10	2.37	72.4	414.6	188.0	110.0	7.6
2011	C	3.24	2.50	73.7	386.7	175.4	105.9	4.2

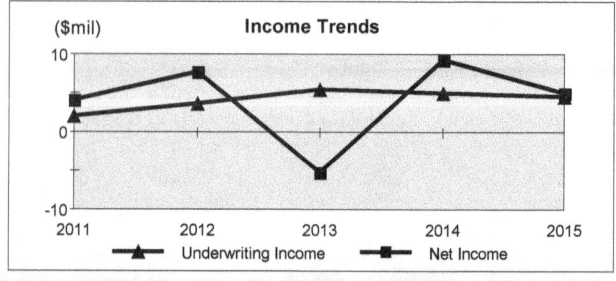

Income Trends

AUTOMOBILE INS CO OF HARTFORD CT   B   Good

Major Rating Factors: Good liquidity (6.7 on a scale of 0 to 10) with sufficient resources (cash flows and marketable investments) to handle a spike in claims. Fair overall results on stability tests (4.7) including weak results on operational trends. Affiliation with Travelers Companies Inc is a strength.

Other Rating Factors: Strong long-term capitalization index (8.3) based on excellent current risk adjusted capital (severe and moderate loss scenarios), despite some fluctuation in capital levels. Ample reserve history (8.6) that helps to protect the company against sharp claims increases. Excellent profitability (7.0) with operating gains in each of the last five years. Return on equity has been good over the last five years, averaging 11.8%.

Principal Business: Homeowners multiple peril (51%), fire (13%), other liability (10%), allied lines (10%), auto liability (8%), auto physical damage (6%), and inland marine (1%).

Principal Investments: Investment grade bonds (97%) and misc. investments (3%).

Investments in Affiliates: None

Group Affiliation: Travelers Companies Inc

Licensed in: All states except CA, PR

Commenced Business: August 1968

Address: One Tower Square, Hartford, CT 06183

Phone: (860) 277-0111   **Domicile State:** CT   **NAIC Code:** 19062

Data Date	Rating	RACR #1	RACR #2	Loss Ratio %	Total Assets ($mil)	Capital ($mil)	Net Premium ($mil)	Net Income ($mil)
6-16	B	3.05	1.93	N/A	1,034.2	340.6	143.5	17.8
6-15	B	3.13	1.97	N/A	1,020.4	343.4	138.3	20.4
2015	B	2.97	1.89	58.7	1,000.8	322.4	284.7	43.1
2014	B	2.97	1.87	60.5	1,013.2	320.8	276.6	43.1
2013	B	2.99	1.90	60.9	1,002.2	317.3	275.9	47.3
2012	B	2.83	1.82	68.4	983.1	295.1	268.0	36.1
2011	B	2.69	1.73	76.9	959.4	282.5	262.4	16.2

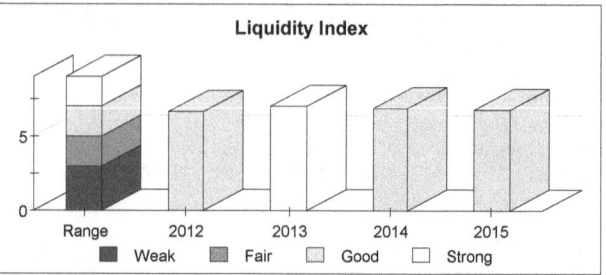

Liquidity Index

AXIS INS CO — B — Good

Major Rating Factors: History of adequate reserve strength (6.6 on a scale of 0 to 10) as reserves have been consistently at an acceptable level. Good liquidity (6.9) with sufficient resources (cash flows and marketable investments) to handle a spike in claims.

Other Rating Factors: Fair overall results on stability tests (4.3) including potential drain of affiliation with AXIS Specialty Ltd and weak results on operational trends. The largest net exposure for one risk is conservative at 1.6% of capital. Fair profitability index (4.6) with operating losses during 2012, 2013, 2014 and the first six months of 2016. Return on equity has been low, averaging 0.0% over the past five years. Strong long-term capitalization index (7.4) based on excellent current risk adjusted capital (severe and moderate loss scenarios), despite some fluctuation in capital levels.

Principal Business: Other liability (65%), fire (8%), allied lines (7%), group accident & health (7%), earthquake (3%), inland marine (2%), and other lines (8%).

Principal Investments: Investment grade bonds (80%) and misc. investments (20%).

Investments in Affiliates: 20%

Group Affiliation: AXIS Specialty Ltd

Licensed in: All states except PR

Commenced Business: November 1979

Address: 202 W Madison St Ste 500, Chicago, IL 60606

Phone: (678) 746-9400 **Domicile State:** IL **NAIC Code:** 37273

Data Date	Rating	RACR #1	RACR #2	Loss Ratio %	Total Assets ($mil)	Capital ($mil)	Net Premium ($mil)	Net Income ($mil)
6-16	B	1.98	1.30	N/A	1,528.9	577.2	150.0	-2.5
6-15	C+	1.88	1.26	N/A	1,512.1	573.3	141.2	5.1
2015	B	1.96	1.29	62.2	1,488.0	565.1	307.5	32.1
2014	C+	1.91	1.28	78.0	1,483.8	578.1	282.3	-2.1
2013	C+	1.79	1.25	80.0	1,366.0	526.2	306.8	-10.1
2012	C+	1.94	1.52	80.0	1,196.5	538.9	227.4	-17.5
2011	C+	2.08	1.86	80.0	1,044.0	529.3	205.3	2.0

Reserve Deficiency (as % of capital)

* Adequate & redundant reserves show as negatives
■ 1 Yr Dev   □ 2 Yr Dev

AXIS REINS CO — C+ — Fair

Major Rating Factors: Fair overall results on stability tests (4.2 on a scale of 0 to 10) including potential drain of affiliation with AXIS Specialty Ltd and weak results on operational trends. Good overall profitability index (5.3) despite operating losses during the first six months of 2016. Return on equity has been low, averaging 4.5% over the past five years.

Other Rating Factors: Strong long-term capitalization index (7.9) based on excellent current risk adjusted capital (severe and moderate loss scenarios), despite some fluctuation in capital levels. Ample reserve history (9.4) that helps to protect the company against sharp claims increases. Excellent liquidity (7.0) with ample operational cash flow and liquid investments.

Principal Business: Other liability (89%), allied lines (5%), fidelity (4%), fire (2%), and earthquake (1%).

Principal Investments: Investment grade bonds (72%), misc. investments (18%), non investment grade bonds (7%), and cash (3%).

Investments in Affiliates: None

Group Affiliation: AXIS Specialty Ltd

Licensed in: All states, the District of Columbia and Puerto Rico

Commenced Business: January 1992

Address: 1211 Avenue of Americas 24 fL, New York, NY 10036

Phone: (212) 500-7600 **Domicile State:** NY **NAIC Code:** 20370

Data Date	Rating	RACR #1	RACR #2	Loss Ratio %	Total Assets ($mil)	Capital ($mil)	Net Premium ($mil)	Net Income ($mil)
6-16	C+	2.55	1.55	N/A	3,136.3	860.6	257.4	-20.4
6-15	C+	2.60	1.59	N/A	2,998.1	864.5	245.5	-2.1
2015	C+	2.69	1.64	68.1	2,863.3	860.9	513.4	24.6
2014	C+	2.63	1.62	73.7	2,872.8	864.9	528.4	40.5
2013	C+	2.74	1.71	57.8	2,675.9	822.7	494.2	58.0
2012	C+	2.27	1.35	69.4	2,501.2	756.8	407.5	35.0
2011	C+	1.98	1.07	62.4	2,296.1	707.8	407.1	57.5

Rating Indexes

Ranges Cap. 2 Stab. Res. Prof. Liq.
■ Weak   ■ Fair   ▨ Good   □ Strong

AXIS SURPLUS INS CO — C — Fair

Major Rating Factors: Fair overall results on stability tests (4.2 on a scale of 0 to 10) including potential drain of affiliation with AXIS Specialty Ltd, weak results on operational trends and negative cash flow from operations for 2015. The largest net exposure for one risk is conservative at 1.7% of capital. Fair profitability index (3.9). Weak expense controls. Return on equity has been low, averaging 4.6% over the past five years.

Other Rating Factors: Strong long-term capitalization index (10.0) based on excellent current risk adjusted capital (severe and moderate loss scenarios), despite some fluctuation in capital levels. Ample reserve history (8.5) that helps to protect the company against sharp claims increases. Excellent liquidity (8.5) with ample operational cash flow and liquid investments.

Principal Business: Other liability (65%), allied lines (16%), fire (10%), earthquake (4%), auto liability (2%), homeowners multiple peril (1%), and other lines (2%).

Principal Investments: Investment grade bonds (87%) and misc. investments (15%).

Investments in Affiliates: None

Group Affiliation: AXIS Specialty Ltd

Licensed in: All states, the District of Columbia and Puerto Rico

Commenced Business: December 1983

Address: 3030 W Madison St Suite 500, Chicago, IL 60606

Phone: (678) 746-9400 **Domicile State:** IL **NAIC Code:** 26620

Data Date	Rating	RACR #1	RACR #2	Loss Ratio %	Total Assets ($mil)	Capital ($mil)	Net Premium ($mil)	Net Income ($mil)
6-16	C	6.77	4.48	N/A	480.5	194.3	20.1	1.4
6-15	C-	7.21	4.49	N/A	501.4	208.2	19.2	2.6
2015	C	7.09	4.75	53.9	432.3	192.0	41.4	8.2
2014	C-	7.63	4.78	46.5	440.3	205.9	37.7	12.2
2013	C-	7.27	4.71	31.1	428.4	206.2	33.4	14.1
2012	C-	6.64	4.03	64.4	443.1	209.0	29.6	6.8
2011	C-	1.65	1.29	70.6	401.1	197.4	37.9	7.9

AXIS Specialty Ltd
Composite Group Rating: C+
Largest Group Members

	Assets ($mil)	Rating
AXIS REINS CO	2863	C+
AXIS INS CO	1488	B
AXIS SURPLUS INS CO	432	C
AXIS SPECIALTY INS CO	67	U

BAY STATE INS CO

B-   **Good**

Major Rating Factors: Fair overall results on stability tests (4.5 on a scale of 0 to 10) including potential drain of affiliation with Andover Group and weak results on operational trends. History of adequate reserve strength (6.4) as reserves have been consistently at an acceptable level.

Other Rating Factors: Good overall profitability index (5.5) despite operating losses during 2011. Return on equity has been low, averaging 2.5% over the past five years. Strong long-term capitalization index (8.3) based on excellent current risk adjusted capital (severe and moderate loss scenarios), despite some fluctuation in capital levels. Excellent liquidity (7.0) with ample operational cash flow and liquid investments.

Principal Business: Homeowners multiple peril (88%), other liability (5%), inland marine (4%), and commercial multiple peril (3%).

Principal Investments: Misc. investments (70%), investment grade bonds (16%), and cash (14%).

Investments in Affiliates: None
Group Affiliation: Andover Group
Licensed in: CT, IL, ME, MA, NH, NJ, NY, RI
Commenced Business: July 1955
Address: 95 Old River Rd, Andover, MA 01810
Phone: (978) 475-3300   **Domicile State:** MA   **NAIC Code:** 19763

Data Date	Rating	RACR #1	RACR #2	Loss Ratio %	Total Assets ($mil)	Capital ($mil)	Net Premium ($mil)	Net Income ($mil)
6-16	B-	3.26	1.97	N/A	453.0	289.1	37.3	6.9
6-15	B-	3.05	1.86	N/A	449.0	274.8	37.5	-9.2
2015	B-	3.23	1.95	68.5	450.4	284.5	77.8	4.8
2014	B-	3.17	1.93	43.4	456.7	287.3	78.5	15.9
2013	B-	3.33	2.06	43.3	412.6	260.3	73.9	16.6
2012	B-	3.36	2.13	64.9	361.4	217.4	71.9	5.9
2011	B-	3.36	2.16	90.4	326.4	200.1	67.3	-9.7

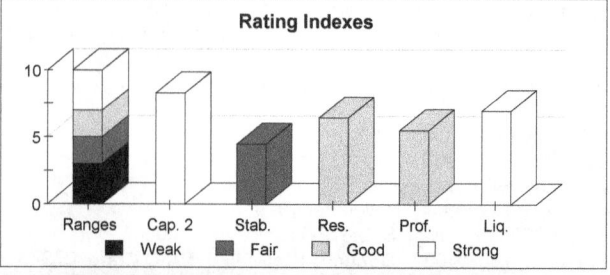

Rating Indexes

BERKLEY INS CO

B-   **Good**

Major Rating Factors: Good overall results on stability tests (5.1 on a scale of 0 to 10) despite potential drain of affiliation with W R Berkley Corp and weak results on operational trends. Good liquidity (6.8) with sufficient resources (cash flows and marketable investments) to handle a spike in claims.

Other Rating Factors: Strong long-term capitalization index (7.2) based on excellent current risk adjusted capital (severe and moderate loss scenarios), despite some fluctuation in capital levels. Ample reserve history (8.0) that helps to protect the company against sharp claims increases. Excellent profitability (7.4) with operating gains in each of the last five years. Return on equity has been good over the last five years, averaging 14.0%.

Principal Business: Other liability (70%), surety (21%), other accident & health (4%), auto liability (4%), and commercial multiple peril (1%).

Principal Investments: Investment grade bonds (57%), misc. investments (38%), non investment grade bonds (2%), real estate (2%), and cash (1%).

Investments in Affiliates: 19%
Group Affiliation: W R Berkley Corp
Licensed in: All states, the District of Columbia and Puerto Rico
Commenced Business: December 1975
Address: 100 Campus Drive, Florham Park, NJ 07932
Phone: (203) 542-3800   **Domicile State:** DE   **NAIC Code:** 32603

Data Date	Rating	RACR #1	RACR #2	Loss Ratio %	Total Assets ($mil)	Capital ($mil)	Net Premium ($mil)	Net Income ($mil)
6-16	B-	1.33	1.08	N/A	17,317.1	5,027.4	2,681.8	196.4
6-15	C	1.30	1.05	N/A	17,015.7	5,183.3	2,529.1	269.4
2015	C+	1.44	1.17	56.5	17,109.3	5,295.6	5,338.8	765.4
2014	C	1.40	1.15	59.3	16,934.1	5,437.2	5,070.0	700.5
2013	C	1.38	1.09	61.6	16,122.7	4,907.2	5,744.1	1,493.8
2012	C	1.44	1.31	67.3	10,223.8	4,656.3	1,719.3	294.5
2011	C	1.64	1.23	68.7	7,830.2	2,611.2	1,525.8	232.8

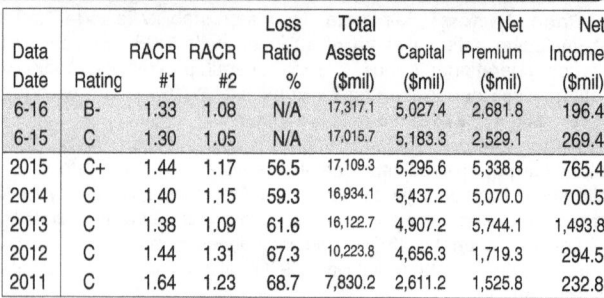

Rating Indexes

BERKLEY REGIONAL INS CO

C+   **Fair**

Major Rating Factors: Fair overall results on stability tests (4.5 on a scale of 0 to 10) including potential drain of affiliation with W R Berkley Corp and weak results on operational trends.

Other Rating Factors: Good overall profitability index (6.1). Fair expense controls. Return on equity has been fair, averaging 9.3% over the past five years. Strong long-term capitalization index (7.8) based on excellent current risk adjusted capital (severe and moderate loss scenarios), despite some fluctuation in capital levels. Excellent liquidity (7.0) with ample operational cash flow and liquid investments.

Principal Business: Fidelity (27%), workers compensation (24%), auto liability (19%), commercial multiple peril (10%), auto physical damage (8%), burglary & theft (4%), and other lines (9%).

Principal Investments: Misc. investments (52%) and investment grade bonds (48%).

Investments in Affiliates: 47%
Group Affiliation: W R Berkley Corp
Licensed in: All states except PR
Commenced Business: January 1987
Address: 1208 Orange St, Wilmington, DE 19801
Phone: (203) 629-3000   **Domicile State:** DE   **NAIC Code:** 29580

Data Date	Rating	RACR #1	RACR #2	Loss Ratio %	Total Assets ($mil)	Capital ($mil)	Net Premium ($mil)	Net Income ($mil)
6-16	C+	1.55	1.53	N/A	723.4	692.7	0.0	4.9
6-15	C+	1.56	1.55	N/A	714.9	673.2	0.0	4.1
2015	C+	1.73	1.88	0.0	711.6	679.9	0.0	11.6
2014	C+	1.75	1.90	0.0	700.4	666.6	0.0	11.0
2013	C+	1.89	2.08	0.0	681.2	643.2	-547.4	134.5
2012	B	1.39	1.17	58.7	2,700.8	717.3	1,185.6	127.2
2011	B	1.38	1.13	66.6	2,683.1	699.8	1,125.5	57.4

Rating Indexes

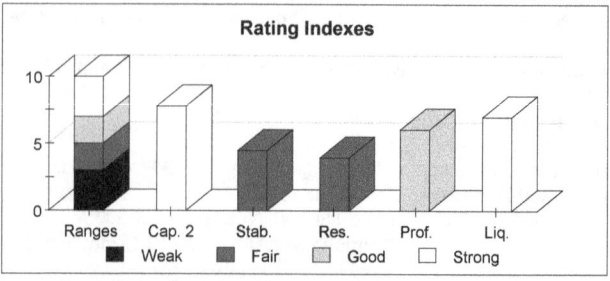

BERKSHIRE HATHAWAY ASR CORP *   A+   Excellent

Major Rating Factors: Strong long-term capitalization index (9.3 on a scale of 0 to 10) based on excellent current risk adjusted capital (severe and moderate loss scenarios). Furthermore, this high level of risk adjusted capital has been consistently maintained in previous years. Excellent profitability (8.5) with operating gains in each of the last five years.

Other Rating Factors: Superior liquidity (10.0) with ample operational cash flow and liquid investments. Excellent overall results on stability tests (7.6). Stability strengths include excellent risk diversification. Fair reserve development (3.6) as reserves have generally been sufficient to cover claims.

Principal Business: Financial guaranty (98%) and surety (2%).

Principal Investments: Misc. investments (61%), investment grade bonds (37%), cash (1%), and non investment grade bonds (1%).

Investments in Affiliates: None

Group Affiliation: Berkshire-Hathaway

Licensed in: All states, the District of Columbia and Puerto Rico

Commenced Business: December 2007

Address: Marine Air Terminal LaGuardia, Flushing, NY 11371

Phone: (402) 916-3000   **Domicile State:** NY   **NAIC Code:** 13070

Data Date	Rating	RACR #1	RACR #2	Loss Ratio %	Total Assets ($mil)	Capital ($mil)	Net Premium ($mil)	Net Income ($mil)
6-16	A+	4.56	2.72	N/A	2,220.4	1,483.1	34.0	37.2
6-15	A+	4.10	2.45	N/A	2,245.6	1,467.5	24.0	35.3
2015	A+	4.18	2.50	N/A	2,176.5	1,449.3	12.9	78.1
2014	A+	4.11	2.46	1.7	2,275.7	1,459.6	2.3	95.2
2013	A+	4.45	2.64	31.1	2,255.6	1,426.8	12.4	195.5
2012	A+	6.70	3.41	0.0	1,841.2	1,149.3	10.2	78.1
2011	A+	15.41	6.96	0.0	1,709.3	1,025.8	5.4	61.6

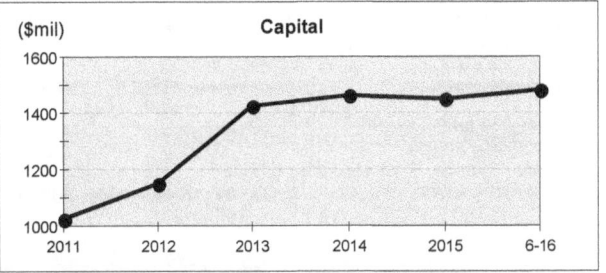

Capital ($mil)

BERKSHIRE HATHAWAY HOMESTATE INS   C+   Fair

Major Rating Factors: Fair overall results on stability tests (3.9 on a scale of 0 to 10) including fair financial strength of affiliated Berkshire-Hathaway and weak results on operational trends. The largest net exposure for one risk is acceptable at 2.2% of capital. History of adequate reserve strength (6.0) as reserves have been consistently at an acceptable level.

Other Rating Factors: Good overall profitability index (6.0) despite operating losses during 2011. Return on equity has been low, averaging 2.9% over the past five years. Strong long-term capitalization index (8.0) based on excellent current risk adjusted capital (severe and moderate loss scenarios), despite some fluctuation in capital levels. Excellent liquidity (7.8) with ample operational cash flow and liquid investments.

Principal Business: Workers compensation (69%), auto liability (16%), commercial multiple peril (5%), auto physical damage (4%), fire (1%), allied lines (1%), and other lines (3%).

Principal Investments: Misc. investments (68%), investment grade bonds (25%), and cash (7%).

Investments in Affiliates: None

Group Affiliation: Berkshire-Hathaway

Licensed in: All states except PR

Commenced Business: February 1970

Address: 1314 Douglas St, Omaha, NE 68102

Phone: (402) 393-7255   **Domicile State:** NE   **NAIC Code:** 20044

Data Date	Rating	RACR #1	RACR #2	Loss Ratio %	Total Assets ($mil)	Capital ($mil)	Net Premium ($mil)	Net Income ($mil)
6-16	C+	2.79	1.68	N/A	2,128.3	1,105.5	216.9	22.2
6-15	C+	1.47	0.94	N/A	2,123.2	1,172.6	208.9	19.4
2015	C+	2.69	1.62	70.4	2,175.0	1,167.7	461.5	55.7
2014	C+	1.63	1.04	64.5	2,008.1	1,159.5	376.5	152.7
2013	C+	1.23	0.80	77.8	1,587.5	963.8	280.1	22.4
2012	C+	1.94	1.25	77.0	1,254.2	884.8	179.5	3.6
2011	C+	3.99	2.32	31.2	776.0	632.4	17.9	-42.0

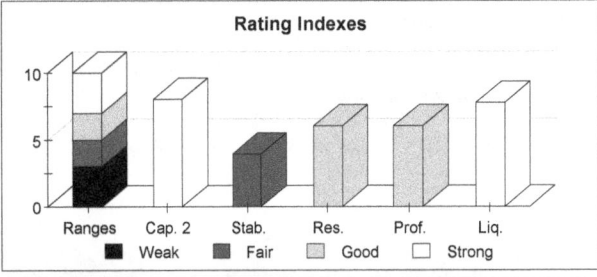

Rating Indexes

BERKSHIRE HATHAWAY SPECIALTY INS CO   C+   Fair

Major Rating Factors: Fair reserve development (4.2 on a scale of 0 to 10) as reserves have generally been sufficient to cover claims. In 2011, the two year reserve development was 43% deficient. Fair overall results on stability tests (3.8) including fair financial strength of affiliated Berkshire-Hathaway, excessive premium growth and weak results on operational trends. The largest net exposure for one risk is conservative at 1.2% of capital.

Other Rating Factors: Good profitability index (5.0) despite operating losses during 2012 and the first six months of 2016. Return on equity has been low, averaging 0.2% over the past five years. Strong long-term capitalization index (9.4) based on excellent current risk adjusted capital (severe and moderate loss scenarios), despite some fluctuation in capital levels. Superior liquidity (10.0) with ample operational cash flow and liquid investments.

Principal Business: Other liability (69%), allied lines (12%), homeowners multiple peril (4%), auto liability (3%), commercial multiple peril (3%), auto physical damage (2%), and other lines (7%).

Principal Investments: Misc. investments (75%), investment grade bonds (15%), and cash (10%).

Investments in Affiliates: None

Group Affiliation: Berkshire-Hathaway

Licensed in: All states except PR

Commenced Business: February 1866

Address: 3024 Harney St, Omaha, NE 68131

Phone: (402) 916-3000   **Domicile State:** NE   **NAIC Code:** 22276

Data Date	Rating	RACR #1	RACR #2	Loss Ratio %	Total Assets ($mil)	Capital ($mil)	Net Premium ($mil)	Net Income ($mil)
6-16	C+	4.28	2.57	N/A	3,479.8	2,998.0	57.6	-12.8
6-15	C+	4.17	2.50	N/A	3,514.4	3,193.6	7.2	18.8
2015	C+	4.32	2.60	75.7	3,371.6	3,044.1	95.5	37.7
2014	C+	4.11	2.46	N/A	3,521.6	3,234.1	0.7	7.6
2013	C+	3.20	1.92	156.6	3,357.7	3,106.7	1.6	0.2
2012	C+	1.81	0.86	339.9	90.2	71.3	2.3	-0.5
2011	C+	2.09	0.88	N/A	96.7	68.8	0.4	0.4

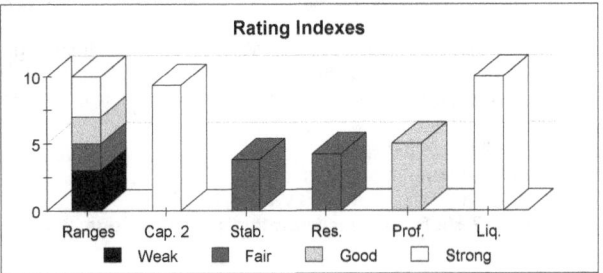

Rating Indexes

BITCO GENERAL INS CORP   B   Good

Major Rating Factors: Good overall profitability index (5.6 on a scale of 0 to 10). Good expense controls. Return on equity has been good over the last five years, averaging 11.2%. Good liquidity (6.8) with sufficient resources (cash flows and marketable investments) to handle a spike in claims.
Other Rating Factors: Fair overall results on stability tests (4.8) including weak results on operational trends. Strong long-term capitalization index (8.4) based on excellent current risk adjusted capital (severe and moderate loss scenarios), despite some fluctuation in capital levels. Ample reserve history (9.1) that helps to protect the company against sharp claims increases.
Principal Business: Workers compensation (34%), commercial multiple peril (21%), auto liability (19%), other liability (12%), auto physical damage (7%), and inland marine (7%).
Principal Investments: Investment grade bonds (75%), misc. investments (21%), and non investment grade bonds (4%).
Investments in Affiliates: None
Group Affiliation: Old Republic Group
Licensed in: All states except HI, NH, PR
Commenced Business: August 1928
Address: 320 18th St, Rock Island, IL 61201
Phone: (800) 475-4477   **Domicile State:** IL   **NAIC Code:** 20095

Data Date	Rating	RACR #1	RACR #2	Loss Ratio %	Total Assets ($mil)	Capital ($mil)	Net Premium ($mil)	Net Income ($mil)
6-16	B	3.01	1.88	N/A	844.8	291.0	114.6	10.0
6-15	B	3.30	2.12	N/A	813.1	280.2	114.6	13.5
2015	B	3.08	1.95	71.9	820.8	275.1	237.6	27.2
2014	B	3.45	2.20	71.2	810.9	288.5	230.2	42.5
2013	A-	3.87	2.49	67.2	788.4	290.2	204.3	39.5
2012	A-	4.18	2.58	65.0	719.8	274.2	178.1	24.3
2011	A-	3.95	2.39	65.0	721.4	250.6	162.8	28.1

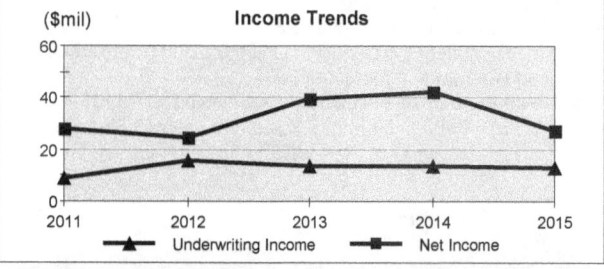

Income Trends

BRICKSTREET MUTUAL INS CO   C   Fair

Major Rating Factors: Fair overall results on stability tests (4.3 on a scale of 0 to 10) including weak results on operational trends. Strong long-term capitalization index (8.0) based on excellent current risk adjusted capital (severe and moderate loss scenarios). Moreover, capital levels have been consistent in recent years.
Other Rating Factors: Ample reserve history (9.5) that helps to protect the company against sharp claims increases. Excellent profitability (8.7) with operating gains in each of the last five years. Excellent liquidity (7.1) with ample operational cash flow and liquid investments.
Principal Business: Workers compensation (100%).
Principal Investments: Investment grade bonds (87%), misc. investments (11%), cash (1%), and real estate (1%).
Investments in Affiliates: 2%
Group Affiliation: BrickStreet Mutual Ins
Licensed in: AL, DC, GA, IL, IN, IA, KY, MD, MO, NC, PA, SC, TN, VA, WV
Commenced Business: January 2006
Address: 400 Quarrier St, Charleston, WV 25301
Phone: (304) 941-1000   **Domicile State:** WV   **NAIC Code:** 12372

Data Date	Rating	RACR #1	RACR #2	Loss Ratio %	Total Assets ($mil)	Capital ($mil)	Net Premium ($mil)	Net Income ($mil)
6-16	C	3.14	2.05	N/A	1,931.4	724.9	127.0	20.7
6-15	C-	2.40	0.89	N/A	1,895.6	681.0	135.3	22.3
2015	C	3.15	2.06	69.2	1,918.0	705.8	245.0	49.2
2014	C-	2.35	0.88	76.1	1,886.9	658.9	290.2	50.9
2013	C-	2.38	0.88	75.1	1,791.0	603.7	301.3	49.6
2012	C-	2.52	0.86	64.8	1,703.1	552.6	287.6	36.8
2011	D+	2.40	0.80	73.9	1,575.1	486.5	253.1	47.1

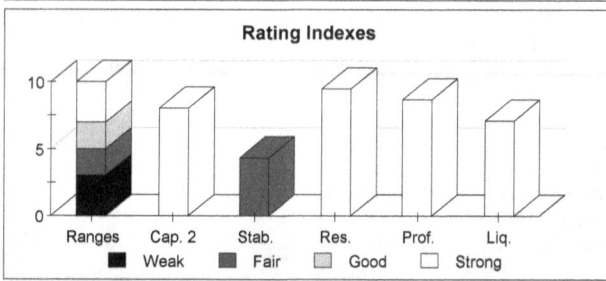

Rating Indexes
Ranges   Cap. 2   Stab.   Res.   Prof.   Liq.
■ Weak   ▨ Fair   ▨ Good   ▢ Strong

BROTHERHOOD MUTUAL INS CO   B   Good

Major Rating Factors: History of adequate reserve strength (5.8 on a scale of 0 to 10) as reserves have been consistently at an acceptable level. Good overall profitability index (5.7) despite operating losses during 2011 and the first six months of 2016.
Other Rating Factors: Good liquidity (6.1) with sufficient resources (cash flows and marketable investments) to handle a spike in claims. Fair overall results on stability tests (4.9) including weak results on operational trends. Strong long-term capitalization index (8.1) based on excellent current risk adjusted capital (severe and moderate loss scenarios). Moreover, capital levels have been consistent in recent years.
Principal Business: Commercial multiple peril (72%), workers compensation (13%), auto liability (5%), other liability (4%), boiler & machinery (3%), and auto physical damage (2%).
Principal Investments: Misc. investments (48%), investment grade bonds (43%), real estate (6%), and cash (3%).
Investments in Affiliates: None
Group Affiliation: None
Licensed in: All states except PR
Commenced Business: November 1935
Address: 6400 Brotherhood Way, Ft Wayne, IN 46825
Phone: (260) 482-8668   **Domicile State:** IN   **NAIC Code:** 13528

Data Date	Rating	RACR #1	RACR #2	Loss Ratio %	Total Assets ($mil)	Capital ($mil)	Net Premium ($mil)	Net Income ($mil)
6-16	B	2.19	1.70	N/A	553.8	228.9	159.0	-1.4
6-15	B	1.97	1.52	N/A	482.5	195.4	143.1	7.8
2015	B	2.35	1.83	61.0	542.0	229.1	304.9	19.1
2014	B	2.02	1.54	66.2	469.7	189.4	277.3	10.0
2013	A-	2.01	1.53	64.5	443.3	178.2	252.5	9.5
2012	A-	2.31	1.80	62.5	384.9	159.7	217.3	7.3
2011	A-	2.45	1.95	80.6	347.4	146.1	190.4	-15.8

Reserve Deficiency (as % of capital)
* Adequate & redundant reserves show as negatives
■ 1 Yr Dev   ▢ 2 Yr Dev

BUILD AMERICA MUTUAL ASR CO D+ Weak

Major Rating Factors: Weak profitability index (2.2) with operating losses during 2012, 2013, 2014 and the first six months of 2016.

Other Rating Factors: Weak overall results on stability tests (1.1) including excessive premium growth, weak results on operational trends and negative cash flow from operations for 2015. The largest net exposure for one risk is excessive at 52.3% of capital. Strong long-term capitalization index (10.0) based on excellent current risk adjusted capital (severe and moderate loss scenarios), despite some fluctuation in capital levels. Superior liquidity (10.0) with ample operational cash flow and liquid investments.

Principal Business: Financial guaranty (100%).

Principal Investments: Investment grade bonds (95%), misc. investments (3%), and cash (2%).

Investments in Affiliates: None

Group Affiliation: None

Licensed in: All states except PR

Commenced Business: July 2012

Address: One World Financial Center, New York, 10 281

Phone: (212) 235-2500 **Domicile State:** NY **NAIC Code:** 14380

Data Date	Rating	RACR #1	RACR #2	Loss Ratio %	Total Assets ($mil)	Capital ($mil)	Net Premium ($mil)	Net Income ($mil)
6-16	D+	8.41	8.17	N/A	485.9	432.5	0.2	-15.9
6-15	D+	8.72	8.56	N/A	472.1	441.1	0.1	-16.0
2015	D+	11.84	11.38	0.0	479.6	437.3	6.3	-32.0
2014	D+	12.00	11.69	0.0	475.7	448.8	3.6	-31.8
2013	D+	14.08	13.68	0.0	486.5	469.0	3.0	-29.3
2012	A+	24.08	23.22	0.0	491.2	483.7	0.0	-18.2
2011	N/A	N/A	N/A	0.0	0.0	0.0	0.0	0.0

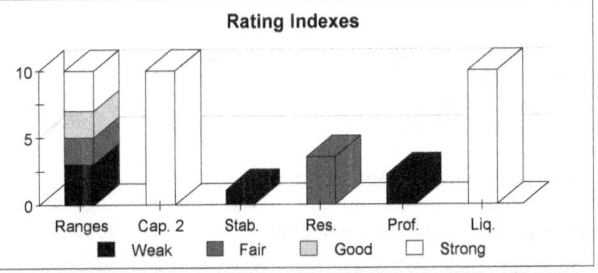

Rating Indexes

BUILDERS INS (A MUTUAL CAPTIVE CO) C Fair

Major Rating Factors: Fair overall results on stability tests (3.5 on a scale of 0 to 10) including potential drain of affiliation with Builders Financial Group Inc and weak results on operational trends. Good liquidity (6.8) with sufficient resources (cash flows and marketable investments) to handle a spike in claims.

Other Rating Factors: Strong long-term capitalization index (8.1) based on excellent current risk adjusted capital (severe and moderate loss scenarios). Moreover, capital levels have been consistent in recent years. Ample reserve history (9.3) that helps to protect the company against sharp claims increases. Excellent profitability (8.4) with operating gains in each of the last five years.

Principal Business: Workers compensation (81%), other liability (13%), and commercial multiple peril (6%).

Principal Investments: Investment grade bonds (62%), misc. investments (35%), real estate (2%), and cash (1%).

Investments in Affiliates: 14%

Group Affiliation: Builders Financial Group Inc

Licensed in: DE, FL, GA, NC, TX

Commenced Business: July 1996

Address: 2410 Paces Ferry Rd Ste 300, Atlanta, GA 30339-1802

Phone: (678) 309-4000 **Domicile State:** GA **NAIC Code:** 10704

Data Date	Rating	RACR #1	RACR #2	Loss Ratio %	Total Assets ($mil)	Capital ($mil)	Net Premium ($mil)	Net Income ($mil)
6-16	C	2.32	1.76	N/A	546.3	239.1	75.4	7.4
6-15	C	2.01	1.51	N/A	497.3	212.1	67.7	7.7
2015	C	2.30	1.77	54.6	518.1	227.3	144.7	19.9
2014	C	1.96	1.47	62.9	482.6	201.8	141.3	13.9
2013	C	1.78	1.34	69.8	441.6	185.9	125.9	7.2
2012	C	1.60	1.20	67.2	406.7	170.0	106.3	4.8
2011	C	2.03	1.45	65.1	378.2	159.2	85.6	7.9

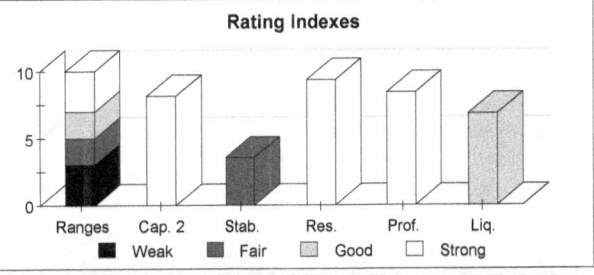

Rating Indexes

BUILDERS MUTUAL INS CO * B+ Good

Major Rating Factors: Good liquidity (6.8 on a scale of 0 to 10) with sufficient resources (cash flows and marketable investments) to handle a spike in claims. Good overall results on stability tests (5.1) despite weak results on operational trends.

Other Rating Factors: Strong long-term capitalization index (8.0) based on excellent current risk adjusted capital (severe and moderate loss scenarios). Moreover, capital levels have been consistent in recent years. Ample reserve history (9.0) that helps to protect the company against sharp claims increases. Excellent profitability (8.4) with operating gains in each of the last five years.

Principal Business: Workers compensation (75%), commercial multiple peril (13%), products liability (4%), inland marine (3%), other liability (3%), and auto liability (2%).

Principal Investments: Investment grade bonds (73%), misc. investments (25%), and cash (2%).

Investments in Affiliates: 2%

Group Affiliation: Builders Group

Licensed in: DC, FL, GA, MD, MS, NC, SC, TN, VA, WI

Commenced Business: September 1997

Address: 5580 Centerview Dr, Raleigh, NC 27606

Phone: (919) 845-1976 **Domicile State:** NC **NAIC Code:** 10844

Data Date	Rating	RACR #1	RACR #2	Loss Ratio %	Total Assets ($mil)	Capital ($mil)	Net Premium ($mil)	Net Income ($mil)
6-16	B+	2.28	1.66	N/A	736.0	295.6	134.2	10.6
6-15	B+	2.23	1.58	N/A	667.0	271.1	109.8	8.3
2015	B+	2.37	1.72	63.1	701.7	281.6	246.8	19.9
2014	B+	2.29	1.63	62.3	638.7	262.6	215.5	18.3
2013	B+	2.24	1.56	61.5	576.4	242.0	181.7	13.4
2012	B+	2.30	1.60	64.8	536.2	218.7	148.4	10.2
2011	B+	3.14	2.14	69.9	490.3	203.7	119.5	5.1

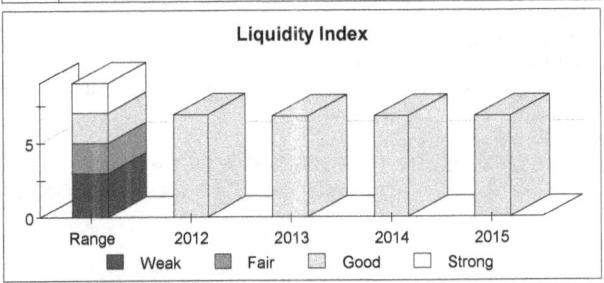

Liquidity Index

CALIFORNIA CAPITAL INS CO

B-   **Good**

Major Rating Factors: Fair overall results on stability tests (4.2 on a scale of 0 to 10) including potential drain of affiliation with CIG Holding Company Inc, weak results on operational trends and negative cash flow from operations for 2015. History of adequate reserve strength (6.0) as reserves have been consistently at an acceptable level.

Other Rating Factors: Good overall profitability index (6.3). Fair expense controls. Return on equity has been low, averaging 2.6% over the past five years. Good liquidity (6.6) with sufficient resources (cash flows and marketable investments) to handle a spike in claims. Strong long-term capitalization index (8.0) based on excellent current risk adjusted capital (severe and moderate loss scenarios), despite some fluctuation in capital levels.

Principal Business: Commercial multiple peril (37%), homeowners multiple peril (21%), auto liability (13%), auto physical damage (10%), fire (5%), farmowners multiple peril (4%), and other lines (10%).

Principal Investments: Investment grade bonds (72%), misc. investments (25%), real estate (2%), and cash (1%).

Investments in Affiliates: 26%

Group Affiliation: CIG Holding Company Inc

Licensed in: AZ, CA, ID, MT, NV, OR, TX

Commenced Business: August 1898

Address: 2300 Garden Rd, Monterey, CA 93942-3110

Phone: (831) 233-5500   **Domicile State:** CA   **NAIC Code:** 13544

Data Date	Rating	RACR #1	RACR #2	Loss Ratio %	Total Assets ($mil)	Capital ($mil)	Net Premium ($mil)	Net Income ($mil)
6-16	B-	2.10	1.73	N/A	588.7	315.0	110.2	1.8
6-15	B-	2.19	1.80	N/A	590.8	324.3	117.8	10.3
2015	B-	2.10	1.73	69.9	580.3	314.1	218.1	13.4
2014	B-	2.16	1.77	65.1	593.5	315.6	245.0	10.8
2013	B-	2.15	1.76	65.1	569.5	303.3	234.0	9.2
2012	B-	2.18	1.79	67.2	536.6	289.7	210.8	6.6
2011	B-	2.19	1.79	70.3	508.1	281.3	191.0	1.8

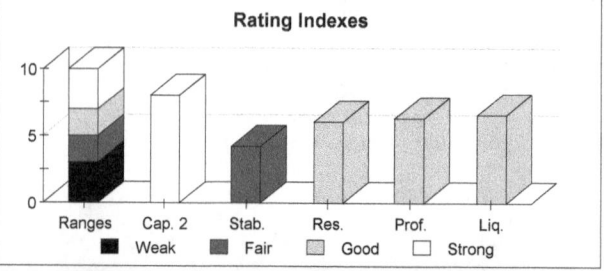

Rating Indexes — Ranges, Cap. 2, Stab., Res., Prof., Liq. — Weak ■ Fair ■ Good ▨ Strong ▫

CALIFORNIA CASUALTY INDEMNITY EXCH

C+   **Fair**

Major Rating Factors: Fair overall results on stability tests (3.4 on a scale of 0 to 10) including weak results on operational trends and excessive premium growth. The largest net exposure for one risk is high at 4.0% of capital. Good liquidity (6.4) with sufficient resources (cash flows and marketable investments) to handle a spike in claims.

Other Rating Factors: Weak profitability index (2.5) with operating losses during 2012, 2014 and the first six months of 2016. Strong long-term capitalization index (7.9) based on excellent current risk adjusted capital (severe and moderate loss scenarios), despite some fluctuation in capital levels. Ample reserve history (7.5) that can protect against increases in claims costs.

Principal Business: Auto liability (37%), auto physical damage (36%), homeowners multiple peril (26%), and earthquake (1%).

Principal Investments: Investment grade bonds (53%) and misc. investments (47%).

Investments in Affiliates: 34%

Group Affiliation: California Casualty Ins Group

Licensed in: All states except MI, NJ, PR

Commenced Business: January 1914

Address: 1900 Alameda De Las Pulgas, San Mateo, CA 94403

Phone: (650) 574-4000   **Domicile State:** CA   **NAIC Code:** 20117

Data Date	Rating	RACR #1	RACR #2	Loss Ratio %	Total Assets ($mil)	Capital ($mil)	Net Premium ($mil)	Net Income ($mil)
6-16	C+	1.80	1.55	N/A	575.5	276.7	118.5	-3.3
6-15	C+	2.00	1.78	N/A	577.6	307.1	90.0	-11.8
2015	C+	1.87	1.63	84.1	582.3	284.3	238.6	-26.7
2014	C+	2.10	1.89	82.5	557.6	319.1	163.8	-6.2
2013	C+	2.08	1.88	79.4	571.8	336.5	158.7	2.6
2012	C+	2.10	1.89	79.9	557.6	320.0	152.7	-1.8
2011	C+	2.10	1.92	76.8	623.4	325.1	150.0	4.3

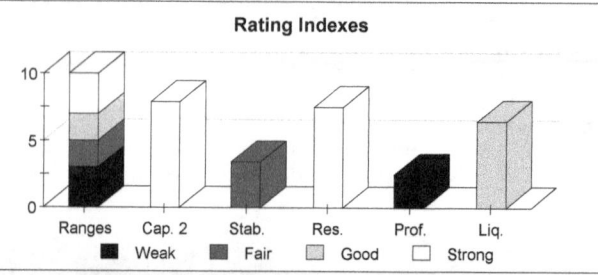

Rating Indexes — Ranges, Cap. 2, Stab., Res., Prof., Liq. — Weak ■ Fair ■ Good ▨ Strong ▫

CALIFORNIA INS CO

B-   **Good**

Major Rating Factors: Fair overall results on stability tests (4.7 on a scale of 0 to 10) including weak results on operational trends. Strong long-term capitalization index (9.7) based on excellent current risk adjusted capital (severe and moderate loss scenarios). Moreover, capital levels have been consistent in recent years.

Other Rating Factors: Ample reserve history (8.7) that helps to protect the company against sharp claims increases. Excellent profitability (9.2) with operating gains in each of the last five years. Return on equity has been excellent over the last five years averaging 17.5%. Excellent liquidity (8.5) with ample operational cash flow and liquid investments.

Principal Business: Workers compensation (98%) and surety (1%).

Principal Investments: Investment grade bonds (80%), misc. investments (12%), and cash (8%).

Investments in Affiliates: None

Group Affiliation: Berkshire-Hathaway

Licensed in: AK, AZ, CA, CT, GA, HI, ID, IL, IN, IA, KS, MD, MO, MT, NV, NJ, NY, NC, ND, OR, PA, TX, UT, VA, WA, WI

Commenced Business: June 1980

Address: 950 Tower Lane 14th Floor, Foster City, CA 94404

Phone: (402) 827-3424   **Domicile State:** CA   **NAIC Code:** 38865

Data Date	Rating	RACR #1	RACR #2	Loss Ratio %	Total Assets ($mil)	Capital ($mil)	Net Premium ($mil)	Net Income ($mil)
6-16	B-	3.83	3.07	N/A	775.7	495.7	114.9	30.2
6-15	B-	3.08	2.41	N/A	680.4	409.8	116.7	35.2
2015	B-	3.67	2.96	21.1	751.2	468.8	255.3	88.5
2014	B-	2.95	2.30	30.1	631.7	379.8	241.6	65.5
2013	B-	3.98	2.18	32.2	521.1	317.4	186.9	48.9
2012	B-	3.99	1.97	12.6	443.9	244.7	136.2	47.6
2011	B-	3.70	1.87	29.6	484.7	192.2	117.9	36.6

Berkshire-Hathaway Composite Group Rating: B Largest Group Members	Assets ($mil)	Rating
NATIONAL INDEMNITY CO	161777	B
GOVERNMENT EMPLOYEES INS CO	24036	B
COLUMBIA INS CO	19102	C+
BERKSHIRE HATHAWAY LIFE INS CO OF NE	16287	C+
GENERAL REINS CORP	15320	C+

CAMBRIDGE MUTUAL FIRE INS CO   B-   Good

Major Rating Factors: Fair overall results on stability tests (4.6 on a scale of 0 to 10) including potential drain of affiliation with Andover Group, weak results on operational trends and negative cash flow from operations for 2015. History of adequate reserve strength (6.5) as reserves have been consistently at an acceptable level.

Other Rating Factors: Good overall profitability index (5.8) despite operating losses during 2011 and 2015. Strong long-term capitalization index (8.5) based on excellent current risk adjusted capital (severe and moderate loss scenarios), despite some fluctuation in capital levels. Excellent liquidity (7.0) with ample operational cash flow and liquid investments.

Principal Business: Homeowners multiple peril (61%), commercial multiple peril (16%), fire (8%), allied lines (7%), other liability (6%), and inland marine (2%).

Principal Investments: Misc. investments (63%), investment grade bonds (20%), and cash (17%).

Investments in Affiliates: None

Group Affiliation: Andover Group

Licensed in: CT, IL, ME, MA, NH, NJ, NY, RI

Commenced Business: January 1834

Address: 95 Old River Rd, Andover, MA 01810

Phone: (978) 475-3300   **Domicile State:** MA   **NAIC Code:** 19771

Data Date	Rating	RACR #1	RACR #2	Loss Ratio %	Total Assets ($mil)	Capital ($mil)	Net Premium ($mil)	Net Income ($mil)
6-16	B-	3.37	2.06	N/A	848.0	502.6	87.1	21.6
6-15	B-	3.03	1.87	N/A	808.7	455.9	87.6	-21.9
2015	B-	3.40	2.08	68.5	805.2	474.1	181.5	-9.3
2014	B-	3.23	1.99	43.4	830.2	479.0	183.3	30.1
2013	B-	3.15	2.01	43.3	738.7	421.9	172.5	51.3
2012	B-	3.02	2.01	64.9	679.7	352.6	167.8	11.9
2011	B-	2.94	1.97	90.4	631.2	331.6	157.1	-22.6

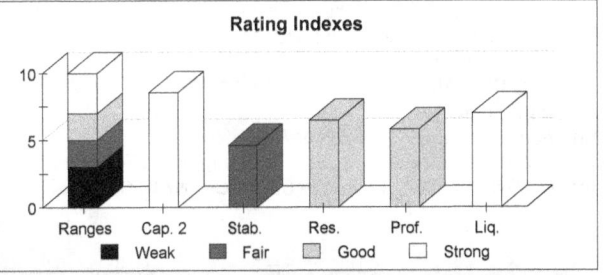

Rating Indexes

CANAL INS CO   B   Good

Major Rating Factors: History of adequate reserve strength (6.0 on a scale of 0 to 10) as reserves have been consistently at an acceptable level. Good liquidity (6.9) with sufficient resources (cash flows and marketable investments) to handle a spike in claims.

Other Rating Factors: Fair profitability index (4.8). Fair expense controls. Return on equity has been low, averaging 2.4% over the past five years. Fair overall results on stability tests (4.6) including weak results on operational trends and negative cash flow from operations for 2015. Strong long-term capitalization index (8.5) based on excellent current risk adjusted capital (severe and moderate loss scenarios), despite some fluctuation in capital levels.

Principal Business: Auto liability (72%), auto physical damage (21%), inland marine (6%), and other liability (1%).

Principal Investments: Misc. investments (53%), investment grade bonds (43%), non investment grade bonds (2%), and real estate (2%).

Investments in Affiliates: 6%

Group Affiliation: Canal Group

Licensed in: All states except AK, HI, PR

Commenced Business: March 1939

Address: 400 E Stone Ave, Greenville, SC 29601

Phone: (864) 242-5365   **Domicile State:** SC   **NAIC Code:** 10464

Data Date	Rating	RACR #1	RACR #2	Loss Ratio %	Total Assets ($mil)	Capital ($mil)	Net Premium ($mil)	Net Income ($mil)
6-16	B	2.85	1.97	N/A	800.7	447.1	94.3	6.8
6-15	B	2.70	1.93	N/A	817.8	444.4	89.7	7.4
2015	B	2.88	2.01	71.6	787.0	428.0	185.5	20.0
2014	B	2.69	1.92	76.9	818.7	447.2	177.4	20.3
2013	B	2.63	1.89	86.6	849.0	444.8	191.9	1.7
2012	B	2.60	1.89	79.1	831.0	421.3	200.1	6.2
2011	B-	2.53	1.80	93.7	850.3	401.9	189.3	2.7

Reserve Deficiency (as % of capital)

* Adequate & redundant reserves show as negatives

CAPITOL INDEMNITY CORP   C   Fair

Major Rating Factors: Fair reserve development (4.0 on a scale of 0 to 10) as reserves have generally been sufficient to cover claims. Fair overall results on stability tests (4.0) including fair financial strength of affiliated Alleghany Corp Group and weak results on operational trends.

Other Rating Factors: Good overall profitability index (5.3) despite operating losses during 2013 and 2014. Return on equity has been low, averaging 1.9% over the past five years. Good liquidity (6.7) with sufficient resources (cash flows and marketable investments) to handle a spike in claims. Strong long-term capitalization index (7.3) based on excellent current risk adjusted capital (severe and moderate loss scenarios), despite some fluctuation in capital levels.

Principal Business: Commercial multiple peril (60%), other liability (24%), surety (7%), auto liability (3%), medical malpractice (2%), products liability (1%), and other lines (4%).

Principal Investments: Misc. investments (60%), investment grade bonds (39%), and cash (1%).

Investments in Affiliates: 22%

Group Affiliation: Alleghany Corp Group

Licensed in: All states except VT, PR

Commenced Business: June 1960

Address: 1600 Aspen Commons, Middleton, WI 53562-4718

Phone: (608) 829-4200   **Domicile State:** WI   **NAIC Code:** 10472

Data Date	Rating	RACR #1	RACR #2	Loss Ratio %	Total Assets ($mil)	Capital ($mil)	Net Premium ($mil)	Net Income ($mil)
6-16	C	1.57	1.19	N/A	508.9	226.6	79.9	2.8
6-15	C	1.54	1.17	N/A	463.3	222.7	68.2	0.3
2015	C	1.55	1.18	54.8	478.8	225.5	154.2	5.1
2014	C	1.58	1.21	55.8	462.4	221.9	134.7	-0.9
2013	C	1.69	1.18	65.6	411.2	172.9	120.0	-11.3
2012	C	1.81	1.28	59.7	386.0	162.5	104.4	7.3
2011	B-	2.31	1.61	55.5	409.4	184.2	99.1	17.1

Reserve Deficiency (as % of capital)

* Adequate & redundant reserves show as negatives

CASTLE KEY INS CO

B-   Good

Major Rating Factors: Fair overall results on stability tests (3.9 on a scale of 0 to 10) including weak results on operational trends. The largest net exposure for one risk is acceptable at 2.4% of capital. History of adequate reserve strength (6.7) as reserves have been consistently at an acceptable level.

Other Rating Factors: Good overall profitability index (5.4) despite operating losses during 2011. Return on equity has been fair, averaging 6.8% over the past five years. Good liquidity (6.8) with sufficient resources (cash flows and marketable investments) to handle a spike in claims. Strong long-term capitalization index (9.5) based on excellent current risk adjusted capital (severe and moderate loss scenarios). Moreover, capital levels have been consistent in recent years.

Principal Business: Homeowners multiple peril (96%) and inland marine (3%).

Principal Investments: Investment grade bonds (86%), misc. investments (14%), and non investment grade bonds (1%).

Investments in Affiliates: 5%

Group Affiliation: Allstate Group

Licensed in: FL, IL, PA

Commenced Business: November 1988

Address: 780 Carillon Parkway, St. Petersburg, FL 33716

Phone: (727) 573-6800   **Domicile State:** IL   **NAIC Code:** 30511

Data Date	Rating	RACR #1	RACR #2	Loss Ratio %	Total Assets ($mil)	Capital ($mil)	Net Premium ($mil)	Net Income ($mil)
6-16	B-	4.64	3.37	N/A	388.5	213.1	62.6	6.3
6-15	B-	2.40	1.74	N/A	358.6	198.8	68.6	9.0
2015	B-	4.49	3.29	60.5	360.4	206.3	123.0	16.6
2014	B-	2.11	1.53	53.5	360.6	190.0	142.5	26.3
2013	B-	0.77	0.56	50.6	354.0	165.7	153.5	24.4
2012	B-	0.69	0.50	53.5	345.8	141.6	130.7	20.2
2011	B-	0.44	0.32	86.5	348.3	117.5	134.1	-19.6

Allstate Group Composite Group Rating: B Largest Group Members	Assets ($mil)	Rating
ALLSTATE INS CO	43271	B
ALLSTATE LIFE INS CO	32348	B
ALLSTATE LIFE INS CO OF NEW YORK	6410	C+
ALLSTATE NJ INS CO	2445	B
AMERICAN HERITAGE LIFE INS CO	1831	B

CATASTROPHE REINS CO

D   Weak

Major Rating Factors: Weak overall results on stability tests (2.3 on a scale of 0 to 10) including weak results on operational trends. History of adequate reserve strength (5.0) as reserves have been consistently at an acceptable level.

Other Rating Factors: Strong long-term capitalization index (10.0) based on excellent current risk adjusted capital (severe and moderate loss scenarios), despite some fluctuation in capital levels. Excellent profitability (7.3) with operating gains in each of the last five years. Excellent expense controls. Return on equity has been good over the last five years, averaging 10.3%. Superior liquidity (9.4) with ample operational cash flow and liquid investments.

Principal Business: (This company is a reinsurer.)

Principal Investments: Investment grade bonds (75%), misc. investments (23%), and non investment grade bonds (2%).

Investments in Affiliates: None

Group Affiliation: USAA Group

Licensed in: TX

Commenced Business: June 2006

Address: 9800 Fredericksburg Rd, San Antonio, TX 78288-0001

Phone: (210) 498-8000   **Domicile State:** TX   **NAIC Code:** 12578

Data Date	Rating	RACR #1	RACR #2	Loss Ratio %	Total Assets ($mil)	Capital ($mil)	Net Premium ($mil)	Net Income ($mil)
6-16	D	14.61	9.07	N/A	1,953.6	1,749.4	81.4	68.2
6-15	D-	12.00	7.16	N/A	1,896.4	1,658.5	88.1	81.4
2015	D	13.80	8.54	N/A	1,775.4	1,659.6	165.5	153.2
2014	D-	9.87	5.93	N/A	1,715.5	1,577.2	178.0	250.6
2013	D-	4.93	3.10	67.6	1,930.5	1,589.2	356.9	136.1
2012	D-	4.94	3.04	24.1	1,976.7	1,680.2	446.7	271.6
2011	E+	3.78	2.32	99.0	1,960.3	1,560.4	434.5	46.4

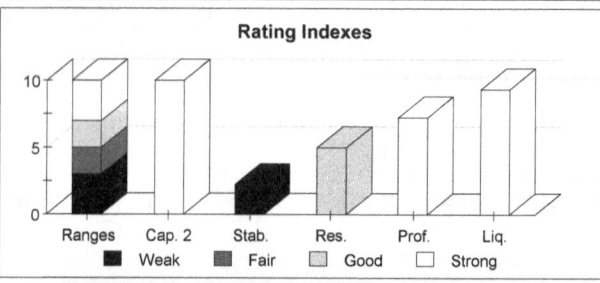

Rating Indexes

Ranges   Cap. 2   Stab.   Res.   Prof.   Liq.
■ Weak   ▨ Fair   ▤ Good   □ Strong

CATERPILLAR INS CO

B   Good

Major Rating Factors: History of adequate reserve strength (6.9 on a scale of 0 to 10) as reserves have been consistently at an acceptable level. Good liquidity (6.9) with sufficient resources (cash flows and marketable investments) to handle a spike in claims.

Other Rating Factors: Fair overall results on stability tests (4.2) including weak results on operational trends. Strong long-term capitalization index (9.0) based on excellent current risk adjusted capital (severe and moderate loss scenarios). Moreover, capital levels have been consistent in recent years. Excellent profitability (8.9) with operating gains in each of the last five years. Return on equity has been good over the last five years, averaging 12.7%.

Principal Business: Other liability (89%), aggregate write-ins for other lines of business (7%), and inland marine (4%).

Principal Investments: Investment grade bonds (71%), misc. investments (25%), and cash (4%).

Investments in Affiliates: None

Group Affiliation: Caterpillar Ins Holdings Inc

Licensed in: All states except PR

Commenced Business: February 1963

Address: 237 E High St, Jefferson City, MO 65101

Phone: (615) 341-8147   **Domicile State:** MO   **NAIC Code:** 11255

Data Date	Rating	RACR #1	RACR #2	Loss Ratio %	Total Assets ($mil)	Capital ($mil)	Net Premium ($mil)	Net Income ($mil)
6-16	B	4.48	3.07	N/A	690.3	305.7	84.2	13.7
6-15	B-	3.27	2.63	N/A	652.4	286.9	99.5	25.6
2015	B	4.38	3.17	63.5	650.3	286.6	142.5	49.0
2014	B-	3.23	2.60	72.9	660.7	271.9	204.7	31.5
2013	B-	2.62	2.16	55.2	639.6	243.4	214.6	33.2
2012	B-	2.26	1.87	51.0	575.6	203.9	199.2	41.5
2011	B-	2.14	1.88	79.5	474.0	151.6	164.4	3.9

Reserve Deficiency (as % of capital)

2011   2012   2013   2014   2015

■ 1 Yr Dev
□ 2 Yr Dev

* Adequate & redundant reserves show as negatives

CATLIN SPECIALTY INS CO · C+ · Fair

Major Rating Factors: Fair reserve development (4.4 on a scale of 0 to 10) as reserves have generally been sufficient to cover claims. Fair profitability index (4.5) with operating losses during 2015. Return on equity has been low, averaging 2.2% over the past five years.

Other Rating Factors: Fair overall results on stability tests (3.2) including weak results on operational trends. The largest net exposure for one risk is excessive at 5.5% of capital. Strong long-term capitalization index (7.8) based on excellent current risk adjusted capital (severe and moderate loss scenarios). Moreover, capital levels have been consistent in recent years. Excellent liquidity (7.2) with ample operational cash flow and liquid investments.

Principal Business: Other liability (72%), products liability (8%), commercial multiple peril (6%), medical malpractice (4%), auto liability (4%), inland marine (3%), and auto physical damage (2%).

Principal Investments: Investment grade bonds (81%), misc. investments (17%), and cash (2%).

Investments in Affiliates: 15%
Group Affiliation: XL Group Ltd
Licensed in: All states except PR
Commenced Business: January 1942
Address: 1209 Orange St, Wilmington, DE 19801
Phone: (404) 443-4910   **Domicile State:** DE   **NAIC Code:** 15989

Data Date	Rating	RACR #1	RACR #2	Loss Ratio %	Total Assets ($mil)	Capital ($mil)	Net Premium ($mil)	Net Income ($mil)
6-16	C+	2.34	1.73	N/A	656.3	222.1	37.0	5.8
6-15	C+	2.02	1.62	N/A	672.9	215.9	40.8	-4.0
2015	C+	2.33	1.74	90.9	668.4	213.1	76.8	-6.8
2014	C+	2.01	1.64	76.3	591.4	204.3	86.8	3.0
2013	C+	2.12	1.68	62.0	483.8	201.5	78.0	7.4
2012	C+	1.70	1.08	71.3	355.2	112.8	63.7	2.5
2011	C+	2.37	1.36	65.1	318.3	111.4	55.9	6.1

Reserve Deficiency (as % of capital)

* Adequate & redundant reserves show as negatives
■ 1 Yr Dev   □ 2 Yr Dev

CENTRAL MUTUAL INS CO · B · Good

Major Rating Factors: Good liquidity (6.8 on a scale of 0 to 10) with sufficient resources (cash flows and marketable investments) to handle a spike in claims. Fair overall results on stability tests (4.6) including weak results on operational trends.

Other Rating Factors: Strong long-term capitalization index (8.8) based on excellent current risk adjusted capital (severe and moderate loss scenarios). Moreover, capital levels have been consistent in recent years. Ample reserve history (9.3) that helps to protect the company against sharp claims increases. Excellent profitability (7.6) despite modest operating losses during 2011.

Principal Business: Homeowners multiple peril (26%), auto liability (22%), commercial multiple peril (20%), auto physical damage (15%), other liability (5%), inland marine (3%), and other lines (8%).

Principal Investments: Investment grade bonds (63%), misc. investments (36%), and real estate (3%).

Investments in Affiliates: 12%
Group Affiliation: Central Mutual Ins Group
Licensed in: AZ, AR, CA, CO, CT, DE, GA, IL, IN, IA, KY, ME, MD, MA, MI, MS, NV, NH, NJ, NM, NY, NC, OH, OK, PA, SC, TN, TX, VT, VA, WI
Commenced Business: October 1876
Address: 800 S Washington St, Van Wert, OH 45891
Phone: (419) 238-1010   **Domicile State:** OH   **NAIC Code:** 20230

Data Date	Rating	RACR #1	RACR #2	Loss Ratio %	Total Assets ($mil)	Capital ($mil)	Net Premium ($mil)	Net Income ($mil)
6-16	B	2.88	2.14	N/A	1,468.5	712.1	248.3	4.0
6-15	B	2.79	2.05	N/A	1,401.3	662.5	229.1	13.2
2015	B	2.93	2.20	57.9	1,451.2	705.8	488.0	57.0
2014	B	2.79	2.08	59.8	1,359.6	640.1	447.6	50.4
2013	B	2.91	2.14	58.4	1,266.0	619.4	402.3	62.9
2012	B	2.63	1.92	70.7	1,184.2	510.5	369.9	23.0
2011	B-	2.38	1.72	79.3	1,163.1	457.8	375.9	-2.9

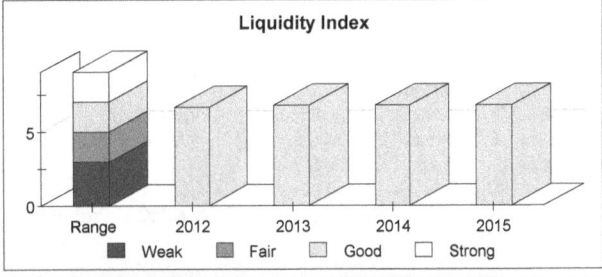

Liquidity Index

■ Weak   ■ Fair   □ Good   □ Strong

CENTRAL STATES INDEMNITY CO OF OMAHA · C+ · Fair

Major Rating Factors: Fair overall results on stability tests (4.5 on a scale of 0 to 10) including potential drain of affiliation with Berkshire-Hathaway and weak results on operational trends. Good overall profitability index (6.8). Weak expense controls. Return on equity has been low, averaging 3.9% over the past five years.

Other Rating Factors: Strong long-term capitalization index (9.3) based on excellent current risk adjusted capital (severe and moderate loss scenarios), despite some fluctuation in capital levels. Ample reserve history (7.5) that can protect against increases in claims costs. Excellent liquidity (7.3) with ample operational cash flow and liquid investments.

Principal Business: Other accident & health (57%), inland marine (26%), aggregate write-ins for other lines of business (10%), credit accident & health (4%), aircraft (2%), and group accident & health (1%).

Principal Investments: Misc. investments (61%), investment grade bonds (33%), non investment grade bonds (5%), and cash (1%).

Investments in Affiliates: 4%
Group Affiliation: Berkshire-Hathaway
Licensed in: All states, the District of Columbia and Puerto Rico
Commenced Business: June 1977
Address: 1212 N 96th St, Omaha, NE 68114
Phone: (402) 997-8000   **Domicile State:** NE   **NAIC Code:** 34274

Data Date	Rating	RACR #1	RACR #2	Loss Ratio %	Total Assets ($mil)	Capital ($mil)	Net Premium ($mil)	Net Income ($mil)
6-16	C+	4.28	2.73	N/A	395.5	340.4	29.1	3.0
6-15	C+	4.25	2.73	N/A	421.1	355.2	27.1	2.2
2015	C+	4.00	2.50	55.4	417.3	354.9	55.0	9.5
2014	C+	4.12	2.63	44.6	435.0	363.7	50.2	11.4
2013	B+	4.34	2.79	36.2	412.3	346.0	43.0	17.7
2012	B+	4.34	2.69	18.3	335.1	285.5	32.2	13.1
2011	B+	4.37	2.58	10.3	287.0	249.6	29.8	12.8

Berkshire-Hathaway Composite Group Rating: B Largest Group Members	Assets ($mil)	Rating
NATIONAL INDEMNITY CO	161777	B
GOVERNMENT EMPLOYEES INS CO	24036	B
COLUMBIA INS CO	19102	C+
BERKSHIRE HATHAWAY LIFE INS CO OF NE	16287	C+
GENERAL REINS CORP	15320	C+

CENTURION CASUALTY CO *

B+

Good

Major Rating Factors: Good overall results on stability tests (5.0 on a scale of 0 to 10) despite weak results on operational trends. Strong long-term capitalization index (10.0) based on excellent current risk adjusted capital (severe and moderate loss scenarios), despite some fluctuation in capital levels.

Other Rating Factors: Ample reserve history (7.3) that can protect against increases in claims costs. Excellent profitability (8.2) with operating gains in each of the last five years. Return on equity has been good over the last five years, averaging 12.1%. Superior liquidity (9.2) with ample operational cash flow and liquid investments.

Principal Business: Aggregate write-ins for other lines of business (100%).

Principal Investments: Investment grade bonds (88%), non investment grade bonds (5%), cash (5%), and misc. investments (2%).

Investments in Affiliates: None

Group Affiliation: Wells Fargo Group

Licensed in: All states except AK, AR, DC, GA, MI, NH, NY, PA, VT, PR

Commenced Business: March 1983

Address: 800 Walnut St, Des Moines, IA 50309

Phone: (515) 557-7346   **Domicile State:** IA   **NAIC Code:** 42765

Data Date	Rating	RACR #1	RACR #2	Loss Ratio %	Total Assets ($mil)	Capital ($mil)	Net Premium ($mil)	Net Income ($mil)
6-16	B+	51.13	23.69	N/A	157.1	156.6	5.2	4.6
6-15	B+	47.06	22.34	N/A	147.9	147.2	6.0	5.2
2015	B+	47.75	22.33	4.0	152.6	152.1	11.7	10.3
2014	B+	44.41	21.58	4.3	142.9	142.0	13.5	11.3
2013	B+	42.92	21.18	6.9	131.9	130.8	15.1	12.6
2012	B+	32.85	14.27	5.8	121.6	118.3	17.6	13.5
2011	B+	20.87	14.19	2.4	194.7	142.7	20.8	40.1

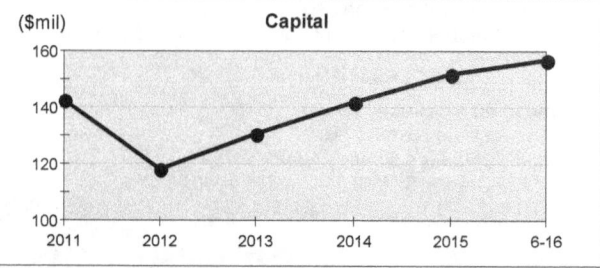

CENTURY-NATIONAL INS CO

B

Good

Major Rating Factors: History of adequate reserve strength (6.6 on a scale of 0 to 10) as reserves have been consistently at an acceptable level. Good overall profitability index (5.1). Fair expense controls. Return on equity has been low, averaging 4.9% over the past five years.

Other Rating Factors: Good liquidity (6.9) with sufficient resources (cash flows and marketable investments) to handle a spike in claims. Fair overall results on stability tests (4.3) including weak results on operational trends and excessive premium growth. Strong long-term capitalization index (8.5) based on excellent current risk adjusted capital (severe and moderate loss scenarios), despite some fluctuation in capital levels.

Principal Business: Homeowners multiple peril (31%), auto liability (29%), commercial multiple peril (13%), auto physical damage (13%), fire (6%), allied lines (4%), and earthquake (3%).

Principal Investments: Investment grade bonds (76%), non investment grade bonds (20%), cash (3%), and misc. investments (1%).

Investments in Affiliates: None

Group Affiliation: National General Holdings Corporatio

Licensed in: All states except DC, HI, MA, NH, NY, RI, PR

Commenced Business: December 1956

Address: 12200 Sylvan St, N Hollywood, CA 91606-3216

Phone: (818) 760-0880   **Domicile State:** CA   **NAIC Code:** 26905

Data Date	Rating	RACR #1	RACR #2	Loss Ratio %	Total Assets ($mil)	Capital ($mil)	Net Premium ($mil)	Net Income ($mil)
6-16	B	2.33	1.59	N/A	485.4	241.7	93.5	16.1
6-15	B	3.54	2.26	N/A	604.0	380.7	74.4	15.2
2015	B	3.65	2.38	70.3	594.1	367.5	165.1	7.5
2014	B	3.64	2.29	72.2	593.1	385.0	141.0	19.4
2013	B	3.54	2.20	78.4	587.7	386.5	124.8	15.5
2012	B	3.52	2.21	66.6	531.6	336.9	117.4	9.7
2011	B-	3.61	2.27	52.7	513.3	326.8	110.5	20.9

CHARTER OAK FIRE INS CO

B

Good

Major Rating Factors: Good liquidity (6.8 on a scale of 0 to 10) with sufficient resources (cash flows and marketable investments) to handle a spike in claims. Fair overall results on stability tests (4.6) including weak results on operational trends. Affiliation with Travelers Companies Inc is a strength.

Other Rating Factors: Strong long-term capitalization index (7.9) based on excellent current risk adjusted capital (severe and moderate loss scenarios), despite some fluctuation in capital levels. Ample reserve history (8.8) that helps to protect the company against sharp claims increases. Excellent profitability (7.5) with operating gains in each of the last five years. Return on equity has been good over the last five years, averaging 13.8%.

Principal Business: Commercial multiple peril (33%), workers compensation (31%), auto liability (12%), homeowners multiple peril (8%), other liability (6%), auto physical damage (4%), and other lines (7%).

Principal Investments: Investment grade bonds (95%) and misc. investments (5%).

Investments in Affiliates: None

Group Affiliation: Travelers Companies Inc

Licensed in: All states except CA

Commenced Business: October 1935

Address: One Tower Square, Hartford, CT 06183

Phone: (860) 277-0111   **Domicile State:** CT   **NAIC Code:** 25615

Data Date	Rating	RACR #1	RACR #2	Loss Ratio %	Total Assets ($mil)	Capital ($mil)	Net Premium ($mil)	Net Income ($mil)
6-16	B	2.60	1.65	N/A	944.7	269.1	133.1	15.0
6-15	B	2.68	1.69	N/A	971.1	273.9	128.2	23.0
2015	B	2.54	1.62	58.7	922.9	255.7	263.9	42.1
2014	B	2.53	1.60	60.5	926.1	253.6	256.4	41.7
2013	B	2.50	1.59	60.9	916.9	245.9	255.8	42.6
2012	B	2.40	1.54	68.4	918.5	232.2	248.4	32.0
2011	B	2.27	1.47	76.9	877.5	221.6	243.2	13.8

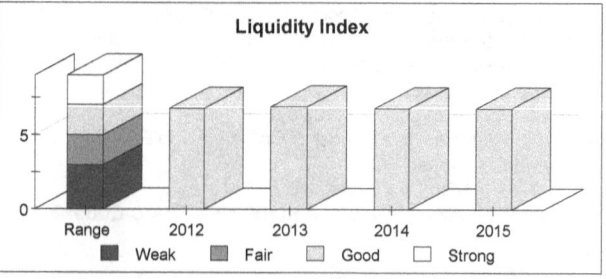

CHESAPEAKE EMPLOYERS INS CO | B | Good

Major Rating Factors: Good long-term capitalization index (6.4 on a scale of 0 to 10) based on good current risk adjusted capital (moderate loss scenario), despite some fluctuation in capital levels. Good overall profitability index (6.2). Fair expense controls.

Other Rating Factors: Fair overall results on stability tests (4.4) including weak results on operational trends. Ample reserve history (9.3) that helps to protect the company against sharp claims increases. Excellent liquidity (7.5) with ample operational cash flow and liquid investments.

Principal Business: Workers compensation (100%).

Principal Investments: Investment grade bonds (75%), misc. investments (23%), and non investment grade bonds (2%).

Investments in Affiliates: None

Group Affiliation: None

Licensed in: MD

Commenced Business: July 1914

Address: 8722 Loch Raven Blvd, Towson, MD 21286-2235

Phone: (410) 494-2000   **Domicile State:** MD   **NAIC Code:** 11039

Data Date	Rating	RACR #1	RACR #2	Loss Ratio %	Total Assets ($mil)	Capital ($mil)	Net Premium ($mil)	Net Income ($mil)
6-16	B	1.77	1.09	N/A	2,168.9	499.1	114.9	32.5
6-15	U	1.41	0.88	N/A	2,003.8	416.8	116.0	29.4
2015	B	1.72	1.05	73.1	2,067.8	463.1	231.1	85.4
2014	U	1.41	0.88	83.8	2,005.8	399.7	227.9	50.8
2013	N/A	N/A	N/A	89.3	1,865.6	337.4	225.6	19.3
2012	N/A	N/A	N/A	98.1	1,843.2	287.2	199.9	7.7
2011	N/A	N/A	N/A	104.9	1,717.4	321.4	176.5	17.7

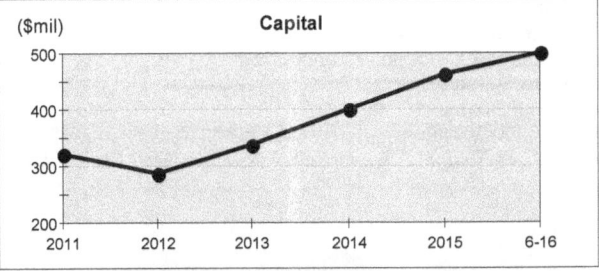

Capital ($mil)

CHUBB CUSTOM INS CO | B- | Good

Major Rating Factors: Fair overall results on stability tests (4.6 on a scale of 0 to 10) including weak results on operational trends. The largest net exposure for one risk is conservative at 1.0% of capital. Strong long-term capitalization index (10.0) based on excellent current risk adjusted capital (severe and moderate loss scenarios). Moreover, capital levels have been consistent in recent years.

Other Rating Factors: Ample reserve history (7.9) that can protect against increases in claims costs. Excellent profitability (8.8) with operating gains in each of the last five years. Excellent liquidity (7.7) with ample operational cash flow and liquid investments.

Principal Business: Commercial multiple peril (43%), fire (19%), other liability (17%), allied lines (12%), products liability (4%), homeowners multiple peril (2%), and other lines (4%).

Principal Investments: Investment grade bonds (86%), misc. investments (13%), and non investment grade bonds (1%).

Investments in Affiliates: None

Group Affiliation: Chubb Limited

Licensed in: All states, the District of Columbia and Puerto Rico

Commenced Business: December 1980

Address: 15 Mountain View Rd, Warren, NJ 07059

Phone: (908) 903-2000   **Domicile State:** NJ   **NAIC Code:** 38989

Data Date	Rating	RACR #1	RACR #2	Loss Ratio %	Total Assets ($mil)	Capital ($mil)	Net Premium ($mil)	Net Income ($mil)
6-16	B-	9.41	5.90	N/A	396.9	206.2	19.4	5.9
6-15	B-	8.21	5.22	N/A	409.2	189.9	24.0	6.1
2015	B-	8.99	5.66	55.1	405.5	200.8	48.9	13.5
2014	B-	8.42	5.36	56.7	398.7	187.4	47.0	13.5
2013	B-	7.78	4.98	51.1	346.3	173.9	45.1	14.1
2012	B-	6.99	4.44	66.4	337.3	160.0	43.3	11.1
2011	B	6.51	4.18	68.0	338.8	148.7	42.5	11.4

Chubb Limited
Composite Group Rating: B
Largest Group Members

Largest Group Members	Assets ($mil)	Rating
FEDERAL INS CO	32241	B
ACE AMERICAN INS CO	12074	B-
ACE PC INS CO	7749	B-
PACIFIC INDEMNITY CO	6916	B
PACIFIC EMPLOYERS INS CO	3542	B-

CHURCH MUTUAL INS CO | B | Good

Major Rating Factors: Good overall profitability index (6.2 on a scale of 0 to 10) despite operating losses during 2011 and 2013. Good liquidity (6.7) with sufficient resources (cash flows and marketable investments) to handle a spike in claims.

Other Rating Factors: Fair overall results on stability tests (4.9) including weak results on operational trends. Strong long-term capitalization index (8.5) based on excellent current risk adjusted capital (severe and moderate loss scenarios). Moreover, capital levels have been consistent in recent years. Ample reserve history (8.8) that helps to protect the company against sharp claims increases.

Principal Business: Commercial multiple peril (69%), workers compensation (20%), auto liability (5%), other liability (3%), auto physical damage (1%), allied lines (1%), and medical malpractice (1%).

Principal Investments: Investment grade bonds (80%), misc. investments (19%), and real estate (1%).

Investments in Affiliates: 4%

Group Affiliation: None

Licensed in: All states except PR

Commenced Business: June 1897

Address: 3000 Schuster Lane, Merrill, WI 54452

Phone: (715) 536-5577   **Domicile State:** WI   **NAIC Code:** 18767

Data Date	Rating	RACR #1	RACR #2	Loss Ratio %	Total Assets ($mil)	Capital ($mil)	Net Premium ($mil)	Net Income ($mil)
6-16	B	2.95	2.09	N/A	1,566.3	615.7	304.5	19.0
6-15	B	3.11	2.26	N/A	1,558.1	550.9	294.1	20.4
2015	B	2.97	2.12	57.7	1,643.9	585.1	615.7	58.1
2014	B	3.18	2.34	58.2	1,453.6	536.7	589.0	76.0
2013	A	2.71	1.83	63.6	1,357.7	473.2	557.3	-4.9
2012	A	2.76	2.22	66.4	1,229.7	415.3	492.5	78.1
2011	A-	2.57	1.98	87.3	1,176.7	376.2	466.6	-28.5

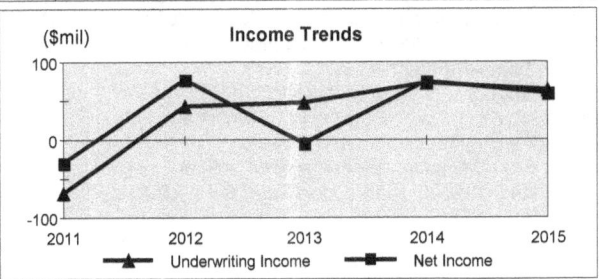

Income Trends ($mil)

CINCINNATI CASUALTY CO   B   Good

Major Rating Factors: Fair overall results on stability tests (4.7 on a scale of 0 to 10) including weak results on operational trends. Strong long-term capitalization index (10.0) based on excellent current risk adjusted capital (severe and moderate loss scenarios). Moreover, capital levels have been consistent in recent years.

Other Rating Factors: Excellent profitability (7.9) with operating gains in each of the last five years. Superior liquidity (10.0) with ample operational cash flow and liquid investments.

Principal Business: Workers compensation (46%), commercial multiple peril (29%), other liability (9%), auto liability (8%), auto physical damage (3%), products liability (3%), and other lines (3%).

Principal Investments: Investment grade bonds (70%), misc. investments (28%), and cash (2%).

Investments in Affiliates: None

Group Affiliation: Cincinnati Financial Corp

Licensed in: All states except PR

Commenced Business: March 1973

Address: 6200 S Gilmore Rd, Fairfield, OH 45014-5141

Phone: (513) 870-2000   **Domicile State:** OH   **NAIC Code:** 28665

Data Date	Rating	RACR #1	RACR #2	Loss Ratio %	Total Assets ($mil)	Capital ($mil)	Net Premium ($mil)	Net Income ($mil)
6-16	B	10.65	6.15	N/A	391.5	349.5	0.0	5.5
6-15	B	11.49	6.63	N/A	373.5	334.2	0.0	6.0
2015	B	12.12	6.96	0.0	377.7	336.5	0.0	12.2
2014	B	10.94	6.34	0.0	371.8	330.2	0.0	12.0
2013	B	10.60	6.13	0.0	361.1	316.5	0.0	9.9
2012	B	12.67	7.29	0.0	329.3	292.6	0.0	9.8
2011	B	13.14	7.54	0.0	313.3	280.0	0.0	15.2

Cincinnati Financial Corp Composite Group Rating: A- Largest Group Members	Assets ($mil)	Rating
CINCINNATI INS CO	11194	A-
CINCINNATI LIFE INS CO	4067	B
CINCINNATI SPECIALTY UNDERWRITER	630	B
CINCINNATI CASUALTY CO	378	B
CINCINNATI INDEMNITY CO	124	A-

CINCINNATI INDEMNITY CO *   A-   Excellent

Major Rating Factors: Strong long-term capitalization index (10.0 on a scale of 0 to 10) based on excellent current risk adjusted capital (severe and moderate loss scenarios). Moreover, capital levels have been consistent in recent years. Excellent profitability (7.9) with operating gains in each of the last five years.

Other Rating Factors: Superior liquidity (10.0) with ample operational cash flow and liquid investments. Good overall results on stability tests (5.5) despite weak results on operational trends. Strengths include potential support from affiliation with Cincinnati Financial Corp.

Principal Business: Workers compensation (31%), commercial multiple peril (24%), other liability (15%), auto liability (13%), auto physical damage (5%), allied lines (4%), and other lines (8%).

Principal Investments: Investment grade bonds (71%), misc. investments (27%), and cash (2%).

Investments in Affiliates: None

Group Affiliation: Cincinnati Financial Corp

Licensed in: All states except PR

Commenced Business: January 1989

Address: 6200 S Gilmore Rd, Fairfield, OH 45014-5141

Phone: (513) 870-2000   **Domicile State:** OH   **NAIC Code:** 23280

Data Date	Rating	RACR #1	RACR #2	Loss Ratio %	Total Assets ($mil)	Capital ($mil)	Net Premium ($mil)	Net Income ($mil)
6-16	A-	10.98	6.34	N/A	123.8	91.4	0.0	2.4
6-15	A-	10.98	6.34	N/A	121.4	86.4	0.0	1.3
2015	A-	11.16	6.44	0.0	124.4	87.8	0.0	2.7
2014	A-	10.55	6.12	0.0	123.0	85.6	0.0	3.1
2013	A-	9.53	5.44	0.0	110.7	82.0	0.0	2.4
2012	A-	10.66	6.00	0.0	101.4	76.2	0.0	2.4
2011	A-	10.76	6.13	0.0	93.4	73.0	0.0	2.1

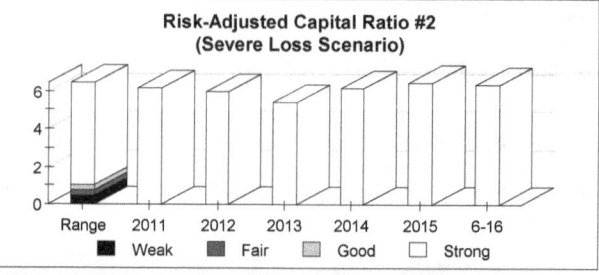

Risk-Adjusted Capital Ratio #2 (Severe Loss Scenario)

Range 2011 2012 2013 2014 2015 6-16
■ Weak ■ Fair ▨ Good □ Strong

CINCINNATI INS CO *   A-   Excellent

Major Rating Factors: Strong long-term capitalization index (8.1 on a scale of 0 to 10) based on excellent current risk adjusted capital (severe and moderate loss scenarios). Furthermore, this high level of risk adjusted capital has been consistently maintained in previous years. Ample reserve history (8.7) that helps to protect the company against sharp claims increases.

Other Rating Factors: Excellent profitability (7.3) with operating gains in each of the last five years. Good liquidity (6.4) with sufficient resources (cash flows and marketable investments) to handle a spike in claims. Good overall results on stability tests (5.7) despite weak results on operational trends.

Principal Business: Commercial multiple peril (27%), auto liability (18%), other liability (16%), homeowners multiple peril (14%), auto physical damage (11%), inland marine (3%), and other lines (12%).

Principal Investments: Investment grade bonds (50%), misc. investments (44%), cash (3%), and non investment grade bonds (3%).

Investments in Affiliates: 10%

Group Affiliation: Cincinnati Financial Corp

Licensed in: All states, the District of Columbia and Puerto Rico

Commenced Business: January 1951

Address: 6200 S Gilmore Rd, Fairfield, OH 45014-5141

Phone: (513) 870-2000   **Domicile State:** OH   **NAIC Code:** 10677

Data Date	Rating	RACR #1	RACR #2	Loss Ratio %	Total Assets ($mil)	Capital ($mil)	Net Premium ($mil)	Net Income ($mil)
6-16	A-	2.33	1.70	N/A	11,749.4	4,600.1	2,125.5	226.0
6-15	A-	2.36	1.73	N/A	11,165.0	4,419.4	2,021.4	244.9
2015	A-	2.36	1.75	60.9	11,194.2	4,412.4	4,189.4	534.1
2014	A-	2.40	1.75	65.5	11,017.2	4,472.2	3,993.2	435.8
2013	A	2.41	1.76	62.1	10,559.8	4,325.7	3,769.2	417.7
2012	A	2.50	1.86	63.7	9,767.3	3,913.6	3,380.3	334.7
2011	A	2.50	1.86	77.4	9,501.8	3,746.8	3,021.6	120.2

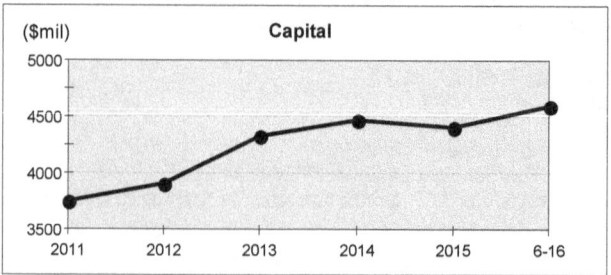

($mil)   **Capital**

CINCINNATI SPECIALTY UNDERWRITER   B   Good

Major Rating Factors: Good liquidity (6.8 on a scale of 0 to 10) with sufficient resources (cash flows and marketable investments) to handle a spike in claims. Fair overall results on stability tests (4.9) including weak results on operational trends.

Other Rating Factors: Strong long-term capitalization index (7.8) based on excellent current risk adjusted capital (severe and moderate loss scenarios). Moreover, capital levels have been consistent in recent years. Ample reserve history (9.4) that helps to protect the company against sharp claims increases. Excellent profitability (8.7) with operating gains in each of the last five years.

Principal Business: Other liability (71%), products liability (16%), fire (7%), and allied lines (6%).

Principal Investments: Investment grade bonds (81%), misc. investments (16%), and cash (3%).

Investments in Affiliates: None

Group Affiliation: Cincinnati Financial Corp

Licensed in: All states except PR

Commenced Business: November 2007

Address: 1807 N Market St, Wilmington, DE 19802-4810

Phone: (513) 870-2000   **Domicile State:** DE   **NAIC Code:** 13037

Data Date	Rating	RACR #1	RACR #2	Loss Ratio %	Total Assets ($mil)	Capital ($mil)	Net Premium ($mil)	Net Income ($mil)
6-16	B	2.98	1.53	N/A	669.5	332.7	88.6	22.2
6-15	B	2.64	1.34	N/A	588.3	279.1	81.4	17.3
2015	B	2.93	1.50	41.9	630.0	306.5	174.7	49.0
2014	B	2.77	1.41	50.5	545.8	265.6	153.3	32.3
2013	B	2.96	1.50	56.7	453.5	228.4	127.7	18.2
2012	B-	3.33	1.65	69.3	377.7	199.1	105.0	5.7
2011	B-	4.45	2.24	60.4	308.9	186.0	79.4	11.1

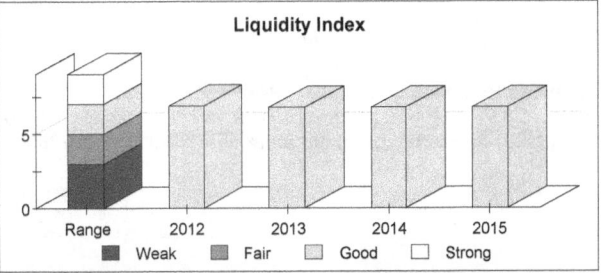

Liquidity Index

CITIZENS INS CO OF AM   B   Good

Major Rating Factors: Good overall profitability index (5.6 on a scale of 0 to 10). Fair expense controls. Return on equity has been good over the last five years, averaging 10.3%. Good liquidity (6.2) with sufficient resources (cash flows and marketable investments) to handle a spike in claims.

Other Rating Factors: Fair overall results on stability tests (4.8) including potential drain of affiliation with Hanover Ins Group Inc and weak results on operational trends. Strong long-term capitalization index (10.0) based on excellent current risk adjusted capital (severe and moderate loss scenarios), despite some fluctuation in capital levels. Ample reserve history (7.8) that can protect against increases in claims costs.

Principal Business: Homeowners multiple peril (32%), commercial multiple peril (30%), auto liability (15%), auto physical damage (11%), workers compensation (6%), other liability (2%), and other lines (3%).

Principal Investments: Investment grade bonds (76%), misc. investments (16%), non investment grade bonds (7%), and real estate (1%).

Investments in Affiliates: None

Group Affiliation: Hanover Ins Group Inc

Licensed in: All states except FL, KY, LA, OR, WY, PR

Commenced Business: August 1974

Address: 645 W Grand River, Howell, MI 48843

Phone: (517) 546-2160   **Domicile State:** MI   **NAIC Code:** 31534

Data Date	Rating	RACR #1	RACR #2	Loss Ratio %	Total Assets ($mil)	Capital ($mil)	Net Premium ($mil)	Net Income ($mil)
6-16	B	4.98	3.35	N/A	1,545.0	734.7	337.8	62.9
6-15	B	4.56	3.03	N/A	1,485.4	682.6	335.8	57.5
2015	B	4.36	2.98	58.3	1,526.4	660.4	680.7	100.8
2014	B	4.03	2.69	76.7	1,501.0	633.6	675.3	35.6
2013	B	4.35	3.04	67.1	1,476.6	662.2	679.8	67.9
2012	B	4.49	3.19	74.0	1,525.1	682.6	716.9	55.8
2011	B	4.95	3.49	68.7	1,515.7	701.7	687.3	60.0

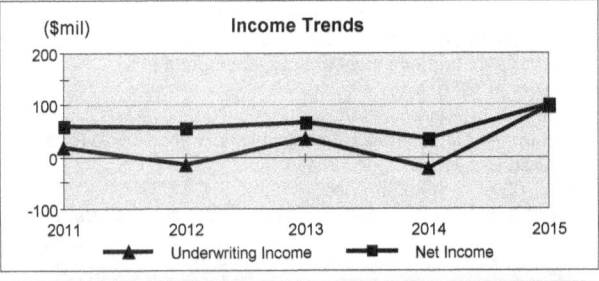

Income Trends

CITIZENS PROPERTY INS CORP *   A+   Excellent

Major Rating Factors: Strong long-term capitalization index (10.0 on a scale of 0 to 10) based on excellent current risk adjusted capital (severe and moderate loss scenarios). Furthermore, this high level of risk adjusted capital has been consistently maintained in previous years. Excellent profitability (8.4) with operating gains in each of the last five years.

Other Rating Factors: Superior liquidity (9.3) with ample operational cash flow and liquid investments. Excellent overall results on stability tests (8.4). Stability strengths include excellent risk diversification. The largest net exposure for one risk is acceptable at 2.7% of capital. History of adequate reserve strength (5.8) as reserves have been consistently at an acceptable level.

Principal Business: Allied lines (56%), homeowners multiple peril (40%), and fire (4%).

Principal Investments: Investment grade bonds (106%) and non investment grade bonds (1%).

Investments in Affiliates: None

Group Affiliation: None

Licensed in: FL

Commenced Business: January 1993

Address: 2312 Killearn Ctr Blvd Bldg A, Tallahassee, FL 32309

Phone: (850) 513-3700   **Domicile State:** FL   **NAIC Code:** 10064

Data Date	Rating	RACR #1	RACR #2	Loss Ratio %	Total Assets ($mil)	Capital ($mil)	Net Premium ($mil)	Net Income ($mil)
6-16	A+	32.44	16.56	N/A	12,538.0	7,568.5	439.7	140.8
6-15	A+	28.16	16.25	N/A	13,904.1	7,584.3	575.4	203.1
2015	A+	29.11	15.06	64.3	13,363.0	7,389.7	578.0	5.7
2014	A+	23.20	13.94	46.5	13,914.2	7,384.0	979.9	387.0
2013	A+	13.10	8.46	39.9	14,766.6	7,008.2	1,702.1	665.3
2012	A+	7.50	5.03	47.8	15,443.2	6,295.2	2,109.5	664.8
2011	A+	6.14	4.20	60.2	13,414.2	5,588.1	2,473.1	448.7

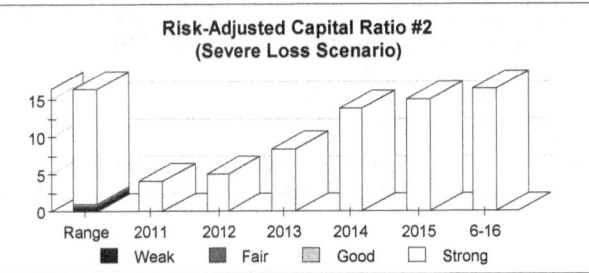

Risk-Adjusted Capital Ratio #2
(Severe Loss Scenario)

CLARENDON NATIONAL INS CO

C   Fair

Major Rating Factors: Fair profitability index (3.0 on a scale of 0 to 10) with operating losses during 2011, 2012 and the first six months of 2016. Return on equity has been fair, averaging 5.1% over the past five years. Fair overall results on stability tests (4.3) including weak results on operational trends and negative cash flow from operations for 2015.

Other Rating Factors: Strong long-term capitalization index (10.0) based on excellent current risk adjusted capital (severe and moderate loss scenarios), despite some fluctuation in capital levels. Ample reserve history (10.0) that helps to protect the company against sharp claims increases. Excellent liquidity (7.0) with ample operational cash flow and liquid investments.

Principal Business: Auto liability (68%) and auto physical damage (32%).
Principal Investments: Investment grade bonds (100%) and cash (2%).
Investments in Affiliates: None
Group Affiliation: Enstar Group Ltd
Licensed in: All states except PR
Commenced Business: November 1941
Address: 198 Princeton Highstown Rd 14A, Princeton Junction, NJ 08550
Phone: (212) 790-9700   **Domicile State:** IL   **NAIC Code:** 20532

Data Date	Rating	RACR #1	RACR #2	Loss Ratio %	Total Assets ($mil)	Capital ($mil)	Net Premium ($mil)	Net Income ($mil)
6-16	C	7.59	4.33	N/A	814.8	204.0	-0.1	-8.0
6-15	C	1.44	1.02	N/A	652.3	247.7	-228.1	5.8
2015	C	5.64	3.22	103.6	933.4	209.8	-204.8	26.0
2014	C	0.92	0.58	813.6	708.6	240.8	-6.7	51.5
2013	C	0.99	0.64	195.9	700.2	311.0	-38.0	8.3
2012	C-	0.90	0.57	308.3	728.8	280.4	-2.8	-10.4
2011	C-	0.73	0.46	N/A	729.8	269.1	0.7	-1.7

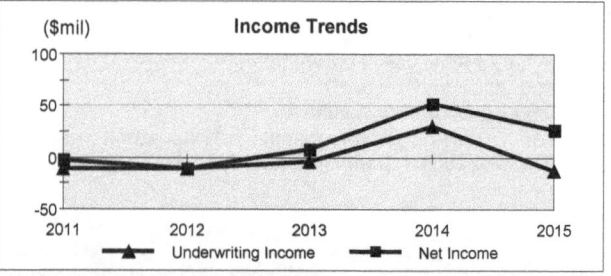
Income Trends

CLEARWATER INS CO

D-   Weak

Major Rating Factors: A history of deficient reserves (0.7 on a scale of 0 to 10) that places pressure on both capital and profits. In four of the last five years reserves (two year development) were between 38% and 66% deficient. Weak profitability index (1.5) with operating losses during 2012, 2013, 2014 and the first six months of 2016. Average return on equity over the last five years has been poor at -9.1%.

Other Rating Factors: Weak overall results on stability tests (1.3) including weak results on operational trends and negative cash flow from operations for 2015. Fair long-term capitalization index (4.6) based on fair current risk adjusted capital (moderate loss scenario), although results have slipped from the good range over the last two years. Superior liquidity (9.4) with ample operational cash flow and liquid investments.

Principal Business: (This company is a reinsurer.)
Principal Investments: Investment grade bonds (49%), misc. investments (47%), cash (3%), and non investment grade bonds (1%).
Investments in Affiliates: 14%
Group Affiliation: Fairfax Financial
Licensed in: All states, the District of Columbia and Puerto Rico
Commenced Business: July 1974
Address: 300 First Stamford Place, Stamford, CT 06902
Phone: (203) 977-8000   **Domicile State:** DE   **NAIC Code:** 25070

Data Date	Rating	RACR #1	RACR #2	Loss Ratio %	Total Assets ($mil)	Capital ($mil)	Net Premium ($mil)	Net Income ($mil)
6-16	D-	0.85	0.67	N/A	1,129.5	276.2	0.1	-10.4
6-15	D	1.16	0.87	N/A	1,139.9	322.4	0.1	-5.4
2015	D-	0.92	0.73	N/A	1,219.1	304.5	0.1	17.3
2014	D	1.14	0.86	N/A	1,202.6	337.3	0.1	-67.5
2013	D	1.22	0.89	N/A	1,306.2	380.1	0.1	-43.0
2012	D	0.93	0.60	N/A	1,200.7	348.9	0.2	-105.1
2011	D	1.09	0.67	N/A	1,239.7	381.4	-1.4	36.0

Reserve Deficiency (as % of capital)

* Adequate & redundant reserves show as negatives

CLEARWATER SELECT INS CO

D   Weak

Major Rating Factors: A history of deficient reserves (0.7 on a scale of 0 to 10). Underreserving can have an adverse impact on capital and profits. In 2013 and 2014 the two year reserve development was 401% and 466% deficient respectively. Weak overall results on stability tests (1.7) including weak results on operational trends. The largest net exposure for one risk is excessive at 7.9% of capital.

Other Rating Factors: Fair long-term capitalization index (3.5) based on fair current risk adjusted capital (severe and moderate loss scenarios). Good liquidity (6.2) with sufficient resources (cash flows and marketable investments) to handle a spike in claims. Excellent profitability (8.7) with operating gains in each of the last five years.

Principal Business: (This company is a reinsurer.)
Principal Investments: Investment grade bonds (71%), misc. investments (24%), non investment grade bonds (4%), and cash (1%).
Investments in Affiliates: 15%
Group Affiliation: Fairfax Financial
Licensed in: All states except CA, FL
Commenced Business: March 1994
Address: 300 First Stamford Place, Stamford, CT 06902
Phone: (203) 977-8000   **Domicile State:** CT   **NAIC Code:** 10019

Data Date	Rating	RACR #1	RACR #2	Loss Ratio %	Total Assets ($mil)	Capital ($mil)	Net Premium ($mil)	Net Income ($mil)
6-16	D	0.88	0.70	N/A	1,223.4	479.8	94.5	35.5
6-15	D	0.75	0.60	N/A	1,202.3	454.4	106.6	24.8
2015	D	0.84	0.68	58.4	1,192.2	476.9	200.4	62.1
2014	D	0.69	0.56	58.4	1,177.7	431.6	222.5	48.3
2013	D	0.11	0.09	93.1	1,111.8	372.6	808.4	2.0
2012	U	43.36	27.71	N/A	118.6	111.3	0.0	6.0
2011	U	40.76	26.39	N/A	113.2	105.4	0.0	4.0

Reserve Deficiency (as % of capital)

* Adequate & redundant reserves show as negatives

COAST NATIONAL INS CO   D+   Weak

Major Rating Factors: Weak overall results on stability tests (2.7 on a scale of 0 to 10) including potential drain of affiliation with Farmers Insurance Group of Companies, weak results on operational trends and negative cash flow from operations for 2015. History of adequate reserve strength (6.0) as reserves have been consistently at an acceptable level.

Other Rating Factors: Good overall profitability index (6.7). Excellent expense controls. Return on equity has been low, averaging 1.9% over the past five years. Strong long-term capitalization index (10.0) based on excellent current risk adjusted capital (severe and moderate loss scenarios), despite some fluctuation in capital levels. Superior liquidity (10.0) with ample operational cash flow and liquid investments.

Principal Business: Auto liability (63%) and auto physical damage (37%).

Principal Investments: Investment grade bonds (80%), misc. investments (13%), cash (6%), and non investment grade bonds (1%).

Investments in Affiliates: 12%

Group Affiliation: Farmers Insurance Group of Companies

Licensed in: AZ, CA, FL, GA, MS, NV, OR, PA, TN, WA

Commenced Business: March 1987

Address: 333 S Anita Dr Suite 150, Orange, CA 92868

Phone: (954) 316-5200   **Domicile State:** CA   **NAIC Code:** 25089

Data Date	Rating	RACR #1	RACR #2	Loss Ratio %	Total Assets ($mil)	Capital ($mil)	Net Premium ($mil)	Net Income ($mil)
6-16	D+	7.84	7.19	N/A	603.8	424.7	0.0	5.4
6-15	D+	7.82	7.21	N/A	611.5	416.2	0.0	4.6
2015	D+	7.81	7.22	0.0	597.5	418.6	0.0	7.4
2014	D+	7.87	7.35	0.0	609.5	411.3	0.0	6.7
2013	D+	7.94	7.38	N/A	587.0	403.1	0.0	7.1
2012	D+	7.47	6.72	0.0	621.8	395.7	0.0	5.7
2011	D+	7.40	6.87	0.0	689.0	387.2	0.0	9.0

Farmers Insurance Group of Companies
Composite Group Rating: C
Largest Group Members

	Assets ($mil)	Rating
FARMERS INS EXCHANGE	15567	C
MID-CENTURY INS CO	3905	B-
FIRE INS EXCHANGE	2335	C+
FOREMOST INS CO	2172	B
TRUCK INS EXCHANGE	2165	C+

COLONY INS CO   C   Fair

Major Rating Factors: Fair overall results on stability tests (3.3 on a scale of 0 to 10) including potential drain of affiliation with Argo Group Intl Holdings Ltd and weak results on operational trends. Good liquidity (6.9) with sufficient resources (cash flows and marketable investments) to handle a spike in claims.

Other Rating Factors: Strong long-term capitalization index (7.2) based on excellent current risk adjusted capital (severe and moderate loss scenarios), despite some fluctuation in capital levels. Ample reserve history (9.4) that helps to protect the company against sharp claims increases. Excellent profitability (7.9) with operating gains in each of the last five years. Return on equity has been excellent over the last five years averaging 20.9%.

Principal Business: Other liability (55%), products liability (19%), commercial multiple peril (11%), allied lines (6%), auto liability (3%), earthquake (2%), and other lines (4%).

Principal Investments: Investment grade bonds (59%), misc. investments (35%), non investment grade bonds (4%), and cash (2%).

Investments in Affiliates: 6%

Group Affiliation: Argo Group Intl Holdings Ltd

Licensed in: All states except PR

Commenced Business: July 1981

Address: 9201 Forest Hill Ave, Ste 200, Richmond, VA 23235-6865

Phone: (804) 560-2000   **Domicile State:** VA   **NAIC Code:** 39993

Data Date	Rating	RACR #1	RACR #2	Loss Ratio %	Total Assets ($mil)	Capital ($mil)	Net Premium ($mil)	Net Income ($mil)
6-16	C	1.60	1.12	N/A	1,450.9	346.0	124.3	11.4
6-15	C	1.86	1.28	N/A	1,380.6	344.5	136.9	17.7
2015	C	1.63	1.14	56.1	1,409.4	349.6	278.8	32.4
2014	C	1.88	1.30	43.3	1,318.8	319.8	234.6	81.1
2013	C	1.97	1.40	42.5	1,309.8	324.4	199.8	46.9
2012	C	1.87	1.31	46.1	1,277.1	328.0	175.7	39.6
2011	C	1.90	1.36	45.1	1,313.2	334.6	146.8	168.0

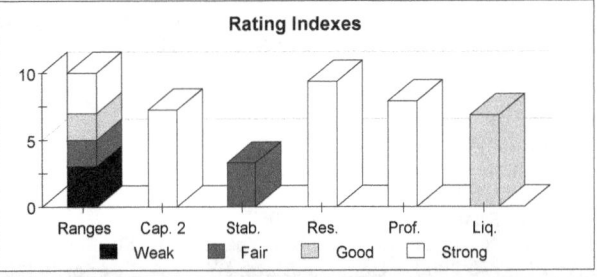

Rating Indexes (Ranges, Cap. 2, Stab., Res., Prof., Liq.) — Weak, Fair, Good, Strong

COLUMBIA CASUALTY CO   C   Fair

Major Rating Factors: Fair overall results on stability tests (3.9 on a scale of 0 to 10) including fair financial strength of affiliated CNA Financial Corp and weak results on operational trends.

Other Rating Factors: Good overall profitability index (6.7). Fair expense controls. Return on equity has been low, averaging 2.9% over the past five years. Strong long-term capitalization index (10.0) based on excellent current risk adjusted capital (severe and moderate loss scenarios), despite some fluctuation in capital levels. Superior liquidity (10.0) with ample operational cash flow and liquid investments.

Principal Business: Other liability (70%), medical malpractice (17%), products liability (8%), fire (3%), allied lines (1%), and burglary & theft (1%).

Principal Investments: Investment grade bonds (102%), non investment grade bonds (1%), and cash (1%).

Investments in Affiliates: None

Group Affiliation: CNA Financial Corp

Licensed in: All states, the District of Columbia and Puerto Rico

Commenced Business: March 1974

Address: 333 S Wabash Ave, Chicago, IL 60604

Phone: (312) 822-5000   **Domicile State:** IL   **NAIC Code:** 31127

Data Date	Rating	RACR #1	RACR #2	Loss Ratio %	Total Assets ($mil)	Capital ($mil)	Net Premium ($mil)	Net Income ($mil)
6-16	C	65.84	27.29	N/A	236.2	234.8	0.0	3.5
6-15	C	67.32	28.15	N/A	248.1	245.6	0.0	3.9
2015	C	68.89	28.58	0.0	247.4	247.3	0.0	5.3
2014	C	68.00	28.39	0.0	242.0	241.6	0.0	6.9
2013	C	67.97	28.36	0.0	235.2	234.9	0.0	6.8
2012	C	65.96	27.41	0.0	234.7	234.3	0.0	7.6
2011	C	68.66	28.71	0.0	235.1	234.9	0.0	7.4

CNA Financial Corp
Composite Group Rating: C+
Largest Group Members

	Assets ($mil)	Rating
CONTINENTAL CASUALTY CO	43531	C+
WESTERN SURETY CO	1824	C
CONTINENTAL INS CO	1667	C
COLUMBIA CASUALTY CO	247	C
AMERICAN CASUALTY CO OF READING	151	C

COLUMBIA INS CO

C+   Fair

Major Rating Factors: Fair overall results on stability tests (3.4 on a scale of 0 to 10) including weak results on operational trends. The largest net exposure for one risk is excessive at 5.2% of capital. Strong long-term capitalization index (7.8) based on excellent current risk adjusted capital (severe and moderate loss scenarios), despite some fluctuation in capital levels.

Other Rating Factors: Ample reserve history (8.2) that helps to protect the company against sharp claims increases. Excellent profitability (7.7) with operating gains in each of the last five years. Superior liquidity (9.8) with ample operational cash flow and liquid investments.

Principal Business: Auto liability (78%), auto physical damage (19%), and inland marine (2%).

Principal Investments: Misc. investments (90%), investment grade bonds (8%), and cash (2%).

Investments in Affiliates: 25%
Group Affiliation: Berkshire-Hathaway
Licensed in: All states except KS, MD, NY, PR
Commenced Business: January 1970
Address: 3024 Harney St, Omaha, NE 68131-3580
Phone: (402) 916-3000   **Domicile State:** NE   **NAIC Code:** 27812

Data Date	Rating	RACR #1	RACR #2	Loss Ratio %	Total Assets ($mil)	Capital ($mil)	Net Premium ($mil)	Net Income ($mil)
6-16	C+	1.99	1.56	N/A	19,039.1	14,203.1	192.8	699.4
6-15	C+	1.97	1.55	N/A	18,862.3	13,950.6	239.4	791.5
2015	C+	1.99	1.57	62.0	19,102.4	14,197.4	448.9	1,154.5
2014	C+	2.07	1.61	160.7	20,054.2	14,990.2	-489.3	769.6
2013	B-	1.83	1.37	37.1	19,012.9	13,454.1	546.8	858.9
2012	C+	1.69	1.26	60.4	15,069.8	10,432.5	611.0	421.2
2011	C+	1.58	1.15	85.4	12,861.8	8,646.5	414.9	298.4

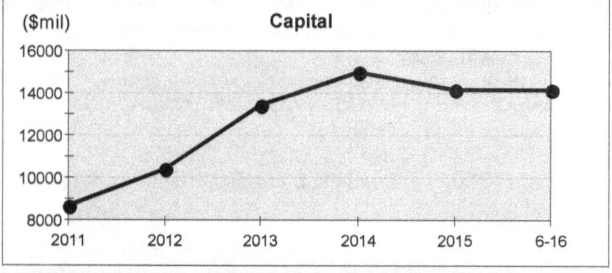

Capital

COMMERCE & INDUSTRY INS CO

C   Fair

Major Rating Factors: Fair reserve development (3.9 on a scale of 0 to 10) as reserves have generally been sufficient to cover claims. In 2011, the two year reserve development was 21% deficient. Weak overall results on stability tests (2.8) including weak results on operational trends and negative cash flow from operations for 2015. The largest net exposure for one risk is excessive at 29.7% of capital. Strengths include potential support from affiliation with AIG.

Other Rating Factors: Weak profitability index (1.9). Fair expense controls. Return on equity has been fair, averaging 26.7% over the past five years. Good liquidity (6.4) with sufficient resources (cash flows and marketable investments) to handle a spike in claims. Strong long-term capitalization index (8.3) based on excellent current risk adjusted capital (severe and moderate loss scenarios), despite some fluctuation in capital levels.

Principal Business: Workers compensation (44%), other liability (30%), aircraft (12%), auto liability (11%), homeowners multiple peril (2%), auto physical damage (1%), and inland marine (1%).

Principal Investments: Investment grade bonds (651%), non investment grade bonds (22%), and cash (1%).

Investments in Affiliates: 2%
Group Affiliation: American International Group
Licensed in: All states except PR
Commenced Business: December 1957
Address: 175 Water St 18th Floor, New York, NY 10038
Phone: (212) 770-7000   **Domicile State:** NY   **NAIC Code:** 19410

Data Date	Rating	RACR #1	RACR #2	Loss Ratio %	Total Assets ($mil)	Capital ($mil)	Net Premium ($mil)	Net Income ($mil)
6-16	C	3.95	3.02	N/A	482.6	465.2	0.0	156.3
6-15	C	2.63	1.82	N/A	4,534.4	1,354.2	445.6	735.8
2015	C	1.92	1.33	91.2	4,142.7	974.0	927.4	650.2
2014	C	2.79	1.87	85.6	4,770.8	1,624.9	590.4	263.8
2013	C	2.05	1.37	73.0	7,339.2	1,905.6	1,569.7	309.1
2012	C	2.28	1.56	85.3	7,350.7	2,041.5	1,353.6	131.7
2011	C-	2.03	1.38	85.2	7,203.9	1,844.1	1,378.8	140.9

Reserve Deficiency (as % of capital)

■ 1 Yr Dev   □ 2 Yr Dev
* Adequate & redundant reserves show as negatives

COMMERCE INS CO

C   Fair

Major Rating Factors: Fair reserve development (4.2 on a scale of 0 to 10) as reserves have generally been sufficient to cover claims. Fair profitability index (3.1) with operating losses during 2015. Return on equity has been fair, averaging 6.9% over the past five years.

Other Rating Factors: Fair overall results on stability tests (4.3) including weak results on operational trends and negative cash flow from operations for 2015. Vulnerable liquidity (2.9) as a spike in claims may stretch capacity. Strong long-term capitalization index (8.4) based on excellent current risk adjusted capital (severe and moderate loss scenarios), despite some fluctuation in capital levels.

Principal Business: Auto liability (51%), auto physical damage (36%), homeowners multiple peril (8%), commercial multiple peril (2%), and fire (1%).

Principal Investments: Investment grade bonds (73%), misc. investments (22%), non investment grade bonds (4%), and real estate (3%).

Investments in Affiliates: 4%
Group Affiliation: MAPFRE Ins Group
Licensed in: CA, CT, FL, ME, MA, NH, NJ, NY, OH, OR, RI, TX, VT
Commenced Business: May 1972
Address: 211 W Main St, Webster, MA 01570-0758
Phone: (508) 943-9000   **Domicile State:** MA   **NAIC Code:** 34754

Data Date	Rating	RACR #1	RACR #2	Loss Ratio %	Total Assets ($mil)	Capital ($mil)	Net Premium ($mil)	Net Income ($mil)
6-16	C	2.50	1.92	N/A	2,244.5	674.4	616.7	19.9
6-15	C	2.15	1.71	N/A	2,174.7	615.1	632.1	-58.0
2015	C	2.37	1.90	84.1	2,235.2	660.6	1,157.6	-1.7
2014	C	2.32	1.91	76.6	2,217.4	682.8	1,370.1	63.7
2013	B-	3.04	2.42	73.5	2,272.1	834.8	1,320.3	88.0
2012	B+	3.74	2.94	75.0	2,372.6	987.8	1,209.8	106.1
2011	B+	3.33	2.62	81.2	2,672.5	987.7	1,391.4	44.8

Reserve Deficiency (as % of capital)

■ 1 Yr Dev   □ 2 Yr Dev
* Adequate & redundant reserves show as negatives

CONCORD GENERAL MUTUAL INS CO   B-   Good

Major Rating Factors: Fair overall results on stability tests (4.1 on a scale of 0 to 10) including potential drain of affiliation with Concord Group, weak results on operational trends and negative cash flow from operations for 2015. Fair profitability index (4.6) with operating losses during 2011.

Other Rating Factors: Good liquidity (6.5) with sufficient resources (cash flows and marketable investments) to handle a spike in claims. Strong long-term capitalization index (8.0) based on excellent current risk adjusted capital (severe and moderate loss scenarios), despite some fluctuation in capital levels. Ample reserve history (8.7) that helps to protect the company against sharp claims increases.

Principal Business: Homeowners multiple peril (36%), auto liability (28%), auto physical damage (25%), commercial multiple peril (5%), other liability (4%), and inland marine (1%).

Principal Investments: Misc. investments (54%), investment grade bonds (42%), cash (2%), non investment grade bonds (1%), and real estate (1%).

Investments in Affiliates: 6%
Group Affiliation: Concord Group
Licensed in: ME, NH, SC, VT
Commenced Business: June 1928
Address: 4 Bouton St, Concord, NH 03301
Phone: (603) 224-4086   **Domicile State:** NH   **NAIC Code:** 20672

Data Date	Rating	RACR #1	RACR #2	Loss Ratio %	Total Assets ($mil)	Capital ($mil)	Net Premium ($mil)	Net Income ($mil)
6-16	B-	2.57	1.71	N/A	449.3	228.8	80.2	1.7
6-15	B-	2.49	1.66	N/A	442.0	216.1	82.0	-7.7
2015	B-	2.55	1.71	74.6	438.2	221.6	164.1	0.4
2014	B-	2.60	1.74	72.2	449.5	226.2	167.7	4.4
2013	B-	2.60	1.72	67.4	426.1	211.9	164.6	10.1
2012	B-	2.88	1.90	68.8	373.6	187.2	155.0	7.9
2011	B-	2.73	1.81	84.6	348.4	171.8	144.7	-10.7

Rating Indexes

CONNECTICUT MEDICAL INS CO   B   Good

Major Rating Factors: Fair overall results on stability tests (4.2 on a scale of 0 to 10) including weak results on operational trends and negative cash flow from operations for 2015. Strong long-term capitalization index (7.5) based on excellent current risk adjusted capital (severe and moderate loss scenarios). Moreover, capital levels have been consistent in recent years.

Other Rating Factors: Ample reserve history (9.4) that helps to protect the company against sharp claims increases. Excellent profitability (8.1) with operating gains in each of the last five years. Excellent liquidity (8.1) with ample operational cash flow and liquid investments.

Principal Business: Medical malpractice (100%).

Principal Investments: Investment grade bonds (80%), misc. investments (19%), and cash (1%).

Investments in Affiliates: None
Group Affiliation: Connecticut Medical
Licensed in: CT, MA
Commenced Business: October 1984
Address: 80 Glastonbury Blvd, Glastonbury, CT 06033
Phone: (860) 633-7788   **Domicile State:** CT   **NAIC Code:** 15890

Data Date	Rating	RACR #1	RACR #2	Loss Ratio %	Total Assets ($mil)	Capital ($mil)	Net Premium ($mil)	Net Income ($mil)
6-16	B	1.53	1.31	N/A	493.4	292.0	18.4	2.7
6-15	C+	1.66	1.42	N/A	492.0	285.9	18.0	6.4
2015	B	1.57	1.35	67.5	476.7	286.8	31.8	8.9
2014	C+	1.65	1.41	63.2	480.2	279.1	31.1	10.7
2013	C+	1.73	1.48	58.6	468.6	264.4	35.9	11.2
2012	C+	7.50	5.50	24.7	440.8	243.7	34.1	21.0
2011	C+	6.37	4.83	35.2	422.1	218.2	32.7	17.2

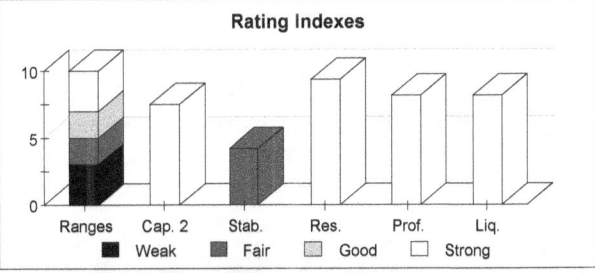

Rating Indexes

CONTINENTAL CASUALTY CO   C+   Fair

Major Rating Factors: Fair overall results on stability tests (3.2 on a scale of 0 to 10) including weak results on operational trends. The largest net exposure for one risk is excessive at 5.0% of capital. History of adequate reserve strength (6.2) as reserves have been consistently at an acceptable level.

Other Rating Factors: Good overall profitability index (5.7). Fair expense controls. Return on equity has been fair, averaging 7.3% over the past five years. Strong long-term capitalization index (7.8) based on excellent current risk adjusted capital (severe and moderate loss scenarios), despite some fluctuation in capital levels. Excellent liquidity (7.0) with ample operational cash flow and liquid investments.

Principal Business: Inland marine (46%), other liability (30%), other accident & health (5%), commercial multiple peril (4%), group accident & health (3%), workers compensation (2%), and other lines (10%).

Principal Investments: Investment grade bonds (75%), misc. investments (20%), and non investment grade bonds (5%).

Investments in Affiliates: 11%
Group Affiliation: CNA Financial Corp
Licensed in: All states, the District of Columbia and Puerto Rico
Commenced Business: December 1897
Address: 333 S Wabash Ave, Chicago, IL 60604
Phone: (312) 822-5000   **Domicile State:** IL   **NAIC Code:** 20443

Data Date	Rating	RACR #1	RACR #2	Loss Ratio %	Total Assets ($mil)	Capital ($mil)	Net Premium ($mil)	Net Income ($mil)
6-16	C+	1.97	1.49	N/A	43,522.7	10,583.9	2,687.9	495.8
6-15	C	2.01	1.53	N/A	43,353.4	10,870.1	2,685.4	367.2
2015	C+	2.01	1.54	83.1	43,531.4	10,723.3	6,036.8	1,078.8
2014	C	2.09	1.60	85.1	43,309.7	11,155.2	6,007.1	839.3
2013	C+	2.04	1.59	87.8	42,642.3	11,136.7	6,246.7	788.0
2012	C+	1.94	1.48	94.8	41,292.2	9,998.4	6,162.5	348.2
2011	C+	2.08	1.59	83.3	40,560.9	9,887.6	6,071.5	746.0

Rating Indexes

CONTINENTAL INS CO

C   Fair

Major Rating Factors: Fair reserve development (3.7 on a scale of 0 to 10) as reserves have generally been sufficient to cover claims. In 2013, the two year reserve development was 16% deficient. Fair overall results on stability tests (4.2) including fair financial strength of affiliated CNA Financial Corp and weak results on operational trends.

Other Rating Factors: Good overall profitability index (6.2). Weak expense controls. Return on equity has been fair, averaging 6.9% over the past five years. Strong long-term capitalization index (10.0) based on excellent current risk adjusted capital (severe and moderate loss scenarios). Moreover, capital levels have been consistent in recent years. Excellent liquidity (7.0) with ample operational cash flow and liquid investments.

Principal Business: Commercial multiple peril (24%), workers compensation (17%), ocean marine (17%), auto liability (11%), surety (4%), fidelity (4%), and other lines (23%).

Principal Investments: Investment grade bonds (86%) and misc. investments (14%).

Investments in Affiliates: 11%

Group Affiliation: CNA Financial Corp

Licensed in: All states, the District of Columbia and Puerto Rico

Commenced Business: December 1977

Address: 100 Matsonford Rd Ste 200, Radnor, PA 19087

Phone: (312) 822-5000   **Domicile State:** PA   **NAIC Code:** 35289

Data Date	Rating	RACR #1	RACR #2	Loss Ratio %	Total Assets ($mil)	Capital ($mil)	Net Premium ($mil)	Net Income ($mil)
6-16	C	6.07	3.29	N/A	1,685.8	1,478.7	0.0	27.8
6-15	C	5.52	3.08	N/A	1,759.7	1,462.7	0.0	30.7
2015	C	6.41	3.56	0.0	1,666.9	1,469.3	0.0	53.1
2014	C	5.27	2.92	0.0	1,995.3	1,437.3	0.0	55.8
2013	C	4.78	2.58	0.0	2,345.5	1,366.9	0.0	121.8
2012	C	5.14	2.85	0.0	2,708.5	1,323.0	0.0	41.4
2011	C	4.88	2.58	0.0	2,668.5	1,240.6	0.0	202.1

Reserve Deficiency (as % of capital)

* Adequate & redundant reserves show as negatives

■ 1 Yr Dev □ 2 Yr Dev

COPIC INS CO

B   Good

Major Rating Factors: Fair overall results on stability tests (4.7 on a scale of 0 to 10) including weak results on operational trends. Strong long-term capitalization index (10.0) based on excellent current risk adjusted capital (severe and moderate loss scenarios). Moreover, capital levels have been consistent in recent years.

Other Rating Factors: Ample reserve history (9.4) that helps to protect the company against sharp claims increases. Excellent profitability (8.2) with operating gains in each of the last five years. Excellent liquidity (7.9) with ample operational cash flow and liquid investments.

Principal Business: Medical malpractice (95%), other liability (4%), and group accident & health (1%).

Principal Investments: Investment grade bonds (55%), misc. investments (43%), and cash (2%).

Investments in Affiliates: None

Group Affiliation: COPIC Trust

Licensed in: AZ, CO, GA, ID, IA, KS, MN, MT, NE, OK, SD, UT, WY

Commenced Business: September 1984

Address: 7800 E Dorado Pl Suite 200, Englewood, CO 80111

Phone: (720) 858-6000   **Domicile State:** CO   **NAIC Code:** 11860

Data Date	Rating	RACR #1	RACR #2	Loss Ratio %	Total Assets ($mil)	Capital ($mil)	Net Premium ($mil)	Net Income ($mil)
6-16	B	6.19	4.05	N/A	690.9	403.5	50.0	5.9
6-15	B	4.73	3.18	N/A	525.6	268.7	41.2	1.4
2015	B	6.43	4.21	56.3	657.3	396.1	82.1	1.9
2014	B	4.75	3.19	49.3	526.5	268.1	81.1	12.8
2013	A-	4.57	3.08	59.4	525.0	260.6	82.0	11.9
2012	A-	4.44	3.08	56.5	525.0	238.9	88.2	27.8
2011	A-	4.11	2.90	54.5	501.2	218.2	88.1	30.0

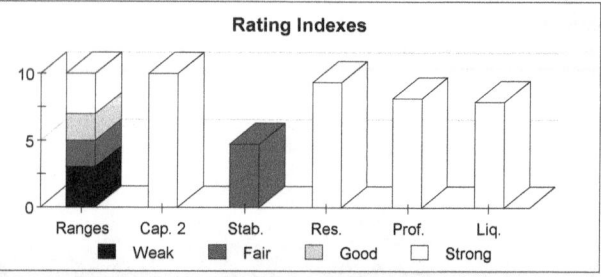

Rating Indexes

Ranges   Cap. 2   Stab.   Res.   Prof.   Liq.

■ Weak ■ Fair ▨ Good □ Strong

COPPERPOINT MUTUAL INS CO *

A+   Excellent

Major Rating Factors: Strong long-term capitalization index (8.4 on a scale of 0 to 10) based on excellent current risk adjusted capital (severe and moderate loss scenarios). Furthermore, this high level of risk adjusted capital has been consistently maintained in previous years. Excellent liquidity (8.4) with ample operational cash flow and liquid investments.

Other Rating Factors: Excellent overall results on stability tests (7.7). Stability strengths include excellent risk diversification. History of adequate reserve strength (6.9) as reserves have been consistently at an acceptable level. Good overall profitability index (6.6). Fair expense controls. Return on equity has been good over the last five years, averaging 10.6%.

Principal Business: Workers compensation (100%).

Principal Investments: Investment grade bonds (77%), misc. investments (22%), and real estate (1%).

Investments in Affiliates: 2%

Group Affiliation: CopperPoint Group

Licensed in: AZ

Commenced Business: January 2013

Address: 3030 N 3rd St, Phoenix, AZ 85012-3039

Phone: (602) 631-2240   **Domicile State:** AZ   **NAIC Code:** 14216

Data Date	Rating	RACR #1	RACR #2	Loss Ratio %	Total Assets ($mil)	Capital ($mil)	Net Premium ($mil)	Net Income ($mil)
6-16	A+	3.15	1.96	N/A	3,573.1	1,290.5	121.1	26.4
6-15	A+	2.57	1.61	N/A	3,576.3	1,258.7	121.8	33.1
2015	A+	3.16	1.96	78.5	3,562.5	1,258.8	242.1	61.9
2014	A+	2.59	1.61	78.2	3,560.4	1,229.7	239.6	51.2
2013	A+	2.22	1.38	89.2	3,536.2	1,186.2	222.5	44.7
2012	U	266.05	133.00	101.8	3,729.6	1,066.6	183.5	287.6
2011	N/A	N/A	N/A	102.6	3,479.6	762.0	172.8	124.1

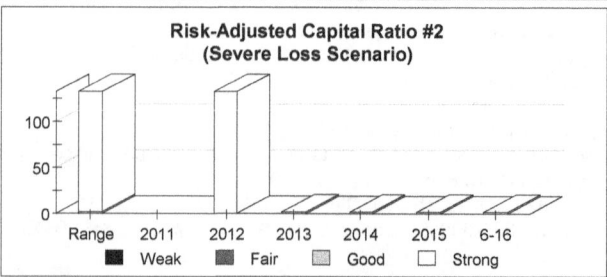

Risk-Adjusted Capital Ratio #2 (Severe Loss Scenario)

Range   2011   2012   2013   2014   2015   6-16

■ Weak ■ Fair ▨ Good □ Strong

COUNTRY CASUALTY INS CO *   B+   Good

Major Rating Factors: Good overall profitability index (6.6 on a scale of 0 to 10). Excellent expense controls. Return on equity has been low, averaging 1.6% over the past five years. Good overall results on stability tests (5.0) despite weak results on operational trends. Strengths include potential support from affiliation with COUNTRY Financial.

Other Rating Factors: Strong long-term capitalization index (10.0) based on excellent current risk adjusted capital (severe and moderate loss scenarios), despite some fluctuation in capital levels. Superior liquidity (10.0) with ample operational cash flow and liquid investments.

Principal Business: Auto liability (40%), homeowners multiple peril (39%), and auto physical damage (21%).

Principal Investments: Investment grade bonds (97%), misc. investments (2%), and cash (1%).

Investments in Affiliates: None

Group Affiliation: COUNTRY Financial

Licensed in: AL, AK, AZ, AR, CO, CT, DE, GA, ID, IL, IN, IA, KS, KY, ME, MD, MA, MI, MN, MO, MT, NE, NV, NM, ND, OH, OK, OR, PA, RI, SD, TN, TX, WA, WI, WY

Commenced Business: March 1964

Address: 1701 N. Towanda Ave, Bloomington, IL 61701

Phone: (309) 821-3000   **Domicile State:** IL   **NAIC Code:** 20982

Data Date	Rating	RACR #1	RACR #2	Loss Ratio %	Total Assets ($mil)	Capital ($mil)	Net Premium ($mil)	Net Income ($mil)
6-16	B+	24.15	21.74	N/A	83.4	69.3	0.0	0.5
6-15	B+	26.17	23.55	N/A	80.0	68.3	0.0	0.3
2015	B+	25.60	23.04	0.0	81.3	68.9	0.0	0.8
2014	B+	27.50	24.75	0.0	78.2	67.9	0.0	1.0
2013	B+	26.67	24.00	0.0	77.7	67.0	0.0	1.2
2012	B+	26.57	23.91	0.0	77.0	66.4	0.0	1.1
2011	B+	25.11	22.60	0.0	77.1	65.5	0.0	1.2

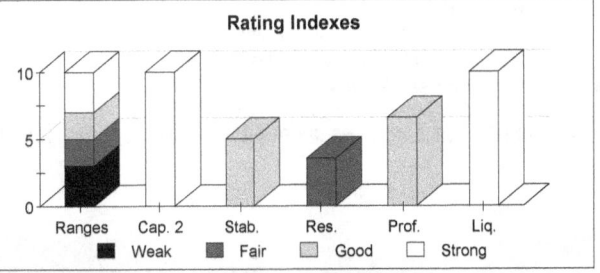

Rating Indexes

Ranges Cap. 2 Stab. Res. Prof. Liq.
■ Weak ■ Fair ▦ Good □ Strong

COUNTRY MUTUAL INS CO *   A-   Excellent

Major Rating Factors: Strong long-term capitalization index (9.7 on a scale of 0 to 10) based on excellent current risk adjusted capital (severe and moderate loss scenarios). Furthermore, this high level of risk adjusted capital has been consistently maintained in previous years. History of adequate reserve strength (6.2) as reserves have been consistently at an acceptable level.

Other Rating Factors: Good overall profitability index (6.2) despite operating losses during 2011. Good liquidity (6.2) with sufficient resources (cash flows and marketable investments) to handle a spike in claims. Good overall results on stability tests (5.9) despite weak results on operational trends.

Principal Business: Homeowners multiple peril (42%), auto liability (16%), auto physical damage (11%), farmowners multiple peril (10%), allied lines (7%), commercial multiple peril (7%), and other lines (8%).

Principal Investments: Investment grade bonds (70%), misc. investments (27%), and non investment grade bonds (3%).

Investments in Affiliates: 4%

Group Affiliation: COUNTRY Financial

Licensed in: All states except DC, FL, HI, LA, MS, PR

Commenced Business: November 1925

Address: 1701 N. Towanda Ave, Bloomington, IL 61701

Phone: (309) 821-3000   **Domicile State:** IL   **NAIC Code:** 20990

Data Date	Rating	RACR #1	RACR #2	Loss Ratio %	Total Assets ($mil)	Capital ($mil)	Net Premium ($mil)	Net Income ($mil)
6-16	A-	4.42	3.16	N/A	4,421.1	2,143.9	993.0	67.1
6-15	A-	3.83	2.78	N/A	4,410.0	2,018.1	1,025.3	51.4
2015	A-	4.26	3.05	70.7	4,295.7	2,072.0	2,023.5	120.0
2014	A-	3.74	2.70	70.3	4,255.7	1,964.2	2,055.1	178.0
2013	A-	3.56	2.56	69.3	4,150.3	1,825.5	2,051.7	151.3
2012	B+	3.41	2.46	75.5	3,930.7	1,635.9	1,979.7	47.1
2011	B+	3.56	2.50	85.8	3,860.7	1,587.0	1,947.2	-140.8

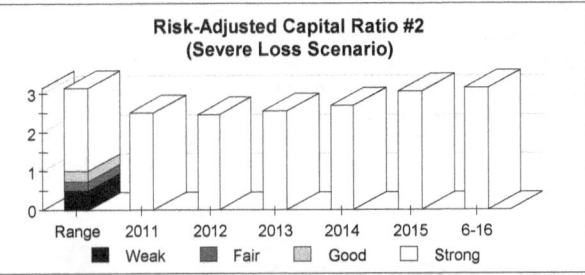

Risk-Adjusted Capital Ratio #2
(Severe Loss Scenario)

Range 2011 2012 2013 2014 2015 6-16
■ Weak ■ Fair ▦ Good □ Strong

COURTESY INS CO   B   Good

Major Rating Factors: History of adequate reserve strength (6.1 on a scale of 0 to 10) as reserves have been consistently at an acceptable level. Fair overall results on stability tests (4.2) including potential drain of affiliation with J M Family Enterprise Group and weak results on operational trends.

Other Rating Factors: Strong long-term capitalization index (10.0) based on excellent current risk adjusted capital (severe and moderate loss scenarios). Moreover, capital levels have been consistent in recent years. Excellent profitability (8.9) with operating gains in each of the last five years. Excellent liquidity (7.6) with ample operational cash flow and liquid investments.

Principal Business: Aggregate write-ins for other lines of business (26%).

Principal Investments: Investment grade bonds (84%) and misc. investments (16%).

Investments in Affiliates: None

Group Affiliation: J M Family Enterprise Group

Licensed in: All states except MI

Commenced Business: May 1988

Address: 100 Jim Moran Blvd, Deerfield Beach, FL 33442

Phone: (954) 429-2150   **Domicile State:** FL   **NAIC Code:** 26492

Data Date	Rating	RACR #1	RACR #2	Loss Ratio %	Total Assets ($mil)	Capital ($mil)	Net Premium ($mil)	Net Income ($mil)
6-16	B	9.94	5.61	N/A	785.7	368.4	62.4	5.6
6-15	B	9.56	5.42	N/A	755.4	353.1	58.6	12.6
2015	B	10.51	5.95	67.6	764.8	360.1	135.6	23.2
2014	B	9.84	5.60	57.9	735.4	341.6	121.7	33.2
2013	B	9.23	5.31	52.7	686.5	308.4	124.9	38.3
2012	B	8.81	5.04	45.1	627.2	265.0	138.6	29.8
2011	B	10.55	5.92	50.1	536.1	226.9	108.8	30.5

Reserve Deficiency (as % of capital)

2011 2012 2013 2014 2015
■ 1 Yr Dev □ 2 Yr Dev

* Adequate & redundant reserves show as negatives

CSAA INS EXCHANGE   B-   Good

Major Rating Factors: Fair overall results on stability tests (4.8 on a scale of 0 to 10) including weak results on operational trends. History of adequate reserve strength (6.2) as reserves have been consistently at an acceptable level.

Other Rating Factors: Good liquidity (5.9) with sufficient resources (cash flows and marketable investments) to handle a spike in claims. Strong long-term capitalization index (8.8) based on excellent current risk adjusted capital (severe and moderate loss scenarios), despite some fluctuation in capital levels. Weak profitability index (2.9) with operating losses during the first six months of 2016.

Principal Business: Auto physical damage (37%), auto liability (36%), homeowners multiple peril (25%), other liability (1%), and allied lines (1%).

Principal Investments: Investment grade bonds (48%), misc. investments (44%), non investment grade bonds (6%), and real estate (2%).

Investments in Affiliates: 6%

Group Affiliation: CSAA Insurance Group

Licensed in: AZ, CA, IN, MO, NV, NJ, NY, UT, WY

Commenced Business: August 1914

Address: 3055 Oak Rd, Walnut Creek, CA 94597-2098

Phone: (800) 207-3618   **Domicile State:** CA   **NAIC Code:** 15539

Data Date	Rating	RACR #1	RACR #2	Loss Ratio %	Total Assets ($mil)	Capital ($mil)	Net Premium ($mil)	Net Income ($mil)
6-16	B-	3.12	2.15	N/A	6,651.6	3,319.5	1,560.0	-25.7
6-15	B	3.35	2.34	N/A	6,723.6	3,608.1	1,467.3	38.3
2015	B-	3.17	2.19	81.6	6,572.3	3,378.1	3,116.8	-120.8
2014	B	3.51	2.45	73.4	6,983.9	3,749.3	2,899.6	122.6
2013	A-	3.82	2.68	74.1	6,672.1	3,830.2	2,714.9	114.9
2012	A-	3.79	2.69	69.5	6,430.9	3,624.9	2,637.5	131.2
2011	A-	3.88	2.79	70.7	6,285.5	3,440.5	2,582.8	211.1

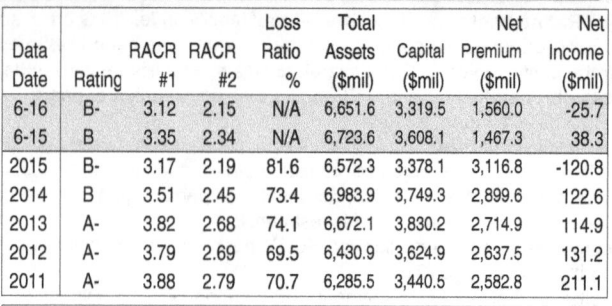

Rating Indexes

CUMIS INS SOCIETY INC   B   Good

Major Rating Factors: Good liquidity (6.3 on a scale of 0 to 10) with sufficient resources (cash flows and marketable investments) to handle a spike in claims. Fair overall results on stability tests (4.9) including weak results on operational trends. The largest net exposure for one risk is conservative at 1.2% of capital.

Other Rating Factors: Strong long-term capitalization index (10.0) based on excellent current risk adjusted capital (severe and moderate loss scenarios). Moreover, capital levels have been consistent in recent years. Ample reserve history (8.9) that helps to protect the company against sharp claims increases. Excellent profitability (8.8) with operating gains in each of the last five years.

Principal Business: Other liability (64%), fidelity (17%), commercial multiple peril (14%), auto physical damage (2%), auto liability (1%), and credit (1%).

Principal Investments: Investment grade bonds (81%), misc. investments (15%), non investment grade bonds (3%), and cash (1%).

Investments in Affiliates: 4%

Group Affiliation: CUNA Mutual Ins Group

Licensed in: All states, the District of Columbia and Puerto Rico

Commenced Business: June 1960

Address: 5910 Mineral Point Rd, Madison, WI 53705

Phone: (608) 238-5851   **Domicile State:** IA   **NAIC Code:** 10847

Data Date	Rating	RACR #1	RACR #2	Loss Ratio %	Total Assets ($mil)	Capital ($mil)	Net Premium ($mil)	Net Income ($mil)
6-16	B	5.33	3.80	N/A	1,789.0	844.0	385.0	40.1
6-15	B	4.52	3.22	N/A	2,234.4	747.9	403.9	56.7
2015	B	4.99	3.58	64.4	1,711.8	800.5	826.3	110.9
2014	B	4.48	3.25	63.4	2,062.8	714.9	652.2	80.9
2013	B	4.63	3.27	63.8	1,637.6	621.7	621.0	58.5
2012	B	4.67	3.28	63.5	1,636.9	562.0	553.1	29.1
2011	B	4.06	2.86	61.6	1,623.3	501.8	491.0	35.9

Liquidity Index

CYPRESS INS CO   C+   Fair

Major Rating Factors: Fair overall results on stability tests (4.4 on a scale of 0 to 10) including fair financial strength of affiliated Berkshire-Hathaway, excessive premium growth and weak results on operational trends. Good long-term capitalization index (5.3) based on good current risk adjusted capital (moderate loss scenario). Over the last several years, capital levels have remained relatively consistent.

Other Rating Factors: Good overall profitability index (5.5) despite operating losses during 2011. Return on equity has been low, averaging 4.5% over the past five years. Ample reserve history (9.1) that helps to protect the company against sharp claims increases. Excellent liquidity (7.3) with ample operational cash flow and liquid investments.

Principal Business: Workers compensation (90%), auto liability (6%), auto physical damage (2%), commercial multiple peril (1%), and inland marine (1%).

Principal Investments: Investment grade bonds (61%), misc. investments (38%), and cash (1%).

Investments in Affiliates: None

Group Affiliation: Berkshire-Hathaway

Licensed in: AL, AR, CA, CO, DE, GA, HI, ID, IA, MS, NE, NM, OK, SC, TN, TX, VA

Commenced Business: March 1963

Address: 525 Market St Ste 3110, San Francisco, CA 94105

Phone: (888) 495-8949   **Domicile State:** CA   **NAIC Code:** 10855

Data Date	Rating	RACR #1	RACR #2	Loss Ratio %	Total Assets ($mil)	Capital ($mil)	Net Premium ($mil)	Net Income ($mil)
6-16	C+	1.04	0.74	N/A	1,363.6	313.8	212.1	41.3
6-15	C	1.19	0.80	N/A	1,165.3	303.0	116.9	11.0
2015	C+	1.21	0.84	77.3	1,284.2	305.7	327.0	6.8
2014	C	1.26	0.85	77.4	1,203.2	311.5	254.3	26.6
2013	C	1.45	1.01	78.9	1,140.2	264.4	271.9	25.3
2012	C	1.22	0.87	85.7	1,065.2	207.2	265.5	12.7
2011	C	1.04	0.76	88.5	897.9	187.4	297.8	-28.4

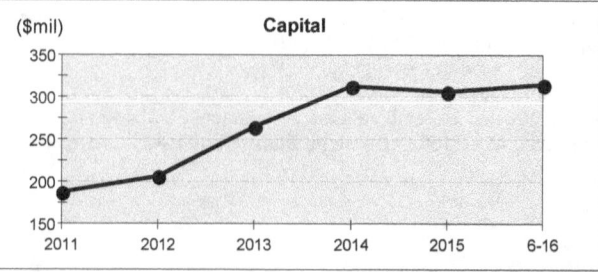

Capital

DAIRYLAND INS CO *   B+   Good

Major Rating Factors: Good overall profitability index (6.0 on a scale of 0 to 10). Fair expense controls. Return on equity has been fair, averaging 5.6% over the past five years. Good liquidity (6.9) with sufficient resources (cash flows and marketable investments) to handle a spike in claims.

Other Rating Factors: Good overall results on stability tests (5.3) despite weak results on operational trends. Strong long-term capitalization index (9.8) based on excellent current risk adjusted capital (severe and moderate loss scenarios), despite some fluctuation in capital levels. Ample reserve history (8.1) that helps to protect the company against sharp claims increases.

Principal Business: Auto liability (68%) and auto physical damage (32%).

Principal Investments: Investment grade bonds (88%), misc. investments (11%), and non investment grade bonds (1%).

Investments in Affiliates: None

Group Affiliation: Sentry Ins Group

Licensed in: All states except CA, DC, HI, LA, NJ, OK, PR

Commenced Business: February 1953

Address: 1800 North Point Dr, Stevens Point, WI 54481

Phone: (715) 346-6000   **Domicile State:** WI   **NAIC Code:** 21164

Data Date	Rating	RACR #1	RACR #2	Loss Ratio %	Total Assets ($mil)	Capital ($mil)	Net Premium ($mil)	Net Income ($mil)
6-16	B+	4.47	2.82	N/A	1,282.3	491.1	168.7	8.9
6-15	B+	5.08	3.34	N/A	1,235.3	499.7	154.9	19.4
2015	B+	4.57	2.92	72.7	1,239.6	482.0	328.5	29.3
2014	B+	5.05	3.38	74.9	1,194.9	485.3	317.4	34.8
2013	A+	4.86	3.30	76.3	1,163.2	471.7	318.1	25.6
2012	A+	4.95	3.35	77.3	1,129.0	460.8	302.3	21.7
2011	A+	4.99	3.40	79.1	1,130.0	455.7	285.8	25.6

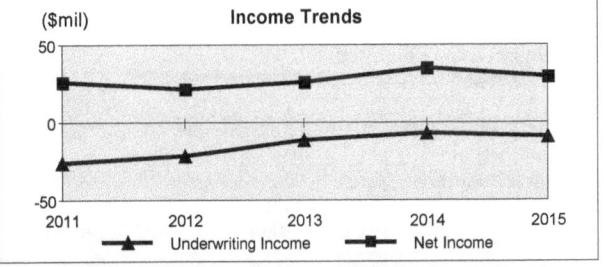

Income Trends

DOCTORS CO AN INTERINS   B-   Good

Major Rating Factors: Fair overall results on stability tests (4.7 on a scale of 0 to 10) including potential drain of affiliation with Doctors Co Group and weak results on operational trends. Fair profitability index (4.5) with operating losses during the first six months of 2016.

Other Rating Factors: Strong long-term capitalization index (7.6) based on excellent current risk adjusted capital (severe and moderate loss scenarios), despite some fluctuation in capital levels. Ample reserve history (9.1) that helps to protect the company against sharp claims increases. Excellent liquidity (7.5) with ample operational cash flow and liquid investments.

Principal Business: Medical malpractice (100%).

Principal Investments: Misc. investments (62%), investment grade bonds (33%), cash (3%), and non investment grade bonds (2%).

Investments in Affiliates: 19%

Group Affiliation: Doctors Co Group

Licensed in: All states except PR

Commenced Business: April 1976

Address: 185 Greenwood Dr, Napa, CA 94558

Phone: (707) 226-0100   **Domicile State:** CA   **NAIC Code:** 34495

Data Date	Rating	RACR #1	RACR #2	Loss Ratio %	Total Assets ($mil)	Capital ($mil)	Net Premium ($mil)	Net Income ($mil)
6-16	B-	1.90	1.48	N/A	4,063.5	1,824.0	309.9	-2.1
6-15	B-	1.91	1.51	N/A	3,587.6	1,815.1	312.0	22.3
2015	B-	1.95	1.54	74.5	3,585.4	1,808.9	622.9	-72.8
2014	B-	1.93	1.53	78.3	3,559.8	1,821.9	644.0	31.3
2013	B-	1.88	1.54	75.1	3,313.2	1,731.7	675.7	27.7
2012	B-	1.61	1.40	69.1	2,769.5	1,358.3	596.5	120.9
2011	B-	1.30	1.18	63.0	2,601.5	1,192.0	564.5	175.1

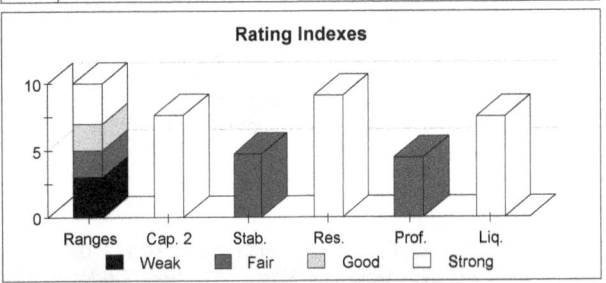

Rating Indexes

DONEGAL MUTUAL INS CO   B-   Good

Major Rating Factors: Fair overall results on stability tests (4.2 on a scale of 0 to 10) including potential drain of affiliation with Donegal Mutual Insurance Company and weak results on operational trends. Good long-term capitalization index (6.3) based on good current risk adjusted capital (severe and moderate loss scenarios), although results have slipped from the excellent range over the last two years.

Other Rating Factors: History of adequate reserve strength (6.0) as reserves have been consistently at an acceptable level. Good liquidity (6.5) with sufficient resources (cash flows and marketable investments) to handle a spike in claims. Excellent profitability (7.2) with operating gains in each of the last five years.

Principal Business: Homeowners multiple peril (25%), auto liability (22%), commercial multiple peril (16%), auto physical damage (16%), workers compensation (10%), other liability (5%), and other lines (5%).

Principal Investments: Misc. investments (77%), real estate (10%), investment grade bonds (8%), and cash (5%).

Investments in Affiliates: 70%

Group Affiliation: Donegal Mutual Insurance Company

Licensed in: AL, DC, DE, GA, IL, IN, IA, ME, MD, MI, NE, NH, NY, NC, OH, OK, PA, SC, SD, TN, VT, VA, WV, WI

Commenced Business: May 1889

Address: 1195 River Rd, Marietta, PA 17547-0302

Phone: (717) 426-1931   **Domicile State:** PA   **NAIC Code:** 13692

Data Date	Rating	RACR #1	RACR #2	Loss Ratio %	Total Assets ($mil)	Capital ($mil)	Net Premium ($mil)	Net Income ($mil)
6-16	B-	0.99	0.93	N/A	451.0	223.9	56.2	6.3
6-15	B-	1.07	1.01	N/A	405.4	207.7	52.1	2.7
2015	B-	0.94	0.90	65.7	431.2	209.4	109.8	14.0
2014	B-	1.08	1.02	75.7	393.7	204.4	102.7	3.5
2013	B-	1.09	1.02	59.2	383.8	204.4	97.8	15.4
2012	B-	1.03	0.96	73.0	350.7	187.7	84.7	5.9
2011	B-	1.01	0.94	86.3	333.8	175.7	79.7	9.4

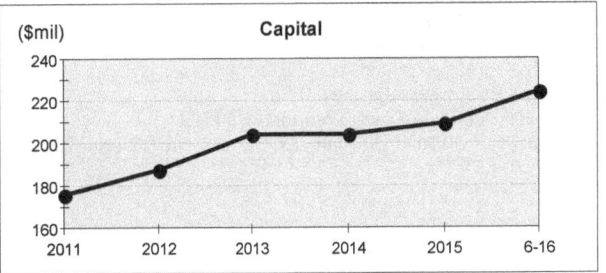

Capital

DORINCO REINS CO
C- **Fair**

Major Rating Factors: Weak overall results on stability tests (2.6 on a scale of 0 to 10) including potential drain of affiliation with Dow Chemical Co and weak results on operational trends. The largest net exposure for one risk is high at 4.4% of capital. Good long-term capitalization index (6.3) based on good current risk adjusted capital (moderate loss scenario), despite some fluctuation in capital levels.

Other Rating Factors: History of adequate reserve strength (6.9) as reserves have been consistently at an acceptable level. Good overall profitability index (5.1). Good expense controls. Return on equity has been good over the last five years, averaging 13.7%. Good liquidity (6.8) with sufficient resources (cash flows and marketable investments) to handle a spike in claims.

Principal Business: Fire (57%) and other liability (42%).

Principal Investments: Investment grade bonds (74%) and misc. investments (26%).

Investments in Affiliates: None

Group Affiliation: Dow Chemical Co

Licensed in: AL, AZ, CA, CT, DE, FL, GA, ID, IL, IN, IA, KS, KY, LA, MD, MI, MN, MS, MO, NE, NH, NY, NC, ND, OH, OK, OR, PA, SC, SD, TX, UT, VT, VA, WV, WI, WY

Commenced Business: March 1977

Address: 1320 Waldo Rd #200, Midland, MI 48642

Phone: (989) 636-0047   **Domicile State:** MI   **NAIC Code:** 33499

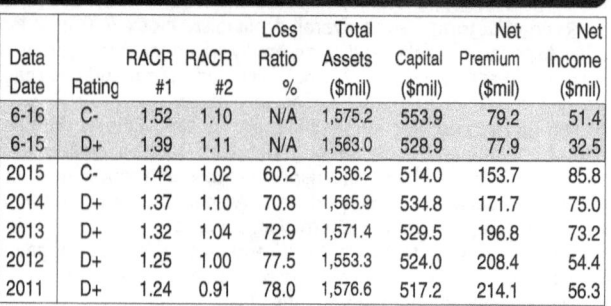

Data Date	Rating	RACR #1	RACR #2	Loss Ratio %	Total Assets ($mil)	Capital ($mil)	Net Premium ($mil)	Net Income ($mil)
6-16	C-	1.52	1.10	N/A	1,575.2	553.9	79.2	51.4
6-15	D+	1.39	1.11	N/A	1,563.0	528.9	77.9	32.5
2015	C-	1.42	1.02	60.2	1,536.2	514.0	153.7	85.8
2014	D+	1.37	1.10	70.8	1,565.9	534.8	171.7	75.0
2013	D+	1.32	1.04	72.9	1,571.4	529.5	196.8	73.2
2012	D+	1.25	1.00	77.5	1,553.3	524.0	208.4	54.4
2011	D+	1.24	0.91	78.0	1,576.6	517.2	214.1	56.3

EAGLESTONE REINS CO
B **Good**

Major Rating Factors: Good long-term capitalization index (6.6 on a scale of 0 to 10) based on good current risk adjusted capital (moderate loss scenario), despite some fluctuation in capital levels. Fair overall results on stability tests (4.4) including excessive premium growth and weak results on operational trends. The largest net exposure for one risk is high at 4.8% of capital. Strengths include potentially strong support from affiliation with American International Group.

Other Rating Factors: Fair profitability index (4.2) with operating losses during 2014 and the first six months of 2016. Return on equity has been low, averaging 3.3% over the past five years. Excellent liquidity (7.7) with ample operational cash flow and liquid investments. A history of deficient reserves (2.4) that places pressure on both capital and profits. Deficiencies in the two year reserve development occurred in three of the previous five years and ranged between 21% and 31%.

Principal Business: (This company is a reinsurer.)

Principal Investments: Investment grade bonds (93%), non investment grade bonds (4%), misc. investments (2%), and cash (1%).

Investments in Affiliates: None

Group Affiliation: American International Group

Licensed in: (No states)

Commenced Business: April 1996

Address: 2595 Interstate Dr Suite 103, Harrisburg, PA 17110

Phone: (212) 770-7000   **Domicile State:** PA   **NAIC Code:** 10651

Data Date	Rating	RACR #1	RACR #2	Loss Ratio %	Total Assets ($mil)	Capital ($mil)	Net Premium ($mil)	Net Income ($mil)
6-16	B	1.62	1.09	N/A	6,494.1	1,812.0	47.5	-42.7
6-15	U	2.42	1.54	N/A	5,399.9	1,826.5	22.7	98.7
2015	B	1.63	1.10	N/A	6,792.3	1,858.7	40.4	-3.4
2014	U	2.14	1.37	N/A	5,593.6	1,727.9	0.0	-209.4
2013	B	2.32	1.46	N/A	5,805.7	1,937.4	0.5	377.9
2012	B	1.41	0.91	223.5	6,199.7	1,358.8	539.9	49.8
2011	U	1.63	0.99	0.0	4,971.3	1,333.3	0.0	125.2

ECONOMY FIRE & CAS CO
B- **Good**

Major Rating Factors: Fair overall results on stability tests (4.7 on a scale of 0 to 10) including weak results on operational trends. Good overall profitability index (6.4). Fair expense controls. Return on equity has been low, averaging 4.4% over the past five years.

Other Rating Factors: Strong long-term capitalization index (10.0) based on excellent current risk adjusted capital (severe and moderate loss scenarios), despite some fluctuation in capital levels. Superior liquidity (10.0) with ample operational cash flow and liquid investments.

Principal Business: Auto liability (40%), auto physical damage (36%), homeowners multiple peril (22%), and earthquake (1%).

Principal Investments: Investment grade bonds (83%), misc. investments (16%), and real estate (1%).

Investments in Affiliates: 15%

Group Affiliation: MetLife Inc

Licensed in: All states except DC, DE, HI, ME, MA, NH, NJ, RI, SC, VT, VA, PR

Commenced Business: January 1935

Address: 500 Economy Court, Freeport, IL 61032

Phone: (401) 827-2400   **Domicile State:** IL   **NAIC Code:** 22926

Data Date	Rating	RACR #1	RACR #2	Loss Ratio %	Total Assets ($mil)	Capital ($mil)	Net Premium ($mil)	Net Income ($mil)
6-16	B-	6.75	6.15	N/A	486.0	383.8	0.0	7.3
6-15	B-	6.82	6.18	N/A	475.2	377.7	0.0	7.2
2015	B-	6.68	6.13	0.0	477.8	375.5	0.0	12.7
2014	B-	6.75	6.16	0.0	467.9	369.3	0.0	15.1
2013	B-	6.85	6.23	0.0	456.3	362.8	0.0	17.4
2012	B-	7.15	6.50	0.0	450.6	364.1	0.0	18.2
2011	B-	7.41	6.69	0.0	447.7	364.0	0.0	18.4

MetLife Inc Composite Group Rating: B- Largest Group Members	Assets ($mil)	Rating
METROPOLITAN LIFE INS CO	390843	B-
METLIFE INS CO USA	173762	B
GENERAL AMERICAN LIFE INS CO	12305	B
AMERICAN LIFE INS CO	11097	C
NEW ENGLAND LIFE INS CO	10173	B

ELECTRIC INS CO   C+   Fair

Major Rating Factors: Fair overall results on stability tests (3.4 on a scale of 0 to 10) including potential drain of affiliation with Wilmington Trust and weak results on operational trends. The largest net exposure for one risk is conservative at 1.3% of capital. Good overall profitability index (6.7). Good expense controls. Return on equity has been low, averaging 5.0% over the past five years.

Other Rating Factors: Good liquidity (6.7) with sufficient resources (cash flows and marketable investments) to handle a spike in claims. Strong long-term capitalization index (8.8) based on excellent current risk adjusted capital (severe and moderate loss scenarios), despite some fluctuation in capital levels. Ample reserve history (7.0) that can protect against increases in claims costs.

Principal Business: Workers compensation (27%), auto liability (20%), homeowners multiple peril (20%), products liability (17%), auto physical damage (13%), other liability (2%), and inland marine (1%).

Principal Investments: Investment grade bonds (84%), misc. investments (16%), and real estate (1%).

Investments in Affiliates: 2%

Group Affiliation: Wilmington Trust

Licensed in: All states, the District of Columbia and Puerto Rico

Commenced Business: September 1966

Address: 75 Sam Fonzo Dr., Beverly, MA 01915

Phone: (978) 921-2080   **Domicile State:** MA   **NAIC Code:** 21261

Data Date	Rating	RACR #1	RACR #2	Loss Ratio %	Total Assets ($mil)	Capital ($mil)	Net Premium ($mil)	Net Income ($mil)
6-16	C+	3.54	2.18	N/A	1,643.4	562.7	200.1	9.3
6-15	C+	3.49	2.17	N/A	1,600.5	537.4	205.9	6.5
2015	C+	3.62	2.24	81.6	1,507.8	545.5	346.5	23.6
2014	C+	3.68	2.30	82.4	1,467.2	537.6	302.0	25.4
2013	C+	3.16	1.92	79.8	1,448.7	522.6	353.3	33.6
2012	C+	2.64	1.63	85.5	1,442.4	481.7	367.0	25.6
2011	C+	2.46	1.46	88.2	1,444.6	460.2	377.1	22.6

Rating Indexes

EMC REINS CO   C+   Fair

Major Rating Factors: Fair overall results on stability tests (3.4 on a scale of 0 to 10) including weak results on operational trends. The largest net exposure for one risk is high at 4.4% of capital. Good liquidity (6.9) with sufficient resources (cash flows and marketable investments) to handle a spike in claims.

Other Rating Factors: Strong long-term capitalization index (7.8) based on excellent current risk adjusted capital (severe and moderate loss scenarios). Moreover, capital levels have been consistent in recent years. Ample reserve history (9.4) that helps to protect the company against sharp claims increases. Excellent profitability (7.0).

Principal Business: (This company is a reinsurer.)

Principal Investments: Investment grade bonds (79%) and misc. investments (21%).

Investments in Affiliates: None

Group Affiliation: Employers Mutual Group

Licensed in: CO, CT, FL, GA, IA, KS, MD, NY, NC, PA, SC, TX

Commenced Business: February 1981

Address: 717 Mulberry St, Des Moines, IA 50309-3872

Phone: (515) 280-2511   **Domicile State:** IA   **NAIC Code:** 40509

Data Date	Rating	RACR #1	RACR #2	Loss Ratio %	Total Assets ($mil)	Capital ($mil)	Net Premium ($mil)	Net Income ($mil)
6-16	C+	2.55	1.72	N/A	465.6	201.7	67.0	10.2
6-15	C+	2.29	1.53	N/A	440.6	184.6	63.9	10.2
2015	C+	2.50	1.70	64.1	443.9	191.2	124.5	20.4
2014	C+	2.24	1.50	73.9	409.2	177.0	118.9	12.4
2013	C+	2.02	1.38	59.0	378.9	160.4	129.0	22.3
2012	C+	2.00	1.40	68.4	327.7	132.7	107.2	16.4
2011	C+	1.90	1.34	96.6	306.4	116.8	96.5	-1.6

Employers Mutual Group Composite Group Rating: B- Largest Group Members	Assets ($mil)	Rating
EMPLOYERS MUTUAL CAS CO	2891	B-
EMCASCO INS CO	463	B-
EMC REINS CO	444	C+
ILLINOIS EMCASCO INS CO	345	C+
DAKOTA FIRE INS CO	221	C

EMPLOYERS ASSURANCE CO   C   Fair

Major Rating Factors: Fair overall results on stability tests (3.3 on a scale of 0 to 10) including potential drain of affiliation with Employers Group Inc and weak results on operational trends. Good overall profitability index (6.5). Fair expense controls. Return on equity has been low, averaging 2.7% over the past five years.

Other Rating Factors: Strong long-term capitalization index (8.6) based on excellent current risk adjusted capital (severe and moderate loss scenarios), despite some fluctuation in capital levels. Ample reserve history (8.3) that helps to protect the company against sharp claims increases. Excellent liquidity (7.0) with ample operational cash flow and liquid investments.

Principal Business: Workers compensation (100%).

Principal Investments: Investment grade bonds (102%) and cash (2%).

Investments in Affiliates: None

Group Affiliation: Employers Group Inc

Licensed in: All states except AK, DE, HI, ME, NH, ND, RI, SD, VT, WA, WY, PR

Commenced Business: November 1979

Address: 851 Trafalgar Ct Suite 400E, Maitland, FL 32751

Phone: (775) 327-2700   **Domicile State:** FL   **NAIC Code:** 25402

Data Date	Rating	RACR #1	RACR #2	Loss Ratio %	Total Assets ($mil)	Capital ($mil)	Net Premium ($mil)	Net Income ($mil)
6-16	C	2.74	1.82	N/A	489.8	171.1	41.9	4.0
6-15	C	3.09	2.19	N/A	501.6	204.7	39.5	2.6
2015	C	3.57	2.34	65.1	502.1	209.9	88.6	10.1
2014	C	3.47	2.49	67.4	617.8	201.6	68.8	5.5
2013	C	3.00	2.14	73.8	548.7	196.8	67.8	2.6
2012	C	3.26	2.34	57.4	474.3	152.9	57.0	1.6
2011	C	2.48	1.75	77.6	390.2	80.5	41.0	2.3

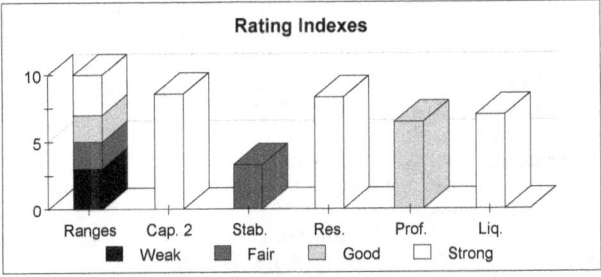

Rating Indexes

EMPLOYERS COMPENSATION INS CO

B **Good**

Major Rating Factors: Good liquidity (6.8 on a scale of 0 to 10) with sufficient resources (cash flows and marketable investments) to handle a spike in claims. Fair overall results on stability tests (4.6) including weak results on operational trends and negative cash flow from operations for 2015.

Other Rating Factors: Strong long-term capitalization index (7.4) based on excellent current risk adjusted capital (severe and moderate loss scenarios), despite some fluctuation in capital levels. Ample reserve history (8.3) that helps to protect the company against sharp claims increases. Excellent profitability (7.8) with operating gains in each of the last five years.

Principal Business: Workers compensation (100%).

Principal Investments: Investment grade bonds (100%).

Investments in Affiliates: None

Group Affiliation: Employers Group Inc

Licensed in: AL, AZ, AR, CA, CO, CT, DC, FL, GA, ID, IL, IN, IA, KS, KY, LA, MD, MA, MI, MN, MS, MO, MT, NE, NV, NJ, NM, NY, OK, OR, PA, SC, TN, TX, UT, VA, WI

Commenced Business: September 2002

Address: 500 North Brand Blvd, Glendale, CA 91203-3392

Phone: (775) 327-2700   **Domicile State:** CA   **NAIC Code:** 11512

Data Date	Rating	RACR #1	RACR #2	Loss Ratio %	Total Assets ($mil)	Capital ($mil)	Net Premium ($mil)	Net Income ($mil)
6-16	B	1.80	1.20	N/A	1,063.5	326.2	122.3	11.8
6-15	B	1.71	1.21	N/A	1,222.4	322.2	115.3	10.5
2015	B	1.93	1.27	65.1	1,094.1	335.1	265.0	19.6
2014	B	2.04	1.46	67.4	1,802.2	318.5	185.7	15.7
2013	B	1.69	1.20	73.8	1,712.3	299.0	183.2	8.3
2012	B	2.32	1.59	57.4	1,477.8	292.9	153.8	5.8
2011	B-	3.11	2.19	77.6	1,283.9	274.6	110.7	11.5

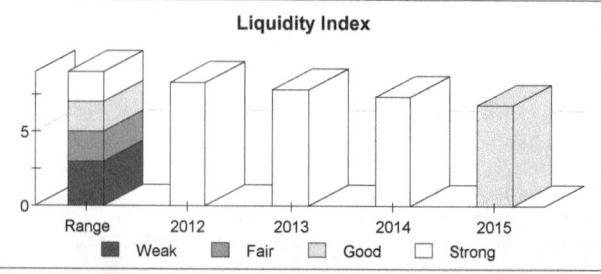

Liquidity Index

Range — 2012 — 2013 — 2014 — 2015
■ Weak ■ Fair □ Good □ Strong

EMPLOYERS INS CO OF NV

B- **Good**

Major Rating Factors: Fair overall results on stability tests (4.5 on a scale of 0 to 10) including weak results on operational trends. Good long-term capitalization index (5.1) based on excellent current risk adjusted capital (severe and moderate loss scenarios). Moreover, capital levels have been consistent in recent years.

Other Rating Factors: Good liquidity (6.2) with sufficient resources (cash flows and marketable investments) to handle a spike in claims. Ample reserve history (9.1) that helps to protect the company against sharp claims increases. Excellent profitability (8.1) with operating gains in each of the last five years.

Principal Business: (Not applicable due to unusual reinsurance transactions.)

Principal Investments: Misc. investments (62%) and investment grade bonds (38%).

Investments in Affiliates: 45%

Group Affiliation: Employers Group Inc

Licensed in: AZ, FL, ID, IL, MT, NV, OR, TX, UT

Commenced Business: January 2000

Address: 10375 Professional Circle, Reno, NV 89521-4802

Phone: (775) 327-2700   **Domicile State:** NV   **NAIC Code:** 10640

Data Date	Rating	RACR #1	RACR #2	Loss Ratio %	Total Assets ($mil)	Capital ($mil)	Net Premium ($mil)	Net Income ($mil)
6-16	B-	1.36	1.22	N/A	839.8	462.9	62.9	44.1
6-15	C	1.01	0.87	N/A	776.7	402.9	59.3	39.1
2015	C+	1.25	1.12	65.1	792.2	425.1	20.4	52.3
2014	C	0.82	0.66	67.4	2,342.4	374.3	364.4	34.5
2013	C	0.65	0.51	73.8	2,182.0	314.7	359.6	8.8
2012	C	0.76	0.62	57.4	1,968.8	295.5	301.9	6.3
2011	C-	0.79	0.67	77.6	1,759.8	251.8	217.3	30.6

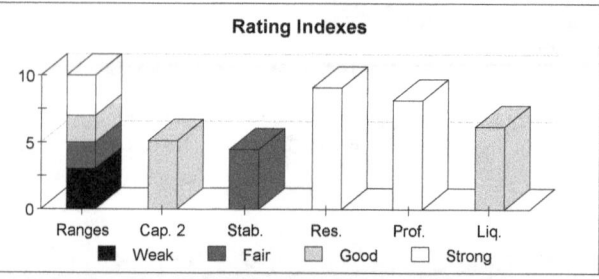

Rating Indexes

Ranges Cap. 2 Stab. Res. Prof. Liq.
■ Weak ■ Fair □ Good □ Strong

EMPLOYERS INS OF WAUSAU

B- **Good**

Major Rating Factors: Fair overall results on stability tests (3.6 on a scale of 0 to 10) including fair financial strength of affiliated Liberty Mutual Group and weak results on operational trends. The largest net exposure for one risk is high at 3.2% of capital. History of adequate reserve strength (5.7) as reserves have been consistently at an acceptable level.

Other Rating Factors: Good overall profitability index (6.2) despite operating losses during 2011 and 2012. Return on equity has been low, averaging 2.9% over the past five years. Good liquidity (6.3) with sufficient resources (cash flows and marketable investments) to handle a spike in claims. Strong long-term capitalization index (8.0) based on excellent current risk adjusted capital (severe and moderate loss scenarios). Moreover, capital levels have been consistent in recent years.

Principal Business: Workers compensation (74%), auto liability (12%), other liability (7%), commercial multiple peril (3%), auto physical damage (2%), and products liability (1%).

Principal Investments: Investment grade bonds (79%), misc. investments (17%), and non investment grade bonds (5%).

Investments in Affiliates: 3%

Group Affiliation: Liberty Mutual Group

Licensed in: All states, the District of Columbia and Puerto Rico

Commenced Business: September 1911

Address: 2000 Westwood Dr, Wausau, WI 54401

Phone: (617) 357-9500   **Domicile State:** WI   **NAIC Code:** 21458

Data Date	Rating	RACR #1	RACR #2	Loss Ratio %	Total Assets ($mil)	Capital ($mil)	Net Premium ($mil)	Net Income ($mil)
6-16	B-	2.41	1.66	N/A	5,526.4	1,513.3	1,014.4	-0.4
6-15	B-	2.24	1.53	N/A	5,463.7	1,444.5	983.1	80.7
2015	B-	2.44	1.69	68.4	5,477.2	1,514.4	2,050.6	155.1
2014	B-	2.19	1.51	70.0	5,277.7	1,393.2	2,030.1	119.7
2013	B-	1.83	1.26	73.5	5,599.8	1,283.7	2,427.2	48.9
2012	B-	2.77	1.89	90.3	3,940.7	1,229.7	1,044.5	-47.7
2011	B-	2.77	1.85	90.1	3,795.7	1,228.8	915.9	-32.8

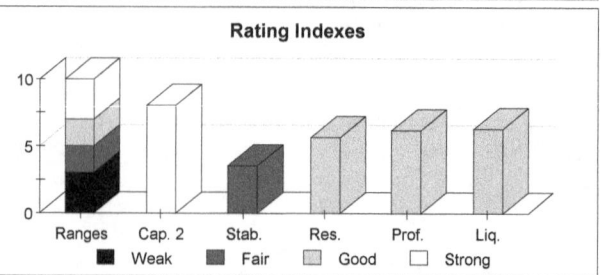

Rating Indexes

Ranges Cap. 2 Stab. Res. Prof. Liq.
■ Weak ■ Fair □ Good □ Strong

EMPLOYERS MUTUAL CAS CO   B-   Good

Major Rating Factors: Fair overall results on stability tests (4.8 on a scale of 0 to 10) including potential drain of affiliation with Employers Mutual Group and weak results on operational trends. Good overall profitability index (5.6) despite operating losses during 2011.

Other Rating Factors: Good liquidity (6.6) with sufficient resources (cash flows and marketable investments) to handle a spike in claims. Strong long-term capitalization index (7.9) based on excellent current risk adjusted capital (severe and moderate loss scenarios). Moreover, capital levels have been consistent in recent years. Ample reserve history (7.8) that can protect against increases in claims costs.

Principal Business: Other liability (22%), auto liability (21%), workers compensation (15%), auto physical damage (11%), allied lines (9%), inland marine (6%), and other lines (17%).

Principal Investments: Misc. investments (52%), investment grade bonds (43%), and real estate (5%).

Investments in Affiliates: 21%

Group Affiliation: Employers Mutual Group

Licensed in: All states except PR

Commenced Business: July 1913

Address: 717 Mulberry St, Des Moines, IA 50309-3872

Phone: (515) 280-2511   **Domicile State:** IA   **NAIC Code:** 21415

Data Date	Rating	RACR #1	RACR #2	Loss Ratio %	Total Assets ($mil)	Capital ($mil)	Net Premium ($mil)	Net Income ($mil)
6-16	B-	2.07	1.62	N/A	3,116.3	1,331.3	525.4	22.3
6-15	B-	2.07	1.64	N/A	2,831.9	1,246.2	457.1	30.4
2015	B-	2.08	1.66	65.7	2,890.6	1,276.3	946.0	61.4
2014	B-	2.06	1.65	70.0	2,721.4	1,215.0	902.2	45.4
2013	B-	2.06	1.65	66.7	2,538.0	1,121.9	845.0	56.1
2012	B-	1.99	1.57	66.4	2,308.9	963.0	772.9	36.1
2011	B-	2.02	1.59	80.3	2,200.5	892.4	695.8	-12.4

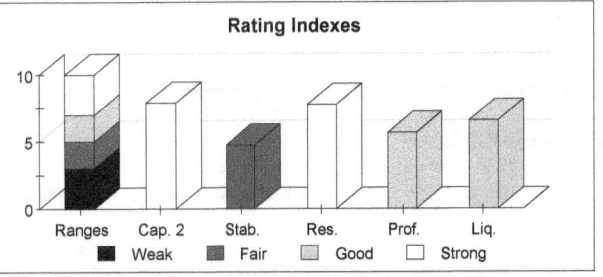

Rating Indexes

EMPLOYERS PREFERRED INS CO   C   Fair

Major Rating Factors: Fair overall results on stability tests (3.3 on a scale of 0 to 10) including potential drain of affiliation with Employers Group Inc and weak results on operational trends. Good long-term capitalization index (5.7) based on good current risk adjusted capital (moderate loss scenario). Moreover, capital levels have been consistent over the last several years.

Other Rating Factors: Good liquidity (6.5) with sufficient resources (cash flows and marketable investments) to handle a spike in claims. Ample reserve history (8.0) that helps to protect the company against sharp claims increases. Excellent profitability (8.3) despite modest operating losses during 2012 and 2013.

Principal Business: Workers compensation (100%).

Principal Investments: Investment grade bonds (68%), misc. investments (31%), and cash (1%).

Investments in Affiliates: 25%

Group Affiliation: Employers Group Inc

Licensed in: AL, AZ, AR, CA, CO, CT, DC, FL, GA, ID, IL, IN, IA, KS, KY, LA, MD, MA, MI, MN, MS, MO, MT, NE, NV, NJ, NM, NY, NC, OK, OR, PA, SC, SD, TN, TX, UT, VA, WI

Commenced Business: January 1982

Address: 851 Trafalgar Ct Suite 400e, Maitland, FL 32751

Phone: (775) 327-2700   **Domicile State:** FL   **NAIC Code:** 10346

Data Date	Rating	RACR #1	RACR #2	Loss Ratio %	Total Assets ($mil)	Capital ($mil)	Net Premium ($mil)	Net Income ($mil)
6-16	C	1.08	0.85	N/A	1,089.3	292.6	122.3	39.2
6-15	C	1.15	0.94	N/A	1,041.7	261.6	115.3	-12.1
2015	C	1.06	0.83	65.1	1,049.9	280.6	315.3	5.9
2014	C	1.37	1.27	67.4	752.3	261.1	68.8	3.1
2013	C	1.30	1.18	73.8	673.1	254.0	67.8	-0.3
2012	C	1.45	1.33	57.4	580.6	206.2	57.0	-0.2
2011	C	1.92	1.70	77.6	432.6	136.1	41.0	8.5

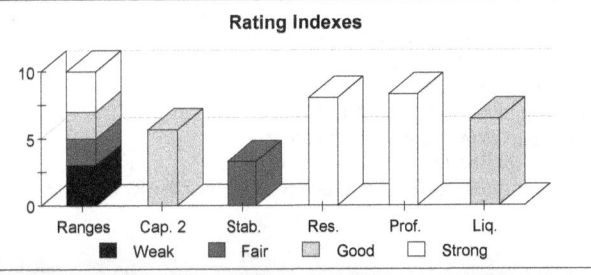

Rating Indexes

ENDURANCE AMERICAN INS CO   C+   Fair

Major Rating Factors: Good long-term capitalization index (5.0 on a scale of 0 to 10) based on good current risk adjusted capital (severe loss scenario). Over the last several years, capital levels have remained relatively consistent. Fair profitability index (3.9) with operating losses during 2011, 2012, 2013 and 2014. Average return on equity over the last five years has been poor at -10.1%.

Other Rating Factors: Fair overall results on stability tests (3.9) including weak results on operational trends. The largest net exposure for one risk is acceptable at 2.1% of capital. History of adequate reserve strength (6.5) as reserves have been consistently at an acceptable level. Vulnerable liquidity (2.5) as a spike in claims may stretch capacity.

Principal Business: Other liability (79%), ocean marine (8%), inland marine (6%), surety (4%), and commercial multiple peril (3%).

Principal Investments: Investment grade bonds (68%), misc. investments (19%), and cash (13%).

Investments in Affiliates: 21%

Group Affiliation: Endurance Specialty Holdings

Licensed in: All states except CA, MN, PR

Commenced Business: April 1996

Address: 1209 Orange St, Wilmington, DE 19801

Phone: (914) 468-8000   **Domicile State:** DE   **NAIC Code:** 10641

Data Date	Rating	RACR #1	RACR #2	Loss Ratio %	Total Assets ($mil)	Capital ($mil)	Net Premium ($mil)	Net Income ($mil)
6-16	C+	1.30	0.94	N/A	1,660.6	267.9	105.4	3.3
6-15	C	1.27	0.91	N/A	1,654.5	239.4	106.3	-0.8
2015	C+	1.29	0.94	78.4	1,227.4	262.7	233.1	16.5
2014	C	1.31	0.94	87.3	1,243.9	241.2	312.0	-4.9
2013	D+	1.27	0.87	94.4	1,313.8	247.5	362.2	-42.9
2012	D	0.73	0.56	103.1	1,305.2	231.0	358.0	-71.4
2011	C+	1.12	0.84	89.3	1,264.9	235.7	239.2	-30.7

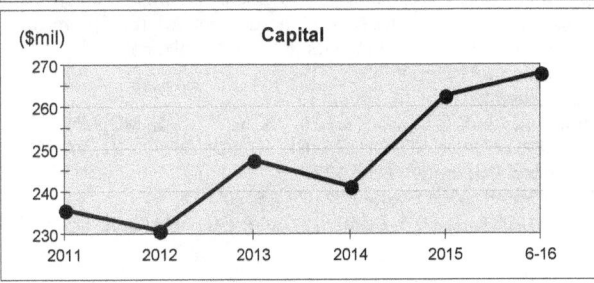

Capital

ENDURANCE ASR CORP   B   Good

Major Rating Factors: Good overall profitability index (5.1 on a scale of 0 to 10) despite operating losses during 2011 and 2012. Return on equity has been low, averaging 1.3% over the past five years. Fair overall results on stability tests (4.6) including weak results on operational trends. The largest net exposure for one risk is conservative at 1.4% of capital.

Other Rating Factors: Strong long-term capitalization index (8.2) based on excellent current risk adjusted capital (severe and moderate loss scenarios), despite some fluctuation in capital levels. Ample reserve history (8.3) that helps to protect the company against sharp claims increases. Excellent liquidity (7.2) with ample operational cash flow and liquid investments.

Principal Business: Other liability (44%), surety (34%), ocean marine (16%), and inland marine (5%).

Principal Investments: Investment grade bonds (65%), misc. investments (28%), and cash (7%).

Investments in Affiliates: 26%

Group Affiliation: Endurance Specialty Holdings

Licensed in: All states, the District of Columbia and Puerto Rico

Commenced Business: December 2002

Address: 333 Westchester Ave, White Plains, NY 10604

Phone: (914) 468-8000   **Domicile State:** DE   **NAIC Code:** 11551

Data Date	Rating	RACR #1	RACR #2	Loss Ratio %	Total Assets ($mil)	Capital ($mil)	Net Premium ($mil)	Net Income ($mil)
6-16	B	2.23	1.91	N/A	1,801.5	753.5	137.3	1.8
6-15	B	2.22	1.91	N/A	1,653.4	688.8	115.7	10.5
2015	B	2.24	1.94	47.7	1,642.9	739.3	262.4	35.7
2014	B	2.18	1.89	49.5	1,562.1	674.1	250.9	33.5
2013	B	1.92	1.61	51.2	1,489.7	629.0	263.2	28.4
2012	B-	1.84	1.50	81.6	1,466.6	587.4	239.8	-19.9
2011	B-	1.74	1.23	91.6	1,779.2	598.4	335.1	-24.3

Income Trends

ERIE INS CO   B-   Good

Major Rating Factors: Fair overall results on stability tests (4.7 on a scale of 0 to 10) including potential drain of affiliation with Erie Ins Group and weak results on operational trends. Good liquidity (6.6) with sufficient resources (cash flows and marketable investments) to handle a spike in claims.

Other Rating Factors: Strong long-term capitalization index (10.0) based on excellent current risk adjusted capital (severe and moderate loss scenarios). Moreover, capital levels have been consistent in recent years. Ample reserve history (8.1) that helps to protect the company against sharp claims increases. Excellent profitability (7.1) with operating gains in each of the last five years.

Principal Business: Homeowners multiple peril (49%), auto liability (23%), auto physical damage (15%), commercial multiple peril (8%), workers compensation (3%), other liability (1%), and surety (1%).

Principal Investments: Investment grade bonds (90%), misc. investments (8%), and non investment grade bonds (2%).

Investments in Affiliates: 5%

Group Affiliation: Erie Ins Group

Licensed in: DC, IL, IN, KY, MD, MN, NY, NC, OH, PA, TN, VA, WV, WI

Commenced Business: January 1973

Address: 100 Erie Ins Place, Erie, PA 16530

Phone: (814) 870-2000   **Domicile State:** PA   **NAIC Code:** 26263

Data Date	Rating	RACR #1	RACR #2	Loss Ratio %	Total Assets ($mil)	Capital ($mil)	Net Premium ($mil)	Net Income ($mil)
6-16	B-	5.15	3.58	N/A	944.4	347.4	150.2	11.8
6-15	B-	5.07	3.54	N/A	879.3	321.3	140.6	7.9
2015	B-	5.15	3.65	69.4	899.7	334.6	294.6	19.2
2014	B-	5.13	3.66	73.0	839.3	311.9	274.4	12.0
2013	B-	5.04	3.48	69.4	771.8	294.4	252.3	17.1
2012	B-	5.16	3.57	76.0	713.3	276.4	230.1	13.8
2011	B-	5.13	3.56	80.3	667.0	260.0	212.7	9.4

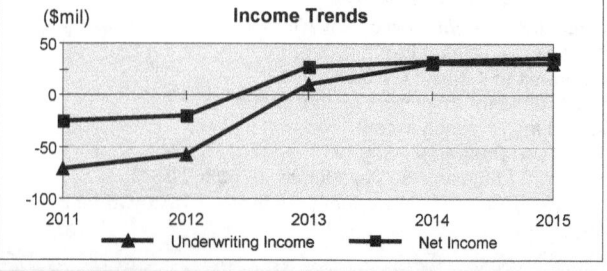

Erie Ins Group Composite Group Rating: B Largest Group Members	Assets ($mil)	Rating
ERIE INS EXCHANGE	13931	B
ERIE FAMILY LIFE INS CO	2169	A-
ERIE INS CO	900	B-
ERIE INS CO OF NEW YORK	101	B
ERIE INS PC CO	96	B-

ERIE INS EXCHANGE   B   Good

Major Rating Factors: Good overall results on stability tests (5.1 on a scale of 0 to 10) despite potential drain of affiliation with Erie Ins Group and weak results on operational trends. Good liquidity (6.6) with sufficient resources (cash flows and marketable investments) to handle a spike in claims.

Other Rating Factors: Strong long-term capitalization index (9.5) based on excellent current risk adjusted capital (severe and moderate loss scenarios). Moreover, capital levels have been consistent in recent years. Ample reserve history (8.0) that helps to protect the company against sharp claims increases. Excellent profitability (7.1) with operating gains in each of the last five years.

Principal Business: Auto liability (31%), auto physical damage (23%), homeowners multiple peril (21%), commercial multiple peril (16%), workers compensation (4%), other liability (3%), and inland marine (1%).

Principal Investments: Investment grade bonds (53%), misc. investments (38%), non investment grade bonds (8%), and real estate (1%).

Investments in Affiliates: 5%

Group Affiliation: Erie Ins Group

Licensed in: AL, CT, DC, DE, GA, IL, IN, IA, KY, ME, MD, MN, MO, MT, NE, NV, NH, NJ, NM, NY, NC, ND, OH, PA, RI, SC, SD, TN, TX, VT, VA, WV, WI, WY

Commenced Business: April 1925

Address: 100 Erie Ins Place, Erie, PA 16530

Phone: (814) 870-2000   **Domicile State:** PA   **NAIC Code:** 26271

Data Date	Rating	RACR #1	RACR #2	Loss Ratio %	Total Assets ($mil)	Capital ($mil)	Net Premium ($mil)	Net Income ($mil)
6-16	B	4.08	2.70	N/A	14,449.8	7,412.0	2,838.2	260.6
6-15	B	3.84	2.55	N/A	13,749.9	7,031.5	2,658.1	244.8
2015	B	3.97	2.65	69.4	13,930.7	7,141.5	5,567.1	465.6
2014	B	3.74	2.51	73.0	13,344.7	6,816.6	5,185.5	353.0
2013	B	3.68	2.51	69.4	12,591.7	6,467.0	4,767.7	478.8
2012	B	3.70	2.57	76.0	11,229.2	5,633.4	4,349.3	311.0
2011	B	3.62	2.50	80.3	10,382.3	5,166.0	4,020.7	182.4

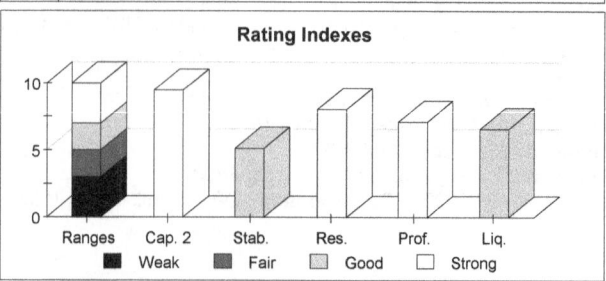

Rating Indexes

Ranges   Cap. 2   Stab.   Res.   Prof.   Liq.
■ Weak   ▨ Fair   ▢ Good   ▢ Strong

ESSENT GUARANTY INC *   A-   Excellent

Major Rating Factors: Strong long-term capitalization index (10.0 on a scale of 0 to 10) based on excellent current risk adjusted capital (severe and moderate loss scenarios). Furthermore, this high level of risk adjusted capital has been consistently maintained in previous years. Excellent liquidity (7.8) with ample operational cash flow and liquid investments.

Other Rating Factors: Good overall profitability index (5.1) despite operating losses during 2011 and 2012. Return on equity has been good over the last five years, averaging 10.4%. Good overall results on stability tests (5.7) despite weak results on operational trends. Fair reserve development (4.6) as reserves have generally been sufficient to cover claims.

Principal Business: Mortgage guaranty (100%).

Principal Investments: Investment grade bonds (89%) and misc. investments (11%).

Investments in Affiliates: None

Group Affiliation: Essent Group Ltd

Licensed in: All states except PR

Commenced Business: July 2009

Address: 201 King of Prussia Rd Ste 501, Radnor, PA 19087

Phone: (610) 230-0555   **Domicile State:** PA   **NAIC Code:** 13634

Data Date	Rating	RACR #1	RACR #2	Loss Ratio %	Total Assets ($mil)	Capital ($mil)	Net Premium ($mil)	Net Income ($mil)
6-16	A-	7.63	4.61	N/A	1,194.6	545.7	155.7	100.0
6-15	A-	7.74	4.90	N/A	953.0	503.0	130.2	84.4
2015	A-	6.05	3.77	3.6	1,072.6	522.2	299.0	172.7
2014	A-	6.33	4.08	2.8	817.3	465.2	239.6	118.2
2013	A-	6.30	4.22	1.9	546.8	346.4	169.8	49.8
2012	A-	3.11	2.58	3.4	246.2	163.8	66.8	-16.3
2011	A-	3.35	3.16	0.8	175.9	141.9	16.6	-34.1

Risk-Adjusted Capital Ratio #2
(Severe Loss Scenario)

Range · 2011 · 2012 · 2013 · 2014 · 2015 · 6-16
■ Weak ■ Fair ▨ Good □ Strong

EVANSTON INS CO   C   Fair

Major Rating Factors: Fair overall results on stability tests (3.8 on a scale of 0 to 10) including excessive premium growth and weak results on operational trends. The largest net exposure for one risk is conservative at 1.1% of capital. History of adequate reserve strength (6.0) as reserves have been consistently at an acceptable level.

Other Rating Factors: Strong long-term capitalization index (7.1) based on excellent current risk adjusted capital (severe and moderate loss scenarios), despite some fluctuation in capital levels. Excellent profitability (8.4) with operating gains in each of the last five years. Return on equity has been excellent over the last five years averaging 16.1%. Excellent liquidity (7.3) with ample operational cash flow and liquid investments.

Principal Business: Other liability (56%), medical malpractice (14%), allied lines (10%), products liability (9%), fire (5%), earthquake (3%), and other lines (3%).

Principal Investments: Misc. investments (53%) and investment grade bonds (47%).

Investments in Affiliates: None

Group Affiliation: Markel Corp

Licensed in: All states, the District of Columbia and Puerto Rico

Commenced Business: December 1977

Address: Ten Parkway North, Deerfield, IL 60015

Phone: (847) 572-6000   **Domicile State:** IL   **NAIC Code:** 35378

Data Date	Rating	RACR #1	RACR #2	Loss Ratio %	Total Assets ($mil)	Capital ($mil)	Net Premium ($mil)	Net Income ($mil)
6-16	C	1.72	1.16	N/A	4,264.1	1,207.5	653.7	85.4
6-15	C	1.55	1.03	N/A	2,505.5	690.2	358.3	60.8
2015	C	1.52	1.03	46.2	2,869.2	719.5	838.4	140.8
2014	C	1.45	0.97	52.7	2,792.9	635.3	758.8	86.7
2013	C	1.34	0.90	48.7	2,152.3	574.2	642.2	82.0
2012	C	1.42	0.99	53.5	2,010.2	568.4	451.1	84.1
2011	C	1.20	0.93	45.2	2,073.6	611.3	477.4	117.9

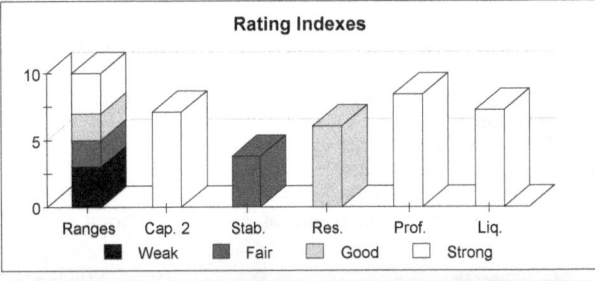

Rating Indexes

Ranges · Cap. 2 · Stab. · Res. · Prof. · Liq.
■ Weak ■ Fair ▨ Good □ Strong

EVEREST REINS CO   B-   Good

Major Rating Factors: Fair overall results on stability tests (4.7 on a scale of 0 to 10) including potential drain of affiliation with Everest Reinsurance Group and weak results on operational trends. History of adequate reserve strength (5.3) as reserves have been consistently at an acceptable level.

Other Rating Factors: Good overall profitability index (5.6) despite operating losses during 2011. Return on equity has been fair, averaging 9.8% over the past five years. Good liquidity (6.7) with sufficient resources (cash flows and marketable investments) to handle a spike in claims. Strong long-term capitalization index (8.0) based on excellent current risk adjusted capital (severe and moderate loss scenarios). Moreover, capital levels have been consistent in recent years.

Principal Business: Other liability (95%), fidelity (4%), and surety (1%).

Principal Investments: Investment grade bonds (60%), misc. investments (36%), cash (2%), and non investment grade bonds (2%).

Investments in Affiliates: 3%

Group Affiliation: Everest Reinsurance Group

Licensed in: All states, the District of Columbia and Puerto Rico

Commenced Business: June 1973

Address: 477 Martinsville Road, Liberty Corner, NJ 07938-0830

Phone: (908) 604-3000   **Domicile State:** DE   **NAIC Code:** 26921

Data Date	Rating	RACR #1	RACR #2	Loss Ratio %	Total Assets ($mil)	Capital ($mil)	Net Premium ($mil)	Net Income ($mil)
6-16	B-	2.78	1.82	N/A	9,863.2	3,442.3	981.0	252.0
6-15	C+	2.40	1.55	N/A	9,688.7	3,096.4	1,043.8	211.8
2015	B-	2.61	1.71	58.8	9,979.6	3,210.9	2,079.5	498.5
2014	C+	2.27	1.47	61.7	9,616.2	2,893.0	2,121.8	357.3
2013	C+	1.13	0.93	59.5	9,288.4	2,814.3	2,024.4	540.0
2012	C+	1.11	0.92	64.9	9,046.7	2,613.0	1,581.0	359.8
2011	C	0.98	0.80	106.4	8,610.6	2,322.1	1,653.4	-326.4

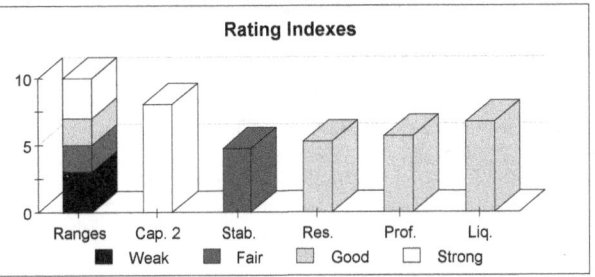

Rating Indexes

Ranges · Cap. 2 · Stab. · Res. · Prof. · Liq.
■ Weak ■ Fair ▨ Good □ Strong

EXECUTIVE RISK INDEMNITY INC   B   Good

Major Rating Factors: Good liquidity (6.8 on a scale of 0 to 10) with sufficient resources (cash flows and marketable investments) to handle a spike in claims. Fair overall results on stability tests (4.3) including weak results on operational trends. The largest net exposure for one risk is acceptable at 2.6% of capital.

Other Rating Factors: Strong long-term capitalization index (9.0) based on excellent current risk adjusted capital (severe and moderate loss scenarios), despite some fluctuation in capital levels. Ample reserve history (8.5) that helps to protect the company against sharp claims increases. Excellent profitability (8.5) with operating gains in each of the last five years. Return on equity has been good over the last five years, averaging 12.7%.

Principal Business: Other liability (84%), commercial multiple peril (7%), homeowners multiple peril (6%), fidelity (1%), inland marine (1%), and burglary & theft (1%).

Principal Investments: Investment grade bonds (86%), misc. investments (12%), non investment grade bonds (1%), and real estate (1%).

Investments in Affiliates: 6%

Group Affiliation: Chubb Limited

Licensed in: All states except PR

Commenced Business: January 1978

Address: 1209 Orange St, Wilmington, DE 19801-1120

Phone: (908) 903-2000   **Domicile State:** DE   **NAIC Code:** 35181

Data Date	Rating	RACR #1	RACR #2	Loss Ratio %	Total Assets ($mil)	Capital ($mil)	Net Premium ($mil)	Net Income ($mil)
6-16	B	3.61	2.47	N/A	3,093.7	1,261.8	311.2	116.3
6-15	B	3.36	2.29	N/A	3,062.7	1,269.1	383.3	66.7
2015	B	3.41	2.32	56.5	3,068.2	1,267.1	782.7	168.4
2014	B	3.42	2.33	56.7	3,024.8	1,258.0	751.6	164.2
2013	B+	3.43	2.34	52.7	2,977.3	1,218.6	721.2	174.1
2012	B+	3.17	2.12	67.3	2,899.9	1,100.6	694.2	115.4
2011	B+	3.19	2.15	68.4	2,832.4	1,076.9	682.0	105.2

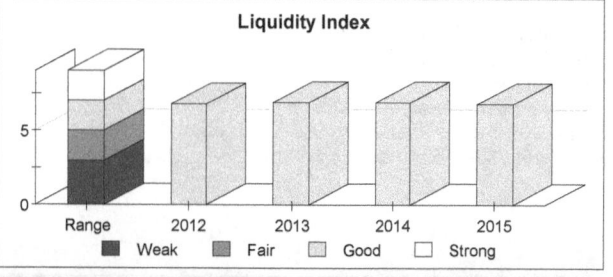

Liquidity Index

Range · 2012 · 2013 · 2014 · 2015
■ Weak ■ Fair ☐ Good ☐ Strong

FACTORY MUTUAL INS CO   B-   Good

Major Rating Factors: Fair overall results on stability tests (3.7 on a scale of 0 to 10) including potential drain of affiliation with Factory Mutual Ins and weak results on operational trends. The largest net exposure for one risk is acceptable at 2.9% of capital. History of adequate reserve strength (6.2) as reserves have been consistently at an acceptable level.

Other Rating Factors: Good liquidity (6.9) with sufficient resources (cash flows and marketable investments) to handle a spike in claims. Strong long-term capitalization index (8.2) based on excellent current risk adjusted capital (severe and moderate loss scenarios). Moreover, capital levels have been consistent in recent years. Excellent profitability (8.0) despite modest operating losses during 2011.

Principal Business: Inland marine (37%), allied lines (30%), boiler & machinery (18%), and fire (15%).

Principal Investments: Misc. investments (70%), investment grade bonds (27%), non investment grade bonds (2%), and cash (1%).

Investments in Affiliates: 18%

Group Affiliation: Factory Mutual Ins

Licensed in: All states, the District of Columbia and Puerto Rico

Commenced Business: December 1835

Address: 1301 Atwood Avenue, Johnston, RI 02919-4908

Phone: (401) 275-3000   **Domicile State:** RI   **NAIC Code:** 21482

Data Date	Rating	RACR #1	RACR #2	Loss Ratio %	Total Assets ($mil)	Capital ($mil)	Net Premium ($mil)	Net Income ($mil)
6-16	B-	2.60	1.99	N/A	16,582.9	10,849.0	1,378.2	198.3
6-15	C	2.58	1.97	N/A	15,877.1	10,505.8	1,336.7	304.7
2015	C+	2.57	1.98	58.0	15,682.9	10,546.7	2,782.1	550.1
2014	C	2.50	1.91	50.2	15,070.1	10,141.8	2,838.5	670.8
2013	C	2.48	1.90	50.6	13,795.7	9,153.5	2,824.5	662.5
2012	C	2.47	1.89	59.8	12,239.9	7,525.1	2,855.3	612.1
2011	C	2.40	1.82	95.3	10,978.4	6,431.6	2,594.5	-5.6

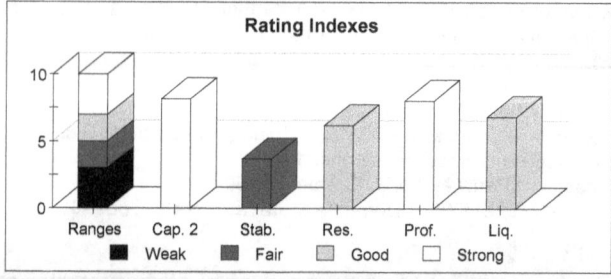

Rating Indexes

Ranges · Cap. 2 · Stab. · Res. · Prof. · Liq.
■ Weak ■ Fair ☐ Good ☐ Strong

FAIR AMERICAN INS & REINS CO   B   Good

Major Rating Factors: History of adequate reserve strength (5.2 on a scale of 0 to 10) as reserves have been consistently at an acceptable level. Good overall profitability index (5.2). Weak expense controls. Return on equity has been fair, averaging 6.0% over the past five years.

Other Rating Factors: Fair overall results on stability tests (4.6) including weak results on operational trends. Affiliation with Alleghany Corp Group is a strength. Strong long-term capitalization index (10.0) based on excellent current risk adjusted capital (severe and moderate loss scenarios), despite some fluctuation in capital levels. Superior liquidity (10.0) with ample operational cash flow and liquid investments.

Principal Business: Medical malpractice (99%) and allied lines (1%).

Principal Investments: Investment grade bonds (99%) and misc. investments (1%).

Investments in Affiliates: None

Group Affiliation: Alleghany Corp Group

Licensed in: All states except PR

Commenced Business: September 1985

Address: 80 Pine St, 7th Floor, New York, NY 10005

Phone: (212) 365-2200   **Domicile State:** NY   **NAIC Code:** 35157

Data Date	Rating	RACR #1	RACR #2	Loss Ratio %	Total Assets ($mil)	Capital ($mil)	Net Premium ($mil)	Net Income ($mil)
6-16	B	76.35	46.92	N/A	255.8	242.4	1.9	3.0
6-15	B	5.42	5.17	N/A	262.6	239.0	1.8	2.4
2015	B	81.08	49.01	52.8	256.9	241.8	3.5	6.0
2014	B	5.55	5.32	64.2	256.9	243.1	3.7	4.6
2013	B	5.35	5.15	78.6	254.8	230.6	3.6	0.3
2012	B	11.85	8.65	65.2	291.8	250.9	66.8	64.3
2011	B	2.08	1.34	85.7	750.1	233.1	173.2	3.6

Reserve Deficiency (as % of capital)

2011 · 2012 · 2013 · 2014 · 2015
■ 1 Yr Dev ☐ 2 Yr Dev

* Adequate & redundant reserves show as negatives

FARM BUREAU GENERAL INS CO OF MI   B   Good

Major Rating Factors: History of adequate reserve strength (6.5 on a scale of 0 to 10) as reserves have been consistently at an acceptable level. Good overall profitability index (6.7). Good expense controls. Return on equity has been low, averaging 4.5% over the past five years.

Other Rating Factors: Good liquidity (5.8) with sufficient resources (cash flows and marketable investments) to handle a spike in claims. Fair overall results on stability tests (4.9) including weak results on operational trends. Strong long-term capitalization index (9.4) based on excellent current risk adjusted capital (severe and moderate loss scenarios). Moreover, capital levels have been consistent in recent years.

Principal Business: Auto liability (34%), homeowners multiple peril (27%), auto physical damage (25%), commercial multiple peril (7%), workers compensation (3%), fire (1%), and other lines (4%).

Principal Investments: Investment grade bonds (84%), misc. investments (17%), and non investment grade bonds (1%).

Investments in Affiliates: None

Group Affiliation: Michigan Farm Bureau

Licensed in: MI

Commenced Business: July 1962

Address: 7373 West Saginaw Highway, Lansing, MI 48917

Phone: (517) 323-7000 **Domicile State:** MI **NAIC Code:** 21547

Data Date	Rating	RACR #1	RACR #2	Loss Ratio %	Total Assets ($mil)	Capital ($mil)	Net Premium ($mil)	Net Income ($mil)
6-16	B	4.56	3.15	N/A	661.8	286.9	161.3	12.5
6-15	B	4.42	3.04	N/A	641.8	260.6	147.0	5.9
2015	B	4.41	3.06	72.1	651.5	273.2	312.7	20.9
2014	B	3.26	2.31	79.7	528.8	178.5	287.3	7.3
2013	B	3.12	2.20	74.8	503.8	170.3	286.4	5.3
2012	B	3.86	2.64	77.9	413.2	147.7	182.6	7.8
2011	B	3.92	2.74	85.8	385.0	134.3	169.0	0.5

Reserve Deficiency (as % of capital)

* Adequate & redundant reserves show as negatives   ■ 1 Yr Dev   □ 2 Yr Dev

FARM BUREAU MUTUAL INS CO OF AR   B   Good

Major Rating Factors: Good overall profitability index (6.5 on a scale of 0 to 10) despite operating losses during 2011. Return on equity has been good over the last five years, averaging 10.6%. Good liquidity (6.1) with sufficient resources (cash flows and marketable investments) to handle a spike in claims.

Other Rating Factors: Fair overall results on stability tests (4.2) including weak results on operational trends. Strong long-term capitalization index (9.9) based on excellent current risk adjusted capital (severe and moderate loss scenarios). Moreover, capital levels have been consistent in recent years. Ample reserve history (8.2) that helps to protect the company against sharp claims increases.

Principal Business: Homeowners multiple peril (57%), fire (16%), inland marine (15%), allied lines (8%), other liability (2%), and commercial multiple peril (1%).

Principal Investments: Investment grade bonds (91%), misc. investments (13%), and real estate (1%).

Investments in Affiliates: 1%

Group Affiliation: None

Licensed in: AR

Commenced Business: March 1950

Address: 10720 Kanis Rd, Little Rock, AR 72211

Phone: (501) 224-4400 **Domicile State:** AR **NAIC Code:** 13757

Data Date	Rating	RACR #1	RACR #2	Loss Ratio %	Total Assets ($mil)	Capital ($mil)	Net Premium ($mil)	Net Income ($mil)
6-16	B	5.18	3.53	N/A	399.9	229.8	99.6	4.3
6-15	C+	4.75	3.24	N/A	375.8	206.3	101.4	13.4
2015	B	5.06	3.47	60.6	387.2	224.9	201.9	32.0
2014	C+	4.58	3.14	71.0	355.5	192.5	195.2	18.9
2013	C+	4.04	2.77	55.3	336.4	172.8	194.5	37.0
2012	C	2.75	1.86	70.2	294.1	126.5	186.8	23.3
2011	C	2.27	1.54	88.7	271.8	102.8	185.6	-7.8

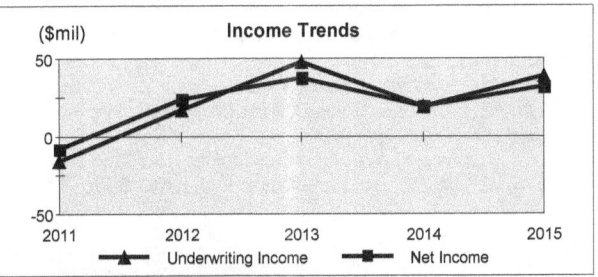

($mil)   Income Trends

▲ Underwriting Income   ■ Net Income

FARM BUREAU MUTUAL INS CO OF ID   B   Good

Major Rating Factors: History of adequate reserve strength (5.9 on a scale of 0 to 10) as reserves have been consistently at an acceptable level. Good liquidity (6.3) with sufficient resources (cash flows and marketable investments) to handle a spike in claims.

Other Rating Factors: Fair overall results on stability tests (4.1) including potential drain of affiliation with Farm Bureau Group of Idaho and weak results on operational trends. Fair profitability index (4.2) with operating losses during 2012 and 2015. Strong long-term capitalization index (9.1) based on excellent current risk adjusted capital (severe and moderate loss scenarios), despite some fluctuation in capital levels.

Principal Business: Auto liability (31%), auto physical damage (24%), homeowners multiple peril (19%), farmowners multiple peril (18%), inland marine (3%), allied lines (3%), and other liability (2%).

Principal Investments: Investment grade bonds (64%), misc. investments (31%), real estate (3%), and cash (2%).

Investments in Affiliates: 18%

Group Affiliation: Farm Bureau Group of Idaho

Licensed in: ID

Commenced Business: May 1947

Address: 275 Tierra Vista Dr, Pocatello, ID 83201

Phone: (208) 232-7914 **Domicile State:** ID **NAIC Code:** 13765

Data Date	Rating	RACR #1	RACR #2	Loss Ratio %	Total Assets ($mil)	Capital ($mil)	Net Premium ($mil)	Net Income ($mil)
6-16	B	2.91	2.39	N/A	458.5	243.2	86.1	4.4
6-15	B	3.07	2.52	N/A	450.5	244.3	80.4	2.2
2015	B	2.90	2.40	82.1	447.8	238.5	169.0	-2.9
2014	B	3.08	2.55	77.9	440.3	241.5	162.4	4.8
2013	B+	3.30	2.70	78.2	418.0	233.1	151.7	5.4
2012	B+	3.46	2.76	86.9	396.6	220.7	137.4	-8.9
2011	B+	3.68	2.98	76.0	388.5	224.4	134.8	4.5

Reserve Deficiency (as % of capital)

* Adequate & redundant reserves show as negatives   ■ 1 Yr Dev   □ 2 Yr Dev

FARM BUREAU MUTUAL INS CO OF MI   B   Good

Major Rating Factors: Good overall profitability index (5.5 on a scale of 0 to 10) despite operating losses during 2011. Good liquidity (6.0) with sufficient resources (cash flows and marketable investments) to handle a spike in claims.
Other Rating Factors: Fair overall results on stability tests (4.6) including weak results on operational trends. Affiliation with Michigan Farm Bureau is a strength. Strong long-term capitalization index (9.2) based on excellent current risk adjusted capital (severe and moderate loss scenarios). Moreover, capital levels have been consistent in recent years. Ample reserve history (8.5) that helps to protect the company against sharp claims increases.
Principal Business: Farmowners multiple peril (45%), auto liability (26%), auto physical damage (18%), workers compensation (6%), inland marine (2%), other liability (1%), and boiler & machinery (1%).
Principal Investments: Investment grade bonds (79%), misc. investments (21%), and non investment grade bonds (1%).
Investments in Affiliates: None
Group Affiliation: Michigan Farm Bureau
Licensed in: AL, CA, CT, DE, GA, IL, IN, IA, KS, KY, LA, ME, MD, MA, MI, MN, MO, MT, NE, NH, NJ, NC, ND, OH, OK, OR, PA, RI, SC, SD, TN, TX, UT, VT, VA, WV, WI
Commenced Business: March 1949
Address: 7373 W Saginaw Hwy, Lansing, MI 48917
Phone: (517) 323-7000 **Domicile State:** MI **NAIC Code:** 21555

Data Date	Rating	RACR #1	RACR #2	Loss Ratio %	Total Assets ($mil)	Capital ($mil)	Net Premium ($mil)	Net Income ($mil)
6-16	B	4.32	2.83	N/A	725.2	349.3	174.9	17.8
6-15	B-	4.20	2.74	N/A	687.3	314.2	165.5	17.3
2015	B	4.22	2.75	65.5	706.3	331.1	345.3	36.7
2014	B-	4.08	2.65	70.8	651.9	290.3	324.9	23.7
2013	B-	3.82	2.49	69.8	630.6	262.8	286.9	21.4
2012	C+	2.76	1.84	74.4	597.8	203.9	337.8	12.4
2011	C	2.63	1.77	86.8	567.2	189.4	324.9	-28.7

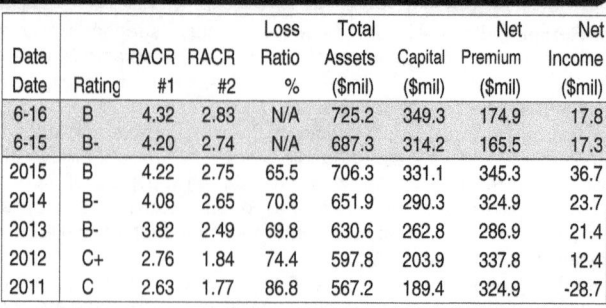

FARM BUREAU P&C INS CO *   B+   Good

Major Rating Factors: Good liquidity (5.9 on a scale of 0 to 10) with sufficient resources (cash flows and marketable investments) to handle a spike in claims. Good overall results on stability tests (5.3) despite weak results on operational trends.
Other Rating Factors: Strong long-term capitalization index (9.4) based on excellent current risk adjusted capital (severe and moderate loss scenarios). Moreover, capital levels have been consistent in recent years. Ample reserve history (8.2) that helps to protect the company against sharp claims increases. Excellent profitability (8.7) with operating gains in each of the last five years.
Principal Business: Farmowners multiple peril (25%), homeowners multiple peril (24%), auto liability (20%), auto physical damage (20%), commercial multiple peril (4%), workers compensation (3%), and other liability (2%).
Principal Investments: Investment grade bonds (78%), misc. investments (23%), non investment grade bonds (1%), and real estate (1%).
Investments in Affiliates: 5%
Group Affiliation: Iowa Farm Bureau
Licensed in: AZ, ID, IA, KS, MN, MO, NE, NM, SD, UT, WI
Commenced Business: May 1939
Address: 5400 University Ave, West Des Moines, IA 50266-5997
Phone: (515) 225-5400 **Domicile State:** IA **NAIC Code:** 13773

Data Date	Rating	RACR #1	RACR #2	Loss Ratio %	Total Assets ($mil)	Capital ($mil)	Net Premium ($mil)	Net Income ($mil)
6-16	B+	4.00	3.08	N/A	2,379.2	1,066.5	572.6	41.6
6-15	B+	3.64	2.79	N/A	2,194.8	933.6	555.6	44.8
2015	B+	3.85	2.91	62.2	2,243.1	1,020.4	1,209.0	129.0
2014	B+	3.57	2.69	70.3	2,036.2	880.6	1,166.7	65.4
2013	A-	3.45	2.57	70.2	1,931.3	802.3	1,127.9	68.6
2012	A-	3.38	2.49	71.4	1,768.5	714.8	1,052.9	74.0
2011	A-	3.18	2.38	75.2	1,664.3	661.7	1,009.1	29.0

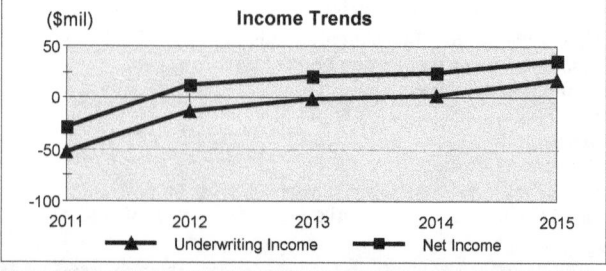

FARM FAMILY CASUALTY INS CO *   B+   Good

Major Rating Factors: Good overall profitability index (6.5 on a scale of 0 to 10). Fair expense controls. Return on equity has been fair, averaging 5.6% over the past five years. Good liquidity (6.3) with sufficient resources (cash flows and marketable investments) to handle a spike in claims.
Other Rating Factors: Good overall results on stability tests (5.3) despite weak results on operational trends. Strong long-term capitalization index (9.3) based on excellent current risk adjusted capital (severe and moderate loss scenarios). Moreover, capital levels have been consistent in recent years. Ample reserve history (9.3) that helps to protect the company against sharp claims increases.
Principal Business: Auto liability (20%), workers compensation (15%), other liability (13%), commercial multiple peril (12%), allied lines (10%), fire (10%), and other lines (21%).
Principal Investments: Investment grade bonds (83%), misc. investments (14%), cash (2%), and non investment grade bonds (1%).
Investments in Affiliates: None
Group Affiliation: American National Group Inc
Licensed in: CT, DE, ME, MD, MA, MO, NH, NJ, NY, PA, RI, VT, VA, WV
Commenced Business: November 1956
Address: 344 Route 9W, Glenmont, NY 12077-2910
Phone: (518) 431-5000 **Domicile State:** NY **NAIC Code:** 13803

Data Date	Rating	RACR #1	RACR #2	Loss Ratio %	Total Assets ($mil)	Capital ($mil)	Net Premium ($mil)	Net Income ($mil)
6-16	B+	3.83	2.50	N/A	1,160.0	389.7	205.5	7.4
6-15	B+	3.43	2.27	N/A	1,097.9	354.7	197.2	-2.8
2015	B+	3.85	2.55	71.0	1,096.5	376.5	407.6	24.9
2014	B+	3.64	2.43	72.8	1,080.0	365.7	392.7	17.5
2013	B+	3.57	2.39	72.1	1,036.7	347.1	371.1	27.6
2012	B+	3.40	2.29	78.9	984.6	308.3	352.7	13.5
2011	B	3.24	2.19	81.4	966.6	293.2	354.9	14.6

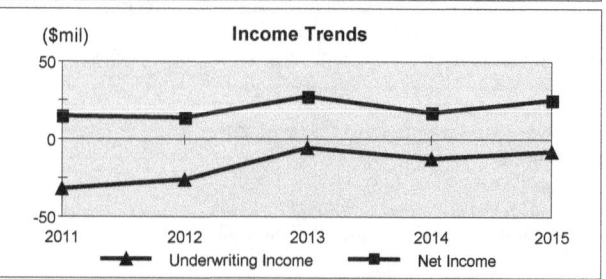

FARMERS AUTOMOBILE INS ASN * B+ Good

Major Rating Factors: Good liquidity (6.4 on a scale of 0 to 10) with sufficient resources (cash flows and marketable investments) to handle a spike in claims. Good overall results on stability tests (5.0) despite weak results on operational trends.

Other Rating Factors: Strong long-term capitalization index (8.3) based on excellent current risk adjusted capital (severe and moderate loss scenarios), despite some fluctuation in capital levels. Ample reserve history (8.8) that helps to protect the company against sharp claims increases. Fair profitability index (4.9) with operating losses during the first six months of 2016.

Principal Business: Homeowners multiple peril (33%), auto liability (31%), auto physical damage (30%), allied lines (3%), fire (2%), and inland marine (1%).

Principal Investments: Investment grade bonds (66%), misc. investments (31%), real estate (2%), and cash (1%).

Investments in Affiliates: 21%

Group Affiliation: Farmers Automobile Ins Assn

Licensed in: AZ, IL, IN, IA, MI, OH, WI

Commenced Business: April 1921

Address: 2505 Court St, Pekin, IL 61558

Phone: (309) 346-1161   **Domicile State:** IL   **NAIC Code:** 24201

Data Date	Rating	RACR #1	RACR #2	Loss Ratio %	Total Assets ($mil)	Capital ($mil)	Net Premium ($mil)	Net Income ($mil)
6-16	B+	2.16	1.84	N/A	1,283.7	503.9	237.7	-7.7
6-15	B+	2.27	1.94	N/A	1,241.4	506.7	228.6	9.7
2015	B+	2.25	1.95	71.5	1,228.6	519.1	480.8	15.4
2014	B+	2.24	1.95	74.3	1,171.2	491.2	455.1	10.5
2013	B+	2.36	2.06	75.4	1,153.5	497.8	428.5	10.2
2012	B+	2.35	2.07	75.1	1,079.7	471.3	402.0	22.8
2011	B+	2.35	2.06	83.5	1,031.5	447.4	368.5	5.0

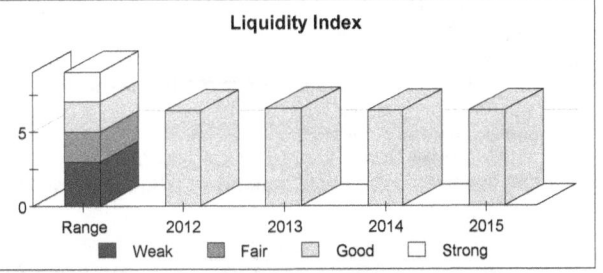

Liquidity Index

Range 2012 2013 2014 2015
■ Weak ▦ Fair ▤ Good □ Strong

FARMERS INS CO OF OREGON B Good

Major Rating Factors: History of adequate reserve strength (6.0 on a scale of 0 to 10) as reserves have been consistently at an acceptable level. Good liquidity (6.1) with sufficient resources (cash flows and marketable investments) to handle a spike in claims.

Other Rating Factors: Fair overall results on stability tests (4.7) including potential drain of affiliation with Farmers Insurance Group of Companies and weak results on operational trends. Fair profitability index (4.8) with operating losses during 2011 and the first six months of 2016. Return on equity has been low, averaging 1.6% over the past five years. Strong long-term capitalization index (8.1) based on excellent current risk adjusted capital (severe and moderate loss scenarios), despite some fluctuation in capital levels.

Principal Business: Auto liability (57%), auto physical damage (22%), homeowners multiple peril (14%), commercial multiple peril (4%), earthquake (1%), and allied lines (1%).

Principal Investments: Investment grade bonds (97%) and cash (3%).

Investments in Affiliates: None

Group Affiliation: Farmers Insurance Group of Companies

Licensed in: CA, MI, OR

Commenced Business: October 1970

Address: 13333 SW 68th Parkway, Tigard, OR 97223

Phone: (503) 372-2000   **Domicile State:** OR   **NAIC Code:** 21636

Data Date	Rating	RACR #1	RACR #2	Loss Ratio %	Total Assets ($mil)	Capital ($mil)	Net Premium ($mil)	Net Income ($mil)
6-16	B	2.43	1.74	N/A	1,713.8	518.9	526.4	-10.0
6-15	B	2.51	1.83	N/A	1,676.6	528.4	524.8	12.8
2015	B	2.48	1.77	68.7	1,681.5	529.8	1,045.1	18.0
2014	B	2.56	1.85	65.7	1,627.9	514.6	984.4	21.3
2013	B	2.48	1.81	66.8	1,614.9	490.3	954.6	21.9
2012	B-	2.36	1.73	72.3	1,600.3	470.2	969.9	6.4
2011	B-	2.28	1.66	73.2	1,577.2	458.7	990.9	-11.8

Reserve Deficiency (as % of capital)

2011 2012 2013 2014 2015
■ 1 Yr Dev □ 2 Yr Dev

* Adequate & redundant reserves show as negatives

FARMERS INS CO OF WA B- Good

Major Rating Factors: Fair overall results on stability tests (4.6 on a scale of 0 to 10) including fair financial strength of affiliated Farmers Insurance Group of Companies and weak results on operational trends. History of adequate reserve strength (6.1) as reserves have been consistently at an acceptable level.

Other Rating Factors: Good profitability index (5.0) despite operating losses during 2011 and the first six months of 2016. Return on equity has been low, averaging 2.2% over the past five years. Good liquidity (6.3) with sufficient resources (cash flows and marketable investments) to handle a spike in claims. Strong long-term capitalization index (9.1) based on excellent current risk adjusted capital (severe and moderate loss scenarios), despite some fluctuation in capital levels.

Principal Business: Auto liability (49%), auto physical damage (22%), homeowners multiple peril (21%), commercial multiple peril (6%), allied lines (1%), and earthquake (1%).

Principal Investments: Investment grade bonds (94%), cash (4%), misc. investments (1%), and non investment grade bonds (1%).

Investments in Affiliates: None

Group Affiliation: Farmers Insurance Group of Companies

Licensed in: CA, WA

Commenced Business: October 1970

Address: 3003 77th Ave SE, Mercer Island, WA 98040-2890

Phone: (503) 372-2000   **Domicile State:** WA   **NAIC Code:** 21644

Data Date	Rating	RACR #1	RACR #2	Loss Ratio %	Total Assets ($mil)	Capital ($mil)	Net Premium ($mil)	Net Income ($mil)
6-16	B-	3.34	2.37	N/A	557.5	203.1	150.4	-0.5
6-15	B-	3.38	2.45	N/A	542.3	202.1	149.9	4.1
2015	B-	3.36	2.37	68.5	548.9	203.4	298.6	6.6
2014	B-	3.46	2.49	65.5	531.4	197.1	281.2	6.9
2013	B-	3.39	2.46	66.9	513.8	189.4	272.7	7.5
2012	C+	3.23	2.36	71.3	511.4	181.7	277.1	4.5
2011	C+	3.08	2.24	73.1	514.7	176.5	283.1	-1.5

Farmers Insurance Group of Companies
Composite Group Rating: C

Largest Group Members	Assets ($mil)	Rating
FARMERS INS EXCHANGE	15567	C
MID-CENTURY INS CO	3905	B-
FIRE INS EXCHANGE	2335	C+
FOREMOST INS CO	2172	B
TRUCK INS EXCHANGE	2165	C+

FARMERS INS EXCHANGE

C   **Fair**

Major Rating Factors: Fair profitability index (3.6 on a scale of 0 to 10) with operating losses during 2011, 2012 and the first six months of 2016. Fair overall results on stability tests (4.3) including weak results on operational trends and negative cash flow from operations for 2015.

Other Rating Factors: Vulnerable liquidity (2.7) as a spike in claims may stretch capacity. Good long-term capitalization index (5.4) based on good current risk adjusted capital (severe and moderate loss scenarios). Over the last several years, capital levels have remained relatively consistent. History of adequate reserve strength (5.9) as reserves have been consistently at an acceptable level.

Principal Business: Homeowners multiple peril (34%), auto liability (28%), auto physical damage (19%), commercial multiple peril (13%), other liability (2%), and workers compensation (2%).

Principal Investments: Misc. investments (49%), investment grade bonds (47%), real estate (3%), and non investment grade bonds (1%).

Investments in Affiliates: 46%

Group Affiliation: Farmers Insurance Group of Companies

Licensed in: All states except AK, CT, HI, PR

Commenced Business: April 1928

Address: 4680 Wilshire Blvd, Los Angeles, CA 90010

Phone: (323) 932-3200   **Domicile State:** CA   **NAIC Code:** 21652

Data Date	Rating	RACR #1	RACR #2	Loss Ratio %	Total Assets ($mil)	Capital ($mil)	Net Premium ($mil)	Net Income ($mil)
6-16	C	0.86	0.79	N/A	16,189.6	4,108.1	3,891.5	-150.3
6-15	C	0.92	0.85	N/A	15,934.3	4,251.3	3,879.6	-19.1
2015	C	0.89	0.82	69.0	15,566.6	4,206.8	7,726.6	-113.7
2014	C	0.92	0.85	65.8	15,591.3	4,181.5	7,277.2	2.5
2013	C	0.90	0.84	66.8	15,557.1	3,879.7	7,057.1	55.0
2012	C	0.91	0.85	73.4	15,530.2	3,750.8	7,170.1	-162.0
2011	C	0.96	0.89	73.2	15,237.4	3,820.2	7,325.7	-229.1

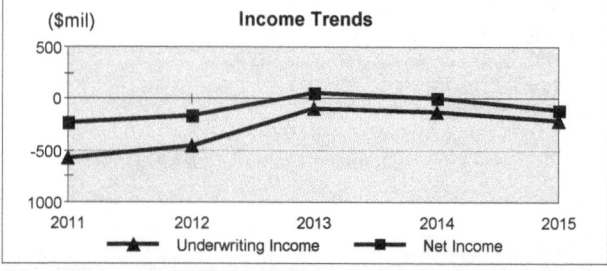

FARMERS MUTUAL HAIL INS CO OF IA

B-   **Good**

Major Rating Factors: Fair overall results on stability tests (4.1 on a scale of 0 to 10) including potential drain of affiliation with Farmers Mutual Hail Ins Co and weak results on operational trends. The largest net exposure for one risk is conservative at 1.8% of capital. Fair profitability index (3.7) with operating losses during 2012 and 2014.

Other Rating Factors: Good liquidity (6.5) with sufficient resources (cash flows and marketable investments) to handle a spike in claims. Strong long-term capitalization index (7.1) based on excellent current risk adjusted capital (severe and moderate loss scenarios), despite some fluctuation in capital levels. Ample reserve history (7.7) that can protect against increases in claims costs.

Principal Business: Allied lines (95%), fire (3%), auto liability (1%), and auto physical damage (1%).

Principal Investments: Investment grade bonds (47%), misc. investments (45%), cash (3%), real estate (3%), and non investment grade bonds (2%).

Investments in Affiliates: 38%

Group Affiliation: Farmers Mutual Hail Ins Co

Licensed in: All states except AK, DC, HI, ME, NV, PR

Commenced Business: March 1893

Address: 6785 Westown Parkway, West Des Moines, IA 50266

Phone: (515) 724-5007   **Domicile State:** IA   **NAIC Code:** 13897

Data Date	Rating	RACR #1	RACR #2	Loss Ratio %	Total Assets ($mil)	Capital ($mil)	Net Premium ($mil)	Net Income ($mil)
6-16	B-	1.64	1.23	N/A	792.3	373.0	145.7	-0.2
6-15	B-	2.06	1.31	N/A	642.1	319.5	145.4	-27.1
2015	B-	1.67	1.27	77.9	744.5	366.6	360.4	9.4
2014	B-	1.77	1.14	91.0	676.3	309.5	390.2	-31.2
2013	B-	1.98	1.24	85.9	832.8	358.3	431.1	3.9
2012	B-	1.91	1.18	92.6	879.9	317.5	470.4	-15.1
2011	B-	2.64	1.63	79.4	679.4	360.0	405.2	19.9

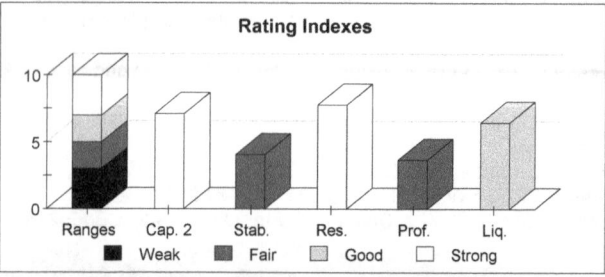

FARMERS MUTUAL INS CO OF NE

B   **Good**

Major Rating Factors: Good overall profitability index (6.1 on a scale of 0 to 10) despite operating losses during 2011 and 2014. Good liquidity (6.7) with sufficient resources (cash flows and marketable investments) to handle a spike in claims.

Other Rating Factors: Fair overall results on stability tests (4.8) including weak results on operational trends. Strong long-term capitalization index (10.0) based on excellent current risk adjusted capital (severe and moderate loss scenarios), despite some fluctuation in capital levels. Ample reserve history (7.9) that can protect against increases in claims costs.

Principal Business: Farmowners multiple peril (30%), homeowners multiple peril (28%), auto physical damage (20%), auto liability (16%), allied lines (2%), fire (2%), and other liability (2%).

Principal Investments: Investment grade bonds (65%), misc. investments (19%), cash (11%), and real estate (5%).

Investments in Affiliates: None

Group Affiliation: None

Licensed in: IL, IN, IA, KS, NE, ND, SD

Commenced Business: November 1891

Address: 501 S 13th St, Lincoln, NE 68508

Phone: (402) 434-8300   **Domicile State:** NE   **NAIC Code:** 13889

Data Date	Rating	RACR #1	RACR #2	Loss Ratio %	Total Assets ($mil)	Capital ($mil)	Net Premium ($mil)	Net Income ($mil)
6-16	B	4.21	3.08	N/A	624.1	327.5	156.4	18.4
6-15	B	4.27	3.11	N/A	577.4	294.6	148.4	18.1
2015	B	4.08	2.92	65.8	591.0	304.3	315.3	27.3
2014	B	4.31	3.01	83.8	536.2	282.4	267.3	-7.7
2013	B	4.70	3.34	67.1	512.4	293.2	264.9	20.0
2012	B	5.08	3.60	70.0	461.8	269.7	224.5	18.2
2011	B	5.35	3.90	86.9	433.8	254.2	206.4	-10.5

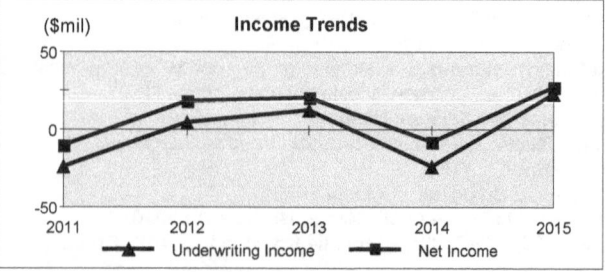

FARMERS REINS CO   C   Fair

Major Rating Factors: Fair overall results on stability tests (3.4 on a scale of 0 to 10) including weak results on operational trends and negative cash flow from operations for 2015. Weak profitability index (2.2). Fair expense controls. Return on equity has been fair, averaging 5.6% over the past five years.

Other Rating Factors: History of adequate reserve strength (5.1) as reserves have been consistently at an acceptable level. Good liquidity (6.7) with sufficient resources (cash flows and marketable investments) to handle a spike in claims. Strong long-term capitalization index (10.0) based on excellent current risk adjusted capital (severe and moderate loss scenarios), despite some fluctuation in capital levels.

Principal Business: Auto physical damage (100%).

Principal Investments: Investment grade bonds (97%), cash (2%), and misc. investments (1%).

Investments in Affiliates: None

Group Affiliation: Zurich Financial Services Group

Licensed in: CA

Commenced Business: August 1997

Address: 6301 Owensmouth Ave, Woodland Hills, CA 91367

Phone: (323) 932-3200   **Domicile State:** CA   **NAIC Code:** 10873

Data Date	Rating	RACR #1	RACR #2	Loss Ratio %	Total Assets ($mil)	Capital ($mil)	Net Premium ($mil)	Net Income ($mil)
6-16	C	27.17	17.24	N/A	591.9	484.5	0.0	9.2
6-15	B-	19.45	13.17	N/A	1,242.5	940.2	112.2	19.1
2015	C	16.36	11.05	70.5	652.1	482.3	158.5	58.2
2014	B-	15.60	10.74	67.0	1,282.9	926.3	373.4	65.5
2013	B-	11.88	8.08	68.9	1,400.2	949.7	517.6	48.3
2012	B-	8.83	6.05	72.4	1,606.1	1,015.5	790.5	31.9
2011	C+	9.54	5.40	70.5	1,602.0	974.1	705.8	13.4

Zurich Financial Services Group
Composite Group Rating: C+

Largest Group Members	Assets ($mil)	Rating
ZURICH AMERICAN INS CO	30471	B-
ZURICH AMERICAN LIFE INS CO	12271	C
FARMERS NEW WORLD LIFE INS CO	7049	B-
RURAL COMMUNITY INS CO	3680	B
CENTRE LIFE INS CO	1884	B-

FARMINGTON CASUALTY CO   B   Good

Major Rating Factors: Good overall profitability index (6.9 on a scale of 0 to 10). Fair expense controls. Return on equity has been good over the last five years, averaging 12.6%. Good liquidity (6.6) with sufficient resources (cash flows and marketable investments) to handle a spike in claims.

Other Rating Factors: Fair overall results on stability tests (4.6) including weak results on operational trends. Affiliation with Travelers Companies Inc is a strength. Strong long-term capitalization index (7.9) based on excellent current risk adjusted capital (severe and moderate loss scenarios), despite some fluctuation in capital levels. Ample reserve history (8.8) that helps to protect the company against sharp claims increases.

Principal Business: Workers compensation (58%), homeowners multiple peril (40%), and auto liability (1%).

Principal Investments: Investment grade bonds (96%) and misc. investments (4%).

Investments in Affiliates: 0%

Group Affiliation: Travelers Companies Inc

Licensed in: All states except PR

Commenced Business: October 1982

Address: One Tower Square, Hartford, CT 06183

Phone: (860) 277-0111   **Domicile State:** CT   **NAIC Code:** 41483

Data Date	Rating	RACR #1	RACR #2	Loss Ratio %	Total Assets ($mil)	Capital ($mil)	Net Premium ($mil)	Net Income ($mil)
6-16	B	2.58	1.63	N/A	1,033.6	309.8	155.1	16.8
6-15	B	2.60	1.64	N/A	1,017.9	307.5	149.4	19.8
2015	B	2.49	1.59	58.7	1,005.4	291.3	307.5	42.0
2014	B	2.48	1.56	60.5	1,009.6	287.7	298.8	46.4
2013	B	2.52	1.60	60.9	1,000.6	287.4	298.1	45.9
2012	B	2.39	1.54	68.4	1,003.0	269.2	289.5	29.7
2011	B	2.31	1.49	76.9	974.4	261.2	283.4	16.9

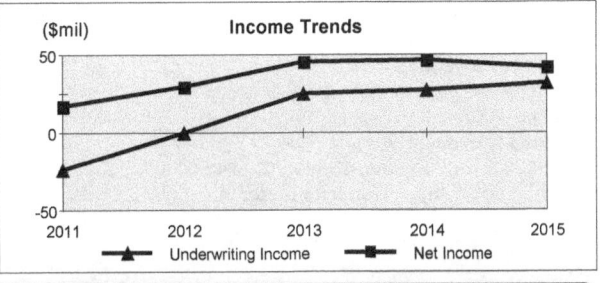

Income Trends

FCCI INS CO   C+   Fair

Major Rating Factors: Fair overall results on stability tests (4.2 on a scale of 0 to 10) including potential drain of affiliation with FCCI Ins Group and weak results on operational trends. Good overall profitability index (6.9) despite modest operating losses during the first six months of 2016. Return on equity has been fair, averaging 5.2% over the past five years.

Other Rating Factors: Good liquidity (6.6) with sufficient resources (cash flows and marketable investments) to handle a spike in claims. Strong long-term capitalization index (8.1) based on excellent current risk adjusted capital (severe and moderate loss scenarios), despite some fluctuation in capital levels. Ample reserve history (9.3) that helps to protect the company against sharp claims increases.

Principal Business: Workers compensation (48%), auto liability (15%), commercial multiple peril (13%), other liability (9%), auto physical damage (4%), fire (2%), and other lines (10%).

Principal Investments: Investment grade bonds (72%), misc. investments (22%), non investment grade bonds (4%), and real estate (2%).

Investments in Affiliates: 8%

Group Affiliation: FCCI Ins Group

Licensed in: AL, AZ, AR, CO, DC, FL, GA, IL, IN, IA, KS, KY, LA, MD, MI, MS, MO, NE, NC, OH, OK, PA, SC, TN, TX, VA

Commenced Business: April 1959

Address: 6300 University Parkway, Sarasota, FL 34240

Phone: (800) 226-3224   **Domicile State:** FL   **NAIC Code:** 10178

Data Date	Rating	RACR #1	RACR #2	Loss Ratio %	Total Assets ($mil)	Capital ($mil)	Net Premium ($mil)	Net Income ($mil)
6-16	C+	2.35	1.69	N/A	1,915.8	584.1	366.4	-2.5
6-15	C+	2.45	1.76	N/A	1,804.3	582.9	327.3	8.5
2015	C+	2.51	1.83	65.8	1,802.2	581.1	711.1	35.5
2014	C+	2.54	1.85	63.4	1,709.1	578.7	639.2	39.4
2013	C+	2.63	1.90	66.0	1,628.9	552.1	559.1	26.7
2012	C+	2.63	1.91	67.1	1,529.4	520.8	492.2	24.7
2011	C+	2.57	1.84	67.1	1,473.3	491.4	441.9	32.1

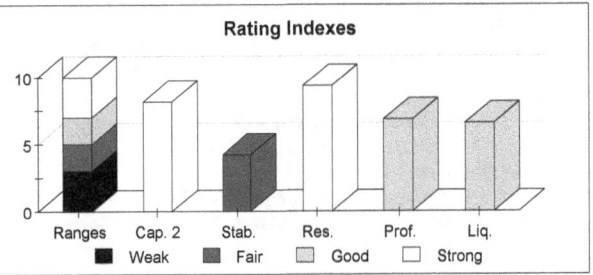

Rating Indexes

FEDERAL INS CO
B **Good**

Major Rating Factors: Good liquidity (6.8 on a scale of 0 to 10) with sufficient resources (cash flows and marketable investments) to handle a spike in claims. Fair profitability index (3.9). Fair expense controls. Return on equity has been fair, averaging 14.3% over the past five years.

Other Rating Factors: Fair overall results on stability tests (4.5) including weak results on operational trends. The largest net exposure for one risk is acceptable at 2.2% of capital. Strong long-term capitalization index (7.2) based on excellent current risk adjusted capital (severe and moderate loss scenarios), despite some fluctuation in capital levels. Ample reserve history (8.2) that helps to protect the company against sharp claims increases.

Principal Business: Other liability (34%), commercial multiple peril (17%), workers compensation (11%), homeowners multiple peril (9%), fidelity (4%), inland marine (4%), and other lines (20%).

Principal Investments: Investment grade bonds (51%), misc. investments (47%), and non investment grade bonds (2%).

Investments in Affiliates: 39%

Group Affiliation: Chubb Limited

Licensed in: All states, the District of Columbia and Puerto Rico

Commenced Business: March 1901

Address: 211 N Pennsylvania St #1350, Indianapolis, IN 46204-1927

Phone: (908) 903-2000 **Domicile State:** IN **NAIC Code:** 20281

Data Date	Rating	RACR #1	RACR #2	Loss Ratio %	Total Assets ($mil)	Capital ($mil)	Net Premium ($mil)	Net Income ($mil)
6-16	B	1.21	1.13	N/A	30,306.0	12,782.2	2,969.8	1,520.7
6-15	B	1.35	1.24	N/A	32,250.0	14,682.1	3,605.7	881.4
2015	B	1.24	1.15	54.3	32,240.6	13,278.7	7,338.2	2,154.1
2014	B	1.36	1.26	56.8	32,484.3	14,828.4	7,113.5	1,855.3
2013	B+	1.42	1.31	51.7	31,761.3	14,741.3	6,844.9	2,021.9
2012	B+	1.36	1.25	64.8	31,246.7	13,841.0	6,586.4	1,564.7
2011	B+	1.39	1.28	65.0	30,726.6	13,707.5	6,473.8	1,760.6

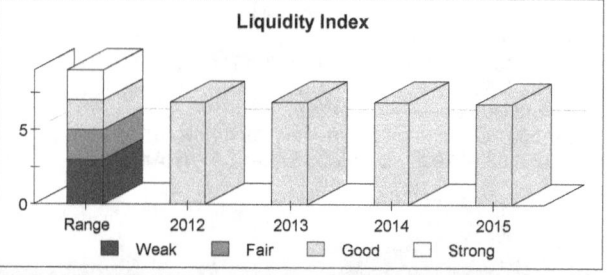

Liquidity Index

Range — 2012 — 2013 — 2014 — 2015
■ Weak ■ Fair ☐ Good ☐ Strong

FEDERATED MUTUAL INS CO
B **Good**

Major Rating Factors: Good overall results on stability tests (5.1 on a scale of 0 to 10) despite potential drain of affiliation with Federated Mutual Ins Group and weak results on operational trends. Good liquidity (6.8) with sufficient resources (cash flows and marketable investments) to handle a spike in claims.

Other Rating Factors: Strong long-term capitalization index (10.0) based on excellent current risk adjusted capital (severe and moderate loss scenarios). Moreover, capital levels have been consistent in recent years. Ample reserve history (9.0) that helps to protect the company against sharp claims increases. Excellent profitability (8.2) with operating gains in each of the last five years.

Principal Business: Group accident & health (33%), workers compensation (18%), other liability (14%), auto liability (12%), commercial multiple peril (6%), auto physical damage (5%), and other lines (14%).

Principal Investments: Investment grade bonds (74%), misc. investments (25%), and real estate (1%).

Investments in Affiliates: 14%

Group Affiliation: Federated Mutual Ins Group

Licensed in: All states except HI, PR

Commenced Business: August 1904

Address: 121 E Park Square, Owatonna, MN 55060

Phone: (507) 455-5200 **Domicile State:** MN **NAIC Code:** 13935

Data Date	Rating	RACR #1	RACR #2	Loss Ratio %	Total Assets ($mil)	Capital ($mil)	Net Premium ($mil)	Net Income ($mil)
6-16	B	3.88	3.14	N/A	5,260.8	2,988.8	702.0	94.6
6-15	B	3.85	3.11	N/A	4,948.9	2,776.0	623.7	86.0
2015	B	3.82	3.13	66.9	5,076.2	2,862.4	1,301.0	189.1
2014	B	3.79	3.11	63.2	4,783.7	2,657.1	1,183.9	187.6
2013	A-	3.67	3.00	69.6	4,523.5	2,518.3	1,083.5	127.9
2012	A-	3.86	3.19	74.6	4,233.8	2,365.4	942.3	106.1
2011	A-	3.71	3.03	79.6	4,075.1	2,237.2	875.9	52.5

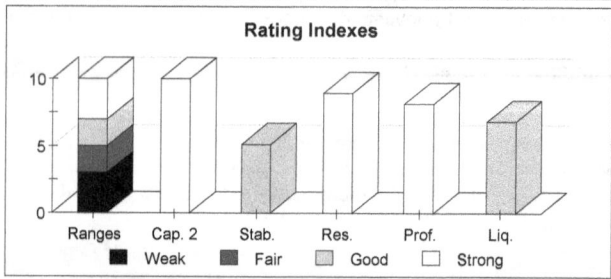

Rating Indexes

Ranges — Cap. 2 — Stab. — Res. — Prof. — Liq.
■ Weak ■ Fair ☐ Good ☐ Strong

FEDERATED SERVICE INS CO
B- **Good**

Major Rating Factors: Fair overall results on stability tests (4.5 on a scale of 0 to 10) including potential drain of affiliation with Federated Mutual Ins Group and weak results on operational trends. The largest net exposure for one risk is conservative at 1.3% of capital. Good liquidity (6.8) with sufficient resources (cash flows and marketable investments) to handle a spike in claims.

Other Rating Factors: Strong long-term capitalization index (10.0) based on excellent current risk adjusted capital (severe and moderate loss scenarios). Moreover, capital levels have been consistent in recent years. Ample reserve history (9.3) that helps to protect the company against sharp claims increases. Excellent profitability (8.1) with operating gains in each of the last five years.

Principal Business: Auto liability (25%), other liability (24%), workers compensation (19%), auto physical damage (10%), allied lines (8%), fire (6%), and other lines (8%).

Principal Investments: Investment grade bonds (98%) and misc. investments (2%).

Investments in Affiliates: None

Group Affiliation: Federated Mutual Ins Group

Licensed in: All states except HI, NH, NJ, VT, PR

Commenced Business: January 1975

Address: 121 E Park Square, Owatonna, MN 55060

Phone: (507) 455-5200 **Domicile State:** MN **NAIC Code:** 28304

Data Date	Rating	RACR #1	RACR #2	Loss Ratio %	Total Assets ($mil)	Capital ($mil)	Net Premium ($mil)	Net Income ($mil)
6-16	B-	6.25	3.97	N/A	470.4	221.1	78.0	10.1
6-15	B-	5.74	3.75	N/A	439.7	202.7	69.3	9.0
2015	B-	6.40	4.08	66.9	455.8	211.2	144.6	20.2
2014	B-	5.82	3.81	63.2	428.3	193.3	131.5	19.6
2013	B	5.31	3.50	69.6	406.0	184.1	120.4	11.6
2012	B	5.97	3.82	74.6	377.3	171.1	104.7	8.4
2011	B	6.04	3.80	79.6	370.6	165.6	97.3	3.5

Federated Mutual Ins Group Composite Group Rating: B Largest Group Members	Assets ($mil)	Rating
FEDERATED MUTUAL INS CO	5076	B
FEDERATED LIFE INS CO	1649	A
FEDERATED SERVICE INS CO	456	B-

FINIAL REINS CO | D+ | Weak

Major Rating Factors: Weak overall results on stability tests (2.5 on a scale of 0 to 10) including potential drain of affiliation with Berkshire-Hathaway and weak results on operational trends. The largest net exposure for one risk is conservative at 1.5% of capital. History of adequate reserve strength (6.6) as reserves have been consistently at an acceptable level.

Other Rating Factors: Strong long-term capitalization index (10.0) based on excellent current risk adjusted capital (severe and moderate loss scenarios), despite some fluctuation in capital levels. Excellent profitability (8.3) with operating gains in each of the last five years. Excellent expense controls. Superior liquidity (10.0) with ample operational cash flow and liquid investments.

Principal Business: (This company is a reinsurer.)

Principal Investments: Investment grade bonds (53%), misc. investments (41%), and cash (6%).

Investments in Affiliates: None

Group Affiliation: Berkshire-Hathaway

Licensed in: All states except MS, PR

Commenced Business: February 1993

Address: 100 First Stamford Pl, Stamford, CT 06902

Phone: (402) 916-3000   **Domicile State:** CT   **NAIC Code:** 39136

Data Date	Rating	RACR #1	RACR #2	Loss Ratio %	Total Assets ($mil)	Capital ($mil)	Net Premium ($mil)	Net Income ($mil)
6-16	D+	5.79	3.72	N/A	1,226.1	840.1	0.1	19.6
6-15	D+	6.37	3.90	N/A	1,202.9	836.4	0.4	6.4
2015	D+	5.21	3.30	73.0	1,274.1	850.4	99.4	31.7
2014	D+	6.13	3.75	N/A	1,230.2	848.2	-0.5	29.6
2013	D+	7.17	4.28	N/A	1,257.7	812.1	-2.2	59.1
2012	U	6.71	3.93	N/A	1,203.0	716.3	-0.1	47.1
2011	D+	5.97	3.37	N/A	1,168.8	609.7	-0.4	34.9

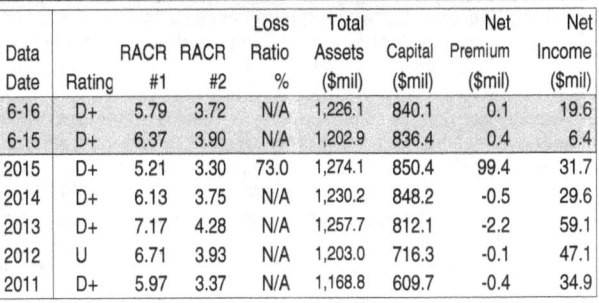

Rating Indexes

FIRE INS EXCHANGE | C+ | Fair

Major Rating Factors: Fair profitability index (3.9 on a scale of 0 to 10) with operating losses during 2011, 2012 and the first six months of 2016. Fair liquidity (4.3) as cash resources may not be adequate to cover a spike in claims.

Other Rating Factors: Fair overall results on stability tests (4.8) including weak results on operational trends and negative cash flow from operations for 2015. Good long-term capitalization index (5.2) based on good current risk adjusted capital (severe and moderate loss scenarios). Over the last several years, capital levels have remained relatively consistent. History of adequate reserve strength (5.9) as reserves have been consistently at an acceptable level.

Principal Business: Homeowners multiple peril (66%), commercial multiple peril (15%), allied lines (10%), fire (6%), other liability (1%), and inland marine (1%).

Principal Investments: Misc. investments (66%), investment grade bonds (24%), cash (6%), and real estate (4%).

Investments in Affiliates: 57%

Group Affiliation: Farmers Insurance Group of Companies

Licensed in: AL, AZ, AR, CA, CO, FL, GA, ID, IL, IN, IA, KS, MI, MN, MO, MT, NE, NV, NH, NJ, NM, NY, ND, OH, OK, OR, SD, TX, UT, WA, WI, WY

Commenced Business: November 1942

Address: 4680 Wilshire Blvd, Los Angeles, CA 90010

Phone: (323) 932-3200   **Domicile State:** CA   **NAIC Code:** 21660

Data Date	Rating	RACR #1	RACR #2	Loss Ratio %	Total Assets ($mil)	Capital ($mil)	Net Premium ($mil)	Net Income ($mil)
6-16	C+	0.82	0.77	N/A	2,431.5	764.4	564.0	-17.2
6-15	C+	0.85	0.80	N/A	2,448.5	789.8	562.3	-0.9
2015	C+	0.84	0.79	69.0	2,335.3	786.9	1,119.8	12.5
2014	C+	0.84	0.80	65.8	2,281.7	771.1	1,054.7	6.8
2013	C+	0.83	0.78	66.9	2,254.8	721.3	1,022.8	12.7
2012	C+	0.83	0.78	73.3	2,204.0	662.2	1,039.1	-10.7
2011	C+	0.85	0.80	73.2	2,277.5	653.1	1,061.7	-26.2

Income Trends

FIREMANS FUND INS CO | C | Fair

Major Rating Factors: Fair long-term capitalization (4.5 on a scale of 0 to 10) based on good current risk adjusted capital (moderate loss scenario) reflecting improvement over results in 2015. Fair overall results on stability tests (3.6) including weak results on operational trends and negative cash flow from operations for 2015. The largest net exposure for one risk is conservative at 1.5% of capital.

Other Rating Factors: Weak profitability index (2.1) with operating losses during 2011 and 2012. Return on equity has been low, averaging 4.6% over the past five years. History of adequate reserve strength (5.0) as reserves have been consistently at an acceptable level. Good liquidity (6.6) with sufficient resources (cash flows and marketable investments) to handle a spike in claims.

Principal Business: Homeowners multiple peril (23%), other liability (21%), commercial multiple peril (19%), inland marine (12%), auto liability (7%), auto physical damage (5%), and other lines (14%).

Principal Investments: Investment grade bonds (178%), non investment grade bonds (6%), and cash (1%).

Investments in Affiliates: 22%

Group Affiliation: Allianz Ins Group

Licensed in: All states, the District of Columbia and Puerto Rico

Commenced Business: September 1864

Address: 777 San Marin Dr, Novato, CA 94998

Phone: (415) 899-2000   **Domicile State:** CA   **NAIC Code:** 21873

Data Date	Rating	RACR #1	RACR #2	Loss Ratio %	Total Assets ($mil)	Capital ($mil)	Net Premium ($mil)	Net Income ($mil)
6-16	C	1.94	1.85	N/A	2,208.8	1,565.9	0.0	371.4
6-15	C	1.32	0.95	N/A	7,536.3	1,982.5	-99.7	283.0
2015	C	1.25	0.97	132.5	5,500.4	1,296.3	-1,189.5	292.2
2014	C	1.12	0.75	90.0	9,434.6	2,134.2	2,460.5	62.9
2013	C	1.39	0.92	68.6	9,843.7	2,478.7	2,577.7	237.4
2012	C	1.15	0.75	103.2	11,835.8	2,522.1	3,638.2	-814.8
2011	C	1.52	1.11	88.2	9,922.8	2,985.9	2,685.5	-42.9

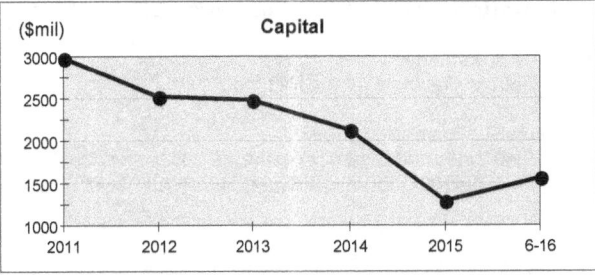

Capital

FIRST COLONIAL INS CO *

B+   Good

Major Rating Factors: Strong long-term capitalization index (10.0 on a scale of 0 to 10) based on excellent current risk adjusted capital (severe and moderate loss scenarios), despite some fluctuation in capital levels. Ample reserve history (7.7) that can protect against increases in claims costs.

Other Rating Factors: Excellent liquidity (7.6) with ample operational cash flow and liquid investments. Fair profitability index (3.6) with operating losses during the first six months of 2016. Return on equity has been fair, averaging 6.7% over the past five years. Good overall results on stability tests (5.0) despite weak results on operational trends. Strengths include potential support from affiliation with Allstate Group.

Principal Business: Credit (32%), other liability (1%), and auto physical damage (1%).

Principal Investments: Investment grade bonds (103%).

Investments in Affiliates: None

Group Affiliation: Allstate Group

Licensed in: All states except CA, PR

Commenced Business: April 1987

Address: 1776 American Heritage Life Dr, Jacksonville, FL 32224-6688

Phone: (904) 992-1776   **Domicile State:** FL   **NAIC Code:** 29980

Data Date	Rating	RACR #1	RACR #2	Loss Ratio %	Total Assets ($mil)	Capital ($mil)	Net Premium ($mil)	Net Income ($mil)
6-16	B+	15.77	8.91	N/A	370.3	157.1	32.3	-3.8
6-15	B+	10.33	7.11	N/A	363.4	159.0	31.5	0.4
2015	B+	16.01	10.14	69.9	374.2	159.7	76.8	1.2
2014	B+	11.28	7.82	48.5	353.3	159.0	65.8	8.8
2013	B+	8.50	6.78	34.0	380.8	193.8	64.5	17.8
2012	B	6.02	5.12	24.9	350.8	183.6	64.6	42.3
2011	B	2.01	1.87	22.6	349.7	150.4	72.3	1.1

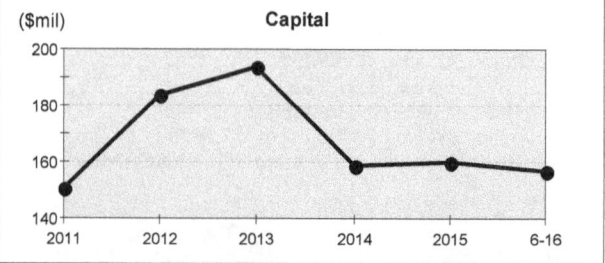

FIRST FINANCIAL INS CO

C-   Fair

Major Rating Factors: Weak overall results on stability tests (2.6 on a scale of 0 to 10) including potential drain of affiliation with IFG Companies and weak results on operational trends. Strong long-term capitalization index (7.3) based on excellent current risk adjusted capital (severe and moderate loss scenarios), despite some fluctuation in capital levels.

Other Rating Factors: Ample reserve history (8.0) that helps to protect the company against sharp claims increases. Excellent profitability (7.6) with operating gains in each of the last five years. Excellent liquidity (7.8) with ample operational cash flow and liquid investments.

Principal Business: Other liability (48%), auto liability (29%), inland marine (19%), and auto physical damage (3%).

Principal Investments: Misc. investments (80%), investment grade bonds (19%), and cash (1%).

Investments in Affiliates: 79%

Group Affiliation: IFG Companies

Licensed in: All states except PR

Commenced Business: May 1970

Address: 400 S Ninth St Suite 200, Springfield, IL 62701-1822

Phone: (336) 586-2500   **Domicile State:** IL   **NAIC Code:** 11177

Data Date	Rating	RACR #1	RACR #2	Loss Ratio %	Total Assets ($mil)	Capital ($mil)	Net Premium ($mil)	Net Income ($mil)
6-16	C-	1.25	1.23	N/A	557.6	439.8	10.9	2.9
6-15	C-	1.22	1.20	N/A	550.0	424.6	13.6	5.5
2015	C-	1.21	1.19	35.1	544.2	423.7	24.6	5.6
2014	C-	1.18	1.17	56.3	540.2	406.4	27.4	5.0
2013	C-	1.18	1.17	36.2	533.6	393.5	30.5	16.3
2012	C-	1.13	1.13	26.2	507.2	354.7	32.3	18.8
2011	C-	1.20	1.20	33.8	519.7	365.4	27.0	12.9

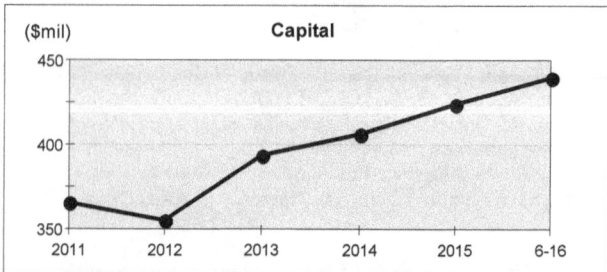

FIRST FLORIDIAN AUTO & HOME INS CO

B   Good

Major Rating Factors: History of adequate reserve strength (6.2 on a scale of 0 to 10) as reserves have been consistently at an acceptable level. Good overall profitability index (6.3). Good expense controls. Return on equity has been fair, averaging 6.7% over the past five years.

Other Rating Factors: Good liquidity (6.9) with sufficient resources (cash flows and marketable investments) to handle a spike in claims. Fair overall results on stability tests (4.0) including weak results on operational trends. The largest net exposure for one risk is acceptable at 2.9% of capital. Strong long-term capitalization index (10.0) based on excellent current risk adjusted capital (severe and moderate loss scenarios), despite some fluctuation in capital levels.

Principal Business: Auto liability (48%), homeowners multiple peril (36%), auto physical damage (15%), other liability (1%), and inland marine (1%).

Principal Investments: Investment grade bonds (100%) and misc. investments (1%).

Investments in Affiliates: None

Group Affiliation: Travelers Companies Inc

Licensed in: FL

Commenced Business: June 1996

Address: 7840 Woodland Ctr Blvd, Tampa, FL 33614

Phone: (813) 890-4200   **Domicile State:** FL   **NAIC Code:** 10647

Data Date	Rating	RACR #1	RACR #2	Loss Ratio %	Total Assets ($mil)	Capital ($mil)	Net Premium ($mil)	Net Income ($mil)
6-16	B	13.06	9.91	N/A	275.9	201.7	28.8	3.8
6-15	B-	12.27	9.62	N/A	280.9	204.1	32.3	7.3
2015	B	11.90	9.26	62.0	273.2	198.1	59.8	13.2
2014	B-	10.95	8.78	68.9	278.7	197.3	67.5	10.6
2013	B	10.38	8.42	57.6	288.6	201.8	73.8	17.0
2012	B	9.29	7.20	75.3	287.6	192.6	81.1	9.2
2011	B	8.00	5.89	63.6	289.9	187.4	91.2	18.4

FIRST INS CO OF HI LTD   C   Fair

Major Rating Factors: Fair overall results on stability tests (4.2 on a scale of 0 to 10) including fair financial strength of affiliated Tokio Marine Holdings Inc and weak results on operational trends. The largest net exposure for one risk is conservative at 1.7% of capital. Good overall profitability index (5.8) despite modest operating losses during the first six months of 2016. Return on equity has been fair, averaging 7.9% over the past five years.

Other Rating Factors: Good liquidity (6.8) with sufficient resources (cash flows and marketable investments) to handle a spike in claims. Strong long-term capitalization index (10.0) based on excellent current risk adjusted capital (severe and moderate loss scenarios), despite some fluctuation in capital levels. Ample reserve history (9.4) that helps to protect the company against sharp claims increases.

Principal Business: Workers compensation (26%), allied lines (20%), other liability (13%), commercial multiple peril (12%), auto liability (10%), homeowners multiple peril (10%), and other lines (9%).

Principal Investments: Investment grade bonds (94%) and misc. investments (6%).

Investments in Affiliates: 4%

Group Affiliation: Tokio Marine Holdings Inc

Licensed in: HI

Commenced Business: September 1982

Address: 1100 Ward Ave, Honolulu, HI 96814

Phone: (808) 527-7777   **Domicile State:** HI   **NAIC Code:** 41742

Data Date	Rating	RACR #1	RACR #2	Loss Ratio %	Total Assets ($mil)	Capital ($mil)	Net Premium ($mil)	Net Income ($mil)
6-16	C	5.26	3.72	N/A	653.7	286.8	96.5	-0.6
6-15	C	5.03	3.51	N/A	636.8	294.6	90.0	8.1
2015	C	5.24	3.75	67.2	640.2	274.9	190.1	15.8
2014	C	5.03	3.55	62.9	631.0	288.8	181.0	20.0
2013	C	5.23	3.66	59.2	640.8	286.4	171.8	19.6
2012	C	6.38	4.14	41.1	646.9	286.9	148.7	50.8
2011	C	3.95	2.74	59.6	619.0	241.0	142.9	15.3

Tokio Marine Holdings Inc
Composite Group Rating: B
Largest Group Members

	Assets ($mil)	Rating
RELIANCE STANDARD LIFE INS CO	9581	B
PHILADELPHIA INDEMNITY INS CO	7362	B-
SAFETY NATIONAL CASUALTY CORP	5611	C
HOUSTON CASUALTY CO	3404	B-
US SPECIALTY INS CO	1793	B-

FLORIDA FARM BU CASUALTY INS CO   B-   Good

Major Rating Factors: Fair overall results on stability tests (4.5 on a scale of 0 to 10) including potential drain of affiliation with Southern Farm Bureau Casualty and weak results on operational trends. Good liquidity (6.6) with sufficient resources (cash flows and marketable investments) to handle a spike in claims.

Other Rating Factors: Strong long-term capitalization index (10.0) based on excellent current risk adjusted capital (severe and moderate loss scenarios). Moreover, capital levels have been consistent in recent years. Ample reserve history (7.7) that can protect against increases in claims costs. Excellent profitability (8.5) with operating gains in each of the last five years.

Principal Business: Homeowners multiple peril (72%), auto liability (20%), and auto physical damage (7%).

Principal Investments: Investment grade bonds (93%), misc. investments (4%), real estate (2%), and cash (1%).

Investments in Affiliates: 3%

Group Affiliation: Southern Farm Bureau Casualty

Licensed in: FL

Commenced Business: July 1974

Address: 5700 SW 34th St, Gainesville, FL 32608

Phone: (352) 378-8100   **Domicile State:** FL   **NAIC Code:** 31216

Data Date	Rating	RACR #1	RACR #2	Loss Ratio %	Total Assets ($mil)	Capital ($mil)	Net Premium ($mil)	Net Income ($mil)
6-16	B-	5.11	3.66	N/A	559.1	292.4	122.8	0.9
6-15	B-	4.64	3.26	N/A	551.2	281.2	121.0	13.7
2015	B-	5.05	3.71	73.4	554.4	292.3	238.6	21.4
2014	B-	4.43	3.19	71.3	532.2	269.0	237.3	24.6
2013	B-	3.02	2.11	73.4	502.8	246.3	235.5	19.9
2012	B-	3.00	2.08	74.6	474.0	227.5	226.3	14.8
2011	B-	2.59	1.80	78.2	444.1	212.3	217.0	9.0

Southern Farm Bureau Casualty
Composite Group Rating: B-
Largest Group Members

	Assets ($mil)	Rating
SOUTHERN FARM BUREAU CAS INS CO	2150	B-
FLORIDA FARM BU CASUALTY INS CO	554	B-
MISSISSIPPI FARM BUREAU CAS INS CO	418	B-
SOUTHERN FARM BUREAU PROPERTY	55	U
LOUISIANA FARM BUREAU CAS INS CO	11	B

FOREMOST INS CO   B   Good

Major Rating Factors: History of adequate reserve strength (6.2 on a scale of 0 to 10) as reserves have been consistently at an acceptable level. Fair overall results on stability tests (4.9) including potential drain of affiliation with Farmers Insurance Group of Companies and weak results on operational trends.

Other Rating Factors: Strong long-term capitalization index (10.0) based on excellent current risk adjusted capital (severe and moderate loss scenarios), despite some fluctuation in capital levels. Excellent profitability (7.8) with operating gains in each of the last five years. Superior liquidity (9.4) with ample operational cash flow and liquid investments.

Principal Business: Homeowners multiple peril (44%), fire (19%), allied lines (10%), auto physical damage (9%), auto liability (7%), other liability (4%), and other lines (7%).

Principal Investments: Investment grade bonds (79%), misc. investments (13%), real estate (6%), cash (1%), and non investment grade bonds (1%).

Investments in Affiliates: 7%

Group Affiliation: Farmers Insurance Group of Companies

Licensed in: All states except PR

Commenced Business: June 1952

Address: 5600 Beech Tree Lane, Caledonia, MI 49316-0050

Phone: (616) 942-3000   **Domicile State:** MI   **NAIC Code:** 11185

Data Date	Rating	RACR #1	RACR #2	Loss Ratio %	Total Assets ($mil)	Capital ($mil)	Net Premium ($mil)	Net Income ($mil)
6-16	B	9.59	6.84	N/A	2,292.9	1,112.9	0.0	18.6
6-15	B	9.50	6.79	N/A	2,240.5	1,079.0	0.0	18.1
2015	B	9.74	7.04	0.0	2,172.2	1,093.2	0.0	33.9
2014	B	8.71	6.20	0.0	2,093.3	1,060.1	0.0	27.1
2013	B	10.90	7.99	0.0	1,938.6	1,029.9	0.0	38.5
2012	B	10.73	7.90	0.0	1,774.4	993.5	0.0	40.4
2011	B	8.18	6.59	0.0	1,691.6	948.4	0.0	50.4

Reserve Deficiency (as % of capital)

* Adequate & redundant reserves show as negatives

■ 1 Yr Dev
□ 2 Yr Dev

FRANKENMUTH MUTUAL INS CO

B   **Good**

Major Rating Factors: Good overall profitability index (6.3 on a scale of 0 to 10) despite operating losses during 2011. Good liquidity (6.5) with sufficient resources (cash flows and marketable investments) to handle a spike in claims.
Other Rating Factors: Fair overall results on stability tests (4.9) including weak results on operational trends. Strong long-term capitalization index (8.9) based on excellent current risk adjusted capital (severe and moderate loss scenarios). Moreover, capital levels have been consistent in recent years. Ample reserve history (9.2) that helps to protect the company against sharp claims increases.
Principal Business: Auto liability (24%), commercial multiple peril (21%), auto physical damage (16%), homeowners multiple peril (16%), workers compensation (13%), other liability (4%), and other lines (5%).
Principal Investments: Investment grade bonds (71%), misc. investments (27%), and real estate (3%).
Investments in Affiliates: 13%
Group Affiliation: Frankenmuth Mutual Group
Licensed in: All states except AK, CA, DC, HI, PR
Commenced Business: March 1922
Address: One Mutual Avenue, Frankenmuth, MI 48787-0001
Phone: (989) 652-6121   **Domicile State:** MI   **NAIC Code:** 13986

Data Date	Rating	RACR #1	RACR #2	Loss Ratio %	Total Assets ($mil)	Capital ($mil)	Net Premium ($mil)	Net Income ($mil)
6-16	B	3.34	2.67	N/A	1,242.1	541.9	227.1	26.1
6-15	B	3.04	2.38	N/A	1,154.4	483.6	218.2	16.2
2015	B	3.02	2.40	62.1	1,174.2	508.3	450.8	33.2
2014	B	3.06	2.45	68.9	1,107.4	463.8	427.9	22.1
2013	A	3.13	2.51	63.2	1,069.3	445.0	410.9	40.1
2012	A-	2.81	2.16	70.2	1,015.6	389.8	396.8	29.2
2011	A-	2.68	2.05	84.4	955.0	356.0	399.2	-15.6

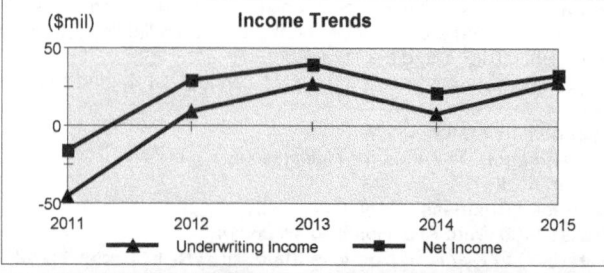

Income Trends

GARRISON P&C INS CO

B   **Good**

Major Rating Factors: History of adequate reserve strength (6.9 on a scale of 0 to 10) as reserves have been consistently at an acceptable level. Good overall profitability index (5.5) despite operating losses during 2011 and the first six months of 2016. Return on equity has been low, averaging 4.1% over the past five years.
Other Rating Factors: Fair liquidity (3.2) as cash resources may not be adequate to cover a spike in claims. Fair overall results on stability tests (4.9) including weak results on operational trends. The largest net exposure for one risk is conservative at 1.4% of capital. Strong long-term capitalization index (8.3) based on excellent current risk adjusted capital (severe and moderate loss scenarios), despite some fluctuation in capital levels.
Principal Business: Auto liability (44%), auto physical damage (34%), homeowners multiple peril (19%), inland marine (1%), allied lines (1%), and fire (1%).
Principal Investments: Investment grade bonds (81%), misc. investments (16%), and non investment grade bonds (3%).
Investments in Affiliates: None
Group Affiliation: USAA Group
Licensed in: All states except PR
Commenced Business: December 1997
Address: 9800 Fredericksburg Rd, San Antonio, TX 78288-0344
Phone: (210) 498-8000   **Domicile State:** TX   **NAIC Code:** 21253

Data Date	Rating	RACR #1	RACR #2	Loss Ratio %	Total Assets ($mil)	Capital ($mil)	Net Premium ($mil)	Net Income ($mil)
6-16	B	2.41	1.79	N/A	1,779.1	649.6	628.6	-17.6
6-15	B	2.17	1.58	N/A	1,555.4	622.5	546.0	21.7
2015	B	2.49	1.89	86.0	1,707.7	655.3	1,190.8	19.0
2014	B	2.10	1.56	81.3	1,492.6	600.1	1,048.0	43.4
2013	B	2.70	2.06	77.4	1,255.5	506.4	710.0	49.2
2012	B	2.69	2.10	83.6	1,107.9	417.8	617.7	22.9
2011	B	2.24	1.88	84.6	972.7	363.2	675.3	-1.3

Reserve Deficiency (as % of capital)

* Adequate & redundant reserves show as negatives

GEICO ADVANTAGE INS CO

B-   **Good**

Major Rating Factors: Fair reserve development (4.7 on a scale of 0 to 10) as reserves have generally been sufficient to cover claims. Fair liquidity (3.9) as cash resources may not be adequate to cover a spike in claims.
Other Rating Factors: Fair overall results on stability tests (4.7) including excessive premium growth, weak results on operational trends and negative cash flow from operations for 2015. Strong long-term capitalization index (7.5) based on excellent current risk adjusted capital (severe and moderate loss scenarios), despite some fluctuation in capital levels. Weak profitability index (2.7) with operating losses during each of the last five years and the first six months of 2016. Average return on equity over the last five years has been poor at -14.0%.
Principal Business: Auto liability (59%) and auto physical damage (41%).
Principal Investments: Misc. investments (63%) and investment grade bonds (37%).
Investments in Affiliates: None
Group Affiliation: Berkshire-Hathaway
Licensed in: All states except CA, FL, HI, ME, MA, MI, MN, NY, ND, SD, VT, PR
Commenced Business: November 2011
Address: 1440 Kiewit Plaza, Omaha, NE 68131
Phone: (800) 841-3000   **Domicile State:** NE   **NAIC Code:** 14138

Data Date	Rating	RACR #1	RACR #2	Loss Ratio %	Total Assets ($mil)	Capital ($mil)	Net Premium ($mil)	Net Income ($mil)
6-16	B-	1.61	1.21	N/A	1,177.8	537.2	307.0	-91.3
6-15	C+	1.81	1.25	N/A	791.2	376.5	177.8	-53.6
2015	B-	1.89	1.39	100.5	1,011.4	532.8	476.5	-115.2
2014	C+	2.49	1.65	103.0	779.7	446.6	192.6	-54.7
2013	C+	4.75	3.61	107.4	629.6	484.6	215.6	-85.3
2012	A-	10.23	7.53	102.7	249.1	208.2	44.3	-17.1
2011	U	133.64	66.82	0.0	225.0	225.0	0.0	0.0

Reserve Deficiency (as % of capital)

* Adequate & redundant reserves show as negatives

GEICO CASUALTY CO   C-   Fair

Major Rating Factors: Weak profitability index (2.7 on a scale of 0 to 10) with operating losses during each of the last five years and the first six months of 2016. Average return on equity over the last five years has been poor at -22.7%. Vulnerable liquidity (2.4) as a spike in claims may stretch capacity.

Other Rating Factors: Fair overall results on stability tests (3.3) including weak results on operational trends. Strong long-term capitalization index (7.4) based on excellent current risk adjusted capital (severe and moderate loss scenarios), despite some fluctuation in capital levels. Ample reserve history (9.6) that helps to protect the company against sharp claims increases.

Principal Business: Auto liability (60%) and auto physical damage (40%).

Principal Investments: Misc. investments (66%) and investment grade bonds (34%).

Investments in Affiliates: None
Group Affiliation: Berkshire-Hathaway
Licensed in: All states except MI, PR
Commenced Business: May 1983
Address: 5260 Western Ave, Chevy Chasse, MD 20815-3799
Phone: (800) 841-3000   **Domicile State:** MD   **NAIC Code:** 41491

Data Date	Rating	RACR #1	RACR #2	Loss Ratio %	Total Assets ($mil)	Capital ($mil)	Net Premium ($mil)	Net Income ($mil)
6-16	C-	1.65	1.21	N/A	2,755.4	918.5	859.3	-5.9
6-15	D	2.06	1.42	N/A	2,485.2	911.5	752.9	-70.2
2015	D+	1.74	1.28	90.8	2,605.9	929.8	1,619.8	-125.3
2014	D	2.45	1.63	83.2	2,347.3	979.9	657.8	-44.1
2013	D-	1.64	1.37	90.9	2,707.2	1,001.0	2,209.4	-342.5
2012	D-	1.73	1.48	87.7	1,712.6	661.8	1,381.8	-252.0
2011	D-	1.30	1.16	81.5	856.1	250.4	680.6	-84.5

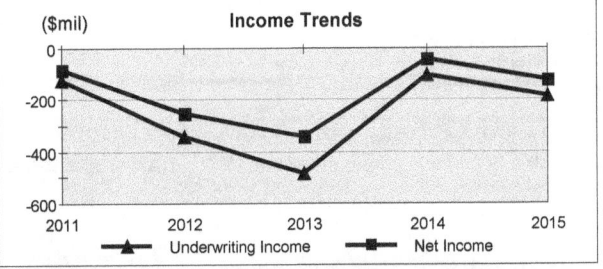

Income Trends (Underwriting Income / Net Income)

GEICO CHOICE INS CO *   A-   Excellent

Major Rating Factors: Strong long-term capitalization index (7.8 on a scale of 0 to 10) based on excellent current risk adjusted capital (severe and moderate loss scenarios), despite some fluctuation in capital levels. Good liquidity (5.7) with sufficient resources (cash flows and marketable investments) to handle a spike in claims.

Other Rating Factors: Good overall results on stability tests (5.5) despite excessive premium growth, weak results on operational trends and negative cash flow from operations for 2015. Fair reserve development (3.9) as reserves have generally been sufficient to cover claims. Weak profitability index (2.8) with operating losses during each of the last five years and the first six months of 2016. Average return on equity over the last five years has been poor at -9.5%.

Principal Business: Auto liability (61%) and auto physical damage (39%).

Principal Investments: Misc. investments (53%) and investment grade bonds (47%).

Investments in Affiliates: None
Group Affiliation: Berkshire-Hathaway
Licensed in: All states except CA, FL, HI, ME, MA, MI, MN, NY, ND, SD, VT, PR
Commenced Business: November 2011
Address: 1440 Kiewit Plaza, Omaha, NE 68131
Phone: (800) 841-3000   **Domicile State:** NE   **NAIC Code:** 14139

Data Date	Rating	RACR #1	RACR #2	Loss Ratio %	Total Assets ($mil)	Capital ($mil)	Net Premium ($mil)	Net Income ($mil)
6-16	A-	1.94	1.35	N/A	647.0	266.3	192.5	-28.2
6-15	A-	2.11	1.38	N/A	450.7	203.5	124.7	-20.5
2015	A-	2.37	1.65	93.2	600.9	295.7	315.1	-41.5
2014	A-	2.58	1.65	90.7	411.4	229.4	134.5	-13.9
2013	A-	3.88	2.79	99.4	339.5	236.8	163.6	-37.4
2012	A-	13.29	9.34	104.2	248.5	212.9	40.1	-12.5
2011	U	133.64	66.82	0.0	225.0	225.0	0.0	0.0

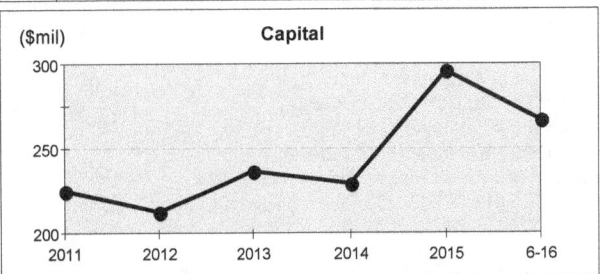

Capital

GEICO GENERAL INS CO *   B+   Good

Major Rating Factors: Good overall results on stability tests (5.0 on a scale of 0 to 10) despite weak results on operational trends. Strong long-term capitalization index (10.0) based on excellent current risk adjusted capital (severe and moderate loss scenarios). Moreover, capital levels have been consistent in recent years.

Other Rating Factors: Excellent profitability (7.1) with operating gains in each of the last five years. Excellent expense controls. Superior liquidity (10.0) with ample operational cash flow and liquid investments.

Principal Business: (Not applicable due to unusual reinsurance transactions.)

Principal Investments: Investment grade bonds (75%), cash (19%), and misc. investments (6%).

Investments in Affiliates: None
Group Affiliation: Berkshire-Hathaway
Licensed in: All states except PR
Commenced Business: May 1934
Address: 5260 Western Avenue, Chevy Chase, MD 20815-3799
Phone: (800) 841-3000   **Domicile State:** MD   **NAIC Code:** 35882

Data Date	Rating	RACR #1	RACR #2	Loss Ratio %	Total Assets ($mil)	Capital ($mil)	Net Premium ($mil)	Net Income ($mil)
6-16	B+	19.76	17.79	N/A	226.3	153.6	0.0	0.2
6-15	B+	17.17	15.45	N/A	222.0	140.4	0.0	0.1
2015	B+	18.69	16.82	0.0	209.5	141.4	0.0	0.2
2014	B+	15.86	14.27	0.0	214.8	131.1	0.0	0.3
2013	B+	14.30	12.87	0.0	215.7	123.6	0.0	2.8
2012	B+	14.96	13.47	0.0	184.2	114.4	0.0	1.7
2011	B+	13.46	12.11	0.0	180.3	105.7	0.0	2.5

Berkshire-Hathaway Composite Group Rating: B Largest Group Members	Assets ($mil)	Rating
NATIONAL INDEMNITY CO	161777	B
GOVERNMENT EMPLOYEES INS CO	24036	B
COLUMBIA INS CO	19102	C+
BERKSHIRE HATHAWAY LIFE INS CO OF NE	16287	C+
GENERAL REINS CORP	15320	C+

GEICO INDEMNITY CO | B | Good

Major Rating Factors: Good overall results on stability tests (5.1 on a scale of 0 to 10) despite potential drain of affiliation with Berkshire-Hathaway and weak results on operational trends. Good liquidity (6.4) with sufficient resources (cash flows and marketable investments) to handle a spike in claims.

Other Rating Factors: Strong long-term capitalization index (7.3) based on excellent current risk adjusted capital (severe and moderate loss scenarios), despite some fluctuation in capital levels. Ample reserve history (9.6) that helps to protect the company against sharp claims increases. Excellent profitability (8.4) with operating gains in each of the last five years. Return on equity has been good over the last five years, averaging 13.4%.

Principal Business: Auto liability (64%) and auto physical damage (36%).

Principal Investments: Misc. investments (79%) and investment grade bonds (21%).

Investments in Affiliates: 16%

Group Affiliation: Berkshire-Hathaway

Licensed in: All states except PR

Commenced Business: September 1961

Address: 5260 Western Ave, Chevy Chase, MD 20815-3799

Phone: (800) 841-3000   **Domicile State:** MD   **NAIC Code:** 22055

Data Date	Rating	RACR #1	RACR #2	Loss Ratio %	Total Assets ($mil)	Capital ($mil)	Net Premium ($mil)	Net Income ($mil)
6-16	B	2.19	1.67	N/A	7,092.5	3,906.9	1,218.7	82.5
6-15	B	2.28	1.69	N/A	7,212.7	4,050.4	1,164.8	79.5
2015	B	2.19	1.66	80.3	7,138.7	4,075.9	2,397.8	133.0
2014	B	2.25	1.67	47.4	6,962.8	4,018.3	530.9	409.2
2013	B+	1.75	1.38	73.2	7,811.2	3,636.3	4,411.5	663.6
2012	B+	1.71	1.38	69.0	6,443.7	2,748.9	4,206.7	607.7
2011	B+	1.55	1.22	76.6	5,845.4	2,097.7	4,069.7	376.0

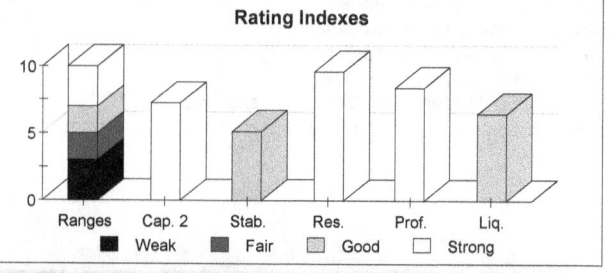

Rating Indexes

(Ranges, Cap. 2, Stab., Res., Prof., Liq. — Weak, Fair, Good, Strong)

GEICO SECURE INS CO * | A- | Excellent

Major Rating Factors: Strong long-term capitalization index (8.7 on a scale of 0 to 10) based on excellent current risk adjusted capital (severe and moderate loss scenarios). Furthermore, this high level of risk adjusted capital has been consistently maintained in previous years. Good liquidity (6.7) with sufficient resources (cash flows and marketable investments) to handle a spike in claims.

Other Rating Factors: Good overall results on stability tests (5.9) despite weak results on operational trends and excessive premium growth. Fair reserve development (4.7) as reserves have generally been sufficient to cover claims. Fair profitability index (3.5) with operating losses during 2012, 2013, 2014 and the first six months of 2016. Average return on equity over the last five years has been poor at -2.8%.

Principal Business: Auto liability (67%) and auto physical damage (33%).

Principal Investments: Misc. investments (68%) and investment grade bonds (32%).

Investments in Affiliates: None

Group Affiliation: Berkshire-Hathaway

Licensed in: All states except CA, FL, HI, ME, MA, MI, MN, NY, ND, SD, VT, PR

Commenced Business: November 2011

Address: 1440 Kiewit Plaza, Omaha, NE 68131

Phone: (800) 841-3000   **Domicile State:** NE   **NAIC Code:** 14137

Data Date	Rating	RACR #1	RACR #2	Loss Ratio %	Total Assets ($mil)	Capital ($mil)	Net Premium ($mil)	Net Income ($mil)
6-16	A-	3.29	2.20	N/A	436.8	259.4	89.0	-6.0
6-15	A-	3.57	2.22	N/A	427.9	263.2	60.6	-5.8
2015	A-	3.26	2.12	86.7	417.5	269.1	147.3	-13.3
2014	A-	3.65	2.24	80.4	413.6	273.1	66.3	-1.9
2013	A-	7.75	5.16	91.7	322.2	266.6	82.7	-14.3
2012	A-	20.77	13.14	92.2	238.9	220.3	21.1	-5.1
2011	U	133.64	66.82	0.0	225.0	225.0	0.0	0.0

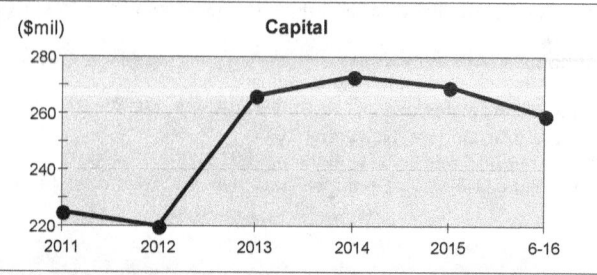

($mil) Capital

(2011, 2012, 2013, 2014, 2015, 6-16)

GENERAL CASUALTY CO OF WI | C | Fair

Major Rating Factors: Fair overall results on stability tests (4.2 on a scale of 0 to 10) including potential drain of affiliation with QBE Ins Group Ltd, excessive premium growth, weak results on operational trends and negative cash flow from operations for 2015. Fair reserve development (4.7) as reserves have generally been sufficient to cover claims.

Other Rating Factors: Fair profitability index (3.1) with operating losses during 2011, 2012 and 2013. Return on equity has been low, averaging 0.6% over the past five years. Good liquidity (5.6) with sufficient resources (cash flows and marketable investments) to handle a spike in claims. Strong long-term capitalization index (7.3) based on excellent current risk adjusted capital (severe and moderate loss scenarios), despite some fluctuation in capital levels.

Principal Business: Commercial multiple peril (35%), auto liability (18%), workers compensation (14%), homeowners multiple peril (11%), auto physical damage (9%), other liability (8%), and other lines (5%).

Principal Investments: Misc. investments (61%), investment grade bonds (36%), and real estate (6%).

Investments in Affiliates: 44%

Group Affiliation: QBE Ins Group Ltd

Licensed in: All states, the District of Columbia and Puerto Rico

Commenced Business: May 1925

Address: One General Dr, Sun Prairie, WI 53596

Phone: (608) 825-5160   **Domicile State:** WI   **NAIC Code:** 24414

Data Date	Rating	RACR #1	RACR #2	Loss Ratio %	Total Assets ($mil)	Capital ($mil)	Net Premium ($mil)	Net Income ($mil)
6-16	C	1.63	1.32	N/A	1,086.9	316.1	187.0	10.3
6-15	C	1.66	1.44	N/A	866.9	320.0	105.4	4.2
2015	C	1.75	1.51	63.9	695.7	317.9	180.2	13.0
2014	C	1.62	1.41	69.2	762.3	309.6	228.3	1.7
2013	C	1.41	1.20	75.2	866.6	312.7	312.2	0.0
2012	B-	1.57	1.36	73.5	1,025.0	448.1	280.2	-0.1
2011	B-	1.68	1.49	74.3	1,205.3	481.5	447.8	-21.9

QBE Ins Group Ltd
Composite Group Rating: B-
Largest Group Members

	Assets ($mil)	Rating
QBE INS CORP	2136	B-
NAU COUNTRY INS CO	1306	C
QBE REINS CORP	1148	B
PRAETORIAN INS CO	872	C
GENERAL CASUALTY CO OF WI	696	C

GENERAL REINS CORP   C+   Fair

Major Rating Factors: Fair overall results on stability tests (3.6 on a scale of 0 to 10) including fair financial strength of affiliated Berkshire-Hathaway and weak results on operational trends. The largest net exposure for one risk is high at 3.4% of capital. Good overall profitability index (6.4). Weak expense controls. Return on equity has been fair, averaging 6.7% over the past five years.

Other Rating Factors: Strong long-term capitalization index (7.5) based on excellent current risk adjusted capital (severe and moderate loss scenarios), despite some fluctuation in capital levels. Ample reserve history (7.9) that can protect against increases in claims costs. Superior liquidity (9.1) with ample operational cash flow and liquid investments.

Principal Business: Aircraft (100%).

Principal Investments: Misc. investments (82%), investment grade bonds (17%), and non investment grade bonds (1%).

Investments in Affiliates: 45%

Group Affiliation: Berkshire-Hathaway

Licensed in: All states, the District of Columbia and Puerto Rico

Commenced Business: January 1973

Address: 1209 ORANGE St, Wilmington, DE 19801

Phone: (203) 328-5000   **Domicile State:** DE   **NAIC Code:** 22039

Data Date	Rating	RACR #1	RACR #2	Loss Ratio %	Total Assets ($mil)	Capital ($mil)	Net Premium ($mil)	Net Income ($mil)
6-16	C+	1.60	1.44	N/A	15,099.1	11,105.1	274.2	609.3
6-15	C+	1.58	1.39	N/A	16,251.0	11,845.8	300.2	189.4
2015	C+	1.51	1.34	56.8	15,320.5	11,050.5	548.5	570.7
2014	C+	1.56	1.36	41.8	16,157.5	11,706.6	593.4	538.2
2013	B-	1.51	1.33	30.7	16,219.7	11,561.7	543.0	930.9
2012	B-	1.51	1.31	54.8	15,532.9	10,693.2	567.5	432.9
2011	B-	1.43	1.24	65.1	14,004.1	9,160.4	541.4	858.5

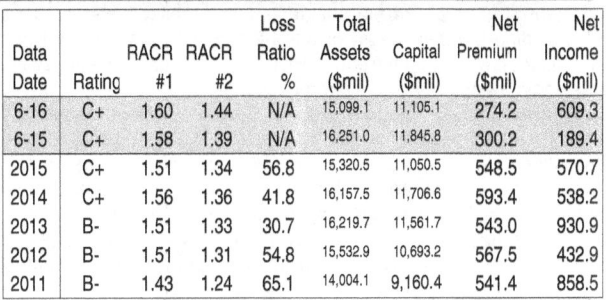

Rating Indexes

(Ranges, Cap. 2, Stab., Res., Prof., Liq. — Weak, Fair, Good, Strong)

GENERAL STAR INDEMNITY CO   C   Fair

Major Rating Factors: Fair profitability index (3.8 on a scale of 0 to 10). Weak expense controls. Return on equity has been low, averaging 4.1% over the past five years. Fair overall results on stability tests (4.0) including weak results on operational trends. The largest net exposure for one risk is conservative at 1.7% of capital.

Other Rating Factors: Strong long-term capitalization index (9.8) based on excellent current risk adjusted capital (severe and moderate loss scenarios), despite some fluctuation in capital levels. Ample reserve history (8.8) that helps to protect the company against sharp claims increases. Superior liquidity (9.7) with ample operational cash flow and liquid investments.

Principal Business: Other liability (40%), allied lines (30%), fire (11%), products liability (7%), medical malpractice (7%), inland marine (2%), and other lines (3%).

Principal Investments: Investment grade bonds (62%) and misc. investments (38%).

Investments in Affiliates: None

Group Affiliation: Berkshire-Hathaway

Licensed in: All states, the District of Columbia and Puerto Rico

Commenced Business: May 1979

Address: 1209 Orange St, Wilmington, DE 19801

Phone: (203) 328-5700   **Domicile State:** DE   **NAIC Code:** 37362

Data Date	Rating	RACR #1	RACR #2	Loss Ratio %	Total Assets ($mil)	Capital ($mil)	Net Premium ($mil)	Net Income ($mil)
6-16	C	5.13	3.21	N/A	749.0	523.8	32.2	4.8
6-15	C	4.82	3.01	N/A	849.1	613.3	35.3	2.5
2015	C	4.60	2.85	60.3	774.7	543.3	66.8	7.9
2014	C	4.82	3.00	54.6	848.9	616.0	72.3	10.4
2013	B-	6.24	3.84	39.8	859.4	645.8	70.3	47.6
2012	B-	7.17	4.49	27.6	748.4	566.4	58.6	14.0
2011	B-	7.74	4.99	15.1	696.6	508.7	47.7	43.2

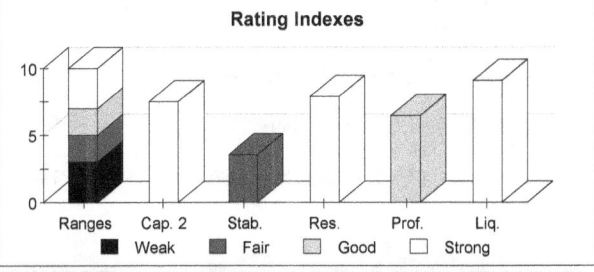

($mil) Income Trends

2011 2012 2013 2014 2015

Underwriting Income   Net Income

GENWORTH MORTGAGE INS CORP   C   Fair

Major Rating Factors: Fair overall results on stability tests (4.0 on a scale of 0 to 10) including weak results on operational trends. Strengths include potentially strong support from affiliation with Genworth Financial. Fair reserve development (3.2) as the level of reserves has at times been insufficient to cover claims. In 2012 and 2011 the two year reserve development was 43% and 138% deficient respectively.

Other Rating Factors: Fair profitability index (3.6) with operating losses during 2011 and 2012. Average return on equity over the last five years has been poor at -14.3%. Good liquidity (6.6) with sufficient resources (cash flows and marketable investments) to handle a spike in claims. Strong long-term capitalization index (7.4) based on excellent current risk adjusted capital (severe and moderate loss scenarios), despite some fluctuation in capital levels.

Principal Business: Mortgage guaranty (100%).

Principal Investments: Investment grade bonds (74%), misc. investments (23%), and non investment grade bonds (3%).

Investments in Affiliates: 18%

Group Affiliation: Genworth Financial

Licensed in: All states except PR

Commenced Business: May 1980

Address: 6601 Six Forks Road, Raleigh, NC 27615

Phone: (919) 846-4100   **Domicile State:** NC   **NAIC Code:** 38458

Data Date	Rating	RACR #1	RACR #2	Loss Ratio %	Total Assets ($mil)	Capital ($mil)	Net Premium ($mil)	Net Income ($mil)
6-16	C	1.57	1.34	N/A	2,817.4	1,162.9	288.8	174.8
6-15	C	1.56	1.37	N/A	2,745.3	1,397.2	259.2	158.1
2015	C	1.42	1.21	35.9	2,627.1	1,073.1	621.1	261.7
2014	C	1.50	1.30	61.0	2,866.0	1,395.8	572.6	179.1
2013	C-	0.88	0.77	77.1	2,390.3	990.2	477.9	77.3
2012	D+	0.41	0.32	139.4	2,247.3	485.6	455.3	-152.3
2011	D+	0.41	0.32	232.0	2,682.2	564.0	483.0	-604.5

Rating Indexes

(Ranges, Cap. 2, Stab., Res., Prof., Liq. — Weak, Fair, Good, Strong)

GEORGIA FARM BUREAU MUTUAL INS CO   B-   Good

Major Rating Factors: Fair overall results on stability tests (4.1 on a scale of 0 to 10) including potential drain of affiliation with Georgia Farm Bureau Ins and weak results on operational trends. History of adequate reserve strength (5.9) as reserves have been consistently at an acceptable level.

Other Rating Factors: Good liquidity (5.6) with sufficient resources (cash flows and marketable investments) to handle a spike in claims. Strong long-term capitalization index (7.4) based on excellent current risk adjusted capital (severe and moderate loss scenarios), despite some fluctuation in capital levels. Weak profitability index (2.9) with operating losses during 2011 and 2015.

Principal Business: Auto liability (32%), homeowners multiple peril (26%), auto physical damage (22%), farmowners multiple peril (16%), commercial multiple peril (2%), allied lines (1%), and fire (1%).

Principal Investments: Investment grade bonds (75%), misc. investments (20%), and cash (5%).

Investments in Affiliates: 2%
Group Affiliation: Georgia Farm Bureau Ins
Licensed in: GA
Commenced Business: January 1959
Address: 1620 Bass Rd, Macon, GA 31210
Phone: (478) 474-8411   **Domicile State:** GA   **NAIC Code:** 14001

Data Date	Rating	RACR #1	RACR #2	Loss Ratio %	Total Assets ($mil)	Capital ($mil)	Net Premium ($mil)	Net Income ($mil)
6-16	B-	1.88	1.28	N/A	674.5	242.8	226.3	6.1
6-15	C	2.11	1.43	N/A	671.7	262.8	214.8	4.0
2015	C+	1.85	1.28	73.5	665.6	237.2	437.9	-4.1
2014	C	2.13	1.47	67.7	651.1	260.4	414.2	19.7
2013	C	2.07	1.41	74.3	620.6	258.1	401.4	2.6
2012	C	2.06	1.40	69.7	609.5	243.5	380.7	19.3
2011	C-	1.92	1.32	88.4	594.8	226.6	400.7	-49.7

Rating Indexes

GOVERNMENT EMPLOYEES INS CO   B   Good

Major Rating Factors: Good overall results on stability tests (5.1 on a scale of 0 to 10) despite potential drain of affiliation with Berkshire-Hathaway and weak results on operational trends. Good liquidity (6.6) with sufficient resources (cash flows and marketable investments) to handle a spike in claims.

Other Rating Factors: Strong long-term capitalization index (7.8) based on excellent current risk adjusted capital (severe and moderate loss scenarios), despite some fluctuation in capital levels. Ample reserve history (9.5) that helps to protect the company against sharp claims increases. Excellent profitability (8.6) with operating gains in each of the last five years. Return on equity has been good over the last five years, averaging 12.4%.

Principal Business: Auto liability (59%), auto physical damage (39%), and other liability (2%).

Principal Investments: Misc. investments (76%), investment grade bonds (24%), non investment grade bonds (1%), and real estate (1%).

Investments in Affiliates: 1%
Group Affiliation: Berkshire-Hathaway
Licensed in: All states except PR
Commenced Business: December 1937
Address: 5260 Western Ave, Chevy Chase, MD 20815-3799
Phone: (800) 841-3000   **Domicile State:** MD   **NAIC Code:** 22063

Data Date	Rating	RACR #1	RACR #2	Loss Ratio %	Total Assets ($mil)	Capital ($mil)	Net Premium ($mil)	Net Income ($mil)
6-16	B	3.37	2.15	N/A	23,562.9	13,622.6	3,344.0	384.8
6-15	B	3.21	1.99	N/A	24,162.4	13,863.5	3,094.3	280.4
2015	B	3.21	2.04	82.3	24,036.2	13,930.5	6,468.3	1,152.6
2014	B	3.43	2.13	36.2	23,472.6	13,443.0	649.5	1,725.3
2013	B+	2.67	1.81	77.3	25,778.8	12,089.8	11,644.8	2,010.1
2012	B+	2.14	1.52	80.2	19,089.6	8,017.6	11,118.7	1,026.0
2011	B+	1.91	1.40	81.3	16,974.9	6,132.3	10,628.3	901.7

Rating Indexes

GRANGE MUTUAL CAS CO   B   Good

Major Rating Factors: History of adequate reserve strength (6.2 on a scale of 0 to 10) as reserves have been consistently at an acceptable level. Good liquidity (6.2) with sufficient resources (cash flows and marketable investments) to handle a spike in claims.

Other Rating Factors: Fair overall results on stability tests (4.8) including potential drain of affiliation with Grange Mutual Casualty Group and weak results on operational trends. Strong long-term capitalization index (8.6) based on excellent current risk adjusted capital (severe and moderate loss scenarios). Moreover, capital levels have been consistent in recent years. Excellent profitability (8.3) with operating gains in each of the last five years.

Principal Business: Auto liability (28%), auto physical damage (21%), commercial multiple peril (19%), homeowners multiple peril (19%), farmowners multiple peril (4%), fire (2%), and other lines (6%).

Principal Investments: Investment grade bonds (45%), misc. investments (40%), non investment grade bonds (7%), real estate (5%), and cash (3%).

Investments in Affiliates: 12%
Group Affiliation: Grange Mutual Casualty Group
Licensed in: AL, GA, IL, IN, IA, KS, KY, MN, MO, OH, PA, SC, TN, VA, WI
Commenced Business: April 1935
Address: 650 S Front St, Columbus, OH 43206-1014
Phone: (614) 445-2900   **Domicile State:** OH   **NAIC Code:** 14060

Data Date	Rating	RACR #1	RACR #2	Loss Ratio %	Total Assets ($mil)	Capital ($mil)	Net Premium ($mil)	Net Income ($mil)
6-16	B	2.89	2.09	N/A	2,258.8	1,119.8	498.9	43.1
6-15	B	3.05	2.24	N/A	2,202.2	1,080.8	511.3	38.8
2015	B	2.83	2.06	69.1	2,192.2	1,068.1	1,026.8	57.2
2014	B	3.01	2.22	68.9	2,120.6	1,047.3	1,021.2	33.1
2013	B+	3.02	2.18	67.0	2,011.8	1,010.2	957.4	47.4
2012	B+	2.97	2.14	69.0	1,858.6	915.3	888.7	37.7
2011	B+	2.88	2.01	70.5	1,716.5	838.6	863.9	25.2

Reserve Deficiency (as % of capital)

* Adequate & redundant reserves show as negatives

GREAT AMERICAN INS CO
B-   **Good**

Major Rating Factors: Fair overall results on stability tests (3.6 on a scale of 0 to 10) including weak results on operational trends. The largest net exposure for one risk is high at 4.1% of capital. Good liquidity (6.7) with sufficient resources (cash flows and marketable investments) to handle a spike in claims.

Other Rating Factors: Strong long-term capitalization index (7.5) based on excellent current risk adjusted capital (severe and moderate loss scenarios), despite some fluctuation in capital levels. Ample reserve history (8.2) that helps to protect the company against sharp claims increases. Excellent profitability (8.5) with operating gains in each of the last five years. Return on equity has been excellent over the last five years averaging 16.8%.

Principal Business: Allied lines (48%), other liability (21%), credit (6%), surety (5%), ocean marine (5%), fidelity (5%), and other lines (11%).

Principal Investments: Investment grade bonds (59%), misc. investments (36%), non investment grade bonds (3%), cash (1%), and real estate (1%).

Investments in Affiliates: 11%

Group Affiliation: American Financial Group Inc

Licensed in: All states, the District of Columbia and Puerto Rico

Commenced Business: March 1872

Address: 580 Walnut St, Cincinnati, OH 45202

Phone: (513) 369-5000   **Domicile State:** OH   **NAIC Code:** 16691

Data Date	Rating	RACR #1	RACR #2	Loss Ratio %	Total Assets ($mil)	Capital ($mil)	Net Premium ($mil)	Net Income ($mil)
6-16	B-	1.88	1.37	N/A	6,188.9	1,685.9	1,081.0	147.5
6-15	B-	1.70	1.25	N/A	5,703.0	1,473.1	990.5	141.0
2015	B-	1.76	1.28	55.6	6,110.9	1,550.9	2,354.2	294.2
2014	B-	1.62	1.19	59.0	5,811.7	1,413.6	2,256.9	221.5
2013	B-	1.79	1.31	59.1	5,376.9	1,403.3	2,100.1	273.7
2012	C+	1.86	1.40	65.4	5,132.6	1,469.6	1,862.4	141.1
2011	C+	1.84	1.35	61.2	5,273.6	1,411.3	1,786.2	276.8

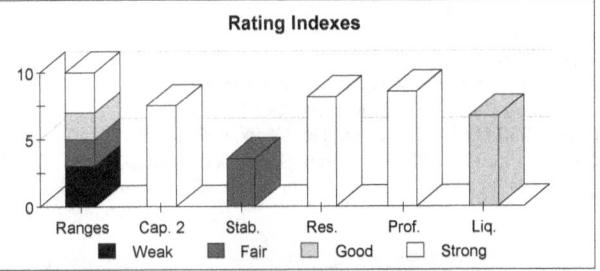

Rating Indexes

GREAT NORTHERN INS CO
B   **Good**

Major Rating Factors: Good overall profitability index (6.5 on a scale of 0 to 10). Fair expense controls. Return on equity has been excellent over the last five years averaging 15.9%. Good liquidity (6.8) with sufficient resources (cash flows and marketable investments) to handle a spike in claims.

Other Rating Factors: Fair overall results on stability tests (4.3) including weak results on operational trends. The largest net exposure for one risk is high at 3.5% of capital. Strong long-term capitalization index (8.3) based on excellent current risk adjusted capital (severe and moderate loss scenarios), despite some fluctuation in capital levels. Ample reserve history (8.9) that helps to protect the company against sharp claims increases.

Principal Business: Homeowners multiple peril (42%), commercial multiple peril (22%), inland marine (10%), auto liability (7%), other liability (5%), auto physical damage (5%), and other lines (9%).

Principal Investments: Investment grade bonds (93%), misc. investments (6%), and non investment grade bonds (1%).

Investments in Affiliates: None

Group Affiliation: Chubb Limited

Licensed in: All states except PR

Commenced Business: August 1952

Address: 100 S 5th St #1800, Minneapolis, MN 55402-1225

Phone: (908) 903-2000   **Domicile State:** IN   **NAIC Code:** 20303

Data Date	Rating	RACR #1	RACR #2	Loss Ratio %	Total Assets ($mil)	Capital ($mil)	Net Premium ($mil)	Net Income ($mil)
6-16	B	2.91	1.86	N/A	1,666.2	459.6	155.6	49.3
6-15	B	2.79	1.79	N/A	1,663.1	471.1	191.6	30.8
2015	B	2.87	1.83	56.5	1,647.5	469.2	391.3	81.2
2014	B	2.94	1.88	56.7	1,641.7	477.0	375.8	80.3
2013	B	2.97	1.92	52.7	1,653.1	478.8	360.6	83.4
2012	B	2.68	1.71	67.3	1,625.6	438.6	347.1	54.2
2011	B+	2.69	1.74	68.4	1,581.5	436.7	341.0	55.1

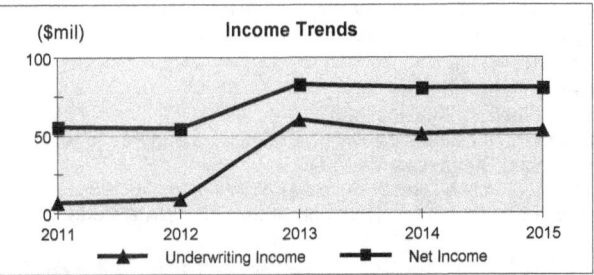

($mil)   Income Trends

GREAT WEST CASUALTY CO
B   **Good**

Major Rating Factors: Good liquidity (6.4 on a scale of 0 to 10) with sufficient resources (cash flows and marketable investments) to handle a spike in claims. Fair overall results on stability tests (4.8) including weak results on operational trends.

Other Rating Factors: Strong long-term capitalization index (8.7) based on excellent current risk adjusted capital (severe and moderate loss scenarios), despite some fluctuation in capital levels. Ample reserve history (9.4) that helps to protect the company against sharp claims increases. Excellent profitability (8.8) with operating gains in each of the last five years. Return on equity has been good over the last five years, averaging 12.0%.

Principal Business: Auto liability (47%), auto physical damage (28%), workers compensation (14%), inland marine (8%), and other liability (3%).

Principal Investments: Investment grade bonds (72%), misc. investments (24%), and non investment grade bonds (4%).

Investments in Affiliates: None

Group Affiliation: Old Republic Group

Licensed in: All states except HI, PR

Commenced Business: April 1956

Address: 1100 W 29th St, South Sioux City, NE 68776

Phone: (402) 494-2411   **Domicile State:** NE   **NAIC Code:** 11371

Data Date	Rating	RACR #1	RACR #2	Loss Ratio %	Total Assets ($mil)	Capital ($mil)	Net Premium ($mil)	Net Income ($mil)
6-16	B	3.39	2.06	N/A	2,008.2	613.3	414.6	33.1
6-15	B	3.72	2.27	N/A	1,892.1	574.7	392.2	33.4
2015	B	3.58	2.20	71.4	1,953.1	586.2	849.2	70.5
2014	B	3.89	2.38	71.4	1,848.4	573.1	787.9	88.9
2013	A-	4.30	2.67	71.3	1,736.6	546.9	712.5	65.1
2012	A-	4.47	2.79	74.0	1,635.6	514.9	668.8	44.1
2011	A-	4.83	3.02	72.3	1,571.2	507.4	594.5	65.0

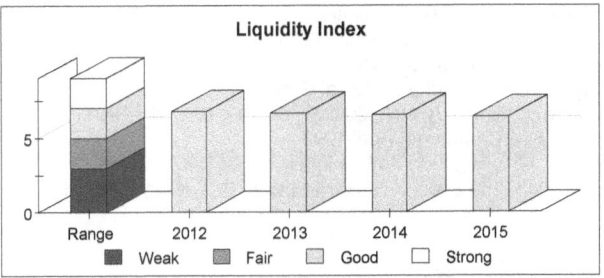

Liquidity Index

GREATER NEW YORK MUTUAL INS CO   B-   Good

Major Rating Factors: Fair overall results on stability tests (4.3 on a scale of 0 to 10) including potential drain of affiliation with Greater New York Group and weak results on operational trends. History of adequate reserve strength (6.2) as reserves have been consistently at an acceptable level.

Other Rating Factors: Good overall profitability index (5.1) despite operating losses during 2011. Good liquidity (6.9) with sufficient resources (cash flows and marketable investments) to handle a spike in claims. Strong long-term capitalization index (8.4) based on excellent current risk adjusted capital (severe and moderate loss scenarios), despite some fluctuation in capital levels.

Principal Business: Commercial multiple peril (95%), workers compensation (2%), and other liability (1%).

Principal Investments: Investment grade bonds (69%), misc. investments (28%), cash (2%), and non investment grade bonds (1%).

Investments in Affiliates: 16%

Group Affiliation: Greater New York Group

Licensed in: All states except AK, CA, FL, HI, TX, PR

Commenced Business: November 1927

Address: 200 Madison Avenue, New York, NY 10016

Phone: (212) 683-9700   **Domicile State:** NY   **NAIC Code:** 22187

Data Date	Rating	RACR #1	RACR #2	Loss Ratio %	Total Assets ($mil)	Capital ($mil)	Net Premium ($mil)	Net Income ($mil)
6-16	B-	2.30	1.96	N/A	971.5	458.7	116.7	6.9
6-15	B-	2.29	1.93	N/A	939.9	431.9	110.2	0.1
2015	B-	2.29	1.97	68.7	942.0	443.9	228.8	13.4
2014	B-	2.37	2.02	67.6	905.4	430.8	213.1	15.6
2013	B-	2.41	2.00	61.1	863.7	414.5	196.7	18.0
2012	B-	2.53	2.26	75.1	859.6	388.6	179.2	2.9
2011	B	2.57	2.19	94.2	840.4	387.0	168.2	-19.0

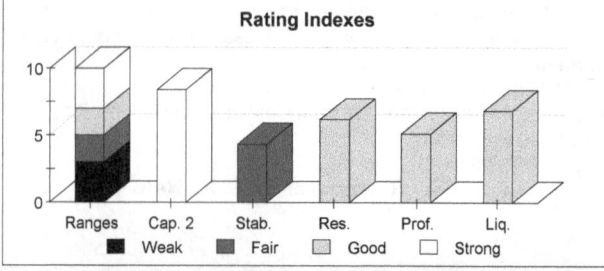

Rating Indexes

GREENWICH INS CO   C   Fair

Major Rating Factors: Fair overall results on stability tests (3.8 on a scale of 0 to 10) including potential drain of affiliation with XL Group Ltd and weak results on operational trends. The largest net exposure for one risk is conservative at 1.5% of capital. Fair profitability index (3.5). Fair expense controls. Return on equity has been fair, averaging 6.6% over the past five years.

Other Rating Factors: Strong long-term capitalization index (7.6) based on excellent current risk adjusted capital (severe and moderate loss scenarios), despite some fluctuation in capital levels. Ample reserve history (7.5) that can protect against increases in claims costs. Excellent liquidity (7.7) with ample operational cash flow and liquid investments.

Principal Business: Other liability (58%), allied lines (17%), auto liability (13%), workers compensation (3%), commercial multiple peril (3%), aggregate write-ins for other lines of business (2%), and other lines (4%).

Principal Investments: Investment grade bonds (65%), cash (18%), and misc. investments (17%).

Investments in Affiliates: 25%

Group Affiliation: XL Group Ltd

Licensed in: All states, the District of Columbia and Puerto Rico

Commenced Business: May 1946

Address: 1201 N Market St Suite 501, Wilmington, DE 19801

Phone: (203) 964-5200   **Domicile State:** DE   **NAIC Code:** 22322

Data Date	Rating	RACR #1	RACR #2	Loss Ratio %	Total Assets ($mil)	Capital ($mil)	Net Premium ($mil)	Net Income ($mil)
6-16	C	1.62	1.40	N/A	1,118.6	352.2	83.3	21.1
6-15	C	1.50	1.32	N/A	1,050.6	351.2	76.0	23.7
2015	C	1.63	1.42	71.2	1,088.3	350.4	159.3	21.0
2014	C	1.71	1.51	61.5	1,073.1	397.3	152.0	35.3
2013	C	1.69	1.51	65.3	1,053.3	416.6	159.7	30.8
2012	C	1.75	1.55	73.4	1,102.6	440.8	155.3	9.4
2011	C-	1.81	1.57	82.9	913.1	406.6	138.0	22.9

XL Group Ltd
Composite Group Rating: C

Largest Group Members	Assets ($mil)	Rating
XL REINS AMERICA INC	5308	C
GREENWICH INS CO	1088	C
XL INS AMERICA INC	678	C
CATLIN SPECIALTY INS CO	668	C+
XL SPECIALTY INS CO	462	C

GRINNELL MUTUAL REINS CO   B-   Good

Major Rating Factors: Fair overall results on stability tests (4.3 on a scale of 0 to 10) including potential drain of affiliation with Grinnell Mutual Group and weak results on operational trends. Good liquidity (6.2) with sufficient resources (cash flows and marketable investments) to handle a spike in claims.

Other Rating Factors: Strong long-term capitalization index (8.9) based on excellent current risk adjusted capital (severe and moderate loss scenarios). Moreover, capital levels have been consistent in recent years. Ample reserve history (8.3) that helps to protect the company against sharp claims increases. Excellent profitability (7.9) despite modest operating losses during 2012.

Principal Business: Commercial multiple peril (19%), other liability (16%), workers compensation (16%), allied lines (15%), auto liability (13%), auto physical damage (12%), and other lines (8%).

Principal Investments: Investment grade bonds (77%), misc. investments (17%), cash (4%), and real estate (2%).

Investments in Affiliates: 3%

Group Affiliation: Grinnell Mutual Group

Licensed in: IL, IN, IA, MN, MO, MT, NE, NY, ND, OH, OK, PA, SD, WI

Commenced Business: April 1909

Address: 4211 Highway 146, Grinnell, IA 50112-0790

Phone: (641) 269-8000   **Domicile State:** IA   **NAIC Code:** 14117

Data Date	Rating	RACR #1	RACR #2	Loss Ratio %	Total Assets ($mil)	Capital ($mil)	Net Premium ($mil)	Net Income ($mil)
6-16	B-	3.60	2.45	N/A	1,078.2	559.3	269.0	41.3
6-15	B-	3.30	2.30	N/A	980.7	474.6	249.8	34.5
2015	B-	3.47	2.38	53.2	1,008.1	517.0	525.1	89.4
2014	B-	3.20	2.25	63.8	913.7	440.1	483.5	58.7
2013	B-	2.90	2.07	65.9	858.6	399.9	451.7	36.8
2012	B-	2.64	1.95	76.0	796.0	351.0	410.5	-2.1
2011	B-	2.78	2.04	75.7	742.9	336.5	375.1	1.1

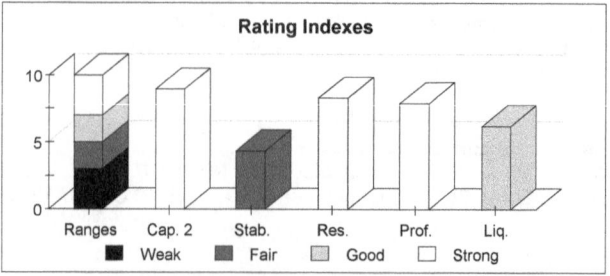

Rating Indexes

GUIDEONE MUTUAL INS CO
B   Good

Major Rating Factors: Good liquidity (6.8 on a scale of 0 to 10) with sufficient resources (cash flows and marketable investments) to handle a spike in claims. Fair overall results on stability tests (4.5) including potential drain of affiliation with GuideOne Group and weak results on operational trends.
Other Rating Factors: Fair profitability index (3.6) with operating losses during 2013 and the first six months of 2016. Strong long-term capitalization index (7.5) based on excellent current risk adjusted capital (severe and moderate loss scenarios), despite some fluctuation in capital levels. Ample reserve history (9.0) that helps to protect the company against sharp claims increases.
Principal Business: Commercial multiple peril (50%), workers compensation (16%), auto liability (12%), homeowners multiple peril (8%), other liability (7%), auto physical damage (6%), and allied lines (1%).
Principal Investments: Investment grade bonds (66%), misc. investments (34%), non investment grade bonds (1%), and real estate (1%).
Investments in Affiliates: 23%
Group Affiliation: GuideOne Group
Licensed in: All states except PR
Commenced Business: April 1947
Address: 1111 Ashworth Rd, West Des Moines, IA 50265-3538
Phone: (515) 267-5000 **Domicile State:** IA **NAIC Code:** 15032

Data Date	Rating	RACR #1	RACR #2	Loss Ratio %	Total Assets ($mil)	Capital ($mil)	Net Premium ($mil)	Net Income ($mil)
6-16	B	1.51	1.26	N/A	1,249.1	421.2	171.8	-68.2
6-15	B-	1.36	1.10	N/A	1,820.0	424.9	170.4	-0.5
2015	B	1.66	1.39	67.1	1,232.0	464.1	360.2	19.6
2014	B-	1.44	1.17	68.0	1,695.2	442.1	355.0	22.3
2013	B-	1.51	1.23	70.5	1,814.5	460.0	334.8	-9.4
2012	B-	1.90	1.66	59.8	1,134.8	423.4	295.7	24.4
2011	B-	1.99	1.75	72.4	1,074.1	408.4	282.3	10.9

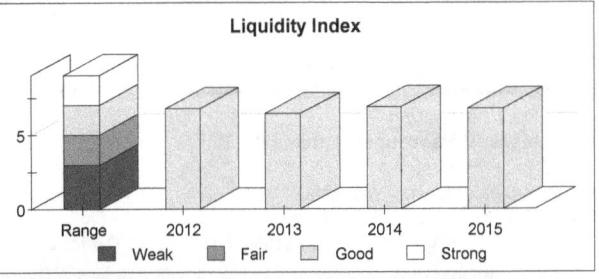

Liquidity Index

GUIDEONE P&C INS CO
B   Good

Major Rating Factors: Good liquidity (6.9 on a scale of 0 to 10) with sufficient resources (cash flows and marketable investments) to handle a spike in claims. Fair profitability index (4.5) with operating losses during the first six months of 2016. Return on equity has been low, averaging 2.0% over the past five years.
Other Rating Factors: Fair overall results on stability tests (4.5) including weak results on operational trends. Strong long-term capitalization index (8.7) based on excellent current risk adjusted capital (severe and moderate loss scenarios), despite some fluctuation in capital levels. Ample reserve history (8.2) that helps to protect the company against sharp claims increases.
Principal Business: (This company is a reinsurer.)
Principal Investments: Investment grade bonds (66%) and misc. investments (34%).
Investments in Affiliates: 21%
Group Affiliation: GuideOne Group
Licensed in: IA
Commenced Business: December 1993
Address: 1111 Ashworth Rd, West Des Moines, IA 50265-3538
Phone: (515) 267-5000 **Domicile State:** IA **NAIC Code:** 13984

Data Date	Rating	RACR #1	RACR #2	Loss Ratio %	Total Assets ($mil)	Capital ($mil)	Net Premium ($mil)	Net Income ($mil)
6-16	B	2.55	2.15	N/A	456.3	245.7	53.7	-3.6
6-15	B	2.28	1.86	N/A	579.5	246.3	53.2	0.3
2015	B	2.57	2.17	67.1	450.3	248.6	112.6	5.3
2014	B	2.31	1.90	68.0	547.5	245.6	110.9	6.3
2013	B	2.77	2.18	70.5	526.5	241.4	104.6	1.8
2012	B	4.07	3.34	59.8	417.1	234.9	92.4	9.2
2011	B	4.21	3.52	72.4	399.6	222.3	88.2	6.7

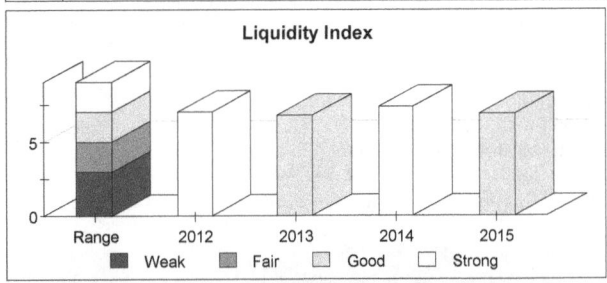

Liquidity Index

GUILFORD INS CO
C-   Fair

Major Rating Factors: Weak overall results on stability tests (2.6 on a scale of 0 to 10) including potential drain of affiliation with IFG Companies and weak results on operational trends. Good overall profitability index (6.8). Weak expense controls. Return on equity has been low, averaging 3.1% over the past five years.
Other Rating Factors: Strong long-term capitalization index (7.9) based on excellent current risk adjusted capital (severe and moderate loss scenarios), despite some fluctuation in capital levels. Ample reserve history (8.0) that helps to protect the company against sharp claims increases. Excellent liquidity (8.2) with ample operational cash flow and liquid investments.
Principal Business: Other liability (64%), inland marine (25%), fire (9%), auto liability (1%), and allied lines (1%).
Principal Investments: Investment grade bonds (52%) and misc. investments (48%).
Investments in Affiliates: 47%
Group Affiliation: IFG Companies
Licensed in: All states except CA, PR
Commenced Business: December 1998
Address: 238 International Road, Burlington, NC 27215
Phone: (336) 586-2500 **Domicile State:** IL **NAIC Code:** 10956

Data Date	Rating	RACR #1	RACR #2	Loss Ratio %	Total Assets ($mil)	Capital ($mil)	Net Premium ($mil)	Net Income ($mil)
6-16	C-	1.68	1.64	N/A	385.7	278.0	14.6	3.5
6-15	C-	1.67	1.62	N/A	398.7	283.1	18.2	4.6
2015	C-	1.66	1.62	44.4	386.9	275.2	32.8	9.5
2014	C-	1.63	1.59	56.5	393.3	274.3	36.6	6.9
2013	C-	1.61	1.57	50.6	390.3	267.5	40.7	12.3
2012	C-	1.61	1.57	60.2	377.8	250.7	43.1	7.6
2011	C-	1.59	1.55	58.9	369.8	246.0	35.9	5.6

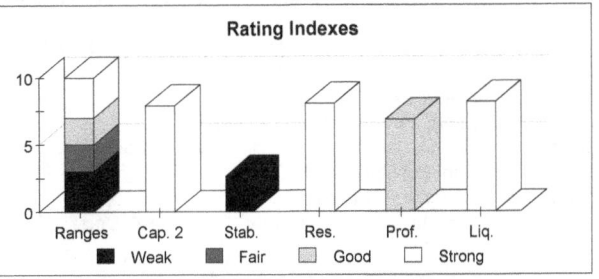

Rating Indexes

HANOVER INS CO   B   Good

Major Rating Factors: Good overall results on stability tests (5.1 on a scale of 0 to 10) despite potential drain of affiliation with Hanover Ins Group Inc and weak results on operational trends. Good overall profitability index (6.3) despite operating losses during 2011 and 2012. Return on equity has been low, averaging 4.9% over the past five years.

Other Rating Factors: Good liquidity (6.1) with sufficient resources (cash flows and marketable investments) to handle a spike in claims. Fair reserve development (4.2) as reserves have generally been sufficient to cover claims. Strong long-term capitalization index (7.3) based on excellent current risk adjusted capital (severe and moderate loss scenarios), despite some fluctuation in capital levels.

Principal Business: Other liability (25%), commercial multiple peril (20%), inland marine (15%), homeowners multiple peril (7%), surety (7%), auto liability (7%), and other lines (19%).

Principal Investments: Investment grade bonds (61%), misc. investments (33%), non investment grade bonds (5%), and real estate (1%).

Investments in Affiliates: 20%

Group Affiliation: Hanover Ins Group Inc

Licensed in: All states except PR

Commenced Business: April 1852

Address: 100 North Parkway, Worcester, MA 01605

Phone: (508) 853-7200   **Domicile State:** NH   **NAIC Code:** 22292

Data Date	Rating	RACR #1	RACR #2	Loss Ratio %	Total Assets ($mil)	Capital ($mil)	Net Premium ($mil)	Net Income ($mil)
6-16	B	1.48	1.20	N/A	6,972.7	2,147.8	1,533.5	69.2
6-15	B	1.54	1.25	N/A	6,671.9	2,121.9	1,477.2	30.8
2015	B	1.56	1.28	66.4	6,926.3	2,188.0	3,046.3	128.8
2014	B	1.53	1.27	63.3	6,482.1	2,052.4	2,905.8	225.0
2013	B	1.42	1.21	64.8	6,047.1	1,829.7	2,759.4	184.3
2012	B-	1.21	1.03	76.1	5,696.5	1,518.9	2,661.5	-42.6
2011	B-	1.31	1.13	73.6	5,288.6	1,578.3	2,478.5	-7.1

Rating Indexes

HARFORD MUTUAL INS CO   B-   Good

Major Rating Factors: Fair overall results on stability tests (4.1 on a scale of 0 to 10) including potential drain of affiliation with Harford Group Inc and weak results on operational trends. History of adequate reserve strength (6.9) as reserves have been consistently at an acceptable level.

Other Rating Factors: Strong long-term capitalization index (8.3) based on excellent current risk adjusted capital (severe and moderate loss scenarios), despite some fluctuation in capital levels. Excellent profitability (7.5) despite modest operating losses during 2011. Excellent liquidity (7.0) with ample operational cash flow and liquid investments.

Principal Business: Commercial multiple peril (48%), workers compensation (25%), auto liability (12%), other liability (8%), auto physical damage (4%), homeowners multiple peril (1%), and other lines (2%).

Principal Investments: Investment grade bonds (52%), misc. investments (42%), cash (5%), and real estate (1%).

Investments in Affiliates: 14%

Group Affiliation: Harford Group Inc

Licensed in: DC, DE, MD, NJ, NC, PA, TN, VA, WV

Commenced Business: January 1843

Address: 200 North Main Street, Bel Air, MD 21014-3544

Phone: (410) 838-4000   **Domicile State:** MD   **NAIC Code:** 14141

Data Date	Rating	RACR #1	RACR #2	Loss Ratio %	Total Assets ($mil)	Capital ($mil)	Net Premium ($mil)	Net Income ($mil)
6-16	B-	2.37	1.83	N/A	404.4	194.3	57.0	0.4
6-15	B-	2.41	1.88	N/A	380.6	187.2	51.8	-0.6
2015	B-	2.42	1.89	60.9	384.5	193.4	114.1	10.9
2014	B-	2.52	1.96	62.3	370.6	194.6	104.0	8.8
2013	B-	2.66	2.06	55.6	352.8	187.5	95.3	11.5
2012	B-	2.76	2.13	55.8	317.8	162.6	81.8	11.6
2011	B-	2.77	2.09	77.1	305.4	145.8	75.5	-1.3

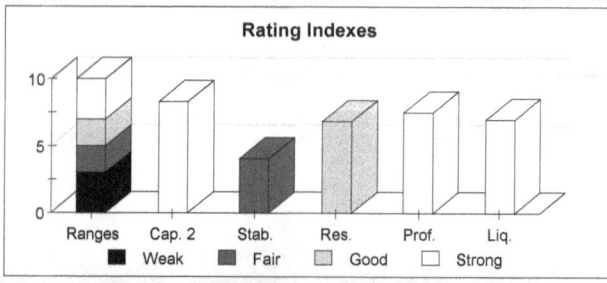

Rating Indexes

HARTFORD ACCIDENT & INDEMNITY CO   B   Good

Major Rating Factors: History of adequate reserve strength (5.8 on a scale of 0 to 10) as reserves have been consistently at an acceptable level. Good overall profitability index (6.5). Fair expense controls. Return on equity has been good over the last five years, averaging 13.2%.

Other Rating Factors: Good liquidity (6.7) with sufficient resources (cash flows and marketable investments) to handle a spike in claims. Fair overall results on stability tests (4.5) including weak results on operational trends. The largest net exposure for one risk is conservative at 1.3% of capital. Strong long-term capitalization index (7.7) based on excellent current risk adjusted capital (severe and moderate loss scenarios), despite some fluctuation in capital levels.

Principal Business: Workers compensation (49%), auto liability (22%), auto physical damage (10%), homeowners multiple peril (6%), commercial multiple peril (6%), other liability (5%), and surety (2%).

Principal Investments: Investment grade bonds (70%), misc. investments (26%), and non investment grade bonds (4%).

Investments in Affiliates: 9%

Group Affiliation: Hartford Financial Services Inc

Licensed in: All states, the District of Columbia and Puerto Rico

Commenced Business: August 1913

Address: Hartford Plaza, Hartford, CT 06115

Phone: (860) 547-5000   **Domicile State:** CT   **NAIC Code:** 22357

Data Date	Rating	RACR #1	RACR #2	Loss Ratio %	Total Assets ($mil)	Capital ($mil)	Net Premium ($mil)	Net Income ($mil)
6-16	B	2.01	1.46	N/A	11,729.7	3,218.0	1,708.5	122.3
6-15	B	2.24	1.63	N/A	11,722.8	3,582.9	1,675.7	222.4
2015	B	2.09	1.53	66.1	11,521.7	3,276.6	3,444.7	582.3
2014	B	2.18	1.60	67.0	11,348.4	3,324.9	3,349.1	509.1
2013	B	2.18	1.60	68.8	11,122.4	3,271.5	3,252.5	468.7
2012	B	2.17	1.60	72.7	11,063.3	3,107.6	3,218.3	362.2
2011	B-	2.03	1.52	78.5	10,631.4	2,823.1	3,219.4	269.3

Reserve Deficiency (as % of capital)

* Adequate & redundant reserves show as negatives

HARTFORD CASUALTY INS CO — B — Good

Major Rating Factors: History of adequate reserve strength (5.9 on a scale of 0 to 10) as reserves have been consistently at an acceptable level. Good overall profitability index (5.9). Fair expense controls. Return on equity has been fair, averaging 8.8% over the past five years.

Other Rating Factors: Good liquidity (6.9) with sufficient resources (cash flows and marketable investments) to handle a spike in claims. Fair overall results on stability tests (4.9) including weak results on operational trends. Strong long-term capitalization index (10.0) based on excellent current risk adjusted capital (severe and moderate loss scenarios), despite some fluctuation in capital levels.

Principal Business: Workers compensation (33%), commercial multiple peril (25%), other liability (13%), auto liability (13%), auto physical damage (7%), homeowners multiple peril (4%), and other lines (3%).

Principal Investments: Investment grade bonds (84%), misc. investments (14%), and non investment grade bonds (2%).

Investments in Affiliates: None

Group Affiliation: Hartford Financial Services Inc

Licensed in: All states except PR

Commenced Business: July 1987

Address: 4040 Vincennes Cir Suite 100, Indianapolis, IN 46268

Phone: (860) 547-5000   **Domicile State:** IN   **NAIC Code:** 29424

Data Date	Rating	RACR #1	RACR #2	Loss Ratio %	Total Assets ($mil)	Capital ($mil)	Net Premium ($mil)	Net Income ($mil)
6-16	B	4.89	3.16	N/A	2,370.8	950.3	287.5	34.3
6-15	B	5.07	3.26	N/A	2,305.6	962.3	281.9	52.4
2015	B	4.80	3.13	66.1	2,249.9	904.4	579.6	95.0
2014	B	4.97	3.23	67.0	2,233.8	913.3	563.5	95.9
2013	B	5.01	3.28	68.8	2,207.0	905.8	547.2	83.6
2012	B	5.13	3.36	72.7	2,196.5	907.3	541.5	82.2
2011	B	5.32	3.55	78.5	2,192.4	895.5	541.6	48.0

Reserve Deficiency (as % of capital)

* Adequate & redundant reserves show as negatives   ■ 1 Yr Dev   □ 2 Yr Dev

HARTFORD FIRE INS CO — B — Good

Major Rating Factors: Good overall profitability index (5.8 on a scale of 0 to 10). Fair expense controls. Return on equity has been fair, averaging 7.2% over the past five years. Good liquidity (6.9) with sufficient resources (cash flows and marketable investments) to handle a spike in claims.

Other Rating Factors: Good overall results on stability tests (5.1) despite weak results on operational trends. Fair reserve development (4.9) as reserves have generally been sufficient to cover claims. Strong long-term capitalization index (7.7) based on excellent current risk adjusted capital (severe and moderate loss scenarios), despite some fluctuation in capital levels.

Principal Business: Commercial multiple peril (30%), workers compensation (19%), inland marine (13%), other liability (10%), surety (8%), auto liability (8%), and other lines (11%).

Principal Investments: Non investment grade bonds (34%), investment grade bonds (32%), misc. investments (32%), and real estate (2%).

Investments in Affiliates: 26%

Group Affiliation: Hartford Financial Services Inc

Licensed in: All states, the District of Columbia and Puerto Rico

Commenced Business: August 1810

Address: Hartford Plaza, Hartford, CT 06115

Phone: (860) 547-5000   **Domicile State:** CT   **NAIC Code:** 19682

Data Date	Rating	RACR #1	RACR #2	Loss Ratio %	Total Assets ($mil)	Capital ($mil)	Net Premium ($mil)	Net Income ($mil)
6-16	B	2.04	1.44	N/A	25,602.1	13,094.5	2,169.0	328.5
6-15	B	2.06	1.45	N/A	25,822.0	13,717.3	2,127.3	184.5
2015	B	2.09	1.48	66.1	25,426.3	13,440.5	4,373.1	1,188.3
2014	B	2.11	1.48	67.0	25,520.2	13,797.4	4,251.7	1,068.2
2013	B	2.16	1.50	68.8	25,684.8	14,081.4	4,129.1	1,006.6
2012	B	2.09	1.47	72.7	24,620.3	13,012.5	4,085.7	735.6
2011	B	2.56	2.31	78.5	24,140.3	12,594.3	4,087.0	987.6

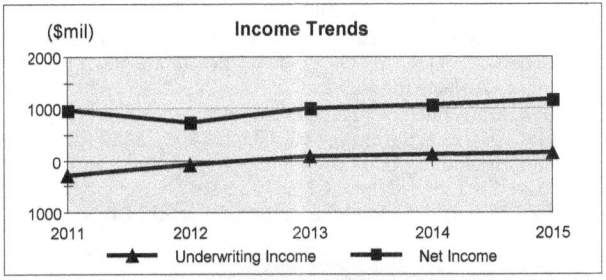

Income Trends ($mil)

▲ Underwriting Income   ■ Net Income

HARTFORD INS CO OF IL — B — Good

Major Rating Factors: History of adequate reserve strength (5.9 on a scale of 0 to 10) as reserves have been consistently at an acceptable level. Good overall profitability index (5.6). Fair expense controls. Return on equity has been fair, averaging 9.9% over the past five years.

Other Rating Factors: Good liquidity (6.8) with sufficient resources (cash flows and marketable investments) to handle a spike in claims. Fair overall results on stability tests (4.8) including weak results on operational trends. Strong long-term capitalization index (9.2) based on excellent current risk adjusted capital (severe and moderate loss scenarios), despite some fluctuation in capital levels.

Principal Business: Workers compensation (36%), auto liability (34%), auto physical damage (17%), homeowners multiple peril (11%), and other liability (1%).

Principal Investments: Investment grade bonds (86%), misc. investments (11%), and non investment grade bonds (3%).

Investments in Affiliates: None

Group Affiliation: Hartford Financial Services Inc

Licensed in: CT, HI, IL, MI, NY, PA

Commenced Business: January 1980

Address: 4245 Meridian Parkway, Aurora, IL 60504

Phone: (860) 547-5000   **Domicile State:** IL   **NAIC Code:** 38288

Data Date	Rating	RACR #1	RACR #2	Loss Ratio %	Total Assets ($mil)	Capital ($mil)	Net Premium ($mil)	Net Income ($mil)
6-16	B	3.83	2.48	N/A	3,931.9	1,345.1	527.9	54.3
6-15	B	4.09	2.63	N/A	3,887.4	1,406.1	517.7	76.5
2015	B	3.78	2.47	66.1	3,787.8	1,289.3	1,064.3	151.8
2014	B	4.00	2.59	67.0	3,781.9	1,334.8	1,034.8	164.6
2013	B	3.99	2.60	68.8	3,725.2	1,309.1	1,004.9	136.4
2012	B	4.06	2.67	72.7	3,698.8	1,301.0	994.3	123.1
2011	B	3.96	2.66	78.5	3,636.4	1,258.7	994.7	77.6

Reserve Deficiency (as % of capital)

* Adequate & redundant reserves show as negatives   ■ 1 Yr Dev   □ 2 Yr Dev

HARTFORD INS CO OF THE MIDWEST — B — Good

Major Rating Factors: History of adequate reserve strength (5.0 on a scale of 0 to 10) as reserves have been consistently at an acceptable level. Fair overall results on stability tests (4.7) including weak results on operational trends.

Other Rating Factors: Strong long-term capitalization index (10.0) based on excellent current risk adjusted capital (severe and moderate loss scenarios). Moreover, capital levels have been consistent in recent years. Excellent profitability (8.2) with operating gains in each of the last five years. Excellent liquidity (7.9) with ample operational cash flow and liquid investments.

Principal Business: Workers compensation (33%), allied lines (23%), auto liability (16%), homeowners multiple peril (14%), auto physical damage (8%), commercial multiple peril (4%), and other liability (1%).

Principal Investments: Investment grade bonds (94%) and misc. investments (6%).

Investments in Affiliates: None

Group Affiliation: Hartford Financial Services Inc

Licensed in: All states except PR

Commenced Business: January 1980

Address: 4040 Vincennes Cir Suite 100, Indianapolis, IN 46268

Phone: (860) 547-5000　**Domicile State:** IN　**NAIC Code:** 37478

Data Date	Rating	RACR #1	RACR #2	Loss Ratio %	Total Assets ($mil)	Capital ($mil)	Net Premium ($mil)	Net Income ($mil)
6-16	B	26.11	16.94	N/A	633.3	482.3	26.1	9.1
6-15	B	25.73	16.73	N/A	586.9	463.1	25.6	10.2
2015	B	26.66	17.49	66.1	595.6	473.3	52.7	20.4
2014	B	25.97	17.00	67.0	581.5	452.9	51.2	21.2
2013	B	25.12	16.51	68.8	550.1	432.1	49.7	19.2
2012	B+	20.83	13.70	72.7	470.1	352.7	49.2	21.0
2011	B+	19.50	12.97	78.5	451.5	330.0	49.2	19.7

Reserve Deficiency (as % of capital)

* Adequate & redundant reserves show as negatives

■ 1 Yr Dev　□ 2 Yr Dev

HARTFORD SM BOIL INSPECTION & INS — B — Good

Major Rating Factors: Good overall profitability index (5.5 on a scale of 0 to 10). Weak expense controls. Return on equity has been excellent over the last five years averaging 20.6%. Good liquidity (6.9) with sufficient resources (cash flows and marketable investments) to handle a spike in claims.

Other Rating Factors: Fair overall results on stability tests (4.7) including weak results on operational trends and negative cash flow from operations for 2015. The largest net exposure for one risk is conservative at 1.6% of capital. Strong long-term capitalization index (8.4) based on excellent current risk adjusted capital (severe and moderate loss scenarios), despite some fluctuation in capital levels. Ample reserve history (9.0) that helps to protect the company against sharp claims increases.

Principal Business: Boiler & machinery (94%), inland marine (3%), commercial multiple peril (2%), and other liability (1%).

Principal Investments: Investment grade bonds (83%), misc. investments (11%), real estate (4%), cash (1%), and non investment grade bonds (1%).

Investments in Affiliates: 14%

Group Affiliation: Münchener Rückversicherungs-Gesellsc

Licensed in: All states, the District of Columbia and Puerto Rico

Commenced Business: October 1866

Address: One State St, Hartford, CT 06102-5024

Phone: (860) 722-1866　**Domicile State:** CT　**NAIC Code:** 11452

Data Date	Rating	RACR #1	RACR #2	Loss Ratio %	Total Assets ($mil)	Capital ($mil)	Net Premium ($mil)	Net Income ($mil)
6-16	B	2.96	2.51	N/A	1,179.3	558.4	221.9	52.1
6-15	B	2.35	2.08	N/A	1,250.8	592.6	206.4	86.7
2015	B	3.40	2.89	27.3	1,293.0	635.8	271.5	151.5
2014	B	2.24	1.98	29.4	1,406.6	641.1	771.8	127.8
2013	B	2.30	2.08	26.8	1,372.0	640.9	727.6	105.2
2012	B	2.40	2.19	26.8	1,353.9	649.2	668.4	128.0
2011	B	2.85	2.56	27.4	1,313.9	644.9	622.9	156.6

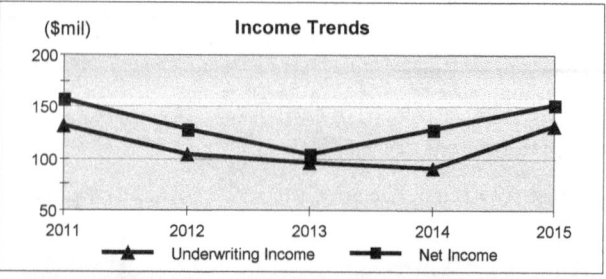

Income Trends ($mil)

▲ Underwriting Income　■ Net Income

HARTFORD UNDERWRITERS INS CO — B — Good

Major Rating Factors: History of adequate reserve strength (5.9 on a scale of 0 to 10) as reserves have been consistently at an acceptable level. Good overall profitability index (5.7). Fair expense controls. Return on equity has been fair, averaging 9.2% over the past five years.

Other Rating Factors: Good liquidity (6.8) with sufficient resources (cash flows and marketable investments) to handle a spike in claims. Fair overall results on stability tests (4.8) including weak results on operational trends. Strong long-term capitalization index (9.8) based on excellent current risk adjusted capital (severe and moderate loss scenarios), despite some fluctuation in capital levels.

Principal Business: Workers compensation (35%), auto liability (31%), auto physical damage (16%), homeowners multiple peril (11%), other liability (3%), commercial multiple peril (2%), and other lines (2%).

Principal Investments: Investment grade bonds (88%), misc. investments (10%), and non investment grade bonds (2%).

Investments in Affiliates: None

Group Affiliation: Hartford Financial Services Inc

Licensed in: All states except PR

Commenced Business: December 1987

Address: Hartford Plaza, Hartford, CT 06115

Phone: (860) 547-5000　**Domicile State:** CT　**NAIC Code:** 30104

Data Date	Rating	RACR #1	RACR #2	Loss Ratio %	Total Assets ($mil)	Capital ($mil)	Net Premium ($mil)	Net Income ($mil)
6-16	B	4.37	2.85	N/A	1,651.2	632.4	209.1	25.0
6-15	B	4.63	3.00	N/A	1,629.8	652.8	205.0	36.0
2015	B	4.36	2.86	66.1	1,590.0	608.8	421.5	66.1
2014	B	4.53	2.97	67.0	1,581.8	620.3	409.8	69.3
2013	B+	4.53	2.99	68.8	1,561.3	611.4	398.0	52.8
2012	B+	4.65	3.07	72.7	1,558.0	614.3	393.8	53.2
2011	B+	4.65	3.12	78.5	1,571.9	608.3	393.9	43.7

Reserve Deficiency (as % of capital)

* Adequate & redundant reserves show as negatives

■ 1 Yr Dev　□ 2 Yr Dev

HASTINGS MUTUAL INS CO   B   Good

Major Rating Factors: History of adequate reserve strength (5.8 on a scale of 0 to 10) as reserves have been consistently at an acceptable level. Good liquidity (6.7) with sufficient resources (cash flows and marketable investments) to handle a spike in claims.

Other Rating Factors: Fair overall results on stability tests (4.7) including weak results on operational trends. Strong long-term capitalization index (10.0) based on excellent current risk adjusted capital (severe and moderate loss scenarios). Moreover, capital levels have been consistent in recent years. Excellent profitability (8.1) with operating gains in each of the last five years.

Principal Business: Auto liability (19%), workers compensation (17%), commercial multiple peril (16%), farmowners multiple peril (16%), homeowners multiple peril (14%), auto physical damage (12%), and other lines (6%).

Principal Investments: Investment grade bonds (82%), misc. investments (12%), non investment grade bonds (4%), and cash (2%).

Investments in Affiliates: None

Group Affiliation: None

Licensed in: IL, IN, IA, KY, MI, OH, PA, TN, WI

Commenced Business: April 1885

Address: 404 E Woodlawn Ave, Hastings, MI 49058-1091

Phone: (800) 442-8277   **Domicile State:** MI   **NAIC Code:** 14176

Data Date	Rating	RACR #1	RACR #2	Loss Ratio %	Total Assets ($mil)	Capital ($mil)	Net Premium ($mil)	Net Income ($mil)
6-16	B	5.17	3.54	N/A	862.9	409.1	196.7	18.2
6-15	B	4.89	3.40	N/A	818.3	373.2	188.1	20.5
2015	B	5.10	3.47	58.2	830.1	386.4	388.6	38.3
2014	B	4.74	3.26	67.9	783.1	354.0	374.2	18.7
2013	A-	4.73	3.30	76.8	759.0	335.5	354.9	3.3
2012	A-	5.18	3.65	71.0	697.4	327.3	328.7	6.6
2011	A-	5.35	3.73	69.3	667.5	314.1	308.8	16.8

Reserve Deficiency (as % of capital)
* Adequate & redundant reserves show as negatives
■ 1 Yr Dev   □ 2 Yr Dev

HAWAII EMPLOYERS MUTUAL INS CO   C   Fair

Major Rating Factors: Fair overall results on stability tests (4.1 on a scale of 0 to 10) including weak results on operational trends. History of adequate reserve strength (5.5) as reserves have been consistently at an acceptable level.

Other Rating Factors: Good overall profitability index (6.9). Fair expense controls. Strong long-term capitalization index (10.0) based on excellent current risk adjusted capital (severe and moderate loss scenarios). Moreover, capital levels have been consistent in recent years. Excellent liquidity (7.1) with ample operational cash flow and liquid investments.

Principal Business: Workers compensation (100%).

Principal Investments: Investment grade bonds (77%), misc. investments (16%), non investment grade bonds (4%), real estate (2%), and cash (1%).

Investments in Affiliates: None

Group Affiliation: None

Licensed in: HI

Commenced Business: October 1996

Address: 1100 Alakea St Suite 1400, Honolulu, HI 96813-3407

Phone: (808) 524-3642   **Domicile State:** HI   **NAIC Code:** 10781

Data Date	Rating	RACR #1	RACR #2	Loss Ratio %	Total Assets ($mil)	Capital ($mil)	Net Premium ($mil)	Net Income ($mil)
6-16	C	4.23	2.97	N/A	376.8	228.3	34.1	5.1
6-15	C-	4.43	3.13	N/A	355.4	222.0	32.2	4.8
2015	C	4.28	3.00	72.9	360.6	221.0	67.6	7.5
2014	C-	4.68	3.26	75.8	341.2	217.5	61.3	11.5
2013	C-	5.90	3.93	72.0	313.6	209.4	45.5	9.3
2012	C-	7.08	4.60	67.7	285.0	190.1	33.6	10.6
2011	C-	6.79	4.42	71.0	273.6	173.8	31.1	8.2

Rating Indexes
Ranges Cap. 2 Stab. Res. Prof. Liq.
■ Weak   ■ Fair   □ Good   □ Strong

HERITAGE P&C INS CO   C+   Fair

Major Rating Factors: Good long-term capitalization (5.0 on a scale of 0 to 10) based on good current risk adjusted capital (severe loss scenario) reflecting some improvement over results in 2015. Fair reserve development (4.6) as reserves have generally been sufficient to cover claims.

Other Rating Factors: Fair overall results on stability tests (3.9) including weak results on operational trends and fair risk adjusted capital in prior years. Good overall profitability index (5.7) despite operating losses during 2012 and the first six months of 2016. Good liquidity (6.9) with sufficient resources (cash flows and marketable investments) to handle a spike in claims.

Principal Business: Homeowners multiple peril (69%), commercial multiple peril (21%), allied lines (8%), and fire (1%).

Principal Investments: Investment grade bonds (65%), misc. investments (27%), and cash (8%).

Investments in Affiliates: None

Group Affiliation: Heritage Ins Holdings LLC

Licensed in: AL, FL, GA, MS, NC, SC

Commenced Business: August 2012

Address: 700 Central Ave Suite 330, St Petersburg, FL 33701

Phone: (727) 362-7200   **Domicile State:** FL   **NAIC Code:** 14407

Data Date	Rating	RACR #1	RACR #2	Loss Ratio %	Total Assets ($mil)	Capital ($mil)	Net Premium ($mil)	Net Income ($mil)
6-16	C+	1.16	0.77	N/A	663.9	208.6	200.4	-8.8
6-15	C	1.06	0.83	N/A	555.0	200.3	194.1	28.3
2015	C+	1.06	0.65	44.7	601.9	216.4	391.7	43.4
2014	C	1.01	0.69	46.5	496.7	172.7	331.7	9.8
2013	C	0.81	0.60	44.4	207.8	63.1	139.6	21.0
2012	B-	0.90	0.70	27.2	78.0	26.5	45.2	-1.1
2011	N/A	N/A	N/A	0.0	0.0	0.0	0.0	0.0

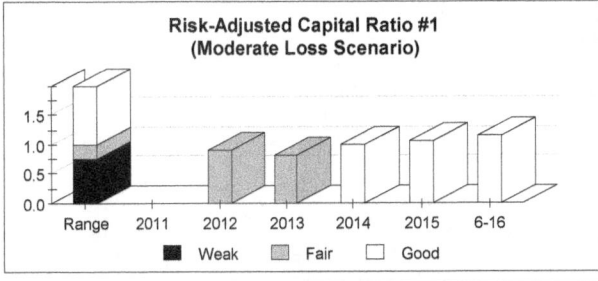

Risk-Adjusted Capital Ratio #1
(Moderate Loss Scenario)
Range 2011 2012 2013 2014 2015 6-16
■ Weak   □ Fair   □ Good

HOLYOKE MUTUAL INS CO IN SALEM *   B+   Good

Major Rating Factors: Good overall profitability index (5.9 on a scale of 0 to 10) despite operating losses during 2011 and 2012. Good liquidity (6.4) with sufficient resources (cash flows and marketable investments) to handle a spike in claims.

Other Rating Factors: Good overall results on stability tests (5.0) despite weak results on operational trends. Strong long-term capitalization index (10.0) based on excellent current risk adjusted capital (severe and moderate loss scenarios), despite some fluctuation in capital levels. Ample reserve history (7.6) that can protect against increases in claims costs.

Principal Business: Commercial multiple peril (85%), homeowners multiple peril (9%), allied lines (2%), auto liability (1%), auto physical damage (1%), and fire (1%).

Principal Investments: Investment grade bonds (80%), misc. investments (19%), and non investment grade bonds (1%).

Investments in Affiliates: 1%

Group Affiliation: COUNTRY Financial

Licensed in: AZ, AR, CO, CT, GA, ID, IL, ME, MA, MN, MO, MT, NE, NV, NH, NJ, NM, NY, NC, ND, OR, RI, SC, SD, TX, UT, VT, WA, WY

Commenced Business: May 1843

Address: Holyoke Square, Salem, MA 01970-6506

Phone: (978) 744-6123   **Domicile State:** MA   **NAIC Code:** 14206

Data Date	Rating	RACR #1	RACR #2	Loss Ratio %	Total Assets ($mil)	Capital ($mil)	Net Premium ($mil)	Net Income ($mil)
6-16	B+	4.74	3.34	N/A	217.0	102.4	49.7	2.8
6-15	B+	4.18	2.97	N/A	224.6	97.2	51.3	2.0
2015	B+	4.54	3.21	70.7	215.4	99.5	101.2	4.5
2014	B+	4.11	2.88	70.3	223.2	95.3	102.8	7.0
2013	B+	3.91	2.69	69.3	224.3	89.9	102.6	5.7
2012	B	3.71	2.58	75.5	216.6	81.7	104.1	-0.2
2011	B	4.34	2.92	85.8	200.8	82.4	83.8	-4.7

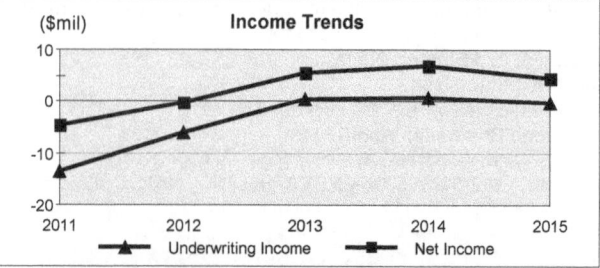

Income Trends

HOME-OWNERS INS CO *   A-   Excellent

Major Rating Factors: Strong long-term capitalization index (10.0 on a scale of 0 to 10) based on excellent current risk adjusted capital (severe and moderate loss scenarios). Furthermore, this high level of risk adjusted capital has been consistently maintained in previous years. Excellent profitability (8.4) with operating gains in each of the last five years.

Other Rating Factors: History of adequate reserve strength (5.9) as reserves have been consistently at an acceptable level. Good liquidity (6.7) with sufficient resources (cash flows and marketable investments) to handle a spike in claims. Good overall results on stability tests (5.9) despite weak results on operational trends and negative cash flow from operations for 2015.

Principal Business: Auto liability (48%), auto physical damage (32%), commercial multiple peril (9%), homeowners multiple peril (4%), workers compensation (3%), other liability (2%), and inland marine (1%).

Principal Investments: Investment grade bonds (85%), misc. investments (14%), and cash (1%).

Investments in Affiliates: None

Group Affiliation: Auto-Owners Group

Licensed in: AL, AR, CO, GA, IL, IN, IA, KY, MI, MO, NE, NV, ND, OH, PA, SC, SD, UT, VA, WI

Commenced Business: May 1863

Address: 6101 Anacapri Blvd, Lansing, MI 48917-3999

Phone: (517) 323-1200   **Domicile State:** MI   **NAIC Code:** 26638

Data Date	Rating	RACR #1	RACR #2	Loss Ratio %	Total Assets ($mil)	Capital ($mil)	Net Premium ($mil)	Net Income ($mil)
6-16	A-	6.38	4.54	N/A	2,106.0	1,042.3	410.8	59.2
6-15	A-	5.20	3.63	N/A	2,064.7	955.6	466.6	76.6
2015	A-	5.27	3.99	66.8	2,063.8	976.4	809.4	102.6
2014	A-	4.42	3.16	72.3	2,104.5	886.7	993.4	89.4
2013	A-	3.77	2.62	69.3	2,069.7	799.4	1,045.3	73.7
2012	A-	3.32	2.29	73.3	1,854.4	684.9	980.9	46.6
2011	A-	3.28	2.27	81.4	1,716.2	612.4	921.8	10.0

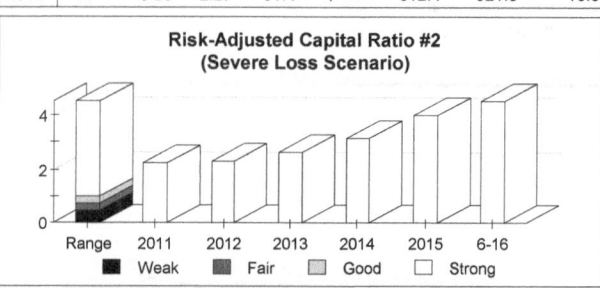

Risk-Adjusted Capital Ratio #2
(Severe Loss Scenario)

HOMEOWNERS CHOICE PROP & CAS INS CO   C-   Fair

Major Rating Factors: Fair reserve development (4.7 on a scale of 0 to 10) as reserves have generally been sufficient to cover claims. Fair overall results on stability tests (3.3) including weak results on operational trends.

Other Rating Factors: Good long-term capitalization index (6.8) based on good current risk adjusted capital (moderate loss scenario), despite some fluctuation in capital levels. Good overall profitability index (5.8) despite operating losses during 2011 and the first six months of 2016. Return on equity has been good over the last five years, averaging 19.3%. Excellent liquidity (7.0) with ample operational cash flow and liquid investments.

Principal Business: Homeowners multiple peril (91%) and fire (9%).

Principal Investments: Cash (47%), investment grade bonds (37%), misc. investments (15%), and non investment grade bonds (1%).

Investments in Affiliates: None

Group Affiliation: HCI Group Inc

Licensed in: FL, MD, NJ, SC, VA

Commenced Business: June 2007

Address: 5300 W Cypress St Suite 100, Tampa, FL 33607

Phone: (813) 405-3600   **Domicile State:** FL   **NAIC Code:** 12944

Data Date	Rating	RACR #1	RACR #2	Loss Ratio %	Total Assets ($mil)	Capital ($mil)	Net Premium ($mil)	Net Income ($mil)
6-16	C-	2.50	1.59	N/A	396.2	172.9	101.0	-1.7
6-15	D	1.84	1.54	N/A	448.9	183.7	153.3	44.1
2015	D+	2.40	1.31	37.0	401.5	194.9	215.8	57.4
2014	D	1.52	1.00	36.8	415.6	168.0	280.1	48.9
2013	D	1.02	0.61	33.5	321.2	116.9	218.8	45.7
2012	D	0.80	0.53	49.6	266.9	69.8	176.2	13.2
2011	D	0.93	0.66	63.0	175.1	46.5	126.1	-4.3

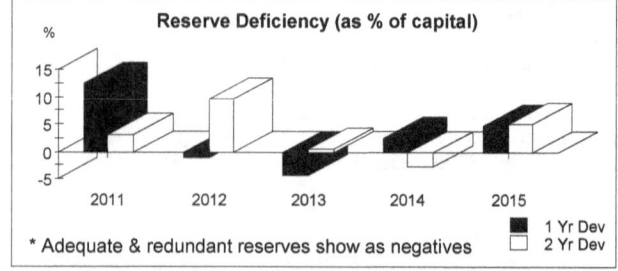

Reserve Deficiency (as % of capital)

* Adequate & redundant reserves show as negatives

HORACE MANN INS CO   B   Good

Major Rating Factors: Good overall profitability index (6.8 on a scale of 0 to 10) despite operating losses during 2011. Return on equity has been fair, averaging 7.9% over the past five years. Good liquidity (5.2) with sufficient resources (cash flows and marketable investments) to handle a spike in claims.

Other Rating Factors: Fair overall results on stability tests (4.4) including weak results on operational trends. Affiliation with Horace Mann Educators Corp is a strength. Strong long-term capitalization index (8.5) based on excellent current risk adjusted capital (severe and moderate loss scenarios), despite some fluctuation in capital levels. Ample reserve history (8.6) that helps to protect the company against sharp claims increases.

Principal Business: Auto liability (37%), homeowners multiple peril (31%), auto physical damage (27%), fire (2%), other liability (1%), allied lines (1%), and earthquake (1%).

Principal Investments: Investment grade bonds (82%), non investment grade bonds (12%), and misc. investments (9%).

Investments in Affiliates: None

Group Affiliation: Horace Mann Educators Corp

Licensed in: All states except HI, NJ, PR

Commenced Business: December 1963

Address: 1 Horace Mann Plaza, Springfield, IL 62715

Phone: (217) 789-2500   **Domicile State:** IL   **NAIC Code:** 22578

Data Date	Rating	RACR #1	RACR #2	Loss Ratio %	Total Assets ($mil)	Capital ($mil)	Net Premium ($mil)	Net Income ($mil)
6-16	B	3.05	1.96	N/A	456.9	184.3	124.8	2.7
6-15	B	1.83	1.18	N/A	460.3	190.3	120.1	7.3
2015	B	3.09	2.01	70.9	447.5	186.4	247.2	15.6
2014	B	1.44	0.94	69.0	444.3	186.3	238.5	20.5
2013	B	1.44	0.94	69.0	432.5	177.0	232.7	19.0
2012	B	1.36	0.91	71.6	414.4	166.9	222.6	23.4
2011	B	2.27	1.39	86.1	362.5	151.2	212.6	-3.4

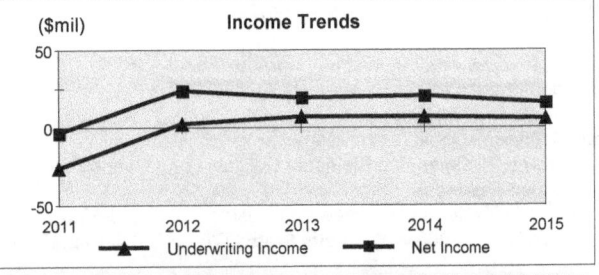

Income Trends

HOSPITALS INS CO   C-   Fair

Major Rating Factors: Weak overall results on stability tests (2.3 on a scale of 0 to 10) including weak results on operational trends. The largest net exposure for one risk is excessive at 10.1% of capital. Fair long-term capitalization (4.6) based on fair current risk adjusted capital (moderate loss scenario), although results have slipped from the good range over the last two years.

Other Rating Factors: History of adequate reserve strength (5.1) as reserves have been consistently at an acceptable level. Good overall profitability index (6.7). Excellent expense controls. Return on equity has been good over the last five years, averaging 12.3%. Good liquidity (6.9) with sufficient resources (cash flows and marketable investments) to handle a spike in claims.

Principal Business: Medical malpractice (97%) and other liability (3%).

Principal Investments: Misc. investments (50%), investment grade bonds (45%), non investment grade bonds (4%), and cash (1%).

Investments in Affiliates: None

Group Affiliation: None

Licensed in: NY

Commenced Business: August 1987

Address: 217 Great Oaks Blvd, Albany, NY 12203-5964

Phone: (914) 220-1800   **Domicile State:** NY   **NAIC Code:** 30317

Data Date	Rating	RACR #1	RACR #2	Loss Ratio %	Total Assets ($mil)	Capital ($mil)	Net Premium ($mil)	Net Income ($mil)
6-16	C-	0.98	0.83	N/A	1,559.0	449.0	92.5	2.9
6-15	D	1.08	0.91	N/A	1,531.1	475.3	107.7	11.6
2015	D+	0.99	0.84	88.7	1,472.8	448.2	216.1	11.5
2014	D	1.08	0.92	9.5	1,414.4	460.2	229.2	134.6
2013	D	0.65	0.56	55.3	1,397.5	318.7	234.1	76.5
2012	D-	0.40	0.34	100.0	1,282.6	214.6	221.5	17.1
2011	E+	0.32	0.27	106.6	1,135.4	179.5	219.4	6.0

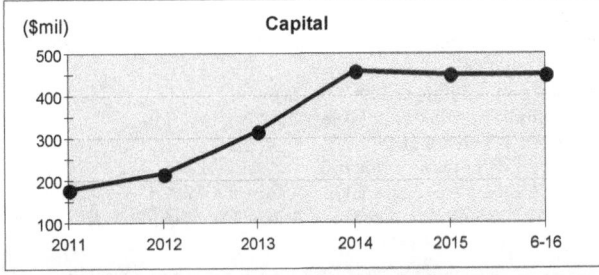

Capital

HOUSING AUTHORITY RISK RET GROUP INC   B-   Good

Major Rating Factors: Fair overall results on stability tests (4.1 on a scale of 0 to 10) including weak results on operational trends. Good overall profitability index (5.6) despite modest operating losses during the first six months of 2016.

Other Rating Factors: Strong long-term capitalization index (10.0) based on excellent current risk adjusted capital (severe and moderate loss scenarios), despite some fluctuation in capital levels. Ample reserve history (9.4) that helps to protect the company against sharp claims increases. Excellent liquidity (7.4) with ample operational cash flow and liquid investments.

Principal Business: Other liability (88%) and auto liability (12%).

Principal Investments: Investment grade bonds (76%), misc. investments (19%), real estate (4%), and cash (1%).

Investments in Affiliates: 12%

Group Affiliation: Housing Investment Group Inc

Licensed in: All states except AK, PR

Commenced Business: June 1987

Address: 189 Commerce Court, Cheshire, CT 06410-0189

Phone: (203) 272-8220   **Domicile State:** VT   **NAIC Code:** 26797

Data Date	Rating	RACR #1	RACR #2	Loss Ratio %	Total Assets ($mil)	Capital ($mil)	Net Premium ($mil)	Net Income ($mil)
6-16	B-	3.72	2.95	N/A	307.2	189.8	15.6	-0.7
6-15	C	4.35	3.44	N/A	308.6	196.0	15.3	2.9
2015	C+	3.86	3.08	77.7	311.8	192.3	30.9	3.8
2014	C	4.42	3.52	49.8	313.2	196.7	29.8	8.0
2013	C	4.68	3.75	43.6	314.8	194.7	28.3	7.0
2012	C	5.25	4.14	27.8	305.8	192.4	28.5	17.9
2011	C	4.55	3.71	N/A	307.1	179.3	28.6	26.8

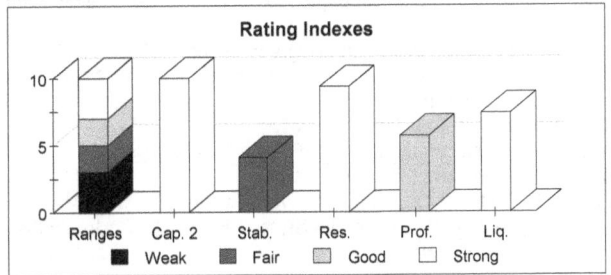

Rating Indexes

HOUSTON CASUALTY CO   B-   Good

Major Rating Factors: Fair overall results on stability tests (4.6 on a scale of 0 to 10) including weak results on operational trends and excessive premium growth. The largest net exposure for one risk is conservative at 1.2% of capital. Strong long-term capitalization index (8.1) based on excellent current risk adjusted capital (severe and moderate loss scenarios), despite some fluctuation in capital levels.

Other Rating Factors: Ample reserve history (7.6) that can protect against increases in claims costs. Excellent profitability (7.3) with operating gains in each of the last five years. Return on equity has been good over the last five years, averaging 13.4%. Excellent liquidity (8.1) with ample operational cash flow and liquid investments.

Principal Business: Other liability (49%), ocean marine (18%), inland marine (6%), fire (5%), other accident & health (4%), earthquake (4%), and other lines (14%).

Principal Investments: Investment grade bonds (53%), misc. investments (44%), non investment grade bonds (2%), and cash (1%).

Investments in Affiliates: 40%

Group Affiliation: HCC Ins Holdings Inc

Licensed in: All states, the District of Columbia and Puerto Rico

Commenced Business: June 1981

Address: 13403 Northwest Freeway, Houston, TX 77040-6094

Phone: (713) 462-1000   **Domicile State:** TX   **NAIC Code:** 42374

Data Date	Rating	RACR #1	RACR #2	Loss Ratio %	Total Assets ($mil)	Capital ($mil)	Net Premium ($mil)	Net Income ($mil)
6-16	B-	1.92	1.73	N/A	3,769.6	2,058.8	290.3	17.2
6-15	B-	1.78	1.62	N/A	3,304.0	2,034.0	232.2	22.1
2015	B-	1.87	1.73	66.4	3,404.1	1,936.9	808.3	313.8
2014	B-	1.72	1.60	51.2	2,960.2	1,891.9	336.7	215.3
2013	B-	1.88	1.71	40.6	2,967.1	1,909.7	301.7	323.6
2012	B-	1.87	1.70	50.1	2,930.4	1,795.1	332.1	264.2
2011	B-	1.91	1.73	70.1	2,911.7	1,699.0	337.0	229.4

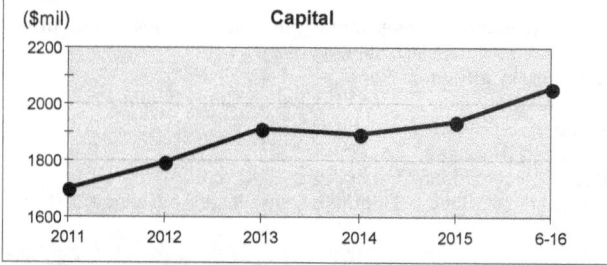

Capital ($mil)

HOUSTON SPECIALTY INS CO   B-   Good

Major Rating Factors: Fair profitability index (4.7 on a scale of 0 to 10) with operating losses during 2012 and 2015. Return on equity has been low, averaging 1.8% over the past five years. Fair overall results on stability tests (4.2) including excessive premium growth and weak results on operational trends.

Other Rating Factors: Good long-term capitalization index (6.5) based on good current risk adjusted capital (moderate loss scenario). Over the last several years, capital levels have remained relatively consistent. History of adequate reserve strength (5.7) as reserves have been consistently at an acceptable level. Good liquidity (6.9) with sufficient resources (cash flows and marketable investments) to handle a spike in claims.

Principal Business: Other liability (59%), auto liability (18%), allied lines (7%), auto physical damage (5%), commercial multiple peril (4%), ocean marine (2%), and other lines (5%).

Principal Investments: Misc. investments (47%), investment grade bonds (44%), and cash (9%).

Investments in Affiliates: 45%

Group Affiliation: Houston International Ins Group Ltd

Licensed in: All states except PR

Commenced Business: April 2007

Address: 800 Gessner Suite 600, Houston, TX 77024

Phone: (713) 935-4820   **Domicile State:** TX   **NAIC Code:** 12936

Data Date	Rating	RACR #1	RACR #2	Loss Ratio %	Total Assets ($mil)	Capital ($mil)	Net Premium ($mil)	Net Income ($mil)
6-16	B-	1.07	0.96	N/A	482.7	277.0	65.6	3.5
6-15	B-	1.07	0.96	N/A	533.5	267.2	39.0	-4.0
2015	B-	1.03	0.91	63.5	497.3	268.9	122.1	-5.8
2014	B	1.01	0.90	61.0	471.1	263.6	74.3	14.0
2013	B	0.78	0.70	51.1	361.7	187.7	109.1	8.2
2012	A-	1.18	1.08	58.6	281.8	187.6	67.5	-0.2
2011	A-	1.26	1.19	67.6	246.4	191.9	12.0	1.9

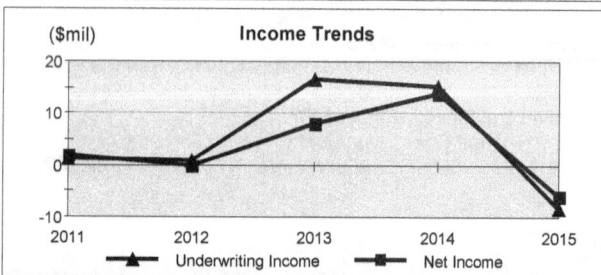

Income Trends ($mil)

Underwriting Income   Net Income

HUDSON INS CO   C-   Fair

Major Rating Factors: Fair overall results on stability tests (3.3 on a scale of 0 to 10) including weak financial strength of affiliated Fairfax Financial and weak results on operational trends. History of adequate reserve strength (6.2) as reserves have been consistently at an acceptable level.

Other Rating Factors: Good overall profitability index (6.9). Fair expense controls. Return on equity has been low, averaging 3.8% over the past five years. Good liquidity (5.5) with sufficient resources (cash flows and marketable investments) to handle a spike in claims. Strong long-term capitalization index (8.3) based on excellent current risk adjusted capital (severe and moderate loss scenarios). Moreover, capital levels have been consistent in recent years.

Principal Business: Allied lines (41%), other liability (37%), surety (8%), auto liability (6%), auto physical damage (6%), commercial multiple peril (1%), and inland marine (1%).

Principal Investments: Investment grade bonds (50%), misc. investments (36%), cash (8%), and non investment grade bonds (6%).

Investments in Affiliates: 37%

Group Affiliation: Fairfax Financial

Licensed in: All states, the District of Columbia and Puerto Rico

Commenced Business: December 1918

Address: 22 Cortlandt St. 18th Floor, New York, NY 10007

Phone: (212) 978-2800   **Domicile State:** DE   **NAIC Code:** 25054

Data Date	Rating	RACR #1	RACR #2	Loss Ratio %	Total Assets ($mil)	Capital ($mil)	Net Premium ($mil)	Net Income ($mil)
6-16	C-	2.15	1.94	N/A	1,138.5	477.9	76.6	20.9
6-15	C-	2.25	2.00	N/A	1,067.3	489.0	68.4	30.6
2015	C-	2.06	1.87	76.0	1,082.8	457.9	149.4	40.0
2014	C-	2.11	1.91	81.4	1,042.7	440.2	166.6	9.6
2013	C-	2.48	2.22	86.0	819.0	413.9	129.6	6.0
2012	C-	2.76	2.54	82.8	821.1	398.9	108.4	14.0
2011	C-	2.78	2.57	90.9	736.6	388.6	102.2	2.7

Fairfax Financial
Composite Group Rating: C

Largest Group Members	Assets ($mil)	Rating
ODYSSEY REINS CO	7308	C
US FIRE INS CO	3736	C
TIG INS CO	1924	U
ZENITH INS CO	1909	C+
CLEARWATER INS CO	1219	D-

HUDSON SPECIALTY INS CO   D+   Weak

Major Rating Factors: Weak overall results on stability tests (2.6 on a scale of 0 to 10) including potential drain of affiliation with Fairfax Financial and weak results on operational trends. The largest net exposure for one risk is conservative at 1.1% of capital. Good liquidity (6.9) with sufficient resources (cash flows and marketable investments) to handle a spike in claims.

Other Rating Factors: Strong long-term capitalization index (9.2) based on excellent current risk adjusted capital (severe and moderate loss scenarios). Moreover, capital levels have been consistent in recent years. Ample reserve history (7.7) that can protect against increases in claims costs. Excellent profitability (8.9) with operating gains in each of the last five years. Return on equity has been good over the last five years, averaging 10.8%.

Principal Business: Other liability (49%), medical malpractice (19%), ocean marine (17%), commercial multiple peril (9%), and fire (5%).

Principal Investments: Investment grade bonds (74%), misc. investments (15%), cash (7%), and non investment grade bonds (4%).

Investments in Affiliates: 19%

Group Affiliation: Fairfax Financial

Licensed in: All states, the District of Columbia and Puerto Rico

Commenced Business: December 1985

Address: 22 Cortlandt St 18th Fl, New York, NY 10007

Phone: (212) 978-2800   **Domicile State:** NY   **NAIC Code:** 37079

Data Date	Rating	RACR #1	RACR #2	Loss Ratio %	Total Assets ($mil)	Capital ($mil)	Net Premium ($mil)	Net Income ($mil)
6-16	D+	3.37	2.95	N/A	360.9	207.9	25.3	8.4
6-15	D+	3.12	2.62	N/A	400.1	216.3	27.9	36.5
2015	D+	3.20	2.78	46.8	373.2	201.2	51.0	50.6
2014	D+	2.79	2.39	60.9	366.9	186.8	63.2	22.2
2013	D+	2.70	2.27	68.7	311.7	157.7	50.5	12.5
2012	D+	2.86	2.58	87.9	263.5	143.8	35.1	7.7
2011	D+	11.30	7.78	61.8	227.1	138.0	26.0	6.9

Fairfax Financial Composite Group Rating: C Largest Group Members	Assets ($mil)	Rating
ODYSSEY REINS CO	7308	C
US FIRE INS CO	3736	C
TIG INS CO	1924	U
ZENITH INS CO	1909	C+
CLEARWATER INS CO	1219	D-

ICI MUTUAL INS CO A RRG   B   Good

Major Rating Factors: Fair overall results on stability tests (4.3 on a scale of 0 to 10) including weak results on operational trends. The largest net exposure for one risk is acceptable at 3.0% of capital. Strong long-term capitalization index (10.0) based on excellent current risk adjusted capital (severe and moderate loss scenarios), despite some fluctuation in capital levels.

Other Rating Factors: Ample reserve history (8.9) that helps to protect the company against sharp claims increases. Excellent profitability (7.9) with operating gains in each of the last five years. Excellent liquidity (8.0) with ample operational cash flow and liquid investments.

Principal Business: Other liability (89%) and fidelity (11%).

Principal Investments: Investment grade bonds (82%), misc. investments (17%), and cash (1%).

Investments in Affiliates: 0%

Group Affiliation: None

Licensed in: AZ, CA, CO, CT, DC, FL, GA, IL, IA, KS, MD, MA, MI, MN, MO, NE, NJ, NY, ND, OH, PA, SC, TN, TX, VT, VA, WA, WI

Commenced Business: March 1988

Address: 40 Main St Suite 500, Burlington, VT 05401

Phone: (800) 643-4246   **Domicile State:** VT   **NAIC Code:** 11268

Data Date	Rating	RACR #1	RACR #2	Loss Ratio %	Total Assets ($mil)	Capital ($mil)	Net Premium ($mil)	Net Income ($mil)
6-16	B	11.42	7.09	N/A	353.4	262.1	14.5	6.7
6-15	B	11.92	7.16	N/A	335.6	249.9	13.5	2.1
2015	B	11.20	6.98	59.5	340.8	249.1	31.0	3.8
2014	B	12.56	7.50	18.6	333.9	249.6	30.1	12.0
2013	A-	10.76	6.82	17.7	322.1	235.8	29.2	12.5
2012	A-	11.83	7.43	45.3	314.0	224.6	28.3	9.4
2011	A-	13.07	8.27	38.3	304.6	213.1	31.7	10.2

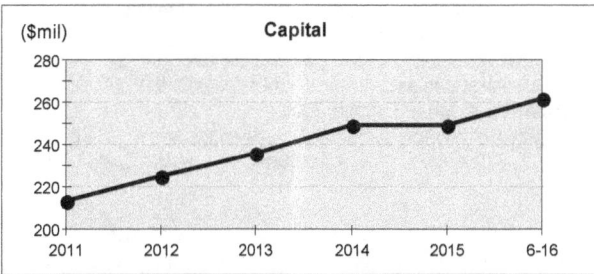

Capital ($mil) chart 2011 through 6-16.

IDS PROPERTY CASUALTY INS CO   B-   Good

Major Rating Factors: Fair reserve development (3.3 on a scale of 0 to 10) as reserves have generally been sufficient to cover claims. In 2015, the two year reserve development was 18% deficient. Fair profitability index (3.6) with operating losses during 2014 and the first six months of 2016. Average return on equity over the last five years has been poor at -0.2%.

Other Rating Factors: Fair liquidity (4.3) as cash resources may not be adequate to cover a spike in claims. Fair overall results on stability tests (4.8) including weak results on operational trends. Strong long-term capitalization index (8.2) based on excellent current risk adjusted capital (severe and moderate loss scenarios). Moreover, capital levels have been consistent in recent years.

Principal Business: Auto liability (37%), homeowners multiple peril (33%), auto physical damage (29%), inland marine (1%), and other liability (1%).

Principal Investments: Investment grade bonds (90%) and misc. investments (13%).

Investments in Affiliates: 3%

Group Affiliation: Ameriprise Financial Group

Licensed in: All states except PR

Commenced Business: January 1973

Address: 3500 Packerland Dr, De Pere, WI 54115

Phone: (920) 330-5100   **Domicile State:** WI   **NAIC Code:** 29068

Data Date	Rating	RACR #1	RACR #2	Loss Ratio %	Total Assets ($mil)	Capital ($mil)	Net Premium ($mil)	Net Income ($mil)
6-16	B-	2.59	2.02	N/A	1,765.1	736.4	529.6	-22.9
6-15	B	2.75	2.17	N/A	1,643.9	726.7	512.9	-9.7
2015	B-	2.49	1.91	97.7	1,661.8	683.6	1,068.2	-44.4
2014	B	2.25	1.74	95.6	1,414.3	559.9	1,000.9	-25.3
2013	B	2.57	2.13	88.2	1,268.3	530.7	883.7	11.3
2012	B	2.45	2.02	87.0	1,109.4	462.2	801.0	27.4
2011	B	2.50	2.12	88.1	1,039.9	431.0	741.7	22.5

Reserve Deficiency (as % of capital) chart, 2011 through 2015.
■ 1 Yr Dev   □ 2 Yr Dev
* Adequate & redundant reserves show as negatives

INDIANA OLD NATIONAL INS CO — C — Fair

Major Rating Factors: Fair overall results on stability tests (3.2 on a scale of 0 to 10) including weak results on operational trends. The largest net exposure for one risk is high at 4.7% of capital. Fair reserve development (3.6) as reserves have generally been sufficient to cover claims.

Other Rating Factors: Strong long-term capitalization index (10.0) based on excellent current risk adjusted capital (severe and moderate loss scenarios). Moreover, capital levels have been consistent in recent years. Excellent profitability (7.5) with operating gains in each of the last five years. Superior liquidity (10.0) with ample operational cash flow and liquid investments.

Principal Business: Aggregate write-ins for other lines of business (56%), other liability (31%), commercial multiple peril (11%), earthquake (2%), and surety (1%).

Principal Investments: Investment grade bonds (65%), misc. investments (30%), and cash (5%).

Investments in Affiliates: None

Group Affiliation: Old National Bancorp

Licensed in: IN, VT

Commenced Business: March 1999

Address: 7 Burlington Square,6th Floor, Burlington, VT 05401

Phone: (812) 464-1530   **Domicile State:** VT   **NAIC Code:** 11021

Data Date	Rating	RACR #1	RACR #2	Loss Ratio %	Total Assets ($mil)	Capital ($mil)	Net Premium ($mil)	Net Income ($mil)
6-16	C	59.21	22.24	N/A	2,150.0	2,147.8	0.6	19.5
6-15	C-	73.81	28.58	N/A	2,122.5	2,104.6	0.6	24.0
2015	C	62.60	23.73	4.6	2,129.5	2,129.3	1.3	48.7
2014	C-	77.54	30.25	23.0	2,096.8	2,079.4	1.3	49.0
2013	C-	66.31	24.93	11.2	2,037.5	2,030.9	1.2	30.2
2012	D+	144.54	72.04	29.3	1,026.5	1,023.1	0.9	12.2
2011	D+	164.74	82.07	30.1	1,012.7	1,010.2	1.1	10.1

Rating Indexes

Weak | Fair | Good | Strong

INFINITY INS CO — B — Good

Major Rating Factors: History of adequate reserve strength (6.5 on a scale of 0 to 10) as reserves have been consistently at an acceptable level. Good overall profitability index (6.1). Good expense controls. Return on equity has been fair, averaging 8.0% over the past five years.

Other Rating Factors: Fair overall results on stability tests (4.5) including potential drain of affiliation with Infinity Property & Casualty Group and weak results on operational trends. Fair liquidity (4.4) as cash resources may not be adequate to cover a spike in claims. Strong long-term capitalization index (7.9) based on excellent current risk adjusted capital (severe and moderate loss scenarios), despite some fluctuation in capital levels.

Principal Business: Auto liability (60%) and auto physical damage (40%).

Principal Investments: Investment grade bonds (80%), misc. investments (10%), non investment grade bonds (8%), and real estate (4%).

Investments in Affiliates: 4%

Group Affiliation: Infinity Property & Casualty Group

Licensed in: All states except KS, LA, NH, NJ, VT, WY, PR

Commenced Business: October 1978

Address: 2204 Lakeshore Dr,Suite 125, Birmingham, AL 35209-6787

Phone: (205) 870-4000   **Domicile State:** IN   **NAIC Code:** 22268

Data Date	Rating	RACR #1	RACR #2	Loss Ratio %	Total Assets ($mil)	Capital ($mil)	Net Premium ($mil)	Net Income ($mil)
6-16	B	1.84	1.58	N/A	2,018.9	652.9	670.8	24.6
6-15	B	1.85	1.58	N/A	2,059.9	669.0	666.6	20.6
2015	B	1.79	1.59	77.1	1,992.7	652.8	1,360.9	61.4
2014	B	1.84	1.63	75.7	1,991.5	674.6	1,334.7	68.0
2013	B	1.73	1.53	78.2	1,966.4	666.6	1,316.0	47.8
2012	B	1.60	1.39	79.7	1,860.6	605.7	1,233.1	33.8
2011	B	1.85	1.67	75.4	1,568.7	526.8	1,061.9	42.1

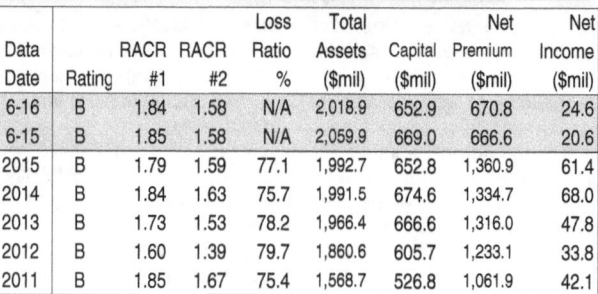

Reserve Deficiency (as % of capital)

* Adequate & redundant reserves show as negatives   1 Yr Dev   2 Yr Dev

INS CO OF NORTH AMERICA — C — Fair

Major Rating Factors: Fair overall results on stability tests (3.7 on a scale of 0 to 10) including fair financial strength of affiliated Chubb Limited and weak results on operational trends. The largest net exposure for one risk is high at 3.0% of capital. Good liquidity (6.9) with sufficient resources (cash flows and marketable investments) to handle a spike in claims.

Other Rating Factors: Strong long-term capitalization index (7.5) based on excellent current risk adjusted capital (severe and moderate loss scenarios), despite some fluctuation in capital levels. Ample reserve history (7.9) that can protect against increases in claims costs. Excellent profitability (7.7) with operating gains in each of the last five years.

Principal Business: Other accident & health (22%), other liability (20%), fire (16%), international (12%), group accident & health (12%), ocean marine (7%), and other lines (11%).

Principal Investments: Investment grade bonds (83%), cash (16%), and real estate (4%).

Investments in Affiliates: None

Group Affiliation: Chubb Limited

Licensed in: All states, the District of Columbia and Puerto Rico

Commenced Business: January 1792

Address: 1601 Chestnut St, Philadelphia, PA 19192

Phone: (215) 640-1000   **Domicile State:** PA   **NAIC Code:** 22713

Data Date	Rating	RACR #1	RACR #2	Loss Ratio %	Total Assets ($mil)	Capital ($mil)	Net Premium ($mil)	Net Income ($mil)
6-16	C	2.08	1.39	N/A	898.7	242.2	108.1	8.5
6-15	C	2.25	1.49	N/A	868.7	231.4	102.2	5.6
2015	C	2.08	1.40	72.8	883.8	233.6	237.9	8.6
2014	C	2.29	1.53	77.6	869.9	225.2	223.9	12.7
2013	C	1.88	1.26	72.2	787.1	182.8	217.7	15.3
2012	C	2.22	1.46	89.9	831.8	195.6	224.1	3.2
2011	C	2.13	1.37	80.7	755.6	180.5	212.8	29.2

Chubb Limited Composite Group Rating: B Largest Group Members	Assets ($mil)	Rating
FEDERAL INS CO	32241	B
ACE AMERICAN INS CO	12074	B-
ACE PC INS CO	7749	B-
PACIFIC INDEMNITY CO	6916	B
PACIFIC EMPLOYERS INS CO	3542	B-

INS CO OF THE WEST   C   Fair

Major Rating Factors: Fair overall results on stability tests (3.7 on a scale of 0 to 10) including potential drain of affiliation with American Assets Inc and weak results on operational trends. The largest net exposure for one risk is conservative at 1.4% of capital. Fair reserve development (4.7) as reserves have generally been sufficient to cover claims.

Other Rating Factors: Good liquidity (6.4) with sufficient resources (cash flows and marketable investments) to handle a spike in claims. Strong long-term capitalization index (7.1) based on excellent current risk adjusted capital (severe and moderate loss scenarios). Moreover, capital levels have been consistent in recent years. Excellent profitability (8.3) despite modest operating losses during 2011.

Principal Business: Workers compensation (93%), earthquake (5%), and inland marine (1%).

Principal Investments: Investment grade bonds (56%), misc. investments (36%), non investment grade bonds (5%), and cash (3%).

Investments in Affiliates: 10%

Group Affiliation: American Assets Inc

Licensed in: All states except PR

Commenced Business: May 1972

Address: 11455 El Camino Real, San Diego, CA 92130-2045

Phone: (858) 350-2400   **Domicile State:** CA   **NAIC Code:** 27847

Data Date	Rating	RACR #1	RACR #2	Loss Ratio %	Total Assets ($mil)	Capital ($mil)	Net Premium ($mil)	Net Income ($mil)
6-16	C	1.50	1.09	N/A	2,066.2	818.2	396.9	51.3
6-15	C	1.52	1.07	N/A	1,801.2	715.3	356.2	59.8
2015	C	1.47	1.08	63.0	1,917.0	753.3	744.1	90.4
2014	C	1.50	1.07	64.0	1,613.2	658.2	621.4	68.1
2013	C	1.72	1.21	61.1	1,314.5	533.5	514.8	68.8
2012	C	1.78	1.20	71.3	1,032.3	417.5	367.5	14.4
2011	C	1.80	1.20	79.1	875.6	350.4	284.7	-1.3

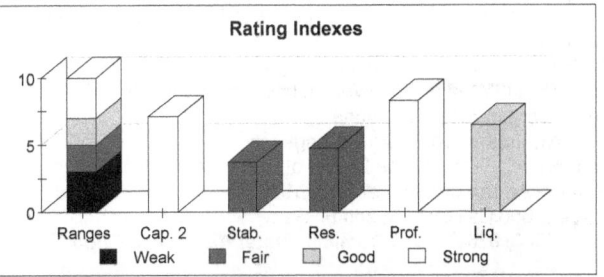

Rating Indexes

INTEGON NATIONAL INS CO   C   Fair

Major Rating Factors: Fair reserve development (3.7 on a scale of 0 to 10) as the level of reserves has at times been insufficient to cover claims. In 2011 and 2012 the two year reserve development was 36% and 40% deficient respectively. Fair profitability index (3.1) with operating losses during 2012, 2013 and 2015. Average return on equity over the last five years has been poor at -5.2%.

Other Rating Factors: Fair liquidity (4.3) as cash resources may not be adequate to cover a spike in claims. Fair overall results on stability tests (3.9) including excessive premium growth and weak results on operational trends. The largest net exposure for one risk is conservative at 1.6% of capital. Good long-term capitalization index (5.1) based on fair current risk adjusted capital (severe loss scenario), although results have slipped from the good range during the last year.

Principal Business: Auto liability (50%), auto physical damage (32%), homeowners multiple peril (16%), and group accident & health (2%).

Principal Investments: Investment grade bonds (95%), non investment grade bonds (5%), misc. investments (2%), and real estate (1%).

Investments in Affiliates: 6%

Group Affiliation: AmTrust Financial Services Inc

Licensed in: All states except PR

Commenced Business: December 1988

Address: 500 W Fifth St, Winston Salem, NC 27152

Phone: (336) 435-2000   **Domicile State:** NC   **NAIC Code:** 29742

Data Date	Rating	RACR #1	RACR #2	Loss Ratio %	Total Assets ($mil)	Capital ($mil)	Net Premium ($mil)	Net Income ($mil)
6-16	C	0.89	0.65	N/A	2,215.7	389.6	678.9	11.9
6-15	C-	1.24	0.99	N/A	1,651.3	326.2	335.2	0.1
2015	C	1.18	0.85	75.2	2,339.5	448.3	1,155.3	-10.0
2014	C-	1.22	0.97	74.3	1,741.0	332.4	928.7	11.4
2013	D+	1.27	0.96	87.6	1,149.5	159.8	349.1	-33.2
2012	D	0.31	0.26	79.1	1,145.1	139.7	869.0	-34.3
2011	D+	1.63	1.30	78.1	400.4	74.5	118.9	9.1

Reserve Deficiency (as % of capital)

* Adequate & redundant reserves show as negatives   1 Yr Dev   2 Yr Dev

INTERINS EXCHANGE *   B+   Good

Major Rating Factors: Good overall results on stability tests (5.1 on a scale of 0 to 10) despite potential drain of affiliation with Auto Club Enterprises Ins Group and weak results on operational trends. Good liquidity (6.6) with sufficient resources (cash flows and marketable investments) to handle a spike in claims.

Other Rating Factors: Strong long-term capitalization index (10.0) based on excellent current risk adjusted capital (severe and moderate loss scenarios). Moreover, capital levels have been consistent in recent years. Ample reserve history (7.4) that can protect against increases in claims costs. Excellent profitability (7.9) despite modest operating losses during the first six months of 2016.

Principal Business: Auto liability (45%), auto physical damage (34%), homeowners multiple peril (19%), fire (1%), and other liability (1%).

Principal Investments: Investment grade bonds (49%), misc. investments (43%), non investment grade bonds (7%), and real estate (2%).

Investments in Affiliates: 1%

Group Affiliation: Auto Club Enterprises Ins Group

Licensed in: CA, FL, HI, ME, MI, MO, NH, NM, OH, PA, TX, VT, VA

Commenced Business: October 1912

Address: 3333 Fairview Road, Costa Mesa, CA 92626

Phone: (714) 850-5111   **Domicile State:** CA   **NAIC Code:** 15598

Data Date	Rating	RACR #1	RACR #2	Loss Ratio %	Total Assets ($mil)	Capital ($mil)	Net Premium ($mil)	Net Income ($mil)
6-16	B+	4.92	3.02	N/A	9,074.7	5,674.9	1,528.7	-13.9
6-15	B+	5.04	3.09	N/A	8,770.2	5,583.3	1,435.0	84.4
2015	B+	5.05	3.13	71.9	8,707.0	5,633.7	3,017.0	183.2
2014	B+	5.11	3.16	71.6	8,547.9	5,496.7	2,864.6	200.7
2013	A+	5.26	3.26	71.1	8,106.5	5,214.6	2,752.1	269.8
2012	A+	5.69	3.60	72.4	7,254.0	4,609.7	2,612.8	220.0
2011	A+	5.78	3.72	73.7	6,733.5	4,265.3	2,514.2	188.5

Rating Indexes

IRONSHORE SPECIALTY INS CO   C   Fair

Major Rating Factors: Fair overall results on stability tests (3.7 on a scale of 0 to 10) including potential drain of affiliation with Ironshore Holdings Inc and weak results on operational trends. The largest net exposure for one risk is conservative at 1.2% of capital. History of adequate reserve strength (6.0) as reserves have been consistently at an acceptable level.

Other Rating Factors: Good liquidity (6.9) with sufficient resources (cash flows and marketable investments) to handle a spike in claims. Strong long-term capitalization index (7.5) based on excellent current risk adjusted capital (severe and moderate loss scenarios). Moreover, capital levels have been consistent in recent years. Excellent profitability (7.9) despite modest operating losses during the first six months of 2016.

Principal Business: Other liability (65%), medical malpractice (11%), fire (10%), homeowners multiple peril (7%), products liability (4%), allied lines (1%), and other lines (2%).

Principal Investments: Investment grade bonds (74%), misc. investments (20%), cash (3%), and non investment grade bonds (3%).

Investments in Affiliates: None

Group Affiliation: Ironshore Holdings Inc

Licensed in: All states, the District of Columbia and Puerto Rico

Commenced Business: February 1953

Address: 650 California St 2nd Fl, San Francisco, CA 94108-2702

Phone: (646) 826-6600   **Domicile State:** AZ   **NAIC Code:** 25445

Data Date	Rating	RACR #1	RACR #2	Loss Ratio %	Total Assets ($mil)	Capital ($mil)	Net Premium ($mil)	Net Income ($mil)
6-16	C	2.38	1.42	N/A	1,111.8	340.7	59.7	-1.2
6-15	C	2.12	1.29	N/A	1,038.2	322.6	64.9	12.3
2015	C	2.41	1.46	76.6	987.1	334.0	112.0	20.9
2014	C	2.28	1.40	85.1	974.0	325.8	127.1	31.3
2013	C	2.59	1.58	68.3	832.9	300.3	119.2	21.4
2012	C	3.02	1.76	84.5	804.3	291.3	101.4	17.1
2011	C	3.21	1.93	85.0	698.0	282.2	90.4	6.2

Rating Indexes

ISMIE MUTUAL INS CO   B-   Good

Major Rating Factors: Fair overall results on stability tests (4.5 on a scale of 0 to 10) including potential drain of affiliation with ISMIE Group, weak results on operational trends and negative cash flow from operations for 2015. Good overall profitability index (6.3) despite operating losses during the first six months of 2016.

Other Rating Factors: Strong long-term capitalization index (9.7) based on excellent current risk adjusted capital (severe and moderate loss scenarios), despite some fluctuation in capital levels. Ample reserve history (9.6) that helps to protect the company against sharp claims increases. Excellent liquidity (7.6) with ample operational cash flow and liquid investments.

Principal Business: Medical malpractice (99%) and aggregate write-ins for other lines of business (1%).

Principal Investments: Investment grade bonds (89%), misc. investments (8%), cash (2%), and non investment grade bonds (1%).

Investments in Affiliates: 4%

Group Affiliation: ISMIE Group

Licensed in: GA, IL, IN, IA, KS, KY, LA, MI, MO, NE, PA, SC, WI

Commenced Business: June 1976

Address: 20 N Michigan Ave, Chicago, IL 60602-4811

Phone: (312) 782-2749   **Domicile State:** IL   **NAIC Code:** 32921

Data Date	Rating	RACR #1	RACR #2	Loss Ratio %	Total Assets ($mil)	Capital ($mil)	Net Premium ($mil)	Net Income ($mil)
6-16	B-	4.12	3.43	N/A	1,482.7	666.8	76.5	-5.0
6-15	B-	3.65	3.01	N/A	1,540.2	637.7	90.3	2.4
2015	B-	4.15	3.48	57.9	1,525.9	670.1	168.4	37.4
2014	B-	3.73	3.10	53.4	1,625.1	647.4	189.2	34.8
2013	B-	3.66	2.98	37.6	1,616.4	609.9	229.6	80.1
2012	B-	2.99	2.47	52.9	1,544.7	522.9	242.2	57.0
2011	B-	2.63	2.18	53.0	1,492.8	461.0	236.5	47.1

Rating Indexes

JEWELERS MUTUAL INS CO   B   Good

Major Rating Factors: History of adequate reserve strength (6.4 on a scale of 0 to 10) as reserves have been consistently at an acceptable level. Good liquidity (6.7) with sufficient resources (cash flows and marketable investments) to handle a spike in claims.

Other Rating Factors: Fair overall results on stability tests (4.4) including weak results on operational trends. The largest net exposure for one risk is acceptable at 2.1% of capital. Strong long-term capitalization index (10.0) based on excellent current risk adjusted capital (severe and moderate loss scenarios). Moreover, capital levels have been consistent in recent years. Excellent profitability (8.6) with operating gains in each of the last five years.

Principal Business: Inland marine (86%) and commercial multiple peril (14%).

Principal Investments: Investment grade bonds (61%), misc. investments (32%), real estate (4%), and cash (3%).

Investments in Affiliates: 0%

Group Affiliation: None

Licensed in: All states except PR

Commenced Business: June 1914

Address: 24 Jewelers Park Dr, Neenah, WI 54957-3703

Phone: (920) 725-4326   **Domicile State:** WI   **NAIC Code:** 14354

Data Date	Rating	RACR #1	RACR #2	Loss Ratio %	Total Assets ($mil)	Capital ($mil)	Net Premium ($mil)	Net Income ($mil)
6-16	B	5.56	3.45	N/A	380.0	235.9	84.3	5.5
6-15	B	5.49	3.45	N/A	349.1	216.4	77.7	8.1
2015	B	5.77	3.60	45.0	365.3	226.5	165.9	15.5
2014	B	5.50	3.45	44.2	338.7	207.7	154.0	16.3
2013	A-	5.07	3.14	43.5	304.9	182.6	143.8	17.4
2012	A-	5.10	3.12	54.2	261.7	153.2	133.4	14.5
2011	A-	5.12	3.10	63.1	247.0	144.7	123.6	2.2

Reserve Deficiency (as % of capital)

* Adequate & redundant reserves show as negatives

KENTUCKY EMPLOYERS MUTUAL INS
B-   **Good**

Major Rating Factors: Fair overall results on stability tests (4.0 on a scale of 0 to 10) including weak results on operational trends. Good long-term capitalization (6.8) based on good current risk adjusted capital (moderate loss scenario) reflecting improvement over results in 2015.

Other Rating Factors: History of adequate reserve strength (6.8) as reserves have been consistently at an acceptable level. Good overall profitability index (5.5) despite operating losses during 2015. Good liquidity (6.9) with sufficient resources (cash flows and marketable investments) to handle a spike in claims.

Principal Business: Workers compensation (100%).

Principal Investments: Investment grade bonds (90%), misc. investments (9%), and cash (1%).

Investments in Affiliates: None

Group Affiliation: None

Licensed in: KY

Commenced Business: September 1995

Address: 250 W Main Street, Ste 900, Lexington, KY 40507

Phone: (859) 425-7800   **Domicile State:** KY   **NAIC Code:** 10320

Data Date	Rating	RACR #1	RACR #2	Loss Ratio %	Total Assets ($mil)	Capital ($mil)	Net Premium ($mil)	Net Income ($mil)
6-16	B-	1.56	1.03	N/A	917.8	208.5	67.5	6.7
6-15	C+	1.48	1.03	N/A	968.4	219.5	77.3	15.6
2015	C+	1.49	0.99	90.2	918.5	196.7	141.1	-4.3
2014	C+	1.49	1.03	87.9	932.2	208.3	157.7	12.5
2013	C+	1.51	1.04	80.9	816.2	196.4	142.8	16.8
2012	C+	1.51	1.04	89.1	747.9	173.1	124.2	9.0
2011	C+	1.47	0.78	105.3	709.5	159.6	112.8	12.9

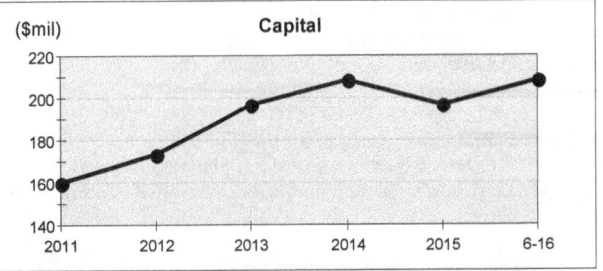

Capital

KENTUCKY FARM BUREAU MUTUAL INS CO
B   **Good**

Major Rating Factors: History of adequate reserve strength (6.5 on a scale of 0 to 10) as reserves have been consistently at an acceptable level. Good overall profitability index (6.3) despite operating losses during 2011.

Other Rating Factors: Good liquidity (6.1) with sufficient resources (cash flows and marketable investments) to handle a spike in claims. Fair overall results on stability tests (4.8) including potential drain of affiliation with Kentucky Farm Bureau Group and weak results on operational trends. Strong long-term capitalization index (10.0) based on excellent current risk adjusted capital (severe and moderate loss scenarios). Moreover, capital levels have been consistent in recent years.

Principal Business: Auto liability (33%), homeowners multiple peril (26%), auto physical damage (20%), farmowners multiple peril (12%), commercial multiple peril (7%), other liability (1%), and allied lines (1%).

Principal Investments: Investment grade bonds (76%) and misc. investments (24%).

Investments in Affiliates: 1%

Group Affiliation: Kentucky Farm Bureau Group

Licensed in: CA, CT, GA, ID, IL, IN, IA, KY, LA, MD, MA, MI, MO, MT, NH, NJ, NC, ND, OH, OK, OR, PA, RI, SD, TX, UT, VT, VA, WV, WI

Commenced Business: December 1943

Address: 9201 Bunsen Parkway, Louisville, KY 40220-3793

Phone: (502) 495-5000   **Domicile State:** KY   **NAIC Code:** 22993

Data Date	Rating	RACR #1	RACR #2	Loss Ratio %	Total Assets ($mil)	Capital ($mil)	Net Premium ($mil)	Net Income ($mil)
6-16	B	5.56	3.62	N/A	2,373.1	1,254.3	451.3	27.8
6-15	B	5.57	3.58	N/A	2,277.5	1,185.6	426.2	30.1
2015	B	5.58	3.68	79.6	2,286.1	1,226.1	877.8	39.9
2014	B	5.53	3.62	71.1	2,222.2	1,155.1	851.1	120.4
2013	A-	5.04	3.32	67.2	2,119.7	1,066.3	845.5	147.6
2012	A-	4.27	2.84	85.9	1,915.4	938.4	850.8	19.6
2011	A-	3.90	2.60	91.5	1,838.2	900.4	862.1	-26.7

Reserve Deficiency (as % of capital)

* Adequate & redundant reserves show as negatives

LAMMICO
B   **Good**

Major Rating Factors: Fair overall results on stability tests (4.2 on a scale of 0 to 10) including weak results on operational trends. Strong long-term capitalization index (10.0) based on excellent current risk adjusted capital (severe and moderate loss scenarios). Moreover, capital levels have been consistent in recent years.

Other Rating Factors: Ample reserve history (9.1) that helps to protect the company against sharp claims increases. Excellent profitability (8.6) with operating gains in each of the last five years. Excellent liquidity (8.7) with ample operational cash flow and liquid investments.

Principal Business: Medical malpractice (99%) and other liability (1%).

Principal Investments: Investment grade bonds (85%), misc. investments (13%), and cash (2%).

Investments in Affiliates: 0%

Group Affiliation: None

Licensed in: AR, LA, MS, TN, TX

Commenced Business: January 1982

Address: One Galleria Blvd Suite 700, Metairie, LA 70001

Phone: (504) 831-3756   **Domicile State:** LA   **NAIC Code:** 43656

Data Date	Rating	RACR #1	RACR #2	Loss Ratio %	Total Assets ($mil)	Capital ($mil)	Net Premium ($mil)	Net Income ($mil)
6-16	B	5.41	4.16	N/A	408.4	219.3	23.7	3.6
6-15	C+	5.21	3.98	N/A	402.0	211.4	23.4	5.4
2015	B	5.38	4.17	64.3	427.1	214.9	49.0	11.6
2014	C+	5.12	3.95	63.8	421.5	206.0	49.3	12.3
2013	C+	4.81	3.76	57.6	411.9	194.0	49.4	13.9
2012	C+	4.35	3.38	57.2	412.5	177.7	54.9	17.1
2011	C+	4.08	3.34	69.6	379.6	153.0	47.3	10.2

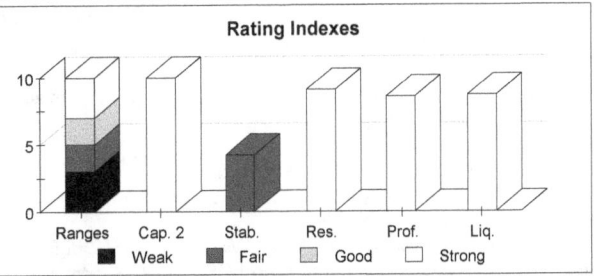

Rating Indexes

LANDMARK AMERICAN INS CO   C   Fair

Major Rating Factors: Fair overall results on stability tests (3.5 on a scale of 0 to 10) including potential drain of affiliation with Alleghany Corp Group and weak results on operational trends. Strong long-term capitalization index (10.0) based on excellent current risk adjusted capital (severe and moderate loss scenarios), despite some fluctuation in capital levels.

Other Rating Factors: Ample reserve history (7.7) that can protect against increases in claims costs. Excellent profitability (8.8) with operating gains in each of the last five years. Excellent liquidity (7.3) with ample operational cash flow and liquid investments.

Principal Business: Other liability (30%), allied lines (29%), fire (20%), medical malpractice (8%), inland marine (8%), products liability (3%), and earthquake (2%).

Principal Investments: Investment grade bonds (97%), misc. investments (1%), cash (1%), and non investment grade bonds (1%).

Investments in Affiliates: None

Group Affiliation: Alleghany Corp Group

Licensed in: All states, the District of Columbia and Puerto Rico

Commenced Business: April 1976

Address: 201 Robert S Kerr Ave Ste 600, Oklahoma City, OK 73102-4267

Phone: (404) 231-2366   **Domicile State:** OK   **NAIC Code:** 33138

Data Date	Rating	RACR #1	RACR #2	Loss Ratio %	Total Assets ($mil)	Capital ($mil)	Net Premium ($mil)	Net Income ($mil)
6-16	C	15.74	9.71	N/A	402.9	238.5	19.9	8.9
6-15	C	13.14	8.18	N/A	415.3	218.0	22.5	8.6
2015	C	14.75	9.18	33.6	387.8	228.7	42.9	19.7
2014	C	13.79	8.66	44.4	388.9	224.4	45.2	17.0
2013	C	12.07	7.60	43.7	397.2	208.1	48.9	16.5
2012	C	8.35	4.56	58.0	370.4	191.6	51.4	11.3
2011	C	9.29	4.54	45.4	367.0	195.0	46.9	14.1

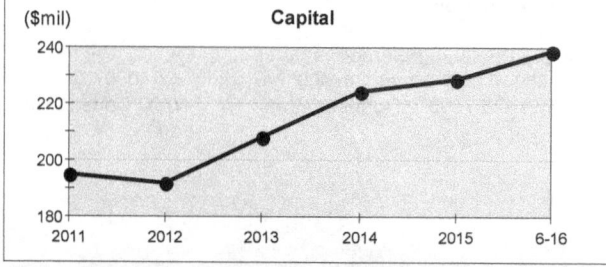

Capital ($mil)

LAWYERS MUTUAL INS CO   B-   Good

Major Rating Factors: Fair overall results on stability tests (4.0 on a scale of 0 to 10) including weak results on operational trends. Strong long-term capitalization index (10.0) based on excellent current risk adjusted capital (severe and moderate loss scenarios). Moreover, capital levels have been consistent in recent years.

Other Rating Factors: Ample reserve history (9.4) that helps to protect the company against sharp claims increases. Excellent profitability (8.9) with operating gains in each of the last five years. Excellent liquidity (7.9) with ample operational cash flow and liquid investments.

Principal Business: Other liability (100%).

Principal Investments: Investment grade bonds (82%), misc. investments (15%), cash (2%), and real estate (1%).

Investments in Affiliates: 0%

Group Affiliation: None

Licensed in: CA

Commenced Business: September 1978

Address: 3110 W Empire Ave, Burbank, CA 91504

Phone: (818) 565-5512   **Domicile State:** CA   **NAIC Code:** 36706

Data Date	Rating	RACR #1	RACR #2	Loss Ratio %	Total Assets ($mil)	Capital ($mil)	Net Premium ($mil)	Net Income ($mil)
6-16	B-	9.39	5.94	N/A	318.3	218.1	17.9	7.9
6-15	C	8.52	5.43	N/A	311.3	204.6	18.2	7.6
2015	C+	9.16	5.82	44.8	308.5	208.7	36.4	15.2
2014	C	8.41	5.40	42.9	303.2	196.0	35.9	16.3
2013	C	6.95	4.43	53.6	296.0	183.2	35.7	14.4
2012	C	6.16	3.99	63.7	288.2	164.0	36.1	15.0
2011	C	5.64	3.70	75.0	277.9	149.3	36.8	13.3

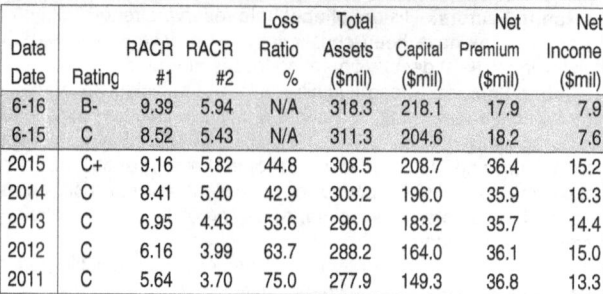

Rating Indexes

Ranges | Cap. 2 | Stab. | Res. | Prof. | Liq.
■ Weak   ▨ Fair   ▢ Good   ☐ Strong

LEXINGTON INS CO   C   Fair

Major Rating Factors: Fair reserve development (4.4 on a scale of 0 to 10) as reserves have generally been sufficient to cover claims. Fair profitability index (3.7). Fair expense controls. Return on equity has been fair, averaging 10.5% over the past five years.

Other Rating Factors: Weak overall results on stability tests (2.8) including weak results on operational trends and negative cash flow from operations for 2015. The largest net exposure for one risk is excessive at 12.2% of capital. Strengths include potentially strong support from affiliation with American International Group. Good liquidity (6.3) with sufficient resources (cash flows and marketable investments) to handle a spike in claims. Strong long-term capitalization index (7.7) based on excellent current risk adjusted capital (severe and moderate loss scenarios), despite some fluctuation in capital levels.

Principal Business: Other liability (27%), fire (24%), allied lines (17%), medical malpractice (7%), homeowners multiple peril (7%), inland marine (6%), and other lines (12%).

Principal Investments: Investment grade bonds (76%), misc. investments (18%), and non investment grade bonds (6%).

Investments in Affiliates: 0%

Group Affiliation: American International Group

Licensed in: All states, the District of Columbia and Puerto Rico

Commenced Business: April 1965

Address: 2711 Centerville Rd Suite 400, Wilmington, DE 19808

Phone: (617) 330-1100   **Domicile State:** DE   **NAIC Code:** 19437

Data Date	Rating	RACR #1	RACR #2	Loss Ratio %	Total Assets ($mil)	Capital ($mil)	Net Premium ($mil)	Net Income ($mil)
6-16	C	2.12	1.44	N/A	25,270.1	6,289.3	2,639.8	604.3
6-15	C+	2.07	1.42	N/A	25,097.6	6,341.9	2,673.5	429.6
2015	C+	2.22	1.51	88.8	25,504.7	6,593.0	5,564.4	6.0
2014	C+	2.11	1.45	62.3	25,340.5	6,534.1	6,098.6	862.0
2013	C+	2.85	1.92	69.4	22,120.5	7,224.1	3,755.8	1,660.2
2012	C+	2.87	1.94	100.0	24,567.8	7,925.6	3,621.9	409.0
2011	C+	2.71	1.75	94.7	24,208.4	7,797.9	4,314.5	517.6

Reserve Deficiency (as % of capital)

* Adequate & redundant reserves show as negatives   ■ 1 Yr Dev   ☐ 2 Yr Dev

LIBERTY INS CORP   C-   Fair

Major Rating Factors: Fair profitability index (3.6) with operating losses during 2011 and 2012. Average return on equity over the last five years has been poor at -1.1%.

Other Rating Factors: Fair overall results on stability tests (3.3) including weak results on operational trends. Strong long-term capitalization index (10.0) based on excellent current risk adjusted capital (severe and moderate loss scenarios), despite some fluctuation in capital levels. Excellent liquidity (7.0) with ample operational cash flow and liquid investments.

Principal Business: Homeowners multiple peril (59%), workers compensation (19%), other liability (8%), auto liability (8%), auto physical damage (3%), and inland marine (1%).

Principal Investments: Investment grade bonds (91%) and misc. investments (9%).

Investments in Affiliates: None

Group Affiliation: Liberty Mutual Group

Licensed in: All states, the District of Columbia and Puerto Rico

Commenced Business: November 1988

Address: 175 Berkeley St, Mailstop 3E, Boston, MA 02117

Phone: (617) 357-9500   **Domicile State:** IL   **NAIC Code:** 42404

Data Date	Rating	RACR #1	RACR #2	Loss Ratio %	Total Assets ($mil)	Capital ($mil)	Net Premium ($mil)	Net Income ($mil)
6-16	C-	124.30	63.29	N/A	245.6	239.4	0.0	2.7
6-15	D	111.26	50.76	N/A	231.9	225.1	0.0	4.9
2015	C-	135.45	65.78	0.0	244.8	239.7	0.0	16.6
2014	D	96.71	51.72	0.0	232.0	223.2	0.0	8.3
2013	D	135.89	66.60	0.0	218.6	215.4	-215.2	48.2
2012	D	0.80	0.53	90.3	1,449.7	168.7	522.2	-48.5
2011	C	1.18	0.76	90.1	1,428.3	245.0	458.0	-28.4

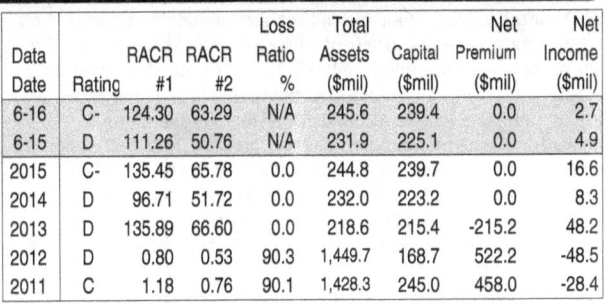

Rating Indexes

LIBERTY MUTUAL FIRE INS CO   B-   Good

Major Rating Factors: Fair reserve development (4.4 on a scale of 0 to 10) as reserves have generally been sufficient to cover claims. Fair overall results on stability tests (3.6) including fair financial strength of affiliated Liberty Mutual Group and weak results on operational trends. The largest net exposure for one risk is high at 3.5% of capital.

Other Rating Factors: Good overall profitability index (5.4) despite operating losses during 2011, 2012 and the first six months of 2016. Return on equity has been low, averaging 2.1% over the past five years. Good liquidity (6.1) with sufficient resources (cash flows and marketable investments) to handle a spike in claims. Strong long-term capitalization index (7.6) based on excellent current risk adjusted capital (severe and moderate loss scenarios), despite some fluctuation in capital levels.

Principal Business: Auto liability (28%), homeowners multiple peril (23%), auto physical damage (16%), workers compensation (11%), other liability (8%), fire (7%), and other lines (8%).

Principal Investments: Investment grade bonds (72%), misc. investments (24%), and non investment grade bonds (5%).

Investments in Affiliates: 5%

Group Affiliation: Liberty Mutual Group

Licensed in: All states, the District of Columbia and Puerto Rico

Commenced Business: November 1908

Address: 175 Berkeley St, Mailstop 3E, Boston, MA 02117

Phone: (617) 357-9500   **Domicile State:** WI   **NAIC Code:** 23035

Data Date	Rating	RACR #1	RACR #2	Loss Ratio %	Total Assets ($mil)	Capital ($mil)	Net Premium ($mil)	Net Income ($mil)
6-16	B-	2.09	1.45	N/A	5,500.1	1,395.3	1,014.4	-12.2
6-15	C+	1.96	1.36	N/A	5,400.8	1,336.1	983.1	188.3
2015	B-	2.12	1.48	68.4	5,477.8	1,399.0	2,050.6	252.1
2014	C+	1.93	1.34	70.0	5,297.9	1,302.1	2,030.1	132.2
2013	C+	1.75	1.20	73.5	5,561.6	1,216.3	2,163.5	87.5
2012	C	1.37	0.92	90.3	5,235.7	939.1	1,684.2	-130.8
2011	B-	1.57	1.04	90.1	4,876.8	1,073.0	1,476.9	-99.4

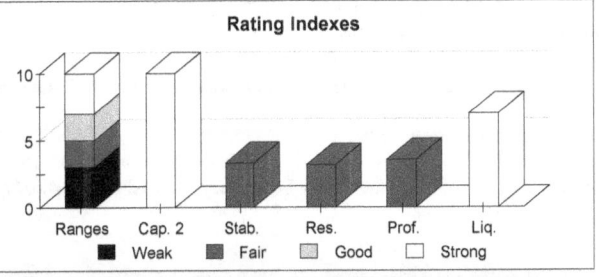

Reserve Deficiency (as % of capital)

* Adequate & redundant reserves show as negatives

1 Yr Dev
2 Yr Dev

LIBERTY MUTUAL INS CO   B   Good

Major Rating Factors: History of adequate reserve strength (5.8 on a scale of 0 to 10) as reserves have been consistently at an acceptable level. Good overall profitability index (5.4) despite operating losses during 2011 and the first six months of 2016. Return on equity has been low, averaging 2.0% over the past five years.

Other Rating Factors: Good liquidity (6.4) with sufficient resources (cash flows and marketable investments) to handle a spike in claims. Fair overall results on stability tests (4.3) including weak results on operational trends. The largest net exposure for one risk is conservative at 1.9% of capital. Strong long-term capitalization index (7.6) based on excellent current risk adjusted capital (severe and moderate loss scenarios), despite some fluctuation in capital levels.

Principal Business: Inland marine (44%), surety (18%), other liability (12%), auto liability (9%), auto physical damage (7%), ocean marine (2%), and other lines (8%).

Principal Investments: Misc. investments (62%), investment grade bonds (35%), non investment grade bonds (3%), and real estate (1%).

Investments in Affiliates: 27%

Group Affiliation: Liberty Mutual Group

Licensed in: All states, the District of Columbia and Puerto Rico

Commenced Business: July 1912

Address: 175 Berkeley St, Mailstop 3E, Boston, MA 02117

Phone: (617) 357-9500   **Domicile State:** MA   **NAIC Code:** 23043

Data Date	Rating	RACR #1	RACR #2	Loss Ratio %	Total Assets ($mil)	Capital ($mil)	Net Premium ($mil)	Net Income ($mil)
6-16	B	1.60	1.40	N/A	42,340.6	15,926.0	6,340.2	-162.7
6-15	B	1.63	1.40	N/A	42,237.6	15,797.7	6,144.5	233.8
2015	B	1.60	1.40	68.4	42,343.2	15,815.3	12,816.1	973.0
2014	B	1.73	1.49	70.0	42,655.2	16,569.3	12,688.4	888.4
2013	B	1.63	1.39	73.5	44,475.8	15,126.4	13,889.2	507.4
2012	B	1.73	1.46	90.3	40,205.4	14,510.5	9,635.4	163.6
2011	B	1.61	1.36	90.1	37,394.8	13,596.4	8,449.3	-536.2

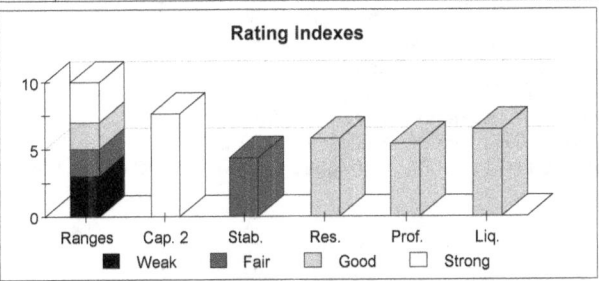

Rating Indexes

MAG MUTUAL INS CO

B-   **Good**

Major Rating Factors: Fair overall results on stability tests (4.7 on a scale of 0 to 10) including potential drain of affiliation with MAG Mutual Group and weak results on operational trends. Strong long-term capitalization index (8.9) based on excellent current risk adjusted capital (severe and moderate loss scenarios). Moreover, capital levels have been consistent in recent years.

Other Rating Factors: Ample reserve history (9.4) that helps to protect the company against sharp claims increases. Excellent profitability (8.4) despite modest operating losses during the first six months of 2016. Excellent liquidity (7.3) with ample operational cash flow and liquid investments.

Principal Business: Medical malpractice (95%), workers compensation (4%), and commercial multiple peril (1%).

Principal Investments: Investment grade bonds (58%), misc. investments (33%), and non investment grade bonds (9%).

Investments in Affiliates: 13%

Group Affiliation: MAG Mutual Group

Licensed in: AL, AZ, AR, FL, GA, IN, KY, MD, MS, NM, NC, OH, SC, TN, VA, WV

Commenced Business: June 1982

Address: 3525 Piedmont Rd NE Bldg 8-600, Atlanta, GA 30305-1556

Phone: (404) 842-5600   **Domicile State:** GA   **NAIC Code:** 42617

Data Date	Rating	RACR #1	RACR #2	Loss Ratio %	Total Assets ($mil)	Capital ($mil)	Net Premium ($mil)	Net Income ($mil)
6-16	B-	3.27	2.56	N/A	1,748.4	890.7	117.8	-0.9
6-15	B-	5.26	3.45	N/A	1,634.4	790.7	99.2	19.5
2015	B-	3.25	2.55	71.3	1,719.2	880.7	200.2	40.8
2014	B-	5.19	3.44	74.4	1,635.6	773.3	194.1	45.2
2013	B-	4.96	3.43	64.5	1,609.9	740.3	197.5	52.0
2012	B-	4.86	3.53	71.6	1,543.7	667.5	197.3	43.7
2011	B-	4.44	3.28	47.3	1,510.4	610.1	214.4	66.2

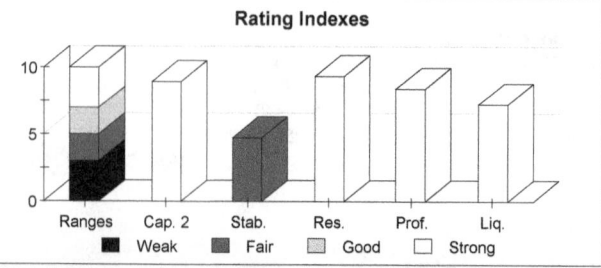

Rating Indexes

MAIDEN RE NORTH AMERICA INC

B-   **Good**

Major Rating Factors: Good long-term capitalization index (5.4 on a scale of 0 to 10) based on fair current risk adjusted capital (severe loss scenario), although results have slipped from the good range during the last year. Fair profitability index (4.6) with operating losses during 2011, 2012, 2013 and the first six months of 2016. Return on equity has been low, averaging 0.1% over the past five years.

Other Rating Factors: Fair overall results on stability tests (4.1) including weak results on operational trends. The largest net exposure for one risk is conservative at 1.9% of capital. History of adequate reserve strength (6.0) as reserves have been consistently at an acceptable level. Good liquidity (6.5) with sufficient resources (cash flows and marketable investments) to handle a spike in claims.

Principal Business: (This company is a reinsurer.)

Principal Investments: Investment grade bonds (94%), non investment grade bonds (3%), misc. investments (2%), and cash (1%).

Investments in Affiliates: None

Group Affiliation: Maiden Holdings Ltd

Licensed in: All states except PR

Commenced Business: August 2000

Address: 13736 Riverport Dr Suite 700, Maryland Heights, MO 63043

Phone: (856) 359-2400   **Domicile State:** MO   **NAIC Code:** 11054

Data Date	Rating	RACR #1	RACR #2	Loss Ratio %	Total Assets ($mil)	Capital ($mil)	Net Premium ($mil)	Net Income ($mil)
6-16	B-	1.25	0.72	N/A	1,319.8	293.0	203.4	-8.5
6-15	B-	1.37	0.74	N/A	1,298.0	284.8	203.2	-3.2
2015	B-	1.31	0.75	69.9	1,240.0	294.3	416.4	17.4
2014	B-	1.46	0.80	68.9	1,216.1	289.2	438.7	16.6
2013	B-	1.55	0.87	75.6	1,159.6	269.6	391.8	-1.3
2012	B-	1.13	0.68	78.4	1,189.0	267.9	346.2	-19.2
2011	B-	1.48	0.91	74.6	1,115.3	268.1	196.3	-1.7

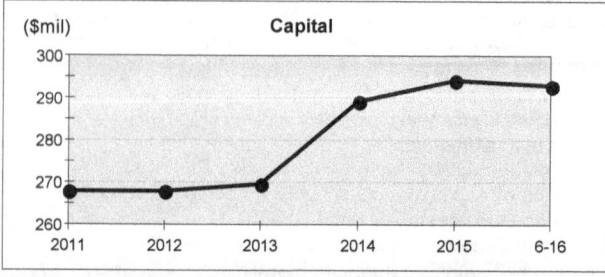

Capital

MARKEL GLOBAL REINS CO

B   **Good**

Major Rating Factors: Fair profitability index (4.2 on a scale of 0 to 10) with operating losses during the first six months of 2016. Return on equity has been low, averaging 1.0% over the past five years. Fair overall results on stability tests (4.8) including weak results on operational trends. The largest net exposure for one risk is acceptable at 2.1% of capital.

Other Rating Factors: Strong long-term capitalization index (8.1) based on excellent current risk adjusted capital (severe and moderate loss scenarios), despite some fluctuation in capital levels. Ample reserve history (7.5) that can protect against increases in claims costs. Excellent liquidity (7.4) with ample operational cash flow and liquid investments.

Principal Business: (This company is a reinsurer.)

Principal Investments: Investment grade bonds (51%), misc. investments (47%), cash (1%), and non investment grade bonds (1%).

Investments in Affiliates: 14%

Group Affiliation: Markel Corp

Licensed in: All states except PR

Commenced Business: September 1997

Address: 20 Horseneck Ln, Greenwich, CT 06830

Phone: (908) 630-2700   **Domicile State:** DE   **NAIC Code:** 10829

Data Date	Rating	RACR #1	RACR #2	Loss Ratio %	Total Assets ($mil)	Capital ($mil)	Net Premium ($mil)	Net Income ($mil)
6-16	B	2.60	1.72	N/A	1,649.7	753.1	110.6	-6.6
6-15	B+	2.84	1.94	N/A	1,565.5	768.8	105.6	3.3
2015	B	2.58	1.72	71.7	1,546.4	727.1	211.7	1.7
2014	B+	3.21	2.22	71.4	1,491.6	749.4	220.7	11.6
2013	B+	3.62	2.60	68.0	1,364.7	715.0	186.9	19.6
2012	B+	5.26	3.44	73.5	1,299.2	671.6	201.7	9.7
2011	B	4.69	3.74	72.6	1,177.7	676.5	205.6	3.8

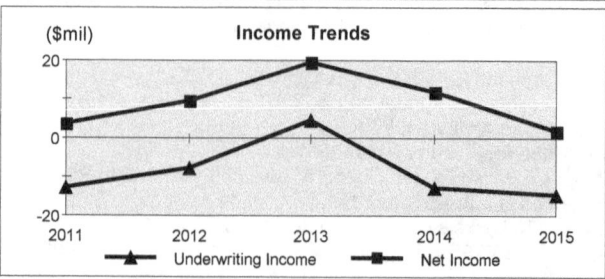

Income Trends

MARKEL INS CO   C   Fair

Major Rating Factors: Fair overall results on stability tests (3.6 on a scale of 0 to 10) including potential drain of affiliation with Markel Corp and weak results on operational trends. The largest net exposure for one risk is high at 3.3% of capital. Fair profitability index (4.5) with operating losses during 2011 and 2012. Return on equity has been low, averaging 0.4% over the past five years.

Other Rating Factors: Good overall long-term capitalization (6.4) based on good current risk adjusted capital (moderate loss scenario). However, capital levels have fluctuated somewhat during past years. Good liquidity (6.8) with sufficient resources (cash flows and marketable investments) to handle a spike in claims. Ample reserve history (9.4) that helps to protect the company against sharp claims increases.

Principal Business: Workers compensation (36%), other liability (20%), commercial multiple peril (20%), auto liability (8%), inland marine (7%), other accident & health (4%), and other lines (6%).

Principal Investments: Investment grade bonds (66%), misc. investments (33%), and cash (1%).

Investments in Affiliates: None
Group Affiliation: Markel Corp
Licensed in: All states except PR
Commenced Business: December 1980
Address: Ten Parkway North, Deerfield, IL 60015
Phone: (800) 431-1270   **Domicile State:** IL   **NAIC Code:** 38970

Data Date	Rating	RACR #1	RACR #2	Loss Ratio %	Total Assets ($mil)	Capital ($mil)	Net Premium ($mil)	Net Income ($mil)
6-16	C	1.84	0.94	N/A	1,525.8	380.0	264.5	16.9
6-15	C	1.79	1.06	N/A	1,435.7	412.4	259.7	6.0
2015	C	1.77	0.91	68.2	1,459.2	352.9	534.2	8.8
2014	C	1.85	1.11	65.0	1,439.9	407.2	517.9	5.6
2013	C	1.74	1.07	61.3	1,225.7	347.4	493.9	7.3
2012	C	1.80	1.10	64.6	1,019.5	272.8	416.6	-5.3
2011	C	0.71	0.49	73.3	839.7	206.4	332.6	-13.5

Markel Corp
Composite Group Rating: C
Largest Group Members

	Assets ($mil)	Rating
EVANSTON INS CO	2869	C
MARKEL GLOBAL REINS CO	1546	B
MARKEL INS CO	1459	C
ESSEX INS CO	1319	C
ALTERRA AMERICA INS CO	455	B-

MBIA INS CORP   D   Weak

Major Rating Factors: Weak overall results on stability tests (1.4 on a scale of 0 to 10) including weak risk adjusted capital in prior years, weak results on operational trends and negative cash flow from operations for 2015. The largest net exposure for one risk is excessive at 20.1% of capital. Strengths include potentially strong support from affiliation with MBIA Inc. Poor long-term capitalization index (0.7) based on weak current risk adjusted capital (severe and moderate loss scenarios).

Other Rating Factors: A history of deficient reserves (1.0) that places pressure on both capital and profits. In 2015 and 2014 the one year reserve development was 26% and 38% deficient respectively. Weak profitability index (1.7) with operating losses during 2011, 2012, 2013, 2014 and the first six months of 2016. Average return on equity over the last five years has been poor at -47.9%. Vulnerable liquidity (1.0) as a spike in claims may stretch capacity.

Principal Business: Financial guaranty (100%).

Principal Investments: Misc. investments (74%), cash (14%), investment grade bonds (11%), and non investment grade bonds (1%).

Investments in Affiliates: 51%
Group Affiliation: MBIA Inc
Licensed in: All states, the District of Columbia and Puerto Rico
Commenced Business: May 1968
Address: 113 King St, Armonk, NY 10504-1610
Phone: (914) 273-4545   **Domicile State:** NY   **NAIC Code:** 12041

Data Date	Rating	RACR #1	RACR #2	Loss Ratio %	Total Assets ($mil)	Capital ($mil)	Net Premium ($mil)	Net Income ($mil)
6-16	D	0.76	0.25	N/A	752.7	489.7	38.7	-103.8
6-15	D	0.81	0.27	N/A	931.9	491.6	49.5	-43.4
2015	D	0.77	0.26	81.8	796.8	609.1	87.0	24.6
2014	D	0.75	0.25	131.4	960.2	541.5	104.6	-35.2
2013	D	0.78	0.26	378.6	1,280.1	403.0	133.5	-494.0
2012	D+	1.20	0.41	338.8	1,012.7	965.1	204.2	-843.4
2011	D+	1.53	0.52	240.5	1,612.5	1,596.6	294.1	-477.2

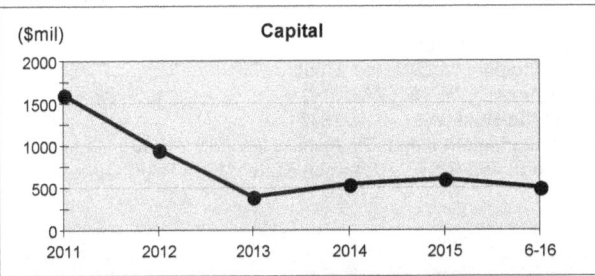

Capital

MEDICAL LIABILITY MUTUAL INS CO   D+   Weak

Major Rating Factors: Weak overall results on stability tests (2.4 on a scale of 0 to 10) including weak results on operational trends and negative cash flow from operations for 2015. The largest net exposure for one risk is conservative at 1.2% of capital. Good overall profitability index (6.9). Good expense controls. Return on equity has been excellent over the last five years averaging 15.1%.

Other Rating Factors: Strong long-term capitalization index (7.1) based on excellent current risk adjusted capital (severe and moderate loss scenarios). Moreover, capital levels have been consistent in recent years. Ample reserve history (9.6) that helps to protect the company against sharp claims increases. Excellent liquidity (7.6) with ample operational cash flow and liquid investments.

Principal Business: Medical malpractice (100%).

Principal Investments: Investment grade bonds (74%), non investment grade bonds (15%), misc. investments (10%), and cash (1%).

Investments in Affiliates: 0%
Group Affiliation: None
Licensed in: CT, DE, ME, MA, NJ, NY, PA, RI, VT
Commenced Business: May 1977
Address: 8 British American Blvd, Latham, NY 12110
Phone: (212) 576-9801   **Domicile State:** NY   **NAIC Code:** 34231

Data Date	Rating	RACR #1	RACR #2	Loss Ratio %	Total Assets ($mil)	Capital ($mil)	Net Premium ($mil)	Net Income ($mil)
6-16	D+	1.70	1.42	N/A	5,539.7	1,865.5	199.1	57.7
6-15	D+	1.60	1.34	N/A	5,871.1	1,859.1	232.2	99.2
2015	D+	1.64	1.38	77.6	5,452.2	1,826.9	410.9	114.5
2014	D+	1.52	1.28	78.4	5,881.1	1,783.9	490.3	263.8
2013	D+	1.27	1.08	93.4	5,777.6	1,538.8	533.9	172.2
2012	D+	1.04	0.89	106.5	5,567.8	1,271.0	550.1	94.5
2011	D+	0.91	0.76	107.9	5,889.0	1,164.6	552.9	466.5

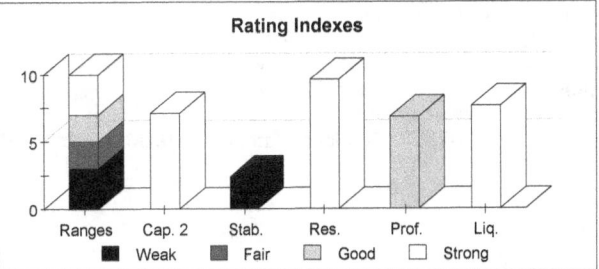

Rating Indexes

■ Weak   ■ Fair   ▨ Good   □ Strong

MEDICAL MUTUAL INS CO OF NC

B- **Good**

Major Rating Factors: Fair overall results on stability tests (4.1 on a scale of 0 to 10) including potential drain of affiliation with Medical Ins Group, excessive premium growth and weak results on operational trends. Fair profitability index (3.5). Good expense controls. Return on equity has been fair, averaging 10.3% over the past five years.

Other Rating Factors: Strong long-term capitalization index (10.0) based on excellent current risk adjusted capital (severe and moderate loss scenarios), despite some fluctuation in capital levels. Ample reserve history (9.3) that helps to protect the company against sharp claims increases. Excellent liquidity (8.5) with ample operational cash flow and liquid investments.

Principal Business: Medical malpractice (100%).

Principal Investments: Investment grade bonds (59%), misc. investments (34%), cash (6%), and non investment grade bonds (1%).

Investments in Affiliates: 4%

Group Affiliation: Medical Ins Group

Licensed in: AL, AR, DE, FL, GA, KY, LA, MD, MS, NJ, NC, OH, PA, SC, TN, TX, VA, WV

Commenced Business: October 1975

Address: 700 Spring Forest Rd, Raleigh, NC 27609

Phone: (919) 872-7117   **Domicile State:** NC   **NAIC Code:** 32522

Data Date	Rating	RACR #1	RACR #2	Loss Ratio %	Total Assets ($mil)	Capital ($mil)	Net Premium ($mil)	Net Income ($mil)
6-16	B-	4.09	2.94	N/A	516.9	246.0	46.8	16.5
6-15	B-	4.78	3.66	N/A	470.5	225.7	30.2	15.5
2015	B-	4.50	3.35	57.2	485.7	229.0	64.0	21.8
2014	B-	4.83	3.72	55.0	475.5	221.3	68.7	30.3
2013	B-	6.28	4.56	54.7	598.0	334.2	75.4	26.1
2012	B-	6.22	4.43	54.4	558.2	295.1	72.2	23.4
2011	B-	5.54	4.08	47.1	527.2	261.5	79.9	28.8

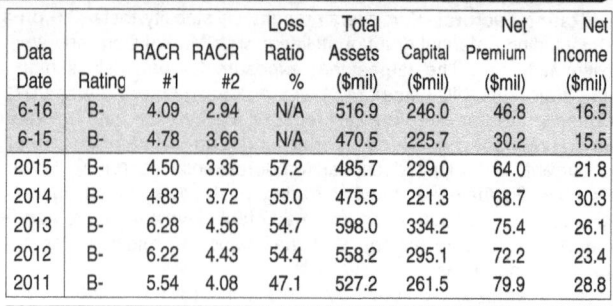

Rating Indexes

MEDICAL MUTUAL LIAB INS SOC OF MD

B- **Good**

Major Rating Factors: Fair overall results on stability tests (4.3 on a scale of 0 to 10) including potential drain of affiliation with Medical Ins Group Of MD, weak results on operational trends and negative cash flow from operations for 2015. Strong long-term capitalization index (9.9) based on excellent current risk adjusted capital (severe and moderate loss scenarios). Moreover, capital levels have been consistent in recent years.

Other Rating Factors: Ample reserve history (9.5) that helps to protect the company against sharp claims increases. Excellent profitability (7.7) with operating gains in each of the last five years. Excellent liquidity (7.5) with ample operational cash flow and liquid investments.

Principal Business: Medical malpractice (100%).

Principal Investments: Investment grade bonds (87%) and misc. investments (13%).

Investments in Affiliates: 13%

Group Affiliation: Medical Ins Group Of MD

Licensed in: MD, MI, NC, PA

Commenced Business: June 1975

Address: 225 International Cir, Hunt Valley, MD 21030

Phone: (410) 785-0050   **Domicile State:** MD   **NAIC Code:** 32328

Data Date	Rating	RACR #1	RACR #2	Loss Ratio %	Total Assets ($mil)	Capital ($mil)	Net Premium ($mil)	Net Income ($mil)
6-16	B-	3.64	3.26	N/A	811.1	393.9	52.6	4.6
6-15	B-	3.50	3.13	N/A	804.4	374.2	53.3	4.4
2015	B-	3.68	3.33	53.9	800.7	385.8	108.1	15.1
2014	B-	3.50	3.15	52.2	812.1	369.3	114.5	15.8
2013	B-	3.35	2.99	50.3	804.9	339.9	120.7	3.4
2012	B-	3.41	3.02	65.3	785.6	331.8	128.9	3.2
2011	B-	3.64	3.20	55.5	777.8	322.1	126.4	10.8

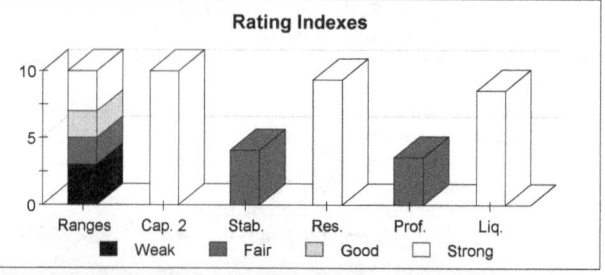

Rating Indexes

MEDICAL PROFESSIONAL MUTUAL INS CO

B- **Good**

Major Rating Factors: Fair overall results on stability tests (4.5 on a scale of 0 to 10) including potential drain of affiliation with Medical Professional Mutual and weak results on operational trends. Strong long-term capitalization index (7.9) based on excellent current risk adjusted capital (severe and moderate loss scenarios). Moreover, capital levels have been consistent in recent years.

Other Rating Factors: Ample reserve history (9.4) that helps to protect the company against sharp claims increases. Excellent profitability (8.5) with operating gains in each of the last five years. Excellent liquidity (7.1) with ample operational cash flow and liquid investments.

Principal Business: Medical malpractice (98%) and other liability (2%).

Principal Investments: Investment grade bonds (51%), misc. investments (44%), non investment grade bonds (4%), and cash (1%).

Investments in Affiliates: 24%

Group Affiliation: Medical Professional Mutual

Licensed in: CO, FL, MA, NY, NC, TN, VA

Commenced Business: July 1975

Address: 101 Arch St, Boston, MA 02110

Phone: (617) 330-1755   **Domicile State:** MA   **NAIC Code:** 10206

Data Date	Rating	RACR #1	RACR #2	Loss Ratio %	Total Assets ($mil)	Capital ($mil)	Net Premium ($mil)	Net Income ($mil)
6-16	B-	2.03	1.79	N/A	2,998.9	1,552.1	127.4	17.9
6-15	B-	1.96	1.74	N/A	3,032.7	1,521.1	129.6	40.3
2015	B-	2.03	1.80	60.0	2,997.3	1,538.2	241.3	72.9
2014	B-	1.93	1.72	65.3	3,012.9	1,474.0	263.6	107.8
2013	B-	2.36	2.01	60.1	3,151.4	1,423.4	277.0	135.3
2012	B-	2.23	1.92	72.0	3,103.7	1,282.8	280.3	87.5
2011	B-	2.04	1.79	46.1	2,955.2	1,132.2	291.6	146.3

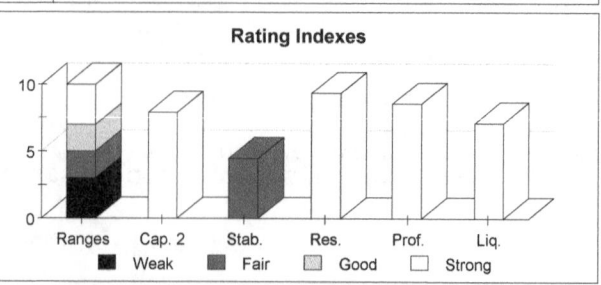

Rating Indexes

MEDICAL PROTECTIVE CO   B   Good

Major Rating Factors: Good overall results on stability tests (5.0 on a scale of 0 to 10) despite weak results on operational trends. Affiliation with Berkshire-Hathaway is a strength. Strong long-term capitalization index (8.9) based on excellent current risk adjusted capital (severe and moderate loss scenarios), despite some fluctuation in capital levels.

Other Rating Factors: Ample reserve history (9.9) that helps to protect the company against sharp claims increases. Excellent profitability (8.7) with operating gains in each of the last five years. Return on equity has been good over the last five years, averaging 10.7%. Excellent liquidity (8.5) with ample operational cash flow and liquid investments.

Principal Business: Medical malpractice (99%) and other liability (1%).

Principal Investments: Investment grade bonds (57%), misc. investments (23%), and cash (20%).

Investments in Affiliates: None

Group Affiliation: Berkshire-Hathaway

Licensed in: All states except PR

Commenced Business: January 1910

Address: 5814 Reed Rd, Fort Wayne, IN 46835

Phone: (260) 485-9622   **Domicile State:** IN   **NAIC Code:** 11843

Data Date	Rating	RACR #1	RACR #2	Loss Ratio %	Total Assets ($mil)	Capital ($mil)	Net Premium ($mil)	Net Income ($mil)
6-16	B	4.41	3.10	N/A	2,726.3	1,577.2	102.8	53.8
6-15	B	5.15	3.43	N/A	2,753.0	1,640.5	97.0	59.2
2015	B	4.32	3.00	59.5	2,790.4	1,570.8	226.5	130.1
2014	B	4.98	3.33	114.6	2,699.6	1,589.1	-680.0	140.1
2013	B	2.74	2.15	51.3	3,286.3	1,405.7	366.9	205.3
2012	B	1.79	1.45	71.7	3,013.5	1,075.4	643.8	133.3
2011	B	2.08	1.61	48.7	2,442.5	863.9	327.2	96.1

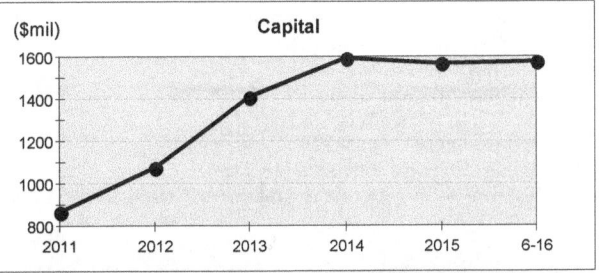

MERCURY CASUALTY CO   B   Good

Major Rating Factors: History of adequate reserve strength (5.8 on a scale of 0 to 10) as reserves have been consistently at an acceptable level. Good liquidity (6.8) with sufficient resources (cash flows and marketable investments) to handle a spike in claims.

Other Rating Factors: Fair profitability index (3.7). Fair expense controls. Return on equity has been fair, averaging 13.1% over the past five years. Fair overall results on stability tests (4.9) including weak results on operational trends.
  Strong long-term capitalization index (7.5) based on excellent current risk adjusted capital (severe and moderate loss scenarios), despite some fluctuation in capital levels.

Principal Business: Homeowners multiple peril (52%), commercial multiple peril (18%), auto liability (16%), auto physical damage (7%), fire (4%), other liability (2%), and boiler & machinery (1%).

Principal Investments: Investment grade bonds (49%), misc. investments (45%), real estate (5%), and cash (1%).

Investments in Affiliates: 39%

Group Affiliation: Mercury General Group

Licensed in: AZ, CA, FL, GA, IL, MI, NV, NJ, NY, OK, PA, TX, VA, WA

Commenced Business: April 1962

Address: 4484 Wilshire Blvd, Los Angeles, CA 90010

Phone: (714) 671-6600   **Domicile State:** CA   **NAIC Code:** 11908

Data Date	Rating	RACR #1	RACR #2	Loss Ratio %	Total Assets ($mil)	Capital ($mil)	Net Premium ($mil)	Net Income ($mil)
6-16	B	1.43	1.34	N/A	1,905.1	937.0	398.3	28.3
6-15	B	1.58	1.46	N/A	1,945.6	1,026.2	361.2	44.4
2015	B	1.50	1.40	77.5	1,849.4	977.7	662.7	119.9
2014	B	1.58	1.46	74.7	1,952.2	1,024.6	735.8	133.9
2013	B+	1.73	1.57	69.4	2,041.5	1,151.3	738.1	226.2
2012	B+	1.49	1.32	77.9	2,040.1	1,065.5	889.0	120.6
2011	B+	1.51	1.35	73.2	2,194.2	1,125.6	1,033.0	145.4

MERCURY INS CO *   B+   Good

Major Rating Factors: History of adequate reserve strength (5.8 on a scale of 0 to 10) as reserves have been consistently at an acceptable level. Good overall profitability index (5.7). Fair expense controls. Return on equity has been fair, averaging 9.3% over the past five years.

Other Rating Factors: Good liquidity (5.1) with sufficient resources (cash flows and marketable investments) to handle a spike in claims. Good overall results on stability tests (5.2) despite weak results on operational trends. Strong long-term capitalization index (8.0) based on excellent current risk adjusted capital (severe and moderate loss scenarios), despite some fluctuation in capital levels.

Principal Business: Auto liability (58%) and auto physical damage (42%).

Principal Investments: Investment grade bonds (95%), misc. investments (5%), and non investment grade bonds (2%).

Investments in Affiliates: None

Group Affiliation: Mercury General Group

Licensed in: CA

Commenced Business: July 1978

Address: 4484 Wilshire Blvd, Los Angeles, CA 90010

Phone: (714) 671-6600   **Domicile State:** CA   **NAIC Code:** 27553

Data Date	Rating	RACR #1	RACR #2	Loss Ratio %	Total Assets ($mil)	Capital ($mil)	Net Premium ($mil)	Net Income ($mil)
6-16	B+	1.78	1.59	N/A	1,600.5	645.5	760.0	15.8
6-15	B+	1.91	1.71	N/A	1,544.3	654.8	713.3	47.0
2015	B+	1.82	1.68	69.6	1,559.3	657.0	1,472.7	90.3
2014	B+	1.84	1.69	70.3	1,561.2	648.7	1,415.9	66.6
2013	A-	1.99	1.81	75.2	1,532.9	652.6	1,350.1	66.5
2012	A-	2.05	1.84	77.1	1,476.2	645.4	1,287.8	24.2
2011	A-	2.34	2.12	71.8	1,416.8	688.5	1,225.6	75.4

MERRIMACK MUTUAL FIRE INS CO   B-   Good

Major Rating Factors: Fair overall results on stability tests (4.7 on a scale of 0 to 10) including potential drain of affiliation with Andover Group, weak results on operational trends and negative cash flow from operations for 2015. History of adequate reserve strength (6.4) as reserves have been consistently at an acceptable level.

Other Rating Factors: Good overall profitability index (5.5) despite operating losses during 2011. Good liquidity (6.9) with sufficient resources (cash flows and marketable investments) to handle a spike in claims. Strong long-term capitalization index (7.8) based on excellent current risk adjusted capital (severe and moderate loss scenarios), despite some fluctuation in capital levels.

Principal Business: Homeowners multiple peril (54%), commercial multiple peril (14%), fire (13%), allied lines (9%), other liability (8%), and inland marine (2%).

Principal Investments: Misc. investments (73%), investment grade bonds (16%), cash (9%), and real estate (2%).

Investments in Affiliates: 24%

Group Affiliation: Andover Group

Licensed in: CT, IL, ME, MA, NH, NJ, NY, RI

Commenced Business: April 1828

Address: 95 Old River Rd, Andover, MA 01810

Phone: (978) 475-3300   **Domicile State:** MA   **NAIC Code:** 19798

Data Date	Rating	RACR #1	RACR #2	Loss Ratio %	Total Assets ($mil)	Capital ($mil)	Net Premium ($mil)	Net Income ($mil)
6-16	B-	2.04	1.57	N/A	1,409.3	900.9	124.5	19.9
6-15	B-	1.91	1.49	N/A	1,314.0	803.5	125.1	-36.0
2015	B-	2.01	1.58	68.5	1,341.1	844.1	259.3	8.7
2014	B	2.02	1.58	43.4	1,363.6	857.8	261.8	49.7
2013	B	2.02	1.58	43.3	1,251.0	785.2	246.4	60.1
2012	B	1.92	1.49	64.9	1,117.6	643.9	239.8	19.4
2011	B+	1.96	1.51	90.4	1,036.1	606.7	224.4	-35.5

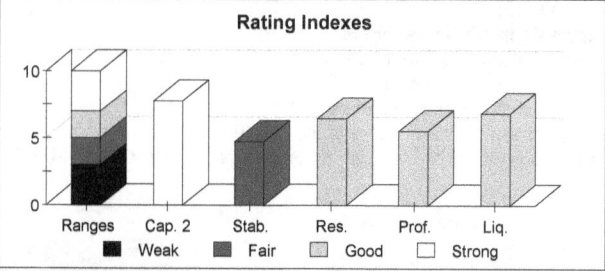

Rating Indexes

METROPOLITAN GROUP PROP & CAS INS CO   B   Good

Major Rating Factors: Good overall profitability index (6.8 on a scale of 0 to 10). Good expense controls. Return on equity has been low, averaging 4.7% over the past five years.

Other Rating Factors: Fair overall results on stability tests (4.9) including weak results on operational trends and negative cash flow from operations for 2015. Strong long-term capitalization index (10.0) based on excellent current risk adjusted capital (severe and moderate loss scenarios), despite some fluctuation in capital levels. Superior liquidity (9.7) with ample operational cash flow and liquid investments.

Principal Business: Auto liability (46%), auto physical damage (34%), and homeowners multiple peril (19%).

Principal Investments: Investment grade bonds (93%), misc. investments (4%), cash (2%), and non investment grade bonds (1%).

Investments in Affiliates: None

Group Affiliation: MetLife Inc

Licensed in: All states except HI, KY, ME, MN, NM, NC, OR, VA, WY, PR

Commenced Business: December 1977

Address: 700 Quaker Lane, Warwick, RI 02886

Phone: (401) 827-2400   **Domicile State:** RI   **NAIC Code:** 34339

Data Date	Rating	RACR #1	RACR #2	Loss Ratio %	Total Assets ($mil)	Capital ($mil)	Net Premium ($mil)	Net Income ($mil)
6-16	B	32.50	14.95	N/A	673.2	404.6	0.0	23.0
6-15	B	21.67	9.98	N/A	632.1	370.0	0.0	-7.8
2015	B	27.20	12.43	0.0	651.1	379.2	0.0	3.4
2014	B	22.37	10.27	0.0	611.7	378.3	0.0	25.7
2013	B	16.98	8.60	0.0	582.5	344.9	0.0	13.0
2012	B	14.32	7.10	0.0	555.8	305.5	0.0	14.4
2011	B	15.56	7.44	0.0	550.2	316.0	0.0	13.2

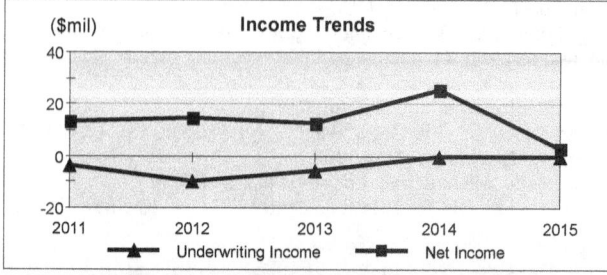

Income Trends

METROPOLITAN P&C INS CO   B-   Good

Major Rating Factors: Good overall results on stability tests (5.1 on a scale of 0 to 10) despite weak results on operational trends. Strong long-term capitalization index (8.0) based on excellent current risk adjusted capital (severe and moderate loss scenarios), despite some fluctuation in capital levels.

Other Rating Factors: Ample reserve history (8.6) that helps to protect the company against sharp claims increases. Excellent profitability (7.7) with operating gains in each of the last five years. Vulnerable liquidity (2.6) as a spike in claims may stretch capacity.

Principal Business: Homeowners multiple peril (48%), auto liability (25%), auto physical damage (20%), other liability (3%), inland marine (1%), other accident & health (1%), and allied lines (1%).

Principal Investments: Investment grade bonds (68%), misc. investments (32%), and non investment grade bonds (4%).

Investments in Affiliates: 22%

Group Affiliation: MetLife Inc

Licensed in: All states except AK, CA, PR

Commenced Business: December 1972

Address: 700 Quaker Lane, Warwick, RI 02886

Phone: (401) 827-2400   **Domicile State:** RI   **NAIC Code:** 26298

Data Date	Rating	RACR #1	RACR #2	Loss Ratio %	Total Assets ($mil)	Capital ($mil)	Net Premium ($mil)	Net Income ($mil)
6-16	B-	2.13	1.71	N/A	5,739.6	2,390.1	1,747.1	14.6
6-15	B	2.26	1.81	N/A	5,716.1	2,484.0	1,713.6	108.2
2015	B-	2.10	1.69	70.2	5,599.1	2,335.5	3,524.3	191.6
2014	B	2.16	1.73	67.3	5,645.6	2,388.0	3,465.7	253.5
2013	B	2.07	1.65	68.8	5,499.7	2,224.9	3,372.1	265.8
2012	B	1.95	1.54	71.7	5,146.4	1,987.3	3,173.9	235.2
2011	B	1.83	1.42	78.9	4,967.4	1,857.3	3,055.4	2.2

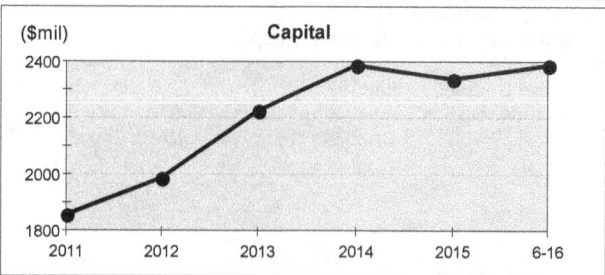

Capital

MHA INS CO   C   Fair

Major Rating Factors: Fair reserve development (4.8 on a scale of 0 to 10) as reserves have generally been sufficient to cover claims. Weak overall results on stability tests (2.3) including weak results on operational trends. The largest net exposure for one risk is excessive at 11.0% of capital.

Other Rating Factors: Good overall profitability index (5.6). Fair expense controls. Return on equity has been low, averaging 3.5% over the past five years. Strong long-term capitalization index (10.0) based on excellent current risk adjusted capital (severe and moderate loss scenarios), despite some fluctuation in capital levels. Excellent liquidity (7.4) with ample operational cash flow and liquid investments.

Principal Business: Medical malpractice (84%), workers compensation (10%), and other liability (7%).

Principal Investments: Investment grade bonds (95%), misc. investments (4%), and cash (1%).

Investments in Affiliates: None

Group Affiliation: Medical Professional Mutual

Licensed in: IL, IN, IA, KS, KY, MI, MN, MO, NE, ND, OH, OK, SD, WA, WI

Commenced Business: May 1976

Address: 6215 W St. Joseph Highway, Lansing, MI 48917

Phone: (517) 703-8500   **Domicile State:** MI   **NAIC Code:** 33111

Data Date	Rating	RACR #1	RACR #2	Loss Ratio %	Total Assets ($mil)	Capital ($mil)	Net Premium ($mil)	Net Income ($mil)
6-16	C	5.02	3.77	N/A	561.1	277.2	37.3	6.8
6-15	C	4.88	3.50	N/A	544.0	262.6	35.7	2.4
2015	C	5.03	3.80	79.6	542.9	271.3	73.2	6.5
2014	C	5.01	3.61	79.1	539.6	261.9	72.7	8.9
2013	B	6.36	4.80	84.5	528.8	277.8	68.2	8.3
2012	B	6.63	5.19	91.4	482.7	269.1	61.9	5.2
2011	B	7.75	5.86	65.9	458.8	262.7	65.2	16.1

Reserve Deficiency (as % of capital)

* Adequate & redundant reserves show as negatives   ■ 1 Yr Dev   □ 2 Yr Dev

MID-CENTURY INS CO   B-   Good

Major Rating Factors: Fair liquidity (4.9 on a scale of 0 to 10) as cash resources may not be adequate to cover a spike in claims. Fair overall results on stability tests (4.9) including fair financial strength of affiliated Farmers Insurance Group of Companies and weak results on operational trends.

Other Rating Factors: History of adequate reserve strength (6.6) as reserves have been consistently at an acceptable level. Good overall profitability index (5.4) despite operating losses during 2011 and the first six months of 2016. Return on equity has been low, averaging 3.4% over the past five years. Strong long-term capitalization index (7.5) based on excellent current risk adjusted capital (severe and moderate loss scenarios), despite some fluctuation in capital levels.

Principal Business: Auto liability (38%), auto physical damage (24%), homeowners multiple peril (20%), commercial multiple peril (11%), and workers compensation (6%).

Principal Investments: Investment grade bonds (84%), misc. investments (12%), real estate (2%), cash (1%), and non investment grade bonds (1%).

Investments in Affiliates: 8%

Group Affiliation: Farmers Insurance Group of Companies

Licensed in: All states except AK, ME, PR

Commenced Business: February 1953

Address: 4680 Wilshire Blvd, Los Angeles, CA 90010

Phone: (323) 932-3200   **Domicile State:** CA   **NAIC Code:** 21687

Data Date	Rating	RACR #1	RACR #2	Loss Ratio %	Total Assets ($mil)	Capital ($mil)	Net Premium ($mil)	Net Income ($mil)
6-16	B-	1.85	1.36	N/A	4,005.3	1,013.3	1,203.2	-16.6
6-15	C	1.89	1.42	N/A	3,909.3	1,019.5	1,199.5	24.9
2015	C+	1.88	1.38	68.3	3,904.9	1,023.6	2,388.9	45.1
2014	C	1.86	1.40	65.0	3,765.9	986.4	2,250.0	58.9
2013	C	1.82	1.38	67.2	3,714.7	921.3	2,181.9	56.0
2012	C	1.70	1.28	70.9	3,657.5	854.4	2,216.8	37.2
2011	C	1.60	1.20	72.1	3,749.8	823.4	2,264.9	-5.7

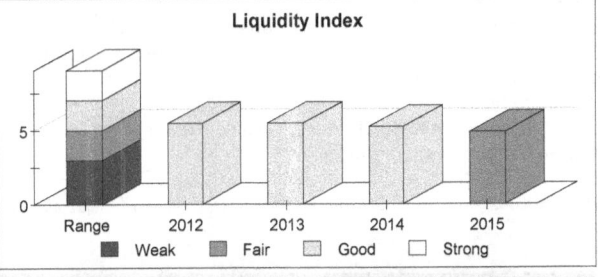

Liquidity Index

Range   2012   2013   2014   2015
■ Weak   ■ Fair   □ Good   □ Strong

MIDDLESEX INS CO   B   Good

Major Rating Factors: Good overall profitability index (6.1 on a scale of 0 to 10). Fair expense controls. Return on equity has been fair, averaging 5.2% over the past five years. Good liquidity (6.9) with sufficient resources (cash flows and marketable investments) to handle a spike in claims.

Other Rating Factors: Fair overall results on stability tests (4.8) including weak results on operational trends. The largest net exposure for one risk is conservative at 1.2% of capital. Strong long-term capitalization index (9.2) based on excellent current risk adjusted capital (severe and moderate loss scenarios), despite some fluctuation in capital levels. Ample reserve history (8.2) that helps to protect the company against sharp claims increases.

Principal Business: Workers compensation (58%), auto liability (30%), allied lines (3%), auto physical damage (3%), fire (2%), other liability (2%), and products liability (1%).

Principal Investments: Investment grade bonds (89%) and misc. investments (11%).

Investments in Affiliates: 4%

Group Affiliation: Sentry Ins Group

Licensed in: All states except PR

Commenced Business: March 1826

Address: 1800 N Point Dr, Stevens Point, WI 54481

Phone: (715) 346-6000   **Domicile State:** WI   **NAIC Code:** 23434

Data Date	Rating	RACR #1	RACR #2	Loss Ratio %	Total Assets ($mil)	Capital ($mil)	Net Premium ($mil)	Net Income ($mil)
6-16	B	3.71	2.43	N/A	719.1	254.4	96.4	3.8
6-15	B	4.11	2.83	N/A	700.1	258.6	88.5	7.9
2015	B	3.79	2.52	72.7	695.2	249.9	187.7	15.8
2014	B	4.08	2.86	74.9	673.1	251.1	181.4	16.5
2013	B	3.92	2.77	76.3	653.2	242.8	181.8	11.8
2012	B	4.00	2.81	77.3	628.2	237.4	172.7	10.3
2011	B	4.05	2.86	79.1	622.2	235.1	163.3	11.9

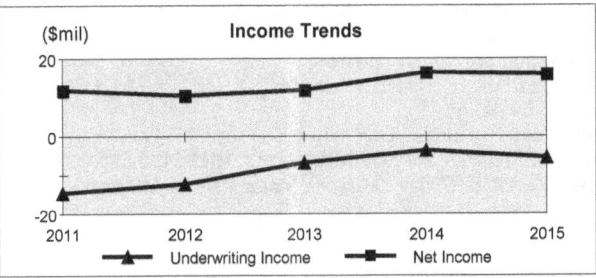

Income Trends

2011   2012   2013   2014   2015
▲ Underwriting Income   ■ Net Income

MISSISSIPPI FARM BUREAU CAS INS CO   B-   Good

Major Rating Factors: Fair overall results on stability tests (4.5 on a scale of 0 to 10) including potential drain of affiliation with Southern Farm Bureau Casualty and weak results on operational trends. Good overall profitability index (6.7) despite operating losses during 2011. Return on equity has been fair, averaging 6.6% over the past five years.

Other Rating Factors: Good liquidity (6.9) with sufficient resources (cash flows and marketable investments) to handle a spike in claims. Strong long-term capitalization index (10.0) based on excellent current risk adjusted capital (severe and moderate loss scenarios). Moreover, capital levels have been consistent in recent years. Ample reserve history (7.6) that can protect against increases in claims costs.

Principal Business: Homeowners multiple peril (39%), auto liability (26%), auto physical damage (22%), allied lines (4%), fire (3%), inland marine (2%), and other lines (4%).

Principal Investments: Investment grade bonds (97%) and cash (3%).

Investments in Affiliates: None

Group Affiliation: Southern Farm Bureau Casualty

Licensed in: FL, LA, MS, SC, TX

Commenced Business: September 1986

Address: 6310 I-55 North, Jackson, MS 39211

Phone: (601) 977-4301   **Domicile State:** MS   **NAIC Code:** 27669

Data Date	Rating	RACR #1	RACR #2	Loss Ratio %	Total Assets ($mil)	Capital ($mil)	Net Premium ($mil)	Net Income ($mil)
6-16	B-	5.44	4.93	N/A	414.9	255.4	86.7	9.9
6-15	B-	5.20	4.77	N/A	399.1	245.8	84.7	21.4
2015	B-	5.45	4.52	59.4	417.6	255.4	175.3	31.6
2014	B-	4.93	4.16	72.9	375.4	228.5	170.2	15.3
2013	B	4.81	3.70	70.4	351.8	212.0	159.2	15.7
2012	B	4.69	3.56	69.8	331.3	197.8	151.3	14.6
2011	B	4.66	3.54	86.4	303.1	181.0	140.5	-2.8

Southern Farm Bureau Casualty
Composite Group Rating: B-
Largest Group Members

	Assets ($mil)	Rating
SOUTHERN FARM BUREAU CAS INS CO	2150	B-
FLORIDA FARM BU CASUALTY INS CO	554	B-
MISSISSIPPI FARM BUREAU CAS INS CO	418	B-
SOUTHERN FARM BUREAU PROPERTY	55	U
LOUISIANA FARM BUREAU CAS INS CO	11	B

MITSUI SUMITOMO INS CO OF AMER *   B+   Good

Major Rating Factors: Good overall profitability index (6.8 on a scale of 0 to 10). Fair expense controls. Return on equity has been fair, averaging 5.8% over the past five years. Good liquidity (6.9) with sufficient resources (cash flows and marketable investments) to handle a spike in claims.

Other Rating Factors: Good overall results on stability tests (5.1) despite weak results on operational trends. The largest net exposure for one risk is conservative at 1.0% of capital. Strong long-term capitalization index (9.3) based on excellent current risk adjusted capital (severe and moderate loss scenarios), despite some fluctuation in capital levels. Ample reserve history (9.3) that helps to protect the company against sharp claims increases.

Principal Business: Workers compensation (29%), commercial multiple peril (23%), other liability (11%), allied lines (11%), ocean marine (7%), aircraft (7%), and other lines (13%).

Principal Investments: Investment grade bonds (79%), misc. investments (15%), real estate (3%), cash (2%), and non investment grade bonds (1%).

Investments in Affiliates: None

Group Affiliation: MS & AD Ins Group Holdings Inc

Licensed in: All states, the District of Columbia and Puerto Rico

Commenced Business: January 1971

Address: 560 Lexington Ave 20th Floor, New York, NY 10022-6828

Phone: (908) 604-2900   **Domicile State:** NY   **NAIC Code:** 20362

Data Date	Rating	RACR #1	RACR #2	Loss Ratio %	Total Assets ($mil)	Capital ($mil)	Net Premium ($mil)	Net Income ($mil)
6-16	B+	3.94	2.48	N/A	925.8	331.5	93.8	7.8
6-15	B+	3.98	2.56	N/A	891.0	331.8	88.3	9.7
2015	B+	4.18	2.65	71.2	904.3	335.3	174.4	21.3
2014	B+	3.99	2.58	71.3	900.6	332.3	191.9	20.3
2013	B+	4.02	2.65	73.5	845.2	319.6	182.7	18.5
2012	B+	4.28	2.60	77.9	789.8	298.2	156.6	13.4
2011	B+	4.14	2.80	68.7	763.9	285.2	146.3	19.0

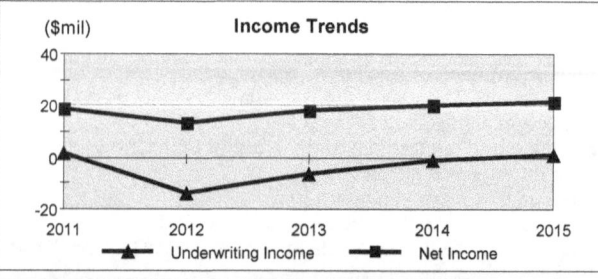

Income Trends

MMIC INS INC   B   Good

Major Rating Factors: Fair overall results on stability tests (4.7 on a scale of 0 to 10) including weak results on operational trends. Strong long-term capitalization index (7.6) based on excellent current risk adjusted capital (severe and moderate loss scenarios). Moreover, capital levels have been consistent in recent years.

Other Rating Factors: Ample reserve history (9.4) that helps to protect the company against sharp claims increases. Excellent profitability (8.8) with operating gains in each of the last five years. Return on equity has been good over the last five years, averaging 10.3%. Excellent liquidity (7.2) with ample operational cash flow and liquid investments.

Principal Business: Medical malpractice (96%) and other liability (4%).

Principal Investments: Investment grade bonds (59%), misc. investments (40%), and non investment grade bonds (1%).

Investments in Affiliates: 24%

Group Affiliation: Constellation Inc

Licensed in: AR, CO, ID, IL, IN, IA, KS, KY, MI, MN, MO, MT, NE, ND, OH, OR, SD, TN, UT, WA, WI, WY

Commenced Business: October 1980

Address: 7701 France Ave S, Minneapolis, MN 55435-5981

Phone: (952) 838-6700   **Domicile State:** MN   **NAIC Code:** 16942

Data Date	Rating	RACR #1	RACR #2	Loss Ratio %	Total Assets ($mil)	Capital ($mil)	Net Premium ($mil)	Net Income ($mil)
6-16	B	1.80	1.56	N/A	704.6	328.2	49.9	27.0
6-15	B	1.83	1.56	N/A	705.4	317.5	51.8	29.6
2015	B	1.76	1.52	77.4	718.1	327.1	108.7	36.9
2014	B	1.79	1.53	68.8	706.5	310.2	106.5	33.1
2013	A-	1.66	1.40	72.9	708.2	273.6	110.4	14.4
2012	A-	3.78	2.64	72.0	554.2	257.0	115.9	27.0
2011	A-	3.85	2.91	64.2	525.5	234.3	117.6	25.1

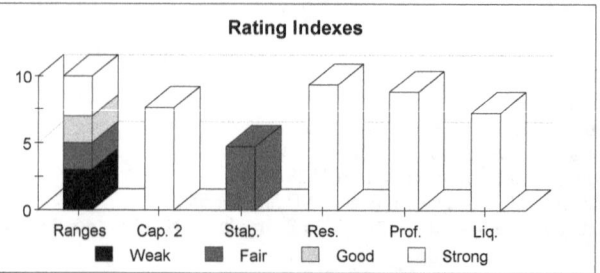

Rating Indexes

MO EMPLOYERS MUTUAL INS CO   B-   Good

Major Rating Factors: Fair overall results on stability tests (4.1 on a scale of 0 to 10) including weak results on operational trends. Good liquidity (6.7) with sufficient resources (cash flows and marketable investments) to handle a spike in claims.

Other Rating Factors: Strong long-term capitalization index (7.9) based on excellent current risk adjusted capital (severe and moderate loss scenarios). Moreover, capital levels have been consistent in recent years. Ample reserve history (9.3) that helps to protect the company against sharp claims increases. Excellent profitability (7.1).

Principal Business: Workers compensation (100%).

Principal Investments: Investment grade bonds (78%), misc. investments (17%), real estate (3%), and non investment grade bonds (2%).

Investments in Affiliates: 0%

Group Affiliation: Missouri Employers Mutual

Licensed in: MO

Commenced Business: March 1995

Address: 101 N Keene St, Columbia, MO 65201

Phone: (573) 499-9714   **Domicile State:** MO   **NAIC Code:** 10191

Data Date	Rating	RACR #1	RACR #2	Loss Ratio %	Total Assets ($mil)	Capital ($mil)	Net Premium ($mil)	Net Income ($mil)
6-16	B-	2.16	1.64	N/A	637.0	252.7	99.2	11.6
6-15	C	2.07	1.59	N/A	594.3	222.8	94.3	12.5
2015	C+	2.12	1.62	62.1	614.5	237.8	202.6	30.6
2014	C	2.10	1.61	72.3	563.2	211.0	189.5	14.9
2013	C	2.01	1.51	72.3	508.8	194.4	166.1	5.9
2012	C	2.32	1.76	83.7	446.1	172.6	137.2	-1.9
2011	C	2.47	1.91	73.0	404.9	167.7	139.9	7.5

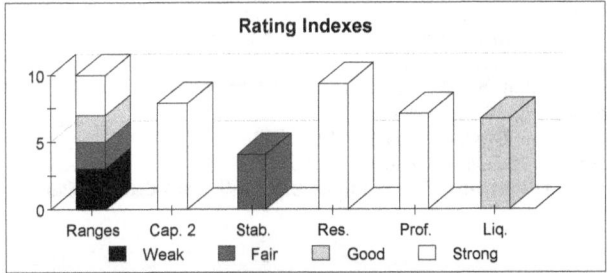

Rating Indexes

MORTGAGE GUARANTY INS CORP   D+   Weak

Major Rating Factors: Weak profitability index (2.7 on a scale of 0 to 10) with operating losses during each of the last five years. However, profits have turned positive in the first six months of 2016. Average return on equity over the last five years has been poor at -26.9%. Weak overall results on stability tests (2.4) including weak results on operational trends.

Other Rating Factors: Fair reserve development (3.1) as the level of reserves has at times been insufficient to cover claims. In 2012 and 2013 the two year reserve development was 29% and 53% deficient respectively. Good overall long-term capitalization (6.3) based on good current risk adjusted capital (moderate loss scenario). However, capital levels have fluctuated somewhat during past years. Good liquidity (6.3) with sufficient resources (cash flows and marketable investments) to handle a spike in claims.

Principal Business: Mortgage guaranty (100%).

Principal Investments: Investment grade bonds (90%) and misc. investments (10%).

Investments in Affiliates: 7%

Group Affiliation: MGIC Investment Corp

Licensed in: All states, the District of Columbia and Puerto Rico

Commenced Business: March 1979

Address: 250 East Kilbourn Avenue, Milwaukee, WI 53202

Phone: (800) 558-9900   **Domicile State:** WI   **NAIC Code:** 29858

Data Date	Rating	RACR #1	RACR #2	Loss Ratio %	Total Assets ($mil)	Capital ($mil)	Net Premium ($mil)	Net Income ($mil)
6-16	D+	1.06	0.91	N/A	4,375.5	1,476.6	395.0	9.6
6-15	D+	1.09	0.92	N/A	4,203.4	1,545.5	396.5	18.9
2015	D+	1.08	0.92	36.8	4,274.8	1,573.9	905.5	-77.9
2014	D+	1.04	0.87	59.2	4,162.5	1,517.7	758.1	-7.8
2013	D+	0.99	0.79	91.1	4,406.2	1,520.6	793.5	-7.0
2012	D+	0.34	0.27	202.5	4,355.0	689.1	904.2	-808.5
2011	D+	0.87	0.68	152.6	5,528.9	1,568.8	957.7	-397.1

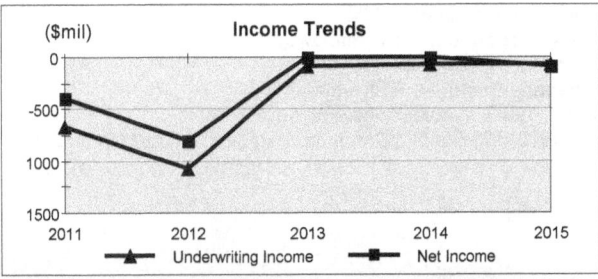

Income Trends

MOTORISTS MUTUAL INS CO *   B+   Good

Major Rating Factors: Good overall profitability index (5.3 on a scale of 0 to 10) despite operating losses during 2011. Good liquidity (6.5) with sufficient resources (cash flows and marketable investments) to handle a spike in claims.

Other Rating Factors: Good overall results on stability tests (5.1) despite weak results on operational trends. Strong long-term capitalization index (8.8) based on excellent current risk adjusted capital (severe and moderate loss scenarios), despite some fluctuation in capital levels. Ample reserve history (7.9) that can protect against increases in claims costs.

Principal Business: Auto liability (28%), homeowners multiple peril (18%), auto physical damage (17%), other liability (14%), commercial multiple peril (12%), workers compensation (5%), and other lines (7%).

Principal Investments: Investment grade bonds (68%), misc. investments (29%), and real estate (3%).

Investments in Affiliates: 10%

Group Affiliation: Motorists Insurance Group

Licensed in: AL, CA, CT, DE, GA, IL, IN, IA, KY, ME, MD, MA, MI, MO, MT, NE, NH, NJ, NY, NC, OH, OK, OR, PA, RI, SC, SD, TN, TX, UT, VT, VA, WV, WI

Commenced Business: November 1928

Address: 471 E Broad St, Columbus, OH 43215

Phone: (614) 225-8211   **Domicile State:** OH   **NAIC Code:** 14621

Data Date	Rating	RACR #1	RACR #2	Loss Ratio %	Total Assets ($mil)	Capital ($mil)	Net Premium ($mil)	Net Income ($mil)
6-16	B+	2.90	2.18	N/A	1,375.1	545.2	242.3	7.1
6-15	B+	3.12	2.27	N/A	1,395.8	556.6	246.1	6.3
2015	B+	2.96	2.24	64.5	1,387.4	553.9	491.5	7.8
2014	B+	3.24	2.37	64.0	1,373.9	557.4	500.9	40.4
2013	A-	3.53	2.48	66.8	1,335.8	568.8	480.0	37.9
2012	B+	3.06	2.17	70.9	1,272.1	480.6	458.1	7.3
2011	B+	2.91	2.06	77.9	1,228.4	460.8	442.9	-20.8

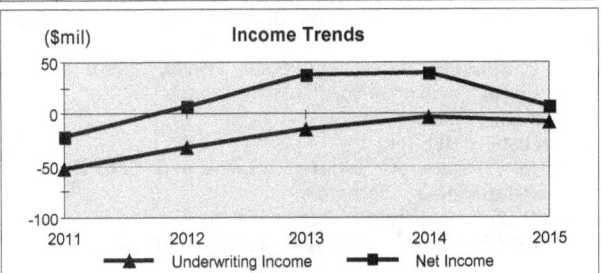

Income Trends

MOTORS INS CORP   D   Weak

Major Rating Factors: Weak overall results on stability tests (0.9 on a scale of 0 to 10) including weak results on operational trends. The largest net exposure for one risk is excessive at 21.3% of capital. Strengths include potentially strong support from affiliation with Ally Financial Inc. Weak profitability index (2.6) with operating losses during the first six months of 2016. Return on equity has been fair, averaging 8.9% over the past five years.

Other Rating Factors: Strong long-term capitalization index (10.0) based on excellent current risk adjusted capital (severe and moderate loss scenarios), despite some fluctuation in capital levels. Ample reserve history (7.8) that can protect against increases in claims costs. Excellent liquidity (7.1) with ample operational cash flow and liquid investments.

Principal Business: Auto physical damage (60%).

Principal Investments: Investment grade bonds (77%), misc. investments (12%), cash (10%), and non investment grade bonds (1%).

Investments in Affiliates: 4%

Group Affiliation: Ally Financial Inc

Licensed in: All states except PR

Commenced Business: November 1939

Address: 300 Galleria Officentre, Southfield, MI 48034

Phone: (313) 656-5437   **Domicile State:** MI   **NAIC Code:** 22012

Data Date	Rating	RACR #1	RACR #2	Loss Ratio %	Total Assets ($mil)	Capital ($mil)	Net Premium ($mil)	Net Income ($mil)
6-16	D	4.37	2.96	N/A	2,054.9	749.7	221.6	-15.0
6-15	C	5.03	3.38	N/A	2,449.8	1,065.6	242.6	32.1
2015	D	4.49	3.07	54.7	2,077.4	746.8	420.5	115.1
2014	C	5.19	3.53	72.1	2,458.7	1,059.9	475.5	84.4
2013	C	4.35	2.71	66.9	2,605.0	1,095.6	462.9	117.7
2012	C	2.49	1.63	73.2	2,770.1	1,183.2	479.8	93.0
2011	C	6.26	3.70	62.9	3,042.0	1,348.9	553.4	118.7

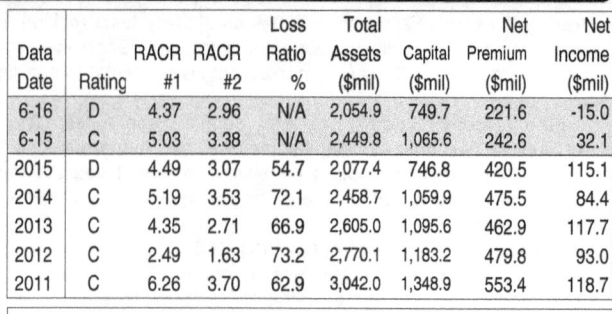

Rating Indexes

MOUNT VERNON FIRE INS CO   C   Fair

Major Rating Factors: Fair overall results on stability tests (4.3 on a scale of 0 to 10) including weak results on operational trends. Strong long-term capitalization index (7.7) based on excellent current risk adjusted capital (severe and moderate loss scenarios), despite some fluctuation in capital levels.

Other Rating Factors: Ample reserve history (9.0) that helps to protect the company against sharp claims increases. Excellent profitability (8.0) with operating gains in each of the last five years. Excellent liquidity (8.5) with ample operational cash flow and liquid investments.

Principal Business: Other liability (78%), fire (19%), products liability (1%), inland marine (1%), and auto physical damage (1%).

Principal Investments: Misc. investments (69%), investment grade bonds (30%), and cash (1%).

Investments in Affiliates: 23%

Group Affiliation: Berkshire-Hathaway

Licensed in: All states except PR

Commenced Business: December 1958

Address: 190 S. Warner Road, Wayne, PA 19087

Phone: (800) 523-5545   **Domicile State:** PA   **NAIC Code:** 26522

Data Date	Rating	RACR #1	RACR #2	Loss Ratio %	Total Assets ($mil)	Capital ($mil)	Net Premium ($mil)	Net Income ($mil)
6-16	C	2.10	1.68	N/A	555.8	385.0	33.8	5.7
6-15	C	2.00	1.56	N/A	579.6	395.9	33.6	7.4
2015	C	2.09	1.64	37.8	580.2	399.7	67.7	17.0
2014	C	1.97	1.53	33.8	586.9	395.2	67.3	18.0
2013	B-	1.84	1.48	33.5	526.4	348.2	63.0	24.1
2012	B-	1.80	1.41	43.7	433.8	273.7	59.4	15.6
2011	B-	1.80	1.44	47.2	379.5	226.3	57.3	10.3

Berkshire-Hathaway Composite Group Rating: B Largest Group Members	Assets ($mil)	Rating
NATIONAL INDEMNITY CO	161777	B
GOVERNMENT EMPLOYEES INS CO	24036	B
COLUMBIA INS CO	19102	C+
BERKSHIRE HATHAWAY LIFE INS CO OF NE	16287	C+
GENERAL REINS CORP	15320	C+

MT HAWLEY INS CO   C   Fair

Major Rating Factors: Fair profitability index (3.5 on a scale of 0 to 10). Weak expense controls. Return on equity has been fair, averaging 16.6% over the past five years. Fair overall results on stability tests (4.0) including weak results on operational trends. The largest net exposure for one risk is conservative at 1.7% of capital.

Other Rating Factors: Good liquidity (6.9) with sufficient resources (cash flows and marketable investments) to handle a spike in claims. Strong long-term capitalization index (8.3) based on excellent current risk adjusted capital (severe and moderate loss scenarios), despite some fluctuation in capital levels. Ample reserve history (9.3) that helps to protect the company against sharp claims increases.

Principal Business: Other liability (52%), allied lines (17%), earthquake (9%), fire (9%), inland marine (8%), medical malpractice (5%), and products liability (1%).

Principal Investments: Investment grade bonds (70%), misc. investments (27%), non investment grade bonds (2%), and cash (1%).

Investments in Affiliates: 14%

Group Affiliation: RLI Corp

Licensed in: All states, the District of Columbia and Puerto Rico

Commenced Business: December 1979

Address: 9025 N Lindbergh Dr, Peoria, IL 61615

Phone: (309) 692-1000   **Domicile State:** IL   **NAIC Code:** 37974

Data Date	Rating	RACR #1	RACR #2	Loss Ratio %	Total Assets ($mil)	Capital ($mil)	Net Premium ($mil)	Net Income ($mil)
6-16	C	2.41	1.88	N/A	924.7	486.5	104.3	22.3
6-15	C	2.38	1.87	N/A	897.7	489.4	103.7	27.0
2015	C	2.31	1.82	37.4	861.2	447.8	208.2	85.5
2014	C	2.27	1.79	32.3	874.2	461.1	209.5	111.8
2013	C	2.63	2.01	26.0	925.3	523.0	202.9	76.0
2012	C	3.13	2.30	42.4	978.0	546.2	166.9	71.5
2011	C	3.17	2.34	21.4	1,032.9	574.5	157.3	91.6

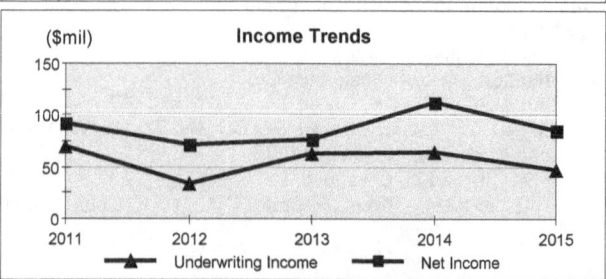

Income Trends

MUNICH REINS AMERICA INC   C+   Fair

Major Rating Factors: Fair overall results on stability tests (3.4 on a scale of 0 to 10) including weak results on operational trends and negative cash flow from operations for 2015. The largest net exposure for one risk is high at 4.4% of capital. Good overall profitability index (6.3). Fair expense controls. Return on equity has been good over the last five years, averaging 11.7%.

Other Rating Factors: Good liquidity (6.9) with sufficient resources (cash flows and marketable investments) to handle a spike in claims. Strong long-term capitalization index (8.4) based on excellent current risk adjusted capital (severe and moderate loss scenarios), despite some fluctuation in capital levels. Ample reserve history (9.2) that helps to protect the company against sharp claims increases.

Principal Business: (This company is a reinsurer.)

Principal Investments: Investment grade bonds (91%), non investment grade bonds (5%), misc. investments (3%), and real estate (1%).

Investments in Affiliates: None

Group Affiliation: Münchener Rückversicherungs-Gesellsc

Licensed in: All states, the District of Columbia and Puerto Rico

Commenced Business: April 1917

Address: 555 College Rd E, Princeton, NJ 08543

Phone: (609) 243-4200   **Domicile State:** DE   **NAIC Code:** 10227

Data Date	Rating	RACR #1	RACR #2	Loss Ratio %	Total Assets ($mil)	Capital ($mil)	Net Premium ($mil)	Net Income ($mil)
6-16	C+	2.98	1.88	N/A	17,460.2	4,833.9	1,493.1	188.2
6-15	C+	2.68	1.61	N/A	17,747.2	4,997.2	1,539.1	219.9
2015	C+	3.08	1.95	62.4	17,497.9	4,957.4	3,120.4	436.6
2014	C+	2.83	1.72	57.2	16,484.8	5,254.8	3,247.7	781.7
2013	C+	2.31	1.40	57.1	16,840.8	5,288.0	3,195.8	806.1
2012	C+	1.80	1.12	66.4	17,362.6	4,624.8	3,113.0	378.2
2011	C+	1.65	1.02	66.9	16,096.5	4,262.0	3,101.6	576.9

Rating Indexes

MUNICIPAL ASR CORP *   A+   Excellent

Major Rating Factors: Strong long-term capitalization index (10.0 on a scale of 0 to 10) based on excellent current risk adjusted capital (severe and moderate loss scenarios). Furthermore, this high level of risk adjusted capital has been consistently maintained in previous years. Superior liquidity (10.0) with ample operational cash flow and liquid investments.

Other Rating Factors: Good overall profitability index (5.1). Excellent expense controls. Return on equity has been fair, averaging 9.2% over the past five years. Good overall results on stability tests (6.5) despite weak results on operational trends. The largest net exposure for one risk is excessive at 17.4% of capital.

Principal Business: Financial guaranty (100%).

Principal Investments: Investment grade bonds (133%).

Investments in Affiliates: None

Group Affiliation: Assured Guaranty Ltd

Licensed in: All states except PR

Commenced Business: October 2008

Address: 31 W 52nd St, New York, NY 10019

Phone: (212) 974-0100   **Domicile State:** NY   **NAIC Code:** 13559

Data Date	Rating	RACR #1	RACR #2	Loss Ratio %	Total Assets ($mil)	Capital ($mil)	Net Premium ($mil)	Net Income ($mil)
6-16	A+	25.61	15.58	N/A	1,125.1	379.3	68.2	69.3
6-15	A+	40.03	20.36	N/A	1,523.7	642.0	64.4	56.2
2015	A+	48.25	27.40	0.0	1,509.3	729.5	-4.8	101.9
2014	A+	37.58	22.45	0.0	1,519.8	611.5	-5.0	74.8
2013	A+	3.74	2.27	0.0	1,516.2	514.4	709.9	25.7
2012	U	111.74	55.87	0.0	77.0	76.9	0.0	0.6
2011	U	107.24	53.62	0.0	75.1	75.1	0.0	0.0

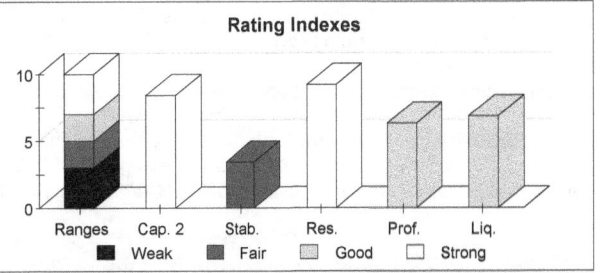

Risk-Adjusted Capital Ratio #2
(Severe Loss Scenario)

MUTUAL INS CO OF AZ   B   Good

Major Rating Factors: Fair overall results on stability tests (4.9 on a scale of 0 to 10) including weak results on operational trends. Strong long-term capitalization index (10.0) based on excellent current risk adjusted capital (severe and moderate loss scenarios). Moreover, capital levels have been consistent in recent years.

Other Rating Factors: Ample reserve history (9.4) that helps to protect the company against sharp claims increases. Excellent profitability (8.4) with operating gains in each of the last five years. Excellent liquidity (8.3) with ample operational cash flow and liquid investments.

Principal Business: Medical malpractice (100%).

Principal Investments: Investment grade bonds (84%), misc. investments (15%), and cash (1%).

Investments in Affiliates: None

Group Affiliation: None

Licensed in: AZ, CA, CO, NV, NM, UT

Commenced Business: March 1976

Address: 2602 East Thomas Rd, Phoenix, AZ 85016

Phone: (602) 956-5276   **Domicile State:** AZ   **NAIC Code:** 32832

Data Date	Rating	RACR #1	RACR #2	Loss Ratio %	Total Assets ($mil)	Capital ($mil)	Net Premium ($mil)	Net Income ($mil)
6-16	B	7.13	5.01	N/A	1,032.8	603.9	52.3	14.5
6-15	B	6.92	4.88	N/A	1,000.8	579.2	51.7	13.9
2015	B	7.31	5.15	53.7	1,038.1	588.8	105.2	28.0
2014	B	7.02	4.95	57.9	1,017.4	565.6	105.4	27.4
2013	A	6.77	4.81	63.3	1,008.0	536.5	109.5	20.9
2012	A	7.08	5.44	41.3	989.4	504.2	113.3	33.2
2011	A	6.19	4.77	26.1	982.2	463.6	116.8	44.4

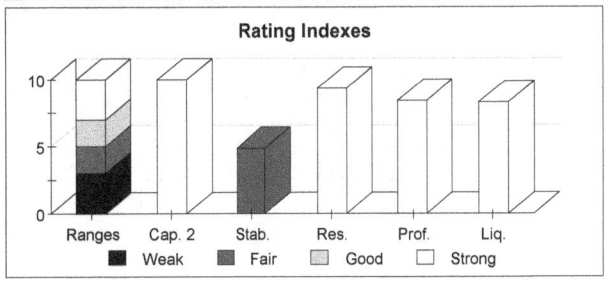

Rating Indexes

MUTUAL OF ENUMCLAW INS CO   B   Good

Major Rating Factors: History of adequate reserve strength (6.9 on a scale of 0 to 10) as reserves have been consistently at an acceptable level. Good liquidity (6.4) with sufficient resources (cash flows and marketable investments) to handle a spike in claims.

Other Rating Factors: Fair profitability index (4.6) with operating losses during 2015. Fair overall results on stability tests (4.7) including weak results on operational trends. Strong long-term capitalization index (9.4) based on excellent current risk adjusted capital (severe and moderate loss scenarios), despite some fluctuation in capital levels.

Principal Business: Auto liability (31%), homeowners multiple peril (20%), commercial multiple peril (18%), auto physical damage (14%), farmowners multiple peril (12%), other liability (3%), and other lines (3%).

Principal Investments: Investment grade bonds (77%), misc. investments (17%), cash (4%), and real estate (2%).

Investments in Affiliates: 4%

Group Affiliation: Enumclaw Ins Group

Licensed in: AK, AZ, CO, ID, MT, NV, NM, OR, UT, WA

Commenced Business: March 1898

Address: 4000 Kruse Way Pl Bldg 3 #200, Lake Oswego, OR 97035

Phone: (360) 825-2591   **Domicile State:** OR   **NAIC Code:** 14761

Data Date	Rating	RACR #1	RACR #2	Loss Ratio %	Total Assets ($mil)	Capital ($mil)	Net Premium ($mil)	Net Income ($mil)
6-16	B	3.81	2.75	N/A	738.6	319.4	187.6	3.1
6-15	B	3.75	2.72	N/A	689.3	300.8	177.9	-1.1
2015	B	3.45	2.48	77.5	697.0	290.0	376.1	-11.6
2014	B	3.86	2.80	68.1	666.7	302.9	350.2	11.3
2013	B	4.05	2.99	68.4	634.8	286.9	331.0	8.0
2012	B	3.90	2.89	68.0	598.9	266.3	309.1	18.2
2011	B	3.66	2.71	66.9	575.9	248.1	297.9	20.3

Reserve Deficiency (as % of capital)

* Adequate & redundant reserves show as negatives

1 Yr Dev / 2 Yr Dev

NATIONAL CASUALTY CO *   B+   Good

Major Rating Factors: Good overall results on stability tests (5.0 on a scale of 0 to 10) despite weak results on operational trends and negative cash flow from operations for 2015. Strengths include potential support from affiliation with Nationwide Corp. Strong long-term capitalization index (10.0) based on excellent current risk adjusted capital (severe and moderate loss scenarios), despite some fluctuation in capital levels.

Other Rating Factors: Excellent profitability (7.7) with operating gains in each of the last five years. Excellent liquidity (7.8) with ample operational cash flow and liquid investments.

Principal Business: Inland marine (28%), auto liability (26%), other liability (14%), commercial multiple peril (9%), auto physical damage (9%), workers compensation (7%), and other lines (6%).

Principal Investments: Investment grade bonds (96%) and misc. investments (4%).

Investments in Affiliates: None

Group Affiliation: Nationwide Corp

Licensed in: All states except PR

Commenced Business: December 1904

Address: 8877 N Gainey Center Dr, Scottsdale, AZ 85258-2108

Phone: (480) 365-4000   **Domicile State:** WI   **NAIC Code:** 11991

Data Date	Rating	RACR #1	RACR #2	Loss Ratio %	Total Assets ($mil)	Capital ($mil)	Net Premium ($mil)	Net Income ($mil)
6-16	B+	13.03	11.72	N/A	402.1	136.6	0.0	1.6
6-15	B+	13.79	12.41	N/A	296.3	132.1	0.0	3.8
2015	B+	14.13	12.72	0.0	288.5	134.1	0.0	5.5
2014	B+	13.70	12.33	0.0	285.4	130.1	0.0	3.0
2013	B+	13.26	11.93	0.0	280.9	125.9	0.0	2.7
2012	B+	12.92	11.63	0.0	277.2	122.6	0.0	2.6
2011	B+	12.89	11.60	0.0	248.9	119.4	0.0	3.3

Nationwide Corp Composite Group Rating: B- Largest Group Members	Assets ($mil)	Rating
NATIONWIDE LIFE INS CO	126861	B-
NATIONWIDE MUTUAL INS CO	35924	B
NATIONWIDE LIFE ANNUITY INS CO	10758	C
NATIONWIDE MUTUAL FIRE INS CO	5938	B+
NATIONWIDE INDEMNITY CO	2995	C+

NATIONAL FIRE & MARINE INS CO   C   Fair

Major Rating Factors: Fair overall results on stability tests (3.9 on a scale of 0 to 10) including weak results on operational trends. The largest net exposure for one risk is acceptable at 2.0% of capital. History of adequate reserve strength (6.1) as reserves have been consistently at an acceptable level.

Other Rating Factors: Strong long-term capitalization index (7.9) based on excellent current risk adjusted capital (severe and moderate loss scenarios), despite some fluctuation in capital levels. Excellent profitability (7.4) with operating gains in each of the last five years. Excellent liquidity (8.3) with ample operational cash flow and liquid investments.

Principal Business: Other liability (33%), allied lines (17%), medical malpractice (13%), fire (11%), earthquake (10%), auto liability (7%), and other lines (8%).

Principal Investments: Misc. investments (74%), investment grade bonds (17%), and cash (9%).

Investments in Affiliates: 7%

Group Affiliation: Berkshire-Hathaway

Licensed in: All states, the District of Columbia and Puerto Rico

Commenced Business: January 1950

Address: 3024 Harney St, Omaha, NE 68131

Phone: (402) 916-3000   **Domicile State:** NE   **NAIC Code:** 20079

Data Date	Rating	RACR #1	RACR #2	Loss Ratio %	Total Assets ($mil)	Capital ($mil)	Net Premium ($mil)	Net Income ($mil)
6-16	C	2.35	1.56	N/A	8,533.9	4,980.3	418.2	234.2
6-15	C	2.45	1.61	N/A	8,554.0	5,637.4	339.8	142.9
2015	C	2.53	1.67	44.7	8,664.8	5,695.9	822.2	327.2
2014	C	2.40	1.58	49.2	8,437.0	5,604.7	710.9	657.8
2013	C	2.57	1.70	69.8	7,335.1	5,010.4	316.5	233.2
2012	C	2.80	1.86	54.6	5,597.0	3,857.6	131.4	279.5
2011	C	2.39	1.60	84.5	4,596.3	3,117.7	102.1	110.8

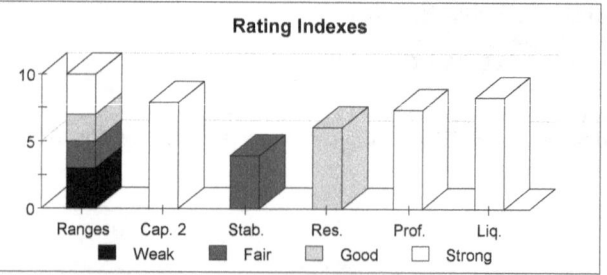

Rating Indexes

Ranges   Cap. 2   Stab.   Res.   Prof.   Liq.

Weak   Fair   Good   Strong

NATIONAL INDEMNITY CO   B   Good

Major Rating Factors: History of adequate reserve strength (5.9 on a scale of 0 to 10) as reserves have been consistently at an acceptable level. Good overall profitability index (6.8). Fair expense controls. Return on equity has been fair, averaging 8.5% over the past five years.

Other Rating Factors: Good liquidity (6.7) with sufficient resources (cash flows and marketable investments) to handle a spike in claims. Fair overall results on stability tests (4.1) including weak results on operational trends. The largest net exposure for one risk is conservative at 1.9% of capital. Strong long-term capitalization index (7.5) based on excellent current risk adjusted capital (severe and moderate loss scenarios), despite some fluctuation in capital levels.

Principal Business: Auto liability (63%), auto physical damage (16%), aircraft (9%), surety (5%), inland marine (5%), and other liability (2%).

Principal Investments: Misc. investments (88%), investment grade bonds (10%), and cash (2%).

Investments in Affiliates: 22%

Group Affiliation: Berkshire-Hathaway

Licensed in: All states except PR

Commenced Business: May 1940

Address: 3024 Harney St, Omaha, NE 68131

Phone: (402) 916-3000   **Domicile State:** NE   **NAIC Code:** 20087

Data Date	Rating	RACR #1	RACR #2	Loss Ratio %	Total Assets ($mil)	Capital ($mil)	Net Premium ($mil)	Net Income ($mil)
6-16	B	1.81	1.51	N/A	163,246.0	90,361.0	9,347.7	2,805.1
6-15	B-	1.74	1.46	N/A	162,002.0	89,526.2	8,159.6	4,747.9
2015	B	1.81	1.52	75.1	161,776.7	89,828.6	18,456.6	7,270.9
2014	B-	1.66	1.43	79.3	166,985.4	93,997.7	26,655.0	12,007.5
2013	B-	2.24	1.87	49.2	151,911.7	97,226.1	5,650.4	8,390.8
2012	B-	2.48	2.01	62.8	128,202.6	79,408.9	7,469.8	5,489.3
2011	B-	2.58	2.05	83.2	118,802.0	72,576.9	5,859.3	5,324.6

Reserve Deficiency (as % of capital)

* Adequate & redundant reserves show as negatives

■ 1 Yr Dev   □ 2 Yr Dev

NATIONAL INTERSTATE INS CO   C+   Fair

Major Rating Factors: Fair overall results on stability tests (4.6 on a scale of 0 to 10) including potential drain of affiliation with American Financial Group Inc and weak results on operational trends. The largest net exposure for one risk is conservative at 1.1% of capital. Fair reserve development (4.4) as reserves have generally been sufficient to cover claims.

Other Rating Factors: Good overall profitability index (6.5). Fair expense controls. Return on equity has been fair, averaging 8.4% over the past five years. Good liquidity (6.7) with sufficient resources (cash flows and marketable investments) to handle a spike in claims. Strong long-term capitalization index (7.3) based on excellent current risk adjusted capital (severe and moderate loss scenarios), despite some fluctuation in capital levels.

Principal Business: Auto liability (46%), workers compensation (31%), auto physical damage (13%), other liability (8%), inland marine (1%), and allied lines (1%).

Principal Investments: Investment grade bonds (67%), misc. investments (29%), non investment grade bonds (2%), and real estate (2%).

Investments in Affiliates: 18%

Group Affiliation: American Financial Group Inc

Licensed in: All states except PR

Commenced Business: March 1989

Address: 3250 Interstate Drive, Richfield, OH 44286

Phone: (330) 659-8900   **Domicile State:** OH   **NAIC Code:** 32620

Data Date	Rating	RACR #1	RACR #2	Loss Ratio %	Total Assets ($mil)	Capital ($mil)	Net Premium ($mil)	Net Income ($mil)
6-16	C+	1.50	1.22	N/A	1,237.9	315.1	145.4	6.3
6-15	C+	1.48	1.21	N/A	1,189.8	297.8	142.9	6.8
2015	C+	1.43	1.18	75.1	1,200.1	295.6	295.3	12.5
2014	C+	1.45	1.20	78.7	1,117.6	284.7	291.2	5.4
2013	C+	1.52	1.26	70.8	1,054.1	283.4	277.6	21.9
2012	C+	1.61	1.36	62.3	1,017.5	269.7	260.7	52.9
2011	C+	1.65	1.37	63.6	994.7	293.6	251.5	31.0

American Financial Group Inc Composite Group Rating: B- Largest Group Members	Assets ($mil)	Rating
GREAT AMERICAN LIFE INS CO	25936	B-
GREAT AMERICAN INS CO	6111	B-
ANNUITY INVESTORS LIFE INS CO	3014	A-
REPUBLIC INDEMNITY CO OF AMERICA	2292	B-
NATIONAL INTERSTATE INS CO	1200	C+

NATIONAL LIABILITY & FIRE INS CO   B-   Good

Major Rating Factors: Fair overall results on stability tests (4.9 on a scale of 0 to 10) including potential drain of affiliation with Berkshire-Hathaway and weak results on operational trends. Good overall profitability index (5.1) despite operating losses during 2014 and 2015. Return on equity has been low, averaging 3.4% over the past five years.

Other Rating Factors: Strong long-term capitalization index (8.2) based on excellent current risk adjusted capital (severe and moderate loss scenarios), despite some fluctuation in capital levels. Ample reserve history (8.5) that helps to protect the company against sharp claims increases. Excellent liquidity (8.6) with ample operational cash flow and liquid investments.

Principal Business: Auto liability (47%), other liability (14%), ocean marine (11%), auto physical damage (9%), workers compensation (9%), inland marine (5%), and other lines (6%).

Principal Investments: Misc. investments (47%), investment grade bonds (36%), and cash (17%).

Investments in Affiliates: None

Group Affiliation: Berkshire-Hathaway

Licensed in: All states except PR

Commenced Business: December 1958

Address: 100 First Stamford Place, Stamford, CT 68131-3580

Phone: (402) 916-3000   **Domicile State:** CT   **NAIC Code:** 20052

Data Date	Rating	RACR #1	RACR #2	Loss Ratio %	Total Assets ($mil)	Capital ($mil)	Net Premium ($mil)	Net Income ($mil)
6-16	B-	2.78	1.75	N/A	2,341.1	935.9	358.5	37.6
6-15	B-	2.87	1.84	N/A	2,335.4	942.5	344.8	-9.0
2015	B-	2.86	1.81	68.9	2,377.3	957.1	762.1	-12.5
2014	B-	2.89	1.83	74.2	2,229.9	967.4	631.8	-0.9
2013	B+	4.12	2.55	64.8	1,836.1	899.0	388.3	70.5
2012	B+	3.88	2.35	77.5	1,419.0	714.5	343.0	18.1
2011	B+	3.98	2.13	62.5	1,132.0	557.1	259.8	31.7

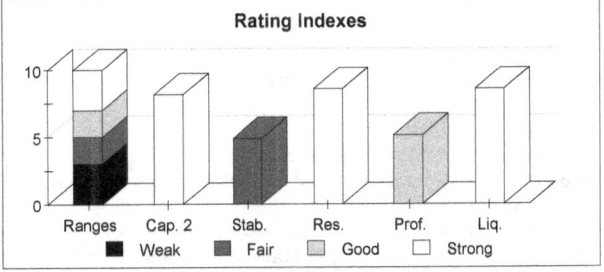

Rating Indexes

Ranges   Cap. 2   Stab.   Res.   Prof.   Liq.

■ Weak   ▨ Fair   ▨ Good   □ Strong

NATIONAL MORTGAGE INS CORP *

A-   Excellent

Major Rating Factors: Strong long-term capitalization index (10.0 on a scale of 0 to 10) based on excellent current risk adjusted capital (severe and moderate loss scenarios). Furthermore, this high level of risk adjusted capital has been consistently maintained in previous years. Excellent liquidity (7.0) with ample operational cash flow and liquid investments.

Other Rating Factors: Good overall results on stability tests (5.7) despite excessive premium growth and weak results on operational trends. Weak profitability index (0.2) with operating losses during each of the last five years and the first six months of 2016. Average return on equity over the last five years has been poor at -22.3%.

Principal Business: Mortgage guaranty (100%).

Principal Investments: Investment grade bonds (88%), misc. investments (7%), and cash (5%).

Investments in Affiliates: None

Group Affiliation: NMI Holdings Inc

Licensed in: All states except PR

Commenced Business: N/A

Address: 1834 Steven St, Sun Prairie, WI 53590-3530

Phone: (925) 300-6375   **Domicile State:** WI   **NAIC Code:** 13695

Data Date	Rating	RACR #1	RACR #2	Loss Ratio %	Total Assets ($mil)	Capital ($mil)	Net Premium ($mil)	Net Income ($mil)
6-16	A-	2.90	2.55	N/A	530.6	345.8	42.0	-21.1
6-15	A-	2.30	2.17	N/A	257.8	197.4	14.7	-25.7
2015	A-	4.06	3.43	1.4	487.7	366.9	103.9	-50.3
2014	A-	3.69	3.41	0.6	261.9	223.1	31.3	-47.2
2013	A-	4.93	4.85	0.0	194.2	180.3	3.3	-32.7
2012	U	23.24	23.15	0.0	210.0	210.0	0.0	0.0
2011	N/A	N/A	N/A	0.0	0.0	-1.4	0.0	-0.6

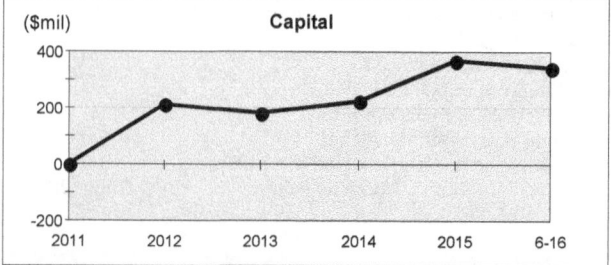

NATIONAL PUBLIC FINANCE GUAR CORP

B   Good

Major Rating Factors: History of adequate reserve strength (5.9 on a scale of 0 to 10) as reserves have been consistently at an acceptable level. Fair overall results on stability tests (4.0) including weak results on operational trends and negative cash flow from operations for 2015. The largest net exposure for one risk is excessive at 9.1% of capital. Strengths include potentially strong support from affiliation with MBIA Inc.

Other Rating Factors: Strong long-term capitalization index (10.0) based on excellent current risk adjusted capital (severe and moderate loss scenarios). Moreover, capital levels have been consistent in recent years. Excellent profitability (8.6) with operating gains in each of the last five years. Return on equity has been excellent over the last five years averaging 16.9%. Excellent liquidity (7.0) with ample operational cash flow and liquid investments.

Principal Business: Financial guaranty (100%).

Principal Investments: Investment grade bonds (91%), cash (7%), and non investment grade bonds (3%).

Investments in Affiliates: 0%

Group Affiliation: MBIA Inc

Licensed in: All states, the District of Columbia and Puerto Rico

Commenced Business: March 1960

Address: 113 King St, Armonk, NY 10504-1610

Phone: (914) 273-4545   **Domicile State:** NY   **NAIC Code:** 23825

Data Date	Rating	RACR #1	RACR #2	Loss Ratio %	Total Assets ($mil)	Capital ($mil)	Net Premium ($mil)	Net Income ($mil)
6-16	B	28.91	19.00	N/A	4,754.2	2,651.5	124.6	99.7
6-15	B	24.51	13.13	N/A	4,799.1	2,327.8	162.8	136.2
2015	B	21.59	13.94	N/A	4,676.6	2,477.5	17.0	283.8
2014	B	25.38	13.47	27.9	5,142.4	2,190.4	13.5	238.1
2013	B	11.85	5.09	18.3	5,339.7	2,086.1	12.1	255.9
2012	B	12.49	6.44	5.5	5,726.2	1,998.5	-4.8	415.5
2011	B	8.76	4.49	1.3	6,656.1	1,423.7	-21.9	477.9

* Adequate & redundant reserves show as negatives

NATIONAL UNION FIRE INS CO OF PITTSB

C   Fair

Major Rating Factors: Fair reserve development (3.7 on a scale of 0 to 10) as the level of reserves has at times been insufficient to cover claims. In 2011 and 2015 the two year reserve development was 16% and 17% deficient respectively. Fair profitability index (3.7). Fair expense controls. Return on equity has been fair, averaging 31.0% over the past five years.

Other Rating Factors: Weak overall results on stability tests (2.8) including weak results on operational trends and negative cash flow from operations for 2015. The largest net exposure for one risk is excessive at 11.7% of capital. Strengths include potential support from AIG. Good liquidity (6.4) with sufficient resources (cash flows and marketable investments) to handle a spike in claims. Strong long-term capitalization index (7.9) based on excellent current risk adjusted capital, despite some fluctuation in capital levels.

Principal Business: Other liability (39%), ocean marine (12%), group accident & health (12%), workers compensation (6%), auto liability (6%), inland marine (6%), and other lines (19%).

Principal Investments: Investment grade bonds (59%), misc. investments (39%), and non investment grade bonds (3%).

Investments in Affiliates: 1%

Group Affiliation: American International Group

Licensed in: All states, the District of Columbia and Puerto Rico

Commenced Business: March 1901

Address: 3595 Interstate Dr Suite 103, Harrisburg, PA 17110

Phone: (212) 458-7000   **Domicile State:** PA   **NAIC Code:** 19445

Data Date	Rating	RACR #1	RACR #2	Loss Ratio %	Total Assets ($mil)	Capital ($mil)	Net Premium ($mil)	Net Income ($mil)
6-16	C	2.40	1.61	N/A	27,169.5	6,639.7	2,639.8	631.5
6-15	C	2.19	1.48	N/A	26,413.9	6,558.8	2,673.5	628.2
2015	C	2.43	1.64	88.8	26,764.2	6,682.8	5,564.4	110.6
2014	C	2.20	1.50	80.2	26,171.1	6,680.8	5,616.6	572.0
2013	C	2.03	1.38	76.7	24,709.6	5,836.5	5,422.5	8,102.0
2012	B-	1.60	1.46	87.1	32,520.8	14,398.9	4,676.2	1,039.0
2011	B-	1.74	1.55	84.1	30,962.5	12,774.8	4,861.3	604.4

* Adequate & redundant reserves show as negatives

NATIONWIDE INDEMNITY CO   C+   Fair

Major Rating Factors: Fair overall results on stability tests (4.5 on a scale of 0 to 10) including weak results on operational trends and negative cash flow from operations for 2015. Strengths include potentially strong support from affiliation with Nationwide Corp. Fair profitability index (3.8) with small operating losses during 2013. Return on equity has been low, averaging 4.4% over the past five years.

Other Rating Factors: Good overall long-term capitalization (6.1) based on good current risk adjusted capital (severe loss scenario). However, capital levels have fluctuated during prior years. A history of deficient reserves (2.3) that places pressure on both capital and profits. Deficiencies in the two year reserve development occurred in three of the previous five years and ranged between 21% and 26%. Superior liquidity (9.7) with ample operational cash flow and liquid investments.

Principal Business: (This company is a reinsurer.)

Principal Investments: Investment grade bonds (93%), misc. investments (4%), and non investment grade bonds (3%).

Investments in Affiliates: None

Group Affiliation: Nationwide Corp

Licensed in: IL, IA, NY, OH, WI

Commenced Business: April 1994

Address: One Nationwide Plaza, Columbus, OH 43216

Phone: (614) 249-7111   **Domicile State:** OH   **NAIC Code:** 10070

Data Date	Rating	RACR #1	RACR #2	Loss Ratio %	Total Assets ($mil)	Capital ($mil)	Net Premium ($mil)	Net Income ($mil)
6-16	C+	1.85	0.86	N/A	3,004.2	1,061.9	0.1	48.8
6-15	C+	1.99	0.90	N/A	3,127.3	1,088.2	0.1	53.9
2015	C+	1.71	0.79	N/A	2,995.0	1,010.1	0.4	54.7
2014	C+	1.84	0.83	N/A	3,165.3	1,044.9	-0.4	4.0
2013	B-	2.21	0.89	N/A	3,251.9	1,069.4	0.2	-8.5
2012	B-	2.66	1.02	N/A	3,357.2	1,120.6	1.4	65.6
2011	C+	2.27	0.93	440.1	3,482.3	1,123.6	1.0	101.0

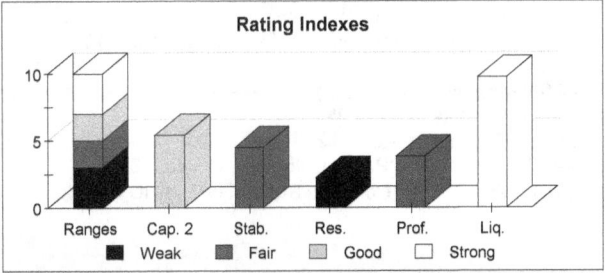

Rating Indexes

(Ranges, Cap. 2, Stab., Res., Prof., Liq.) — Weak, Fair, Good, Strong

NATIONWIDE INS CO OF FL   C+   Fair

Major Rating Factors: Fair overall results on stability tests (3.1 on a scale of 0 to 10) including weak results on operational trends. The largest net exposure for one risk is excessive at 7.8% of capital. History of adequate reserve strength (5.2) as reserves have been consistently at an acceptable level.

Other Rating Factors: Strong long-term capitalization index (10.0) based on excellent current risk adjusted capital (severe and moderate loss scenarios), despite some fluctuation in capital levels. Excellent profitability (7.7) with operating gains in each of the last five years. Excellent liquidity (8.7) with ample operational cash flow and liquid investments.

Principal Business: Homeowners multiple peril (98%) and inland marine (2%).

Principal Investments: Investment grade bonds (107%).

Investments in Affiliates: None

Group Affiliation: Nationwide Corp

Licensed in: FL, OH

Commenced Business: August 1998

Address: One Nationwide Plaza, Columbus, OH 43216

Phone: (614) 249-7111   **Domicile State:** OH   **NAIC Code:** 10948

Data Date	Rating	RACR #1	RACR #2	Loss Ratio %	Total Assets ($mil)	Capital ($mil)	Net Premium ($mil)	Net Income ($mil)
6-16	C+	53.46	38.77	N/A	316.9	305.8	0.0	5.2
6-15	C+	19.72	13.65	N/A	342.1	296.5	19.1	8.2
2015	C+	23.60	18.48	54.2	344.6	302.1	34.9	13.3
2014	C+	19.09	13.23	48.0	338.4	288.9	37.6	14.9
2013	C+	6.12	4.44	52.1	325.4	272.9	33.8	12.4
2012	C+	5.32	3.82	80.8	330.1	257.8	33.6	5.3
2011	B-	4.41	3.17	88.9	368.1	278.2	32.4	5.1

Nationwide Corp Composite Group Rating: B- Largest Group Members	Assets ($mil)	Rating
NATIONWIDE LIFE INS CO	126861	B-
NATIONWIDE MUTUAL INS CO	35924	B
NATIONWIDE LIFE ANNUITY INS CO	10758	C
NATIONWIDE MUTUAL FIRE INS CO	5938	B+
NATIONWIDE INDEMNITY CO	2995	C+

NATIONWIDE MUTUAL FIRE INS CO *   B+   Good

Major Rating Factors: History of adequate reserve strength (6.2 on a scale of 0 to 10) as reserves have been consistently at an acceptable level. Good liquidity (6.5) with sufficient resources (cash flows and marketable investments) to handle a spike in claims.

Other Rating Factors: Good overall results on stability tests (5.1) despite weak results on operational trends. Strong long-term capitalization index (10.0) based on excellent current risk adjusted capital (severe and moderate loss scenarios), despite some fluctuation in capital levels. Fair profitability index (4.3) with operating losses during 2011 and the first six months of 2016.

Principal Business: Homeowners multiple peril (47%), auto liability (16%), auto physical damage (10%), allied lines (9%), commercial multiple peril (7%), other liability (4%), and other lines (6%).

Principal Investments: Investment grade bonds (80%), misc. investments (15%), and non investment grade bonds (5%).

Investments in Affiliates: 5%

Group Affiliation: Nationwide Corp

Licensed in: All states except PR

Commenced Business: April 1934

Address: One Nationwide Plaza, Columbus, OH 43216

Phone: (614) 249-7111   **Domicile State:** OH   **NAIC Code:** 23779

Data Date	Rating	RACR #1	RACR #2	Loss Ratio %	Total Assets ($mil)	Capital ($mil)	Net Premium ($mil)	Net Income ($mil)
6-16	B+	4.78	3.46	N/A	6,045.9	2,623.6	1,146.4	-13.2
6-15	B+	4.94	3.58	N/A	5,933.0	2,605.5	1,089.4	23.1
2015	B+	4.90	3.59	71.1	5,938.4	2,604.3	2,242.5	-10.6
2014	B+	5.00	3.67	71.1	5,733.3	2,559.1	2,163.3	64.1
2013	B+	4.96	3.51	66.2	5,410.1	2,445.1	2,162.4	73.7
2012	B+	5.59	4.02	71.9	4,729.7	2,317.4	1,691.9	33.9
2011	B+	5.53	3.97	77.0	4,553.4	2,243.2	1,617.1	-8.6

Reserve Deficiency (as % of capital)

2011 2012 2013 2014 2015 — 1 Yr Dev, 2 Yr Dev

* Adequate & redundant reserves show as negatives

NATIONWIDE MUTUAL INS CO   B   Good

Major Rating Factors: History of adequate reserve strength (5.3 on a scale of 0 to 10) as reserves have been consistently at an acceptable level. Good liquidity (5.1) with sufficient resources (cash flows and marketable investments) to handle a spike in claims.

Other Rating Factors: Good overall results on stability tests (5.1) despite weak results on operational trends. Fair profitability index (4.5) with operating losses during 2011 and the first six months of 2016. Strong long-term capitalization index (7.4) based on excellent current risk adjusted capital (severe and moderate loss scenarios), despite some fluctuation in capital levels.

Principal Business: Auto liability (40%), auto physical damage (26%), commercial multiple peril (11%), other liability (6%), homeowners multiple peril (6%), allied lines (3%), and other lines (7%).

Principal Investments: Misc. investments (54%), investment grade bonds (40%), non investment grade bonds (5%), and real estate (2%).

Investments in Affiliates: 29%

Group Affiliation: Nationwide Corp

Licensed in: All states except PR

Commenced Business: April 1926

Address: One Nationwide Plaza, Columbus, OH 43216

Phone: (614) 249-7111   **Domicile State:** OH   **NAIC Code:** 23787

Data Date	Rating	RACR #1	RACR #2	Loss Ratio %	Total Assets ($mil)	Capital ($mil)	Net Premium ($mil)	Net Income ($mil)
6-16	B	1.44	1.25	N/A	36,667.7	12,353.5	7,929.3	-272.9
6-15	B	1.48	1.29	N/A	35,438.8	12,475.7	7,534.9	181.4
2015	B	1.45	1.27	71.1	35,923.7	12,315.9	15,510.8	184.1
2014	B	1.46	1.29	71.1	34,711.2	12,138.0	14,962.7	718.4
2013	B	1.49	1.31	66.2	32,675.8	11,792.5	14,630.9	499.8
2012	B	1.44	1.28	71.9	29,551.8	11,344.0	12,492.6	21.7
2011	B	1.48	1.31	77.2	29,149.9	11,294.7	12,326.8	-894.5

Reserve Deficiency (as % of capital)

* Adequate & redundant reserves show as negatives

■ 1 Yr Dev
□ 2 Yr Dev

NAU COUNTRY INS CO   C   Fair

Major Rating Factors: Fair overall results on stability tests (4.3 on a scale of 0 to 10) including potential drain of affiliation with QBE Ins Group Ltd, weak results on operational trends and negative cash flow from operations for 2015. Fair reserve development (3.7) as reserves have generally been sufficient to cover claims. In 2013, the two year reserve development was 17% deficient.

Other Rating Factors: Fair profitability index (3.9) with operating losses during 2012, 2013 and the first six months of 2016. Return on equity has been low, averaging 0.3% over the past five years. Strong long-term capitalization index (7.3) based on excellent current risk adjusted capital (severe and moderate loss scenarios), despite some fluctuation in capital levels. Excellent liquidity (7.5) with ample operational cash flow and liquid investments.

Principal Business: Allied lines (100%).

Principal Investments: Investment grade bonds (129%), cash (8%), and real estate (1%).

Investments in Affiliates: None

Group Affiliation: QBE Ins Group Ltd

Licensed in: All states except AK, DC, HI, ME, NY, PR

Commenced Business: May 1919

Address: 7333 Sunwood Dr, Ramsey, MN 55303-5119

Phone: (608) 825-5160   **Domicile State:** MN   **NAIC Code:** 25240

Data Date	Rating	RACR #1	RACR #2	Loss Ratio %	Total Assets ($mil)	Capital ($mil)	Net Premium ($mil)	Net Income ($mil)
6-16	C	2.23	1.48	N/A	1,291.9	356.1	240.0	-0.9
6-15	C	1.87	1.28	N/A	1,155.1	273.4	193.9	6.3
2015	C	2.32	1.54	63.9	1,305.9	309.3	343.9	19.7
2014	C	1.72	1.19	69.2	1,330.5	254.3	415.4	2.0
2013	C	1.53	1.04	75.2	1,300.1	286.9	444.3	-29.0
2012	C	1.28	0.90	73.5	1,458.6	335.4	693.9	-23.7
2011	C-	2.66	1.61	90.2	1,346.0	379.8	811.2	45.8

QBE Ins Group Ltd Composite Group Rating: B- Largest Group Members	Assets ($mil)	Rating
QBE INS CORP	2136	B-
NAU COUNTRY INS CO	1306	C
QBE REINS CORP	1148	B
PRAETORIAN INS CO	872	C
GENERAL CASUALTY CO OF WI	696	C

NAVIGATORS INS CO   B   Good

Major Rating Factors: History of adequate reserve strength (6.8 on a scale of 0 to 10) as reserves have been consistently at an acceptable level. Good liquidity (6.8) with sufficient resources (cash flows and marketable investments) to handle a spike in claims.

Other Rating Factors: Fair overall results on stability tests (4.6) including weak results on operational trends. The largest net exposure for one risk is conservative at 1.5% of capital. Strong long-term capitalization index (8.1) based on excellent current risk adjusted capital (severe and moderate loss scenarios). Moreover, capital levels have been consistent in recent years. Excellent profitability (7.5) with operating gains in each of the last five years.

Principal Business: Other liability (65%), ocean marine (26%), auto liability (3%), inland marine (3%), surety (1%), international (1%), and auto physical damage (1%).

Principal Investments: Investment grade bonds (72%), misc. investments (25%), and cash (3%).

Investments in Affiliates: 6%

Group Affiliation: Navigators Group Inc

Licensed in: All states, the District of Columbia and Puerto Rico

Commenced Business: March 1983

Address: One Penn Plaza, 55th Floor, New York, NY 10119

Phone: (914) 934-8999   **Domicile State:** NY   **NAIC Code:** 42307

Data Date	Rating	RACR #1	RACR #2	Loss Ratio %	Total Assets ($mil)	Capital ($mil)	Net Premium ($mil)	Net Income ($mil)
6-16	B	2.39	1.88	N/A	2,764.8	997.0	379.6	36.2
6-15	B	2.28	1.77	N/A	2,538.7	899.1	350.6	31.3
2015	B	2.31	1.83	62.4	2,568.5	950.3	757.1	58.7
2014	B	2.33	1.81	61.7	2,454.0	893.9	752.8	72.4
2013	B	2.26	1.70	65.0	2,215.0	804.1	680.0	56.6
2012	B	2.48	1.88	73.0	2,102.4	682.9	623.0	25.2
2011	B	2.51	1.96	72.3	1,903.9	662.2	542.4	13.0

Reserve Deficiency (as % of capital)

* Adequate & redundant reserves show as negatives

■ 1 Yr Dev
□ 2 Yr Dev

NCMIC INS CO   B   Good

Major Rating Factors: Fair overall results on stability tests (4.2 on a scale of 0 to 10) including weak results on operational trends. Strong long-term capitalization index (7.8) based on excellent current risk adjusted capital (severe and moderate loss scenarios). Moreover, capital levels have been consistent in recent years.

Other Rating Factors: Ample reserve history (9.6) that helps to protect the company against sharp claims increases. Excellent profitability (8.9) with operating gains in each of the last five years. Excellent liquidity (7.4) with ample operational cash flow and liquid investments.

Principal Business: Medical malpractice (100%).

Principal Investments: Investment grade bonds (81%), misc. investments (17%), cash (1%), and non investment grade bonds (1%).

Investments in Affiliates: 1%

Group Affiliation: NCMIC Group

Licensed in: All states, the District of Columbia and Puerto Rico

Commenced Business: January 1946

Address: 1452 29th St Ste 102, W Des Moines, IA 50266-1307

Phone: (515) 313-4500   **Domicile State:** IA   **NAIC Code:** 15865

Data Date	Rating	RACR #1	RACR #2	Loss Ratio %	Total Assets ($mil)	Capital ($mil)	Net Premium ($mil)	Net Income ($mil)
6-16	B	2.19	1.49	N/A	731.1	274.4	63.1	9.9
6-15	B	2.17	1.53	N/A	679.1	259.8	61.2	8.3
2015	B	2.20	1.51	58.1	713.0	261.7	145.6	17.7
2014	B	2.23	1.57	50.2	654.9	252.1	147.1	21.1
2013	B	2.68	2.02	50.2	593.9	241.5	102.2	27.2
2012	B	2.40	1.80	43.4	583.1	218.2	100.7	29.5
2011	B	2.11	1.56	55.0	570.5	197.9	96.0	17.9

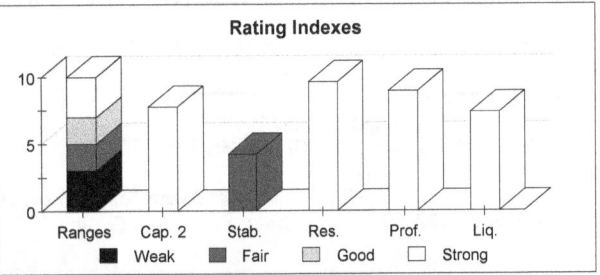

Rating Indexes

NEW JERSEY RE-INS CO   B   Good

Major Rating Factors: History of adequate reserve strength (6.9 on a scale of 0 to 10) as reserves have been consistently at an acceptable level. Fair overall results on stability tests (4.7) including potential drain of affiliation with NJ Manufacturers, weak results on operational trends and negative cash flow from operations for 2015.

Other Rating Factors: Strong long-term capitalization index (9.1) based on excellent current risk adjusted capital (severe and moderate loss scenarios). Moreover, capital levels have been consistent in recent years. Excellent profitability (8.0) with operating gains in each of the last five years. Excellent liquidity (8.6) with ample operational cash flow and liquid investments.

Principal Business: Allied lines (32%), other liability (32%), auto liability (13%), workers compensation (12%), auto physical damage (5%), homeowners multiple peril (5%), and fire (3%).

Principal Investments: Investment grade bonds (99%) and cash (1%).

Investments in Affiliates: None

Group Affiliation: NJ Manufacturers

Licensed in: All states except AR, CA, CO, DC, ID, KS, LA, NM, UT, WY, PR

Commenced Business: January 1978

Address: 301 Sullivan Way, West Trenton, NJ 08628

Phone: (609) 883-1300   **Domicile State:** NJ   **NAIC Code:** 35432

Data Date	Rating	RACR #1	RACR #2	Loss Ratio %	Total Assets ($mil)	Capital ($mil)	Net Premium ($mil)	Net Income ($mil)
6-16	B	4.37	2.57	N/A	548.6	409.8	9.2	7.1
6-15	B	3.85	2.30	N/A	559.2	398.2	15.6	4.1
2015	B	4.06	2.36	95.1	549.8	400.6	21.5	6.2
2014	B	3.86	2.28	33.1	556.8	393.1	33.6	19.8
2013	B	2.99	1.77	47.4	553.6	362.3	37.1	21.1
2012	B	2.52	1.49	92.5	546.8	330.4	41.2	12.0
2011	B-	11.40	6.81	88.5	550.3	313.0	44.4	14.2

Reserve Deficiency (as % of capital)

* Adequate & redundant reserves show as negatives

NEW YORK MARINE & GENERAL INS CO   B-   Good

Major Rating Factors: Fair overall results on stability tests (4.3 on a scale of 0 to 10) including potential drain of affiliation with ProSight Specialty Ins Group Inc and weak results on operational trends. The largest net exposure for one risk is conservative at 1.3% of capital. Fair profitability index (3.8) with operating losses during 2011 and the first six months of 2016. Average return on equity over the last five years has been poor at -1.2%.

Other Rating Factors: Good long-term capitalization index (6.7) based on good current risk adjusted capital (moderate loss scenario). Over the last several years, capital levels have remained relatively consistent. History of adequate reserve strength (6.8) as reserves have been consistently at an acceptable level. Good liquidity (6.9) with sufficient resources (cash flows and marketable investments) to handle a spike in claims.

Principal Business: Auto liability (27%), workers compensation (18%), other liability (17%), ocean marine (8%), commercial multiple peril (7%), fire (4%), and other lines (19%).

Principal Investments: Investment grade bonds (68%), misc. investments (29%), cash (2%), and non investment grade bonds (1%).

Investments in Affiliates: 15%

Group Affiliation: ProSight Specialty Ins Group Inc

Licensed in: All states, the District of Columbia and Puerto Rico

Commenced Business: July 1972

Address: 919 Third Ave, New York, NY 10022

Phone: (212) 551-0600   **Domicile State:** NY   **NAIC Code:** 16608

Data Date	Rating	RACR #1	RACR #2	Loss Ratio %	Total Assets ($mil)	Capital ($mil)	Net Premium ($mil)	Net Income ($mil)
6-16	B-	1.34	0.95	N/A	1,274.9	374.9	200.1	-10.3
6-15	B-	1.39	1.01	N/A	1,186.6	371.2	172.9	-4.4
2015	B-	1.37	0.98	70.3	1,191.9	379.2	401.2	-8.3
2014	B-	1.10	0.79	57.7	1,062.9	352.6	347.1	12.6
2013	B-	1.21	0.88	60.6	891.7	240.1	270.9	1.8
2012	B	1.55	1.16	60.0	738.9	230.6	197.9	8.0
2011	B	1.82	1.50	65.8	666.1	216.0	128.9	-20.9

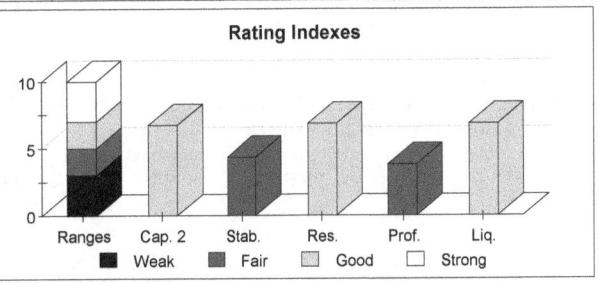

Rating Indexes

NGM INS CO
B-   Good

Major Rating Factors: Fair overall results on stability tests (4.6 on a scale of 0 to 10) including potential drain of affiliation with Main Street America Group Inc and weak results on operational trends. History of adequate reserve strength (5.9) as reserves have been consistently at an acceptable level.

Other Rating Factors: Good overall profitability index (6.7). Fair expense controls. Return on equity has been low, averaging 4.9% over the past five years. Good liquidity (6.4) with sufficient resources (cash flows and marketable investments) to handle a spike in claims. Strong long-term capitalization index (8.7) based on excellent current risk adjusted capital (severe and moderate loss scenarios). Moreover, capital levels have been consistent in recent years.

Principal Business: Auto liability (31%), homeowners multiple peril (21%), auto physical damage (15%), workers compensation (14%), surety (7%), other liability (4%), and other lines (8%).

Principal Investments: Investment grade bonds (67%), misc. investments (29%), and non investment grade bonds (4%).

Investments in Affiliates: 12%

Group Affiliation: Main Street America Group Inc

Licensed in: All states except AK, CA, HI, MN, PR

Commenced Business: July 1923

Address: 4601 Touchton Rd E Suite 3400, Jacksonville, FL 32245

Phone: (904) 380-7282   **Domicile State:** FL   **NAIC Code:** 14788

Data Date	Rating	RACR #1	RACR #2	Loss Ratio %	Total Assets ($mil)	Capital ($mil)	Net Premium ($mil)	Net Income ($mil)
6-16	B-	2.99	2.29	N/A	2,412.3	1,033.2	502.2	8.9
6-15	B-	3.04	2.29	N/A	2,339.9	987.6	479.6	26.0
2015	B-	2.99	2.31	68.0	2,344.8	1,020.6	967.6	66.2
2014	B-	3.07	2.34	70.6	2,314.4	968.2	968.6	30.3
2013	B-	2.98	2.26	68.2	2,265.3	936.9	1,018.2	53.7
2012	B-	2.56	1.87	69.2	2,120.1	838.4	981.6	62.1
2011	B-	2.54	1.84	74.5	2,018.2	770.5	889.4	26.5

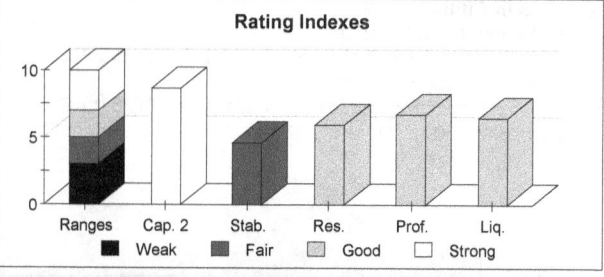

Rating Indexes

NJ MANUFACTURERS INS CO
B   Good

Major Rating Factors: Good overall results on stability tests (5.1 on a scale of 0 to 10) despite potential drain of affiliation with NJ Manufacturers and weak results on operational trends. History of adequate reserve strength (6.6) as reserves have been consistently at an acceptable level.

Other Rating Factors: Good liquidity (6.8) with sufficient resources (cash flows and marketable investments) to handle a spike in claims. Fair profitability index (4.6) with operating losses during 2011 and 2012. Average return on equity over the last five years has been poor at -0.7%. Strong long-term capitalization index (8.2) based on excellent current risk adjusted capital (severe and moderate loss scenarios), despite some fluctuation in capital levels.

Principal Business: Auto liability (40%), workers compensation (26%), auto physical damage (20%), and homeowners multiple peril (14%).

Principal Investments: Investment grade bonds (72%), misc. investments (26%), and real estate (2%).

Investments in Affiliates: 12%

Group Affiliation: NJ Manufacturers

Licensed in: CT, DE, ME, NJ, NY, PA, RI

Commenced Business: July 1913

Address: 301 Sullivan Way, West Trenton, NJ 08628

Phone: (609) 883-1300   **Domicile State:** NJ   **NAIC Code:** 12122

Data Date	Rating	RACR #1	RACR #2	Loss Ratio %	Total Assets ($mil)	Capital ($mil)	Net Premium ($mil)	Net Income ($mil)
6-16	B	2.41	1.80	N/A	6,882.1	2,580.6	813.4	20.4
6-15	B-	2.36	1.75	N/A	6,712.3	2,353.4	780.1	4.5
2015	B	2.39	1.82	78.6	6,687.0	2,445.0	1,629.6	79.7
2014	B-	2.48	1.87	79.7	6,568.2	2,379.9	1,660.1	162.5
2013	B-	2.38	1.80	83.1	6,282.4	2,273.9	1,597.6	123.6
2012	C+	2.25	1.69	107.5	5,945.3	2,057.3	1,459.1	-289.4
2011	B	2.70	2.06	95.8	5,892.8	2,253.7	1,365.5	-134.0

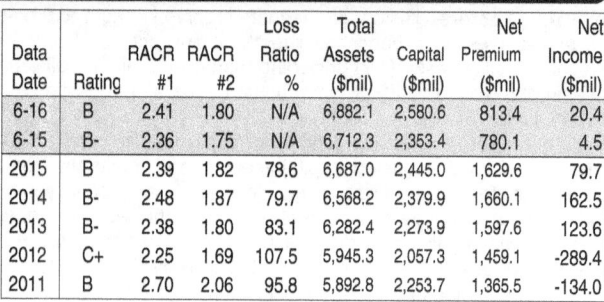

Rating Indexes

NORCAL MUTUAL INS CO
B-   Good

Major Rating Factors: Fair overall results on stability tests (4.6 on a scale of 0 to 10) including potential drain of affiliation with NORCAL Mutual, excessive premium growth, weak results on operational trends and negative cash flow from operations for 2015. Good overall profitability index (5.3) despite operating losses during the first six months of 2016.

Other Rating Factors: Strong long-term capitalization index (7.7) based on excellent current risk adjusted capital (severe and moderate loss scenarios), despite some fluctuation in capital levels. Ample reserve history (9.3) that helps to protect the company against sharp claims increases. Excellent liquidity (7.0) with ample operational cash flow and liquid investments.

Principal Business: Medical malpractice (100%).

Principal Investments: Misc. investments (56%), investment grade bonds (41%), and non investment grade bonds (3%).

Investments in Affiliates: 27%

Group Affiliation: NORCAL Mutual

Licensed in: All states except CO, ID, MT, NH, NY, ND, WY, PR

Commenced Business: November 1975

Address: 560 Davis Street 2nd Floor, San Francisco, CA 94111-1902

Phone: (415) 397-9700   **Domicile State:** CA   **NAIC Code:** 33200

Data Date	Rating	RACR #1	RACR #2	Loss Ratio %	Total Assets ($mil)	Capital ($mil)	Net Premium ($mil)	Net Income ($mil)
6-16	B-	1.65	1.41	N/A	1,623.1	670.3	184.8	-4.9
6-15	B-	1.87	1.57	N/A	1,451.8	642.6	103.7	7.9
2015	B-	1.69	1.46	80.3	1,610.5	670.1	314.1	25.8
2014	B-	1.87	1.58	74.9	1,359.3	642.1	207.8	16.8
2013	B-	1.86	1.56	79.3	1,323.3	634.2	212.3	31.6
2012	B-	1.75	1.46	71.9	1,323.6	607.6	209.6	29.8
2011	B-	1.74	1.45	76.8	1,304.6	579.5	231.9	32.7

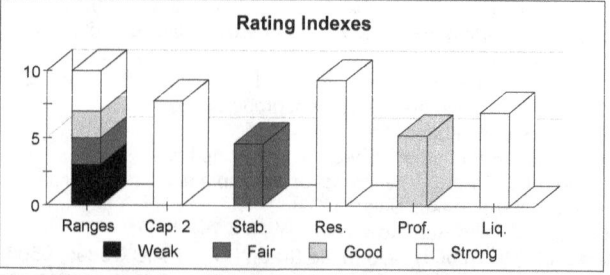

Rating Indexes

NORCAL SPECIALTY INS CO

B-   **Good**

Major Rating Factors: Fair overall results on stability tests (4.4 on a scale of 0 to 10) including potential drain of affiliation with NORCAL Mutual and weak results on operational trends.

Other Rating Factors: Good overall profitability index (6.8). Fair expense controls. Return on equity has been low, averaging 3.9% over the past five years. Good liquidity (6.8) with sufficient resources (cash flows and marketable investments) to handle a spike in claims. Strong long-term capitalization index (10.0) based on excellent current risk adjusted capital (severe and moderate loss scenarios), despite some fluctuation in capital levels.

Principal Business: Medical malpractice (100%).

Principal Investments: Investment grade bonds (149%) and non investment grade bonds (2%).

Investments in Affiliates: None

Group Affiliation: NORCAL Mutual

Licensed in: All states except PR

Commenced Business: January 1978

Address: 777 E Park Dr, Harrisburg, PA 17111

Phone: (717) 791-1212   **Domicile State:** PA   **NAIC Code:** 35114

Data Date	Rating	RACR #1	RACR #2	Loss Ratio %	Total Assets ($mil)	Capital ($mil)	Net Premium ($mil)	Net Income ($mil)
6-16	B-	16.33	9.35	N/A	264.8	245.4	0.0	8.0
6-15	B-	4.51	3.59	N/A	505.6	228.9	38.4	0.3
2015	B-	16.34	8.91	N/A	507.7	236.7	-35.7	14.8
2014	B-	4.70	3.77	74.9	457.4	229.7	76.9	8.5
2013	B-	4.66	3.53	79.3	472.1	220.1	78.5	3.5
2012	B-	4.79	3.63	71.9	476.4	220.8	77.5	10.7
2011	B-	4.36	3.24	76.8	452.6	207.2	85.8	3.6

Rating Indexes

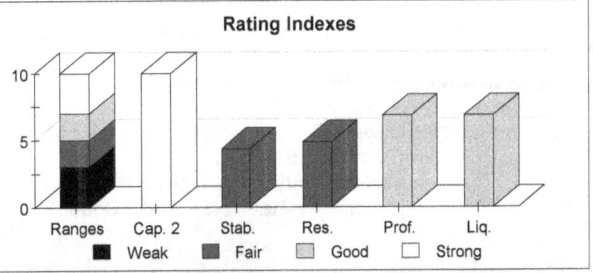

NORTH AMERICAN SPECIALTY INS CO

C   **Fair**

Major Rating Factors: Fair overall results on stability tests (3.6 on a scale of 0 to 10) including potential drain of affiliation with Swiss Reinsurance, weak results on operational trends and negative cash flow from operations for 2015. The largest net exposure for one risk is high at 3.3% of capital. History of adequate reserve strength (6.4) as reserves have been consistently at an acceptable level.

Other Rating Factors: Strong long-term capitalization index (10.0) based on excellent current risk adjusted capital (severe and moderate loss scenarios), despite some fluctuation in capital levels. Excellent profitability (7.0) with operating gains in each of the last five years. Excellent expense controls. Superior liquidity (10.0) with ample operational cash flow and liquid investments.

Principal Business: Other liability (39%), surety (32%), inland marine (21%), ocean marine (5%), fire (1%), allied lines (1%), and other lines (2%).

Principal Investments: Investment grade bonds (105%) and non investment grade bonds (2%).

Investments in Affiliates: 15%

Group Affiliation: Swiss Reinsurance

Licensed in: All states, the District of Columbia and Puerto Rico

Commenced Business: October 1974

Address: 650 Elm St, Manchester, NH 03101-2524

Phone: (603) 644-6600   **Domicile State:** NH   **NAIC Code:** 29874

Data Date	Rating	RACR #1	RACR #2	Loss Ratio %	Total Assets ($mil)	Capital ($mil)	Net Premium ($mil)	Net Income ($mil)
6-16	C	4.13	3.82	N/A	462.5	305.8	0.0	7.8
6-15	C	5.34	4.84	N/A	554.2	389.8	7.0	3.7
2015	C	5.34	4.93	16.6	576.7	395.3	2.8	9.5
2014	C	5.35	4.92	34.3	547.3	384.2	14.2	6.4
2013	C	5.38	4.98	8.4	514.2	373.0	11.4	4.6
2012	C	5.50	5.09	N/A	503.5	363.7	10.4	12.5
2011	C	5.23	4.96	N/A	472.1	344.6	10.7	23.4

Swiss Reinsurance
Composite Group Rating: C+

Largest Group Members	Assets ($mil)	Rating
SWISS REINS AMERICA CORP	12796	C+
SWISS RE LIFE HEALTH AMER INC	12264	C
WESTPORT INS CORP	4693	B-
NORTH AMERICAN SPECIALTY INS CO	577	C
FIRST SPECIALTY INS CORP	174	C

NORTH CAROLINA FARM BU MUTUAL INS CO

B   **Good**

Major Rating Factors: Good liquidity (6.6 on a scale of 0 to 10) with sufficient resources (cash flows and marketable investments) to handle a spike in claims. Fair overall results on stability tests (4.7) including potential drain of affiliation with NC Farm Bureau Ins and weak results on operational trends.

Other Rating Factors: Fair profitability index (4.3) with operating losses during 2011. Strong long-term capitalization index (10.0) based on excellent current risk adjusted capital (severe and moderate loss scenarios). Moreover, capital levels have been consistent in recent years. Ample reserve history (8.7) that helps to protect the company against sharp claims increases.

Principal Business: Homeowners multiple peril (31%), auto liability (31%), auto physical damage (22%), allied lines (3%), farmowners multiple peril (3%), workers compensation (2%), and other lines (8%).

Principal Investments: Investment grade bonds (83%) and misc. investments (18%).

Investments in Affiliates: 1%

Group Affiliation: NC Farm Bureau Ins

Licensed in: NC

Commenced Business: October 1953

Address: 5301 Glenwood Ave, Raleigh, NC 27612

Phone: (919) 782-1705   **Domicile State:** NC   **NAIC Code:** 14842

Data Date	Rating	RACR #1	RACR #2	Loss Ratio %	Total Assets ($mil)	Capital ($mil)	Net Premium ($mil)	Net Income ($mil)
6-16	B	6.00	4.01	N/A	1,860.2	1,106.8	368.9	15.4
6-15	B-	5.86	3.92	N/A	1,781.8	1,034.8	352.1	38.7
2015	B	6.02	4.06	68.5	1,815.1	1,077.2	716.6	78.8
2014	B-	5.77	3.90	68.0	1,740.3	1,008.9	675.7	94.7
2013	B-	3.87	2.60	68.5	1,664.7	933.1	737.3	86.8
2012	C+	3.82	2.56	76.0	1,568.5	836.0	701.8	33.1
2011	C	2.83	1.91	111.0	1,535.8	762.3	813.0	-235.0

Liquidity Index

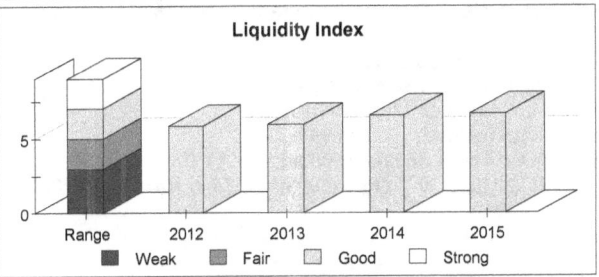

NORTH RIVER INS CO   C-   Fair

Major Rating Factors: Fair overall results on stability tests (3.3 on a scale of 0 to 10) including weak financial strength of affiliated Fairfax Financial and weak results on operational trends. Good long-term capitalization index (6.7) based on good current risk adjusted capital (moderate loss scenario), despite some fluctuation in capital levels.

Other Rating Factors: History of adequate reserve strength (5.7) as reserves have been consistently at an acceptable level. Good overall profitability index (6.0) despite operating losses during 2012. Return on equity has been good over the last five years, averaging 13.3%. Excellent liquidity (7.3) with ample operational cash flow and liquid investments.

Principal Business: Other liability (46%), workers compensation (28%), products liability (8%), auto liability (6%), commercial multiple peril (6%), auto physical damage (2%), and other lines (3%).

Principal Investments: Investment grade bonds (67%), misc. investments (27%), and non investment grade bonds (6%).

Investments in Affiliates: 21%
Group Affiliation: Fairfax Financial
Licensed in: All states except PR
Commenced Business: October 1972
Address: 305 Madison Avenue, Morristown, NJ 07960
Phone: (973) 490-6600   **Domicile State:** NJ   **NAIC Code:** 21105

Data Date	Rating	RACR #1	RACR #2	Loss Ratio %	Total Assets ($mil)	Capital ($mil)	Net Premium ($mil)	Net Income ($mil)
6-16	C-	1.18	0.90	N/A	1,050.7	288.0	188.4	6.4
6-15	C-	1.32	1.03	N/A	1,001.9	308.4	154.3	35.8
2015	C-	1.31	1.02	64.1	1,030.5	306.2	365.6	55.3
2014	C-	1.16	0.92	67.5	945.8	264.8	296.7	4.4
2013	C-	1.13	0.89	71.4	938.2	263.1	281.3	87.7
2012	C-	1.19	0.94	81.2	869.7	277.0	234.5	-17.2
2011	C-	1.52	1.13	81.0	816.8	282.3	201.8	68.3

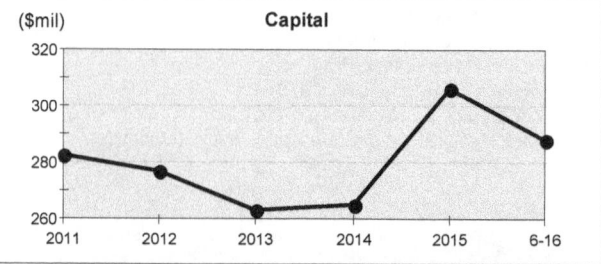

NORTH STAR MUTUAL INS CO   B-   Good

Major Rating Factors: Fair overall results on stability tests (4.2 on a scale of 0 to 10) including potential drain of affiliation with North Star Companies and weak results on operational trends. Good liquidity (6.8) with sufficient resources (cash flows and marketable investments) to handle a spike in claims.

Other Rating Factors: Strong long-term capitalization index (10.0) based on excellent current risk adjusted capital (severe and moderate loss scenarios). Moreover, capital levels have been consistent in recent years. Ample reserve history (7.5) that can protect against increases in claims costs. Excellent profitability (8.6) with operating gains in each of the last five years.

Principal Business: Allied lines (25%), homeowners multiple peril (23%), auto physical damage (14%), auto liability (12%), farmowners multiple peril (11%), other liability (6%), and other lines (9%).

Principal Investments: Investment grade bonds (78%), misc. investments (21%), and real estate (2%).

Investments in Affiliates: 1%
Group Affiliation: North Star Companies
Licensed in: IA, MN, NE, ND, OK, SD, WI
Commenced Business: February 1920
Address: 269 Barstad Rd S, Cottonwood, MN 56229
Phone: (507) 423-6262   **Domicile State:** MN   **NAIC Code:** 14850

Data Date	Rating	RACR #1	RACR #2	Loss Ratio %	Total Assets ($mil)	Capital ($mil)	Net Premium ($mil)	Net Income ($mil)
6-16	B-	6.06	4.20	N/A	684.9	392.1	170.2	30.3
6-15	B-	4.98	3.46	N/A	619.7	333.6	162.0	25.5
2015	B-	5.90	4.01	49.2	637.4	361.9	338.6	57.4
2014	B-	4.93	3.40	63.0	566.7	306.5	317.4	29.0
2013	B-	4.61	3.18	64.3	520.2	280.0	288.7	20.9
2012	B-	5.17	3.63	70.9	460.3	253.3	251.5	11.5
2011	B	5.84	4.06	74.0	424.7	240.5	211.3	6.9

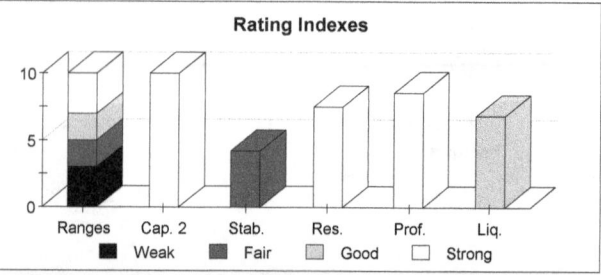

NORTHLAND INS CO   B   Good

Major Rating Factors: Good overall profitability index (6.5 on a scale of 0 to 10). Fair expense controls. Return on equity has been fair, averaging 9.3% over the past five years. Good liquidity (6.9) with sufficient resources (cash flows and marketable investments) to handle a spike in claims.

Other Rating Factors: Fair overall results on stability tests (4.7) including weak results on operational trends. Affiliation with Travelers Companies Inc is a strength. Strong long-term capitalization index (9.2) based on excellent current risk adjusted capital (severe and moderate loss scenarios), despite some fluctuation in capital levels. Ample reserve history (7.9) that can protect against increases in claims costs.

Principal Business: Auto liability (59%), auto physical damage (27%), inland marine (10%), other liability (2%), and commercial multiple peril (1%).

Principal Investments: Investment grade bonds (81%) and misc. investments (21%).

Investments in Affiliates: 16%
Group Affiliation: Travelers Companies Inc
Licensed in: All states except AK, PR
Commenced Business: March 1948
Address: One Tower Square, Hartford, CT 06183
Phone: (651) 310-4100   **Domicile State:** CT   **NAIC Code:** 24015

Data Date	Rating	RACR #1	RACR #2	Loss Ratio %	Total Assets ($mil)	Capital ($mil)	Net Premium ($mil)	Net Income ($mil)
6-16	B	3.02	2.45	N/A	1,211.3	569.1	127.8	16.5
6-15	B	3.06	2.47	N/A	1,223.1	569.0	123.2	20.9
2015	B	2.96	2.42	58.7	1,171.6	544.0	253.5	62.1
2014	B	2.97	2.41	60.5	1,166.2	538.9	246.3	60.6
2013	B	2.97	2.43	60.9	1,157.6	533.3	245.7	56.8
2012	B	3.05	2.48	68.4	1,150.6	524.6	238.6	41.9
2011	B	3.15	2.56	76.9	1,158.0	535.1	233.6	36.7

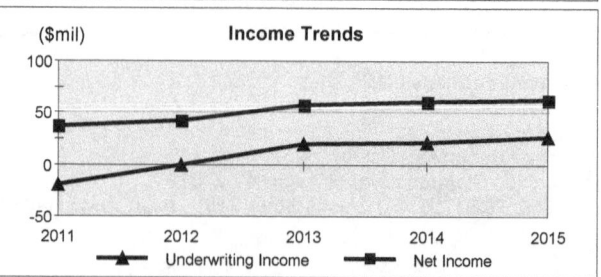

NUTMEG INS CO   C-   Fair

Major Rating Factors: Weak overall results on stability tests (2.9 on a scale of 0 to 10) including weak results on operational trends. Fair reserve development (4.9) as reserves have generally been sufficient to cover claims.

Other Rating Factors: Strong long-term capitalization index (10.0) based on excellent current risk adjusted capital (severe and moderate loss scenarios), despite some fluctuation in capital levels. Excellent profitability (8.2) with operating gains in each of the last five years. Excellent liquidity (8.4) with ample operational cash flow and liquid investments.

Principal Business: Other liability (-17%).

Principal Investments: Misc. investments (61%), investment grade bonds (38%), and non investment grade bonds (1%).

Investments in Affiliates: 43%

Group Affiliation: Hartford Financial Services Inc

Licensed in: All states except PR

Commenced Business: December 1980

Address: Hartford Plaza, Hartford, CT 06115

Phone: (860) 547-5000 **Domicile State:** CT **NAIC Code:** 39608

Data Date	Rating	RACR #1	RACR #2	Loss Ratio %	Total Assets ($mil)	Capital ($mil)	Net Premium ($mil)	Net Income ($mil)
6-16	C-	58.83	52.95	N/A	770.2	578.5	36.6	13.5
6-15	D	0.06	0.04	N/A	490.7	319.1	35.9	31.6
2015	D	54.75	49.28	66.1	706.6	530.6	73.8	102.6
2014	D	0.06	0.04	67.0	448.1	280.2	71.7	11.8
2013	C-	26.77	24.09	68.8	421.7	256.6	69.6	28.3
2012	C-	23.82	21.44	72.7	392.0	227.9	68.9	8.9
2011	D+	0.05	0.03	78.5	416.5	246.1	68.9	11.4

Hartford Financial Services Inc
Composite Group Rating: C+
Largest Group Members

	Assets ($mil)	Rating
HARTFORD LIFE INS CO	114421	C+
HARTFORD LIFE ANNUITY INS CO	40189	B-
HARTFORD FIRE INS CO	25426	B
HARTFORD ACCIDENT INDEMNITY CO	11522	B
HARTFORD LIFE ACCIDENT INS CO	8992	C+

OAK RIVER INS CO   C   Fair

Major Rating Factors: Fair overall results on stability tests (4.1 on a scale of 0 to 10) including weak results on operational trends. Good overall profitability index (6.2) despite operating losses during 2011 and 2012. Return on equity has been low, averaging 3.4% over the past five years.

Other Rating Factors: Strong long-term capitalization index (7.2) based on excellent current risk adjusted capital (severe and moderate loss scenarios), despite some fluctuation in capital levels. Ample reserve history (9.2) that helps to protect the company against sharp claims increases. Excellent liquidity (8.0) with ample operational cash flow and liquid investments.

Principal Business: Workers compensation (94%), commercial multiple peril (3%), auto liability (1%), allied lines (1%), and fire (1%).

Principal Investments: Investment grade bonds (60%), misc. investments (33%), and cash (7%).

Investments in Affiliates: None

Group Affiliation: Berkshire-Hathaway

Licensed in: All states except ME, OR, WA, WY, PR

Commenced Business: December 1993

Address: 9290 W Dodge Rd, Ste 300, Omaha, NE 68114-3363

Phone: (402) 393-7255 **Domicile State:** NE **NAIC Code:** 34630

Data Date	Rating	RACR #1	RACR #2	Loss Ratio %	Total Assets ($mil)	Capital ($mil)	Net Premium ($mil)	Net Income ($mil)
6-16	C	1.79	1.18	N/A	606.1	199.1	55.3	2.0
6-15	C-	0.58	0.36	N/A	569.1	190.0	53.0	6.4
2015	C	1.83	1.20	60.5	594.7	200.4	110.9	18.2
2014	C-	0.60	0.37	67.1	571.1	191.9	108.0	16.0
2013	C	1.64	1.07	66.3	527.4	170.9	111.9	14.0
2012	C	0.85	0.50	81.2	459.0	137.7	100.2	-6.1
2011	C+	1.58	1.04	86.0	336.6	126.5	81.2	-4.4

Berkshire-Hathaway
Composite Group Rating: B
Largest Group Members

	Assets ($mil)	Rating
NATIONAL INDEMNITY CO	161777	B
GOVERNMENT EMPLOYEES INS CO	24036	B
COLUMBIA INS CO	19102	C+
BERKSHIRE HATHAWAY LIFE INS CO OF NE	16287	C+
GENERAL REINS CORP	15320	C+

ODYSSEY REINS CO   C   Fair

Major Rating Factors: Weak overall results on stability tests (2.7 on a scale of 0 to 10) including weak results on operational trends. The largest net exposure for one risk is excessive at 8.7% of capital. Good overall profitability index (5.8) despite operating losses during 2011. Return on equity has been fair, averaging 5.7% over the past five years.

Other Rating Factors: Good liquidity (6.6) with sufficient resources (cash flows and marketable investments) to handle a spike in claims. Strong long-term capitalization index (7.3) based on excellent current risk adjusted capital (severe and moderate loss scenarios), despite some fluctuation in capital levels. Ample reserve history (9.4) that helps to protect the company against sharp claims increases.

Principal Business: (This company is a reinsurer.)

Principal Investments: Misc. investments (54%), investment grade bonds (40%), cash (3%), and non investment grade bonds (3%).

Investments in Affiliates: 29%

Group Affiliation: Fairfax Financial

Licensed in: All states, the District of Columbia and Puerto Rico

Commenced Business: September 1986

Address: 300 First Stamford Pl, Stamford, CT 06902

Phone: (203) 977-8000 **Domicile State:** CT **NAIC Code:** 23680

Data Date	Rating	RACR #1	RACR #2	Loss Ratio %	Total Assets ($mil)	Capital ($mil)	Net Premium ($mil)	Net Income ($mil)
6-16	C	1.52	1.28	N/A	7,394.0	3,265.6	745.7	131.7
6-15	C	1.39	1.12	N/A	7,371.3	3,168.5	868.1	251.5
2015	C	1.48	1.24	52.2	7,308.2	3,288.5	1,575.5	449.6
2014	C	1.41	1.13	51.8	7,577.4	3,248.7	1,799.8	191.7
2013	C	1.63	1.23	29.2	7,448.0	3,102.5	1,267.5	112.5
2012	C	1.65	1.21	57.5	8,171.6	3,154.8	2,129.9	174.7
2011	C	1.87	1.37	91.5	7,875.2	3,024.8	1,807.3	-40.3

Rating Indexes

Ranges   Cap. 2   Stab.   Res.   Prof.   Liq.
■ Weak   ■ Fair   ▨ Good   □ Strong

OGLESBY REINS CO *   A+   Excellent

Major Rating Factors: Strong long-term capitalization index (10.0 on a scale of 0 to 10) based on excellent current risk adjusted capital (severe and moderate loss scenarios). Furthermore, this high level of risk adjusted capital has been consistently maintained in previous years. Excellent profitability (7.9) with operating gains in each of the last five years.

Other Rating Factors: Excellent liquidity (7.3) with ample operational cash flow and liquid investments. Excellent overall results on stability tests (8.4). Stability strengths include excellent risk diversification.

Principal Business: (This company is a reinsurer.)

Principal Investments: Investment grade bonds (88%) and misc. investments (12%).

Investments in Affiliates: None

Group Affiliation: State Farm Group

Licensed in: IL, TX

Commenced Business: July 2011

Address: One State Farm Plaza, Bloomington, IL 61710-0001

Phone: (309) 766-2311   **Domicile State:** IL   **NAIC Code:** 14103

Data Date	Rating	RACR #1	RACR #2	Loss Ratio %	Total Assets ($mil)	Capital ($mil)	Net Premium ($mil)	Net Income ($mil)
6-16	A+	10.68	7.86	N/A	4,277.3	3,181.2	419.0	40.8
6-15	A+	32.60	29.19	N/A	3,629.8	3,135.6	253.7	24.7
2015	A+	12.04	9.41	72.0	3,998.0	3,119.4	1,206.2	34.4
2014	A+	48.48	43.38	0.0	3,171.6	3,071.8	177.2	146.4
2013	A+	52.33	46.32	0.0	3,022.7	2,923.9	155.3	161.7
2012	A+	39.07	35.40	0.0	2,930.5	2,775.3	199.3	165.2
2011	A+	37.91	34.29	0.0	2,761.6	2,609.9	178.2	78.0

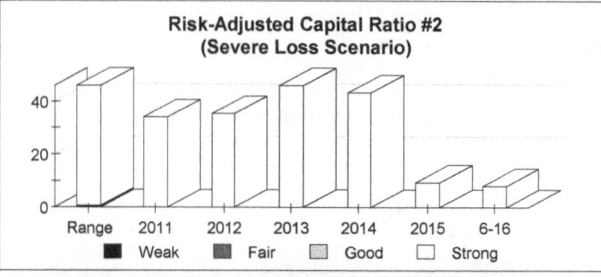

Risk-Adjusted Capital Ratio #2 (Severe Loss Scenario)

Range | 2011 | 2012 | 2013 | 2014 | 2015 | 6-16
■ Weak   ■ Fair   ▨ Good   □ Strong

OHIO CASUALTY INS CO   C   Fair

Major Rating Factors: Fair overall results on stability tests (3.7 on a scale of 0 to 10) including potential drain of affiliation with Liberty Mutual Group and weak results on operational trends. The largest net exposure for one risk is acceptable at 2.9% of capital. History of adequate reserve strength (5.9) as reserves have been consistently at an acceptable level.

Other Rating Factors: Good overall profitability index (6.5). Fair expense controls. Return on equity has been fair, averaging 9.5% over the past five years. Good liquidity (6.2) with sufficient resources (cash flows and marketable investments) to handle a spike in claims. Strong long-term capitalization index (8.1) based on excellent current risk adjusted capital (severe and moderate loss scenarios). Moreover, capital levels have been consistent in recent years.

Principal Business: Other liability (36%), commercial multiple peril (22%), surety (16%), inland marine (8%), auto liability (7%), workers compensation (6%), and other lines (5%).

Principal Investments: Investment grade bonds (75%), misc. investments (20%), non investment grade bonds (5%), and real estate (1%).

Investments in Affiliates: 2%

Group Affiliation: Liberty Mutual Group

Licensed in: All states except PR

Commenced Business: March 1920

Address: 62 Maple Ave, Keene, NH 03431

Phone: (617) 357-9500   **Domicile State:** NH   **NAIC Code:** 24074

Data Date	Rating	RACR #1	RACR #2	Loss Ratio %	Total Assets ($mil)	Capital ($mil)	Net Premium ($mil)	Net Income ($mil)
6-16	C	2.84	1.88	N/A	5,600.3	1,645.1	1,014.4	2.0
6-15	C	2.66	1.75	N/A	5,521.3	1,596.3	983.1	95.8
2015	C	2.82	1.87	68.4	5,578.6	1,637.4	2,050.6	157.4
2014	C	2.56	1.68	70.0	5,408.2	1,529.8	2,030.1	133.7
2013	C	2.34	1.52	73.5	5,639.6	1,384.1	1,791.9	313.5
2012	C	1.97	1.41	66.7	5,100.5	1,274.6	2,227.3	112.0
2011	C	1.74	1.24	74.0	4,860.0	1,087.6	2,169.2	27.8

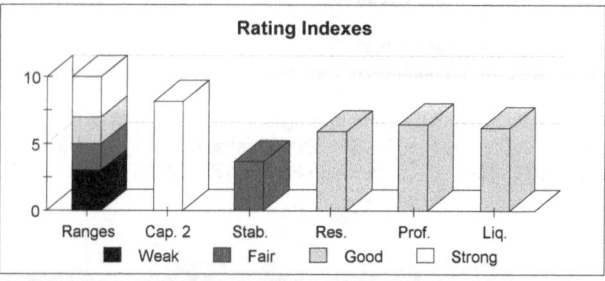

Rating Indexes

Ranges | Cap. 2 | Stab. | Res. | Prof. | Liq.
■ Weak   ■ Fair   ▨ Good   □ Strong

OHIO FARMERS INS CO   B-   Good

Major Rating Factors: Fair overall results on stability tests (4.6 on a scale of 0 to 10) including potential drain of affiliation with Westfield Companies and weak results on operational trends. Fair profitability index (4.7) with operating losses during 2011.

Other Rating Factors: Good liquidity (6.9) with sufficient resources (cash flows and marketable investments) to handle a spike in claims. Strong long-term capitalization index (7.2) based on excellent current risk adjusted capital (severe and moderate loss scenarios). Moreover, capital levels have been consistent in recent years. Ample reserve history (7.5) that can protect against increases in claims costs.

Principal Business: Surety (100%).

Principal Investments: Misc. investments (80%), investment grade bonds (17%), real estate (2%), and cash (1%).

Investments in Affiliates: 69%

Group Affiliation: Westfield Companies

Licensed in: All states except AK, CA, CT, HI, ID, ME, NH, OR, PR

Commenced Business: July 1848

Address: One Park Circle, Westfield Center, OH 44251-5001

Phone: (330) 887-0101   **Domicile State:** OH   **NAIC Code:** 24104

Data Date	Rating	RACR #1	RACR #2	Loss Ratio %	Total Assets ($mil)	Capital ($mil)	Net Premium ($mil)	Net Income ($mil)
6-16	B-	1.28	1.23	N/A	2,815.4	2,114.4	167.6	50.3
6-15	B-	1.25	1.21	N/A	2,656.4	1,965.9	163.7	10.5
2015	B-	1.23	1.20	62.7	2,701.1	1,997.1	336.1	22.0
2014	B-	1.22	1.19	63.5	2,595.1	1,902.4	329.3	39.3
2013	B-	1.25	1.21	59.8	2,404.6	1,808.7	318.3	21.1
2012	B-	1.22	1.18	64.9	2,131.9	1,525.6	305.3	36.9
2011	B-	1.24	1.19	79.3	1,915.6	1,361.7	363.0	-62.4

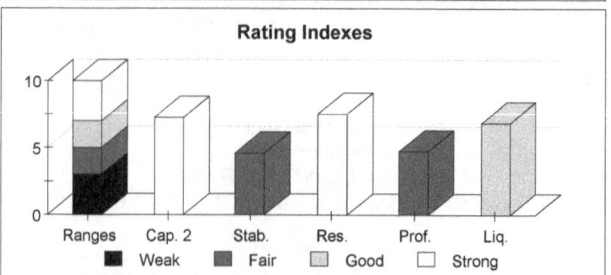

Rating Indexes

Ranges | Cap. 2 | Stab. | Res. | Prof. | Liq.
■ Weak   ■ Fair   ▨ Good   □ Strong

OHIO MUTUAL INS CO   B-   Good

Major Rating Factors: Fair overall results on stability tests (4.1 on a scale of 0 to 10) including potential drain of affiliation with Ohio Mutual Group and weak results on operational trends. Good liquidity (6.9) with sufficient resources (cash flows and marketable investments) to handle a spike in claims.

Other Rating Factors: Strong long-term capitalization index (7.4) based on excellent current risk adjusted capital (severe and moderate loss scenarios). Moreover, capital levels have been consistent in recent years. Ample reserve history (7.7) that can protect against increases in claims costs. Excellent profitability (7.8).

Principal Business: Auto liability (37%), auto physical damage (33%), homeowners multiple peril (21%), fire (5%), farmowners multiple peril (4%), and other liability (1%).

Principal Investments: Misc. investments (72%), investment grade bonds (25%), real estate (2%), and cash (1%).

Investments in Affiliates: 67%

Group Affiliation: Ohio Mutual Group

Licensed in: CT, IN, IA, KS, ME, MN, NE, NH, OH, OR, RI, TN, VT, VA, WI

Commenced Business: March 1901

Address: 1725 Hopley Ave, Bucyrus, OH 44820-0111

Phone: (419) 562-3011   **Domicile State:** OH   **NAIC Code:** 10202

Data Date	Rating	RACR #1	RACR #2	Loss Ratio %	Total Assets ($mil)	Capital ($mil)	Net Premium ($mil)	Net Income ($mil)
6-16	B-	1.39	1.34	N/A	268.7	210.3	26.9	1.8
6-15	B-	1.38	1.33	N/A	246.3	190.7	26.0	0.7
2015	B-	1.36	1.32	61.6	256.8	201.3	53.5	2.9
2014	B-	1.37	1.32	64.0	239.7	187.5	51.9	2.4
2013	B-	1.35	1.31	65.8	227.4	177.8	49.4	1.8
2012	B-	1.38	1.33	67.7	222.7	165.2	45.3	2.1
2011	B-	1.40	1.37	73.6	209.6	154.2	45.7	0.0

Rating Indexes

Ranges   Cap. 2   Stab.   Res.   Prof.   Liq.

■ Weak   ▨ Fair   ▤ Good   □ Strong

OLD GUARD INS CO   C+   Fair

Major Rating Factors: Fair overall results on stability tests (4.3 on a scale of 0 to 10) including potential drain of affiliation with Westfield Companies and weak results on operational trends. The largest net exposure for one risk is conservative at 1.5% of capital. Good overall profitability index (6.6) despite operating losses during 2011. Return on equity has been fair, averaging 7.2% over the past five years.

Other Rating Factors: Good liquidity (6.5) with sufficient resources (cash flows and marketable investments) to handle a spike in claims. Strong long-term capitalization index (9.0) based on excellent current risk adjusted capital (severe and moderate loss scenarios). Moreover, capital levels have been consistent in recent years. Ample reserve history (9.1) that helps to protect the company against sharp claims increases.

Principal Business: (This company is a reinsurer.)

Principal Investments: Investment grade bonds (67%) and misc. investments (33%).

Investments in Affiliates: None

Group Affiliation: Westfield Companies

Licensed in: DE, IN, IA, KY, MD, ND, OH, OR, PA, SD, VA, WV

Commenced Business: December 1896

Address: One Park Circle, Westfield Center, OH 44251-5001

Phone: (330) 887-0101   **Domicile State:** OH   **NAIC Code:** 17558

Data Date	Rating	RACR #1	RACR #2	Loss Ratio %	Total Assets ($mil)	Capital ($mil)	Net Premium ($mil)	Net Income ($mil)
6-16	C+	3.74	2.47	N/A	435.1	196.4	79.4	5.4
6-15	C+	3.70	2.45	N/A	417.5	184.8	77.6	7.8
2015	C+	3.74	2.49	62.7	421.4	185.6	159.2	12.6
2014	C+	3.53	2.32	63.5	410.2	179.8	156.0	13.3
2013	C+	3.31	2.17	59.8	392.0	164.4	150.8	19.5
2012	C+	2.92	1.92	64.9	356.2	136.8	144.6	16.1
2011	C	2.71	1.77	79.3	337.3	118.2	138.2	-1.3

Westfield Companies
Composite Group Rating: B-

Largest Group Members	Assets ($mil)	Rating
OHIO FARMERS INS CO	2701	B-
WESTFIELD INS CO	2594	B-
WESTFIELD NATIONAL INS CO	613	B-
OLD GUARD INS CO	421	C+
AMERICAN SELECT INS CO	234	C

OLD REPUB INS CO   B   Good

Major Rating Factors: History of adequate reserve strength (5.5 on a scale of 0 to 10) as reserves have been consistently at an acceptable level. Fair overall results on stability tests (4.8) including weak results on operational trends. The largest net exposure for one risk is conservative at 1.1% of capital.

Other Rating Factors: Strong long-term capitalization index (9.3) based on excellent current risk adjusted capital (severe and moderate loss scenarios), despite some fluctuation in capital levels. Excellent profitability (8.8) with operating gains in each of the last five years. Excellent liquidity (7.4) with ample operational cash flow and liquid investments.

Principal Business: Workers compensation (37%), other liability (18%), inland marine (12%), auto liability (9%), aircraft (7%), credit (7%), and other lines (10%).

Principal Investments: Investment grade bonds (71%), misc. investments (23%), non investment grade bonds (4%), and cash (2%).

Investments in Affiliates: 1%

Group Affiliation: Old Republic Group

Licensed in: All states, the District of Columbia and Puerto Rico

Commenced Business: April 1935

Address: 414 W Pittsburgh St, Greensburg, PA 15601-0789

Phone: (724) 834-5000   **Domicile State:** PA   **NAIC Code:** 24147

Data Date	Rating	RACR #1	RACR #2	Loss Ratio %	Total Assets ($mil)	Capital ($mil)	Net Premium ($mil)	Net Income ($mil)
6-16	B	4.02	2.49	N/A	2,868.4	1,078.1	213.1	48.9
6-15	B+	3.79	2.33	N/A	2,769.9	1,028.0	199.0	48.5
2015	B	4.16	2.58	53.5	2,668.8	1,034.0	420.9	98.9
2014	B+	3.85	2.35	61.7	2,609.4	1,035.8	400.4	105.6
2013	A-	4.02	2.48	52.2	2,472.7	937.8	365.4	107.4
2012	A-	3.96	2.36	57.2	2,439.8	874.9	359.3	84.4
2011	A-	4.23	2.29	61.6	2,394.1	859.6	358.7	79.3

Reserve Deficiency (as % of capital)

2011   2012   2013   2014   2015

* Adequate & redundant reserves show as negatives

■ 1 Yr Dev   □ 2 Yr Dev

OLD REPUBLIC GENERAL INS CORP   B   Good

Major Rating Factors: History of adequate reserve strength (6.9 on a scale of 0 to 10) as reserves have been consistently at an acceptable level. Fair overall results on stability tests (4.8) including weak results on operational trends.

Other Rating Factors: Strong long-term capitalization index (7.1) based on excellent current risk adjusted capital (severe and moderate loss scenarios). Moreover, capital levels have been consistent in recent years. Excellent profitability (8.9) with operating gains in each of the last five years. Excellent expense controls. Return on equity has been good over the last five years, averaging 11.6%. Excellent liquidity (7.0) with ample operational cash flow and liquid investments.

Principal Business: Workers compensation (65%), other liability (25%), auto liability (9%), and auto physical damage (2%).

Principal Investments: Investment grade bonds (81%), misc. investments (14%), non investment grade bonds (4%), and cash (1%).

Investments in Affiliates: None

Group Affiliation: Old Republic Group

Licensed in: All states, the District of Columbia and Puerto Rico

Commenced Business: January 1961

Address: 307 North Michigan Avenue, Chicago, IL 60601

Phone: (312) 346-8100   **Domicile State:** IL   **NAIC Code:** 24139

Data Date	Rating	RACR #1	RACR #2	Loss Ratio %	Total Assets ($mil)	Capital ($mil)	Net Premium ($mil)	Net Income ($mil)
6-16	B	2.67	1.23	N/A	1,992.7	538.9	97.8	25.4
6-15	B	2.39	1.11	N/A	1,975.7	487.6	151.8	23.9
2015	B	2.48	1.14	81.7	2,004.0	500.2	311.4	60.6
2014	B	2.50	1.18	88.8	1,925.7	494.1	303.1	62.8
2013	A-	2.74	1.63	83.2	1,730.6	431.7	286.3	54.2
2012	A-	2.22	1.06	88.0	1,507.9	332.6	278.6	33.4
2011	A-	2.52	1.32	89.1	1,290.8	308.0	263.8	35.5

Reserve Deficiency (as % of capital)
* Adequate & redundant reserves show as negatives
■ 1 Yr Dev   □ 2 Yr Dev

OMS NATIONAL INS CO RRG   B-   Good

Major Rating Factors: Fair overall results on stability tests (4.1 on a scale of 0 to 10) including potential drain of affiliation with OMS National Ins and weak results on operational trends. The largest net exposure for one risk is conservative at 1.3% of capital. Strong long-term capitalization index (8.2) based on excellent current risk adjusted capital (severe and moderate loss scenarios). Moreover, capital levels have been consistent in recent years.

Other Rating Factors: Ample reserve history (9.2) that helps to protect the company against sharp claims increases. Excellent profitability (8.6) with operating gains in each of the last five years. Excellent liquidity (8.3) with ample operational cash flow and liquid investments.

Principal Business: Medical malpractice (100%).

Principal Investments: Investment grade bonds (54%), misc. investments (41%), and cash (5%).

Investments in Affiliates: 17%

Group Affiliation: OMS National Ins

Licensed in: All states except PR

Commenced Business: April 1988

Address: 6133 N River Rd Ste 650, Rosemont, IL 60018

Phone: (847) 384-0041   **Domicile State:** IL   **NAIC Code:** 44121

Data Date	Rating	RACR #1	RACR #2	Loss Ratio %	Total Assets ($mil)	Capital ($mil)	Net Premium ($mil)	Net Income ($mil)
6-16	B-	2.46	1.97	N/A	391.4	222.7	32.0	1.5
6-15	B-	2.39	1.90	N/A	378.2	216.9	31.1	4.1
2015	B-	2.50	2.03	68.0	384.3	216.8	63.8	8.9
2014	B-	2.46	1.98	67.9	374.8	215.1	65.7	12.9
2013	B-	2.43	1.98	51.3	342.9	191.5	69.9	21.4
2012	B-	2.88	2.19	55.1	383.0	166.6	77.3	15.6
2011	B-	2.53	1.93	53.3	357.3	146.6	76.9	17.1

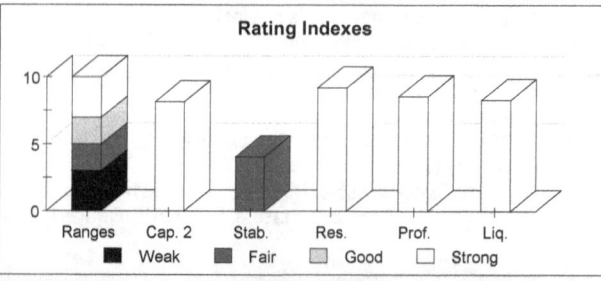

Rating Indexes
Ranges   Cap. 2   Stab.   Res.   Prof.   Liq.
■ Weak   ■ Fair   ▨ Good   □ Strong

OPHTHALMIC MUTUAL INS CO RRG   B   Good

Major Rating Factors: Fair overall results on stability tests (4.2 on a scale of 0 to 10) including weak results on operational trends. Strong long-term capitalization index (10.0) based on excellent current risk adjusted capital (severe and moderate loss scenarios). Moreover, capital levels have been consistent in recent years.

Other Rating Factors: Ample reserve history (9.3) that helps to protect the company against sharp claims increases. Excellent profitability (8.9) with operating gains in each of the last five years. Excellent liquidity (7.8) with ample operational cash flow and liquid investments.

Principal Business: Medical malpractice (100%).

Principal Investments: Investment grade bonds (85%), misc. investments (12%), and cash (3%).

Investments in Affiliates: None

Group Affiliation: None

Licensed in: All states except PR

Commenced Business: September 1987

Address: 655 Beach St Suite 260, San Francisco, CA 94109-1336

Phone: (800) 562-6642   **Domicile State:** VT   **NAIC Code:** 44105

Data Date	Rating	RACR #1	RACR #2	Loss Ratio %	Total Assets ($mil)	Capital ($mil)	Net Premium ($mil)	Net Income ($mil)
6-16	B	12.63	7.92	N/A	274.6	202.4	19.0	8.9
6-15	B	12.07	7.66	N/A	269.3	191.4	18.7	7.9
2015	B	12.61	8.10	39.9	275.1	192.7	39.8	10.8
2014	B	12.43	8.10	8.8	268.5	182.9	41.1	19.7
2013	B	11.20	8.07	30.3	259.9	163.6	39.9	12.7
2012	B	10.21	7.63	52.3	246.0	149.5	38.8	7.5
2011	B	10.80	8.11	46.2	233.0	140.4	33.3	8.1

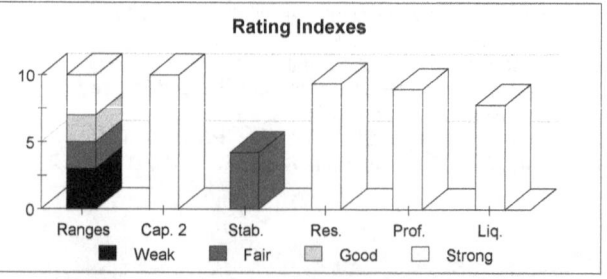

Rating Indexes
Ranges   Cap. 2   Stab.   Res.   Prof.   Liq.
■ Weak   ■ Fair   ▨ Good   □ Strong

OWNERS INS CO *   A-   Excellent

Major Rating Factors: Strong long-term capitalization index (9.5 on a scale of 0 to 10) based on excellent current risk adjusted capital (severe and moderate loss scenarios). Furthermore, this high level of risk adjusted capital has been consistently maintained in previous years. Ample reserve history (8.6) that helps to protect the company against sharp claims increases.

Other Rating Factors: Excellent profitability (8.4) with operating gains in each of the last five years. Good liquidity (6.7) with sufficient resources (cash flows and marketable investments) to handle a spike in claims. Good overall results on stability tests (5.6) despite weak results on operational trends.

Principal Business: Auto liability (27%), commercial multiple peril (21%), homeowners multiple peril (19%), auto physical damage (18%), workers compensation (8%), other liability (4%), and other lines (4%).

Principal Investments: Investment grade bonds (87%) and misc. investments (13%).

Investments in Affiliates: None

Group Affiliation: Auto-Owners Group

Licensed in: AL, AZ, AR, CO, FL, GA, ID, IL, IN, IA, KS, KY, MI, MN, MS, MO, NE, NV, NM, NC, ND, OH, OR, PA, SC, SD, TN, UT, VA, WA, WI

Commenced Business: December 1975

Address: 2325 N Cole St, Lima, OH 45801

Phone: (517) 323-1200   **Domicile State:** OH   **NAIC Code:** 32700

Data Date	Rating	RACR #1	RACR #2	Loss Ratio %	Total Assets ($mil)	Capital ($mil)	Net Premium ($mil)	Net Income ($mil)
6-16	A-	4.56	3.01	N/A	3,891.6	1,660.9	845.3	94.6
6-15	A-	4.00	2.59	N/A	3,840.0	1,500.8	855.4	110.5
2015	A-	4.31	2.89	61.6	3,883.0	1,557.7	1,705.9	179.7
2014	A-	3.79	2.48	68.4	3,721.9	1,395.5	1,690.1	96.2
2013	A+	3.73	2.44	67.5	3,510.8	1,292.1	1,617.0	120.6
2012	A	3.48	2.08	70.3	3,191.7	1,139.3	1,518.7	92.5
2011	A	3.22	1.90	78.2	2,993.1	1,016.7	1,420.7	28.2

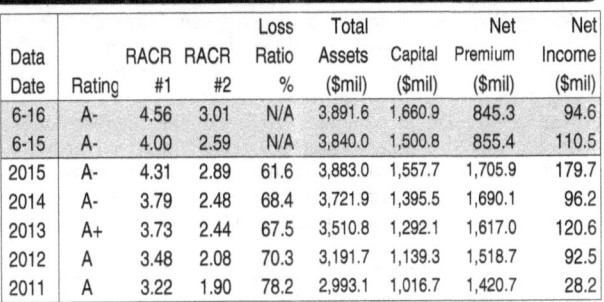

Risk-Adjusted Capital Ratio #2
(Severe Loss Scenario)

PACIFIC EMPLOYERS INS CO   B-   Good

Major Rating Factors: Fair overall results on stability tests (3.9 on a scale of 0 to 10) including potential drain of affiliation with Chubb Limited and weak results on operational trends. The largest net exposure for one risk is acceptable at 2.0% of capital. Strong long-term capitalization index (8.7) based on excellent current risk adjusted capital (severe and moderate loss scenarios). Moreover, capital levels have been consistent in recent years.

Other Rating Factors: Ample reserve history (7.7) that can protect against increases in claims costs. Excellent profitability (8.4) with operating gains in each of the last five years. Excellent liquidity (7.0) with ample operational cash flow and liquid investments.

Principal Business: Workers compensation (24%), other liability (20%), auto liability (16%), fire (15%), products liability (9%), allied lines (5%), and other lines (11%).

Principal Investments: Investment grade bonds (78%), misc. investments (21%), and cash (1%).

Investments in Affiliates: 6%

Group Affiliation: Chubb Limited

Licensed in: All states, the District of Columbia and Puerto Rico

Commenced Business: October 1923

Address: 1601 Chestnut St, Philadelphia, PA 19192

Phone: (215) 640-1000   **Domicile State:** PA   **NAIC Code:** 22748

Data Date	Rating	RACR #1	RACR #2	Loss Ratio %	Total Assets ($mil)	Capital ($mil)	Net Premium ($mil)	Net Income ($mil)
6-16	B-	3.08	2.15	N/A	3,697.7	1,278.3	385.0	35.9
6-15	B-	3.09	2.17	N/A	3,432.8	1,206.1	363.8	32.8
2015	B-	3.10	2.17	72.8	3,541.6	1,240.4	846.9	69.5
2014	B-	3.12	2.20	77.6	3,390.5	1,170.2	796.9	48.4
2013	B-	3.27	2.31	72.2	3,309.0	1,141.6	774.9	89.1
2012	B-	3.27	2.27	89.9	3,329.0	1,085.8	797.6	29.4
2011	B-	3.26	2.23	80.7	3,072.9	1,048.4	757.5	62.4

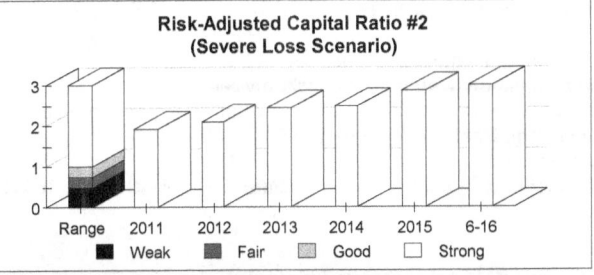

Rating Indexes

PACIFIC INDEMNITY CO   B   Good

Major Rating Factors: Good liquidity (6.8 on a scale of 0 to 10) with sufficient resources (cash flows and marketable investments) to handle a spike in claims. Fair overall results on stability tests (4.3) including weak results on operational trends. The largest net exposure for one risk is acceptable at 2.4% of capital.

Other Rating Factors: Strong long-term capitalization index (9.8) based on excellent current risk adjusted capital (severe and moderate loss scenarios), despite some fluctuation in capital levels. Ample reserve history (8.5) that helps to protect the company against sharp claims increases. Excellent profitability (8.6) with operating gains in each of the last five years. Return on equity has been good over the last five years, averaging 13.8%.

Principal Business: Homeowners multiple peril (45%), workers compensation (24%), inland marine (12%), commercial multiple peril (5%), other liability (4%), auto liability (3%), and other lines (7%).

Principal Investments: Investment grade bonds (93%) and misc. investments (7%).

Investments in Affiliates: 0%

Group Affiliation: Chubb Limited

Licensed in: All states except PR

Commenced Business: February 1926

Address: Two Plaza East Suite 1450, Milwaukee, WI 53202-3146

Phone: (908) 903-2000   **Domicile State:** WI   **NAIC Code:** 20346

Data Date	Rating	RACR #1	RACR #2	Loss Ratio %	Total Assets ($mil)	Capital ($mil)	Net Premium ($mil)	Net Income ($mil)
6-16	B	4.63	2.97	N/A	6,797.0	2,868.6	664.3	255.0
6-15	B	4.22	2.70	N/A	6,953.7	2,903.1	830.7	157.5
2015	B	4.47	2.85	56.7	6,916.0	2,930.2	1,691.9	449.7
2014	B	4.38	2.80	56.2	6,822.4	2,922.2	1,624.5	421.6
2013	B+	4.16	2.69	52.5	6,640.5	2,771.4	1,568.7	425.6
2012	B+	3.74	2.39	66.1	6,465.8	2,496.2	1,506.1	278.8
2011	A-	3.71	2.40	68.3	6,283.8	2,440.8	1,474.5	265.0

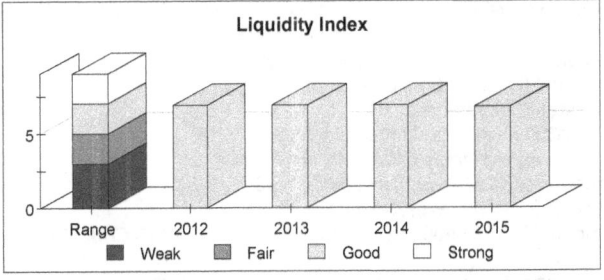

Liquidity Index

PACIFIC INS CO LTD   B   Good

Major Rating Factors: History of adequate reserve strength (5.9 on a scale of 0 to 10) as reserves have been consistently at an acceptable level. Good overall profitability index (6.0). Fair expense controls. Return on equity has been fair, averaging 9.3% over the past five years.

Other Rating Factors: Good liquidity (6.8) with sufficient resources (cash flows and marketable investments) to handle a spike in claims. Fair overall results on stability tests (4.6) including weak results on operational trends. Strong long-term capitalization index (9.2) based on excellent current risk adjusted capital (severe and moderate loss scenarios), despite some fluctuation in capital levels.

Principal Business: Other liability (50%), workers compensation (41%), auto liability (6%), and auto physical damage (3%).

Principal Investments: Investment grade bonds (92%) and misc. investments (8%).

Investments in Affiliates: None

Group Affiliation: Hartford Financial Services Inc

Licensed in: All states, the District of Columbia and Puerto Rico

Commenced Business: January 1995

Address: Hartford Plaza, Hartford, CT 06115

Phone: (860) 547-5000   **Domicile State:** CT   **NAIC Code:** 10046

Data Date	Rating	RACR #1	RACR #2	Loss Ratio %	Total Assets ($mil)	Capital ($mil)	Net Premium ($mil)	Net Income ($mil)
6-16	B	3.72	2.45	N/A	661.0	232.8	88.8	10.2
6-15	B	3.90	2.56	N/A	654.7	238.6	87.1	12.1
2015	B	3.67	2.43	66.1	638.0	222.3	179.1	24.6
2014	B	3.84	2.54	67.0	635.6	227.2	174.2	28.5
2013	B	3.76	2.50	68.8	619.3	218.5	169.1	20.3
2012	B	3.86	2.57	72.7	618.7	220.2	167.4	17.2
2011	B	3.84	2.59	78.5	619.3	218.8	167.4	13.4

Reserve Deficiency (as % of capital)

* Adequate & redundant reserves show as negatives

■ 1 Yr Dev   □ 2 Yr Dev

PARTNER REINSURANCE CO OF THE US   C   Fair

Major Rating Factors: Fair overall results on stability tests (4.3 on a scale of 0 to 10) including potential drain of affiliation with Giovanni Agnelli e C Sapaz, weak results on operational trends and negative cash flow from operations for 2015. The largest net exposure for one risk is conservative at 1.3% of capital. Good liquidity (6.8) with sufficient resources (cash flows and marketable investments) to handle a spike in claims.

Other Rating Factors: Strong long-term capitalization index (7.4) based on excellent current risk adjusted capital (severe and moderate loss scenarios), despite some fluctuation in capital levels. Ample reserve history (9.6) that helps to protect the company against sharp claims increases. Excellent profitability (8.1) with operating gains in each of the last five years. Return on equity has been good over the last five years, averaging 12.1%.

Principal Business: (This company is a reinsurer.)

Principal Investments: Investment grade bonds (92%), misc. investments (7%), and cash (1%).

Investments in Affiliates: 3%

Group Affiliation: Giovanni Agnelli e C Sapaz

Licensed in: All states except PR

Commenced Business: May 1980

Address: 245 Park Ave 24th Floor, New York, NY 10167

Phone: (203) 485-4200   **Domicile State:** NY   **NAIC Code:** 38636

Data Date	Rating	RACR #1	RACR #2	Loss Ratio %	Total Assets ($mil)	Capital ($mil)	Net Premium ($mil)	Net Income ($mil)
6-16	C	1.98	1.26	N/A	5,025.4	1,422.8	575.9	24.0
6-15	C-	1.85	1.19	N/A	4,975.5	1,437.4	596.4	72.1
2015	C	2.00	1.28	61.8	4,865.9	1,405.1	1,201.8	219.2
2014	C-	1.86	1.20	62.8	4,742.6	1,420.0	1,203.9	236.0
2013	C-	1.68	1.09	66.6	4,886.7	1,332.0	1,139.4	122.7
2012	C-	1.93	1.25	64.2	4,528.3	1,260.2	922.9	181.1
2011	D+	1.75	1.14	68.1	4,390.6	1,173.6	892.9	106.4

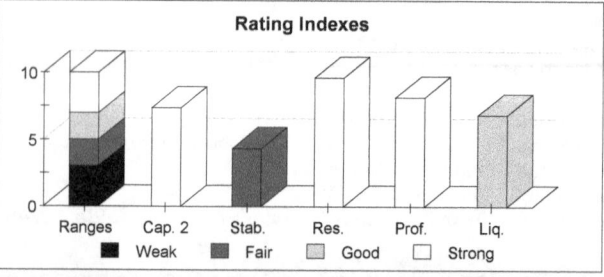

Rating Indexes

Ranges   Cap. 2   Stab.   Res.   Prof.   Liq.

■ Weak   ■ Fair   ▨ Good   □ Strong

PEERLESS INS CO   B-   Good

Major Rating Factors: Fair reserve development (4.7 on a scale of 0 to 10) as reserves have generally been sufficient to cover claims. Fair overall results on stability tests (3.9) including weak results on operational trends. The largest net exposure for one risk is high at 3.6% of capital.

Other Rating Factors: Good overall profitability index (6.4) despite modest operating losses during the first six months of 2016. Return on equity has been fair, averaging 7.7% over the past five years. Good liquidity (6.1) with sufficient resources (cash flows and marketable investments) to handle a spike in claims. Strong long-term capitalization index (7.5) based on excellent current risk adjusted capital (severe and moderate loss scenarios). Moreover, capital levels have been consistent in recent years.

Principal Business: Commercial multiple peril (29%), workers compensation (16%), auto liability (14%), inland marine (11%), other liability (10%), auto physical damage (7%), and other lines (14%).

Principal Investments: Investment grade bonds (72%), misc. investments (25%), and non investment grade bonds (5%).

Investments in Affiliates: 6%

Group Affiliation: Liberty Mutual Group

Licensed in: All states except HI, PR

Commenced Business: November 1903

Address: 62 Maple Ave, Keene, NH 03431

Phone: (617) 357-9500   **Domicile State:** NH   **NAIC Code:** 24198

Data Date	Rating	RACR #1	RACR #2	Loss Ratio %	Total Assets ($mil)	Capital ($mil)	Net Premium ($mil)	Net Income ($mil)
6-16	B-	2.09	1.45	N/A	13,004.0	3,347.6	2,536.1	-7.4
6-15	B-	1.92	1.32	N/A	12,868.5	3,169.4	2,457.8	140.5
2015	B-	2.07	1.44	68.4	13,172.4	3,316.7	5,126.4	304.6
2014	B-	1.88	1.30	70.0	12,800.9	3,058.9	5,075.4	247.2
2013	B-	1.60	1.09	73.5	13,621.2	2,786.4	5,827.5	151.5
2012	B-	1.71	1.33	66.7	7,629.8	1,887.3	2,751.4	349.4
2011	B-	1.45	1.18	74.0	7,361.8	1,802.5	2,679.6	23.6

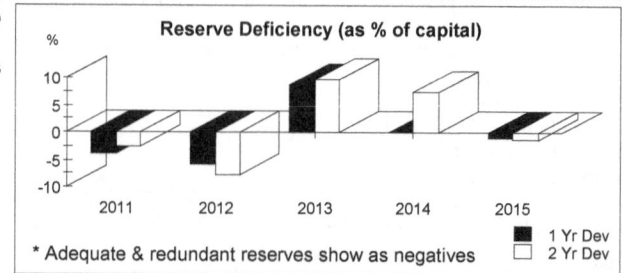

Reserve Deficiency (as % of capital)

* Adequate & redundant reserves show as negatives

■ 1 Yr Dev   □ 2 Yr Dev

PEKIN INS CO *

B+　　**Good**

Major Rating Factors: Good overall profitability index (5.4 on a scale of 0 to 10) despite operating losses during the first six months of 2016. Return on equity has been low, averaging 3.8% over the past five years. Good liquidity (6.5) with sufficient resources (cash flows and marketable investments) to handle a spike in claims.

Other Rating Factors: Good overall results on stability tests (5.0) despite weak results on operational trends. Strong long-term capitalization index (10.0) based on excellent current risk adjusted capital (severe and moderate loss scenarios), despite some fluctuation in capital levels. Ample reserve history (8.9) that helps to protect the company against sharp claims increases.

Principal Business: Commercial multiple peril (26%), workers compensation (20%), auto liability (19%), auto physical damage (14%), homeowners multiple peril (13%), other liability (4%), and other lines (3%).

Principal Investments: Investment grade bonds (85%) and misc. investments (15%).

Investments in Affiliates: 3%

Group Affiliation: Farmers Automobile Ins Assn

Licensed in: AZ, IL, IN, IA, MI, OH, WI

Commenced Business: July 1961

Address: 2505 Court St, Pekin, IL 61558

Phone: (309) 346-1161　**Domicile State:** IL　**NAIC Code:** 24228

Data Date	Rating	RACR #1	RACR #2	Loss Ratio %	Total Assets ($mil)	Capital ($mil)	Net Premium ($mil)	Net Income ($mil)
6-16	B+	4.40	3.08	N/A	312.8	124.7	59.4	-1.1
6-15	B+	4.60	3.22	N/A	301.7	122.6	57.1	3.2
2015	B+	4.60	3.27	71.5	295.9	125.7	120.2	5.5
2014	B+	4.63	3.29	74.3	281.2	118.7	113.8	5.5
2013	B+	4.79	3.39	75.4	281.9	117.1	107.1	4.4
2012	B+	4.80	3.43	75.1	262.7	111.6	100.5	7.6
2011	B+	4.65	3.29	83.5	250.0	104.3	92.1	2.0

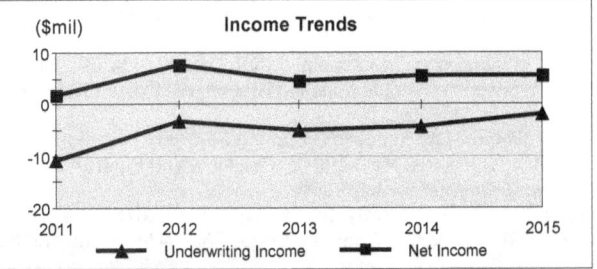

Income Trends

PEMCO MUTUAL INS CO

B-　　**Good**

Major Rating Factors: Fair overall results on stability tests (4.1 on a scale of 0 to 10) including potential drain of affiliation with PEMCO Corp and weak results on operational trends. History of adequate reserve strength (6.2) as reserves have been consistently at an acceptable level.

Other Rating Factors: Good overall profitability index (5.9) despite operating losses during 2012 and 2013. Good liquidity (5.9) with sufficient resources (cash flows and marketable investments) to handle a spike in claims. Strong long-term capitalization index (8.9) based on excellent current risk adjusted capital (severe and moderate loss scenarios), despite some fluctuation in capital levels.

Principal Business: Auto liability (47%), homeowners multiple peril (26%), auto physical damage (23%), other liability (2%), fire (2%), and inland marine (1%).

Principal Investments: Investment grade bonds (79%), real estate (11%), misc. investments (7%), and cash (3%).

Investments in Affiliates: 0%

Group Affiliation: PEMCO Corp

Licensed in: ID, OR, WA

Commenced Business: February 1949

Address: 325 Eastlake Ave E, Seattle, WA 98109-5466

Phone: (206) 628-4000　**Domicile State:** WA　**NAIC Code:** 24341

Data Date	Rating	RACR #1	RACR #2	Loss Ratio %	Total Assets ($mil)	Capital ($mil)	Net Premium ($mil)	Net Income ($mil)
6-16	B-	2.92	2.30	N/A	721.3	276.7	199.8	19.6
6-15	B-	2.97	2.35	N/A	707.2	268.7	186.3	23.6
2015	B-	2.71	2.18	77.0	706.8	259.0	396.6	10.2
2014	B-	2.81	2.33	77.5	687.4	254.5	370.1	24.0
2013	B-	2.82	2.34	72.2	629.4	237.4	346.0	-3.3
2012	B-	2.77	2.23	79.3	611.4	232.7	322.6	-16.3
2011	B-	3.05	2.51	72.8	603.8	241.6	315.4	8.2

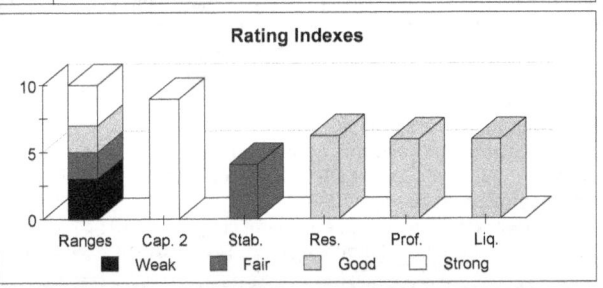

Rating Indexes

PENN NATIONAL SECURITY INS CO

B-　　**Good**

Major Rating Factors: Fair overall results on stability tests (4.4 on a scale of 0 to 10) including potential drain of affiliation with Pennsylvania National Ins Group and weak results on operational trends. History of adequate reserve strength (5.9) as reserves have been consistently at an acceptable level.

Other Rating Factors: Good overall profitability index (5.8) despite operating losses during 2011 and 2012. Return on equity has been low, averaging 3.0% over the past five years. Good liquidity (6.4) with sufficient resources (cash flows and marketable investments) to handle a spike in claims. Strong long-term capitalization index (9.2) based on excellent current risk adjusted capital (severe and moderate loss scenarios). Moreover, capital levels have been consistent in recent years.

Principal Business: Workers compensation (29%), auto liability (21%), fire (13%), other liability (11%), commercial multiple peril (10%), products liability (7%), and other lines (10%).

Principal Investments: Investment grade bonds (93%), misc. investments (6%), and cash (1%).

Investments in Affiliates: None

Group Affiliation: Pennsylvania National Ins Group

Licensed in: AL, DC, DE, MD, NJ, NC, PA, SC, TN, VA

Commenced Business: January 1989

Address: Two North Second Street, Harrisburg, PA 17101

Phone: (717) 234-4941　**Domicile State:** PA　**NAIC Code:** 32441

Data Date	Rating	RACR #1	RACR #2	Loss Ratio %	Total Assets ($mil)	Capital ($mil)	Net Premium ($mil)	Net Income ($mil)
6-16	B-	3.54	2.46	N/A	950.7	309.7	167.1	10.6
6-15	B-	3.34	2.32	N/A	937.3	287.0	162.4	0.9
2015	B-	3.56	2.50	65.0	914.5	299.7	330.9	13.3
2014	B-	3.46	2.43	64.8	894.1	287.2	326.5	18.4
2013	B-	3.04	2.07	65.5	843.2	282.1	315.8	10.3
2012	B-	2.92	2.00	77.4	804.2	254.5	309.5	-1.6
2011	B-	3.80	2.49	78.9	699.0	251.8	226.2	-2.0

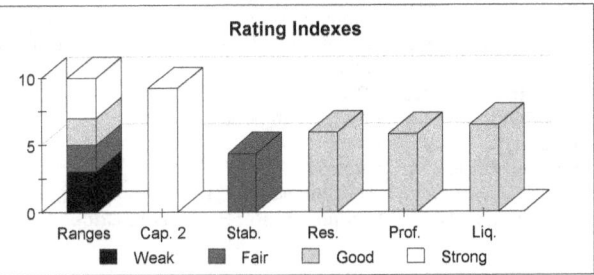

Rating Indexes

PENNSYLVANIA MANUFACTURERS ASN INS | C | Fair

Major Rating Factors: Fair overall results on stability tests (3.7 on a scale of 0 to 10) including weak results on operational trends. A history of deficient reserves (2.4) that places pressure on both capital and profits. In four of the last five years reserves (two year development) were between 18% and 34% deficient.

Other Rating Factors: Good overall profitability index (6.2) with small operating losses during 2014. Return on equity has been low, averaging 2.9% over the past five years. Good liquidity (6.6) with sufficient resources (cash flows and marketable investments) to handle a spike in claims. Strong long-term capitalization index (8.0) based on excellent current risk adjusted capital (severe and moderate loss scenarios), despite some fluctuation in capital levels.

Principal Business: Workers compensation (76%), inland marine (15%), auto liability (4%), other liability (2%), commercial multiple peril (2%), and auto physical damage (1%).

Principal Investments: Investment grade bonds (74%), misc. investments (25%), non investment grade bonds (3%), and real estate (1%).

Investments in Affiliates: None
Group Affiliation: Old Republic Group
Licensed in: All states, the District of Columbia and Puerto Rico
Commenced Business: July 1964
Address: 380 Sentry Parkway, Blue Bell, PA 19422-0754
Phone: (610) 397-5000 **Domicile State:** PA **NAIC Code:** 12262

Data Date	Rating	RACR #1	RACR #2	Loss Ratio %	Total Assets ($mil)	Capital ($mil)	Net Premium ($mil)	Net Income ($mil)
6-16	C	2.56	1.73	N/A	876.8	263.6	80.6	2.8
6-15	C	2.64	1.84	N/A	819.1	260.1	72.3	2.5
2015	C	2.65	1.79	83.1	821.9	251.7	134.7	6.0
2014	C	2.93	2.12	91.2	834.0	266.1	149.5	-2.1
2013	C	2.86	2.11	79.9	761.2	224.5	135.6	18.0
2012	C	2.91	2.22	79.3	730.6	225.4	143.1	1.0
2011	C	3.08	2.35	68.1	699.2	230.1	141.5	11.4

Old Republic Group
Composite Group Rating: B

Largest Group Members	Assets ($mil)	Rating
OLD REPUB INS CO	2669	B
OLD REPUBLIC GENERAL INS CORP	2004	B
GREAT WEST CASUALTY CO	1953	B
OLD REPUBLIC SECURITY ASR CO	1092	U
PENNSYLVANIA MANUFACTURERS ASN INS	822	C

PENNSYLVANIA NTL MUTUAL CAS INS CO | B- | Good

Major Rating Factors: Fair overall results on stability tests (4.5 on a scale of 0 to 10) including potential drain of affiliation with Pennsylvania National Ins Group, weak results on operational trends and negative cash flow from operations for 2015. History of adequate reserve strength (5.9) as reserves have been consistently at an acceptable level.

Other Rating Factors: Good overall profitability index (5.3) despite operating losses during 2011. Good liquidity (6.5) with sufficient resources (cash flows and marketable investments) to handle a spike in claims. Strong long-term capitalization index (7.8) based on excellent current risk adjusted capital (severe and moderate loss scenarios). Moreover, capital levels have been consistent in recent years.

Principal Business: Auto liability (25%), other liability (15%), auto physical damage (15%), homeowners multiple peril (14%), workers compensation (10%), commercial multiple peril (8%), and other lines (14%).

Principal Investments: Investment grade bonds (54%), misc. investments (43%), and cash (3%).

Investments in Affiliates: 34%
Group Affiliation: Pennsylvania National Ins Group
Licensed in: All states except CA, CT, HI, NV, NH, ND, WY, PR
Commenced Business: April 1920
Address: Two North Second Street, Harrisburg, PA 17101
Phone: (717) 234-4941 **Domicile State:** PA **NAIC Code:** 14990

Data Date	Rating	RACR #1	RACR #2	Loss Ratio %	Total Assets ($mil)	Capital ($mil)	Net Premium ($mil)	Net Income ($mil)
6-16	B-	1.73	1.56	N/A	1,268.3	592.1	167.1	12.8
6-15	B-	1.67	1.50	N/A	1,209.6	548.4	162.4	-2.1
2015	B-	1.71	1.56	65.0	1,233.6	571.4	330.9	14.6
2014	B-	1.72	1.55	64.8	1,192.6	558.8	326.5	23.8
2013	B-	1.65	1.47	65.5	1,125.8	541.2	315.8	22.4
2012	B-	1.59	1.42	77.4	1,036.8	473.7	279.4	13.9
2011	B-	1.49	1.32	80.5	1,071.1	451.2	291.5	-23.2

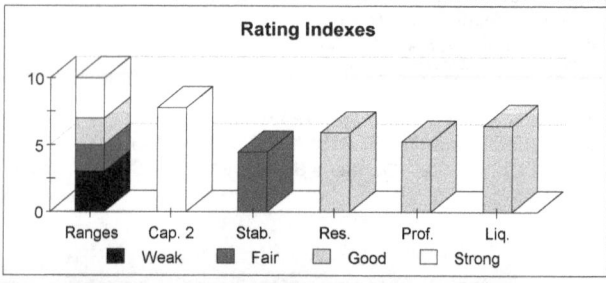

Rating Indexes

Ranges | Cap. 2 | Stab. | Res. | Prof. | Liq.
Weak | Fair | Good | Strong

PHILADELPHIA CBSP FOR INS OF HOUSES | B- | Good

Major Rating Factors: Fair overall results on stability tests (4.1 on a scale of 0 to 10) including potential drain of affiliation with Philadelphia Contrib Group, weak results on operational trends and negative cash flow from operations for 2015. Fair profitability index (4.4) with operating losses during 2011 and the first six months of 2016. Return on equity has been low, averaging 1.0% over the past five years.

Other Rating Factors: History of adequate reserve strength (6.2) as reserves have been consistently at an acceptable level. Good liquidity (6.7) with sufficient resources (cash flows and marketable investments) to handle a spike in claims. Strong long-term capitalization index (7.2) based on excellent current risk adjusted capital (severe and moderate loss scenarios), despite some fluctuation in capital levels.

Principal Business: (This company is a reinsurer.)
Principal Investments: Misc. investments (96%), investment grade bonds (2%), cash (1%), and real estate (1%).
Investments in Affiliates: 50%
Group Affiliation: Philadelphia Contrib Group
Licensed in: IL, NJ, NY, PA
Commenced Business: March 1753
Address: 212 S Fourth St, Philadelphia, PA 19106
Phone: (888) 627-1752 **Domicile State:** PA **NAIC Code:** 17930

Data Date	Rating	RACR #1	RACR #2	Loss Ratio %	Total Assets ($mil)	Capital ($mil)	Net Premium ($mil)	Net Income ($mil)
6-16	B-	1.31	1.13	N/A	312.6	233.7	18.1	-1.6
6-15	B-	1.30	1.12	N/A	320.1	236.7	18.5	0.2
2015	B-	1.31	1.14	75.1	309.5	233.1	36.6	1.1
2014	B-	1.32	1.13	85.2	326.3	245.0	37.1	8.3
2013	B-	1.30	1.10	63.0	316.6	234.8	35.8	6.0
2012	B-	1.27	1.08	87.8	266.3	187.5	33.1	1.1
2011	B-	1.26	1.08	97.7	254.9	181.0	32.0	-1.5

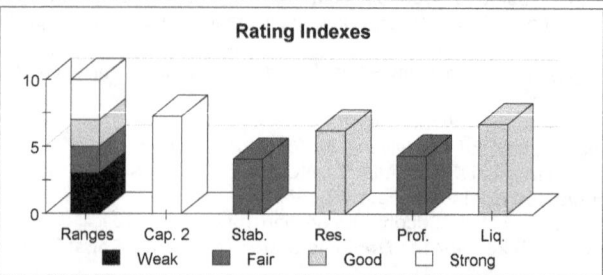

Rating Indexes

Ranges | Cap. 2 | Stab. | Res. | Prof. | Liq.
Weak | Fair | Good | Strong

PHILADELPHIA INDEMNITY INS CO   B-   Good

Major Rating Factors: Fair overall results on stability tests (4.6 on a scale of 0 to 10) including potential drain of affiliation with Tokio Marine Holdings Inc and weak results on operational trends. Good overall profitability index (5.5). Fair expense controls. Return on equity has been good over the last five years, averaging 12.5%.

Other Rating Factors: Good liquidity (6.6) with sufficient resources (cash flows and marketable investments) to handle a spike in claims. Strong long-term capitalization index (8.1) based on excellent current risk adjusted capital (severe and moderate loss scenarios), despite some fluctuation in capital levels. Ample reserve history (7.9) that can protect against increases in claims costs.

Principal Business: Commercial multiple peril (54%), other liability (22%), auto liability (14%), auto physical damage (5%), surety (3%), and allied lines (1%).

Principal Investments: Investment grade bonds (83%), misc. investments (12%), non investment grade bonds (4%), and cash (1%).

Investments in Affiliates: None
Group Affiliation: Tokio Marine Holdings Inc
Licensed in: All states except PR
Commenced Business: March 1927
Address: 1 Bala Plz #100, Bala Cynwyd, PA 19004-1401
Phone: (610) 617-7900   **Domicile State:** PA   **NAIC Code:** 18058

Data Date	Rating	RACR #1	RACR #2	Loss Ratio %	Total Assets ($mil)	Capital ($mil)	Net Premium ($mil)	Net Income ($mil)
6-16	B-	2.38	1.78	N/A	7,811.8	2,225.1	1,357.2	160.0
6-15	B-	2.57	1.91	N/A	7,579.2	2,485.0	1,289.0	140.9
2015	B-	2.30	1.73	60.5	7,361.5	2,047.5	2,696.2	311.2
2014	B-	2.55	1.92	61.5	7,182.2	2,337.4	2,553.3	306.1
2013	B	2.66	2.02	61.0	6,526.1	2,156.7	2,351.5	293.5
2012	B	3.01	2.32	62.8	6,047.3	2,017.2	2,124.8	229.6
2011	B	3.08	2.36	70.3	5,462.8	1,867.0	1,932.8	155.0

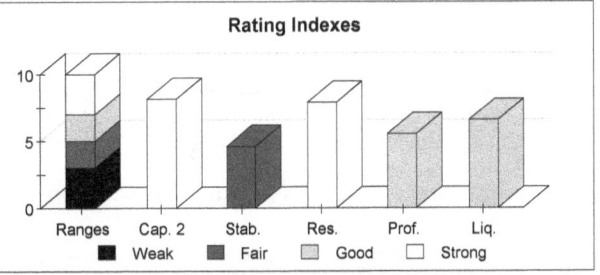

Rating Indexes

PHOENIX INS CO   B   Good

Major Rating Factors: Good liquidity (6.9 on a scale of 0 to 10) with sufficient resources (cash flows and marketable investments) to handle a spike in claims. Good overall results on stability tests (5.0) despite weak results on operational trends. Affiliation with Travelers Companies Inc is a strength.

Other Rating Factors: Strong long-term capitalization index (7.8) based on excellent current risk adjusted capital (severe and moderate loss scenarios). Moreover, capital levels have been consistent in recent years. Ample reserve history (8.2) that helps to protect the company against sharp claims increases. Excellent profitability (8.4) with operating gains in each of the last five years. Return on equity has been good over the last five years, averaging 10.6%.

Principal Business: Workers compensation (38%), commercial multiple peril (25%), auto liability (12%), homeowners multiple peril (8%), other liability (6%), inland marine (5%), and other lines (6%).

Principal Investments: Investment grade bonds (68%) and misc. investments (32%).

Investments in Affiliates: 27%
Group Affiliation: Travelers Companies Inc
Licensed in: All states except CA, PR
Commenced Business: July 1850
Address: One Tower Square, Hartford, CT 06183
Phone: (860) 277-0111   **Domicile State:** CT   **NAIC Code:** 25623

Data Date	Rating	RACR #1	RACR #2	Loss Ratio %	Total Assets ($mil)	Capital ($mil)	Net Premium ($mil)	Net Income ($mil)
6-16	B	1.83	1.61	N/A	4,300.2	1,840.2	524.0	52.5
6-15	B	1.69	1.51	N/A	4,259.6	1,839.1	505.2	67.2
2015	B	1.77	1.56	58.7	4,175.2	1,746.0	1,039.8	312.8
2014	B	1.62	1.45	60.5	4,196.2	1,739.4	1,009.4	207.8
2013	B	1.53	1.37	60.9	4,009.4	1,579.1	1,006.9	194.5
2012	B	1.43	1.27	68.4	3,860.1	1,390.6	978.0	98.5
2011	B	1.39	1.23	76.9	3,697.1	1,294.5	957.5	80.2

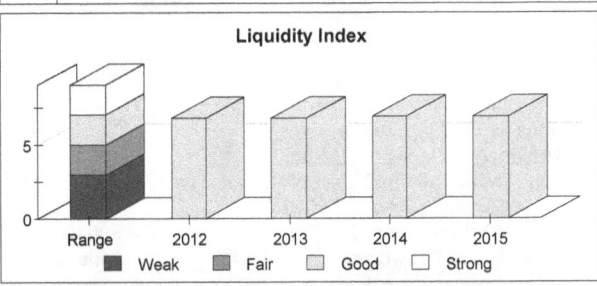

Liquidity Index

PHYSICIANS INS A MUTL CO   B-   Good

Major Rating Factors: Fair overall results on stability tests (4.1 on a scale of 0 to 10) including potential drain of affiliation with Washington State Health and weak results on operational trends. The largest net exposure for one risk is conservative at 1.2% of capital. Good overall profitability index (6.9). Good expense controls.

Other Rating Factors: Strong long-term capitalization index (10.0) based on excellent current risk adjusted capital (severe and moderate loss scenarios), despite some fluctuation in capital levels. Ample reserve history (9.4) that helps to protect the company against sharp claims increases. Excellent liquidity (7.5) with ample operational cash flow and liquid investments.

Principal Business: Medical malpractice (82%) and aggregate write-ins for other lines of business (18%).

Principal Investments: Investment grade bonds (80%), misc. investments (17%), and cash (3%).

Investments in Affiliates: 3%
Group Affiliation: Washington State Health
Licensed in: AK, AZ, CA, CO, GA, HI, ID, IL, MI, MT, NV, NM, OR, UT, WA, WY
Commenced Business: December 1981
Address: 1730 Minor Ave, Suite 1800, Seattle, WA 98101
Phone: (206) 343-7300   **Domicile State:** WA   **NAIC Code:** 40738

Data Date	Rating	RACR #1	RACR #2	Loss Ratio %	Total Assets ($mil)	Capital ($mil)	Net Premium ($mil)	Net Income ($mil)
6-16	B-	4.06	3.11	N/A	499.8	228.1	40.8	8.0
6-15	B-	4.11	3.16	N/A	486.6	227.5	36.5	6.4
2015	B-	4.08	3.15	84.4	471.0	220.0	76.3	6.9
2014	B-	4.08	3.16	82.1	468.3	222.6	76.7	11.6
2013	B-	4.11	3.20	85.2	454.0	211.9	72.9	5.6
2012	B-	4.03	3.21	80.1	428.5	195.4	67.8	8.2
2011	B-	3.76	3.01	82.7	421.0	186.0	73.3	8.4

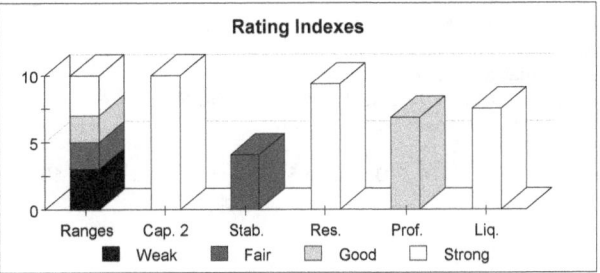

Rating Indexes

PIONEER STATE MUTUAL INS CO   B   Good

Major Rating Factors: Good liquidity (6.9 on a scale of 0 to 10) with sufficient resources (cash flows and marketable investments) to handle a spike in claims. Fair overall results on stability tests (4.7) including weak results on operational trends.

Other Rating Factors: Strong long-term capitalization index (10.0) based on excellent current risk adjusted capital (severe and moderate loss scenarios). Moreover, capital levels have been consistent in recent years. Ample reserve history (8.7) that helps to protect the company against sharp claims increases. Excellent profitability (8.7) with operating gains in each of the last five years.

Principal Business: Auto liability (38%), homeowners multiple peril (29%), auto physical damage (23%), farmowners multiple peril (5%), commercial multiple peril (2%), fire (1%), and workers compensation (1%).

Principal Investments: Investment grade bonds (62%), misc. investments (32%), cash (5%), and real estate (1%).

Investments in Affiliates: None

Group Affiliation: None

Licensed in: IN, MI

Commenced Business: June 1908

Address: 1510 N Elms Rd, Flint, MI 48532

Phone: (810) 733-2300   **Domicile State:** MI   **NAIC Code:** 18309

Data Date	Rating	RACR #1	RACR #2	Loss Ratio %	Total Assets ($mil)	Capital ($mil)	Net Premium ($mil)	Net Income ($mil)
6-16	B	5.12	3.26	N/A	526.4	309.7	91.6	15.0
6-15	B	4.79	3.04	N/A	489.5	285.1	86.1	8.3
2015	B	4.96	3.16	60.6	499.5	292.4	183.3	20.0
2014	B	4.69	2.98	66.3	472.2	277.9	174.4	16.0
2013	A	4.51	2.84	64.4	448.4	260.0	171.1	13.6
2012	A	5.03	3.25	66.2	400.9	233.1	163.7	11.8
2011	A	5.36	3.53	73.5	363.8	215.4	150.5	8.5

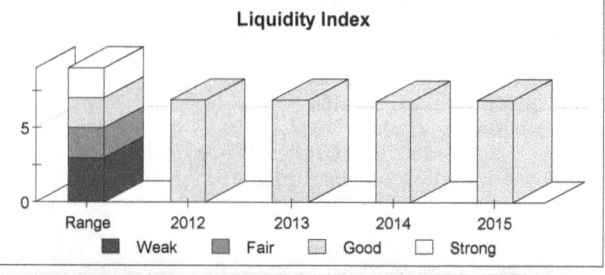

Liquidity Index

PRAETORIAN INS CO   C   Fair

Major Rating Factors: Fair reserve development (3.8 on a scale of 0 to 10) as reserves have generally been sufficient to cover claims. In 2013, the two year reserve development was 17% deficient. Fair overall results on stability tests (4.1) including weak results on operational trends and negative cash flow from operations for 2015.

Other Rating Factors: Weak profitability index (2.4) with operating losses during 2011, 2012, 2013 and 2014. Average return on equity over the last five years has been poor at -3.6%. Vulnerable liquidity (2.7) as a spike in claims may stretch capacity. Strong long-term capitalization index (7.5) based on excellent current risk adjusted capital (severe and moderate loss scenarios), despite some fluctuation in capital levels.

Principal Business: Homeowners multiple peril (24%), workers compensation (21%), auto liability (14%), auto physical damage (14%), commercial multiple peril (14%), inland marine (9%), and other liability (4%).

Principal Investments: Investment grade bonds (69%), misc. investments (23%), and cash (8%).

Investments in Affiliates: None

Group Affiliation: QBE Ins Group Ltd

Licensed in: All states, the District of Columbia and Puerto Rico

Commenced Business: August 1979

Address: 3435 Wilshire Blvd, Ste 700, Los Angeles, CA 90010

Phone: (212) 805-9700   **Domicile State:** PA   **NAIC Code:** 37257

Data Date	Rating	RACR #1	RACR #2	Loss Ratio %	Total Assets ($mil)	Capital ($mil)	Net Premium ($mil)	Net Income ($mil)
6-16	C	3.35	2.26	N/A	658.9	218.7	74.8	1.7
6-15	C	2.22	1.52	N/A	1,156.2	272.0	175.7	5.3
2015	C	2.23	1.49	63.9	871.5	243.9	300.7	13.3
2014	C	2.08	1.43	69.2	996.8	264.9	415.5	-7.1
2013	C-	1.67	1.14	75.2	971.9	248.4	400.0	-28.2
2012	C	1.64	1.12	73.5	1,109.4	316.3	545.2	-13.5
2011	B-	1.59	1.00	77.2	991.8	346.3	287.0	-27.0

Reserve Deficiency (as % of capital)

* Adequate & redundant reserves show as negatives

PREFERRED MUTUAL INS CO   B   Good

Major Rating Factors: Good overall profitability index (6.1 on a scale of 0 to 10) despite operating losses during 2011. Good liquidity (6.7) with sufficient resources (cash flows and marketable investments) to handle a spike in claims.

Other Rating Factors: Fair overall results on stability tests (4.3) including weak results on operational trends. Strong long-term capitalization index (9.8) based on excellent current risk adjusted capital (severe and moderate loss scenarios). Moreover, capital levels have been consistent in recent years. Ample reserve history (9.1) that helps to protect the company against sharp claims increases.

Principal Business: Homeowners multiple peril (42%), auto liability (18%), commercial multiple peril (18%), auto physical damage (13%), other liability (3%), fire (2%), and other lines (3%).

Principal Investments: Investment grade bonds (85%), misc. investments (11%), non investment grade bonds (5%), and real estate (1%).

Investments in Affiliates: None

Group Affiliation: None

Licensed in: CT, MA, NH, NJ, NY, NC, OH, PA, RI, SC

Commenced Business: January 1897

Address: One Preferred Way, New Berlin, NY 13411-1896

Phone: (607) 847-6161   **Domicile State:** NY   **NAIC Code:** 15024

Data Date	Rating	RACR #1	RACR #2	Loss Ratio %	Total Assets ($mil)	Capital ($mil)	Net Premium ($mil)	Net Income ($mil)
6-16	B	4.76	3.08	N/A	526.3	225.4	102.1	10.6
6-15	B	4.23	2.74	N/A	498.4	198.9	99.9	0.2
2015	B	4.54	2.99	67.8	522.7	212.7	204.4	18.6
2014	B	4.38	2.89	68.2	502.3	200.1	199.9	14.3
2013	B	3.43	2.25	65.5	484.8	185.3	193.6	13.3
2012	B	3.18	2.11	66.6	456.4	166.4	182.5	11.9
2011	B-	3.01	1.96	88.3	430.2	155.1	169.4	-14.3

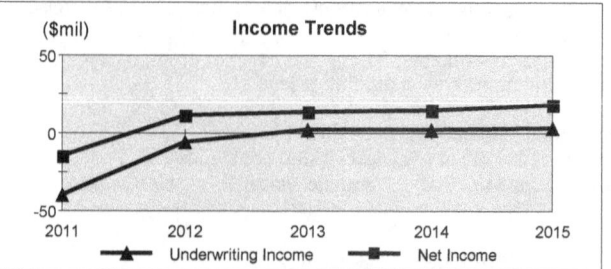

Income Trends

PREMIER INS CO OF MA　　　　　　　　　　　　B　　Good

Major Rating Factors: Good liquidity (6.8 on a scale of 0 to 10) with sufficient resources (cash flows and marketable investments) to handle a spike in claims. Fair reserve development (4.7) as reserves have generally been sufficient to cover claims.

Other Rating Factors: Fair overall results on stability tests (4.6) including weak results on operational trends and negative cash flow from operations for 2015. Strong long-term capitalization index (10.0) based on excellent current risk adjusted capital (severe and moderate loss scenarios), despite some fluctuation in capital levels. Excellent profitability (7.0) despite modest operating losses during 2011.

Principal Business: Auto liability (56%) and auto physical damage (44%).

Principal Investments: Investment grade bonds (106%).

Investments in Affiliates: None

Group Affiliation: Travelers Companies Inc

Licensed in: CT, MA

Commenced Business: July 1993

Address: One Tower Square, Hartford, CT 06183

Phone: (860) 277-0111　**Domicile State:** CT　**NAIC Code:** 12850

Data Date	Rating	RACR #1	RACR #2	Loss Ratio %	Total Assets ($mil)	Capital ($mil)	Net Premium ($mil)	Net Income ($mil)
6-16	B	16.94	13.77	N/A	280.7	243.1	23.0	11.0
6-15	B-	8.62	7.42	N/A	343.0	236.4	52.5	9.5
2015	B	11.11	9.56	59.7	307.2	234.0	73.8	19.7
2014	B-	7.27	6.53	69.1	350.4	227.6	112.3	13.5
2013	B	5.86	5.32	76.9	362.1	219.7	132.1	7.0
2012	B	5.06	4.61	75.6	375.0	218.6	153.4	12.2
2011	B	4.22	3.84	82.7	391.5	210.2	175.1	-0.6

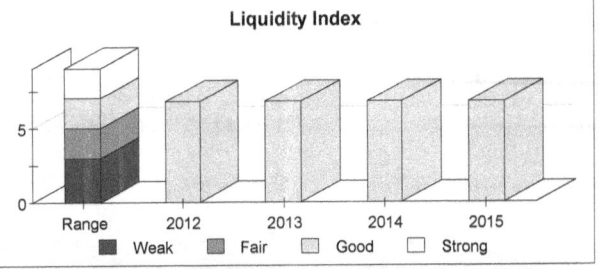

Liquidity Index

PRINCETON INS CO　　　　　　　　　　　　　C　　Fair

Major Rating Factors: Fair overall results on stability tests (3.8 on a scale of 0 to 10) including fair financial strength of affiliated Berkshire Hathaway and weak results on operational trends. Strong long-term capitalization index (10.0) based on excellent current risk adjusted capital (severe and moderate loss scenarios). Moreover, capital levels have been consistent in recent years.

Other Rating Factors: Ample reserve history (9.6) that helps to protect the company against sharp claims increases. Excellent profitability (8.4) with operating gains in each of the last five years. Superior liquidity (9.7) with ample operational cash flow and liquid investments.

Principal Business: (Not applicable due to unusual reinsurance transactions.)

Principal Investments: Investment grade bonds (61%), cash (44%), non investment grade bonds (1%), and real estate (1%).

Investments in Affiliates: None

Group Affiliation: Berkshire Hathaway

Licensed in: AZ, CT, DC, DE, GA, IL, IN, MD, MI, NJ, NY, NC, PA, SC, VA, WA, WV

Commenced Business: February 1982

Address: 746 Alexander Rd, CN-5322, Princeton, NJ 08543-5322

Phone: (609) 452-9404　**Domicile State:** NJ　**NAIC Code:** 42226

Data Date	Rating	RACR #1	RACR #2	Loss Ratio %	Total Assets ($mil)	Capital ($mil)	Net Premium ($mil)	Net Income ($mil)
6-16	C	7.11	5.45	N/A	667.4	464.1	14.8	10.4
6-15	C	6.72	4.89	N/A	662.0	463.9	15.9	7.6
2015	C	6.89	5.14	79.3	666.4	463.9	31.0	12.1
2014	C	6.60	4.76	78.1	665.0	460.7	33.1	13.9
2013	C	8.15	6.06	104.5	628.5	438.8	35.1	12.6
2012	C	10.70	7.63	99.4	585.5	412.6	-502.9	79.6
2011	C-	1.58	1.33	74.8	1,037.4	350.4	135.4	37.9

Berkshire Hathaway Composite Group Rating: B Largest Group Members	Assets ($mil)	Rating
NATIONAL INDEMNITY CO	161777	B
GOVERNMENT EMPLOYEES INS CO	24036	B
COLUMBIA INS CO	19102	C+
BERKSHIRE HATHAWAY LIFE INS CO OF NE	16287	C+
GENERAL REINS CORP	15320	C+

PROASSURANCE CASUALTY CO　　　　　　　　B-　　Good

Major Rating Factors: Fair profitability index (3.4 on a scale of 0 to 10). Fair expense controls. Return on equity has been fair, averaging 15.6% over the past five years. Fair overall results on stability tests (4.6) including weak results on operational trends.

Other Rating Factors: Strong long-term capitalization index (9.1) based on excellent current risk adjusted capital (severe and moderate loss scenarios), despite some fluctuation in capital levels. Ample reserve history (9.7) that helps to protect the company against sharp claims increases. Excellent liquidity (7.4) with ample operational cash flow and liquid investments.

Principal Business: Medical malpractice (92%) and other liability (8%).

Principal Investments: Investment grade bonds (73%), misc. investments (20%), and non investment grade bonds (7%).

Investments in Affiliates: None

Group Affiliation: ProAssurance Corp

Licensed in: AL, CA, CT, DE, FL, GA, IL, IN, IA, KS, KY, MD, MA, MI, MN, MS, MO, NE, NV, NJ, NY, ND, OH, PA, SC, SD, TN, VT, VA, WV, WI

Commenced Business: June 1980

Address: 2600 Professionals Dr, Okemos, MI 48805-0150

Phone: (517) 349-6500　**Domicile State:** MI　**NAIC Code:** 38954

Data Date	Rating	RACR #1	RACR #2	Loss Ratio %	Total Assets ($mil)	Capital ($mil)	Net Premium ($mil)	Net Income ($mil)
6-16	B-	2.98	2.22	N/A	1,074.4	373.6	73.2	16.2
6-15	B-	3.42	2.56	N/A	1,159.1	436.8	80.5	37.4
2015	B-	3.48	2.62	59.9	1,139.9	443.6	151.1	51.5
2014	B-	4.06	3.09	44.5	1,274.1	534.1	158.1	81.4
2013	B-	3.66	2.80	52.4	1,342.0	523.6	166.0	72.1
2012	B-	3.52	2.77	23.2	1,430.7	567.0	190.1	124.4
2011	B-	2.71	2.28	17.7	1,468.8	526.4	183.0	99.3

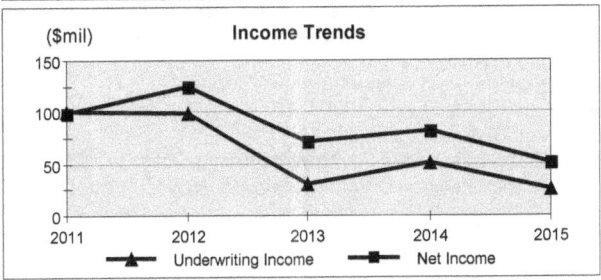

Income Trends

PROASSURANCE INDEMNTIY CO INC   C+   Fair

Major Rating Factors: Fair profitability index (3.0 on a scale of 0 to 10). Good expense controls. Return on equity has been fair, averaging 19.2% over the past five years. Fair overall results on stability tests (4.4) including weak results on operational trends.

Other Rating Factors: Strong long-term capitalization index (9.9) based on excellent current risk adjusted capital (severe and moderate loss scenarios), despite some fluctuation in capital levels. Ample reserve history (9.6) that helps to protect the company against sharp claims increases. Excellent liquidity (7.3) with ample operational cash flow and liquid investments.

Principal Business: Medical malpractice (98%) and other liability (2%).

Principal Investments: Investment grade bonds (66%), misc. investments (27%), non investment grade bonds (6%), and real estate (1%).

Investments in Affiliates: 1%

Group Affiliation: ProAssurance Corp

Licensed in: All states except NY, PR

Commenced Business: April 1977

Address: 100 Brookwood Pl, Birmingham, AL 35209

Phone: (205) 877-4400   **Domicile State:** AL   **NAIC Code:** 33391

Data Date	Rating	RACR #1	RACR #2	Loss Ratio %	Total Assets ($mil)	Capital ($mil)	Net Premium ($mil)	Net Income ($mil)
6-16	C+	4.04	3.03	N/A	1,394.4	596.4	97.1	38.2
6-15	B-	4.51	3.40	N/A	1,559.1	705.0	102.1	49.2
2015	C+	3.75	2.87	52.2	1,382.6	556.3	197.4	84.1
2014	B-	4.38	3.39	43.7	1,539.3	667.3	213.6	120.3
2013	B-	4.72	3.65	26.8	1,718.4	753.7	240.0	147.5
2012	B-	4.31	3.40	24.4	1,861.9	772.5	256.9	180.1
2011	B-	3.88	3.18	17.2	2,042.5	775.9	280.9	179.6

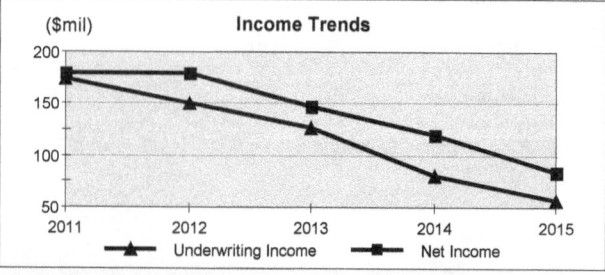

Income Trends

PROGRESSIVE CASUALTY INS CO   B-   Good

Major Rating Factors: Fair overall results on stability tests (4.5 on a scale of 0 to 10) including potential drain of affiliation with Progressive Group and weak results on operational trends. Good long-term capitalization index (5.6) based on good current risk adjusted capital (moderate loss scenario). Over the last several years, capital levels have remained relatively consistent.

Other Rating Factors: History of adequate reserve strength (6.2) as reserves have been consistently at an acceptable level. Excellent profitability (8.9) with operating gains in each of the last five years. Return on equity has been excellent over the last five years averaging 30.3%. Vulnerable liquidity (1.3) as a spike in claims may stretch capacity.

Principal Business: Auto liability (66%), auto physical damage (30%), inland marine (3%), other liability (1%), and homeowners multiple peril (1%).

Principal Investments: Misc. investments (49%), investment grade bonds (39%), real estate (9%), non investment grade bonds (2%), and cash (1%).

Investments in Affiliates: 18%

Group Affiliation: Progressive Group

Licensed in: All states except PR

Commenced Business: December 1956

Address: 6300 Wilson Mills Rd,W33, Mayfield Village, OH 44143-2182

Phone: (440) 461-5000   **Domicile State:** OH   **NAIC Code:** 24260

Data Date	Rating	RACR #1	RACR #2	Loss Ratio %	Total Assets ($mil)	Capital ($mil)	Net Premium ($mil)	Net Income ($mil)
6-16	B-	1.07	0.88	N/A	7,375.3	1,792.4	2,623.9	78.7
6-15	C+	1.11	0.92	N/A	6,922.2	1,836.1	2,437.4	139.0
2015	B-	0.98	0.81	71.7	6,245.6	1,610.1	5,050.3	450.8
2014	C+	0.98	0.83	71.8	6,061.7	1,611.4	4,891.7	528.0
2013	C+	0.94	0.80	72.9	5,781.0	1,543.1	4,657.8	501.3
2012	C+	0.90	0.78	75.1	5,332.1	1,448.5	4,447.9	406.7
2011	C+	0.84	0.73	72.0	5,129.9	1,359.9	4,151.1	556.8

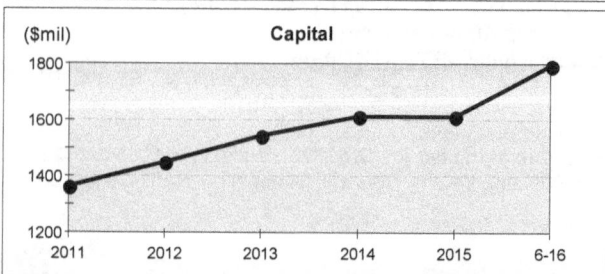

Capital

PROGRESSIVE DIRECT INS CO   C   Fair

Major Rating Factors: Fair overall results on stability tests (4.3 on a scale of 0 to 10) including potential drain of affiliation with Progressive Group and weak results on operational trends. Vulnerable liquidity (1.3) as a spike in claims may stretch capacity.

Other Rating Factors: Strong long-term capitalization index (7.2) based on excellent current risk adjusted capital (severe and moderate loss scenarios). Moreover, capital levels have been consistent in recent years. Ample reserve history (7.7) that can protect against increases in claims costs. Excellent profitability (8.9) with operating gains in each of the last five years. Return on equity has been excellent over the last five years averaging 16.2%.

Principal Business: Auto liability (63%), auto physical damage (35%), and inland marine (1%).

Principal Investments: Investment grade bonds (69%), misc. investments (26%), real estate (3%), and non investment grade bonds (2%).

Investments in Affiliates: None

Group Affiliation: Progressive Group

Licensed in: All states except TX, PR

Commenced Business: January 1987

Address: 6300 Wilson Mills Rd, Mayfield Village, OH 44143-2182

Phone: (440) 461-5000   **Domicile State:** OH   **NAIC Code:** 16322

Data Date	Rating	RACR #1	RACR #2	Loss Ratio %	Total Assets ($mil)	Capital ($mil)	Net Premium ($mil)	Net Income ($mil)
6-16	C	1.35	1.19	N/A	6,529.2	1,922.0	2,976.8	106.7
6-15	C-	1.34	1.17	N/A	5,720.5	1,706.6	2,589.5	119.5
2015	C	1.30	1.17	74.5	5,835.3	1,783.1	5,521.8	265.6
2014	C-	1.26	1.14	74.3	5,180.2	1,571.5	4,966.6	253.6
2013	C-	1.26	1.13	72.4	4,724.2	1,433.3	4,450.2	286.3
2012	C-	1.27	1.15	74.2	4,541.6	1,363.3	4,246.7	222.7
2011	C-	1.29	1.17	71.7	4,185.6	1,272.4	3,955.8	208.4

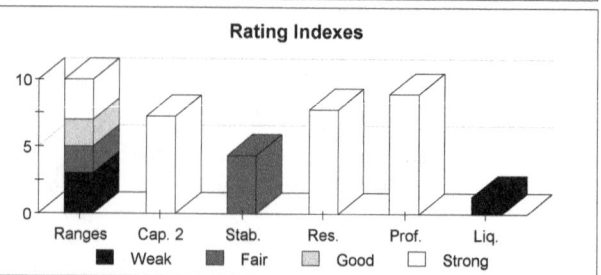

Rating Indexes

PROGRESSIVE NORTHERN INS CO
C+   Fair

Major Rating Factors: Fair overall results on stability tests (4.3 on a scale of 0 to 10) including potential drain of affiliation with Progressive Group and weak results on operational trends. History of adequate reserve strength (6.2) as reserves have been consistently at an acceptable level.

Other Rating Factors: Vulnerable liquidity (2.3) as a spike in claims may stretch capacity. Strong long-term capitalization index (7.2) based on excellent current risk adjusted capital (severe and moderate loss scenarios). Moreover, capital levels have been consistent in recent years. Excellent profitability (9.4) with operating gains in each of the last five years. Return on equity has been excellent over the last five years averaging 19.4%.

Principal Business: Auto liability (59%), auto physical damage (37%), inland marine (3%), homeowners multiple peril (1%), and other liability (1%).

Principal Investments: Investment grade bonds (80%) and misc. investments (20%).

Investments in Affiliates: None

Group Affiliation: Progressive Group

Licensed in: All states except AL, AR, CA, FL, MA, MO, NJ, ND, TN, TX, PR

Commenced Business: March 1981

Address: 8025 Excelsior Dr Suite 200, Madison, WI 53717

Phone: (440) 461-5000 **Domicile State:** WI **NAIC Code:** 38628

Data Date	Rating	RACR #1	RACR #2	Loss Ratio %	Total Assets ($mil)	Capital ($mil)	Net Premium ($mil)	Net Income ($mil)
6-16	C+	1.40	1.20	N/A	1,556.6	425.8	642.6	23.4
6-15	C+	1.47	1.26	N/A	1,471.6	430.5	596.9	40.4
2015	C+	1.32	1.16	71.7	1,408.4	396.9	1,236.8	88.2
2014	C+	1.30	1.16	71.8	1,349.2	385.8	1,198.0	90.7
2013	C+	1.30	1.15	72.9	1,305.4	370.7	1,140.7	78.6
2012	C+	1.30	1.16	75.1	1,245.7	347.5	1,089.3	51.9
2011	C+	1.33	1.20	72.0	1,167.3	329.7	1,016.6	63.7

Progressive Group
Composite Group Rating: C+

Largest Group Members	Assets ($mil)	Rating
PROGRESSIVE CASUALTY INS CO	6246	B-
PROGRESSIVE DIRECT INS CO	5835	C
UNITED FINANCIAL CASUALTY CO	2508	B-
PROGRESSIVE NORTHERN INS CO	1408	C+
PROGRESSIVE NORTHWESTERN INS CO	1372	C+

PROGRESSIVE NORTHWESTERN INS CO
C+   Fair

Major Rating Factors: Fair overall results on stability tests (4.4 on a scale of 0 to 10) including potential drain of affiliation with Progressive Group and weak results on operational trends. Fair liquidity (4.3) as cash resources may not be adequate to cover a spike in claims.

Other Rating Factors: History of adequate reserve strength (6.2) as reserves have been consistently at an acceptable level. Strong long-term capitalization index (7.3) based on excellent current risk adjusted capital (severe and moderate loss scenarios). Moreover, capital levels have been consistent in recent years. Excellent profitability (9.3) with operating gains in each of the last five years. Return on equity has been excellent over the last five years averaging 19.0%.

Principal Business: Auto liability (56%), auto physical damage (39%), inland marine (3%), and other liability (2%).

Principal Investments: Investment grade bonds (78%), misc. investments (20%), and non investment grade bonds (2%).

Investments in Affiliates: None

Group Affiliation: Progressive Group

Licensed in: All states except AL, FL, IL, MA, NH, PA, VT, WY, PR

Commenced Business: September 1983

Address: 6300 Wilson Mills Rd W33, Mayfield Village, OH 44143-2182

Phone: (440) 461-5000 **Domicile State:** OH **NAIC Code:** 42919

Data Date	Rating	RACR #1	RACR #2	Loss Ratio %	Total Assets ($mil)	Capital ($mil)	Net Premium ($mil)	Net Income ($mil)
6-16	C+	1.39	1.18	N/A	1,516.9	421.5	642.6	20.8
6-15	C+	1.45	1.23	N/A	1,420.6	425.8	596.9	37.7
2015	C+	1.31	1.16	71.7	1,372.0	396.2	1,236.8	84.5
2014	C+	1.30	1.15	71.8	1,313.5	387.6	1,198.0	92.9
2013	C+	1.30	1.13	72.9	1,267.5	371.6	1,140.7	66.0
2012	C+	1.29	1.14	75.1	1,207.2	347.3	1,089.3	57.0
2011	C+	1.32	1.17	72.0	1,127.0	328.5	1,016.6	65.5

Progressive Group
Composite Group Rating: C+

Largest Group Members	Assets ($mil)	Rating
PROGRESSIVE CASUALTY INS CO	6246	B-
PROGRESSIVE DIRECT INS CO	5835	C
UNITED FINANCIAL CASUALTY CO	2508	B-
PROGRESSIVE NORTHERN INS CO	1408	C+
PROGRESSIVE NORTHWESTERN INS CO	1372	C+

PROGRESSIVE PREFERRED INS CO
C   Fair

Major Rating Factors: Fair overall results on stability tests (3.9 on a scale of 0 to 10) including potential drain of affiliation with Progressive Group and weak results on operational trends. Fair liquidity (3.0) as cash resources may not be adequate to cover a spike in claims.

Other Rating Factors: History of adequate reserve strength (6.2) as reserves have been consistently at an acceptable level. Strong long-term capitalization index (7.4) based on excellent current risk adjusted capital (severe and moderate loss scenarios). Moreover, capital levels have been consistent in recent years. Excellent profitability (9.3) with operating gains in each of the last five years. Return on equity has been excellent over the last five years averaging 19.1%.

Principal Business: Auto liability (62%), auto physical damage (36%), inland marine (2%), other liability (1%), and homeowners multiple peril (1%).

Principal Investments: Investment grade bonds (99%) and non investment grade bonds (1%).

Investments in Affiliates: None

Group Affiliation: Progressive Group

Licensed in: AK, AZ, CO, DC, DE, GA, HI, ID, IN, IA, KY, ME, MD, MI, MN, MS, MO, MT, NE, NV, NJ, NM, NY, NC, OH, OK, OR, PA, RI, SC, SD, TN, TX, UT, VA, WA, WV

Commenced Business: April 1980

Address: 6300 Wilson Mills Rd, W33, Mayfield Village, OH 44143-2182

Phone: (440) 461-5000 **Domicile State:** OH **NAIC Code:** 37834

Data Date	Rating	RACR #1	RACR #2	Loss Ratio %	Total Assets ($mil)	Capital ($mil)	Net Premium ($mil)	Net Income ($mil)
6-16	C	1.41	1.24	N/A	774.8	211.0	321.3	10.0
6-15	C	1.51	1.34	N/A	734.0	217.5	298.5	20.0
2015	C	1.35	1.23	71.7	705.5	198.7	618.4	43.0
2014	C	1.35	1.23	71.8	677.1	195.9	599.0	49.6
2013	C	1.32	1.20	72.9	652.5	183.7	570.3	35.4
2012	C	1.32	1.21	75.1	620.7	174.3	544.6	22.7
2011	C	1.33	1.22	72.0	582.3	164.0	508.3	34.5

Progressive Group
Composite Group Rating: C+

Largest Group Members	Assets ($mil)	Rating
PROGRESSIVE CASUALTY INS CO	6246	B-
PROGRESSIVE DIRECT INS CO	5835	C
UNITED FINANCIAL CASUALTY CO	2508	B-
PROGRESSIVE NORTHERN INS CO	1408	C+
PROGRESSIVE NORTHWESTERN INS CO	1372	C+

PROGRESSIVE SPECIALTY INS CO   C   Fair

Major Rating Factors: Fair overall results on stability tests (3.9 on a scale of 0 to 10) including weak results on operational trends. Weak profitability index (2.5). Good expense controls. Return on equity has been fair, averaging 16.0% over the past five years.

Other Rating Factors: Vulnerable liquidity (2.3) as a spike in claims may stretch capacity. History of adequate reserve strength (6.1) as reserves have been consistently at an acceptable level. Strong long-term capitalization index (7.5) based on excellent current risk adjusted capital (severe and moderate loss scenarios), despite some fluctuation in capital levels.

Principal Business: Auto liability (63%), auto physical damage (35%), inland marine (1%), and homeowners multiple peril (1%).

Principal Investments: Investment grade bonds (67%), misc. investments (32%), and non investment grade bonds (1%).

Investments in Affiliates: None

Group Affiliation: Progressive Group

Licensed in: All states except LA, MA, NH, NC, WY, PR

Commenced Business: May 1976

Address: 6300 Wilson Mills Rd,W33, Mayfield Village, OH 44143-2182

Phone: (440) 461-5000   **Domicile State:** OH   **NAIC Code:** 32786

Data Date	Rating	RACR #1	RACR #2	Loss Ratio %	Total Assets ($mil)	Capital ($mil)	Net Premium ($mil)	Net Income ($mil)
6-16	C	1.71	1.43	N/A	979.7	310.4	374.8	15.6
6-15	C	1.99	1.67	N/A	965.2	349.0	348.2	22.1
2015	C	1.49	1.29	71.7	864.7	266.4	721.5	48.3
2014	C	1.78	1.54	71.8	880.2	314.1	698.8	56.9
2013	C	2.27	1.96	72.9	941.3	386.2	665.4	87.0
2012	C	2.94	2.54	75.1	994.3	467.3	635.4	60.3
2011	C	3.90	3.38	72.0	1,065.8	574.7	593.0	64.0

Progressive Group Composite Group Rating: C+ Largest Group Members	Assets ($mil)	Rating
PROGRESSIVE CASUALTY INS CO	6246	B-
PROGRESSIVE DIRECT INS CO	5835	C
UNITED FINANCIAL CASUALTY CO	2508	B-
PROGRESSIVE NORTHERN INS CO	1408	C+
PROGRESSIVE NORTHWESTERN INS CO	1372	C+

PROPERTY-OWNERS INS CO *   B+   Good

Major Rating Factors: Good liquidity (6.7 on a scale of 0 to 10) with sufficient resources (cash flows and marketable investments) to handle a spike in claims. Good overall results on stability tests (5.1) despite weak results on operational trends.

Other Rating Factors: Strong long-term capitalization index (8.5) based on excellent current risk adjusted capital (severe and moderate loss scenarios). Moreover, capital levels have been consistent in recent years. Excellent profitability (8.2) with operating gains in each of the last five years. Fair reserve development (4.8) as reserves have generally been sufficient to cover claims.

Principal Business: Commercial multiple peril (39%), homeowners multiple peril (23%), auto liability (10%), workers compensation (10%), auto physical damage (7%), other liability (4%), and other lines (8%).

Principal Investments: Investment grade bonds (82%), misc. investments (17%), and cash (1%).

Investments in Affiliates: None

Group Affiliation: Auto-Owners Group

Licensed in: AL, AR, GA, IL, IN, IA, KY, MI, MO, NE, NV, ND, SC, SD, UT, VA, WI

Commenced Business: September 1976

Address: 3950 W Delphi Pike, Marion, IN 46952-9266

Phone: (517) 323-1200   **Domicile State:** IN   **NAIC Code:** 32905

Data Date	Rating	RACR #1	RACR #2	Loss Ratio %	Total Assets ($mil)	Capital ($mil)	Net Premium ($mil)	Net Income ($mil)
6-16	B+	3.41	1.97	N/A	257.1	121.9	42.9	4.6
6-15	B+	3.41	2.03	N/A	222.7	112.6	37.6	3.1
2015	B+	3.46	1.99	60.7	232.4	115.7	78.9	6.5
2014	B+	3.53	2.09	64.6	216.2	109.6	72.4	5.0
2013	A	3.83	2.21	55.5	209.7	104.5	70.0	9.0
2012	A	3.32	1.77	61.3	193.9	93.5	63.5	7.5
2011	A	2.59	1.42	80.2	179.5	85.3	63.3	1.6

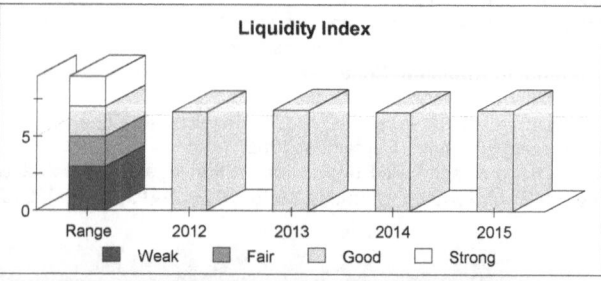

Liquidity Index

Range | 2012 | 2013 | 2014 | 2015
■ Weak ▨ Fair ▥ Good ☐ Strong

PROTECTIVE INS CO   B   Good

Major Rating Factors: Good overall profitability index (6.5 on a scale of 0 to 10) despite operating losses during 2011. Return on equity has been fair, averaging 5.1% over the past five years. Good liquidity (6.7) with sufficient resources (cash flows and marketable investments) to handle a spike in claims.

Other Rating Factors: Fair overall results on stability tests (4.9) including weak results on operational trends. Strong long-term capitalization index (7.2) based on excellent current risk adjusted capital (severe and moderate loss scenarios), despite some fluctuation in capital levels. Ample reserve history (8.7) that helps to protect the company against sharp claims increases.

Principal Business: Workers compensation (46%), other liability (18%), auto physical damage (17%), auto liability (16%), group accident & health (3%), and surety (1%).

Principal Investments: Misc. investments (58%), investment grade bonds (32%), non investment grade bonds (8%), and real estate (4%).

Investments in Affiliates: 27%

Group Affiliation: Protective Ins Group

Licensed in: All states, the District of Columbia and Puerto Rico

Commenced Business: December 1954

Address: 1099 N Meridian St, Indianapolis, IN 46204

Phone: (317) 636-9800   **Domicile State:** IN   **NAIC Code:** 12416

Data Date	Rating	RACR #1	RACR #2	Loss Ratio %	Total Assets ($mil)	Capital ($mil)	Net Premium ($mil)	Net Income ($mil)
6-16	B	1.57	1.15	N/A	763.4	397.9	126.0	24.1
6-15	B	1.50	1.08	N/A	776.0	402.3	120.7	13.3
2015	B	1.54	1.13	57.4	753.5	389.4	233.2	27.1
2014	B	1.51	1.09	56.7	791.8	397.4	235.5	29.7
2013	A-	1.42	1.03	57.6	741.1	375.8	228.0	28.6
2012	A-	1.30	0.94	57.6	680.1	337.5	203.4	24.0
2011	A-	1.22	0.89	93.6	633.5	312.3	199.2	-23.0

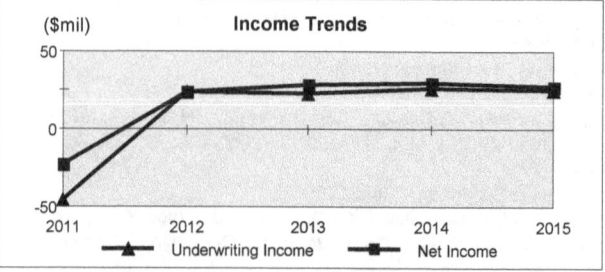

($mil)   Income Trends

2011 | 2012 | 2013 | 2014 | 2015
▲ Underwriting Income ■ Net Income

QBE INS CORP   B-   Good

Major Rating Factors: Fair reserve development (3.8 on a scale of 0 to 10) as reserves have generally been sufficient to cover claims. In 2011, the two year reserve development was 24% deficient. Fair profitability index (3.6) with operating losses during 2011, 2012, 2013 and the first six months of 2016. Average return on equity over the last five years has been poor at -2.3%.

Other Rating Factors: Fair liquidity (4.5) as cash resources may not be adequate to cover a spike in claims. Fair overall results on stability tests (4.8) including weak results on operational trends, negative cash flow from operations for 2015 and excessive premium growth. Strong long-term capitalization index (7.9) based on excellent current risk adjusted capital (severe and moderate loss scenarios), despite some fluctuation in capital levels.

Principal Business: Commercial multiple peril (31%), group accident & health (13%), homeowners multiple peril (12%), other liability (11%), workers compensation (8%), auto physical damage (7%), and other lines (19%).

Principal Investments: Misc. investments (56%), investment grade bonds (37%), non investment grade bonds (5%), and cash (2%).

Investments in Affiliates: 17%

Group Affiliation: QBE Ins Group Ltd

Licensed in: All states except PR

Commenced Business: October 1980

Address: 1209 Orange St, Wilmington, DE 19801

Phone: (212) 805-9700   **Domicile State:** PA   **NAIC Code:** 39217

Data Date	Rating	RACR #1	RACR #2	Loss Ratio %	Total Assets ($mil)	Capital ($mil)	Net Premium ($mil)	Net Income ($mil)
6-16	B-	2.18	1.54	N/A	2,608.9	721.7	455.0	-2.3
6-15	C+	2.21	1.68	N/A	2,307.3	670.9	337.1	8.4
2015	B-	2.46	1.81	63.9	2,135.7	735.7	597.0	28.8
2014	C+	2.08	1.58	69.2	2,113.3	681.2	742.1	4.2
2013	C	1.95	1.49	75.2	2,138.2	678.7	750.5	-61.1
2012	C	2.04	1.55	73.5	2,188.1	802.4	473.1	-24.3
2011	C	1.77	1.16	50.9	2,424.9	840.8	1,600.7	-40.9

Reserve Deficiency (as % of capital)

* Adequate & redundant reserves show as negatives
■ 1 Yr Dev   □ 2 Yr Dev

QBE REINS CORP   B   Good

Major Rating Factors: History of adequate reserve strength (5.9 on a scale of 0 to 10) as reserves have been consistently at an acceptable level. Good liquidity (6.4) with sufficient resources (cash flows and marketable investments) to handle a spike in claims.

Other Rating Factors: Fair overall results on stability tests (4.9) including potential drain of affiliation with QBE Ins Group Ltd and weak results on operational trends. Fair profitability index (3.8) with modest operating losses during the first six months of 2016. Return on equity has been low, averaging 0.6% over the past five years. Strong long-term capitalization index (7.4) based on excellent current risk adjusted capital (severe and moderate loss scenarios), despite some fluctuation in capital levels.

Principal Business: (This company is a reinsurer.)

Principal Investments: Misc. investments (89%), investment grade bonds (9%), and cash (2%).

Investments in Affiliates: 74%

Group Affiliation: QBE Ins Group Ltd

Licensed in: All states, the District of Columbia and Puerto Rico

Commenced Business: October 1964

Address: 88 Pine Street, 16th Floorr, New York, NY 10005

Phone: (212) 805-9700   **Domicile State:** PA   **NAIC Code:** 10219

Data Date	Rating	RACR #1	RACR #2	Loss Ratio %	Total Assets ($mil)	Capital ($mil)	Net Premium ($mil)	Net Income ($mil)
6-16	B	1.35	1.33	N/A	1,212.7	830.0	90.4	-1.4
6-15	B	1.44	1.40	N/A	1,312.3	824.6	98.9	3.6
2015	B	1.33	1.31	63.9	1,148.2	813.3	186.6	11.9
2014	B	1.44	1.41	69.2	1,176.1	826.8	168.3	5.0
2013	B	1.40	1.36	75.2	1,232.9	814.7	210.4	0.0
2012	B	1.33	1.28	73.5	1,545.6	943.1	333.1	5.0
2011	B	1.39	1.30	64.6	1,750.9	1,080.5	369.6	11.7

Reserve Deficiency (as % of capital)

* Adequate & redundant reserves show as negatives
■ 1 Yr Dev   □ 2 Yr Dev

QUINCY MUTUAL FIRE INS CO   B   Good

Major Rating Factors: Good overall profitability index (5.7 on a scale of 0 to 10) despite operating losses during 2011. Good liquidity (6.9) with sufficient resources (cash flows and marketable investments) to handle a spike in claims.

Other Rating Factors: Fair overall results on stability tests (4.7) including potential drain of affiliation with Quincy Mutual Group and weak results on operational trends. Strong long-term capitalization index (9.2) based on excellent current risk adjusted capital (severe and moderate loss scenarios), despite some fluctuation in capital levels. Ample reserve history (7.8) that can protect against increases in claims costs.

Principal Business: Homeowners multiple peril (34%), auto liability (24%), auto physical damage (19%), commercial multiple peril (18%), allied lines (3%), and fire (2%).

Principal Investments: Misc. investments (56%), investment grade bonds (39%), non investment grade bonds (3%), cash (1%), and real estate (1%).

Investments in Affiliates: 3%

Group Affiliation: Quincy Mutual Group

Licensed in: CT, ME, MA, NH, NJ, NY, PA, RI

Commenced Business: May 1851

Address: 57 Washington St, Quincy, MA 02169

Phone: (617) 770-5100   **Domicile State:** MA   **NAIC Code:** 15067

Data Date	Rating	RACR #1	RACR #2	Loss Ratio %	Total Assets ($mil)	Capital ($mil)	Net Premium ($mil)	Net Income ($mil)
6-16	B	3.95	2.49	N/A	1,536.0	1,007.8	145.3	16.5
6-15	B	3.89	2.45	N/A	1,505.3	966.2	135.2	-19.7
2015	B	3.95	2.50	78.5	1,508.0	977.0	313.3	14.6
2014	B	3.82	2.40	45.2	1,510.5	994.7	269.3	77.0
2013	B	3.71	2.30	55.6	1,471.1	927.1	296.3	49.8
2012	B	3.72	2.36	61.7	1,310.9	796.7	284.3	47.8
2011	B	3.55	2.30	101.1	1,186.1	729.1	276.3	-12.9

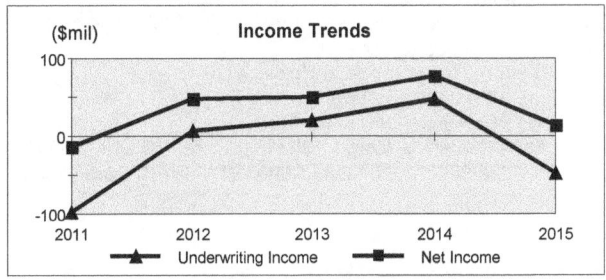

Income Trends

▲ Underwriting Income   ■ Net Income

RADIAN GUARANTY INC   D+   Weak

Major Rating Factors: Weak overall results on stability tests (2.4 on a scale of 0 to 10) including weak results on operational trends. Fair reserve development (3.4) as the level of reserves has at times been insufficient to cover claims. Deficiencies in the two year reserve development occurred in three of the previous five years and ranged between 17% and 74%.

Other Rating Factors: Fair profitability index (3.9) with operating losses during 2011, 2012 and 2013. Average return on equity over the last five years has been poor at -0.5%. Good liquidity (6.8) with sufficient resources (cash flows and marketable investments) to handle a spike in claims. Strong long-term capitalization index (7.7) based on excellent current risk adjusted capital (severe and moderate loss scenarios), despite some fluctuation in capital levels.

Principal Business: Mortgage guaranty (100%).

Principal Investments: Investment grade bonds (102%) and cash (1%).

Investments in Affiliates: 1%

Group Affiliation: Radian Group Inc

Licensed in: All states except PR

Commenced Business: April 1977

Address: 1601 Market Street, 12th Floor, Philadelphia, PA 19103

Phone: (800) 523-1988   **Domicile State:** PA   **NAIC Code:** 33790

Data Date	Rating	RACR #1	RACR #2	Loss Ratio %	Total Assets ($mil)	Capital ($mil)	Net Premium ($mil)	Net Income ($mil)
6-16	D+	1.78	1.51	N/A	3,805.1	1,387.9	380.4	240.0
6-15	D	0.91	0.83	N/A	3,636.6	1,367.0	406.5	295.7
2015	D+	2.04	1.73	22.2	4,009.0	1,686.5	845.7	754.8
2014	D	0.85	0.76	33.0	3,643.3	1,325.2	797.5	273.7
2013	D	0.66	0.59	81.6	3,657.5	1,317.8	814.4	-23.8
2012	D	0.45	0.38	133.2	3,872.0	926.1	686.8	-175.9
2011	D	0.45	0.38	189.8	3,821.8	843.2	631.7	-545.1

Rating Indexes

REDWOOD FIRE & CAS INS CO   C   Fair

Major Rating Factors: Fair overall results on stability tests (3.6 on a scale of 0 to 10) including weak results on operational trends and weak risk adjusted capital in prior years. Fair long-term capitalization index (3.3) based on weak current risk adjusted capital (severe loss scenario).

Other Rating Factors: Ample reserve history (7.9) that can protect against increases in claims costs. Excellent profitability (8.0) with operating gains in each of the last five years. Excellent liquidity (7.3) with ample operational cash flow and liquid investments.

Principal Business: Workers compensation (80%), auto liability (15%), auto physical damage (4%), and inland marine (1%).

Principal Investments: Investment grade bonds (52%), misc. investments (40%), and cash (8%).

Investments in Affiliates: None

Group Affiliation: Berkshire-Hathaway

Licensed in: All states except FL, OR, PA, PR

Commenced Business: January 1970

Address: 9290 W Dodge Road,Ste 300, Omaha, NE 68114-3363

Phone: (402) 393-7255   **Domicile State:** NE   **NAIC Code:** 11673

Data Date	Rating	RACR #1	RACR #2	Loss Ratio %	Total Assets ($mil)	Capital ($mil)	Net Premium ($mil)	Net Income ($mil)
6-16	C	0.79	0.49	N/A	1,512.1	574.0	166.0	13.6
6-15	C	0.62	0.40	N/A	1,336.5	525.7	200.5	5.2
2015	C	0.78	0.49	70.2	1,428.0	552.8	401.2	46.8
2014	C	0.73	0.47	72.6	1,257.7	533.3	377.0	5.1
2013	C	0.93	0.59	66.9	1,031.3	506.0	286.9	49.2
2012	B-	1.50	0.92	53.9	761.7	426.0	97.7	3.1
2011	B	6.13	2.65	N/A	747.3	452.7	15.1	38.8

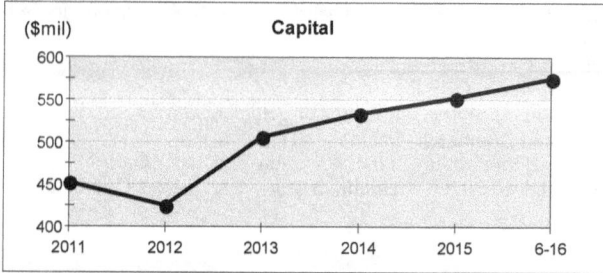

Capital

RENAISSANCE RE US INC   B-   Good

Major Rating Factors: Fair profitability index (4.6 on a scale of 0 to 10). Fair expense controls. Return on equity has been fair, averaging 11.2% over the past five years. Fair overall results on stability tests (3.6) including weak results on operational trends and negative cash flow from operations for 2015. The largest net exposure for one risk is excessive at 5.2% of capital.

Other Rating Factors: Good liquidity (6.8) with sufficient resources (cash flows and marketable investments) to handle a spike in claims. Strong long-term capitalization index (7.9) based on excellent current risk adjusted capital (severe and moderate loss scenarios), despite some fluctuation in capital levels. Ample reserve history (9.5) that helps to protect the company against sharp claims increases.

Principal Business: (This company is a reinsurer.)

Principal Investments: Investment grade bonds (100%) and cash (2%).

Investments in Affiliates: None

Group Affiliation: RenaissanceRe Holdings Ltd

Licensed in: All states except PR

Commenced Business: December 1995

Address: 5801 Centennial Way, LA303, Baltimore, MD 21209-3653

Phone: (212) 238-9600   **Domicile State:** MD   **NAIC Code:** 10357

Data Date	Rating	RACR #1	RACR #2	Loss Ratio %	Total Assets ($mil)	Capital ($mil)	Net Premium ($mil)	Net Income ($mil)
6-16	B-	2.93	1.82	N/A	1,600.5	546.1	133.1	20.7
6-15	B-	2.83	1.75	N/A	1,623.9	549.2	158.1	19.1
2015	B-	2.74	1.71	51.6	1,508.0	521.5	323.7	58.8
2014	B-	2.67	1.66	52.3	1,564.7	531.4	339.3	62.1
2013	B-	2.46	1.53	43.4	1,620.3	549.2	395.4	93.2
2012	B-	2.39	1.53	57.0	1,661.8	555.4	381.6	73.0
2011	C+	2.20	1.43	74.7	1,667.7	529.9	396.5	25.1

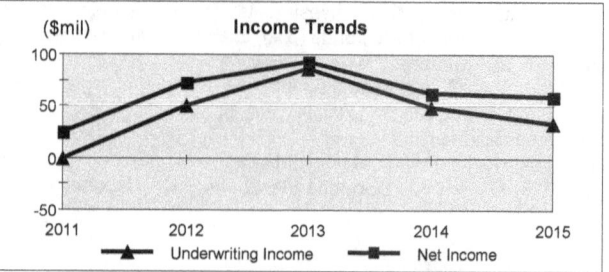

Income Trends

REPUBLIC INDEMNITY CO OF AMERICA   B-   Good

Major Rating Factors: Fair overall results on stability tests (4.7 on a scale of 0 to 10) including potential drain of affiliation with American Financial Group Inc and weak results on operational trends. Good overall long-term capitalization (5.3) based on good current risk adjusted capital (moderate loss scenario). However, capital levels have fluctuated somewhat during past years.

Other Rating Factors: Good liquidity (6.5) with sufficient resources (cash flows and marketable investments) to handle a spike in claims. Ample reserve history (9.2) that helps to protect the company against sharp claims increases. Excellent profitability (7.0) with operating gains in each of the last five years.

Principal Business: Workers compensation (100%).

Principal Investments: Investment grade bonds (88%), misc. investments (10%), cash (1%), and non investment grade bonds (1%).

Investments in Affiliates: 2%

Group Affiliation: American Financial Group Inc

Licensed in: All states except CT, MA, MN, NH, NJ, NY, ND, PA, VT, WY, PR

Commenced Business: March 1973

Address: 15821 Ventura Blvd, Suite 370, Encino, CA 91436

Phone: (818) 990-9860   **Domicile State:** CA   **NAIC Code:** 22179

Data Date	Rating	RACR #1	RACR #2	Loss Ratio %	Total Assets ($mil)	Capital ($mil)	Net Premium ($mil)	Net Income ($mil)
6-16	B-	1.00	0.75	N/A	2,274.5	504.1	393.3	29.2
6-15	C+	1.08	0.81	N/A	2,316.3	547.0	388.3	36.4
2015	C+	1.10	0.82	65.0	2,292.4	537.3	793.3	98.9
2014	C+	1.13	0.83	67.0	2,229.5	503.6	665.9	6.7
2013	C+	1.72	1.24	68.6	847.7	252.3	209.3	30.4
2012	B-	2.21	1.54	80.2	858.5	279.8	158.4	11.9
2011	B-	2.42	1.66	75.4	830.8	278.8	131.4	21.0

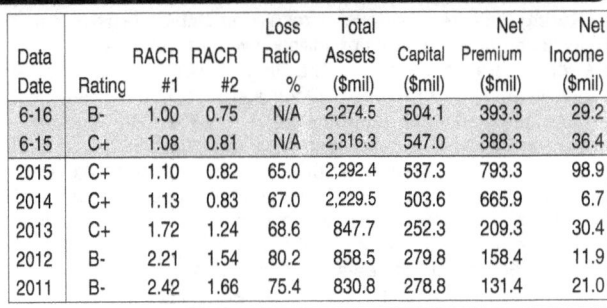

REPUBLIC UNDERWRITERS INS CO   C   Fair

Major Rating Factors: Fair overall results on stability tests (4.1 on a scale of 0 to 10) including potential drain of affiliation with AmTrust Financial Services Inc and weak results on operational trends. Fair reserve development (3.7) as reserves have generally been sufficient to cover claims.

Other Rating Factors: Weak profitability index (2.8) with operating losses during 2011 and the first six months of 2016. Average return on equity over the last five years has been poor at -8.2%. Good liquidity (6.6) with sufficient resources (cash flows and marketable investments) to handle a spike in claims. Strong long-term capitalization index (7.8) based on excellent current risk adjusted capital (severe and moderate loss scenarios), despite some fluctuation in capital levels.

Principal Business: Workers compensation (81%), homeowners multiple peril (7%), commercial multiple peril (4%), auto liability (4%), auto physical damage (2%), allied lines (1%), and fire (1%).

Principal Investments: Investment grade bonds (69%), misc. investments (28%), and cash (3%).

Investments in Affiliates: 14%

Group Affiliation: AmTrust Financial Services Inc

Licensed in: AZ, AR, CA, CO, CT, KS, LA, MS, NV, NM, OK, TX, UT

Commenced Business: October 1965

Address: 2727 Turtle Creek Blvd, Dallas, TX 75219

Phone: (972) 788-6000   **Domicile State:** TX   **NAIC Code:** 24538

Data Date	Rating	RACR #1	RACR #2	Loss Ratio %	Total Assets ($mil)	Capital ($mil)	Net Premium ($mil)	Net Income ($mil)
6-16	C	1.46	1.16	N/A	712.4	158.9	119.4	-72.8
6-15	C+	2.33	1.83	N/A	675.8	253.5	132.5	3.7
2015	C+	2.32	1.84	57.8	676.4	255.9	285.9	10.2
2014	C+	2.50	2.00	61.2	647.4	252.0	244.0	13.2
2013	C+	2.24	1.80	57.9	678.6	246.1	297.1	23.8
2012	C+	1.99	1.57	67.9	658.1	228.4	309.6	10.3
2011	C+	1.81	1.44	78.6	671.0	219.1	354.0	-49.3

AmTrust Financial Services Inc Composite Group Rating: C Largest Group Members	Assets ($mil)	Rating
INTEGON NATIONAL INS CO	2339	C
TECHNOLOGY INS CO	1981	C
WESCO INS CO	1743	B-
SECURITY NATIONAL INS CO	991	B
REPUBLIC UNDERWRITERS INS CO	676	C

RLI INS CO   B   Good

Major Rating Factors: Good liquidity (6.9 on a scale of 0 to 10) with sufficient resources (cash flows and marketable investments) to handle a spike in claims. Fair overall results on stability tests (4.7) including potential drain of affiliation with RLI Corp and weak results on operational trends.

Other Rating Factors: Strong long-term capitalization index (7.3) based on excellent current risk adjusted capital (severe and moderate loss scenarios), despite some fluctuation in capital levels. Ample reserve history (8.2) that helps to protect the company against sharp claims increases. Excellent profitability (8.7) with operating gains in each of the last five years. Return on equity has been excellent over the last five years averaging 21.0%.

Principal Business: Other liability (39%), surety (21%), auto liability (17%), auto physical damage (5%), ocean marine (5%), inland marine (5%), and other lines (9%).

Principal Investments: Misc. investments (58%), investment grade bonds (34%), non investment grade bonds (5%), real estate (2%), and cash (1%).

Investments in Affiliates: 37%

Group Affiliation: RLI Corp

Licensed in: All states, the District of Columbia and Puerto Rico

Commenced Business: November 1960

Address: 9025 N Lindbergh Dr, Peoria, IL 61615

Phone: (309) 692-1000   **Domicile State:** IL   **NAIC Code:** 13056

Data Date	Rating	RACR #1	RACR #2	Loss Ratio %	Total Assets ($mil)	Capital ($mil)	Net Premium ($mil)	Net Income ($mil)
6-16	B	1.41	1.21	N/A	1,808.7	924.0	220.9	38.5
6-15	B	1.34	1.16	N/A	1,745.4	878.1	209.2	30.3
2015	B	1.37	1.18	47.4	1,725.1	865.3	450.9	183.2
2014	B	1.31	1.14	50.6	1,707.0	849.3	437.6	238.4
2013	B	1.25	1.12	50.8	1,679.4	859.2	413.2	205.9
2012	B	1.00	0.91	53.3	1,423.9	684.1	377.2	127.2
2011	B	1.05	0.95	44.7	1,467.2	710.2	362.4	139.0

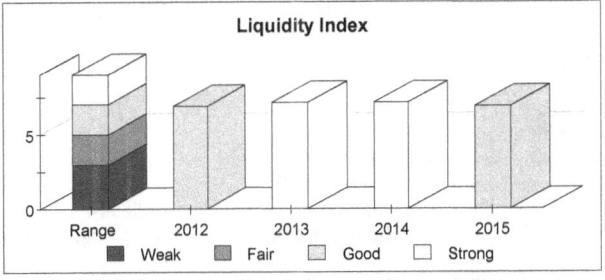

RSUI INDEMNITY CO
C+   Fair

Major Rating Factors: Fair overall results on stability tests (4.3 on a scale of 0 to 10) including potential drain of affiliation with Alleghany Corp Group and weak results on operational trends. The largest net exposure for one risk is conservative at 1.3% of capital. Good liquidity (6.9) with sufficient resources (cash flows and marketable investments) to handle a spike in claims.

Other Rating Factors: Strong long-term capitalization index (8.0) based on excellent current risk adjusted capital (severe and moderate loss scenarios), despite some fluctuation in capital levels. Ample reserve history (8.0) that helps to protect the company against sharp claims increases. Excellent profitability (7.7) with operating gains in each of the last five years. Return on equity has been good over the last five years, averaging 11.4%.

Principal Business: Other liability (73%), allied lines (14%), fire (9%), inland marine (2%), and earthquake (2%).

Principal Investments: Investment grade bonds (54%), misc. investments (41%), and non investment grade bonds (5%).

Investments in Affiliates: 9%

Group Affiliation: Alleghany Corp Group

Licensed in: All states except PR

Commenced Business: December 1977

Address: 900 Elm St, Manchester, NH 03101

Phone: (404) 231-2366   **Domicile State:** NH   **NAIC Code:** 22314

Data Date	Rating	RACR #1	RACR #2	Loss Ratio %	Total Assets ($mil)	Capital ($mil)	Net Premium ($mil)	Net Income ($mil)
6-16	C+	2.38	1.70	N/A	3,423.5	1,476.8	353.0	83.9
6-15	C+	2.41	1.70	N/A	3,392.4	1,503.8	374.2	123.3
2015	C+	2.36	1.69	53.8	3,329.0	1,481.6	720.4	201.0
2014	C+	2.45	1.75	51.8	3,286.8	1,466.1	764.3	197.5
2013	C+	2.68	1.92	53.4	3,323.2	1,492.4	765.1	160.2
2012	C+	2.71	1.96	72.2	3,013.4	1,296.0	661.4	108.7
2011	C+	2.72	1.65	53.7	2,772.7	1,262.3	581.0	137.0

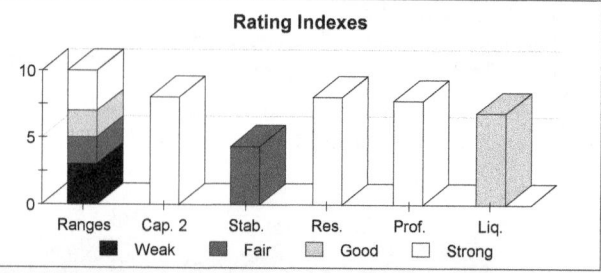

Rating Indexes

RURAL MUTUAL INS CO
B-   Good

Major Rating Factors: Fair overall results on stability tests (4.1 on a scale of 0 to 10) including potential drain of affiliation with Wisconsin Farm Bureau Federation and weak results on operational trends. Good liquidity (6.7) with sufficient resources (cash flows and marketable investments) to handle a spike in claims.

Other Rating Factors: Strong long-term capitalization index (10.0) based on excellent current risk adjusted capital (severe and moderate loss scenarios). Moreover, capital levels have been consistent in recent years. Ample reserve history (8.7) that helps to protect the company against sharp claims increases. Excellent profitability (8.9) with operating gains in each of the last five years.

Principal Business: Farmowners multiple peril (33%), workers compensation (17%), commercial multiple peril (15%), auto liability (14%), auto physical damage (10%), homeowners multiple peril (9%), and allied lines (2%).

Principal Investments: Investment grade bonds (83%), misc. investments (16%), and cash (1%).

Investments in Affiliates: None

Group Affiliation: Wisconsin Farm Bureau Federation

Licensed in: IL, MN, WI

Commenced Business: June 1935

Address: 12421 John Q Hammons Dr #200, Madison, WI 53717-1929

Phone: (608) 836-5525   **Domicile State:** WI   **NAIC Code:** 15091

Data Date	Rating	RACR #1	RACR #2	Loss Ratio %	Total Assets ($mil)	Capital ($mil)	Net Premium ($mil)	Net Income ($mil)
6-16	B-	6.05	4.15	N/A	448.9	223.8	81.0	9.8
6-15	C+	5.87	4.06	N/A	413.0	201.7	76.1	6.3
2015	B-	6.18	4.19	59.9	419.9	213.5	162.6	21.3
2014	C+	5.99	4.08	59.8	385.9	194.0	152.9	20.0
2013	C+	5.74	3.93	59.7	356.6	176.5	144.7	18.1
2012	C+	5.58	3.83	60.4	324.0	156.1	136.0	8.8
2011	C+	5.62	3.85	68.5	305.4	145.5	128.5	8.6

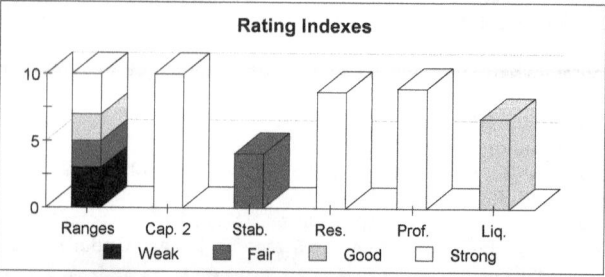

Rating Indexes

SAFECO INS CO OF AMERICA
B-   Good

Major Rating Factors: Fair overall results on stability tests (3.9 on a scale of 0 to 10) including weak results on operational trends. The largest net exposure for one risk is acceptable at 2.5% of capital. History of adequate reserve strength (5.9) as reserves have been consistently at an acceptable level.

Other Rating Factors: Good overall profitability index (6.6) despite modest operating losses during the first six months of 2016. Return on equity has been fair, averaging 9.5% over the past five years. Good liquidity (6.3) with sufficient resources (cash flows and marketable investments) to handle a spike in claims. Strong long-term capitalization index (7.9) based on excellent current risk adjusted capital (severe and moderate loss scenarios). Moreover, capital levels have been consistent in recent years.

Principal Business: Homeowners multiple peril (43%), auto liability (19%), auto physical damage (16%), allied lines (6%), fire (6%), other liability (5%), and other lines (5%).

Principal Investments: Investment grade bonds (68%), misc. investments (28%), and non investment grade bonds (5%).

Investments in Affiliates: 7%

Group Affiliation: Liberty Mutual Group

Licensed in: All states except PR

Commenced Business: October 1953

Address: 1001 Fourth Ave Safeco Plaza, Seattle, WA 98154

Phone: (617) 357-9500   **Domicile State:** NH   **NAIC Code:** 24740

Data Date	Rating	RACR #1	RACR #2	Loss Ratio %	Total Assets ($mil)	Capital ($mil)	Net Premium ($mil)	Net Income ($mil)
6-16	B-	2.59	1.80	N/A	4,349.5	1,417.2	760.8	-2.6
6-15	B-	2.43	1.67	N/A	4,301.8	1,357.9	737.3	56.4
2015	B-	2.56	1.80	68.4	4,356.9	1,393.4	1,537.9	103.6
2014	B-	2.33	1.61	70.0	4,233.3	1,278.9	1,522.6	106.8
2013	B-	2.18	1.48	73.5	4,747.1	1,188.7	1,349.1	154.8
2012	B-	1.79	1.28	66.7	4,029.8	945.1	1,659.6	193.5
2011	C+	1.55	1.14	74.0	3,854.2	870.8	1,616.3	29.2

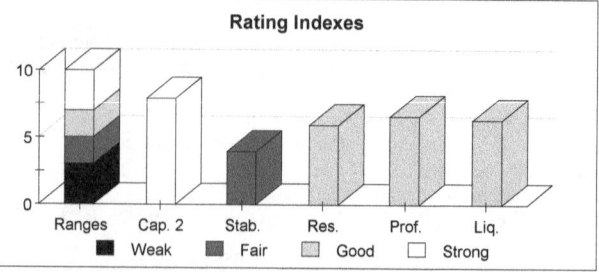

Rating Indexes

SAFETY INS CO   B-   Good

Major Rating Factors: Fair overall results on stability tests (4.4 on a scale of 0 to 10) including potential drain of affiliation with Safety Group, weak results on operational trends and negative cash flow from operations for 2015. Fair profitability index (3.6) with operating losses during 2015. Return on equity has been fair, averaging 5.4% over the past five years.

Other Rating Factors: Good liquidity (5.9) with sufficient resources (cash flows and marketable investments) to handle a spike in claims. Strong long-term capitalization index (8.8) based on excellent current risk adjusted capital (severe and moderate loss scenarios), despite some fluctuation in capital levels. Ample reserve history (8.8) that helps to protect the company against sharp claims increases.

Principal Business: Auto liability (51%), auto physical damage (35%), homeowners multiple peril (8%), commercial multiple peril (3%), other liability (1%), allied lines (1%), and fire (1%).

Principal Investments: Investment grade bonds (74%), misc. investments (18%), and non investment grade bonds (10%).

Investments in Affiliates: 6%

Group Affiliation: Safety Group

Licensed in: ME, MA, NH

Commenced Business: January 1980

Address: 20 Custom House St, Boston, MA 02110

Phone: (617) 951-0600   **Domicile State:** MA   **NAIC Code:** 39454

Data Date	Rating	RACR #1	RACR #2	Loss Ratio %	Total Assets ($mil)	Capital ($mil)	Net Premium ($mil)	Net Income ($mil)
6-16	B-	3.19	2.20	N/A	1,455.7	583.9	335.7	28.1
6-15	B-	3.30	2.42	N/A	1,426.7	567.3	328.5	-35.6
2015	B-	3.15	2.21	83.0	1,434.6	571.0	671.6	-12.2
2014	B-	3.67	2.72	66.5	1,430.1	630.0	661.4	51.2
2013	B+	3.72	2.71	65.7	1,396.8	628.0	627.8	53.1
2012	B+	3.97	2.99	65.7	1,319.7	599.0	597.5	52.4
2011	B+	4.22	3.37	78.0	1,235.4	570.5	558.3	9.0

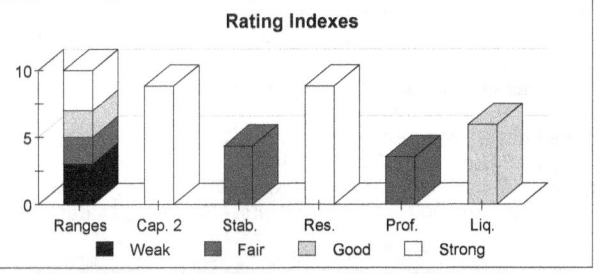

Rating Indexes

SAFETY NATIONAL CASUALTY CORP   C   Fair

Major Rating Factors: Fair overall results on stability tests (3.4 on a scale of 0 to 10) including weak results on operational trends. Strengths include potentially strong support from affiliation with Tokio Marine Holdings Inc. A history of deficient reserves (1.9). Underreserving can have an adverse impact on capital and profits. In four of the last five years reserves (two year development) were between 16% and 47% deficient.

Other Rating Factors: Good overall profitability index (6.3). Good expense controls. Return on equity has been fair, averaging 8.9% over the past five years. Strong long-term capitalization index (7.1) based on excellent current risk adjusted capital (severe and moderate loss scenarios). Moreover, capital levels have been consistent in recent years. Excellent liquidity (7.4) with ample operational cash flow and liquid investments.

Principal Business: Workers compensation (19%), auto liability (3%), other liability (3%), surety (1%), and products liability (1%).

Principal Investments: Investment grade bonds (62%), misc. investments (27%), and non investment grade bonds (11%).

Investments in Affiliates: 4%

Group Affiliation: Tokio Marine Holdings Inc

Licensed in: All states, the District of Columbia and Puerto Rico

Commenced Business: December 1942

Address: 1832 Schuetz Rd, St Louis, MO 63146-3540

Phone: (314) 995-5300   **Domicile State:** MO   **NAIC Code:** 15105

Data Date	Rating	RACR #1	RACR #2	Loss Ratio %	Total Assets ($mil)	Capital ($mil)	Net Premium ($mil)	Net Income ($mil)
6-16	C	1.58	1.17	N/A	6,043.9	1,653.4	361.4	85.6
6-15	C	1.44	1.08	N/A	5,331.3	1,430.6	343.9	70.6
2015	C	1.54	1.16	86.1	5,611.3	1,527.0	728.9	159.3
2014	C	1.46	1.10	87.8	4,985.1	1,367.6	671.2	110.2
2013	C	1.39	1.06	78.4	4,183.6	1,153.8	664.9	122.7
2012	C	1.36	1.06	101.1	3,544.1	960.8	549.0	36.8
2011	C	1.50	0.94	76.9	2,868.9	844.5	449.2	89.9

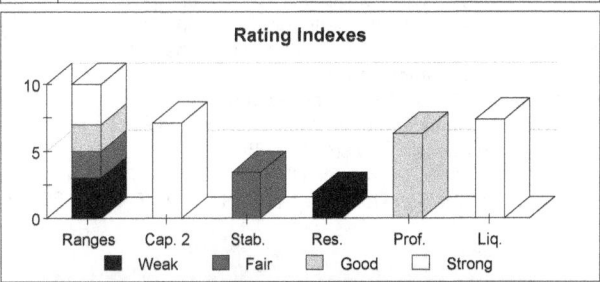

Rating Indexes

SAFEWAY INS CO   B-   Good

Major Rating Factors: Fair overall results on stability tests (4.2 on a scale of 0 to 10) including potential drain of affiliation with Safeway Ins Group and weak results on operational trends. History of adequate reserve strength (5.1) as reserves have been consistently at an acceptable level.

Other Rating Factors: Good overall profitability index (5.6) despite operating losses during 2013 and the first six months of 2016. Return on equity has been low, averaging 3.1% over the past five years. Good liquidity (6.6) with sufficient resources (cash flows and marketable investments) to handle a spike in claims. Strong long-term capitalization index (7.8) based on excellent current risk adjusted capital (severe and moderate loss scenarios), despite some fluctuation in capital levels.

Principal Business: Auto liability (63%) and auto physical damage (37%).

Principal Investments: Misc. investments (61%), investment grade bonds (30%), cash (8%), and real estate (1%).

Investments in Affiliates: 41%

Group Affiliation: Safeway Ins Group

Licensed in: AL, AK, AZ, CA, CO, DC, DE, FL, GA, ID, IL, IN, IA, KS, LA, ME, MD, MA, MI, MN, MS, MO, MT, NE, NV, NJ, NM, ND, OK, OR, PA, SC, SD, TX, UT, WA, WV, WI, WY

Commenced Business: December 1962

Address: 790 Pasquinelli, Westmont, IL 60559

Phone: (630) 887-8300   **Domicile State:** IL   **NAIC Code:** 12521

Data Date	Rating	RACR #1	RACR #2	Loss Ratio %	Total Assets ($mil)	Capital ($mil)	Net Premium ($mil)	Net Income ($mil)
6-16	B-	1.63	1.48	N/A	464.8	286.0	103.9	-3.9
6-15	B-	1.51	1.38	N/A	469.4	295.9	100.0	1.3
2015	B-	1.72	1.57	82.2	463.6	302.1	204.4	33.3
2014	B-	1.53	1.41	76.0	446.1	298.8	167.5	7.3
2013	B-	1.47	1.35	79.1	417.0	279.3	156.1	-0.3
2012	B-	1.65	1.52	78.7	390.6	281.4	126.1	8.1
2011	B-	1.69	1.58	73.5	382.0	283.1	119.2	6.1

Rating Indexes

SAN FRANCISCO REINS CO   C+   Fair

Major Rating Factors: Fair overall results on stability tests (4.4 on a scale of 0 to 10) including weak results on operational trends and fair risk adjusted capital in prior years. Strengths include potentially strong support from affiliation with Allianz Ins Group. Fair long-term capitalization (3.8) based on good current risk adjusted capital (moderate loss scenario) reflecting significant improvement over results in 2015.

Other Rating Factors: Fair profitability index (3.9) with operating losses during 2011, 2012 and 2015. Average return on equity over the last five years has been poor at -0.8%. Good liquidity (6.4) with sufficient resources (cash flows and marketable investments) to handle a spike in claims. A history of deficient reserves (1.0) that places pressure on both capital and profits. In 2012 and 2015 the two year reserve development was 21% and 3048% deficient respectively.

Principal Business: (This company is a reinsurer.)

Principal Investments: Investment grade bonds (90%), misc. investments (8%), and cash (2%).

Investments in Affiliates: None

Group Affiliation: Allianz Ins Group

Licensed in: All states except PR

Commenced Business: August 1964

Address: 777 San Marin Dr, Novato, CA 94998-3452

Phone: (415) 899-2000   **Domicile State:** CA   **NAIC Code:** 21911

Data Date	Rating	RACR #1	RACR #2	Loss Ratio %	Total Assets ($mil)	Capital ($mil)	Net Premium ($mil)	Net Income ($mil)
6-16	C+	1.85	1.22	N/A	3,220.1	649.3	-772.9	14.4
6-15	U	2.44	0.78	N/A	1,405.7	381.3	953.8	-15.7
2015	C+	0.75	0.54	100.0	2,931.1	655.9	2,282.7	-14.9
2014	U	18.37	5.88	0.0	98.4	74.5	0.0	1.8
2013	U	18.21	5.90	0.0	96.5	73.0	0.0	0.7
2012	U	18.78	6.11	0.0	94.3	72.1	0.0	-4.3
2011	U	22.15	7.46	0.0	89.2	74.5	0.0	-1.2

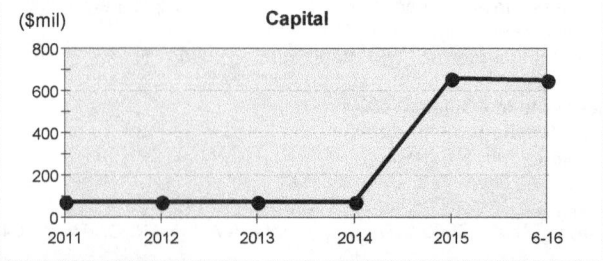

Capital ($mil)

SCOR REINS CO   C-   Fair

Major Rating Factors: Fair overall results on stability tests (3.3 on a scale of 0 to 10) including potential drain of affiliation with SCOR Reinsurance Group and weak results on operational trends. The largest net exposure for one risk is acceptable at 2.1% of capital. History of adequate reserve strength (6.3) as reserves have been consistently at an acceptable level.

Other Rating Factors: Good overall profitability index (6.0) despite operating losses during 2012. Return on equity has been fair, averaging 5.4% over the past five years. Good liquidity (6.7) with sufficient resources (cash flows and marketable investments) to handle a spike in claims. Strong long-term capitalization index (7.1) based on excellent current risk adjusted capital (severe and moderate loss scenarios), despite some fluctuation in capital levels.

Principal Business: (This company is a reinsurer.)

Principal Investments: Investment grade bonds (87%), misc. investments (11%), cash (1%), and non investment grade bonds (1%).

Investments in Affiliates: None

Group Affiliation: SCOR Reinsurance Group

Licensed in: All states, the District of Columbia and Puerto Rico

Commenced Business: September 1985

Address: 199 Water St, New York, NY 10038-3526

Phone: (212) 480-1900   **Domicile State:** NY   **NAIC Code:** 30058

Data Date	Rating	RACR #1	RACR #2	Loss Ratio %	Total Assets ($mil)	Capital ($mil)	Net Premium ($mil)	Net Income ($mil)
6-16	C-	2.13	1.39	N/A	2,929.1	1,086.2	471.1	24.6
6-15	D	1.34	0.87	N/A	2,421.7	754.4	394.5	69.9
2015	D+	1.94	1.26	48.6	2,749.2	962.2	846.9	126.6
2014	D	1.30	0.85	54.8	2,269.6	704.3	798.2	75.1
2013	D	1.39	0.90	62.3	2,364.7	676.4	755.6	66.6
2012	D	1.04	0.69	76.6	2,247.6	618.9	709.3	-89.2
2011	D	1.17	0.77	72.4	2,106.6	658.7	645.2	54.0

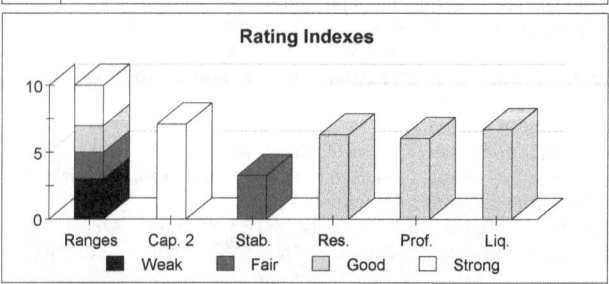

Rating Indexes

Ranges   Cap. 2   Stab.   Res.   Prof.   Liq.
■ Weak   ▨ Fair   ▢ Good   □ Strong

SCOTTSDALE INS CO   B-   Good

Major Rating Factors: Fair profitability index (4.2 on a scale of 0 to 10) with operating losses during 2011, 2012 and the first six months of 2016. Return on equity has been low, averaging 0.4% over the past five years. Fair overall results on stability tests (4.9) including weak results on operational trends.

Other Rating Factors: History of adequate reserve strength (6.2) as reserves have been consistently at an acceptable level. Good liquidity (6.4) with sufficient resources (cash flows and marketable investments) to handle a spike in claims. Strong long-term capitalization index (8.3) based on excellent current risk adjusted capital (severe and moderate loss scenarios), despite some fluctuation in capital levels.

Principal Business: Other liability (51%), commercial multiple peril (23%), allied lines (10%), homeowners multiple peril (5%), fire (4%), auto liability (3%), and other lines (4%).

Principal Investments: Investment grade bonds (82%) and misc. investments (22%).

Investments in Affiliates: 19%

Group Affiliation: Nationwide Corp

Licensed in: All states, the District of Columbia and Puerto Rico

Commenced Business: July 1982

Address: 8877 N. Gainey Center Dr, Scottsdale, AZ 85258

Phone: (480) 365-4000   **Domicile State:** OH   **NAIC Code:** 41297

Data Date	Rating	RACR #1	RACR #2	Loss Ratio %	Total Assets ($mil)	Capital ($mil)	Net Premium ($mil)	Net Income ($mil)
6-16	B-	2.23	1.86	N/A	2,561.9	768.6	382.1	-4.0
6-15	B-	2.26	1.90	N/A	2,339.5	765.6	363.1	10.8
2015	B-	2.27	1.92	71.1	2,313.3	766.1	747.5	8.5
2014	B-	2.30	1.95	71.1	2,222.6	764.9	721.1	9.9
2013	B-	2.42	1.99	66.2	2,133.3	716.4	707.1	16.2
2012	B-	2.42	2.03	71.9	1,879.5	670.2	598.9	-2.3
2011	B-	2.66	2.16	77.0	1,747.5	678.8	572.4	-11.6

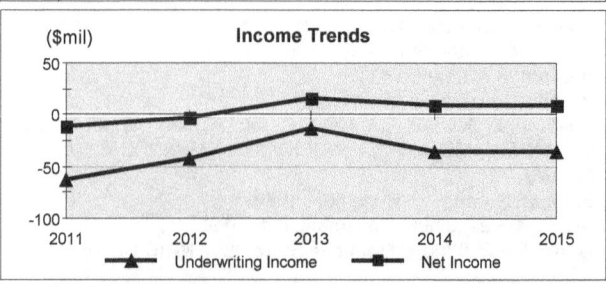

Income Trends ($mil)

▲ Underwriting Income   ■ Net Income

SECURA INS A MUTUAL CO   B-   Good

Major Rating Factors: Fair overall results on stability tests (4.2 on a scale of 0 to 10) including potential drain of affiliation with SECURA Group and weak results on operational trends. Good liquidity (6.5) with sufficient resources (cash flows and marketable investments) to handle a spike in claims.

Other Rating Factors: Strong long-term capitalization index (8.2) based on excellent current risk adjusted capital (severe and moderate loss scenarios). Moreover, capital levels have been consistent in recent years. Ample reserve history (9.3) that helps to protect the company against sharp claims increases. Excellent profitability (8.3) with operating gains in each of the last five years.

Principal Business: Workers compensation (29%), commercial multiple peril (26%), auto liability (15%), farmowners multiple peril (10%), other liability (7%), auto physical damage (7%), and other lines (6%).

Principal Investments: Investment grade bonds (69%), misc. investments (29%), and real estate (2%).

Investments in Affiliates: 7%

Group Affiliation: SECURA Group

Licensed in: AZ, AR, CO, ID, IL, IN, IA, KS, KY, MI, MN, MO, MT, NE, NV, NM, ND, OH, OK, OR, PA, SD, TN, UT, WA, WI, WY

Commenced Business: May 1900

Address: 2401 S Memorial Dr, Appleton, WI 54915

Phone: (920) 739-3161   **Domicile State:** WI   **NAIC Code:** 22543

Data Date	Rating	RACR #1	RACR #2	Loss Ratio %	Total Assets ($mil)	Capital ($mil)	Net Premium ($mil)	Net Income ($mil)
6-16	B-	2.49	1.81	N/A	1,066.5	375.3	234.1	9.1
6-15	B-	2.48	1.81	N/A	984.9	341.7	220.3	12.3
2015	B-	2.50	1.84	60.1	1,018.7	353.1	462.5	24.7
2014	B-	2.53	1.84	62.6	940.4	332.9	424.4	37.9
2013	B-	2.58	1.87	59.4	872.1	321.7	387.1	45.3
2012	B-	1.98	1.43	64.0	797.4	273.3	344.9	22.9
2011	B-	1.95	1.40	74.4	734.2	241.2	320.7	6.8

Rating Indexes

SELECTIVE INS CO OF AM   B   Good

Major Rating Factors: Good liquidity (6.8 on a scale of 0 to 10) with sufficient resources (cash flows and marketable investments) to handle a spike in claims. Fair overall results on stability tests (4.6) including potential drain of affiliation with Selective Ins and weak results on operational trends.

Other Rating Factors: Strong long-term capitalization index (8.2) based on excellent current risk adjusted capital (severe and moderate loss scenarios), despite some fluctuation in capital levels. Ample reserve history (9.1) that helps to protect the company against sharp claims increases. Excellent profitability (7.1) with operating gains in each of the last five years. Return on equity has been good over the last five years, averaging 10.7%.

Principal Business: Other liability (23%), workers compensation (18%), auto liability (16%), allied lines (11%), fire (7%), auto physical damage (6%), and other lines (20%).

Principal Investments: Investment grade bonds (85%), misc. investments (15%), and non investment grade bonds (1%).

Investments in Affiliates: None

Group Affiliation: Selective Ins

Licensed in: All states except AZ, CO, FL, ID, LA, NH, NM, OK, UT, VT, PR

Commenced Business: April 1926

Address: 40 Wantage Ave, Branchville, NJ 07890

Phone: (973) 948-3000   **Domicile State:** NJ   **NAIC Code:** 12572

Data Date	Rating	RACR #1	RACR #2	Loss Ratio %	Total Assets ($mil)	Capital ($mil)	Net Premium ($mil)	Net Income ($mil)
6-16	B	2.74	1.82	N/A	2,216.9	546.6	337.4	33.9
6-15	B-	2.48	1.61	N/A	2,102.4	499.4	309.3	36.1
2015	B	2.67	1.77	57.7	2,140.7	520.8	662.4	69.6
2014	B-	2.60	1.70	62.4	2,044.6	493.0	603.3	83.9
2013	B-	2.47	1.59	64.5	1,951.0	463.4	579.7	53.1
2012	C+	2.19	1.38	70.6	1,708.3	369.9	496.8	29.8
2011	B	2.18	1.42	74.7	2,400.8	507.4	735.2	15.2

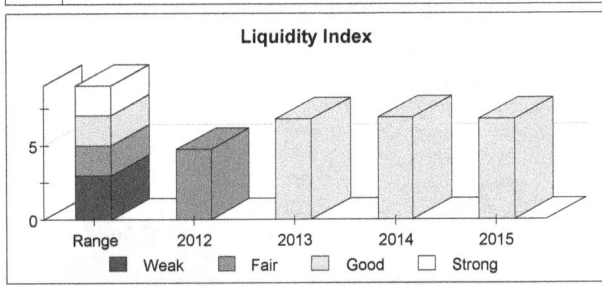

Liquidity Index

SELECTIVE WAY INS CO   B   Good

Major Rating Factors: Good liquidity (6.9 on a scale of 0 to 10) with sufficient resources (cash flows and marketable investments) to handle a spike in claims. Fair overall results on stability tests (4.6) including weak results on operational trends.

Other Rating Factors: Strong long-term capitalization index (7.8) based on excellent current risk adjusted capital (severe and moderate loss scenarios), despite some fluctuation in capital levels. Ample reserve history (9.3) that helps to protect the company against sharp claims increases. Excellent profitability (7.7) with operating gains in each of the last five years. Return on equity has been good over the last five years, averaging 10.1%.

Principal Business: Other liability (24%), auto liability (19%), workers compensation (17%), fire (8%), allied lines (8%), products liability (7%), and other lines (17%).

Principal Investments: Investment grade bonds (90%), misc. investments (9%), and non investment grade bonds (1%).

Investments in Affiliates: None

Group Affiliation: Selective Ins

Licensed in: DC, DE, GA, MD, MI, NJ, NY, NC, PA, SC, VA

Commenced Business: November 1973

Address: 40 Wantage Ave, Branchville, NJ 07890

Phone: (973) 948-3000   **Domicile State:** NJ   **NAIC Code:** 26301

Data Date	Rating	RACR #1	RACR #2	Loss Ratio %	Total Assets ($mil)	Capital ($mil)	Net Premium ($mil)	Net Income ($mil)
6-16	B	2.25	1.51	N/A	1,264.9	291.8	221.4	17.3
6-15	B	2.03	1.35	N/A	1,191.6	255.1	203.0	20.5
2015	B	2.22	1.49	57.7	1,215.0	272.6	434.7	42.3
2014	B	2.07	1.38	62.4	1,167.4	250.3	395.9	37.0
2013	B	2.09	1.36	64.5	1,124.5	250.3	380.4	27.5
2012	B	2.00	1.28	70.7	1,048.0	211.2	350.0	10.1
2011	B	2.22	1.45	74.7	1,021.1	221.6	311.9	7.8

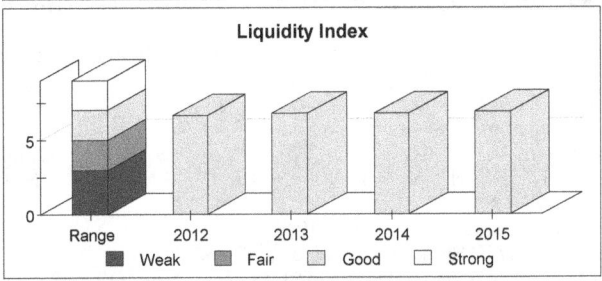

Liquidity Index

SENTRY INS A MUTUAL CO *
A   Excellent

Major Rating Factors: Strong long-term capitalization index (8.5 on a scale of 0 to 10) based on excellent current risk adjusted capital (severe and moderate loss scenarios). Furthermore, this high level of risk adjusted capital has been consistently maintained in previous years. Ample reserve history (7.5) that can protect against increases in claims costs.

Other Rating Factors: Excellent liquidity (7.0) with ample operational cash flow and liquid investments. Good overall profitability index (6.8). Fair expense controls. Good overall results on stability tests (6.1) despite weak results on operational trends.

Principal Business: Workers compensation (33%), auto liability (26%), other liability (10%), allied lines (7%), fire (7%), auto physical damage (6%), and other lines (10%).

Principal Investments: Misc. investments (55%), investment grade bonds (42%), non investment grade bonds (3%), and real estate (1%).

Investments in Affiliates: 23%

Group Affiliation: Sentry Ins Group

Licensed in: All states, the District of Columbia and Puerto Rico

Commenced Business: August 1914

Address: 1800 N Point Dr, Stevens Point, WI 54481

Phone: (715) 346-6000   **Domicile State:** WI   **NAIC Code:** 24988

Data Date	Rating	RACR #1	RACR #2	Loss Ratio %	Total Assets ($mil)	Capital ($mil)	Net Premium ($mil)	Net Income ($mil)
6-16	A	2.51	2.10	N/A	7,458.5	4,520.1	520.6	57.1
6-15	A	2.37	2.00	N/A	7,112.8	4,273.6	486.7	155.7
2015	A	2.49	2.10	72.7	7,214.6	4,404.3	1,014.2	297.6
2014	A	2.34	1.99	74.9	6,981.3	4,164.4	997.7	272.5
2013	A	2.34	2.01	76.3	6,632.0	4,075.3	999.7	308.4
2012	A	2.19	1.92	77.3	6,248.1	3,637.2	950.0	230.0
2011	A	2.07	1.83	79.1	5,891.4	3,417.2	898.3	206.7

Risk-Adjusted Capital Ratio #2
(Severe Loss Scenario)

Range 2011 2012 2013 2014 2015 6-16
■ Weak   ■ Fair   ▨ Good   □ Strong

SENTRY SELECT INS CO *
B+   Good

Major Rating Factors: Good overall profitability index (6.0 on a scale of 0 to 10). Fair expense controls. Return on equity has been fair, averaging 5.7% over the past five years. Good liquidity (6.7) with sufficient resources (cash flows and marketable investments) to handle a spike in claims.

Other Rating Factors: Good overall results on stability tests (5.1) despite weak results on operational trends. The largest net exposure for one risk is conservative at 1.2% of capital. Strong long-term capitalization index (9.2) based on excellent current risk adjusted capital (severe and moderate loss scenarios), despite some fluctuation in capital levels. Ample reserve history (8.3) that helps to protect the company against sharp claims increases.

Principal Business: Auto liability (42%), auto physical damage (16%), inland marine (15%), other liability (10%), workers compensation (6%), allied lines (4%), and other lines (8%).

Principal Investments: Investment grade bonds (92%), misc. investments (7%), and non investment grade bonds (1%).

Investments in Affiliates: None

Group Affiliation: Sentry Ins Group

Licensed in: All states except PR

Commenced Business: August 1929

Address: 3400 80th St, Moline, IL 61265

Phone: (715) 346-6000   **Domicile State:** WI   **NAIC Code:** 21180

Data Date	Rating	RACR #1	RACR #2	Loss Ratio %	Total Assets ($mil)	Capital ($mil)	Net Premium ($mil)	Net Income ($mil)
6-16	B+	3.79	2.39	N/A	706.8	237.0	96.4	4.1
6-15	B+	4.33	2.85	N/A	682.3	242.1	88.5	7.2
2015	B+	3.87	2.48	72.7	679.1	232.0	187.7	11.9
2014	B+	4.30	2.89	74.9	658.6	235.1	181.4	19.0
2013	B+	4.12	2.81	76.3	641.3	227.5	181.8	12.4
2012	B+	4.20	2.84	77.3	620.8	221.5	172.7	11.5
2011	B	4.25	2.89	79.1	616.9	220.3	163.3	12.8

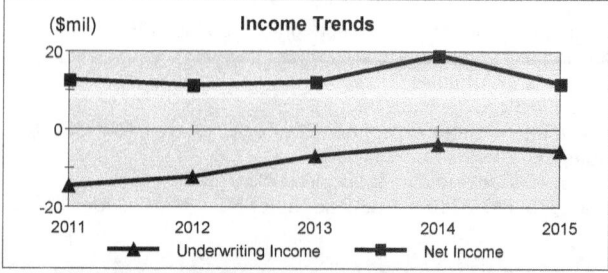

($mil)   Income Trends

2011   2012   2013   2014   2015
—▲— Underwriting Income   —■— Net Income

SHELTER MUTUAL INS CO
B   Good

Major Rating Factors: Good overall results on stability tests (5.0 on a scale of 0 to 10) despite potential drain of affiliation with Shelter Ins Companies and weak results on operational trends. Good overall profitability index (5.4) despite operating losses during 2011.

Other Rating Factors: Good liquidity (5.8) with sufficient resources (cash flows and marketable investments) to handle a spike in claims. Strong long-term capitalization index (8.1) based on excellent current risk adjusted capital (severe and moderate loss scenarios). Moreover, capital levels have been consistent in recent years. Ample reserve history (7.5) that can protect against increases in claims costs.

Principal Business: Auto liability (30%), homeowners multiple peril (29%), auto physical damage (23%), allied lines (6%), fire (3%), farmowners multiple peril (3%), and other lines (5%).

Principal Investments: Investment grade bonds (54%), misc. investments (47%), and real estate (1%).

Investments in Affiliates: 24%

Group Affiliation: Shelter Ins Companies

Licensed in: AL, AR, CO, DE, GA, ID, IL, IN, IA, KS, KY, LA, MD, MA, MN, MS, MO, MT, NE, NV, NH, NJ, NY, NC, OH, OK, OR, PA, SC, SD, TN, TX, VT, VA, WV, WI, WY

Commenced Business: January 1946

Address: 1817 W Broadway, Columbia, MO 65218

Phone: (573) 445-8441   **Domicile State:** MO   **NAIC Code:** 23388

Data Date	Rating	RACR #1	RACR #2	Loss Ratio %	Total Assets ($mil)	Capital ($mil)	Net Premium ($mil)	Net Income ($mil)
6-16	B	2.21	1.77	N/A	3,210.5	1,831.5	705.9	10.3
6-15	B	2.21	1.75	N/A	3,032.7	1,729.5	671.5	31.2
2015	B	2.19	1.77	69.4	3,114.8	1,787.8	1,379.7	80.1
2014	B	2.15	1.72	69.7	2,973.8	1,682.7	1,323.6	66.8
2013	B	2.03	1.62	74.2	2,756.5	1,566.9	1,208.2	65.5
2012	B	2.06	1.60	75.1	2,490.3	1,397.9	1,144.8	70.1
2011	B	1.99	1.56	91.6	2,306.5	1,281.4	1,090.6	-28.8

Rating Indexes

Ranges Cap. 2 Stab. Res. Prof. Liq.
■ Weak   ■ Fair   ▨ Good   □ Strong

SHELTER REINS CO
B- Good

Major Rating Factors: Fair profitability index (4.8 on a scale of 0 to 10) with operating losses during 2011. Return on equity has been low, averaging 4.7% over the past five years. Fair overall results on stability tests (3.7) including fair financial strength of affiliated Shelter Ins Companies and weak results on operational trends. The largest net exposure for one risk is high at 3.1% of capital.

Other Rating Factors: Good liquidity (6.7) with sufficient resources (cash flows and marketable investments) to handle a spike in claims. Strong long-term capitalization index (9.0) based on excellent current risk adjusted capital (severe and moderate loss scenarios). Moreover, capital levels have been consistent in recent years. Ample reserve history (7.0) that can protect against increases in claims costs.

Principal Business: Earthquake (100%).

Principal Investments: Investment grade bonds (97%), misc. investments (1%), cash (1%), and non investment grade bonds (1%).

Investments in Affiliates: None

Group Affiliation: Shelter Ins Companies

Licensed in: CA, IA, KS, MD, MI, MN, MO, ND, PA, SD, TN, WI, PR

Commenced Business: November 1986

Address: 1817 West Broadway, Columbia, MO 65218

Phone: (573) 445-8441 **Domicile State:** MO **NAIC Code:** 26557

Data Date	Rating	RACR #1	RACR #2	Loss Ratio %	Total Assets ($mil)	Capital ($mil)	Net Premium ($mil)	Net Income ($mil)
6-16	B-	4.31	2.86	N/A	437.6	316.1	54.0	20.0
6-15	C	3.86	2.53	N/A	407.8	287.9	48.9	18.2
2015	C+	4.10	2.72	46.7	422.3	296.7	103.5	28.1
2014	C	3.51	2.30	46.1	405.7	271.0	103.4	27.2
2013	C	2.94	2.00	40.6	383.0	245.4	98.0	30.5
2012	C	1.86	1.27	54.1	321.8	165.2	102.1	21.3
2011	C	1.43	1.04	140.8	294.1	143.2	101.7	-35.9

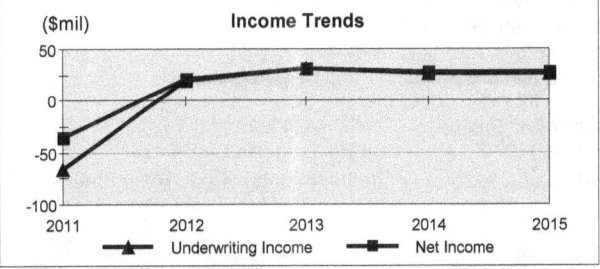

SIRIUS AMERICA INS CO
C+ Fair

Major Rating Factors: Fair profitability index (4.3 on a scale of 0 to 10). Weak expense controls. Return on equity has been fair, averaging 12.5% over the past five years. Fair overall results on stability tests (3.1) including weak results on operational trends and negative cash flow from operations for 2015. The largest net exposure for one risk is excessive at 5.6% of capital.

Other Rating Factors: Good overall long-term capitalization (6.1) based on good current risk adjusted capital (moderate loss scenario). However, capital levels have fluctuated during prior years. History of adequate reserve strength (6.3) as reserves have been consistently at an acceptable level. Excellent liquidity (7.2) with ample operational cash flow and liquid investments.

Principal Business: Group accident & health (99%), commercial multiple peril (1%), and inland marine (1%).

Principal Investments: Investment grade bonds (73%), misc. investments (25%), and cash (2%).

Investments in Affiliates: None

Group Affiliation: China Minsheng Investment Co Ltd

Licensed in: All states, the District of Columbia and Puerto Rico

Commenced Business: January 1980

Address: One Liberty Plaza, 19th Floor, New York, NY 10006

Phone: (212) 312-2500 **Domicile State:** NY **NAIC Code:** 38776

Data Date	Rating	RACR #1	RACR #2	Loss Ratio %	Total Assets ($mil)	Capital ($mil)	Net Premium ($mil)	Net Income ($mil)
6-16	C+	1.47	0.90	N/A	1,444.0	534.5	147.4	59.5
6-15	C+	2.10	1.22	N/A	1,533.4	629.6	139.1	40.0
2015	C+	1.42	0.87	53.7	1,387.6	517.6	283.9	74.7
2014	C+	1.58	0.94	45.1	1,550.5	620.6	267.2	56.1
2013	C+	2.14	1.21	48.9	1,559.4	548.4	252.8	55.9
2012	C	1.64	1.03	76.8	1,669.7	528.3	271.2	26.2
2011	C	1.50	0.95	71.7	1,807.7	533.7	485.3	101.4

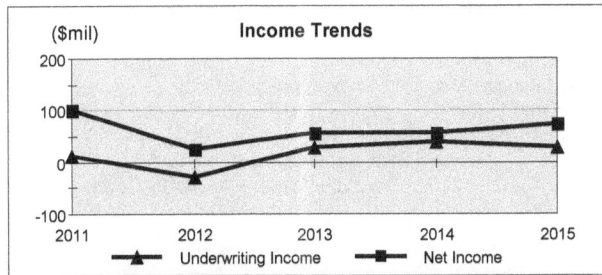

SOMPO JAPAN INS CO OF AM
B Good

Major Rating Factors: Fair profitability index (3.6 on a scale of 0 to 10). Weak expense controls. Return on equity has been low, averaging 3.3% over the past five years. Fair overall results on stability tests (4.6) including weak results on operational trends.

Other Rating Factors: Strong long-term capitalization index (9.6) based on excellent current risk adjusted capital (severe and moderate loss scenarios), despite some fluctuation in capital levels. Ample reserve history (9.0) that helps to protect the company against sharp claims increases. Excellent liquidity (7.2) with ample operational cash flow and liquid investments.

Principal Business: Workers compensation (24%), allied lines (19%), other liability (10%), fire (9%), ocean marine (8%), products liability (8%), and other lines (23%).

Principal Investments: Investment grade bonds (72%), misc. investments (25%), and cash (3%).

Investments in Affiliates: 1%

Group Affiliation: Sompo Holdings Inc

Licensed in: All states, the District of Columbia and Puerto Rico

Commenced Business: January 1963

Address: 777 Third Ave 28th Floor, New York, NY 10017

Phone: (704) 759-2200 **Domicile State:** NY **NAIC Code:** 11126

Data Date	Rating	RACR #1	RACR #2	Loss Ratio %	Total Assets ($mil)	Capital ($mil)	Net Premium ($mil)	Net Income ($mil)
6-16	B	4.50	2.82	N/A	1,236.8	548.6	91.0	13.8
6-15	B	3.06	2.13	N/A	1,195.8	498.1	87.4	18.2
2015	B	4.23	2.66	64.8	1,177.6	488.7	183.0	38.1
2014	B	3.55	2.48	62.8	1,238.5	598.3	191.4	8.8
2013	B	2.44	1.86	67.7	1,187.9	555.2	197.2	1.0
2012	B	3.41	2.47	56.1	1,163.0	586.4	173.5	20.7
2011	B	3.44	2.54	62.4	1,116.2	535.7	151.0	14.3

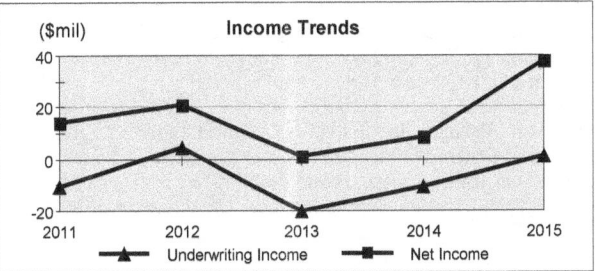

SOUTHERN FARM BUREAU CAS INS CO   B-   Good

Major Rating Factors: Fair overall results on stability tests (4.8 on a scale of 0 to 10) including potential drain of affiliation with Southern Farm Bureau Casualty and weak results on operational trends. Fair profitability index (4.7) with operating losses during the first six months of 2016. Return on equity has been low, averaging 2.5% over the past five years.

Other Rating Factors: Good liquidity (6.4) with sufficient resources (cash flows and marketable investments) to handle a spike in claims. Strong long-term capitalization index (8.4) based on excellent current risk adjusted capital (severe and moderate loss scenarios), despite some fluctuation in capital levels. Ample reserve history (7.8) that can protect against increases in claims costs.

Principal Business: Auto physical damage (49%), auto liability (45%), other liability (5%), and allied lines (1%).

Principal Investments: Investment grade bonds (59%), misc. investments (42%), and real estate (1%).

Investments in Affiliates: 32%

Group Affiliation: Southern Farm Bureau Casualty

Licensed in: AR, CO, FL, LA, MS, SC

Commenced Business: September 1947

Address: 1800 E County Line Rd, Ridgeland, MS 39157

Phone: (601) 957-7777   **Domicile State:** MS   **NAIC Code:** 18325

Data Date	Rating	RACR #1	RACR #2	Loss Ratio %	Total Assets ($mil)	Capital ($mil)	Net Premium ($mil)	Net Income ($mil)
6-16	B-	2.10	1.93	N/A	2,152.0	1,311.0	420.5	-16.1
6-15	B-	2.23	2.01	N/A	2,132.7	1,315.2	415.3	20.9
2015	B-	2.13	1.98	83.9	2,150.3	1,317.8	838.3	9.8
2014	B-	2.21	2.03	79.5	2,094.5	1,275.6	841.7	50.7
2013	B-	2.29	2.09	80.3	1,998.3	1,235.9	825.8	36.4
2012	B-	2.34	2.12	74.3	1,899.2	1,161.1	803.0	70.8
2011	B-	2.28	2.04	85.0	1,804.8	1,064.3	794.0	10.3

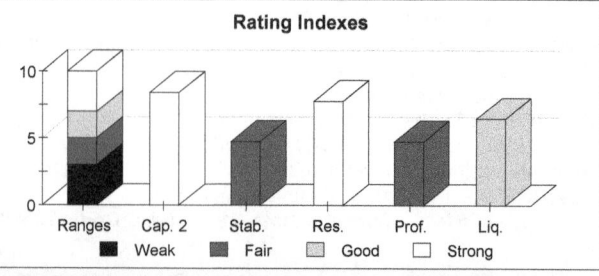

Rating Indexes

SOUTHERN-OWNERS INS CO *   B+   Good

Major Rating Factors: Good liquidity (6.8 on a scale of 0 to 10) with sufficient resources (cash flows and marketable investments) to handle a spike in claims. Good overall results on stability tests (5.2) despite weak results on operational trends.

Other Rating Factors: Strong long-term capitalization index (8.6) based on excellent current risk adjusted capital (severe and moderate loss scenarios). Moreover, capital levels have been consistent in recent years. Ample reserve history (9.0) that helps to protect the company against sharp claims increases. Excellent profitability (7.5) with operating gains in each of the last five years.

Principal Business: Auto liability (38%), other liability (27%), auto physical damage (13%), commercial multiple peril (12%), workers compensation (5%), homeowners multiple peril (3%), and inland marine (2%).

Principal Investments: Investment grade bonds (87%) and misc. investments (13%).

Investments in Affiliates: None

Group Affiliation: Auto-Owners Group

Licensed in: FL, MI

Commenced Business: June 1995

Address: 6101 Anacapri Blvd, Lansing, MI 48917-3968

Phone: (517) 323-1200   **Domicile State:** MI   **NAIC Code:** 10190

Data Date	Rating	RACR #1	RACR #2	Loss Ratio %	Total Assets ($mil)	Capital ($mil)	Net Premium ($mil)	Net Income ($mil)
6-16	B+	2.86	2.03	N/A	695.8	228.5	136.8	6.3
6-15	B+	2.67	1.93	N/A	662.5	206.9	127.3	8.3
2015	B+	2.88	2.08	65.1	665.7	219.5	266.1	24.4
2014	B+	2.64	1.93	70.9	628.8	198.2	247.1	13.1
2013	A	2.73	2.04	74.0	573.8	184.6	224.9	13.5
2012	A-	2.59	1.93	80.4	537.8	161.5	204.4	2.2
2011	A-	2.73	1.80	82.0	497.2	156.3	186.5	0.4

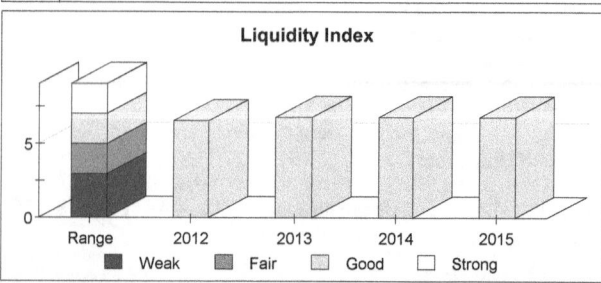

Liquidity Index

ST PAUL FIRE & MARINE INS CO   B   Good

Major Rating Factors: Good liquidity (6.8 on a scale of 0 to 10) with sufficient resources (cash flows and marketable investments) to handle a spike in claims. Good overall results on stability tests (5.1) despite weak results on operational trends.

Other Rating Factors: Fair profitability index (4.0). Fair expense controls. Return on equity has been fair, averaging 13.4% over the past five years. Strong long-term capitalization index (7.7) based on excellent current risk adjusted capital (severe and moderate loss scenarios), despite some fluctuation in capital levels. Ample reserve history (8.6) that helps to protect the company against sharp claims increases.

Principal Business: Other liability (51%), auto liability (16%), products liability (8%), fire (8%), inland marine (6%), auto physical damage (5%), and other lines (7%).

Principal Investments: Investment grade bonds (69%), misc. investments (23%), real estate (5%), and non investment grade bonds (3%).

Investments in Affiliates: 15%

Group Affiliation: Travelers Companies Inc

Licensed in: All states, the District of Columbia and Puerto Rico

Commenced Business: April 1925

Address: One Tower Square, Hartford, CT 06183

Phone: (860) 277-0111   **Domicile State:** CT   **NAIC Code:** 24767

Data Date	Rating	RACR #1	RACR #2	Loss Ratio %	Total Assets ($mil)	Capital ($mil)	Net Premium ($mil)	Net Income ($mil)
6-16	B	1.88	1.42	N/A	18,479.2	5,641.7	2,644.8	275.2
6-15	B	1.53	1.24	N/A	18,463.9	5,843.9	2,562.1	385.2
2015	B	1.90	1.45	58.8	18,297.4	5,563.3	5,252.1	1,186.6
2014	B	1.58	1.28	60.3	18,917.2	5,994.1	5,123.4	933.7
2013	B	1.57	1.29	60.5	18,566.3	5,914.7	5,131.4	883.9
2012	B	1.59	1.32	67.7	18,761.8	6,000.7	5,006.4	594.8
2011	B	1.57	1.28	76.1	18,414.7	5,713.6	4,923.4	401.5

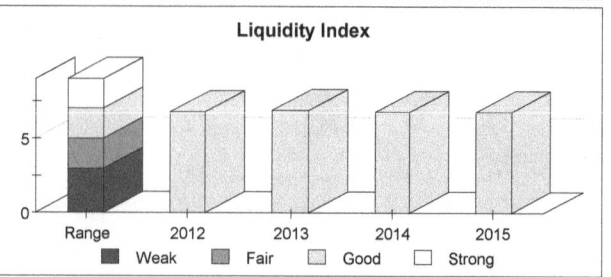

Liquidity Index

ST PAUL PROTECTIVE INS CO   B-   Good

Major Rating Factors: Fair overall results on stability tests (4.6 on a scale of 0 to 10) including fair financial strength of affiliated Travelers Companies Inc and weak results on operational trends. Good overall profitability index (6.1). Fair expense controls. Return on equity has been fair, averaging 7.9% over the past five years.

Other Rating Factors: Good liquidity (6.8) with sufficient resources (cash flows and marketable investments) to handle a spike in claims. Strong long-term capitalization index (10.0) based on excellent current risk adjusted capital (severe and moderate loss scenarios), despite some fluctuation in capital levels. Ample reserve history (7.9) that can protect against increases in claims costs.

Principal Business: Auto liability (71%) and auto physical damage (29%).

Principal Investments: Investment grade bonds (98%) and misc. investments (2%).

Investments in Affiliates: None

Group Affiliation: Travelers Companies Inc

Licensed in: All states, the District of Columbia and Puerto Rico

Commenced Business: February 1932

Address: One Tower Square, Hartford, CT 06183

Phone: (651) 310-7911   **Domicile State:** CT   **NAIC Code:** 19224

Data Date	Rating	RACR #1	RACR #2	Loss Ratio %	Total Assets ($mil)	Capital ($mil)	Net Premium ($mil)	Net Income ($mil)
6-16	B-	4.94	3.13	N/A	520.9	235.2	60.8	7.9
6-15	B-	5.04	3.17	N/A	516.4	235.9	58.6	9.8
2015	B-	4.91	3.12	58.7	507.6	227.3	120.6	21.2
2014	B-	4.91	3.09	60.5	507.8	226.2	117.1	20.4
2013	B-	5.04	3.21	60.9	510.1	228.2	116.8	22.8
2012	B-	5.02	3.23	68.4	506.8	224.2	113.4	16.3
2011	B-	4.92	3.18	76.9	500.4	221.6	111.1	9.7

Travelers Companies Inc
Composite Group Rating: B+
Largest Group Members

	Assets ($mil)	Rating
TRAVELERS INDEMNITY CO	20818	B+
ST PAUL FIRE MARINE INS CO	18297	B
TRAVELERS CASUALTY SURETY CO	16274	A-
TRAVELERS CASUALTY SURETY CO OF AM	4185	C+
PHOENIX INS CO	4175	B

ST PAUL SURPLUS LINES INS CO   C   Fair

Major Rating Factors: Good long-term capitalization index (5.0 on a scale of 0 to 10) based on fair current risk adjusted capital (severe loss scenario), although results have slipped from the good range over the last two years. Fair overall results on stability tests (4.0) including weak results on operational trends and fair risk adjusted capital in prior years.

Other Rating Factors: Good liquidity (6.6) with sufficient resources (cash flows and marketable investments) to handle a spike in claims. Ample reserve history (8.6) that helps to protect the company against sharp claims increases. Excellent profitability (7.0) with operating gains in each of the last five years. Return on equity has been good over the last five years, averaging 11.6%.

Principal Business: Other liability (85%), products liability (5%), fire (4%), inland marine (3%), and allied lines (3%).

Principal Investments: Investment grade bonds (98%) and misc. investments (2%).

Investments in Affiliates: None

Group Affiliation: Travelers Companies Inc

Licensed in: All states, the District of Columbia and Puerto Rico

Commenced Business: December 1974

Address: 2711 Centerville Rd Suite 400, Wilmington, DE 19808

Phone: (651) 310-7911   **Domicile State:** DE   **NAIC Code:** 30481

Data Date	Rating	RACR #1	RACR #2	Loss Ratio %	Total Assets ($mil)	Capital ($mil)	Net Premium ($mil)	Net Income ($mil)
6-16	C	1.04	0.68	N/A	641.4	207.9	92.2	11.2
6-15	C	1.56	1.01	N/A	633.0	207.6	88.9	12.9
2015	C	1.00	0.65	58.7	621.3	196.7	182.9	28.1
2014	C	1.48	0.96	60.5	633.6	194.9	177.7	27.0
2013	C	1.83	1.18	60.9	619.0	193.6	177.2	28.7
2012	C	1.75	1.14	68.4	625.0	181.9	172.1	19.3
2011	C	1.91	1.24	76.9	603.5	173.1	168.5	8.6

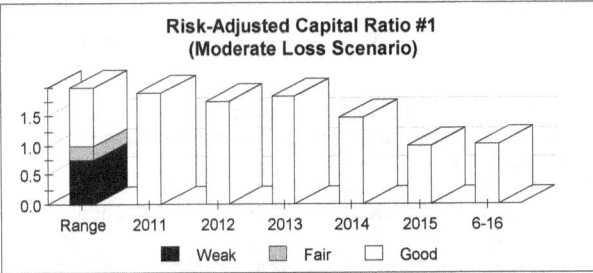

Risk-Adjusted Capital Ratio #1
(Moderate Loss Scenario)

STANDARD FIRE INS CO   B   Good

Major Rating Factors: Good overall profitability index (6.7 on a scale of 0 to 10). Fair expense controls. Return on equity has been good over the last five years, averaging 14.5%. Good liquidity (6.8) with sufficient resources (cash flows and marketable investments) to handle a spike in claims.

Other Rating Factors: Good overall results on stability tests (5.0) despite weak results on operational trends. Affiliation with Travelers Companies Inc is a strength. Strong long-term capitalization index (7.7) based on excellent current risk adjusted capital (severe and moderate loss scenarios), despite some fluctuation in capital levels. Ample reserve history (8.4) that helps to protect the company against sharp claims increases.

Principal Business: Auto liability (36%), homeowners multiple peril (26%), auto physical damage (22%), workers compensation (10%), ocean marine (2%), fire (1%), and other lines (3%).

Principal Investments: Investment grade bonds (69%), misc. investments (28%), and non investment grade bonds (3%).

Investments in Affiliates: 17%

Group Affiliation: Travelers Companies Inc

Licensed in: All states, the District of Columbia and Puerto Rico

Commenced Business: March 1910

Address: One Tower Square, Hartford, CT 06183

Phone: (860) 277-0111   **Domicile State:** CT   **NAIC Code:** 19070

Data Date	Rating	RACR #1	RACR #2	Loss Ratio %	Total Assets ($mil)	Capital ($mil)	Net Premium ($mil)	Net Income ($mil)
6-16	B	1.88	1.47	N/A	3,665.0	1,205.9	507.1	51.6
6-15	B	1.91	1.48	N/A	3,608.7	1,207.9	488.7	62.2
2015	B	1.90	1.49	58.7	3,583.9	1,185.5	1,005.7	204.8
2014	B	1.96	1.53	60.5	3,627.1	1,215.2	977.2	228.2
2013	B	2.02	1.60	60.9	3,605.3	1,234.8	974.8	217.9
2012	B-	1.82	1.43	68.4	3,440.2	1,057.8	946.7	130.7
2011	C+	1.78	1.39	76.9	3,374.0	1,009.9	926.9	94.6

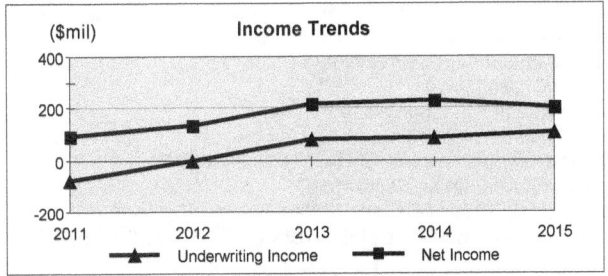

($mil)   Income Trends

STAR INS CO   C   Fair

Major Rating Factors: Fair overall results on stability tests (3.6 on a scale of 0 to 10) including potential drain of affiliation with Meadowbrook Ins Group and weak results on operational trends. Fair reserve development (3.3) as reserves have generally been sufficient to cover claims. In 2013, the two year reserve development was 19% deficient.

Other Rating Factors: Good overall profitability index (5.7) despite operating losses during 2015. Return on equity has been low, averaging 4.5% over the past five years. Good liquidity (6.7) with sufficient resources (cash flows and marketable investments) to handle a spike in claims. Strong long-term capitalization index (7.9) based on excellent current risk adjusted capital (severe and moderate loss scenarios), despite some fluctuation in capital levels.

Principal Business: Workers compensation (73%), commercial multiple peril (8%), inland marine (7%), auto liability (6%), auto physical damage (2%), other liability (2%), and other lines (3%).

Principal Investments: Investment grade bonds (81%), misc. investments (17%), cash (1%), and non investment grade bonds (1%).

Investments in Affiliates: 17%

Group Affiliation: Meadowbrook Ins Group

Licensed in: All states except PR

Commenced Business: November 1985

Address: 26255 American Drive, Southfield, MI 48034-6112

Phone: (248) 358-1100   **Domicile State:** MI   **NAIC Code:** 18023

Data Date	Rating	RACR #1	RACR #2	Loss Ratio %	Total Assets ($mil)	Capital ($mil)	Net Premium ($mil)	Net Income ($mil)
6-16	C	2.13	1.74	N/A	862.8	312.3	104.6	26.3
6-15	C	2.22	1.87	N/A	875.8	335.3	105.9	7.7
2015	C	2.13	1.74	77.1	946.4	314.1	213.0	-9.8
2014	C	2.15	1.82	66.4	963.8	324.3	211.6	14.7
2013	C	2.10	1.73	79.2	1,000.3	309.6	245.7	3.9
2012	C	1.73	1.39	79.3	956.8	263.1	285.7	5.8
2011	C	1.48	1.13	65.9	861.9	229.1	275.0	25.8

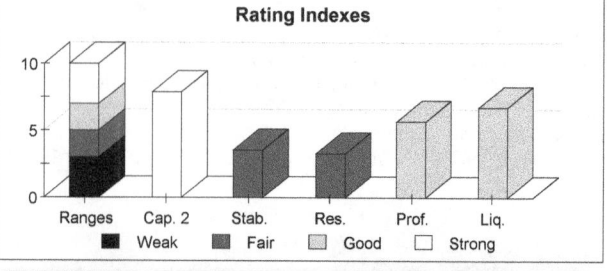

Rating Indexes

STARR INDEMNITY & LIABILITY CO   B   Good

Major Rating Factors: Good liquidity (6.8 on a scale of 0 to 10) with sufficient resources (cash flows and marketable investments) to handle a spike in claims. Fair overall results on stability tests (4.5) including potential drain of affiliation with Starr International Co Inc and weak results on operational trends. The largest net exposure for one risk is conservative at 1.3% of capital.

Other Rating Factors: Fair reserve development (4.9) as reserves have generally been sufficient to cover claims. Strong long-term capitalization index (7.2) based on excellent current risk adjusted capital (severe and moderate loss scenarios), despite some fluctuation in capital levels. Excellent profitability (7.7) with operating gains in each of the last five years.

Principal Business: Other liability (33%), workers compensation (25%), ocean marine (13%), aircraft (10%), auto liability (5%), commercial multiple peril (5%), and other lines (9%).

Principal Investments: Misc. investments (50%), investment grade bonds (47%), and cash (3%).

Investments in Affiliates: 36%

Group Affiliation: Starr International Co Inc

Licensed in: All states, the District of Columbia and Puerto Rico

Commenced Business: May 1919

Address: 2727 Turtle Creek Blvd, Dallas, TX 75219

Phone: (646) 227-6400   **Domicile State:** TX   **NAIC Code:** 38318

Data Date	Rating	RACR #1	RACR #2	Loss Ratio %	Total Assets ($mil)	Capital ($mil)	Net Premium ($mil)	Net Income ($mil)
6-16	B	1.40	1.15	N/A	4,391.4	2,017.5	534.6	32.4
6-15	B	1.33	1.11	N/A	4,037.5	1,924.1	514.4	47.3
2015	B	1.33	1.12	75.0	4,002.0	1,847.6	1,078.1	73.8
2014	B	1.30	1.12	78.2	3,755.1	1,832.3	1,015.8	54.6
2013	B-	1.35	1.13	81.6	3,467.4	1,865.1	847.3	13.2
2012	B-	1.38	1.22	76.7	2,904.1	1,871.3	625.3	14.9
2011	C+	1.85	1.20	79.5	1,158.3	539.0	402.5	1.7

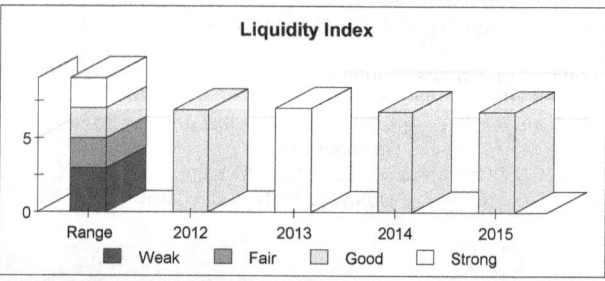

Liquidity Index

STATE AUTO P&C INS CO   C   Fair

Major Rating Factors: Fair overall results on stability tests (4.3 on a scale of 0 to 10) including potential drain of affiliation with State Auto Mutual Group and weak results on operational trends. Fair profitability index (4.6) with operating losses during 2011, 2014 and the first six months of 2016. Return on equity has been low, averaging 0.2% over the past five years.

Other Rating Factors: History of adequate reserve strength (5.8) as reserves have been consistently at an acceptable level. Good liquidity (6.2) with sufficient resources (cash flows and marketable investments) to handle a spike in claims. Strong long-term capitalization index (7.4) based on excellent current risk adjusted capital (severe and moderate loss scenarios), despite some fluctuation in capital levels.

Principal Business: Homeowners multiple peril (27%), auto liability (21%), commercial multiple peril (19%), auto physical damage (13%), other liability (6%), allied lines (5%), and other lines (9%).

Principal Investments: Investment grade bonds (75%), misc. investments (24%), and cash (1%).

Investments in Affiliates: None

Group Affiliation: State Auto Mutual Group

Licensed in: All states except CA, NH, NM, WA, PR

Commenced Business: April 1950

Address: 112 S Main St, Greer, SC 29650

Phone: (614) 464-5000   **Domicile State:** IA   **NAIC Code:** 25127

Data Date	Rating	RACR #1	RACR #2	Loss Ratio %	Total Assets ($mil)	Capital ($mil)	Net Premium ($mil)	Net Income ($mil)
6-16	C	1.97	1.24	N/A	2,404.1	636.0	504.0	-16.3
6-15	C-	1.98	1.22	N/A	2,313.3	642.7	491.8	26.5
2015	C	2.11	1.34	68.5	2,355.6	655.3	999.2	52.3
2014	C-	2.08	1.28	71.6	2,291.5	628.9	937.0	-13.6
2013	C-	2.19	1.40	68.5	2,066.5	607.7	833.3	39.6
2012	D+	1.92	1.26	74.8	1,889.0	505.5	828.0	3.5
2011	D	1.55	0.94	82.4	2,122.2	506.7	1,000.0	-48.7

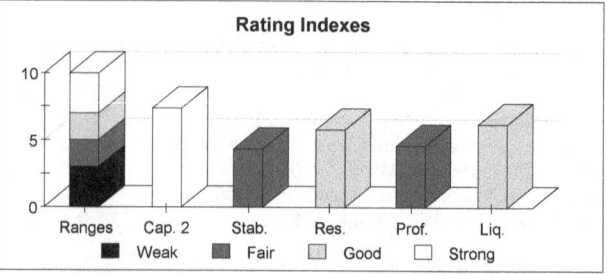

Rating Indexes

STATE AUTOMOBILE MUTUAL INS CO   C+   Fair

Major Rating Factors: Fair overall results on stability tests (4.3 on a scale of 0 to 10) including potential drain of affiliation with State Auto Mutual Group and weak results on operational trends. Fair profitability index (3.7) with operating losses during 2011, 2012, 2013, 2014 and the first six months of 2016.

Other Rating Factors: History of adequate reserve strength (5.9) as reserves have been consistently at an acceptable level. Good liquidity (6.3) with sufficient resources (cash flows and marketable investments) to handle a spike in claims. Strong long-term capitalization index (7.1) based on excellent current risk adjusted capital (severe and moderate loss scenarios), despite some fluctuation in capital levels.

Principal Business: Auto liability (23%), auto physical damage (13%), homeowners multiple peril (12%), other liability (12%), commercial multiple peril (10%), farmowners multiple peril (9%), and other lines (22%).

Principal Investments: Misc. investments (57%), investment grade bonds (38%), cash (4%), and real estate (1%).

Investments in Affiliates: 47%

Group Affiliation: State Auto Mutual Group

Licensed in: All states except PR

Commenced Business: September 1921

Address: 518 E Broad St, Columbus, OH 43215-3976

Phone: (614) 464-5000   **Domicile State:** OH   **NAIC Code:** 25135

Data Date	Rating	RACR #1	RACR #2	Loss Ratio %	Total Assets ($mil)	Capital ($mil)	Net Premium ($mil)	Net Income ($mil)
6-16	C+	1.11	1.01	N/A	2,449.7	775.9	340.9	-16.6
6-15	C+	1.20	1.07	N/A	2,428.6	829.7	332.7	4.6
2015	C+	1.19	1.08	68.5	2,386.4	824.7	675.9	5.2
2014	C+	1.21	1.10	71.5	2,352.1	816.8	633.8	-17.6
2013	C+	1.33	1.22	68.5	2,205.9	866.3	563.7	-2.8
2012	C	1.28	1.17	74.6	2,093.8	748.7	552.0	-10.4
2011	C+	1.16	1.10	82.2	2,156.9	785.5	437.2	-42.5

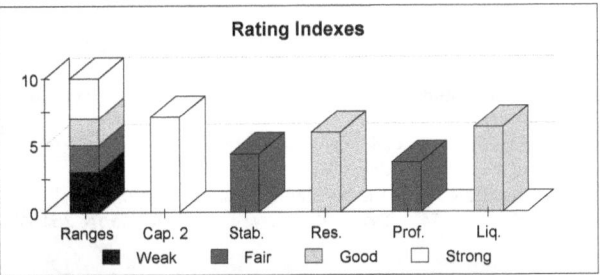

Rating Indexes

STATE FARM FIRE & CAS CO   B   Good

Major Rating Factors: Good overall results on stability tests (5.1 on a scale of 0 to 10) despite weak results on operational trends. Affiliation with State Farm Group is a strength. Good overall profitability index (5.2) despite operating losses during 2011. Return on equity has been fair, averaging 7.5% over the past five years.

Other Rating Factors: Good liquidity (5.5) with sufficient resources (cash flows and marketable investments) to handle a spike in claims. Strong long-term capitalization index (7.4) based on excellent current risk adjusted capital (severe and moderate loss scenarios). Moreover, capital levels have been consistent in recent years. Ample reserve history (8.0) that helps to protect the company against sharp claims increases.

Principal Business: Homeowners multiple peril (71%), auto liability (8%), commercial multiple peril (6%), auto physical damage (4%), other liability (3%), inland marine (3%), and other lines (4%).

Principal Investments: Investment grade bonds (79%) and misc. investments (21%).

Investments in Affiliates: None

Group Affiliation: State Farm Group

Licensed in: All states except PR

Commenced Business: June 1935

Address: One State Farm Plaza, Bloomington, IL 61710

Phone: (309) 766-2311   **Domicile State:** IL   **NAIC Code:** 25143

Data Date	Rating	RACR #1	RACR #2	Loss Ratio %	Total Assets ($mil)	Capital ($mil)	Net Premium ($mil)	Net Income ($mil)
6-16	B	2.58	1.60	N/A	37,184.7	15,447.6	8,100.8	1,089.0
6-15	B-	2.27	1.44	N/A	34,406.0	13,042.3	7,838.2	1,243.1
2015	B	2.41	1.49	60.8	35,495.7	14,196.8	15,914.0	2,543.8
2014	B-	2.15	1.34	65.9	33,481.0	12,193.8	15,917.6	1,853.0
2013	B-	1.99	1.23	63.5	31,460.7	10,951.2	15,276.5	1,803.8
2012	C+	1.64	1.01	77.4	28,999.1	8,805.4	14,409.5	317.2
2011	C	1.45	0.86	91.3	27,243.3	7,748.7	14,161.4	-1,465.1

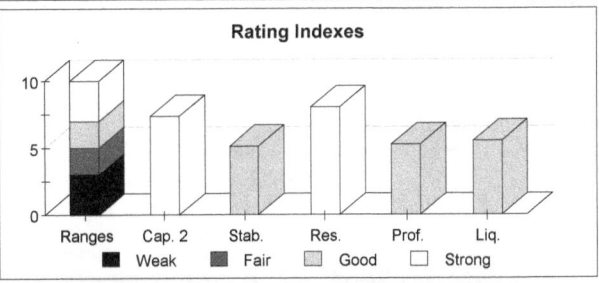

Rating Indexes

STATE FARM FLORIDA INS CO   B-   Good

Major Rating Factors: Fair overall results on stability tests (4.9 on a scale of 0 to 10) including weak results on operational trends. History of adequate reserve strength (6.5) as reserves have been consistently at an acceptable level.

Other Rating Factors: Good liquidity (6.8) with sufficient resources (cash flows and marketable investments) to handle a spike in claims. Strong long-term capitalization index (9.3) based on excellent current risk adjusted capital (severe and moderate loss scenarios). Moreover, capital levels have been consistent in recent years. Excellent profitability (9.1) with operating gains in each of the last five years. Return on equity has been excellent over the last five years averaging 19.2%.

Principal Business: Homeowners multiple peril (87%), other liability (5%), inland marine (5%), and commercial multiple peril (3%).

Principal Investments: Investment grade bonds (88%) and misc. investments (12%).

Investments in Affiliates: None

Group Affiliation: State Farm Group

Licensed in: FL, IL

Commenced Business: December 1998

Address: One State Farm Plaza, Bloomington, IL 61710

Phone: (863) 318-3000   **Domicile State:** FL   **NAIC Code:** 10739

Data Date	Rating	RACR #1	RACR #2	Loss Ratio %	Total Assets ($mil)	Capital ($mil)	Net Premium ($mil)	Net Income ($mil)
6-16	B-	4.98	3.50	N/A	2,073.8	1,103.0	289.3	68.5
6-15	C	4.00	2.77	N/A	1,972.5	965.3	298.7	90.4
2015	C+	4.45	3.14	42.1	1,991.9	1,033.8	584.0	179.8
2014	C	3.79	2.63	36.2	1,915.6	894.5	588.7	155.1
2013	C-	1.60	1.13	40.8	1,793.7	734.6	575.4	174.5
2012	D+	1.04	0.73	53.4	1,766.2	534.5	597.3	144.5
2011	D	0.55	0.39	72.1	1,744.1	368.1	699.4	50.8

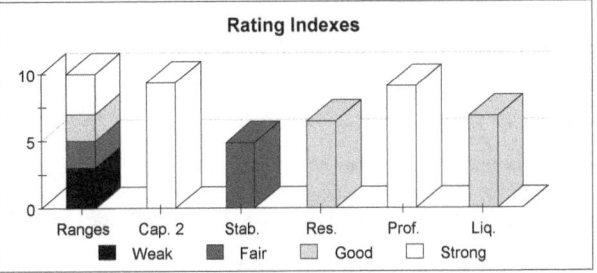

Rating Indexes

STATE FARM GENERAL INS CO | B | Good

Major Rating Factors: Good overall results on stability tests (5.0 on a scale of 0 to 10) despite weak results on operational trends. Affiliation with State Farm Group is a strength. History of adequate reserve strength (6.5) as reserves have been consistently at an acceptable level.

Other Rating Factors: Good liquidity (6.7) with sufficient resources (cash flows and marketable investments) to handle a spike in claims. Strong long-term capitalization index (10.0) based on excellent current risk adjusted capital (severe and moderate loss scenarios). Moreover, capital levels have been consistent in recent years. Excellent profitability (8.8) with operating gains in each of the last five years.

Principal Business: Homeowners multiple peril (73%), commercial multiple peril (15%), other liability (8%), inland marine (3%), earthquake (1%), and farmowners multiple peril (1%).

Principal Investments: Investment grade bonds (97%) and misc. investments (3%).

Investments in Affiliates: None
Group Affiliation: State Farm Group
Licensed in: All states except CT, MA, RI, PR
Commenced Business: May 1962
Address: One State Farm Plaza, Bloomington, IL 61710
Phone: (309) 766-2311 **Domicile State:** IL **NAIC Code:** 25151

Data Date	Rating	RACR #1	RACR #2	Loss Ratio %	Total Assets ($mil)	Capital ($mil)	Net Premium ($mil)	Net Income ($mil)
6-16	B	6.75	4.54	N/A	7,064.0	4,108.0	957.4	106.1
6-15	B	6.60	4.41	N/A	6,794.9	3,971.1	940.4	165.1
2015	B	6.66	4.33	71.5	6,918.7	3,991.2	1,904.2	174.0
2014	B	6.35	4.11	57.6	6,714.9	3,821.2	1,893.1	352.2
2013	B	5.25	3.31	55.5	6,388.1	3,452.6	1,919.0	379.9
2012	B	4.19	2.61	63.1	6,061.2	3,101.9	1,976.9	268.2
2011	B	3.07	1.87	55.1	5,685.5	2,817.9	1,958.9	346.1

Rating Indexes

STATE FARM INDEMNITY CO | B | Good

Major Rating Factors: Good overall profitability index (6.7 on a scale of 0 to 10). Good expense controls. Return on equity has been fair, averaging 6.4% over the past five years. Good liquidity (6.7) with sufficient resources (cash flows and marketable investments) to handle a spike in claims.

Other Rating Factors: Good overall results on stability tests (5.0) despite weak results on operational trends. Affiliation with State Farm Group is a strength. Strong long-term capitalization index (10.0) based on excellent current risk adjusted capital (severe and moderate loss scenarios). Moreover, capital levels have been consistent in recent years. Ample reserve history (9.3) that helps to protect the company against sharp claims increases.

Principal Business: Auto liability (73%) and auto physical damage (27%).

Principal Investments: Investment grade bonds (96%) and misc. investments (4%).

Investments in Affiliates: 1%
Group Affiliation: State Farm Group
Licensed in: IL, NJ
Commenced Business: March 1991
Address: One State Farm Plaza, Bloomington, IL 61710
Phone: (973) 739-5000 **Domicile State:** IL **NAIC Code:** 43796

Data Date	Rating	RACR #1	RACR #2	Loss Ratio %	Total Assets ($mil)	Capital ($mil)	Net Premium ($mil)	Net Income ($mil)
6-16	B	5.83	5.00	N/A	2,231.1	1,209.0	312.1	17.7
6-15	B-	5.46	4.53	N/A	2,180.0	1,152.5	307.2	39.6
2015	B	5.42	4.95	82.5	2,219.7	1,194.6	621.0	78.1
2014	B-	4.95	4.36	81.1	2,158.4	1,113.6	610.1	56.0
2013	B-	4.72	4.14	75.6	2,098.9	1,061.7	603.6	74.5
2012	B-	3.97	3.45	80.2	2,047.2	965.9	597.5	56.5
2011	C+	3.56	3.10	79.3	2,058.9	927.1	614.6	83.5

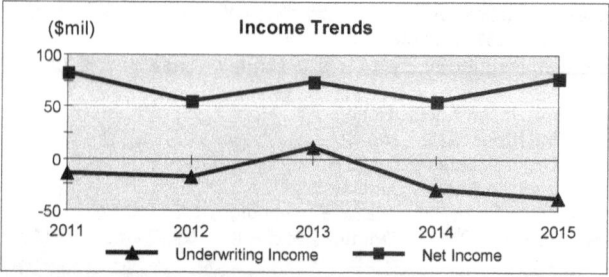

($mil) Income Trends

STATE FARM LLOYDS | B | Good

Major Rating Factors: Good overall results on stability tests (5.0 on a scale of 0 to 10) despite weak results on operational trends and negative cash flow from operations for 2015. Affiliation with State Farm Group is a strength. History of adequate reserve strength (6.9) as reserves have been consistently at an acceptable level.

Other Rating Factors: Good overall profitability index (6.2) despite operating losses during 2011 and 2014. Return on equity has been good over the last five years, averaging 11.4%. Good liquidity (5.9) with sufficient resources (cash flows and marketable investments) to handle a spike in claims. Strong long-term capitalization index (8.4) based on excellent current risk adjusted capital (severe and moderate loss scenarios), despite some fluctuation in capital levels.

Principal Business: Homeowners multiple peril (93%), commercial multiple peril (5%), and farmowners multiple peril (2%).

Principal Investments: Investment grade bonds (96%) and misc. investments (6%).

Investments in Affiliates: None
Group Affiliation: State Farm Group
Licensed in: TX
Commenced Business: June 1983
Address: 17301 Preston Rd, Dallas, TX 75252
Phone: (972) 732-5000 **Domicile State:** TX **NAIC Code:** 43419

Data Date	Rating	RACR #1	RACR #2	Loss Ratio %	Total Assets ($mil)	Capital ($mil)	Net Premium ($mil)	Net Income ($mil)
6-16	B	2.58	2.36	N/A	3,331.5	1,185.5	881.6	42.3
6-15	B-	1.64	1.18	N/A	3,649.4	1,072.0	894.5	47.4
2015	B	2.64	2.22	63.0	3,250.8	1,213.8	1,572.6	412.2
2014	B-	1.67	1.21	51.1	3,490.8	1,039.5	1,799.7	-54.3
2013	B-	2.26	1.93	53.5	3,075.5	1,105.4	1,712.7	215.2
2012	C+	2.39	2.03	59.8	2,927.0	1,073.3	1,484.6	153.4
2011	C	2.02	1.51	76.9	2,803.5	916.9	1,536.7	-32.0

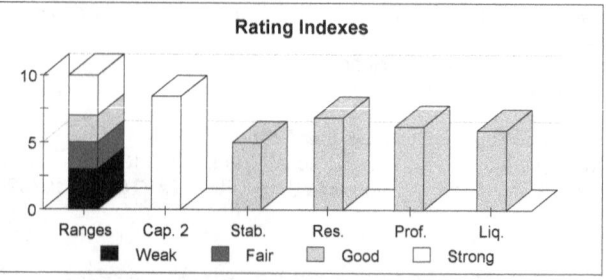

Rating Indexes

STATE FARM MUTUAL AUTOMOBILE INS CO *   B+   Good

Major Rating Factors: Good liquidity (6.5 on a scale of 0 to 10) with sufficient resources (cash flows and marketable investments) to handle a spike in claims. Good overall results on stability tests (5.3) despite weak results on operational trends.

Other Rating Factors: Strong long-term capitalization index (8.0) based on excellent current risk adjusted capital (severe and moderate loss scenarios). Moreover, capital levels have been consistent in recent years. Ample reserve history (7.7) that can protect against increases in claims costs. Fair profitability index (4.6) with operating losses during the first six months of 2016.

Principal Business: Auto liability (58%), auto physical damage (39%), other accident & health (2%), and group accident & health (1%).

Principal Investments: Misc. investments (68%) and investment grade bonds (32%).

Investments in Affiliates: 27%

Group Affiliation: State Farm Group

Licensed in: All states except PR

Commenced Business: June 1922

Address: One State Farm Plaza, Bloomington, IL 61710

Phone: (309) 766-2311   **Domicile State:** IL   **NAIC Code:** 25178

Data Date	Rating	RACR #1	RACR #2	Loss Ratio %	Total Assets ($mil)	Capital ($mil)	Net Premium ($mil)	Net Income ($mil)
6-16	B+	2.08	1.79	N/A	143,802.0	86,467.6	19,444.7	-439.3
6-15	B+	2.13	1.81	N/A	139,365.9	81,442.7	18,232.4	1,859.5
2015	B+	2.03	1.76	84.5	138,494.7	82,630.7	37,511.4	2,137.2
2014	B+	2.10	1.79	82.2	138,797.9	79,876.9	36,928.5	1,045.8
2013	B+	2.18	1.84	79.9	129,337.9	75,678.9	35,163.3	1,836.5
2012	B+	2.14	1.81	78.1	114,933.2	65,241.9	33,697.9	1,525.0
2011	B+	2.17	1.83	82.4	108,097.4	60,791.0	32,844.2	1,088.2

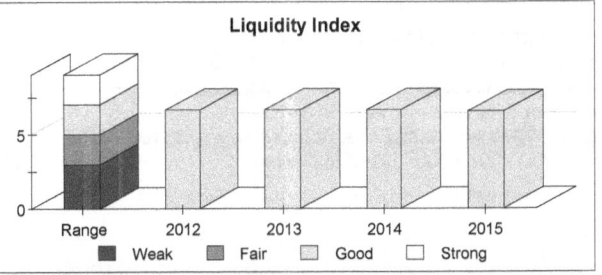

Liquidity Index

STATE NATIONAL INS CO   B-   Good

Major Rating Factors: Fair overall results on stability tests (4.1 on a scale of 0 to 10) including potential drain of affiliation with TX State National Group and weak results on operational trends. History of adequate reserve strength (5.1) as reserves have been consistently at an acceptable level.

Other Rating Factors: Strong long-term capitalization index (8.2) based on excellent current risk adjusted capital (severe and moderate loss scenarios). Moreover, capital levels have been consistent in recent years. Excellent profitability (7.6) with operating gains in each of the last five years. Excellent liquidity (7.0) with ample operational cash flow and liquid investments.

Principal Business: Auto physical damage (29%), other liability (18%), commercial multiple peril (16%), auto liability (14%), workers compensation (6%), aircraft (2%), and other lines (16%).

Principal Investments: Misc. investments (48%), investment grade bonds (43%), real estate (5%), cash (2%), and non investment grade bonds (2%).

Investments in Affiliates: 46%

Group Affiliation: TX State National Group

Licensed in: All states except PR

Commenced Business: September 1984

Address: 8200 Anderson Blvd., Fort Worth, TX 76120

Phone: (817) 265-2000   **Domicile State:** TX   **NAIC Code:** 12831

Data Date	Rating	RACR #1	RACR #2	Loss Ratio %	Total Assets ($mil)	Capital ($mil)	Net Premium ($mil)	Net Income ($mil)
6-16	B-	1.96	1.83	N/A	321.6	236.8	26.8	2.7
6-15	C+	1.98	1.86	N/A	302.6	223.3	24.8	2.7
2015	B-	1.92	1.81	49.1	319.3	229.8	56.2	5.6
2014	C+	1.94	1.84	42.5	290.7	215.8	52.2	3.2
2013	C+	1.94	1.81	40.3	218.8	155.6	42.0	2.5
2012	C+	1.92	1.79	39.3	206.9	147.8	30.3	4.9
2011	C+	2.70	2.40	39.5	204.4	140.7	51.9	5.7

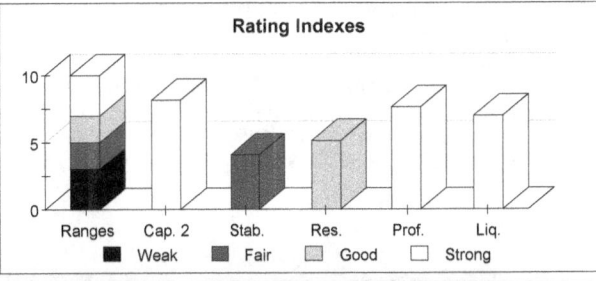

Rating Indexes

STATE VOLUNTEER MUTUAL INS CO   B   Good

Major Rating Factors: Good overall profitability index (6.2 on a scale of 0 to 10) despite operating losses during the first six months of 2016. Fair overall results on stability tests (4.9) including weak results on operational trends.

Other Rating Factors: Strong long-term capitalization index (10.0) based on excellent current risk adjusted capital (severe and moderate loss scenarios). Moreover, capital levels have been consistent in recent years. Ample reserve history (9.4) that helps to protect the company against sharp claims increases. Excellent liquidity (8.7) with ample operational cash flow and liquid investments.

Principal Business: Medical malpractice (100%).

Principal Investments: Investment grade bonds (84%) and misc. investments (16%).

Investments in Affiliates: None

Group Affiliation: None

Licensed in: AL, AR, GA, IN, KY, MS, MO, NC, TN, VA

Commenced Business: May 1976

Address: 101 Westpark Dr Suite 300, Brentwood, TN 37024-1065

Phone: (615) 377-1999   **Domicile State:** TN   **NAIC Code:** 33049

Data Date	Rating	RACR #1	RACR #2	Loss Ratio %	Total Assets ($mil)	Capital ($mil)	Net Premium ($mil)	Net Income ($mil)
6-16	B	4.34	3.30	N/A	1,203.2	537.1	52.7	-3.7
6-15	B	3.95	2.88	N/A	1,199.9	513.3	51.8	-0.1
2015	B	4.43	3.39	79.5	1,193.2	538.0	113.4	25.5
2014	B	4.03	2.96	84.6	1,199.1	516.6	114.6	21.5
2013	A+	3.65	2.76	89.0	1,186.2	496.7	122.2	17.4
2012	A+	3.54	2.71	82.6	1,169.5	464.0	154.6	26.1
2011	A+	3.46	2.67	71.7	1,148.1	436.4	129.9	28.0

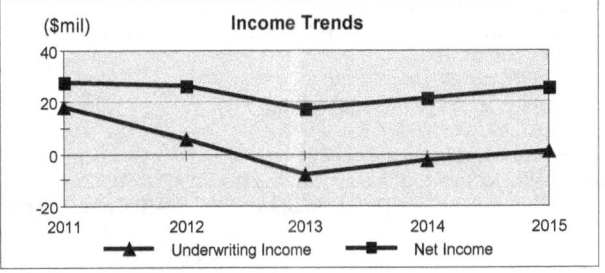

Income Trends

STEADFAST INS CO   C+   Fair

Major Rating Factors: Fair overall results on stability tests (4.5 on a scale of 0 to 10) including weak results on operational trends and negative cash flow from operations for 2015. Good liquidity (6.9) with sufficient resources (cash flows and marketable investments) to handle a spike in claims.

Other Rating Factors: Strong long-term capitalization index (9.1) based on excellent current risk adjusted capital (severe and moderate loss scenarios), despite some fluctuation in capital levels. Excellent profitability (7.4) with operating gains in each of the last five years.

Principal Business: Other liability (64%), commercial multiple peril (11%), medical malpractice (6%), allied lines (6%), fire (5%), auto liability (4%), and other lines (4%).

Principal Investments: Investment grade bonds (55%) and misc. investments (45%).

Investments in Affiliates: 45%

Group Affiliation: Zurich Financial Services Group

Licensed in: All states, the District of Columbia and Puerto Rico

Commenced Business: May 1988

Address: 1400 American Lane, Schaumburg, IL 60196-1056

Phone: (847) 605-6000   **Domicile State:** DE   **NAIC Code:** 26387

Data Date	Rating	RACR #1	RACR #2	Loss Ratio %	Total Assets ($mil)	Capital ($mil)	Net Premium ($mil)	Net Income ($mil)
6-16	C+	2.43	2.39	N/A	674.1	503.7	0.0	2.3
6-15	C	3.04	2.97	N/A	575.6	440.0	0.0	2.4
2015	C+	2.42	2.39	0.0	660.2	499.6	0.0	7.9
2014	C	3.03	2.98	0.0	528.8	436.2	0.0	9.1
2013	C	3.06	3.00	0.0	602.2	430.0	0.0	5.1
2012	C	3.21	3.15	0.0	555.4	444.4	0.0	12.7
2011	C	3.37	3.28	0.0	568.8	442.3	0.0	24.6

Zurich Financial Services Group
Composite Group Rating: C+

Largest Group Members	Assets ($mil)	Rating
ZURICH AMERICAN INS CO	30471	B-
ZURICH AMERICAN LIFE INS CO	12271	C
FARMERS NEW WORLD LIFE INS CO	7049	B-
RURAL COMMUNITY INS CO	3680	B
CENTRE LIFE INS CO	1884	B-

SWISS REINS AMERICA CORP   C+   Fair

Major Rating Factors: Good long-term capitalization index (5.0 on a scale of 0 to 10) based on fair current risk adjusted capital (severe loss scenario), although results have slipped from the good range during the last year. Fair profitability index (3.1). Fair expense controls. Return on equity has been fair, averaging 11.0% over the past five years.

Other Rating Factors: Fair overall results on stability tests (3.2) including weak results on operational trends. The largest net exposure for one risk is excessive at 5.3% of capital. Ample reserve history (9.3) that helps to protect the company against sharp claims increases. Excellent liquidity (7.0) with ample operational cash flow and liquid investments.

Principal Business: (This company is a reinsurer.)

Principal Investments: Investment grade bonds (76%), misc. investments (21%), and non investment grade bonds (3%).

Investments in Affiliates: None

Group Affiliation: Swiss Reinsurance

Licensed in: All states, the District of Columbia and Puerto Rico

Commenced Business: September 1940

Address: 175 King Street, Armonk, NY 10504

Phone: (914) 828-8000   **Domicile State:** NY   **NAIC Code:** 25364

Data Date	Rating	RACR #1	RACR #2	Loss Ratio %	Total Assets ($mil)	Capital ($mil)	Net Premium ($mil)	Net Income ($mil)
6-16	C+	0.93	0.68	N/A	13,573.0	3,124.8	943.1	92.5
6-15	B-	1.03	0.73	N/A	13,654.8	3,350.3	848.6	100.0
2015	B-	1.07	0.79	50.4	12,795.5	3,581.1	1,987.4	389.8
2014	B-	1.30	0.93	48.9	13,109.1	4,259.8	1,881.8	498.1
2013	B-	1.50	1.03	39.0	11,409.4	4,619.3	1,965.0	644.9
2012	B-	1.73	1.15	43.3	12,061.1	4,973.2	1,439.4	431.8
2011	C+	1.93	1.15	55.6	12,608.0	4,960.9	1,641.2	600.7

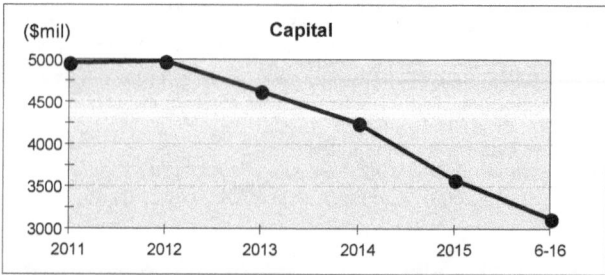

Capital ($mil)

SYNCORA CAPITAL ASR INC   E   Very Weak

Major Rating Factors: A history of deficient reserves (0.5 on a scale of 0 to 10) that places pressure on both capital and profits. Deficiencies in the two year reserve development occurred in three of the previous five years and ranged between 17% and 165%. Weak overall results on stability tests (0.0) including weak results on operational trends and negative cash flow from operations for 2015. The largest net exposure for one risk is excessive at 604.4% of capital.

Other Rating Factors: Fair profitability index (3.5) with operating losses during 2013, 2014 and the first six months of 2016. Average return on equity over the last five years has been poor at -6.5%. Strong long-term capitalization index (8.6) based on excellent current risk adjusted capital (severe and moderate loss scenarios), despite some fluctuation in capital levels. Superior liquidity (10.0) with ample operational cash flow and liquid investments.

Principal Business: Financial guaranty (100%).

Principal Investments: Investment grade bonds (80%), non investment grade bonds (18%), and cash (2%).

Investments in Affiliates: None

Group Affiliation: Syncora Holdings Ltd

Licensed in: ID, KY, MI, NY

Commenced Business: July 2009

Address: 1221 Avenue of the Americas, New York, NY 10020-1001

Phone: (212) 478-3400   **Domicile State:** NY   **NAIC Code:** 13666

Data Date	Rating	RACR #1	RACR #2	Loss Ratio %	Total Assets ($mil)	Capital ($mil)	Net Premium ($mil)	Net Income ($mil)
6-16	E	3.89	2.37	N/A	444.1	203.6	18.7	-9.6
6-15	E	2.76	1.96	N/A	488.6	153.2	23.9	-17.7
2015	E	3.55	2.22	55.3	468.9	192.1	11.7	4.6
2014	E	3.58	2.50	82.8	495.2	164.5	15.3	-74.3
2013	E	3.45	1.91	256.8	618.7	186.5	22.2	-108.6
2012	A-	4.07	2.79	10.3	720.9	172.6	31.5	42.0
2011	A-	2.53	2.02	11.8	716.2	132.7	37.4	60.4

Reserve Deficiency (as % of capital)

* Adequate & redundant reserves show as negatives
■ 1 Yr Dev
□ 2 Yr Dev

SYNCORA GUARANTEE INC   E-   Very Weak

Major Rating Factors: A history of deficient reserves (0.8 on a scale of 0 to 10). Underreserving can have an adverse impact on capital and profits. In 2014 and 2011 the one year reserve development was 114% and 177% deficient respectively. Weak overall results on stability tests (0.0) including weak results on operational trends and negative cash flow from operations for 2015. The largest net exposure for one risk is excessive at 85.5% of capital.

Other Rating Factors: Good profitability index (5.0) despite operating losses during 2011 and 2014. Return on equity has been good over the last five years, averaging 18.5%. Strong long-term capitalization index (10.0) based on excellent current risk adjusted capital (severe and moderate loss scenarios), despite some fluctuation in capital levels. Superior liquidity (10.0) with ample operational cash flow and liquid investments.

Principal Business: (Not applicable due to unusual reinsurance transactions.)
Principal Investments: Investment grade bonds (74%), misc. investments (20%), non investment grade bonds (5%), and cash (1%).
Investments in Affiliates: None
Group Affiliation: Syncora Holdings Ltd
Licensed in: All states except AK, FL, OH, TN, PR
Commenced Business: January 1872
Address: 250 Park Ave 19th Floor, New York, NY 10177-1999
Phone: (212) 478-3400   **Domicile State:** NY   **NAIC Code:** 20311

Data Date	Rating	RACR #1	RACR #2	Loss Ratio %	Total Assets ($mil)	Capital ($mil)	Net Premium ($mil)	Net Income ($mil)
6-16	E-	24.58	13.20	N/A	1,282.2	1,150.7	7.0	49.7
6-15	E-	6.59	4.66	N/A	1,237.2	853.8	16.2	0.1
2015	E-	20.05	12.07	N/A	1,249.4	1,087.0	12.8	209.0
2014	E-	6.94	4.99	240.3	1,219.5	856.0	19.1	-52.7
2013	E-	11.39	8.21	N/A	1,034.5	973.3	23.7	391.5
2012	E-	4.15	2.98	N/A	1,099.9	510.7	27.6	307.8
2011	E-	0.85	0.59	211.2	833.7	186.1	39.8	-30.4

Reserve Deficiency (as % of capital)

* Adequate & redundant reserves show as negatives   ■ 1 Yr Dev   □ 2 Yr Dev

TECHNOLOGY INS CO   C   Fair

Major Rating Factors: Fair reserve development (3.0 on a scale of 0 to 10) as the level of reserves has at times been insufficient to cover claims. In 2014 and 2015 the two year reserve development was 18% and 23% deficient respectively. Fair overall results on stability tests (3.6) including weak results on operational trends and excessive premium growth.

Other Rating Factors: Good long-term capitalization index (5.2) based on good current risk adjusted capital (moderate loss scenario). Over the last several years, capital levels have remained relatively consistent. Good liquidity (6.7) with sufficient resources (cash flows and marketable investments) to handle a spike in claims. Excellent profitability (8.6) with operating gains in each of the last five years.

Principal Business: Workers compensation (85%), other liability (6%), auto liability (4%), commercial multiple peril (2%), allied lines (2%), and auto physical damage (1%).
Principal Investments: Investment grade bonds (60%), misc. investments (22%), cash (17%), and non investment grade bonds (1%).
Investments in Affiliates: 4%
Group Affiliation: AmTrust Financial Services Inc
Licensed in: All states, the District of Columbia and Puerto Rico
Commenced Business: July 1991
Address: 20 Trafalgar Square, Nashua, NH 03063
Phone: (212) 220-7120   **Domicile State:** NH   **NAIC Code:** 42376

Data Date	Rating	RACR #1	RACR #2	Loss Ratio %	Total Assets ($mil)	Capital ($mil)	Net Premium ($mil)	Net Income ($mil)
6-16	C	1.09	0.78	N/A	2,351.4	527.8	521.1	30.8
6-15	C	1.88	1.35	N/A	1,822.0	490.0	386.3	6.4
2015	C	1.08	0.78	71.0	1,981.5	478.7	985.0	0.3
2014	C	2.25	1.63	N/A	1,502.4	479.4	-250.2	21.4
2013	C	1.62	1.11	67.1	1,132.6	236.5	485.6	16.6
2012	C	1.75	1.19	67.9	915.5	206.8	308.4	45.6
2011	C	1.93	1.36	77.8	845.8	193.0	226.9	1.7

Reserve Deficiency (as % of capital)

* Adequate & redundant reserves show as negatives   ■ 1 Yr Dev   □ 2 Yr Dev

TENNESSEE FARMERS ASR CO *   B+   Good

Major Rating Factors: Good liquidity (6.3 on a scale of 0 to 10) with sufficient resources (cash flows and marketable investments) to handle a spike in claims. Good overall results on stability tests (5.1) despite weak results on operational trends.

Other Rating Factors: Strong long-term capitalization index (9.6) based on excellent current risk adjusted capital (severe and moderate loss scenarios). Moreover, capital levels have been consistent in recent years. Ample reserve history (8.0) that helps to protect the company against sharp claims increases. Fair profitability index (4.2) with operating losses during 2011. Return on equity has been fair, averaging 5.5% over the past five years.

Principal Business: (This company is a reinsurer.)
Principal Investments: Investment grade bonds (83%) and misc. investments (17%).
Investments in Affiliates: 3%
Group Affiliation: Tennessee Farmers Mutual
Licensed in: TN
Commenced Business: August 1991
Address: 147 Bear Creek Pike, Columbia, TN 38401-2266
Phone: (931) 388-7872   **Domicile State:** TN   **NAIC Code:** 41220

Data Date	Rating	RACR #1	RACR #2	Loss Ratio %	Total Assets ($mil)	Capital ($mil)	Net Premium ($mil)	Net Income ($mil)
6-16	B+	4.93	3.36	N/A	1,408.6	935.8	293.2	57.0
6-15	B+	4.38	2.99	N/A	1,246.0	802.1	285.8	59.2
2015	B+	4.64	3.20	66.4	1,302.5	874.5	586.1	122.4
2014	B+	4.08	2.82	67.6	1,156.6	743.4	570.9	108.6
2013	B+	2.77	1.92	65.9	1,014.2	635.5	555.8	144.0
2012	B+	2.41	1.67	87.5	874.5	511.9	534.7	25.0
2011	B+	2.76	1.89	126.1	877.2	492.5	480.9	-157.9

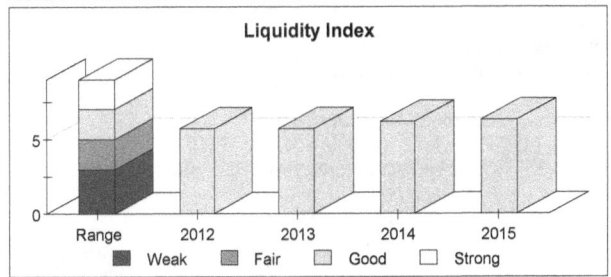

Liquidity Index

■ Weak   ▨ Fair   ▧ Good   □ Strong

TENNESSEE FARMERS MUTUAL INS CO *   B+   Good

Major Rating Factors: Good overall profitability index (5.9 on a scale of 0 to 10) despite operating losses during 2011. Good liquidity (6.6) with sufficient resources (cash flows and marketable investments) to handle a spike in claims.
Other Rating Factors: Good overall results on stability tests (5.1) despite weak results on operational trends. Strong long-term capitalization index (7.8) based on excellent current risk adjusted capital (severe and moderate loss scenarios). Moreover, capital levels have been consistent in recent years. Ample reserve history (7.5) that can protect against increases in claims costs.
Principal Business: Homeowners multiple peril (31%), auto liability (26%), auto physical damage (26%), farmowners multiple peril (10%), fire (4%), other liability (1%), and allied lines (1%).
Principal Investments: Misc. investments (59%) and investment grade bonds (42%).
Investments in Affiliates: 49%
Group Affiliation: Tennessee Farmers Mutual
Licensed in: TN
Commenced Business: December 1952
Address: 147 Bear Creek Pike, Columbia, TN 38401-2266
Phone: (931) 388-7872   **Domicile State:** TN   **NAIC Code:** 15245

Data Date	Rating	RACR #1	RACR #2	Loss Ratio %	Total Assets ($mil)	Capital ($mil)	Net Premium ($mil)	Net Income ($mil)
6-16	B+	1.90	1.78	N/A	2,804.7	2,192.3	294.6	62.1
6-15	B+	1.86	1.73	N/A	2,539.8	1,917.0	287.3	65.9
2015	B+	1.84	1.74	65.8	2,658.9	2,074.6	589.2	141.4
2014	B+	1.80	1.70	67.5	2,410.2	1,807.5	574.3	134.8
2013	B+	1.80	1.67	66.8	2,191.9	1,650.4	559.4	159.8
2012	B+	1.81	1.68	87.9	1,940.0	1,449.4	540.2	34.2
2011	B+	1.85	1.70	137.2	1,978.5	1,405.0	522.8	-146.0

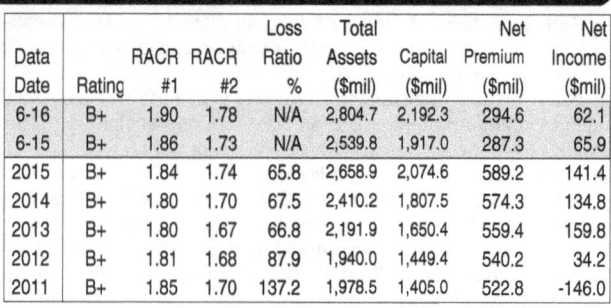

Income Trends. Underwriting Income / Net Income.

TEXAS FARM BUREAU CASUALTY INS CO *   B+   Good

Major Rating Factors: History of adequate reserve strength (6.2 on a scale of 0 to 10) as reserves have been consistently at an acceptable level. Good liquidity (5.7) with sufficient resources (cash flows and marketable investments) to handle a spike in claims.
Other Rating Factors: Good overall results on stability tests (5.2) despite weak results on operational trends. Strong long-term capitalization index (10.0) based on excellent current risk adjusted capital (severe and moderate loss scenarios), despite some fluctuation in capital levels. Fair profitability index (4.0) with operating losses during 2011 and the first six months of 2016. Return on equity has been low, averaging 0.9% over the past five years.
Principal Business: Auto liability (50%), auto physical damage (48%), and other liability (2%).
Principal Investments: Investment grade bonds (69%) and misc. investments (36%).
Investments in Affiliates: None
Group Affiliation: TX Farm Bureau Mutual
Licensed in: TX
Commenced Business: August 2007
Address: 7420 Fish Pond Rd, Waco, TX 76710
Phone: (254) 772-3030   **Domicile State:** TX   **NAIC Code:** 13004

Data Date	Rating	RACR #1	RACR #2	Loss Ratio %	Total Assets ($mil)	Capital ($mil)	Net Premium ($mil)	Net Income ($mil)
6-16	B+	4.21	3.31	N/A	1,179.5	629.4	332.2	-21.2
6-15	B+	4.62	3.66	N/A	1,161.1	652.9	316.5	-4.1
2015	B+	4.39	3.56	88.3	1,180.6	647.8	644.4	-8.6
2014	B+	4.71	3.83	82.3	1,154.8	657.1	620.8	28.4
2013	A	4.80	3.83	81.5	1,099.9	645.0	583.4	28.0
2012	A	4.65	3.60	82.5	1,048.1	606.2	546.4	8.1
2011	A	2.60	1.86	89.7	1,014.1	589.1	563.0	-2.6

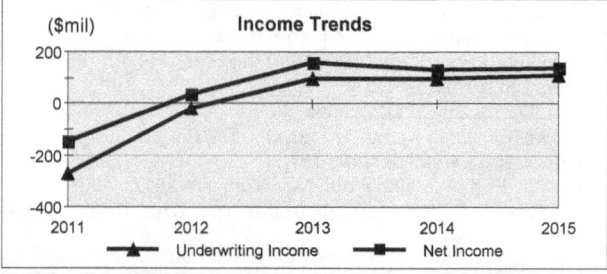

Reserve Deficiency (as % of capital). * Adequate & redundant reserves show as negatives. 1 Yr Dev / 2 Yr Dev.

TEXAS FARM BUREAU MUTUAL INS CO   C-   Fair

Major Rating Factors: Fair profitability index (3.9 on a scale of 0 to 10) with operating losses during 2012, 2013, 2014 and the first six months of 2016. Fair overall results on stability tests (3.3) including weak results on operational trends.
Other Rating Factors: History of adequate reserve strength (6.1) as reserves have been consistently at an acceptable level. Good liquidity (5.8) with sufficient resources (cash flows and marketable investments) to handle a spike in claims. Strong long-term capitalization index (8.8) based on excellent current risk adjusted capital (severe and moderate loss scenarios), despite some fluctuation in capital levels.
Principal Business: Auto liability (35%), homeowners multiple peril (33%), auto physical damage (30%), and other liability (1%).
Principal Investments: Investment grade bonds (95%) and misc. investments (13%).
Investments in Affiliates: 1%
Group Affiliation: TX Farm Bureau Mutual
Licensed in: TX
Commenced Business: February 1950
Address: 7420 Fish Pond Road, Waco, TX 76710
Phone: (254) 772-3030   **Domicile State:** TX   **NAIC Code:** 25380

Data Date	Rating	RACR #1	RACR #2	Loss Ratio %	Total Assets ($mil)	Capital ($mil)	Net Premium ($mil)	Net Income ($mil)
6-16	C-	2.23	2.03	N/A	713.0	271.9	204.7	-61.3
6-15	D	2.30	2.07	N/A	715.9	275.6	188.5	-36.6
2015	D+	2.82	2.38	76.5	741.3	326.8	407.5	20.1
2014	D	2.81	2.36	79.7	705.1	309.8	389.1	-6.8
2013	D	3.28	2.75	82.6	659.9	313.0	343.1	-19.4
2012	B-	3.89	3.26	87.0	616.5	323.2	304.5	-39.1
2011	B-	2.73	2.08	82.7	349.5	152.8	141.2	3.9

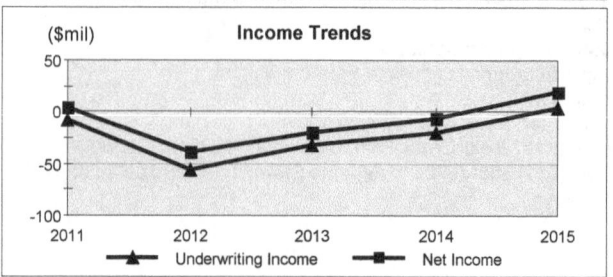

Income Trends. Underwriting Income / Net Income.

TOA REINS CO OF AMERICA *   B+   Good

Major Rating Factors: Good overall profitability index (6.7 on a scale of 0 to 10). Fair expense controls. Return on equity has been fair, averaging 8.7% over the past five years. Good liquidity (6.9) with sufficient resources (cash flows and marketable investments) to handle a spike in claims.

Other Rating Factors: Good overall results on stability tests (5.1) despite weak results on operational trends. The largest net exposure for one risk is conservative at 1.7% of capital. Strong long-term capitalization index (8.0) based on excellent current risk adjusted capital (severe and moderate loss scenarios), despite some fluctuation in capital levels. Ample reserve history (7.9) that can protect against increases in claims costs.

Principal Business: (This company is a reinsurer.)

Principal Investments: Investment grade bonds (82%), misc. investments (16%), cash (1%), and non investment grade bonds (1%).

Investments in Affiliates: None

Group Affiliation: Toa Reinsurance Co Ltd Japan

Licensed in: All states except PR

Commenced Business: January 1972

Address: 2711 Centerville Rd Suite 400, Wilmington, DE 19808

Phone: (973) 898-9480   **Domicile State:** DE   **NAIC Code:** 42439

Data Date	Rating	RACR #1	RACR #2	Loss Ratio %	Total Assets ($mil)	Capital ($mil)	Net Premium ($mil)	Net Income ($mil)
6-16	B+	2.44	1.61	N/A	1,747.5	640.9	190.2	9.0
6-15	B+	2.49	1.65	N/A	1,739.6	681.6	185.3	34.9
2015	B+	2.68	1.77	64.1	1,715.4	672.4	363.9	63.3
2014	B+	2.66	1.76	61.7	1,773.3	714.6	351.5	72.8
2013	B+	2.14	1.43	65.1	1,779.4	682.4	403.1	70.7
2012	B	1.84	1.23	78.3	1,670.3	599.1	391.3	32.6
2011	B	2.32	1.53	67.6	1,577.6	586.9	293.7	63.7

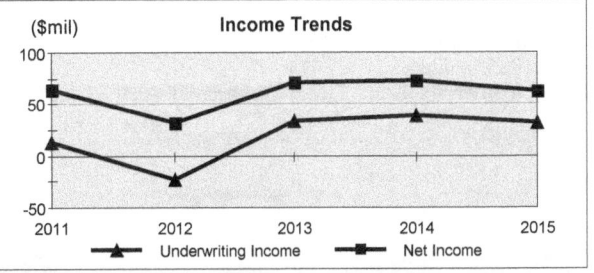

Income Trends ($mil) — Underwriting Income, Net Income (2011–2015)

TOKIO MARINE AMERICA INS CO *   A   Excellent

Major Rating Factors: Strong long-term capitalization index (8.0 on a scale of 0 to 10) based on excellent current risk adjusted capital (severe and moderate loss scenarios). Furthermore, this high level of risk adjusted capital has been consistently maintained in previous years. History of adequate reserve strength (6.8) as reserves have been consistently at an acceptable level.

Other Rating Factors: Good liquidity (6.7) with sufficient resources (cash flows and marketable investments) to handle a spike in claims. Good overall results on stability tests (6.0) despite weak results on operational trends. The largest net exposure for one risk is high at 3.6% of capital. Strengths include potential support from affiliation with Tokio Marine Holdings Inc. Fair profitability index (4.8) with operating losses during 2011. Return on equity has been low, averaging 0.9% over the past five years.

Principal Business: Auto liability (16%), ocean marine (14%), workers compensation (11%), fire (10%), commercial multiple peril (9%), other liability (9%), and other lines (31%).

Principal Investments: Investment grade bonds (81%), misc. investments (15%), and cash (4%).

Investments in Affiliates: 14%

Group Affiliation: Tokio Marine Holdings Inc

Licensed in: All states, the District of Columbia and Puerto Rico

Commenced Business: September 1999

Address: 230 Park Ave, New York, NY 10169-0005

Phone: (610) 227-1300   **Domicile State:** NY   **NAIC Code:** 10945

Data Date	Rating	RACR #1	RACR #2	Loss Ratio %	Total Assets ($mil)	Capital ($mil)	Net Premium ($mil)	Net Income ($mil)
6-16	A	2.20	1.66	N/A	1,410.7	512.7	152.6	0.4
6-15	A	2.89	1.85	N/A	1,401.3	516.2	146.6	12.2
2015	A	2.27	1.73	78.0	1,360.5	510.6	308.5	17.8
2014	A	2.98	1.90	76.7	1,349.2	497.3	248.0	25.4
2013	A	2.78	1.85	73.8	1,383.5	514.4	275.0	16.0
2012	U	41.03	36.93	78.8	1,388.4	499.1	263.0	7.9
2011	U	17.68	12.10	N/A	2.7	2.4	0.0	-0.2

Capital ($mil) (2011 – 6-16)

TOKIO MARINE SPECIALTY INS CO   C   Fair

Major Rating Factors: Fair overall results on stability tests (3.9 on a scale of 0 to 10) including fair financial strength of affiliated Tokio Marine Holdings Inc and weak results on operational trends. Good liquidity (6.8) with sufficient resources (cash flows and marketable investments) to handle a spike in claims.

Other Rating Factors: Strong long-term capitalization index (9.6) based on excellent current risk adjusted capital (severe and moderate loss scenarios). Moreover, capital levels have been consistent in recent years. Ample reserve history (7.7) that can protect against increases in claims costs. Excellent profitability (8.9) with operating gains in each of the last five years.

Principal Business: Other liability (65%), commercial multiple peril (14%), products liability (9%), auto physical damage (6%), and allied lines (5%).

Principal Investments: Investment grade bonds (107%).

Investments in Affiliates: None

Group Affiliation: Tokio Marine Holdings Inc

Licensed in: All states except PR

Commenced Business: October 1986

Address: 1807 N Market St, Wilmington, DE 19802

Phone: (610) 617-7900   **Domicile State:** DE   **NAIC Code:** 23850

Data Date	Rating	RACR #1	RACR #2	Loss Ratio %	Total Assets ($mil)	Capital ($mil)	Net Premium ($mil)	Net Income ($mil)
6-16	C	3.74	2.81	N/A	563.1	207.8	71.4	9.7
6-15	C	3.16	2.37	N/A	499.1	182.1	67.8	8.8
2015	C	3.76	2.86	60.5	517.3	197.8	141.9	19.9
2014	C	3.21	2.42	61.5	465.0	173.9	134.4	17.5
2013	C	3.26	2.47	61.0	416.1	157.3	123.8	17.3
2012	C	3.53	2.71	62.8	381.2	140.8	111.8	14.3
2011	C	3.47	2.65	70.3	332.0	125.7	101.7	10.1

Tokio Marine Holdings Inc
Composite Group Rating: B

Largest Group Members	Assets ($mil)	Rating
RELIANCE STANDARD LIFE INS CO	9581	B
PHILADELPHIA INDEMNITY INS CO	7362	B-
SAFETY NATIONAL CASUALTY CORP	5611	C
HOUSTON CASUALTY CO	3404	B-
US SPECIALTY INS CO	1793	B-

TOKIO MILLENNIUM RE AG (US BRANCH)

C+ **Fair**

Major Rating Factors: Fair overall results on stability tests (3.3) including excessive premium growth and weak results on operational trends. The largest net exposure for one risk is high at 4.0% of capital.

Other Rating Factors: Good long-term capitalization index (6.6) based on good current risk adjusted capital (moderate loss scenario). Moreover, capital levels have been consistent over the last several years. Good liquidity (6.9) with sufficient resources (cash flows and marketable investments) to handle a spike in claims. Weak profitability index (2.0) with operating losses during 2014 and 2015.

Principal Business: (This company is a reinsurer.)

Principal Investments: Investment grade bonds (79%), misc. investments (19%), and cash (2%).

Investments in Affiliates: None

Group Affiliation: Tokio Marine Holdings Inc

Licensed in: All states except PR

Commenced Business: June 2014

Address: 1010 Broad St 14th Floor, Stamford, CT 06901

Phone: (203) 658-1900 **Domicile State:** NY **NAIC Code:** 15529

Data Date	Rating	RACR #1	RACR #2	Loss Ratio %	Total Assets ($mil)	Capital ($mil)	Net Premium ($mil)	Net Income ($mil)
6-16	C+	1.57	0.92	N/A	931.4	247.8	218.1	29.6
6-15	C+	3.07	1.80	N/A	704.8	141.5	103.5	-146.1
2015	C+	1.91	0.97	60.0	817.3	217.9	647.4	-119.7
2014	U	5.10	2.78	60.6	222.6	102.8	121.9	-46.8
2013	N/A	N/A	N/A	0.0	0.0	0.0	0.0	0.0
2012	N/A	N/A	N/A	0.0	0.0	0.0	0.0	0.0
2011	N/A	N/A	N/A	0.0	0.0	0.0	0.0	0.0

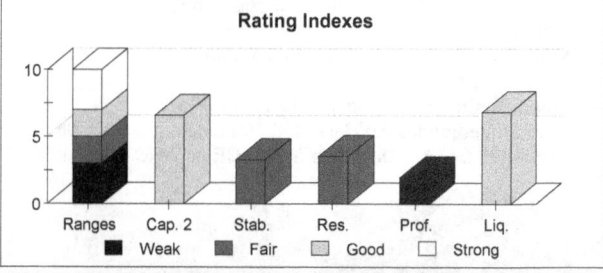

Rating Indexes

Ranges — Cap. 2 — Stab. — Res. — Prof. — Liq.

■ Weak ■ Fair ▨ Good ☐ Strong

TOYOTA MOTOR INS CO

C+ **Fair**

Major Rating Factors: Fair overall results on stability tests (4.0 on a scale of 0 to 10) including potential drain of affiliation with Toyota Motor Corp and weak results on operational trends. History of adequate reserve strength (5.2) as reserves have been consistently at an acceptable level.

Other Rating Factors: Strong long-term capitalization index (10.0) based on excellent current risk adjusted capital (severe and moderate loss scenarios). Moreover, capital levels have been consistent in recent years. Excellent profitability (8.9) with operating gains in each of the last five years. Excellent liquidity (7.3) with ample operational cash flow and liquid investments.

Principal Business: Other liability (69%), credit (9%), and aggregate write-ins for other lines of business (5%).

Principal Investments: Investment grade bonds (86%), misc. investments (5%), cash (5%), and non investment grade bonds (4%).

Investments in Affiliates: None

Group Affiliation: Toyota Motor Corp

Licensed in: All states except PR

Commenced Business: December 1909

Address: 19001 S.Western Ave TC22, Torrance, CA 90509

Phone: (310) 468-4019 **Domicile State:** IA **NAIC Code:** 37621

Data Date	Rating	RACR #1	RACR #2	Loss Ratio %	Total Assets ($mil)	Capital ($mil)	Net Premium ($mil)	Net Income ($mil)
6-16	C+	6.84	5.54	N/A	505.3	241.0	38.0	11.4
6-15	C	8.30	6.91	N/A	475.9	220.2	31.0	8.0
2015	C+	7.24	5.88	48.8	493.8	229.1	91.8	16.3
2014	C	9.12	7.65	43.3	453.0	211.4	79.7	14.9
2013	C	9.87	8.12	38.0	420.0	194.9	65.6	17.1
2012	C	11.31	9.35	34.1	411.6	177.0	52.0	20.1
2011	C	11.79	8.87	33.7	422.8	157.3	43.7	18.6

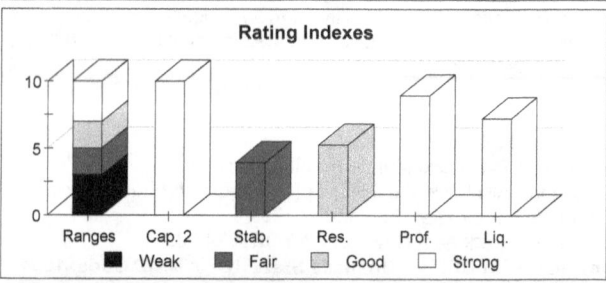

Rating Indexes

Ranges — Cap. 2 — Stab. — Res. — Prof. — Liq.

■ Weak ■ Fair ▨ Good ☐ Strong

TRANSATLANTIC REINS CO

B **Good**

Major Rating Factors: Good liquidity (6.7 on a scale of 0 to 10) with sufficient resources (cash flows and marketable investments) to handle a spike in claims. Fair overall results on stability tests (4.8) including weak results on operational trends, negative cash flow from operations for 2015 and excessive premium growth. The largest net exposure for one risk is conservative at 1.0% of capital.

Other Rating Factors: Strong long-term capitalization index (7.7) based on excellent current risk adjusted capital (severe and moderate loss scenarios), despite some fluctuation in capital levels. Ample reserve history (8.5) that helps to protect the company against sharp claims increases. Excellent profitability (7.9) despite modest operating losses during 2011.

Principal Business: (This company is a reinsurer.)

Principal Investments: Investment grade bonds (72%), misc. investments (23%), non investment grade bonds (3%), and cash (2%).

Investments in Affiliates: 9%

Group Affiliation: Alleghany Corp Group

Licensed in: (No states)

Commenced Business: January 1953

Address: 80 Pine St, New York, NY 10005

Phone: (212) 365-2200 **Domicile State:** NY **NAIC Code:** 19453

Data Date	Rating	RACR #1	RACR #2	Loss Ratio %	Total Assets ($mil)	Capital ($mil)	Net Premium ($mil)	Net Income ($mil)
6-16	B	2.10	1.46	N/A	14,151.9	4,831.3	1,719.5	173.1
6-15	B	2.15	1.47	N/A	14,720.6	4,902.7	1,372.9	275.8
2015	B	2.17	1.52	53.3	13,834.9	4,816.9	2,967.9	512.5
2014	B	2.10	1.44	55.0	14,574.6	4,770.5	2,986.8	562.1
2013	B	2.02	1.39	55.2	15,013.0	4,718.9	2,977.0	770.4
2012	B	1.92	1.28	71.2	14,661.5	4,179.1	3,074.5	345.5
2011	B	1.90	1.26	85.7	13,307.8	3,843.8	3,291.5	-15.3

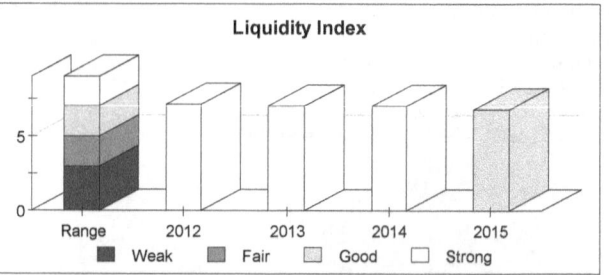

Liquidity Index

Range — 2012 — 2013 — 2014 — 2015

■ Weak ■ Fair ▨ Good ☐ Strong

TRAVELERS CASUALTY & SURETY CO *   A-   Excellent

Major Rating Factors: Strong long-term capitalization index (7.6 on a scale of 0 to 10) based on excellent current risk adjusted capital (severe and moderate loss scenarios), despite some fluctuation in capital levels. Ample reserve history (8.2) that helps to protect the company against sharp claims increases.

Other Rating Factors: Excellent profitability (7.9) with operating gains in each of the last five years. Return on equity has been excellent over the last five years averaging 15.0%. Good liquidity (6.9) with sufficient resources (cash flows and marketable investments) to handle a spike in claims. Good overall results on stability tests (5.5) despite weak results on operational trends.

Principal Business: Workers compensation (75%), surety (14%), homeowners multiple peril (9%), fire (1%), and other liability (1%).

Principal Investments: Investment grade bonds (65%), misc. investments (33%), and non investment grade bonds (2%).

Investments in Affiliates: 27%

Group Affiliation: Travelers Companies Inc

Licensed in: All states, the District of Columbia and Puerto Rico

Commenced Business: May 1907

Address: One Tower Square, Hartford, CT 06183

Phone: (860) 277-0111   **Domicile State:** CT   **NAIC Code:** 19038

Data Date	Rating	RACR #1	RACR #2	Loss Ratio %	Total Assets ($mil)	Capital ($mil)	Net Premium ($mil)	Net Income ($mil)
6-16	A-	1.60	1.39	N/A	16,398.0	6,375.5	2,133.1	188.3
6-15	A-	1.59	1.39	N/A	16,325.5	6,444.7	2,055.7	285.5
2015	A-	1.65	1.45	58.7	16,273.6	6,376.3	4,230.7	1,259.2
2014	A-	1.63	1.43	60.5	16,436.2	6,469.5	4,111.2	1,141.3
2013	A-	1.75	1.53	60.9	16,464.4	6,558.6	4,101.0	1,165.6
2012	B+	1.58	1.36	68.3	15,137.1	5,149.5	3,983.1	610.4
2011	B+	1.59	1.35	76.9	14,784.7	4,897.2	3,899.7	620.3

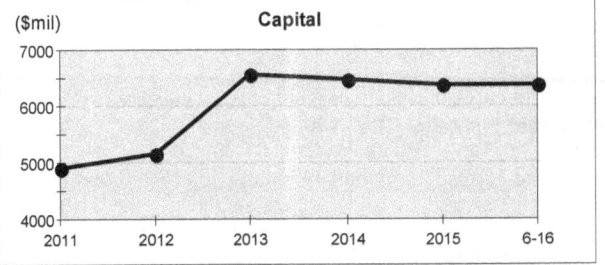

TRAVELERS CASUALTY & SURETY CO OF AM   C+   Fair

Major Rating Factors: Fair overall results on stability tests (3.0 on a scale of 0 to 10) including weak results on operational trends. The largest net exposure for one risk is excessive at 8.4% of capital. Strong long-term capitalization index (10.0) based on excellent current risk adjusted capital (severe and moderate loss scenarios), despite some fluctuation in capital levels.

Other Rating Factors: Ample reserve history (9.6) that helps to protect the company against sharp claims increases. Excellent profitability (9.4) with operating gains in each of the last five years. Return on equity has been excellent over the last five years averaging 24.3%. Excellent liquidity (7.0) with ample operational cash flow and liquid investments.

Principal Business: Other liability (47%), surety (40%), fidelity (10%), and burglary & theft (3%).

Principal Investments: Investment grade bonds (85%), misc. investments (14%), and non investment grade bonds (1%).

Investments in Affiliates: 6%

Group Affiliation: Travelers Companies Inc

Licensed in: All states, the District of Columbia and Puerto Rico

Commenced Business: July 1974

Address: One Tower Square, Hartford, CT 06183

Phone: (860) 277-0111   **Domicile State:** CT   **NAIC Code:** 31194

Data Date	Rating	RACR #1	RACR #2	Loss Ratio %	Total Assets ($mil)	Capital ($mil)	Net Premium ($mil)	Net Income ($mil)
6-16	C+	5.53	3.99	N/A	4,564.3	2,398.7	686.5	229.9
6-15	C+	4.93	3.67	N/A	4,458.7	2,296.9	668.0	206.0
2015	C+	5.05	3.66	20.9	4,184.9	2,103.6	1,372.9	470.0
2014	C+	4.62	3.46	9.0	4,225.2	2,114.7	1,408.3	565.8
2013	C+	4.75	3.18	13.9	4,147.5	1,881.7	1,293.9	500.5
2012	C+	3.99	2.70	26.4	4,339.6	1,780.5	1,223.0	417.0
2011	C+	3.81	2.54	27.2	4,256.4	1,652.1	1,245.3	416.2

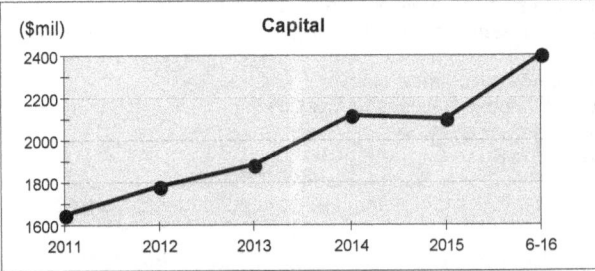

TRAVELERS CASUALTY INS CO OF AMERICA   B   Good

Major Rating Factors: Good liquidity (6.8 on a scale of 0 to 10) with sufficient resources (cash flows and marketable investments) to handle a spike in claims. Fair overall results on stability tests (4.8) including weak results on operational trends. Affiliation with Travelers Companies Inc is a strength.

Other Rating Factors: Strong long-term capitalization index (8.0) based on excellent current risk adjusted capital (severe and moderate loss scenarios). Moreover, capital levels have been consistent in recent years. Ample reserve history (8.7) that helps to protect the company against sharp claims increases. Excellent profitability (8.4) with operating gains in each of the last five years. Return on equity has been good over the last five years, averaging 13.5%.

Principal Business: Commercial multiple peril (70%), workers compensation (16%), auto liability (11%), and auto physical damage (3%).

Principal Investments: Investment grade bonds (93%) and misc. investments (7%).

Investments in Affiliates: None

Group Affiliation: Travelers Companies Inc

Licensed in: All states except PR

Commenced Business: October 1971

Address: One Tower Square, Hartford, CT 06183

Phone: (860) 277-0111   **Domicile State:** CT   **NAIC Code:** 19046

Data Date	Rating	RACR #1	RACR #2	Loss Ratio %	Total Assets ($mil)	Capital ($mil)	Net Premium ($mil)	Net Income ($mil)
6-16	B	2.81	1.78	N/A	1,984.9	617.8	286.0	40.0
6-15	B	2.79	1.75	N/A	1,956.6	605.7	275.6	40.8
2015	B	2.73	1.73	58.7	1,942.2	586.0	567.3	104.2
2014	B	2.66	1.67	60.5	1,918.5	566.2	551.1	91.4
2013	B	2.62	1.66	60.9	1,893.1	549.8	549.8	91.5
2012	B	2.45	1.57	68.4	1,841.4	506.6	534.0	59.7
2011	B	2.35	1.52	76.9	1,826.2	489.0	522.8	26.5

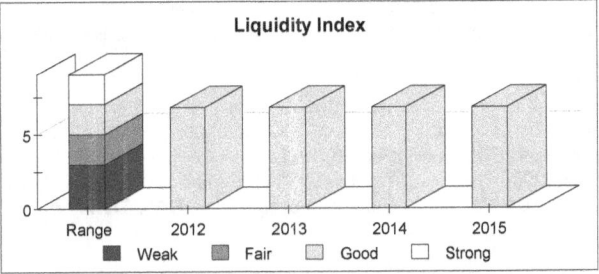

TRAVELERS INDEMNITY CO *   B+   Good

Major Rating Factors: Good overall profitability index (6.0 on a scale of 0 to 10). Fair expense controls. Return on equity has been good over the last five years, averaging 12.4%. Good liquidity (6.9) with sufficient resources (cash flows and marketable investments) to handle a spike in claims.

Other Rating Factors: Good overall results on stability tests (5.1) despite weak results on operational trends. Strong long-term capitalization index (7.7) based on excellent current risk adjusted capital (severe and moderate loss scenarios), despite some fluctuation in capital levels. Ample reserve history (8.2) that helps to protect the company against sharp claims increases.

Principal Business: Workers compensation (22%), other liability (20%), commercial multiple peril (15%), auto liability (12%), allied lines (9%), fire (8%), and other lines (13%).

Principal Investments: Investment grade bonds (69%), misc. investments (29%), non investment grade bonds (3%), and real estate (2%).

Investments in Affiliates: 21%

Group Affiliation: Travelers Companies Inc

Licensed in: All states, the District of Columbia and Puerto Rico

Commenced Business: May 1906

Address: One Tower Square, Hartford, CT 06183

Phone: (860) 277-0111   **Domicile State:** CT   **NAIC Code:** 25658

Data Date	Rating	RACR #1	RACR #2	Loss Ratio %	Total Assets ($mil)	Capital ($mil)	Net Premium ($mil)	Net Income ($mil)
6-16	B+	1.74	1.45	N/A	21,495.2	6,856.9	2,440.1	354.8
6-15	B	1.70	1.42	N/A	20,651.9	6,628.8	2,352.1	408.8
2015	B+	1.78	1.49	58.7	20,817.8	6,844.6	4,840.0	1,164.1
2014	B	1.73	1.46	60.5	20,724.5	6,633.4	4,704.2	942.2
2013	B	1.82	1.52	60.9	20,662.6	6,706.1	4,531.6	1,065.7
2012	A-	1.93	1.63	68.4	21,834.6	7,119.3	4,921.4	706.8
2011	A-	1.95	1.63	76.8	20,948.7	6,975.3	4,462.2	404.2

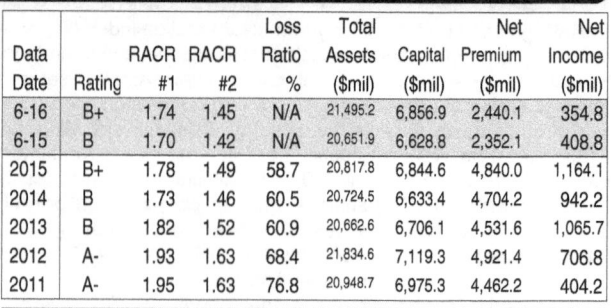

Income Trends

TRAVELERS INDEMNITY CO OF AMERICA   B   Good

Major Rating Factors: Good overall profitability index (6.3 on a scale of 0 to 10). Fair expense controls. Return on equity has been fair, averaging 9.8% over the past five years. Good liquidity (6.8) with sufficient resources (cash flows and marketable investments) to handle a spike in claims.

Other Rating Factors: Fair overall results on stability tests (4.6) including weak results on operational trends. Affiliation with Travelers Companies Inc is a strength. Strong long-term capitalization index (8.5) based on excellent current risk adjusted capital (severe and moderate loss scenarios), despite some fluctuation in capital levels. Ample reserve history (8.5) that helps to protect the company against sharp claims increases.

Principal Business: Workers compensation (39%), commercial multiple peril (31%), auto liability (9%), farmowners multiple peril (5%), other liability (5%), homeowners multiple peril (4%), and other lines (7%).

Principal Investments: Investment grade bonds (97%) and misc. investments (3%).

Investments in Affiliates: None

Group Affiliation: Travelers Companies Inc

Licensed in: All states except CA, PR

Commenced Business: May 1946

Address: One Tower Square, Hartford, CT 06183

Phone: (860) 277-0111   **Domicile State:** CT   **NAIC Code:** 25666

Data Date	Rating	RACR #1	RACR #2	Loss Ratio %	Total Assets ($mil)	Capital ($mil)	Net Premium ($mil)	Net Income ($mil)
6-16	B	3.17	2.01	N/A	631.1	200.2	80.7	9.0
6-15	B	3.46	2.18	N/A	638.2	215.2	77.7	12.5
2015	B	3.11	1.98	58.7	611.7	190.7	160.0	25.8
2014	B	3.32	2.09	60.5	635.7	202.8	155.5	26.1
2013	B	3.24	2.07	60.9	628.0	194.5	155.1	25.1
2012	B	3.05	1.96	68.4	639.0	180.7	150.6	16.9
2011	B	2.78	1.80	76.9	602.7	165.7	147.5	1.6

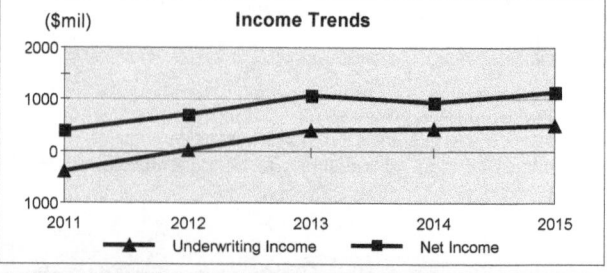

Income Trends

TRAVELERS INDEMNITY CO OF CT   B   Good

Major Rating Factors: Good overall profitability index (5.7 on a scale of 0 to 10). Fair expense controls. Return on equity has been good over the last five years, averaging 11.1%. Good liquidity (6.8) with sufficient resources (cash flows and marketable investments) to handle a spike in claims.

Other Rating Factors: Fair overall results on stability tests (4.7) including weak results on operational trends. Affiliation with Travelers Companies Inc is a strength. Strong long-term capitalization index (8.6) based on excellent current risk adjusted capital (severe and moderate loss scenarios), despite some fluctuation in capital levels. Ample reserve history (8.3) that helps to protect the company against sharp claims increases.

Principal Business: Commercial multiple peril (30%), workers compensation (29%), auto liability (21%), other liability (10%), auto physical damage (6%), farmowners multiple peril (2%), and other lines (3%).

Principal Investments: Investment grade bonds (94%) and misc. investments (6%).

Investments in Affiliates: None

Group Affiliation: Travelers Companies Inc

Licensed in: All states, the District of Columbia and Puerto Rico

Commenced Business: September 1860

Address: One Tower Square, Hartford, CT 06183

Phone: (860) 277-0111   **Domicile State:** CT   **NAIC Code:** 25682

Data Date	Rating	RACR #1	RACR #2	Loss Ratio %	Total Assets ($mil)	Capital ($mil)	Net Premium ($mil)	Net Income ($mil)
6-16	B	3.29	2.09	N/A	1,098.3	368.9	143.5	17.8
6-15	B	3.56	2.24	N/A	1,107.8	392.4	138.3	21.8
2015	B	3.25	2.07	58.7	1,075.7	354.4	284.7	46.2
2014	B	3.53	2.22	60.5	1,117.8	383.1	276.6	56.6
2013	B	3.43	2.18	60.9	1,082.4	365.6	275.9	51.8
2012	B	3.33	2.14	68.4	1,065.2	350.1	268.0	33.9
2011	B	3.12	2.01	76.9	1,017.6	330.5	262.4	15.1

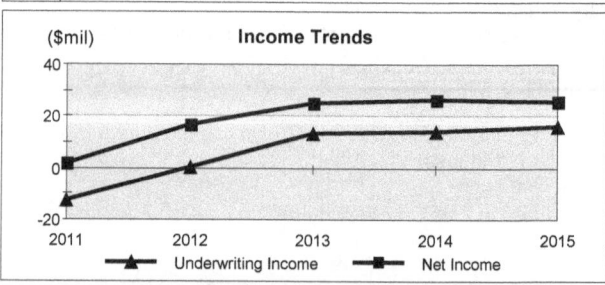

Income Trends

TRAVELERS PROPERTY CAS OF AMERICA — B — Good

Major Rating Factors: Fair profitability index (4.2 on a scale of 0 to 10). Fair expense controls. Return on equity has been low, averaging 3.6% over the past five years. Fair overall results on stability tests (4.7) including weak results on operational trends and negative cash flow from operations for 2015. Affiliation with Travelers Companies Inc is a strength.

Other Rating Factors: Strong long-term capitalization index (10.0) based on excellent current risk adjusted capital (severe and moderate loss scenarios), despite some fluctuation in capital levels. Ample reserve history (7.5) that can protect against increases in claims costs. Excellent liquidity (7.6) with ample operational cash flow and liquid investments.

Principal Business: Workers compensation (34%), other liability (17%), commercial multiple peril (16%), inland marine (9%), auto liability (8%), fire (4%), and other lines (13%).

Principal Investments: Investment grade bonds (99%) and misc. investments (1%).

Investments in Affiliates: None

Group Affiliation: Travelers Companies Inc

Licensed in: All states, the District of Columbia and Puerto Rico

Commenced Business: August 1971

Address: One Tower Square, Hartford, CT 06183

Phone: (860) 277-0111 **Domicile State:** CT **NAIC Code:** 25674

Data Date	Rating	RACR #1	RACR #2	Loss Ratio %	Total Assets ($mil)	Capital ($mil)	Net Premium ($mil)	Net Income ($mil)
6-16	B	14.29	9.00	N/A	840.3	451.4	37.7	7.3
6-15	B	16.47	10.28	N/A	893.7	513.3	36.3	8.5
2015	B	14.66	9.30	58.7	848.4	443.9	74.8	19.7
2014	B	16.67	10.46	60.5	933.2	505.0	72.7	18.4
2013	B	16.40	10.35	60.9	907.0	487.0	72.5	20.2
2012	B	15.37	9.74	68.4	841.7	450.1	70.4	16.0
2011	B	14.73	9.40	76.9	792.2	433.7	68.9	11.4

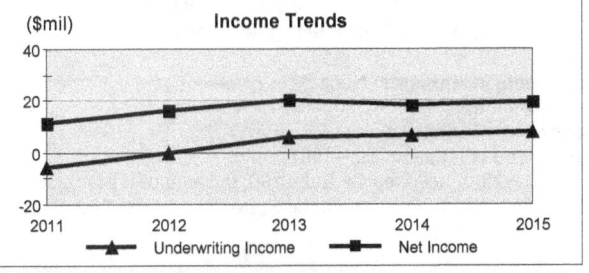

TRINITY UNIVERSAL INS CO — B — Good

Major Rating Factors: Fair profitability index (3.8 on a scale of 0 to 10). Fair expense controls. Return on equity has been fair, averaging 8.2% over the past five years. Fair overall results on stability tests (4.7) including weak results on operational trends and negative cash flow from operations for 2015.

Other Rating Factors: Strong long-term capitalization index (7.9) based on excellent current risk adjusted capital (severe and moderate loss scenarios), despite some fluctuation in capital levels. Ample reserve history (9.1) that helps to protect the company against sharp claims increases. Vulnerable liquidity (2.8) as a spike in claims may stretch capacity.

Principal Business: Homeowners multiple peril (38%), auto liability (33%), auto physical damage (25%), other liability (2%), inland marine (1%), and fire (1%).

Principal Investments: Investment grade bonds (49%), misc. investments (43%), and non investment grade bonds (8%).

Investments in Affiliates: 16%

Group Affiliation: Kemper Corporation

Licensed in: AL, AZ, AR, CA, CO, DE, FL, GA, ID, IL, IN, IA, KS, KY, LA, MI, MN, MS, MO, MT, NE, NH, NM, NY, NC, OH, OK, OR, PA, SC, TN, TX, UT, VA, WA, WV, WI, WY

Commenced Business: February 1926

Address: 10000 N Central Expressway, Dallas, TX 75231

Phone: (904) 245-5600 **Domicile State:** TX **NAIC Code:** 19887

Data Date	Rating	RACR #1	RACR #2	Loss Ratio %	Total Assets ($mil)	Capital ($mil)	Net Premium ($mil)	Net Income ($mil)
6-16	B	2.08	1.57	N/A	1,921.2	772.8	596.9	18.5
6-15	B	2.09	1.56	N/A	2,010.1	786.0	620.2	39.6
2015	B	2.16	1.64	68.4	1,964.7	817.4	1,210.9	89.7
2014	B	2.27	1.69	67.8	2,200.1	943.4	1,279.5	82.5
2013	B	2.19	1.62	66.7	2,380.9	984.1	1,435.7	138.5
2012	B	1.80	1.34	78.1	2,407.9	839.0	1,550.5	41.0
2011	B	1.69	1.29	79.6	2,452.5	824.0	1,614.5	31.3

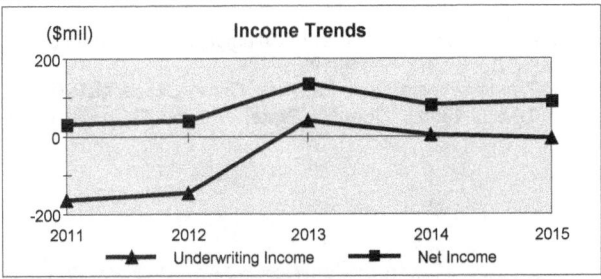

TRUCK INS EXCHANGE — C+ — Fair

Major Rating Factors: Fair profitability index (3.6 on a scale of 0 to 10) with operating losses during 2011, 2012, 2014 and the first six months of 2016. Fair overall results on stability tests (4.8) including weak results on operational trends.

Other Rating Factors: Good long-term capitalization index (5.3) based on good current risk adjusted capital (severe and moderate loss scenarios). Over the last several years, capital levels have remained relatively consistent. History of adequate reserve strength (5.9) as reserves have been consistently at an acceptable level. Vulnerable liquidity (2.9) as a spike in claims may stretch capacity.

Principal Business: Commercial multiple peril (45%), workers compensation (17%), homeowners multiple peril (13%), other liability (11%), auto liability (10%), and auto physical damage (3%).

Principal Investments: Investment grade bonds (56%), misc. investments (50%), and non investment grade bonds (1%).

Investments in Affiliates: 43%

Group Affiliation: Farmers Insurance Group of Companies

Licensed in: All states except PR

Commenced Business: February 1935

Address: 4680 Wilshire Blvd, Los Angeles, CA 90010

Phone: (323) 932-3200 **Domicile State:** CA **NAIC Code:** 21709

Data Date	Rating	RACR #1	RACR #2	Loss Ratio %	Total Assets ($mil)	Capital ($mil)	Net Premium ($mil)	Net Income ($mil)
6-16	C+	0.85	0.77	N/A	2,206.8	606.2	582.8	-23.9
6-15	C+	0.90	0.82	N/A	2,160.6	628.0	581.0	-2.2
2015	C+	0.88	0.80	69.0	2,164.8	624.1	1,157.1	-6.9
2014	C+	0.90	0.83	65.8	2,077.6	618.7	1,089.8	-7.3
2013	C+	0.86	0.80	66.9	1,933.4	563.5	1,056.9	1.5
2012	C+	0.87	0.80	73.3	1,963.0	535.0	1,073.8	-29.3
2011	C+	0.94	0.87	73.2	1,976.4	554.5	1,097.1	-23.4

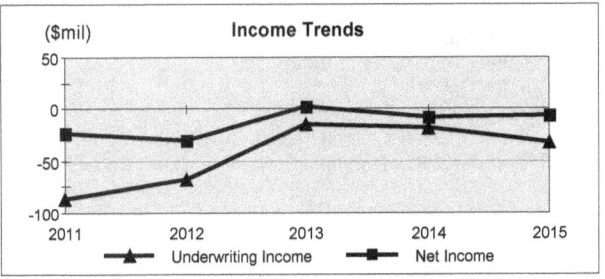

TWIN CITY FIRE INS CO — B — Good

Major Rating Factors: History of adequate reserve strength (5.9 on a scale of 0 to 10) as reserves have been consistently at an acceptable level. Good overall profitability index (5.6). Good expense controls. Return on equity has been fair, averaging 8.7% over the past five years.

Other Rating Factors: Good liquidity (6.9) with sufficient resources (cash flows and marketable investments) to handle a spike in claims. Fair overall results on stability tests (4.6) including weak results on operational trends. Strong long-term capitalization index (10.0) based on excellent current risk adjusted capital (severe and moderate loss scenarios), despite some fluctuation in capital levels.

Principal Business: Workers compensation (50%), other liability (21%), auto liability (12%), auto physical damage (6%), products liability (4%), homeowners multiple peril (4%), and commercial multiple peril (2%).

Principal Investments: Investment grade bonds (95%) and misc. investments (5%).

Investments in Affiliates: None

Group Affiliation: Hartford Financial Services Inc

Licensed in: All states except PR

Commenced Business: July 1987

Address: 4040 Vincennes Cir Suite 100, Indianapolis, IN 46268

Phone: (860) 547-5000   **Domicile State:** IN   **NAIC Code:** 29459

Data Date	Rating	RACR #1	RACR #2	Loss Ratio %	Total Assets ($mil)	Capital ($mil)	Net Premium ($mil)	Net Income ($mil)
6-16	B	5.48	3.60	N/A	690.2	297.8	78.4	10.9
6-15	B	5.67	3.72	N/A	671.4	302.0	76.9	14.9
2015	B	5.45	3.61	66.1	653.2	286.6	158.1	27.6
2014	B	5.60	3.71	67.0	650.4	288.9	153.7	27.6
2013	B	5.67	3.77	68.8	641.7	288.1	149.2	27.7
2012	B	5.82	3.86	72.7	643.1	291.1	147.7	26.4
2011	B	5.81	3.90	78.5	647.6	290.2	147.7	18.9

Reserve Deficiency (as % of capital)

* Adequate & redundant reserves show as negatives

■ 1 Yr Dev   □ 2 Yr Dev

UNITED EDUCATORS INS A RECIP RRG — B- — Good

Major Rating Factors: Fair overall results on stability tests (3.8 on a scale of 0 to 10) including weak results on operational trends. The largest net exposure for one risk is acceptable at 2.6% of capital. Strong long-term capitalization index (7.5) based on excellent current risk adjusted capital (severe and moderate loss scenarios). Moreover, capital levels have been consistent in recent years.

Other Rating Factors: Excellent profitability (8.6) with operating gains in each of the last five years. Excellent liquidity (7.4) with ample operational cash flow and liquid investments.

Principal Business: Other liability (100%).

Principal Investments: Investment grade bonds (85%), misc. investments (14%), and non investment grade bonds (1%).

Investments in Affiliates: None

Group Affiliation: None

Licensed in: All states, the District of Columbia and Puerto Rico

Commenced Business: March 1987

Address: Two Wisconsin Circle, Ste 1040, Chevy Chase, MD 20815-9913

Phone: (301) 907-4908   **Domicile State:** VT   **NAIC Code:** 10020

Data Date	Rating	RACR #1	RACR #2	Loss Ratio %	Total Assets ($mil)	Capital ($mil)	Net Premium ($mil)	Net Income ($mil)
6-16	B-	1.73	1.39	N/A	866.1	309.0	72.4	15.1
6-15	C	1.67	1.35	N/A	803.2	284.1	69.3	12.4
2015	C+	1.63	1.32	78.2	874.5	284.3	144.6	23.4
2014	C	1.74	1.41	77.3	820.4	281.8	139.0	26.1
2013	C	1.68	1.35	76.9	759.7	254.5	123.7	37.7
2012	C	1.81	1.47	83.6	727.9	253.3	110.6	19.7
2011	C	1.79	1.40	81.2	674.5	239.9	101.8	22.1

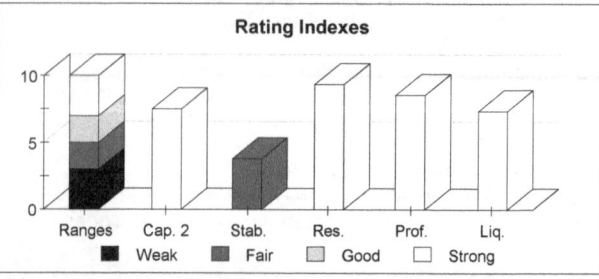

Rating Indexes

Ranges   Cap. 2   Stab.   Res.   Prof.   Liq.

■ Weak   ■ Fair   □ Good   □ Strong

UNITED FARM FAMILY MUTUAL INS CO — B — Good

Major Rating Factors: Good liquidity (5.7 on a scale of 0 to 10) with sufficient resources (cash flows and marketable investments) to handle a spike in claims. Fair profitability index (4.8) with operating losses during 2011 and 2012.

Other Rating Factors: Fair overall results on stability tests (4.5) including weak results on operational trends. Strong long-term capitalization index (8.5) based on excellent current risk adjusted capital (severe and moderate loss scenarios), despite some fluctuation in capital levels. Ample reserve history (8.1) that helps to protect the company against sharp claims increases.

Principal Business: Homeowners multiple peril (24%), auto liability (24%), auto physical damage (21%), farmowners multiple peril (16%), commercial multiple peril (7%), allied lines (4%), and other lines (4%).

Principal Investments: Investment grade bonds (73%) and misc. investments (27%).

Investments in Affiliates: 3%

Group Affiliation: Indiana Farm Bureau Inc

Licensed in: IN, OH

Commenced Business: February 1935

Address: 225 South East St, Indianapolis, IN 46202-4056

Phone: (317) 692-7200   **Domicile State:** IN   **NAIC Code:** 15288

Data Date	Rating	RACR #1	RACR #2	Loss Ratio %	Total Assets ($mil)	Capital ($mil)	Net Premium ($mil)	Net Income ($mil)
6-16	B	3.42	2.28	N/A	1,037.9	424.8	263.0	8.1
6-15	B-	3.44	2.31	N/A	989.8	388.5	255.8	30.3
2015	B	3.40	2.30	65.9	1,015.2	414.4	536.4	55.9
2014	B-	3.18	2.18	71.5	956.8	357.1	509.6	46.9
2013	B-	2.89	2.00	72.6	915.0	323.7	503.3	35.8
2012	C+	2.02	1.35	96.9	877.5	241.4	521.2	-56.2
2011	B	2.92	2.08	84.1	890.9	314.7	498.1	-10.6

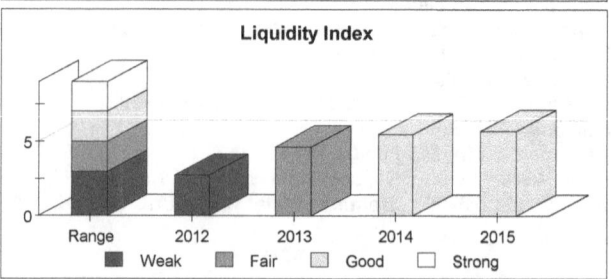

Liquidity Index

Range   2012   2013   2014   2015

■ Weak   ■ Fair   □ Good   □ Strong

UNITED FINANCIAL CASUALTY CO   B-   Good

Major Rating Factors: Fair overall results on stability tests (4.5 on a scale of 0 to 10) including potential drain of affiliation with Progressive Group and weak results on operational trends. History of adequate reserve strength (6.6) as reserves have been consistently at an acceptable level.

Other Rating Factors: Good liquidity (5.3) with sufficient resources (cash flows and marketable investments) to handle a spike in claims. Strong long-term capitalization index (7.6) based on excellent current risk adjusted capital (severe and moderate loss scenarios). Moreover, capital levels have been consistent in recent years. Excellent profitability (9.5) with operating gains in each of the last five years. Return on equity has been excellent over the last five years averaging 23.6%.

Principal Business: Auto liability (65%), auto physical damage (33%), and inland marine (2%).

Principal Investments: Investment grade bonds (76%), misc. investments (22%), and non investment grade bonds (2%).

Investments in Affiliates: None

Group Affiliation: Progressive Group

Licensed in: All states except PR

Commenced Business: August 1984

Address: 6300 Wilson Mills Rd W33, Mayfield Village, OH 44143-2182

Phone: (440) 461-5000   **Domicile State:** OH   **NAIC Code:** 11770

Data Date	Rating	RACR #1	RACR #2	Loss Ratio %	Total Assets ($mil)	Capital ($mil)	Net Premium ($mil)	Net Income ($mil)
6-16	B-	2.07	1.46	N/A	2,805.0	614.3	905.9	48.5
6-15	C+	2.23	1.58	N/A	2,521.8	618.5	816.3	68.1
2015	B-	1.98	1.40	70.0	2,507.6	554.7	1,742.6	146.4
2014	C+	2.07	1.49	69.3	2,301.1	546.1	1,619.0	162.0
2013	C+	1.96	1.41	75.3	2,137.9	492.0	1,501.7	60.4
2012	C+	2.12	1.48	72.8	1,815.9	391.3	1,173.2	74.0
2011	C+	2.38	1.63	64.1	1,630.4	390.3	975.1	134.2

Progressive Group
Composite Group Rating: C+
Largest Group Members

Largest Group Members	Assets ($mil)	Rating
PROGRESSIVE CASUALTY INS CO	6246	B-
PROGRESSIVE DIRECT INS CO	5835	C
UNITED FINANCIAL CASUALTY CO	2508	B-
PROGRESSIVE NORTHERN INS CO	1408	C+
PROGRESSIVE NORTHWESTERN INS CO	1372	C+

UNITED FIRE & CAS CO   B   Good

Major Rating Factors: Good liquidity (6.8 on a scale of 0 to 10) with sufficient resources (cash flows and marketable investments) to handle a spike in claims. Fair overall results on stability tests (4.7) including potential drain of affiliation with United Fire & Casualty Group and weak results on operational trends.

Other Rating Factors: Strong long-term capitalization index (7.2) based on excellent current risk adjusted capital (severe and moderate loss scenarios). Moreover, capital levels have been consistent in recent years. Ample reserve history (8.7) that helps to protect the company against sharp claims increases. Excellent profitability (7.7) with operating gains in each of the last five years.

Principal Business: Other liability (20%), auto liability (18%), workers compensation (14%), products liability (8%), auto physical damage (8%), allied lines (7%), and other lines (24%).

Principal Investments: Misc. investments (57%), investment grade bonds (40%), real estate (2%), and cash (1%).

Investments in Affiliates: 37%

Group Affiliation: United Fire & Casualty Group

Licensed in: All states except ME, MA, NH, PR

Commenced Business: January 1947

Address: 118 Second Ave SE, Cedar Rapids, IA 52407

Phone: (319) 399-5700   **Domicile State:** IA   **NAIC Code:** 13021

Data Date	Rating	RACR #1	RACR #2	Loss Ratio %	Total Assets ($mil)	Capital ($mil)	Net Premium ($mil)	Net Income ($mil)
6-16	B	1.31	1.12	N/A	1,863.5	736.0	289.6	10.6
6-15	B	1.21	1.02	N/A	1,742.3	705.4	266.1	8.1
2015	B	1.31	1.13	61.2	1,777.9	722.4	564.5	37.9
2014	B	1.19	1.02	66.7	1,661.9	685.9	523.1	33.0
2013	B	1.18	1.01	63.3	1,558.7	665.8	469.8	58.9
2012	B	1.14	1.04	70.5	1,434.1	586.0	426.0	19.0
2011	B-	1.14	1.03	75.3	1,309.7	565.8	371.0	19.6

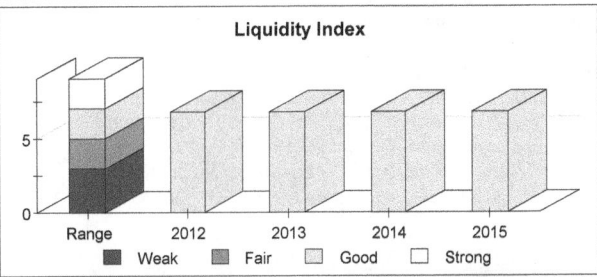

Liquidity Index

Range   2012   2013   2014   2015
■ Weak   ▦ Fair   ▢ Good   □ Strong

UNITED GUAR RESIDENTIAL INS CO OF NC   C+   Fair

Major Rating Factors: Fair overall results on stability tests (4.5 on a scale of 0 to 10) including weak results on operational trends. History of adequate reserve strength (5.8) as reserves have been consistently at an acceptable level.

Other Rating Factors: Good overall profitability index (5.7) despite operating losses during 2011 and 2012. Return on equity has been fair, averaging 7.4% over the past five years. Strong long-term capitalization index (7.2) based on excellent current risk adjusted capital (severe and moderate loss scenarios), despite some fluctuation in capital levels. Excellent liquidity (7.1) with ample operational cash flow and liquid investments.

Principal Business: Credit (100%).

Principal Investments: Misc. investments (67%), investment grade bonds (29%), and cash (4%).

Investments in Affiliates: 68%

Group Affiliation: American International Group

Licensed in: All states except AZ, CA, NY, WY, PR

Commenced Business: May 1963

Address: 230 North Elm Street, Greensboro, NC 27401

Phone: (336) 373-0232   **Domicile State:** NC   **NAIC Code:** 16667

Data Date	Rating	RACR #1	RACR #2	Loss Ratio %	Total Assets ($mil)	Capital ($mil)	Net Premium ($mil)	Net Income ($mil)
6-16	C+	1.37	1.35	N/A	407.8	386.8	14.8	88.9
6-15	C	1.52	1.51	N/A	467.7	443.9	20.7	15.3
2015	C+	1.59	1.57	N/A	477.2	449.9	38.3	23.9
2014	C	1.48	1.46	N/A	461.1	432.3	75.6	62.6
2013	C	1.23	1.21	31.2	448.5	377.9	92.5	40.0
2012	C-	1.06	1.02	174.2	472.2	319.8	97.2	-40.4
2011	D	1.13	1.08	97.5	417.2	257.8	135.0	-0.7

American International Group
Composite Group Rating: B
Largest Group Members

Largest Group Members	Assets ($mil)	Rating
AMERICAN GENERAL LIFE INS CO	166711	B
VARIABLE ANNUITY LIFE INS CO	74141	B
UNITED STATES LIFE INS CO IN NYC	28404	B
NATIONAL UNION FIRE INS CO OF PITTSB	26764	C
AMERICAN HOME ASR CO	26104	C

UNITED GUARANTY MORTGAGE INDEM CO   C+   Fair

Major Rating Factors: Fair reserve development (3.9 on a scale of 0 to 10) as reserves have generally been sufficient to cover claims. In 2011, the one year reserve development was 49% deficient. Fair profitability index (4.7) with operating losses during 2012. Return on equity has been low, averaging 0.9% over the past five years.

Other Rating Factors: Fair overall results on stability tests (4.6) including weak results on operational trends and negative cash flow from operations for 2015. Good liquidity (6.9) with sufficient resources (cash flows and marketable investments) to handle a spike in claims. Strong long-term capitalization index (9.7) based on excellent current risk adjusted capital (severe and moderate loss scenarios). Moreover, capital levels have been consistent in recent years.

Principal Business: Mortgage guaranty (100%).
Principal Investments: Investment grade bonds (100%) and cash (1%).
Investments in Affiliates: None
Group Affiliation: American International Group
Licensed in: All states except IL, WY, PR
Commenced Business: July 1972
Address: 230 North Elm Street, Greensboro, NC 27401
Phone: (336) 373-0232   **Domicile State:** NC   **NAIC Code:** 26999

Data Date	Rating	RACR #1	RACR #2	Loss Ratio %	Total Assets ($mil)	Capital ($mil)	Net Premium ($mil)	Net Income ($mil)
6-16	C+	6.83	5.16	N/A	431.1	290.9	9.0	11.4
6-15	C+	1.74	1.36	N/A	280.6	115.5	19.4	9.0
2015	C+	5.13	3.94	47.6	439.5	283.9	29.4	15.2
2014	C+	1.65	1.29	49.3	284.1	115.1	37.7	13.9
2013	C+	1.41	1.10	71.1	283.8	113.2	44.2	5.4
2012	C+	1.54	1.15	N/A	309.8	109.4	11.4	-28.6
2011	C	0.88	0.70	94.8	390.2	93.3	104.7	4.7

Reserve Deficiency (as % of capital)

* Adequate & redundant reserves show as negatives
1 Yr Dev
2 Yr Dev

UNITED GUARANTY RESIDENTIAL INS CO   C   Fair

Major Rating Factors: Fair reserve development (3.8 on a scale of 0 to 10) as the level of reserves has at times been insufficient to cover claims. In 2013 and 2011 the two year reserve development was 19% and 21% deficient respectively. Fair overall results on stability tests (4.3) including weak results on operational trends.

Other Rating Factors: Good overall profitability index (6.1) despite operating losses during 2012. Return on equity has been good over the last five years, averaging 11.4%. Good liquidity (6.6) with sufficient resources (cash flows and marketable investments) to handle a spike in claims. Strong long-term capitalization index (8.4) based on excellent current risk adjusted capital (severe and moderate loss scenarios), despite some fluctuation in capital levels.

Principal Business: Mortgage guaranty (100%).
Principal Investments: Investment grade bonds (92%), non investment grade bonds (7%), and cash (2%).
Investments in Affiliates: 8%
Group Affiliation: American International Group
Licensed in: All states, the District of Columbia and Puerto Rico
Commenced Business: December 1963
Address: 230 North Elm Street, Greensboro, NC 27401
Phone: (336) 373-0232   **Domicile State:** NC   **NAIC Code:** 15873

Data Date	Rating	RACR #1	RACR #2	Loss Ratio %	Total Assets ($mil)	Capital ($mil)	Net Premium ($mil)	Net Income ($mil)
6-16	C	2.21	1.79	N/A	3,161.8	1,060.6	308.9	141.6
6-15	C-	2.67	2.11	N/A	3,455.9	1,371.0	304.7	115.3
2015	C	2.76	2.22	20.7	3,550.4	1,351.3	564.8	314.6
2014	C-	2.58	2.05	27.4	3,247.7	1,383.8	791.3	254.6
2013	D+	2.58	2.01	64.7	3,059.3	1,465.7	799.9	88.4
2012	D+	1.82	1.46	116.6	2,930.3	1,383.0	576.6	-100.8
2011	D+	2.13	1.78	71.5	2,502.2	1,062.5	524.9	94.7

Reserve Deficiency (as % of capital)

* Adequate & redundant reserves show as negatives
1 Yr Dev
2 Yr Dev

UNITED SERVICES AUTOMOBILE ASN *   B+   Good

Major Rating Factors: Good profitability index (5.0 on a scale of 0 to 10) despite operating losses during the first six months of 2016. Good liquidity (6.8) with sufficient resources (cash flows and marketable investments) to handle a spike in claims.

Other Rating Factors: Good overall results on stability tests (5.2) despite weak results on operational trends. Strong long-term capitalization index (7.5) based on excellent current risk adjusted capital (severe and moderate loss scenarios). Moreover, capital levels have been consistent in recent years. Ample reserve history (7.4) that can protect against increases in claims costs.

Principal Business: Homeowners multiple peril (35%), auto liability (30%), auto physical damage (26%), allied lines (3%), other liability (2%), inland marine (2%), and fire (2%).
Principal Investments: Misc. investments (68%), investment grade bonds (29%), real estate (4%), and non investment grade bonds (1%).
Investments in Affiliates: 58%
Group Affiliation: USAA Group
Licensed in: All states, the District of Columbia and Puerto Rico
Commenced Business: June 1922
Address: 9800 Fredericksburg Rd, San Antonio, TX 78288
Phone: (210) 498-2211   **Domicile State:** TX   **NAIC Code:** 25941

Data Date	Rating	RACR #1	RACR #2	Loss Ratio %	Total Assets ($mil)	Capital ($mil)	Net Premium ($mil)	Net Income ($mil)
6-16	B+	1.49	1.42	N/A	32,870.8	24,702.0	3,465.3	-211.1
6-15	A-	1.54	1.45	N/A	32,019.0	24,200.3	3,318.6	704.5
2015	A-	1.49	1.42	79.3	32,549.4	24,363.6	6,812.7	757.2
2014	A-	1.48	1.39	78.7	30,991.0	22,854.4	6,640.0	850.9
2013	A+	1.48	1.40	73.4	28,667.0	20,754.5	6,189.3	922.6
2012	A+	1.47	1.39	81.9	25,880.7	18,362.9	5,721.4	437.2
2011	A+	1.51	1.45	87.2	23,936.1	16,917.5	5,563.0	486.2

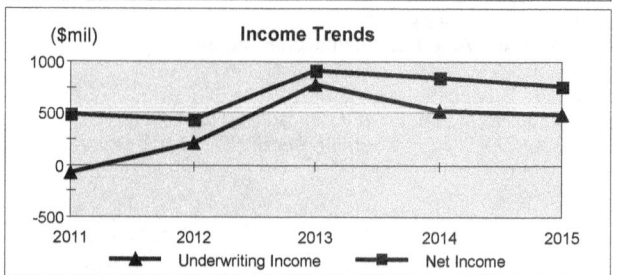

Income Trends

Underwriting Income   Net Income

UNITED STATES FIDELITY & GUARANTY CO　　　　　　　C　　　Fair

Major Rating Factors: Fair overall results on stability tests (3.6 on a scale of 0 to 10) including weak results on operational trends. Weak profitability index (2.4). Fair expense controls. Return on equity has been fair, averaging 9.9% over the past five years.

Other Rating Factors: Strong long-term capitalization index (9.5) based on excellent current risk adjusted capital (severe and moderate loss scenarios), despite some fluctuation in capital levels. Ample reserve history (7.7) that can protect against increases in claims costs. Excellent liquidity (7.0) with ample operational cash flow and liquid investments.

Principal Business: Surety (100%).

Principal Investments: Investment grade bonds (92%), misc. investments (7%), and non investment grade bonds (1%).

Investments in Affiliates: 3%

Group Affiliation: Travelers Companies Inc

Licensed in: All states, the District of Columbia and Puerto Rico

Commenced Business: August 1896

Address: One Tower Square, Hartford, CT 06183

Phone: (860) 277-0111　　**Domicile State:** CT　　**NAIC Code:** 25887

Data Date	Rating	RACR #1	RACR #2	Loss Ratio %	Total Assets ($mil)	Capital ($mil)	Net Premium ($mil)	Net Income ($mil)
6-16	C	4.15	2.71	N/A	3,700.2	1,473.5	462.0	62.5
6-15	B	6.88	4.49	N/A	4,596.5	2,458.1	445.3	90.1
2015	C	4.08	2.67	58.7	3,565.3	1,408.9	916.4	284.3
2014	B	7.00	4.58	60.5	4,677.4	2,466.2	890.3	206.8
2013	B	7.16	4.72	60.9	4,653.9	2,484.4	888.1	224.2
2012	B	7.64	5.08	68.4	4,797.2	2,627.5	862.6	216.7
2011	B	7.20	4.79	76.9	4,646.8	2,488.7	844.5	103.2

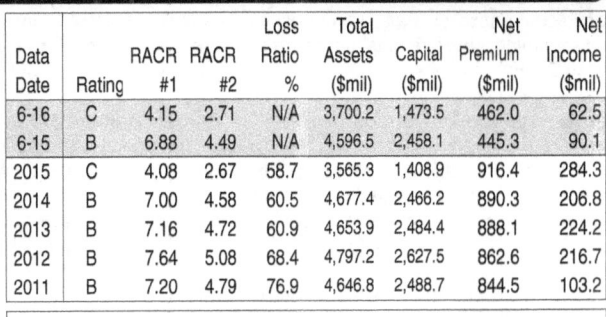

Rating Indexes

UNIVERSAL INS CO (PR)　　　　　　　　　　　　　　B-　　　Good

Major Rating Factors: Fair overall results on stability tests (4.2 on a scale of 0 to 10) including potential drain of affiliation with Universal Ins Co Group and weak results on operational trends. History of adequate reserve strength (6.2) as reserves have been consistently at an acceptable level.

Other Rating Factors: Good overall profitability index (6.1). Fair expense controls. Return on equity has been good over the last five years, averaging 10.4%. Good liquidity (6.7) with sufficient resources (cash flows and marketable investments) to handle a spike in claims. Strong long-term capitalization index (7.6) based on excellent current risk adjusted capital (severe and moderate loss scenarios), despite some fluctuation in capital levels.

Principal Business: Auto physical damage (45%), commercial multiple peril (19%), homeowners multiple peril (12%), auto liability (9%), other liability (6%), allied lines (3%), and other lines (7%).

Principal Investments: Investment grade bonds (53%), misc. investments (34%), real estate (8%), non investment grade bonds (4%), and cash (1%).

Investments in Affiliates: 17%

Group Affiliation: Universal Ins Co Group

Licensed in: PR

Commenced Business: January 1972

Address: Metro Office Park St 1 Lot 10, Guaynabo, PR 00921

Phone: (787) 706-7155　　**Domicile State:** PR　　**NAIC Code:** 31704

Data Date	Rating	RACR #1	RACR #2	Loss Ratio %	Total Assets ($mil)	Capital ($mil)	Net Premium ($mil)	Net Income ($mil)
6-16	B-	1.90	1.44	N/A	851.6	257.5	100.3	7.5
6-15	B-	2.75	1.82	N/A	815.1	252.8	98.1	8.7
2015	B-	1.93	1.47	64.9	779.3	259.7	194.4	23.2
2014	B-	3.20	2.13	66.4	805.5	253.1	196.3	23.4
2013	B-	3.46	2.26	69.4	802.8	253.1	202.7	38.1
2012	B-	3.56	2.32	68.4	778.3	258.9	208.5	25.2
2011	B-	4.89	2.84	66.6	769.7	251.9	207.4	28.6

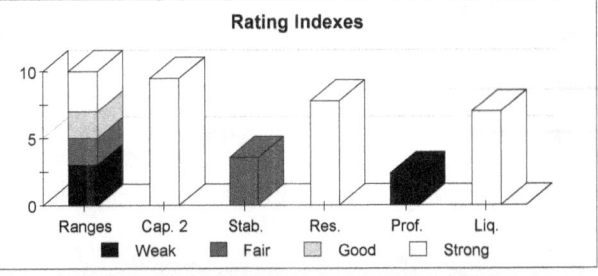

Rating Indexes

UNIVERSAL P&C INS CO　　　　　　　　　　　　　　　D　　　Weak

Major Rating Factors: Weak overall results on stability tests (1.8 on a scale of 0 to 10) including weak results on operational trends and excessive premium growth. Fair profitability index (4.3) with operating losses during 2011 and 2012. Return on equity has been fair, averaging 5.8% over the past five years.

Other Rating Factors: History of adequate reserve strength (5.8) as reserves have been consistently at an acceptable level. Good liquidity (6.8) with sufficient resources (cash flows and marketable investments) to handle a spike in claims. Strong long-term capitalization index (7.2) based on excellent current risk adjusted capital (severe and moderate loss scenarios). Moreover, capital levels have been consistent in recent years.

Principal Business: Homeowners multiple peril (92%), allied lines (6%), and fire (2%).

Principal Investments: Investment grade bonds (59%), cash (21%), misc. investments (17%), and real estate (3%).

Investments in Affiliates: None

Group Affiliation: Universal Insurance Holdings Inc

Licensed in: AL, DE, FL, GA, HI, IN, MD, MA, MI, MN, NH, NJ, NY, NC, PA, SC, VA, WV

Commenced Business: December 1997

Address: 1110 W Commercial Blvd, Ft. Lauderdale, FL 33180

Phone: (954) 958-1200　　**Domicile State:** FL　　**NAIC Code:** 10861

Data Date	Rating	RACR #1	RACR #2	Loss Ratio %	Total Assets ($mil)	Capital ($mil)	Net Premium ($mil)	Net Income ($mil)
6-16	D	1.30	1.22	N/A	967.3	294.2	307.2	34.5
6-15	D-	1.36	1.23	N/A	844.3	213.0	205.3	5.2
2015	D	1.30	1.11	40.9	816.3	257.0	623.0	52.9
2014	D-	1.52	1.27	42.1	626.8	200.2	385.3	38.5
2013	E+	0.26	0.19	46.1	553.6	161.8	260.0	27.7
2012	E+	0.22	0.15	65.1	526.6	134.0	245.8	-25.5
2011	E+	0.25	0.18	75.4	493.6	123.0	187.5	-21.7

Rating Indexes

UNIVERSAL UNDERWRITERS INS CO
C+ **Fair**

Major Rating Factors: Fair overall results on stability tests (4.5 on a scale of 0 to 10) including weak results on operational trends. Good overall profitability index (6.0). Fair expense controls. Return on equity has been low, averaging 4.5% over the past five years.

Other Rating Factors: Strong long-term capitalization index (10.0) based on excellent current risk adjusted capital (severe and moderate loss scenarios), despite some fluctuation in capital levels. Superior liquidity (10.0) with ample operational cash flow and liquid investments.

Principal Business: Auto liability (18%), auto physical damage (17%), other liability (16%), allied lines (4%), fire (3%), boiler & machinery (1%), and other lines (41%).

Principal Investments: Investment grade bonds (86%), misc. investments (11%), and cash (3%).

Investments in Affiliates: 11%
Group Affiliation: Zurich Financial Services Group
Licensed in: All states except PR
Commenced Business: January 1982
Address: 1400 American Lane, Schaumburg, IL 60196-1056
Phone: (847) 605-6000   **Domicile State:** IL   **NAIC Code:** 41181

Data Date	Rating	RACR #1	RACR #2	Loss Ratio %	Total Assets ($mil)	Capital ($mil)	Net Premium ($mil)	Net Income ($mil)
6-16	C+	10.19	9.28	N/A	404.7	345.6	0.0	2.7
6-15	C	10.09	8.68	N/A	412.6	342.5	0.0	2.7
2015	C+	10.35	9.61	0.0	379.9	339.6	0.0	9.5
2014	C	10.14	8.78	0.0	363.8	338.9	0.0	8.6
2013	C	10.82	9.95	0.0	386.2	336.1	0.0	5.2
2012	C	11.63	10.69	0.0	385.4	341.7	0.0	10.4
2011	C	13.23	12.02	0.0	376.0	341.8	0.0	47.2

Zurich Financial Services Group
Composite Group Rating: C+

Largest Group Members	Assets ($mil)	Rating
ZURICH AMERICAN INS CO	30471	B-
ZURICH AMERICAN LIFE INS CO	12271	C
FARMERS NEW WORLD LIFE INS CO	7049	B-
RURAL COMMUNITY INS CO	3680	B
CENTRE LIFE INS CO	1884	B-

US FIRE INS CO
C **Fair**

Major Rating Factors: Fair overall results on stability tests (3.7 on a scale of 0 to 10) including potential drain of affiliation with Fairfax Financial and weak results on operational trends. History of adequate reserve strength (5.6) as reserves have been consistently at an acceptable level.

Other Rating Factors: Good overall profitability index (5.2) despite operating losses during 2011, 2012 and 2013. Return on equity has been low, averaging 3.1% over the past five years. Strong long-term capitalization index (7.2) based on excellent current risk adjusted capital (severe and moderate loss scenarios), despite some fluctuation in capital levels. Excellent liquidity (7.0) with ample operational cash flow and liquid investments.

Principal Business: Group accident & health (28%), inland marine (20%), other liability (13%), workers compensation (12%), auto liability (7%), ocean marine (7%), and other lines (13%).

Principal Investments: Investment grade bonds (54%), misc. investments (36%), cash (5%), non investment grade bonds (3%), and real estate (2%).

Investments in Affiliates: 19%
Group Affiliation: Fairfax Financial
Licensed in: All states, the District of Columbia and Puerto Rico
Commenced Business: April 1824
Address: 305 Madison Avenue, Morristown, NJ 07960
Phone: (973) 490-6600   **Domicile State:** DE   **NAIC Code:** 21113

Data Date	Rating	RACR #1	RACR #2	Loss Ratio %	Total Assets ($mil)	Capital ($mil)	Net Premium ($mil)	Net Income ($mil)
6-16	C	1.43	1.11	N/A	3,914.8	1,202.5	650.9	85.3
6-15	C	1.53	1.07	N/A	3,318.2	860.7	533.1	49.3
2015	C	1.45	1.14	64.1	3,736.1	1,178.0	1,262.9	94.5
2014	C	1.62	1.14	67.5	3,248.6	898.6	1,025.1	195.7
2013	C	1.14	0.87	71.4	3,154.5	812.1	971.7	-75.7
2012	C	1.42	1.07	81.2	2,924.1	881.7	810.0	-50.1
2011	C	1.39	1.06	81.0	2,722.9	894.8	697.3	-43.8

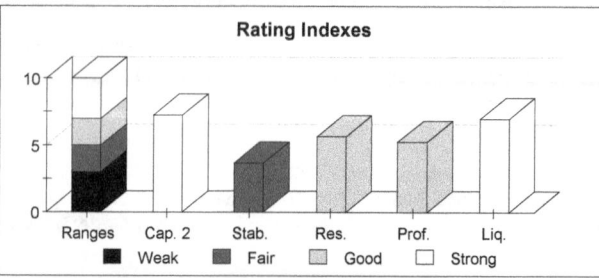

Rating Indexes

US LIABILITY INS CO
C **Fair**

Major Rating Factors: Fair overall results on stability tests (4.3 on a scale of 0 to 10) including weak results on operational trends. Strong long-term capitalization index (7.3) based on excellent current risk adjusted capital (severe and moderate loss scenarios), despite some fluctuation in capital levels.

Other Rating Factors: Ample reserve history (8.8) that helps to protect the company against sharp claims increases. Excellent profitability (7.7) with operating gains in each of the last five years. Excellent liquidity (7.6) with ample operational cash flow and liquid investments.

Principal Business: Other liability (82%), fire (16%), products liability (1%), and inland marine (1%).

Principal Investments: Misc. investments (69%) and investment grade bonds (31%).

Investments in Affiliates: 48%
Group Affiliation: Berkshire-Hathaway
Licensed in: All states except ND, PR
Commenced Business: May 1951
Address: 190 S. Warner Road, Wayne, PA 19087
Phone: (800) 523-5545   **Domicile State:** PA   **NAIC Code:** 25895

Data Date	Rating	RACR #1	RACR #2	Loss Ratio %	Total Assets ($mil)	Capital ($mil)	Net Premium ($mil)	Net Income ($mil)
6-16	C	1.29	1.17	N/A	886.0	539.2	95.2	5.4
6-15	C	1.33	1.20	N/A	887.4	553.2	86.6	5.9
2015	C	1.31	1.18	37.7	897.2	559.2	187.2	24.4
2014	C	1.35	1.22	51.1	885.9	563.3	169.7	4.6
2013	C	1.50	1.35	47.9	811.3	537.5	144.8	25.0
2012	C	1.52	1.31	47.2	675.5	441.1	118.5	15.7
2011	C	1.45	1.22	38.8	577.8	372.4	85.9	11.0

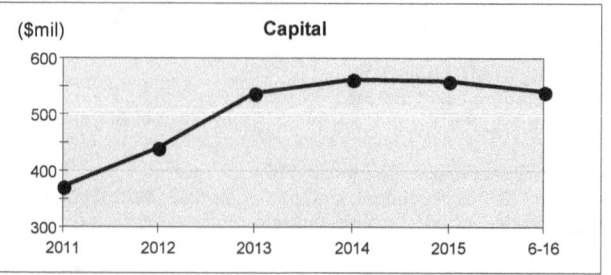

Capital

US SPECIALTY INS CO B- Good

Major Rating Factors: Fair profitability index (4.0 on a scale of 0 to 10). Fair expense controls. Return on equity has been fair, averaging 18.3% over the past five years. Fair overall results on stability tests (3.5) including weak results on operational trends. The largest net exposure for one risk is high at 4.3% of capital.

Other Rating Factors: History of adequate reserve strength (6.9) as reserves have been consistently at an acceptable level. Good liquidity (6.9) with sufficient resources (cash flows and marketable investments) to handle a spike in claims. Strong long-term capitalization index (8.0) based on excellent current risk adjusted capital (severe and moderate loss scenarios), despite some fluctuation in capital levels.

Principal Business: Other liability (61%), surety (12%), aircraft (8%), commercial multiple peril (6%), credit (2%), inland marine (2%), and other lines (9%).

Principal Investments: Investment grade bonds (88%), misc. investments (7%), non investment grade bonds (4%), and cash (1%).

Investments in Affiliates: None
Group Affiliation: HCC Ins Holdings Inc
Licensed in: All states except PR
Commenced Business: April 1987
Address: 13403 Northwest Freeway, Houston, TX 77040-6094
Phone: (713) 462-1000   **Domicile State:** TX   **NAIC Code:** 29599

Data Date	Rating	RACR #1	RACR #2	Loss Ratio %	Total Assets ($mil)	Capital ($mil)	Net Premium ($mil)	Net Income ($mil)
6-16	B-	2.62	1.72	N/A	1,844.9	569.1	218.0	38.9
6-15	B-	2.94	1.88	N/A	1,929.8	631.1	214.6	56.7
2015	B-	2.47	1.63	55.7	1,792.8	525.7	436.2	94.1
2014	B-	2.71	1.76	47.0	1,890.8	577.1	420.1	133.2
2013	B-	2.56	1.66	51.5	1,928.6	580.3	440.5	124.8
2012	B-	2.58	1.71	59.5	2,056.0	552.5	440.2	104.9
2011	B-	1.90	1.18	67.5	1,889.7	507.3	460.9	61.1

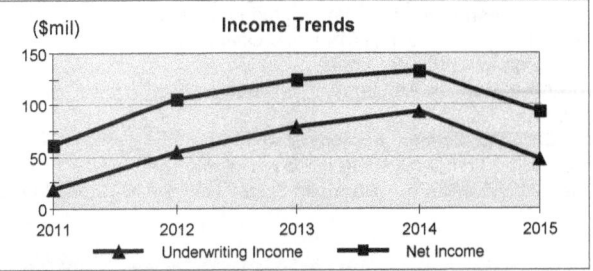

Income Trends

USAA CASUALTY INS CO * A- Excellent

Major Rating Factors: Strong long-term capitalization index (8.9 on a scale of 0 to 10) based on excellent current risk adjusted capital (severe and moderate loss scenarios). Furthermore, this high level of risk adjusted capital has been consistently maintained in previous years. Ample reserve history (7.9) that can protect against increases in claims costs.

Other Rating Factors: Good overall profitability index (5.9) despite operating losses during the first six months of 2016. Return on equity has been fair, averaging 5.2% over the past five years. Good liquidity (5.6) with sufficient resources (cash flows and marketable investments) to handle a spike in claims. Good overall results on stability tests (5.7) despite weak results on operational trends.

Principal Business: Auto liability (37%), auto physical damage (29%), homeowners multiple peril (29%), inland marine (2%), allied lines (1%), other liability (1%), and fire (1%).

Principal Investments: Investment grade bonds (65%), misc. investments (32%), non investment grade bonds (2%), and cash (1%).

Investments in Affiliates: 8%
Group Affiliation: USAA Group
Licensed in: All states except PR
Commenced Business: December 1990
Address: 9800 Fredericksburg Rd, San Antonio, TX 78288
Phone: (210) 498-8000   **Domicile State:** TX   **NAIC Code:** 25968

Data Date	Rating	RACR #1	RACR #2	Loss Ratio %	Total Assets ($mil)	Capital ($mil)	Net Premium ($mil)	Net Income ($mil)
6-16	A-	2.97	2.26	N/A	9,860.1	4,477.7	2,949.4	-46.3
6-15	A-	2.91	2.17	N/A	9,273.7	4,573.4	2,604.1	188.1
2015	A-	2.99	2.31	86.0	9,668.6	4,451.8	5,679.1	164.5
2014	A-	2.86	2.16	81.3	8,699.0	4,392.2	4,836.8	338.4
2013	A+	2.90	2.20	77.4	8,445.8	4,168.8	4,756.9	319.9
2012	A+	2.98	2.29	83.6	7,773.4	3,673.4	4,385.4	151.9
2011	A+	3.79	2.99	84.5	7,294.9	3,570.8	3,848.9	224.9

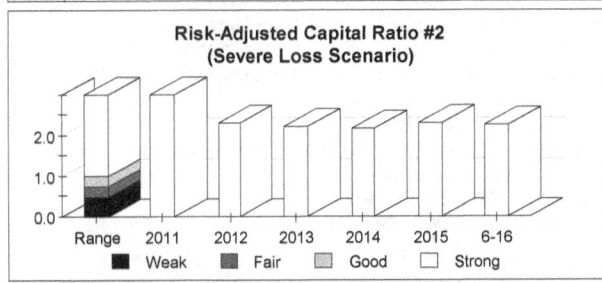

Risk-Adjusted Capital Ratio #2
(Severe Loss Scenario)

USAA GENERAL INDEMNITY CO * B+ Good

Major Rating Factors: Good overall profitability index (6.2 on a scale of 0 to 10) despite operating losses during the first six months of 2016. Return on equity has been fair, averaging 6.4% over the past five years. Good overall results on stability tests (5.0) despite weak results on operational trends.

Other Rating Factors: Strong long-term capitalization index (8.4) based on excellent current risk adjusted capital (severe and moderate loss scenarios), despite some fluctuation in capital levels. Ample reserve history (9.3) that helps to protect the company against sharp claims increases. Fair liquidity (3.6) as cash resources may not be adequate to cover a spike in claims.

Principal Business: Auto liability (38%), auto physical damage (35%), homeowners multiple peril (19%), allied lines (6%), inland marine (1%), and fire (1%).

Principal Investments: Investment grade bonds (81%), misc. investments (16%), non investment grade bonds (2%), and cash (1%).

Investments in Affiliates: None
Group Affiliation: USAA Group
Licensed in: All states, the District of Columbia and Puerto Rico
Commenced Business: August 1972
Address: 9800 Fredericksburg Rd, San Antonio, TX 78288
Phone: (210) 498-8000   **Domicile State:** TX   **NAIC Code:** 18600

Data Date	Rating	RACR #1	RACR #2	Loss Ratio %	Total Assets ($mil)	Capital ($mil)	Net Premium ($mil)	Net Income ($mil)
6-16	B+	2.63	1.94	N/A	3,644.1	1,295.5	1,257.1	-27.7
6-15	B+	2.16	1.56	N/A	3,128.6	1,149.1	1,050.0	52.9
2015	B+	2.78	2.10	85.9	3,503.7	1,303.6	2,289.9	66.0
2014	B+	1.92	1.42	81.2	2,933.6	1,096.7	2,176.6	108.4
2013	B+	1.99	1.53	77.3	2,256.6	835.6	1,633.0	117.0
2012	B+	2.01	1.59	83.2	1,676.2	580.8	1,173.6	42.8
2011	B+	2.35	1.78	87.0	1,099.6	401.3	828.8	4.5

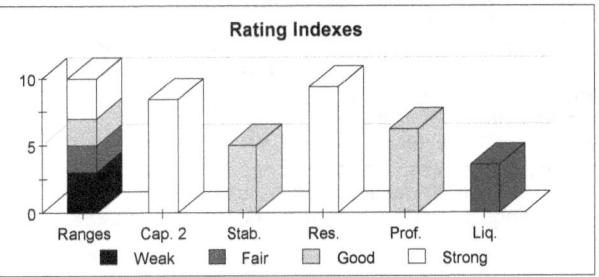

Rating Indexes

USAA TEXAS LLOYDS CO
B   **Good**

Major Rating Factors: Good liquidity (6.3 on a scale of 0 to 10) with sufficient resources (cash flows and marketable investments) to handle a spike in claims. Fair overall results on stability tests (4.8) including weak results on operational trends and negative cash flow from operations for 2015. The largest net exposure for one risk is acceptable at 2.6% of capital.

Other Rating Factors: Strong long-term capitalization index (9.9) based on excellent current risk adjusted capital (severe and moderate loss scenarios). Moreover, capital levels have been consistent in recent years. Ample reserve history (7.7) that can protect against increases in claims costs. Excellent profitability (8.9) with operating gains in each of the last five years.

Principal Business: Homeowners multiple peril (94%), allied lines (5%), and fire (1%).

Principal Investments: Investment grade bonds (88%), misc. investments (7%), non investment grade bonds (3%), and cash (2%).

Investments in Affiliates: None
Group Affiliation: USAA Group
Licensed in: TX
Commenced Business: September 2001
Address: 9800 Fredericksburg Rd, San Antonio, TX 78288
Phone: (210) 498-8000   **Domicile State:** TX   **NAIC Code:** 11120

Data Date	Rating	RACR #1	RACR #2	Loss Ratio %	Total Assets ($mil)	Capital ($mil)	Net Premium ($mil)	Net Income ($mil)
6-16	B	8.50	6.95	N/A	372.7	288.0	38.5	4.7
6-15	B	2.06	1.81	N/A	638.5	272.3	171.6	2.3
2015	B	5.02	3.99	85.6	463.2	283.8	159.5	18.9
2014	B	2.31	1.91	70.9	574.3	275.1	345.0	29.4
2013	B+	2.63	2.17	68.2	505.7	245.1	275.0	26.6
2012	B	3.14	2.56	79.0	462.9	216.9	199.6	3.0
2011	B	3.85	3.22	81.8	417.9	214.8	177.7	2.9

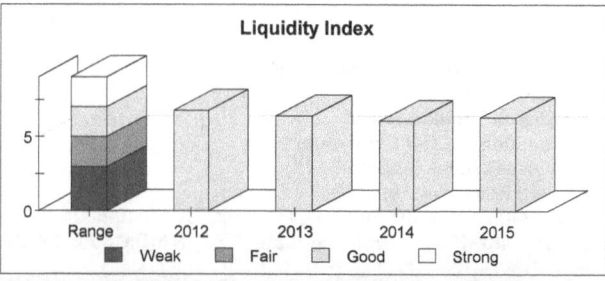

Liquidity Index

UTICA MUTUAL INS CO
B-   **Good**

Major Rating Factors: Fair overall results on stability tests (4.6 on a scale of 0 to 10) including potential drain of affiliation with Utica National Ins Group and weak results on operational trends. The largest net exposure for one risk is conservative at 1.2% of capital. History of adequate reserve strength (6.0) as reserves have been consistently at an acceptable level.

Other Rating Factors: Good overall profitability index (5.1) despite operating losses during 2011 and 2012. Good liquidity (6.7) with sufficient resources (cash flows and marketable investments) to handle a spike in claims. Strong long-term capitalization index (8.1) based on excellent current risk adjusted capital (severe and moderate loss scenarios), despite some fluctuation in capital levels.

Principal Business: Other liability (29%), workers compensation (23%), auto liability (18%), commercial multiple peril (17%), auto physical damage (8%), homeowners multiple peril (3%), and other lines (2%).

Principal Investments: Investment grade bonds (68%), misc. investments (28%), non investment grade bonds (3%), and real estate (1%).

Investments in Affiliates: 12%
Group Affiliation: Utica National Ins Group
Licensed in: All states, the District of Columbia and Puerto Rico
Commenced Business: July 1914
Address: 180 Genesee St, New Hartford, NY 13413
Phone: (315) 734-2000   **Domicile State:** NY   **NAIC Code:** 25976

Data Date	Rating	RACR #1	RACR #2	Loss Ratio %	Total Assets ($mil)	Capital ($mil)	Net Premium ($mil)	Net Income ($mil)
6-16	B-	2.30	1.71	N/A	2,292.1	827.8	352.2	11.2
6-15	B-	2.29	1.70	N/A	2,238.5	812.1	326.9	16.2
2015	B-	2.32	1.75	65.5	2,293.5	811.9	689.9	38.0
2014	B-	2.23	1.66	66.2	2,228.8	805.9	627.9	34.0
2013	B-	2.27	1.65	65.5	2,130.1	775.1	579.5	29.9
2012	B-	2.46	1.85	70.5	2,110.6	742.7	532.3	-5.9
2011	B-	2.25	1.67	94.8	2,334.2	733.0	531.0	-45.9

Rating Indexes

VERMONT MUTUAL INS CO
B-   **Good**

Major Rating Factors: Fair overall results on stability tests (4.2 on a scale of 0 to 10) including potential drain of affiliation with Vermont Mutual Group, weak results on operational trends and negative cash flow from operations for 2015. Good liquidity (6.5) with sufficient resources (cash flows and marketable investments) to handle a spike in claims.

Other Rating Factors: Strong long-term capitalization index (10.0) based on excellent current risk adjusted capital (severe and moderate loss scenarios). Moreover, capital levels have been consistent in recent years. Ample reserve history (9.1) that helps to protect the company against sharp claims increases. Excellent profitability (8.5) with operating gains in each of the last five years.

Principal Business: Homeowners multiple peril (41%), commercial multiple peril (23%), auto physical damage (11%), auto liability (11%), fire (5%), allied lines (4%), and other lines (4%).

Principal Investments: Investment grade bonds (65%), misc. investments (30%), cash (4%), and non investment grade bonds (1%).

Investments in Affiliates: 1%
Group Affiliation: Vermont Mutual Group
Licensed in: CT, ME, MA, NH, NY, RI, VT
Commenced Business: March 1828
Address: 89 State St, Monteplier, VT 05602
Phone: (802) 223-2341   **Domicile State:** VT   **NAIC Code:** 26018

Data Date	Rating	RACR #1	RACR #2	Loss Ratio %	Total Assets ($mil)	Capital ($mil)	Net Premium ($mil)	Net Income ($mil)
6-16	B-	4.68	3.10	N/A	794.0	396.0	179.5	17.8
6-15	C+	4.14	2.73	N/A	723.4	342.8	169.2	-21.8
2015	B-	4.62	3.03	64.7	753.7	376.5	358.5	13.1
2014	C+	4.49	2.91	51.1	753.1	367.8	343.3	43.2
2013	C+	4.12	2.64	54.0	690.7	328.2	313.7	25.9
2012	C+	4.19	2.77	51.0	614.2	283.8	292.3	35.0
2011	C+	3.79	2.56	68.3	557.2	239.8	280.6	8.7

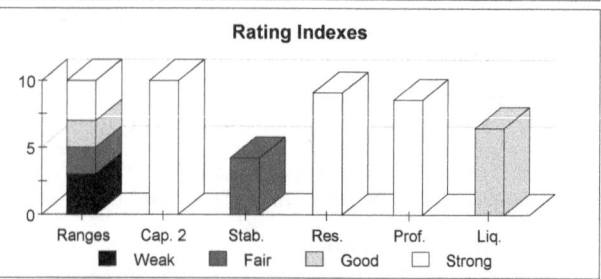

Rating Indexes

VIGILANT INS CO   B   Good

Major Rating Factors: Fair overall results on stability tests (4.7 on a scale of 0 to 10) including weak results on operational trends. Affiliation with Chubb Limited is a strength. Strong long-term capitalization index (10.0) based on excellent current risk adjusted capital (severe and moderate loss scenarios). Moreover, capital levels have been consistent in recent years.

Other Rating Factors: Ample reserve history (7.6) that can protect against increases in claims costs. Excellent profitability (8.7) with operating gains in each of the last five years. Excellent liquidity (7.2) with ample operational cash flow and liquid investments.

Principal Business: Homeowners multiple peril (45%), workers compensation (17%), commercial multiple peril (14%), inland marine (7%), other liability (7%), auto liability (3%), and other lines (8%).

Principal Investments: Investment grade bonds (83%), misc. investments (16%), and non investment grade bonds (1%).

Investments in Affiliates: 7%

Group Affiliation: Chubb Limited

Licensed in: All states except PR

Commenced Business: October 1939

Address: 55 Water St, New York, NY 10041

Phone: (212) 612-4000   **Domicile State:** NY   **NAIC Code:** 20397

Data Date	Rating	RACR #1	RACR #2	Loss Ratio %	Total Assets ($mil)	Capital ($mil)	Net Premium ($mil)	Net Income ($mil)
6-16	B	8.70	6.48	N/A	519.2	311.5	19.4	7.9
6-15	B	5.41	4.53	N/A	498.7	296.3	24.0	6.5
2015	B	9.88	7.48	56.5	514.8	306.2	48.9	22.0
2014	B	6.05	5.29	56.7	502.5	292.3	47.0	23.3
2013	B	5.10	4.72	52.7	467.9	264.9	45.1	16.7
2012	B	4.86	4.36	67.3	451.3	246.8	43.4	12.8
2011	B	5.29	4.51	68.4	440.4	233.6	42.6	15.8

Chubb Limited
Composite Group Rating: B
Largest Group Members

	Assets ($mil)	Rating
FEDERAL INS CO	32241	B
ACE AMERICAN INS CO	12074	B-
ACE PC INS CO	7749	B-
PACIFIC INDEMNITY CO	6916	B
PACIFIC EMPLOYERS INS CO	3542	B-

VIRGINIA SURETY CO INC   B   Good

Major Rating Factors: Good liquidity (6.7 on a scale of 0 to 10) with sufficient resources (cash flows and marketable investments) to handle a spike in claims. Fair overall results on stability tests (4.3) including weak results on operational trends.

Other Rating Factors: Strong long-term capitalization index (10.0) based on excellent current risk adjusted capital (severe and moderate loss scenarios), despite some fluctuation in capital levels. Ample reserve history (8.0) that helps to protect the company against sharp claims increases. Excellent profitability (8.4) with operating gains in each of the last five years. Return on equity has been excellent over the last five years averaging 18.5%.

Principal Business: Other liability (94%), inland marine (2%), and credit (1%).

Principal Investments: Investment grade bonds (88%), misc. investments (9%), and cash (3%).

Investments in Affiliates: 2%

Group Affiliation: Onex Corp

Licensed in: All states, the District of Columbia and Puerto Rico

Commenced Business: July 1982

Address: 175 W Jackson, Chicago, IL 60604

Phone: (312) 356-3000   **Domicile State:** IL   **NAIC Code:** 40827

Data Date	Rating	RACR #1	RACR #2	Loss Ratio %	Total Assets ($mil)	Capital ($mil)	Net Premium ($mil)	Net Income ($mil)
6-16	B	4.05	3.53	N/A	1,231.9	382.0	140.4	21.5
6-15	C+	3.47	3.02	N/A	1,074.4	322.0	133.3	27.7
2015	B	4.05	3.59	62.7	1,147.0	363.6	299.6	44.5
2014	C+	3.15	2.78	64.0	1,022.7	300.8	329.7	50.4
2013	C+	2.85	2.48	55.3	1,007.8	309.2	341.8	73.6
2012	C+	2.90	2.42	62.5	978.9	292.1	327.3	52.1
2011	C	2.20	1.64	46.7	970.1	286.3	292.2	72.2

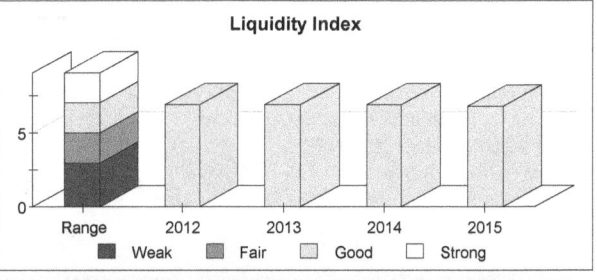

Liquidity Index

Range — Weak, Fair, Good, Strong — 2012, 2013, 2014, 2015

WAWANESA GENERAL INS CO   C+   Fair

Major Rating Factors: Fair reserve development (4.5 on a scale of 0 to 10) as reserves have generally been sufficient to cover claims. Fair overall results on stability tests (4.0) including weak results on operational trends. The largest net exposure for one risk is conservative at 1.4% of capital.

Other Rating Factors: Good liquidity (5.6) with sufficient resources (cash flows and marketable investments) to handle a spike in claims. Weak profitability index (2.5) with operating losses during 2013 and 2015. Average return on equity over the last five years has been poor at -1.0%. Strong long-term capitalization index (7.8) based on excellent current risk adjusted capital (severe and moderate loss scenarios), despite some fluctuation in capital levels.

Principal Business: Auto liability (54%), auto physical damage (38%), homeowners multiple peril (7%), and earthquake (1%).

Principal Investments: Investment grade bonds (99%) and cash (1%).

Investments in Affiliates: None

Group Affiliation: Wawanesa Ins Group

Licensed in: CA, OR

Commenced Business: January 1997

Address: 9050 Friars Road,Suite 200, San Diego, CA 92108-5865

Phone: (858) 874-5310   **Domicile State:** CA   **NAIC Code:** 10683

Data Date	Rating	RACR #1	RACR #2	Loss Ratio %	Total Assets ($mil)	Capital ($mil)	Net Premium ($mil)	Net Income ($mil)
6-16	C+	1.99	1.52	N/A	605.1	202.3	185.6	6.8
6-15	C+	2.64	2.03	N/A	602.8	235.3	172.3	-6.6
2015	C+	1.89	1.50	102.5	590.3	195.5	365.9	-30.8
2014	C+	2.67	2.13	91.9	583.0	240.2	343.4	5.3
2013	C+	2.73	2.17	94.6	558.2	235.1	331.1	-1.3
2012	C+	2.86	2.27	93.8	542.9	235.8	314.4	10.2
2011	C	2.96	2.32	96.7	534.1	228.0	290.9	2.1

Reserve Deficiency (as % of capital)

2011, 2012, 2013, 2014, 2015 — 1 Yr Dev, 2 Yr Dev

* Adequate & redundant reserves show as negatives

WESCO INS CO
B-   Good

Major Rating Factors: Fair overall results on stability tests (4.6 on a scale of 0 to 10) including potential drain of affiliation with AmTrust Financial Services Inc, excessive premium growth and weak results on operational trends. Fair reserve development (4.9) as reserves have generally been sufficient to cover claims.

Other Rating Factors: Good overall profitability index (5.9) despite operating losses during the first six months of 2016. Return on equity has been fair, averaging 6.2% over the past five years. Strong long-term capitalization index (7.2) based on good current risk adjusted capital (severe and moderate loss scenarios), although results have slipped from the excellent range during the last year. Excellent liquidity (7.3) with ample operational cash flow and liquid investments.

Principal Business: Workers compensation (30%), auto liability (14%), other liability (13%), fire (3%), commercial multiple peril (3%), allied lines (2%), and other lines (34%).

Principal Investments: Investment grade bonds (70%), misc. investments (26%), cash (3%), and non investment grade bonds (1%).

Investments in Affiliates: 6%

Group Affiliation: AmTrust Financial Services Inc

Licensed in: All states, the District of Columbia and Puerto Rico

Commenced Business: May 1963

Address: 200 Somerset Corp Blvd,Ste 100, Bridgewater, NJ 08807

Phone: (212) 220-7120   **Domicile State:** DE   **NAIC Code:** 25011

Data Date	Rating	RACR #1	RACR #2	Loss Ratio %	Total Assets ($mil)	Capital ($mil)	Net Premium ($mil)	Net Income ($mil)
6-16	B-	1.55	0.97	N/A	1,794.7	334.5	241.0	-13.7
6-15	C+	3.95	2.27	N/A	1,391.9	275.3	121.9	4.0
2015	C+	1.98	1.26	64.1	1,743.4	333.5	416.8	13.1
2014	C+	4.16	2.41	72.7	1,113.6	215.5	182.6	14.2
2013	C+	5.29	3.08	63.2	804.1	166.8	114.8	21.4
2012	C+	4.38	2.58	76.6	505.2	114.5	80.7	9.3
2011	C+	5.92	3.40	68.8	326.6	82.6	61.3	5.6

AmTrust Financial Services Inc
Composite Group Rating: C

Largest Group Members	Assets ($mil)	Rating
INTEGON NATIONAL INS CO	2339	C
TECHNOLOGY INS CO	1981	C
WESCO INS CO	1743	B-
SECURITY NATIONAL INS CO	991	B
REPUBLIC UNDERWRITERS INS CO	676	C

WEST BEND MUTUAL INS CO *
B+   Good

Major Rating Factors: Good liquidity (6.4 on a scale of 0 to 10) with sufficient resources (cash flows and marketable investments) to handle a spike in claims. Good overall results on stability tests (5.1) despite weak results on operational trends.

Other Rating Factors: Strong long-term capitalization index (8.7) based on excellent current risk adjusted capital (severe and moderate loss scenarios). Moreover, capital levels have been consistent in recent years. Ample reserve history (7.0) that can protect against increases in claims costs. Excellent profitability (8.5) with operating gains in each of the last five years.

Principal Business: Workers compensation (25%), other liability (17%), auto liability (15%), homeowners multiple peril (12%), auto physical damage (10%), allied lines (6%), and other lines (15%).

Principal Investments: Investment grade bonds (67%), misc. investments (22%), non investment grade bonds (7%), real estate (3%), and cash (1%).

Investments in Affiliates: None

Group Affiliation: None

Licensed in: IL, IN, IA, KS, KY, MI, MN, MO, NE, OH, WI

Commenced Business: May 1894

Address: 1900 S 18th Ave, West Bend, WI 53095

Phone: (262) 334-5571   **Domicile State:** WI   **NAIC Code:** 15350

Data Date	Rating	RACR #1	RACR #2	Loss Ratio %	Total Assets ($mil)	Capital ($mil)	Net Premium ($mil)	Net Income ($mil)
6-16	B+	3.10	2.12	N/A	2,456.0	911.6	482.1	20.1
6-15	B+	3.57	2.31	N/A	2,313.5	877.3	452.4	43.1
2015	B+	3.18	2.20	59.3	2,329.3	878.2	960.5	44.8
2014	B+	3.48	2.24	63.6	2,171.2	823.1	895.0	57.5
2013	A-	3.27	2.11	61.1	1,975.4	690.7	814.3	62.8
2012	B+	3.34	2.20	62.3	1,786.2	613.5	726.7	60.3
2011	B+	3.10	2.09	74.1	1,666.6	547.6	656.2	20.1

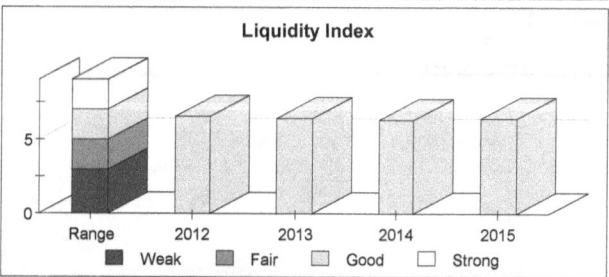

Liquidity Index

WESTCHESTER FIRE INS CO
C+   Fair

Major Rating Factors: Fair profitability index (3.3 on a scale of 0 to 10). Fair expense controls. Return on equity has been fair, averaging 9.4% over the past five years. Fair overall results on stability tests (4.5) including fair financial strength of affiliated Chubb Limited and weak results on operational trends.

Other Rating Factors: Good liquidity (6.9) with sufficient resources (cash flows and marketable investments) to handle a spike in claims. Strong long-term capitalization index (9.3) based on excellent current risk adjusted capital (severe and moderate loss scenarios), despite some fluctuation in capital levels. Ample reserve history (8.2) that helps to protect the company against sharp claims increases.

Principal Business: Other liability (56%), surety (26%), inland marine (7%), products liability (3%), fidelity (2%), fire (1%), and other lines (4%).

Principal Investments: Investment grade bonds (96%) and non investment grade bonds (8%).

Investments in Affiliates: None

Group Affiliation: Chubb Limited

Licensed in: All states, the District of Columbia and Puerto Rico

Commenced Business: April 1967

Address: 1601 Chestnut St, Philadelphia, PA 19192

Phone: (215) 640-1000   **Domicile State:** PA   **NAIC Code:** 10030

Data Date	Rating	RACR #1	RACR #2	Loss Ratio %	Total Assets ($mil)	Capital ($mil)	Net Premium ($mil)	Net Income ($mil)
6-16	C+	3.60	2.38	N/A	1,753.9	674.1	180.0	6.4
6-15	C	4.77	3.12	N/A	1,931.8	858.1	173.2	45.9
2015	C+	3.98	2.65	60.1	1,797.9	731.4	374.1	53.0
2014	C	4.92	3.23	56.5	2,011.9	906.1	342.6	81.9
2013	C	4.31	2.96	46.7	2,056.1	906.6	226.4	114.1
2012	C	2.05	1.25	67.2	2,119.3	813.7	389.8	103.8
2011	C-	1.37	0.96	59.4	2,420.5	1,104.6	343.3	102.0

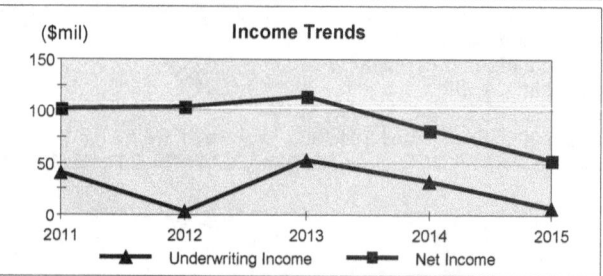

Income Trends

WESTERN AGRICULTURAL INS CO * — B+ — Good

Major Rating Factors: Good liquidity (5.8 on a scale of 0 to 10) with sufficient resources (cash flows and marketable investments) to handle a spike in claims. Good overall results on stability tests (5.1) despite weak results on operational trends.

Other Rating Factors: Strong long-term capitalization index (9.9) based on excellent current risk adjusted capital (severe and moderate loss scenarios). Moreover, capital levels have been consistent in recent years. Ample reserve history (8.1) that helps to protect the company against sharp claims increases. Excellent profitability (8.7) with operating gains in each of the last five years.

Principal Business: Allied lines (52%), farmowners multiple peril (10%), auto liability (10%), homeowners multiple peril (9%), auto physical damage (9%), commercial multiple peril (6%), and other lines (4%).

Principal Investments: Investment grade bonds (86%), misc. investments (12%), and non investment grade bonds (2%).

Investments in Affiliates: 2%

Group Affiliation: Iowa Farm Bureau

Licensed in: AL, AZ, AR, CO, ID, IL, IN, IA, KS, MI, MN, MO, MT, NE, NV, NM, ND, OH, OK, SC, SD, TN, TX, UT, VA, WI, WY

Commenced Business: January 1972

Address: 5400 University Ave, West Des Moines, IA 50266-5997

Phone: (515) 225-5400   **Domicile State:** IA   **NAIC Code:** 27871

Data Date	Rating	RACR #1	RACR #2	Loss Ratio %	Total Assets ($mil)	Capital ($mil)	Net Premium ($mil)	Net Income ($mil)
6-16	B+	4.40	3.41	N/A	206.5	92.8	49.8	3.3
6-15	B+	4.04	3.12	N/A	192.7	81.7	48.3	3.8
2015	B+	4.33	3.25	62.3	190.4	88.9	105.1	11.1
2014	B+	4.00	3.00	70.3	182.7	77.4	101.5	5.8
2013	B+	3.93	2.92	70.2	171.2	70.7	98.1	6.4
2012	B+	3.87	2.83	71.5	163.5	63.9	91.6	7.7
2011	B+	3.48	2.60	75.4	148.8	58.3	87.8	2.9

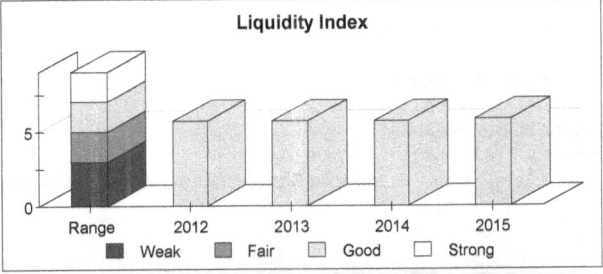

Liquidity Index

WESTERN NATIONAL MUTUAL INS CO — B- — Good

Major Rating Factors: Fair overall results on stability tests (4.3 on a scale of 0 to 10) including potential drain of affiliation with Western National Mutual and weak results on operational trends. Good liquidity (6.7) with sufficient resources (cash flows and marketable investments) to handle a spike in claims.

Other Rating Factors: Strong long-term capitalization index (8.6) based on excellent current risk adjusted capital (severe and moderate loss scenarios). Moreover, capital levels have been consistent in recent years. Ample reserve history (8.2) that helps to protect the company against sharp claims increases. Excellent profitability (8.7) with operating gains in each of the last five years.

Principal Business: Workers compensation (22%), auto liability (19%), homeowners multiple peril (16%), auto physical damage (14%), other liability (11%), products liability (5%), and other lines (12%).

Principal Investments: Investment grade bonds (62%), misc. investments (34%), real estate (3%), and cash (1%).

Investments in Affiliates: 19%

Group Affiliation: Western National Mutual

Licensed in: AK, AZ, AR, CA, CO, DE, ID, IL, IN, IA, KS, MD, MI, MN, MO, MT, NE, NV, NJ, NM, ND, OH, OK, OR, PA, RI, SD, TX, UT, WA, WI, WY

Commenced Business: June 1915

Address: 5350 W 78th St, Minneapolis, MN 55439

Phone: (952) 835-5350   **Domicile State:** MN   **NAIC Code:** 15377

Data Date	Rating	RACR #1	RACR #2	Loss Ratio %	Total Assets ($mil)	Capital ($mil)	Net Premium ($mil)	Net Income ($mil)
6-16	B-	2.49	2.07	N/A	929.6	408.1	164.2	12.0
6-15	B-	2.48	2.08	N/A	828.1	367.6	160.1	13.1
2015	B-	2.47	2.10	65.2	845.5	390.6	340.6	28.2
2014	B-	2.44	2.08	65.7	762.5	350.0	285.0	23.4
2013	B-	2.16	1.78	68.7	696.0	314.2	256.3	15.7
2012	B-	2.23	1.88	70.0	647.0	292.4	233.7	12.4
2011	B-	2.28	1.84	72.1	593.9	275.9	196.8	11.7

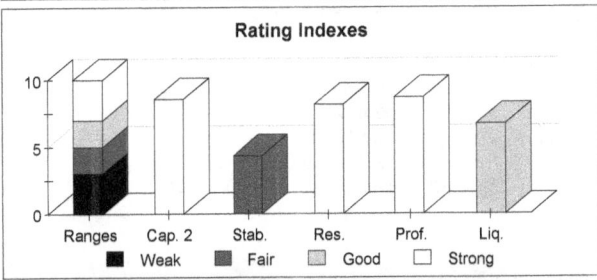

Rating Indexes

WESTERN SURETY CO — C — Fair

Major Rating Factors: Weak overall results on stability tests (2.9 on a scale of 0 to 10) including weak results on operational trends. The largest net exposure for one risk is excessive at 8.3% of capital. Good liquidity (6.9) with sufficient resources (cash flows and marketable investments) to handle a spike in claims.

Other Rating Factors: Strong long-term capitalization index (10.0) based on excellent current risk adjusted capital (severe and moderate loss scenarios), despite some fluctuation in capital levels. Ample reserve history (9.3) that helps to protect the company against sharp claims increases. Excellent profitability (8.0) with operating gains in each of the last five years. Return on equity has been good over the last five years, averaging 10.9%.

Principal Business: (Not applicable due to unusual reinsurance transactions.)

Principal Investments: Investment grade bonds (92%) and misc. investments (8%).

Investments in Affiliates: 1%

Group Affiliation: CNA Financial Corp

Licensed in: All states, the District of Columbia and Puerto Rico

Commenced Business: July 1900

Address: 101 South Phillips Avenue, Sioux Falls, SD 57104-6703

Phone: (605) 336-0850   **Domicile State:** SD   **NAIC Code:** 13188

Data Date	Rating	RACR #1	RACR #2	Loss Ratio %	Total Assets ($mil)	Capital ($mil)	Net Premium ($mil)	Net Income ($mil)
6-16	C	6.93	5.36	N/A	1,962.4	1,369.0	179.8	46.6
6-15	C	7.87	5.92	N/A	1,943.6	1,400.9	161.5	35.2
2015	C	7.42	5.79	21.8	1,823.7	1,323.3	295.8	116.5
2014	C	6.57	4.94	10.6	1,998.3	1,368.0	433.7	164.2
2013	C	5.67	4.30	9.2	1,856.4	1,205.6	418.4	152.7
2012	C	4.57	3.46	15.6	1,732.5	1,052.4	411.7	126.7
2011	C	3.96	2.99	26.6	1,587.1	889.5	419.6	96.2

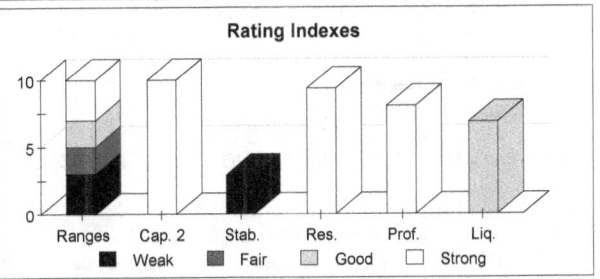

Rating Indexes

287

WESTERN WORLD INS CO | C | Fair

Major Rating Factors: Fair overall results on stability tests (4.1 on a scale of 0 to 10) including weak results on operational trends and negative cash flow from operations for 2015. Good overall profitability index (6.8). Weak expense controls. Return on equity has been fair, averaging 5.3% over the past five years.

Other Rating Factors: Strong long-term capitalization index (7.0) based on excellent current risk adjusted capital (severe and moderate loss scenarios), despite some fluctuation in capital levels. Ample reserve history (9.6) that helps to protect the company against sharp claims increases. Excellent liquidity (7.0) with ample operational cash flow and liquid investments.

Principal Business: Other liability (60%), commercial multiple peril (18%), products liability (13%), allied lines (6%), medical malpractice (2%), and auto liability (1%).

Principal Investments: Investment grade bonds (54%), misc. investments (41%), non investment grade bonds (4%), and cash (1%).

Investments in Affiliates: 31%

Group Affiliation: Western World Group

Licensed in: All states except PR

Commenced Business: April 1964

Address: 50 Washington St, Keene, NH 03431

Phone: (201) 847-8600   **Domicile State:** NH   **NAIC Code:** 13196

Data Date	Rating	RACR #1	RACR #2	Loss Ratio %	Total Assets ($mil)	Capital ($mil)	Net Premium ($mil)	Net Income ($mil)
6-16	C	1.69	1.53	N/A	905.5	426.6	52.0	1.7
6-15	C	1.60	1.34	N/A	1,016.9	463.3	89.3	14.0
2015	C	1.66	1.49	72.3	916.5	421.0	96.7	22.3
2014	C	1.58	1.33	28.9	1,047.6	452.1	239.9	80.3
2013	C	1.39	1.19	69.0	1,047.0	367.7	201.7	7.8
2012	C	1.55	1.36	70.0	1,011.0	357.0	155.1	6.2
2011	C	1.60	1.42	72.0	993.3	351.8	132.2	5.8

Rating Indexes

WESTFIELD INS CO | B- | Good

Major Rating Factors: Fair overall results on stability tests (4.6 on a scale of 0 to 10) including potential drain of affiliation with Westfield Companies and weak results on operational trends. Good liquidity (6.6) with sufficient resources (cash flows and marketable investments) to handle a spike in claims.

Other Rating Factors: Strong long-term capitalization index (9.7) based on excellent current risk adjusted capital (severe and moderate loss scenarios). Moreover, capital levels have been consistent in recent years. Ample reserve history (9.1) that helps to protect the company against sharp claims increases. Excellent profitability (7.7) with operating gains in each of the last five years.

Principal Business: Commercial multiple peril (28%), auto liability (23%), auto physical damage (11%), other liability (10%), homeowners multiple peril (6%), workers compensation (6%), and other lines (16%).

Principal Investments: Investment grade bonds (67%) and misc. investments (33%).

Investments in Affiliates: None

Group Affiliation: Westfield Companies

Licensed in: All states except CA, PR

Commenced Business: July 1929

Address: One Park Circle, Westfield Center, OH 44251-5001

Phone: (330) 887-0101   **Domicile State:** OH   **NAIC Code:** 24112

Data Date	Rating	RACR #1	RACR #2	Loss Ratio %	Total Assets ($mil)	Capital ($mil)	Net Premium ($mil)	Net Income ($mil)
6-16	B-	4.22	2.84	N/A	2,634.5	1,113.3	476.4	40.2
6-15	B-	4.19	2.81	N/A	2,588.1	1,082.2	465.4	39.2
2015	B-	4.26	2.89	62.7	2,594.4	1,092.4	955.3	70.9
2014	B-	4.14	2.78	63.5	2,536.1	1,043.0	935.9	93.3
2013	B-	3.76	2.50	59.8	2,450.5	991.2	904.7	127.7
2012	B-	3.33	2.22	64.9	2,243.1	853.6	867.8	89.6
2011	B-	3.25	2.13	79.3	2,128.8	774.3	757.9	29.5

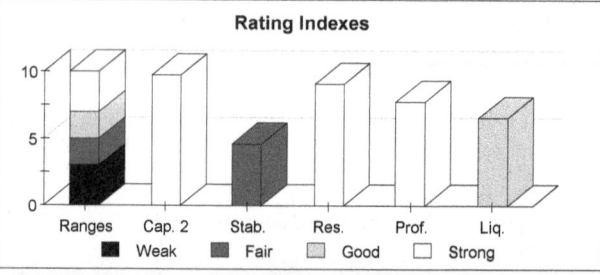

Rating Indexes

WESTFIELD NATIONAL INS CO | B- | Good

Major Rating Factors: Fair overall results on stability tests (4.6 on a scale of 0 to 10) including potential drain of affiliation with Westfield Companies and weak results on operational trends. The largest net exposure for one risk is conservative at 1.0% of capital. Good liquidity (6.6) with sufficient resources (cash flows and marketable investments) to handle a spike in claims.

Other Rating Factors: Strong long-term capitalization index (9.5) based on excellent current risk adjusted capital (severe and moderate loss scenarios). Moreover, capital levels have been consistent in recent years. Ample reserve history (9.0) that helps to protect the company against sharp claims increases. Excellent profitability (7.5) despite modest operating losses during 2011.

Principal Business: Homeowners multiple peril (35%), auto liability (25%), auto physical damage (21%), commercial multiple peril (6%), workers compensation (5%), other liability (4%), and inland marine (2%).

Principal Investments: Investment grade bonds (72%) and misc. investments (28%).

Investments in Affiliates: None

Group Affiliation: Westfield Companies

Licensed in: AL, AZ, AR, CA, CO, DC, DE, FL, GA, ID, IL, IN, IA, KS, KY, MD, MI, MN, MS, MO, MT, NE, NV, NM, NC, ND, OH, OK, PA, SC, SD, TN, TX, UT, VA, WA, WV, WI, WY

Commenced Business: April 1968

Address: One Park Circle, Westfield Center, OH 44251

Phone: (330) 887-0101   **Domicile State:** OH   **NAIC Code:** 24120

Data Date	Rating	RACR #1	RACR #2	Loss Ratio %	Total Assets ($mil)	Capital ($mil)	Net Premium ($mil)	Net Income ($mil)
6-16	B-	4.08	2.74	N/A	634.5	288.0	114.7	8.6
6-15	B-	4.03	2.71	N/A	606.4	269.7	112.0	10.7
2015	B-	4.10	2.79	62.7	613.4	272.8	230.0	16.5
2014	B-	3.92	2.62	63.5	598.7	263.1	225.3	16.6
2013	B+	3.75	2.51	59.8	571.9	243.2	217.8	25.2
2012	B+	3.27	2.18	64.9	524.9	208.0	208.9	19.8
2011	B+	3.06	2.01	79.3	501.8	186.6	199.6	-1.7

Westfield Companies
Composite Group Rating: B-
Largest Group Members

	Assets ($mil)	Rating
OHIO FARMERS INS CO	2701	B-
WESTFIELD INS CO	2594	B-
WESTFIELD NATIONAL INS CO	613	B-
OLD GUARD INS CO	421	C+
AMERICAN SELECT INS CO	234	C

WESTGUARD INS CO   C+   Fair

Major Rating Factors: Fair overall results on stability tests (3.3 on a scale of 0 to 10) including weak results on operational trends, excessive premium growth and negative cash flow from operations for 2015. The largest net exposure for one risk is acceptable at 2.0% of capital. Good long-term capitalization index (6.0) based on excellent current risk adjusted capital (severe and moderate loss scenarios). Moreover, capital levels have been consistent in recent years.

Other Rating Factors: Ample reserve history (9.4) that helps to protect the company against sharp claims increases. Excellent profitability (7.9) with operating gains in each of the last five years. Superior liquidity (10.0) with ample operational cash flow and liquid investments.

Principal Business: Workers compensation (100%).

Principal Investments: Misc. investments (92%), investment grade bonds (4%), cash (3%), and real estate (1%).

Investments in Affiliates: 64%

Group Affiliation: Berkshire-Hathaway

Licensed in: NY, PA, WV

Commenced Business: July 2004

Address: 16 S River St, Wilkes-barre, PA 18702

Phone: (570) 825-9900   **Domicile State:** PA   **NAIC Code:** 11981

Data Date	Rating	RACR #1	RACR #2	Loss Ratio %	Total Assets ($mil)	Capital ($mil)	Net Premium ($mil)	Net Income ($mil)
6-16	C+	1.34	1.21	N/A	884.7	452.0	9.2	2.4
6-15	C+	1.14	1.08	N/A	650.2	310.3	6.1	1.3
2015	C+	1.30	1.19	60.0	780.5	430.9	19.0	0.3
2014	C+	1.09	1.06	63.2	607.1	309.1	11.9	1.2
2013	C	0.82	0.57	67.8	35.1	14.6	6.2	1.4
2012	C	1.02	0.62	N/A	42.0	13.3	3.1	1.1
2011	C	1.15	0.52	66.8	37.6	12.5	13.3	1.2

Berkshire-Hathaway
Composite Group Rating: B

Largest Group Members	Assets ($mil)	Rating
NATIONAL INDEMNITY CO	161777	B
GOVERNMENT EMPLOYEES INS CO	24036	B
COLUMBIA INS CO	19102	C+
BERKSHIRE HATHAWAY LIFE INS CO OF NE	16287	C+
GENERAL REINS CORP	15320	C+

WESTPORT INS CORP   B-   Good

Major Rating Factors: Fair profitability index (3.5 on a scale of 0 to 10). Weak expense controls. Return on equity has been fair, averaging 9.7% over the past five years. Fair overall results on stability tests (4.2) including weak results on operational trends and negative cash flow from operations for 2015. The largest net exposure for one risk is conservative at 1.6% of capital.

Other Rating Factors: Good long-term capitalization index (5.6) based on good current risk adjusted capital (moderate loss scenario), despite some fluctuation in capital levels. History of adequate reserve strength (6.9) as reserves have been consistently at an acceptable level. Excellent liquidity (7.0) with ample operational cash flow and liquid investments.

Principal Business: Allied lines (31%), other liability (24%), fire (19%), earthquake (10%), group accident & health (7%), boiler & machinery (5%), and aircraft (3%).

Principal Investments: Investment grade bonds (71%), misc. investments (27%), and non investment grade bonds (2%).

Investments in Affiliates: 13%

Group Affiliation: Swiss Reinsurance

Licensed in: All states, the District of Columbia and Puerto Rico

Commenced Business: September 1981

Address: 237 E High St, Jefferson City, MO 65101

Phone: (913) 676-5200   **Domicile State:** MO   **NAIC Code:** 39845

Data Date	Rating	RACR #1	RACR #2	Loss Ratio %	Total Assets ($mil)	Capital ($mil)	Net Premium ($mil)	Net Income ($mil)
6-16	B-	1.54	1.08	N/A	4,890.9	1,507.8	135.6	136.4
6-15	C+	1.46	1.02	N/A	5,164.3	1,498.5	159.8	122.0
2015	B-	1.48	1.03	61.5	4,693.0	1,505.3	281.6	177.3
2014	C+	1.56	1.08	67.9	5,215.7	1,630.5	135.9	160.8
2013	C+	1.25	0.85	62.2	5,454.1	1,769.4	580.1	167.8
2012	C	0.57	0.44	64.9	5,331.3	1,726.5	535.1	108.0
2011	C+	1.17	0.80	112.0	5,349.6	1,940.9	99.6	135.3

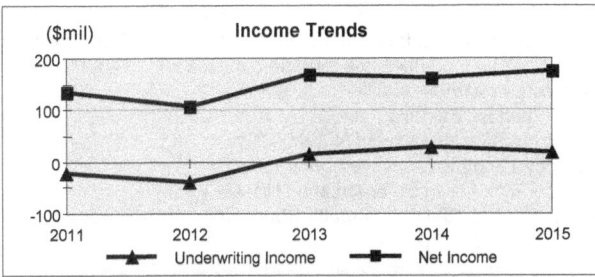

Income Trends

XL INS AMERICA INC   C   Fair

Major Rating Factors: Fair overall results on stability tests (3.6 on a scale of 0 to 10) including potential drain of affiliation with XL Group Ltd, weak results on operational trends and negative cash flow from operations for 2015. The largest net exposure for one risk is acceptable at 2.4% of capital. Fair profitability index (3.6). Fair expense controls. Return on equity has been fair, averaging 5.9% over the past five years.

Other Rating Factors: Good liquidity (6.7) with sufficient resources (cash flows and marketable investments) to handle a spike in claims. Strong long-term capitalization index (7.3) based on excellent current risk adjusted capital (severe and moderate loss scenarios), despite some fluctuation in capital levels. Ample reserve history (7.6) that can protect against increases in claims costs.

Principal Business: Other liability (29%), fire (18%), allied lines (14%), workers compensation (13%), earthquake (7%), inland marine (7%), and other lines (12%).

Principal Investments: Investment grade bonds (66%), misc. investments (19%), and cash (15%).

Investments in Affiliates: 21%

Group Affiliation: XL Group Ltd

Licensed in: All states, the District of Columbia and Puerto Rico

Commenced Business: December 1945

Address: 1201 N Market St Suite 501, Wilmington, DE 19801

Phone: (203) 964-5200   **Domicile State:** DE   **NAIC Code:** 24554

Data Date	Rating	RACR #1	RACR #2	Loss Ratio %	Total Assets ($mil)	Capital ($mil)	Net Premium ($mil)	Net Income ($mil)
6-16	C	1.36	1.10	N/A	742.2	189.7	69.4	4.4
6-15	C	1.47	1.21	N/A	676.6	211.5	63.3	9.2
2015	C	1.54	1.27	71.2	678.0	211.1	132.7	6.9
2014	C	1.62	1.34	61.5	752.9	232.3	126.7	16.3
2013	C	1.35	1.07	65.3	734.2	246.8	133.1	26.0
2012	C	1.65	1.37	73.4	775.6	253.0	129.4	16.7
2011	C	1.54	1.25	82.9	686.3	223.4	115.0	6.0

XL Group Ltd
Composite Group Rating: C

Largest Group Members	Assets ($mil)	Rating
XL REINS AMERICA INC	5308	C
GREENWICH INS CO	1088	C
XL INS AMERICA INC	678	C
CATLIN SPECIALTY INS CO	668	C+
XL SPECIALTY INS CO	462	C

XL REINS AMERICA INC   C   Fair

Major Rating Factors: Fair overall results on stability tests (3.8 on a scale of 0 to 10) including potential drain of affiliation with XL Group Ltd and weak results on operational trends. The largest net exposure for one risk is conservative at 1.4% of capital. Fair profitability index (3.8). Weak expense controls. Return on equity has been fair, averaging 5.1% over the past five years.

Other Rating Factors: Strong long-term capitalization index (8.7) based on excellent current risk adjusted capital (severe and moderate loss scenarios), despite some fluctuation in capital levels. Ample reserve history (7.5) that can protect against increases in claims costs. Excellent liquidity (7.1) with ample operational cash flow and liquid investments.

Principal Business: Other liability (97%) and surety (3%).

Principal Investments: Investment grade bonds (72%), misc. investments (25%), and cash (3%).

Investments in Affiliates: 11%

Group Affiliation: XL Group Ltd

Licensed in: All states, the District of Columbia and Puerto Rico

Commenced Business: October 1929

Address: 111 Broadway Suite 1802, New York, NY 10006

Phone: (203) 964-5200   **Domicile State:** NY   **NAIC Code:** 20583

Data Date	Rating	RACR #1	RACR #2	Loss Ratio %	Total Assets ($mil)	Capital ($mil)	Net Premium ($mil)	Net Income ($mil)
6-16	C	2.70	1.99	N/A	5,935.1	2,025.4	451.2	6.5
6-15	C	2.81	2.14	N/A	5,464.9	2,032.6	411.5	79.0
2015	C	2.96	2.22	71.2	5,307.7	2,021.6	862.6	83.0
2014	C	3.07	2.34	61.5	5,627.6	2,233.6	823.4	219.8
2013	C	2.94	2.26	65.3	5,527.8	2,244.5	865.2	161.4
2012	C	2.93	2.25	73.4	5,413.0	2,237.8	841.2	65.5
2011	C	2.93	2.17	82.9	5,128.5	2,093.7	747.3	73.3

Rating Indexes

ZENITH INS CO   C+   Fair

Major Rating Factors: Fair overall results on stability tests (4.4 on a scale of 0 to 10) including potential drain of affiliation with Fairfax Financial and weak results on operational trends. Fair profitability index (4.2) with operating losses during 2011, 2012 and 2013. Return on equity has been low, averaging 3.0% over the past five years.

Other Rating Factors: Strong long-term capitalization index (7.1) based on excellent current risk adjusted capital (severe and moderate loss scenarios), despite some fluctuation in capital levels. Ample reserve history (7.0) that can protect against increases in claims costs. Excellent liquidity (7.0) with ample operational cash flow and liquid investments.

Principal Business: Workers compensation (92%), commercial multiple peril (3%), auto liability (2%), other liability (1%), fire (1%), and auto physical damage (1%).

Principal Investments: Investment grade bonds (67%), misc. investments (27%), cash (2%), non investment grade bonds (2%), and real estate (2%).

Investments in Affiliates: 6%

Group Affiliation: Fairfax Financial

Licensed in: All states except ND, WY, PR

Commenced Business: December 1950

Address: 21255 Califa St, Woodland Hills, CA 91367

Phone: (818) 713-1000   **Domicile State:** CA   **NAIC Code:** 13269

Data Date	Rating	RACR #1	RACR #2	Loss Ratio %	Total Assets ($mil)	Capital ($mil)	Net Premium ($mil)	Net Income ($mil)
6-16	C+	1.36	1.02	N/A	1,902.7	592.0	376.7	59.5
6-15	C	1.46	1.08	N/A	1,873.8	613.8	358.3	87.0
2015	C+	1.43	1.07	46.6	1,908.8	621.7	754.9	121.0
2014	C	1.37	1.02	52.8	1,834.1	564.5	703.4	110.7
2013	C-	1.12	0.82	62.4	1,783.8	515.8	677.5	-18.1
2012	D+	1.21	0.89	77.8	1,646.3	443.7	596.7	-125.4
2011	C+	1.99	1.45	83.1	1,714.1	620.1	493.8	-4.0

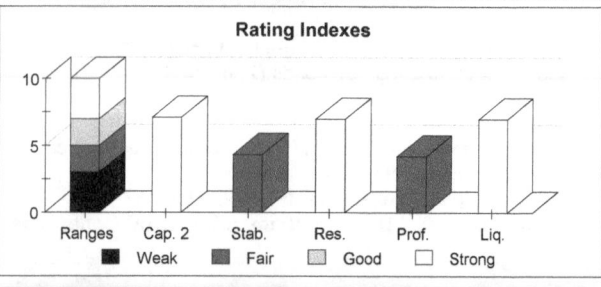

Rating Indexes

ZURICH AMERICAN INS CO   B-   Good

Major Rating Factors: Fair overall results on stability tests (3.5 on a scale of 0 to 10) including weak results on operational trends. The largest net exposure for one risk is excessive at 5.0% of capital. History of adequate reserve strength (6.1) as reserves have been consistently at an acceptable level.

Other Rating Factors: Good overall profitability index (6.5). Good expense controls. Return on equity has been good over the last five years, averaging 11.9%. Good liquidity (6.9) with sufficient resources (cash flows and marketable investments) to handle a spike in claims. Strong long-term capitalization index (8.0) based on excellent current risk adjusted capital (severe and moderate loss scenarios), despite some fluctuation in capital levels.

Principal Business: Workers compensation (27%), other liability (23%), auto liability (10%), commercial multiple peril (8%), inland marine (6%), allied lines (6%), and other lines (20%).

Principal Investments: Investment grade bonds (70%), misc. investments (23%), real estate (4%), and non investment grade bonds (3%).

Investments in Affiliates: 6%

Group Affiliation: Zurich Financial Services Group

Licensed in: All states, the District of Columbia and Puerto Rico

Commenced Business: January 1913

Address: 165 Broadway, 28th Floor, New York, NY 10006

Phone: (847) 605-6000   **Domicile State:** NY   **NAIC Code:** 16535

Data Date	Rating	RACR #1	RACR #2	Loss Ratio %	Total Assets ($mil)	Capital ($mil)	Net Premium ($mil)	Net Income ($mil)
6-16	B-	2.35	1.57	N/A	30,823.4	7,465.3	2,226.4	505.3
6-15	C+	2.50	1.70	N/A	30,873.6	7,586.6	2,258.2	267.7
2015	B-	2.53	1.71	81.4	30,471.5	7,765.5	4,540.4	597.9
2014	C+	2.71	1.86	78.0	30,309.7	8,015.4	4,739.7	1,000.5
2013	C+	2.76	1.90	74.6	30,184.0	7,798.4	4,733.6	772.8
2012	C+	2.75	1.91	81.8	30,011.1	7,642.3	4,437.8	1,156.5
2011	C	2.57	1.72	78.8	28,729.2	7,018.8	4,155.8	960.4

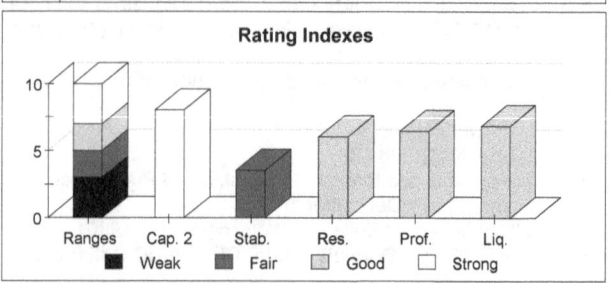

Rating Indexes

Section III

Weiss
Recommended Companies

A compilation of those

U.S. Property and Casualty Insurers

receiving a Weiss Safety Rating

of A+, A, A- or B+.

Companies are listed in alphabetical order.

Section III Contents

This section provides a list of recommended carriers (based strictly on financial safety) along with additional information you should have when shopping for insurance. It contains all insurers receiving a Safety Rating of A+, A, A- or B+. If an insurer is not on this list, it should not be automatically assumed that the firm is weak. Indeed, there are many firms that have not achieved a B+ or better rating but are in relatively good condition with adequate resources to cover their risk during an average recession. Not being included in this list should not be construed as a recommendation to cancel a policy.

Left Pages

1. **Safety Rating**	Our rating is measured on a scale from A to F and considers a wide range of factors. Highly-rated companies are, in our opinion, less likely to experience financial difficulties than lower rated firms. See *About Weiss Safety Ratings* for more information.	
2. **Insurance Company Name**	The legally-registered name, which can sometimes differ from the name that the company uses for advertising. An insurer's name can be very similar to the name of other companies which may not be on our Recommended List, so make sure you note the exact name before contacting your agent.	
3. **Address**	The address of the main office where you can contact the firm for additional financial data or for the location of local branches and/or registered agents.	
4. **Telephone Number**	The number to call for additional financial data or for the phone numbers of local branches and/or registered agents.	

Right Pages

The right-side pages present the percentage of the company's business that is involved in each type of insurance. Specifically, the numbers shown are the amounts of direct premium (received directly from policyholders) for each line of business as a percent of total premiums.

1. **Domicile State**	The state which has primary regulatory responsibility for the company. It may differ from the location of the company's corporate headquarters. You do not have to be living in the domicile state to purchase insurance from this firm, provided it is licensed to do business in your state.	
2. **Auto**	Coverage for damage to a policyholder's own automobile and for the financial loss from auto-related bodily injury or property damage.	
3. **Homeowners Multiple Peril**	Package policies for homeowners providing a broad spectrum of property and liability coverages.	

4. **Farmowners Multiple Peril**   Package policies for farm or ranch owners providing a broad spectrum of property and liability coverages.

5. **Commercial Multiple Peril**   Package policies for businesses and other commercial establishments providing a broad spectrum of property and liability coverages.

6. **Commercial Auto Liability**   Coverage against financial loss because of auto related injuries or damages to third parties.

7. **Other Liability**   Encompasses all third-party liability coverages not included in other business areas. It can include among others: professional liability, environmental liability, product liability, umbrella liability, general liability.

8. **Medical Malpractice**   Errors and omissions liability coverages for persons engaged in the practice of medicine, surgery, dentistry, nursing, pharmacy, or other health care services. Also covers health care institutions.

9. **Workers' Compensation**   Liability coverage issued to employers which provides for the payment of medical care, disability income or possible additional liability amounts to employees who are injured on the job.

10. **Accident and Health**   This includes three categories: (1) group accident and health, which consists of medical and hospitalization insurance plans under which a number of persons and their dependents are insured under a single policy issued to an employer or a common associated entity; (2) credit accident and health, which makes certain debt payments, usually for car or home loans, in the case of accident or illness; and (3) other accident and health, issued to individuals, to pay health care benefits or loss of income due to accidental injury or death.

11. **Other**   Fire, allied lines, mortgage guaranty, ocean marine, inland marine, financial guaranty, product liability, aircraft, fidelity, surety, glass, burglary and theft, boiler and machinery, credit, international, reinsurance, aggregate write-ins for other lines of business and other miscellaneous types of insurance.

Weiss Safety Ratings are not deemed to be a recommendation concerning the purchase or sale of the securities of any insurance company that is publicly owned.

RATING	INSURANCE COMPANY NAME	ADDRESS	CITY	STATE	ZIP	PHONE
B+	ACUITY A MUTUAL INS CO	2800 S TAYLOR DR	SHEBOYGAN	WI	53081	(920) 458-9131
B+	ALFA MUTUAL GENERAL INS CO	2108 EAST SOUTH BLVD	MONTGOMERY	AL	36116	(334) 288-3900
B+	ALL AMERICA INS CO	800 S WASHINGTON ST	VAN WERT	OH	45891	(419) 238-1010
B+	AMERICAN FAMILY MUT INS CO	6000 AMERICAN PKWY	MADISON	WI	53783	(608) 249-2111
B+	AMERICAN STANDARD INS CO OF WI	6000 AMERICAN PARKWAY	MADISON	WI	53783	(608) 249-2111
B+	AMICA MUTUAL INS CO	100 AMICA WAY	LINCOLN	RI	02865	(800) 652-6422
B+	AUTO CLUB INDEMNITY CO	3333 FAIRVIEW ROAD	COSTA MESA	CA	92626	(714) 850-5111
A-	AUTO-OWNERS INS CO	6101 ANACAPRI BLVD	LANSING	MI	48917	(517) 323-1200
A+	BERKSHIRE HATHAWAY ASR CORP	MARINE AIR TERMINAL LAGUARDIA	FLUSHING	NY	11371	(402) 916-3000
B+	BUILDERS MUTUAL INS CO	5580 CENTERVIEW DR	RALEIGH	NC	27606	(919) 845-1976
B+	CENTURION CASUALTY CO	800 WALNUT ST	DES MOINES	IA	50309	515-557-7346
A-	CINCINNATI INDEMNITY CO	6200 S GILMORE RD	FAIRFIELD	OH	45014	(513) 870-2000
A-	CINCINNATI INS CO	6200 S GILMORE RD	FAIRFIELD	OH	45014	(513) 870-2000
A+	CITIZENS PROPERTY INS CORP	2312 KILLEARN CTR BLVD BLDG A	TALLAHASSEE	FL	32309	(850) 513-3700
A+	COPPERPOINT MUTUAL INS CO	3030 N 3RD ST	PHOENIX	AZ	85012	(602) 631-2240
B+	COUNTRY CASUALTY INS CO	1701 N. TOWANDA AVE	BLOOMINGTON	IL	61701	(309) 821-3000
A-	COUNTRY MUTUAL INS CO	1701 N. TOWANDA AVE	BLOOMINGTON	IL	61701	(309) 821-3000
B+	DAIRYLAND INS CO	1800 NORTH POINT DR	STEVENS POINT	WI	54481	(715) 346-6000
A-	ESSENT GUARANTY INC	201 KING OF PRUSSIA RD STE 501	RADNOR	PA	19087	(610) 230-0555
B+	FARM BUREAU P&C INS CO	5400 UNIVERSITY AVE	WEST DES MOINES	IA	50266	(515) 225-5400
B+	FARM FAMILY CASUALTY INS CO	344 ROUTE 9W	GLENMONT	NY	12077	(518) 431-5000
B+	FARMERS AUTOMOBILE INS ASN	2505 COURT ST	PEKIN	IL	61558	(309) 346-1161
B+	FIRST COLONIAL INS CO	1776 AMERICAN HERITAGE LIFE DR	JACKSONVILLE	FL	32224	(904) 992-1776
A-	GEICO CHOICE INS CO	1440 KIEWIT PLAZA	OMAHA	NE	68131	(800) 841-3000
B+	GEICO GENERAL INS CO	5260 WESTERN AVENUE	CHEVY CHASE	MD	20815	(800) 841-3000
A-	GEICO SECURE INS CO	1440 KIEWIT PLAZA	OMAHA	NE	68131	(800) 841-3000
B+	HOLYOKE MUTUAL INS CO IN SALEM	HOLYOKE SQUARE	SALEM	MA	01970	(978) 744-6123
A-	HOME-OWNERS INS CO	6101 ANACAPRI BLVD	LANSING	MI	48917	(517) 323-1200
B+	INTERINS EXCHANGE	3333 FAIRVIEW ROAD	COSTA MESA	CA	92626	(714) 850-5111
B+	MERCURY INS CO	4484 WILSHIRE BLVD	LOS ANGELES	CA	90010	(714) 671-6600
B+	MITSUI SUMITOMO INS CO OF AMER	560 LEXINGTON AVE 20TH FLOOR	NEW YORK	NY	10022	(908) 604-2900
B+	MOTORISTS MUTUAL INS CO	471 E BROAD ST	COLUMBUS	OH	43215	(614) 225-8211
A+	MUNICIPAL ASR CORP	31 W 52ND ST	NEW YORK	NY	10019	212-974-0100
B+	NATIONAL CASUALTY CO	8877 N GAINEY CENTER DR	SCOTTSDALE	AZ	85258	(480) 365-4000
A-	NATIONAL MORTGAGE INS CORP	1834 STEVEN ST	SUN PRAIRIE	WI	53590	(925) 300-6375
B+	NATIONWIDE MUTUAL FIRE INS CO	ONE NATIONWIDE PLAZA	COLUMBUS	OH	43216	(614) 249-7111
A+	OGLESBY REINS CO	ONE STATE FARM PLAZA	BLOOMINGTON	IL	61710	(309) 766-2311
A-	OWNERS INS CO	2325 N COLE ST	LIMA	OH	45801	(517) 323-1200
B+	PEKIN INS CO	2505 COURT ST	PEKIN	IL	61558	(309) 346-1161
B+	PROPERTY-OWNERS INS CO	3950 W DELPHI PIKE	MARION	IN	46952	(517) 323-1200
A	SENTRY INS A MUTUAL CO	1800 N POINT DR	STEVENS POINT	WI	54481	(715) 346-6000
B+	SENTRY SELECT INS CO	3400 80TH ST	MOLINE	IL	61265	(715) 346-6000
B+	SOUTHERN-OWNERS INS CO	6101 ANACAPRI BLVD	LANSING	MI	48917	(517) 323-1200
B+	STATE FARM MUTUAL AUTOMOBILE INS CO	ONE STATE FARM PLAZA	BLOOMINGTON	IL	61710	(309) 766-2311
B+	TENNESSEE FARMERS ASR CO	147 BEAR CREEK PIKE	COLUMBIA	TN	38401	(931) 388-7872
B+	TENNESSEE FARMERS MUTUAL INS CO	147 BEAR CREEK PIKE	COLUMBIA	TN	38401	(931) 388-7872
B+	TEXAS FARM BUREAU CASUALTY INS CO	7420 FISH POND RD	WACO	TX	76710	(254) 772-3030
B+	TOA REINS CO OF AMERICA	2711 CENTERVILLE RD SUITE 400	WILMINGTON	DE	19808	(973) 898-9480
A	TOKIO MARINE AMERICA INS CO	230 PARK AVE	NEW YORK	NY	10169	(610) 227-1300
A-	TRAVELERS CASUALTY & SURETY CO	ONE TOWER SQUARE	HARTFORD	CT	06183	(860) 277-0111
B+	TRAVELERS INDEMNITY CO	ONE TOWER SQUARE	HARTFORD	CT	06183	(860) 277-0111
B+	UNITED SERVICES AUTOMOBILE ASN	9800 FREDERICKSBURG RD	SAN ANTONIO	TX	78288	(210) 498-2211
A-	USAA CASUALTY INS CO	9800 FREDERICKSBURG RD	SAN ANTONIO	TX	78288	(210) 498-8000
B+	USAA GENERAL INDEMNITY CO	9800 FREDERICKSBURG RD	SAN ANTONIO	TX	78288	(210) 498-8000
B+	WEST BEND MUTUAL INS CO	1900 S 18TH AVE	WEST BEND	WI	53095	262-334-5571
B+	WESTERN AGRICULTURAL INS CO	5400 UNIVERSITY AVE	WEST DES MOINES	IA	50266	(515) 225-5400

DOM. STATE	AUTO	HOME MULT. PERIL	FARM MULT. PERIL	COMM. MULT. PERIL	COMM. AUTO LIAB.	OTHER LIABILITY	MED MALPRAC.	WORK. COMP.	ACCID. & HEALTH	OTHER	INSURANCE COMPANY NAME
WI	22	10	0	11	14	10	0	24	0	9	ACUITY A MUTUAL INS CO
AL	47	52	0	0	0	1	0	0	0	0	ALFA MUTUAL GENERAL INS CO
OH	8	0	0	58	20	0	0	8	0	5	ALL AMERICA INS CO
WI	51	32	2	8	1	3	0	1	1	1	AMERICAN FAMILY MUT INS CO
WI	100	0	0	0	0	0	0	0	0	0	AMERICAN STANDARD INS CO OF WI
RI	57	37	0	0	0	3	0	0	0	3	AMICA MUTUAL INS CO
TX	0	99	0	0	0	1	0	0	0	0	AUTO CLUB INDEMNITY CO
MI	20	29	2	11	8	7	0	8	0	16	AUTO-OWNERS INS CO
NY	0	0	0	0	0	0	0	0	0	100	BERKSHIRE HATHAWAY ASR CORP
NC	0	0	0	13	2	3	0	75	0	7	BUILDERS MUTUAL INS CO
IA	0	0	0	0	0	0	0	0	0	100	CENTURION CASUALTY CO
OH	5	0	0	24	13	15	1	31	0	11	CINCINNATI INDEMNITY CO
OH	19	14	0	27	10	16	1	3	0	11	CINCINNATI INS CO
FL	0	40	0	0	0	0	0	0	0	60	CITIZENS PROPERTY INS CORP
AZ	0	0	0	0	0	0	0	100	0	0	COPPERPOINT MUTUAL INS CO
IL	61	39	0	0	0	0	0	0	0	0	COUNTRY CASUALTY INS CO
IL	25	42	10	7	2	3	0	5	0	8	COUNTRY MUTUAL INS CO
WI	100	0	0	0	0	0	0	0	0	0	DAIRYLAND INS CO
PA	0	0	0	0	0	0	0	0	0	100	ESSENT GUARANTY INC
IA	39	24	25	4	1	2	0	3	0	1	FARM BUREAU P&C INS CO
NY	17	6	0	12	13	13	0	15	0	25	FARM FAMILY CASUALTY INS CO
IL	61	33	0	0	0	0	0	0	0	6	FARMERS AUTOMOBILE INS ASN
FL	1	0	0	0	0	1	0	0	0	32	FIRST COLONIAL INS CO
NE	100	0	0	0	0	0	0	0	0	0	GEICO CHOICE INS CO
MD	100	0	0	0	0	0	0	0	0	0	GEICO GENERAL INS CO
NE	100	0	0	0	0	0	0	0	0	0	GEICO SECURE INS CO
MA	2	9	0	85	0	0	0	0	0	3	HOLYOKE MUTUAL INS CO IN SALEM
MI	78	4	0	9	3	2	0	3	0	1	HOME-OWNERS INS CO
CA	79	19	0	0	0	1	0	0	0	1	INTERINS EXCHANGE
CA	100	0	0	0	0	0	0	0	0	0	MERCURY INS CO
NY	2	0	0	23	5	11	0	29	0	29	MITSUI SUMITOMO INS CO OF AMER
OH	33	18	0	12	12	14	0	5	0	7	MOTORISTS MUTUAL INS CO
NY	0	0	0	0	0	0	0	0	0	100	MUNICIPAL ASR CORP
WI	9	0	0	9	26	14	0	7	0	31	NATIONAL CASUALTY CO
WI	0	0	0	0	0	0	0	0	0	100	NATIONAL MORTGAGE INS CORP
OH	24	47	0	7	2	4	0	1	0	15	NATIONWIDE MUTUAL FIRE INS CO
IL (*)	0	0	0	0	0	0	0	0	0	0	OGLESBY REINS CO
OH	35	19	1	21	9	4	0	8	0	3	OWNERS INS CO
IL	24	13	0	26	10	4	0	20	0	3	PEKIN INS CO
IN	7	23	2	39	10	4	0	10	0	6	PROPERTY-OWNERS INS CO
WI	19	0	0	2	13	10	0	33	1	21	SENTRY INS A MUTUAL CO
WI	16	0	0	0	42	10	0	6	1	25	SENTRY SELECT INS CO
MI	50	3	0	12	2	27	0	5	0	2	SOUTHERN-OWNERS INS CO
IL	96	0	0	0	1	0	0	0	3	0	STATE FARM MUTUAL AUTOMOBILE INS CO
TN (*)	0	0	0	0	0	0	0	0	0	0	TENNESSEE FARMERS ASR CO
TN	51	31	10	1	0	1	0	0	0	5	TENNESSEE FARMERS MUTUAL INS CO
TX	96	0	0	0	2	2	0	0	0	0	TEXAS FARM BUREAU CASUALTY INS CO
DE (*)	0	0	0	0	0	0	0	0	0	0	TOA REINS CO OF AMERICA
NY	7	2	0	9	14	9	0	11	0	48	TOKIO MARINE AMERICA INS CO
CT	0	9	0	0	0	1	0	75	0	15	TRAVELERS CASUALTY & SURETY CO
CT	4	3	2	15	12	20	0	22	0	22	TRAVELERS INDEMNITY CO
TX	56	35	0	0	0	2	0	0	0	7	UNITED SERVICES AUTOMOBILE ASN
TX	66	29	0	0	0	1	0	0	0	4	USAA CASUALTY INS CO
TX	73	19	0	0	0	0	0	0	0	8	USAA GENERAL INDEMNITY CO
WI	19	12	0	3	6	17	0	25	0	18	WEST BEND MUTUAL INS CO
IA	16	9	10	6	2	1	0	2	0	53	WESTERN AGRICULTURAL INS CO

(*) Denotes reinsurers, companies that do not sell to consumers

Section IV

Weiss
Recommended Companies
by Type of Business

A compilation of those

U.S. Property and Casualty Insurers

receiving a Weiss Safety Rating

of A+, A, A- or B+.

Companies are ranked by Safety Rating
in each line of business where they have received
more than $1 million in direct premiums.

Section IV Contents

This section is broken into six subsections, each presenting a list of the recommended carriers receiving at least $1 million in direct premiums from a particular line of business: Auto, Commercial Multiple Peril, Fire and Allied, Homeowners Multiple Peril, Medical Malpractice, and Workers' Compensation. Recommended companies are those insurers receiving a Safety Rating of A+, A, A- or B+. If an insurer is not on this list, it should not be automatically assumed that the firm is weak. Indeed, there are many firms that have not achieved a B+ or better rating but are in relatively good condition with adequate resources to cover their risk during an average recession. Not being included in this list should not be construed as a recommendation to cancel policies.

Companies are ranked within each line of business by their Safety Rating. However, companies with the same rating should be viewed as having the same relative financial strength regardless of their ranking in these tables. While the specific order in which they appear on the page is based upon differences in our underlying indexes, you can assume that companies with the same rating have differences that are only minor and relatively inconsequential.

The six lines of business covered in this section are defined as follows:

Auto:	Coverage for auto physical damage and auto liability. Auto physical covers damage to the policyholder's own automobile. Auto liability covers against financial loss from lawsuits (and legal settlements) for auto-related bodily injuries or property damage caused by the insured.
Commercial Multiple Peril:	Package policies for business and other commercial establishments providing a broad spectrum of property and liability coverages.
Fire & Allied:	Coverage for losses caused by fire, lightning, sprinkler damage, windstorm, and water damage.
Homeowners Multiple Peril:	Package policies for homeowners providing a broad spectrum of property and liability coverages.
Medical Malpractice:	Errors and omissions liability coverages for persons engaged in the practice of medicine, surgery, dentistry, nursing, pharmacy, or other health care services. Also covers health care institutions.
Workers' Compensation:	Liability coverage issued to employers which provides for the payment of medical care, certain disability income benefits and possible additional liability amounts to employees who are injured on the job.

Column definitions are as follows:

1. **Insurance Company Name**   The legally-registered name, which can sometimes differ from the name that the company uses for advertising. An insurer's name can be very similar to the name of other companies which may not be on our Recommended List, so make sure you note the exact name before contacting your agent.

2. **Domicile State**   The state which has primary regulatory responsibility for the company. It may differ from the location of the company's corporate headquarters. You do not have to be living in the domicile state to purchase insurance from this firm, provided it is licensed to do business in your state.

3. **Total Premiums**   Total direct premiums received by the company during the year for all types of policies.

4. **Policy-Type Premium**   Direct premiums received by the company for a specific type of insurance coverage, such as Auto Premiums. Companies that have less than $1,000,000 in this type of premium are not listed.

5. **Maximum Benefit**   Conservative consumers may want to limit the size of their policy with this company to the amount shown. This figure is based on the view that a policy's maximum benefits per risk should not exceed 1% of the company's capital and surplus.

Weiss Safety Ratings are not deemed to be a recommendation concerning the purchase or sale of the securities of any insurance company that is publicly owned.

Auto

INSURANCE COMPANY NAME	DOMICILE STATE	TOTAL PREMIUM ($)	AUTO PREMIUM ($)	MAXIMUM BENEFIT ($)
Rating: A				
SENTRY INS A MUTUAL CO	WI	483,300,666	154,627,482	40,000,000
TOKIO MARINE AMERICA INS CO	NY	416,365,360	87,823,791	5,000,000
Rating: A-				
AUTO-OWNERS INS CO	MI	2,687,546,986	761,161,617	90,000,000
CINCINNATI INDEMNITY CO	OH	435,422,908	79,330,714	900,000
CINCINNATI INS CO	OH	3,532,402,509	1,003,369,236	40,000,000
COUNTRY MUTUAL INS CO	IL	1,534,809,274	415,858,114	20,000,000
GEICO CHOICE INS CO	NE	394,050,937	394,050,938	3,000,000
GEICO SECURE INS CO	NE	202,705,326	202,705,326	3,000,000
HOME-OWNERS INS CO	MI	963,052,227	776,448,267	10,000,000
OWNERS INS CO	OH	1,908,752,662	845,928,059	10,000,000
USAA CASUALTY INS CO	TX	5,222,821,998	3,435,039,216	40,000,000
Rating: B+				
ACUITY A MUTUAL INS CO	WI	1,330,076,095	481,848,413	10,000,000
ALFA MUTUAL GENERAL INS CO	AL	51,414,862	24,194,554	600,000
ALL AMERICA INS CO	OH	42,329,551	12,058,830	1,000,000
AMERICAN FAMILY MUT INS CO	WI	5,357,566,732	2,791,989,083	60,000,000
AMERICAN STANDARD INS CO OF WI	WI	232,295,689	232,295,689	3,000,000
AMICA MUTUAL INS CO	RI	1,954,386,358	1,116,377,936	30,000,000
BUILDERS MUTUAL INS CO	NC	224,733,404	5,180,256	3,000,000
COUNTRY CASUALTY INS CO	IL	36,460,429	22,281,574	700,000
DAIRYLAND INS CO	WI	140,326,868	140,326,868	5,000,000
FARM BUREAU P&C INS CO	IA	1,163,158,328	465,252,756	10,000,000
FARM FAMILY CASUALTY INS CO	NY	376,110,308	110,348,244	4,000,000
FARMERS AUTOMOBILE INS ASN	IL	244,618,873	149,902,661	5,000,000
FIRST COLONIAL INS CO	FL	270,346,151	2,567,682	1,000,000
GEICO GENERAL INS CO	MD	7,910,456,898	7,910,456,898	1,000,000
INTERINS EXCHANGE	CA	2,497,488,272	1,977,781,906	60,000,000
MERCURY INS CO	CA	1,472,824,840	1,472,824,840	6,000,000
MITSUI SUMITOMO INS CO OF AMER	NY	232,036,510	16,711,777	3,000,000
MOTORISTS MUTUAL INS CO	OH	441,254,336	200,189,258	5,000,000
NATIONAL CASUALTY CO	WI	881,399,154	312,808,812	1,000,000
NATIONWIDE MUTUAL FIRE INS CO	OH	1,633,354,682	419,660,672	30,000,000
PEKIN INS CO	IL	390,852,731	132,286,205	1,000,000
PROPERTY-OWNERS INS CO	IN	106,493,892	17,653,150	1,000,000
SENTRY SELECT INS CO	WI	466,292,041	267,912,072	2,000,000
SOUTHERN-OWNERS INS CO	MI	315,530,141	163,690,861	2,000,000
STATE FARM MUTUAL AUTOMOBILE INS CO	IL	34,588,540,295	33,628,059,724	800,000,000
TENNESSEE FARMERS MUTUAL INS CO	TN	1,190,438,018	615,728,612	20,000,000
TEXAS FARM BUREAU CASUALTY INS CO	TX	235,126,918	229,515,682	6,000,000
TRAVELERS INDEMNITY CO	CT	1,825,073,050	287,036,772	70,000,000
UNITED SERVICES AUTOMOBILE ASN	TX	7,086,252,957	3,988,322,088	200,000,000
USAA GENERAL INDEMNITY CO	TX	2,811,299,487	2,041,578,697	10,000,000
WEST BEND MUTUAL INS CO	WI	1,057,468,964	267,279,116	9,000,000
WESTERN AGRICULTURAL INS CO	IA	267,757,105	48,660,904	900,000

Commercial Multiple Peril

INSURANCE COMPANY NAME	DOMICILE STATE	TOTAL PREMIUM ($)	COMM. MULT. PERIL PREMIUM ($)	MAXIMUM BENEFIT ($)
Rating: **A**				
SENTRY INS A MUTUAL CO	WI	483,300,666	59,934,853	40,000,000
TOKIO MARINE AMERICA INS CO	NY	416,365,360	74,834,914	5,000,000
Rating: **A-**				
AUTO-OWNERS INS CO	MI	2,687,546,986	470,596,566	90,000,000
CINCINNATI INDEMNITY CO	OH	435,422,908	170,601,624	900,000
CINCINNATI INS CO	OH	3,532,402,509	1,514,947,082	40,000,000
COUNTRY MUTUAL INS CO	IL	1,534,809,274	148,256,752	20,000,000
HOME-OWNERS INS CO	MI	963,052,227	106,372,352	10,000,000
OWNERS INS CO	OH	1,908,752,662	480,802,858	10,000,000
TRAVELERS CASUALTY & SURETY CO	CT	318,854,301	2,451,291	60,000,000
USAA CASUALTY INS CO	TX	5,222,821,998	52,704,274	40,000,000
Rating: **B+**				
ACUITY A MUTUAL INS CO	WI	1,330,076,095	274,400,630	10,000,000
ALL AMERICA INS CO	OH	42,329,551	24,563,776	1,000,000
AMERICAN FAMILY MUT INS CO	WI	5,357,566,732	580,143,118	60,000,000
AMICA MUTUAL INS CO	RI	1,954,386,358	53,300,696	30,000,000
BUILDERS MUTUAL INS CO	NC	224,733,404	35,283,318	3,000,000
FARM BUREAU P&C INS CO	IA	1,163,158,328	79,619,742	10,000,000
FARM FAMILY CASUALTY INS CO	NY	376,110,308	91,786,469	4,000,000
FIRST COLONIAL INS CO	FL	270,346,151	3,019,071	1,000,000
HOLYOKE MUTUAL INS CO IN SALEM	MA	28,636,387	24,569,883	1,000,000
INTERINS EXCHANGE	CA	2,497,488,272	14,269,140	60,000,000
MITSUI SUMITOMO INS CO OF AMER	NY	232,036,510	79,852,130	3,000,000
MOTORISTS MUTUAL INS CO	OH	441,254,336	114,053,119	5,000,000
NATIONAL CASUALTY CO	WI	881,399,154	202,854,706	1,000,000
NATIONWIDE MUTUAL FIRE INS CO	OH	1,633,354,682	187,933,017	30,000,000
PEKIN INS CO	IL	390,852,731	116,884,728	1,000,000
PROPERTY-OWNERS INS CO	IN	106,493,892	45,361,089	1,000,000
SENTRY SELECT INS CO	WI	466,292,041	48,291,195	2,000,000
SOUTHERN-OWNERS INS CO	MI	315,530,141	121,888,651	2,000,000
STATE FARM MUTUAL AUTOMOBILE INS CO	IL	34,588,540,295	2,355,060	800,000,000
TENNESSEE FARMERS MUTUAL INS CO	TN	1,190,438,018	28,957,788	20,000,000
TEXAS FARM BUREAU CASUALTY INS CO	TX	235,126,918	5,611,236	6,000,000
TRAVELERS INDEMNITY CO	CT	1,825,073,050	635,047,119	70,000,000
UNITED SERVICES AUTOMOBILE ASN	TX	7,086,252,957	129,837,817	200,000,000
USAA GENERAL INDEMNITY CO	TX	2,811,299,487	10,114,130	10,000,000
WEST BEND MUTUAL INS CO	WI	1,057,468,964	211,847,288	9,000,000
WESTERN AGRICULTURAL INS CO	IA	267,757,105	19,408,680	900,000

Fire & Allied

INSURANCE COMPANY NAME	DOMICILE STATE	TOTAL PREMIUM ($)	FIRE & ALLIED PREMIUM ($)	MAXIMUM BENEFIT ($)
Rating: A+				
CITIZENS PROPERTY INS CORP	FL	1,267,754,200	763,849,314	70,000,000
Rating: A				
SENTRY INS A MUTUAL CO	WI	483,300,666	68,842,519	40,000,000
TOKIO MARINE AMERICA INS CO	NY	416,365,360	71,887,890	5,000,000
Rating: A-				
AUTO-OWNERS INS CO	MI	2,687,546,986	345,327,817	90,000,000
CINCINNATI INDEMNITY CO	OH	435,422,908	32,104,275	900,000
CINCINNATI INS CO	OH	3,532,402,509	160,503,625	40,000,000
COUNTRY MUTUAL INS CO	IL	1,534,809,274	108,802,143	20,000,000
HOME-OWNERS INS CO	MI	963,052,227	2,327,087	10,000,000
OWNERS INS CO	OH	1,908,752,662	10,211,202	10,000,000
TRAVELERS CASUALTY & SURETY CO	CT	318,854,301	4,284,934	60,000,000
USAA CASUALTY INS CO	TX	5,222,821,998	119,435,572	40,000,000
Rating: B+				
ACUITY A MUTUAL INS CO	WI	1,330,076,095	69,612,430	10,000,000
AMERICAN FAMILY MUT INS CO	WI	5,357,566,732	23,752,655	60,000,000
AMICA MUTUAL INS CO	RI	1,954,386,358	27,374,033	30,000,000
FARM FAMILY CASUALTY INS CO	NY	376,110,308	75,925,011	4,000,000
FARMERS AUTOMOBILE INS ASN	IL	244,618,873	11,663,822	5,000,000
INTERINS EXCHANGE	CA	2,497,488,272	20,705,350	60,000,000
MITSUI SUMITOMO INS CO OF AMER	NY	232,036,510	25,797,898	3,000,000
MOTORISTS MUTUAL INS CO	OH	441,254,336	5,938,203	5,000,000
NATIONAL CASUALTY CO	WI	881,399,154	11,324,178	1,000,000
NATIONWIDE MUTUAL FIRE INS CO	OH	1,633,354,682	207,537,779	30,000,000
PEKIN INS CO	IL	390,852,731	4,736,947	1,000,000
SENTRY SELECT INS CO	WI	466,292,041	32,132,728	2,000,000
TENNESSEE FARMERS MUTUAL INS CO	TN	1,190,438,018	64,868,190	20,000,000
TRAVELERS INDEMNITY CO	CT	1,825,073,050	316,474,568	70,000,000
UNITED SERVICES AUTOMOBILE ASN	TX	7,086,252,957	332,234,131	200,000,000
USAA GENERAL INDEMNITY CO	TX	2,811,299,487	180,280,662	10,000,000
WEST BEND MUTUAL INS CO	WI	1,057,468,964	119,771,056	9,000,000
WESTERN AGRICULTURAL INS CO	IA	267,757,105	140,291,541	900,000

Homeowners Multiple Peril

INSURANCE COMPANY NAME	DOMICILE STATE	TOTAL PREMIUM ($)	HOME OWNERS PREMIUM ($)	MAXIMUM BENEFIT ($)
Rating: A+				
CITIZENS PROPERTY INS CORP	FL	1,267,754,200	503,904,885	70,000,000
Rating: A				
TOKIO MARINE AMERICA INS CO	NY	416,365,360	10,007,127	5,000,000
Rating: A-				
AUTO-OWNERS INS CO	MI	2,687,546,986	779,404,345	90,000,000
CINCINNATI INS CO	OH	3,532,402,509	493,452,790	40,000,000
COUNTRY MUTUAL INS CO	IL	1,534,809,274	638,319,233	20,000,000
HOME-OWNERS INS CO	MI	963,052,227	36,005,681	10,000,000
OWNERS INS CO	OH	1,908,752,662	363,743,322	10,000,000
TRAVELERS CASUALTY & SURETY CO	CT	318,854,301	29,188,258	60,000,000
USAA CASUALTY INS CO	TX	5,222,821,998	1,507,293,427	40,000,000
Rating: B+				
ACUITY A MUTUAL INS CO	WI	1,330,076,095	132,143,327	10,000,000
ALFA MUTUAL GENERAL INS CO	AL	51,414,862	26,751,898	600,000
AMERICAN FAMILY MUT INS CO	WI	5,357,566,732	1,731,306,182	60,000,000
AMICA MUTUAL INS CO	RI	1,954,386,358	717,791,024	30,000,000
AUTO CLUB INDEMNITY CO	TX	105,111,004	104,070,265	50,000
COUNTRY CASUALTY INS CO	IL	36,460,429	14,141,942	700,000
FARM BUREAU P&C INS CO	IA	1,163,158,328	280,804,242	10,000,000
FARM FAMILY CASUALTY INS CO	NY	376,110,308	23,531,963	4,000,000
FARMERS AUTOMOBILE INS ASN	IL	244,618,873	80,096,489	5,000,000
HOLYOKE MUTUAL INS CO IN SALEM	MA	28,636,387	2,612,283	1,000,000
INTERINS EXCHANGE	CA	2,497,488,272	479,509,534	60,000,000
MOTORISTS MUTUAL INS CO	OH	441,254,336	77,343,462	5,000,000
NATIONWIDE MUTUAL FIRE INS CO	OH	1,633,354,682	766,734,806	30,000,000
PEKIN INS CO	IL	390,852,731	52,740,859	1,000,000
PROPERTY-OWNERS INS CO	IN	106,493,892	24,490,291	1,000,000
SOUTHERN-OWNERS INS CO	MI	315,530,141	8,594,781	2,000,000
TENNESSEE FARMERS MUTUAL INS CO	TN	1,190,438,018	366,280,106	20,000,000
TRAVELERS INDEMNITY CO	CT	1,825,073,050	50,536,194	70,000,000
UNITED SERVICES AUTOMOBILE ASN	TX	7,086,252,957	2,480,924,698	200,000,000
USAA GENERAL INDEMNITY CO	TX	2,811,299,487	547,705,365	10,000,000
WEST BEND MUTUAL INS CO	WI	1,057,468,964	124,208,995	9,000,000
WESTERN AGRICULTURAL INS CO	IA	267,757,105	25,383,812	900,000

Medical Malpractice

INSURANCE COMPANY NAME	DOMICILE STATE	TOTAL PREMIUM ($)	MEDICAL MALPRACTICE PREMIUM ($)	MAXIMUM BENEFIT ($)
Rating: A-				
CINCINNATI INDEMNITY CO	OH	435,422,908	2,301,799	900,000
CINCINNATI INS CO	OH	3,532,402,509	30,748,050	40,000,000

Workers' Compensation

INSURANCE COMPANY NAME	DOMICILE STATE	TOTAL PREMIUM ($)	WORKERS' COMPENSATION PREMIUM ($)	MAXIMUM BENEFIT ($)
Rating: A+				
COPPERPOINT MUTUAL INS CO	AZ	60,324,406	60,324,406	10,000,000
Rating: A				
SENTRY INS A MUTUAL CO	WI	483,300,666	161,791,271	40,000,000
TOKIO MARINE AMERICA INS CO	NY	416,365,360	44,657,196	5,000,000
Rating: A-				
AUTO-OWNERS INS CO	MI	2,687,546,986	209,975,659	90,000,000
CINCINNATI INDEMNITY CO	OH	435,422,908	134,475,219	900,000
CINCINNATI INS CO	OH	3,532,402,509	91,380,378	40,000,000
COUNTRY MUTUAL INS CO	IL	1,534,809,274	69,448,109	20,000,000
HOME-OWNERS INS CO	MI	963,052,227	32,281,667	10,000,000
OWNERS INS CO	OH	1,908,752,662	147,319,806	10,000,000
TRAVELERS CASUALTY & SURETY CO	CT	318,854,301	237,990,326	60,000,000
Rating: B+				
ACUITY A MUTUAL INS CO	WI	1,330,076,095	318,540,210	10,000,000
ALL AMERICA INS CO	OH	42,329,551	3,567,342	1,000,000
AMERICAN FAMILY MUT INS CO	WI	5,357,566,732	56,764,416	60,000,000
BUILDERS MUTUAL INS CO	NC	224,733,404	168,096,588	3,000,000
FARM BUREAU P&C INS CO	IA	1,163,158,328	34,076,363	10,000,000
FARM FAMILY CASUALTY INS CO	NY	376,110,308	54,700,718	4,000,000
MITSUI SUMITOMO INS CO OF AMER	NY	232,036,510	66,789,425	3,000,000
MOTORISTS MUTUAL INS CO	OH	441,254,336	20,039,629	5,000,000
NATIONAL CASUALTY CO	WI	881,399,154	65,147,854	1,000,000
NATIONWIDE MUTUAL FIRE INS CO	OH	1,633,354,682	17,210,190	30,000,000
PEKIN INS CO	IL	390,852,731	78,189,337	1,000,000
PROPERTY-OWNERS INS CO	IN	106,493,892	10,393,791	1,000,000
SENTRY SELECT INS CO	WI	466,292,041	27,169,558	2,000,000
SOUTHERN-OWNERS INS CO	MI	315,530,141	14,971,910	2,000,000
TRAVELERS INDEMNITY CO	CT	1,825,073,050	405,355,653	70,000,000
WEST BEND MUTUAL INS CO	WI	1,057,468,964	260,272,466	9,000,000
WESTERN AGRICULTURAL INS CO	IA	267,757,105	6,229,398	900,000

Section V

Weiss
Recommended Companies
by State

A compilation of those

U.S. Property and Casualty Insurers

receiving a Weiss Safety Rating

of A+, A, A- or B+.

Companies are ranked by Safety Rating
in each state where they are licensed to do business.

Section V Contents

This section provides a list of the recommended carriers licensed to do business in each state. It contains all insurers receiving a Safety Rating of A+, A, A- or B+. If an insurer is not on this list, it should not be automatically assumed that the firm is weak. Indeed, there are many firms that have not achieved a B+ or better rating but are in relatively good condition with adequate resources to cover their risk during an average recession. Not being included in this list should not be construed as a recommendation to cancel policies.

Companies are ranked within each state by their Safety Rating. However, companies with the same rating should be viewed as having the same relative safety regardless of their ranking in this table. While the specific order in which they appear on the page is based upon differences in our underlying indexes, you can assume that companies with the same rating have differences that are only minor and relatively inconsequential.

1. **Insurance Company Name**
   The legally-registered name, which can sometimes differ from the name that the company uses for advertising. An insurer's name can be very similar to the name of other companies which may not be on our Recommended List, so make sure you note the exact name before contacting your agent.

2. **Domicile State**
   The state which has primary regulatory responsibility for the company. It may differ from the location of the company's corporate headquarters. You do not have to be living in the domicile state to purchase insurance from this firm, provided it is licensed to do business in your state.

3. **Total Assets**
   All assets admitted by state insurance regulators in millions of dollars. This includes investments and current business assets such as receivables from agents and reinsurers.

Weiss Safety Ratings are not deemed to be a recommendation concerning the purchase or sale of the securities of any insurance company that is publicly owned.

Alabama

INSURANCE COMPANY NAME	DOM. STATE	TOTAL ASSETS ($MIL)
Rating:	**A+**	
BERKSHIRE HATHAWAY ASR CORP	NY	2,220.4
MUNICIPAL ASR CORP	NY	1,125.1
Rating:	**A**	
SENTRY INS A MUTUAL CO	WI	7,458.5
TOKIO MARINE AMERICA INS CO	NY	1,410.7
Rating:	**A-**	
AUTO-OWNERS INS CO	MI	13,712.2
CINCINNATI INDEMNITY CO	OH	123.8
CINCINNATI INS CO	OH	11,749.4
COUNTRY MUTUAL INS CO	IL	4,421.1
ESSENT GUARANTY INC	PA	1,194.6
GEICO CHOICE INS CO	NE	647.0
GEICO SECURE INS CO	NE	436.8
HOME-OWNERS INS CO	MI	2,106.0
NATIONAL MORTGAGE INS CORP	WI	530.6
OWNERS INS CO	OH	3,891.6
TRAVELERS CASUALTY & SURETY CO	CT	16,398.0
USAA CASUALTY INS CO	TX	9,860.1
Rating:	**B+**	
ACUITY A MUTUAL INS CO	WI	3,483.6
ALFA MUTUAL GENERAL INS CO	AL	103.4
AMICA MUTUAL INS CO	RI	4,974.1
CENTURION CASUALTY CO	IA	157.1
COUNTRY CASUALTY INS CO	IL	83.4
DAIRYLAND INS CO	WI	1,282.3
FIRST COLONIAL INS CO	FL	370.3
GEICO GENERAL INS CO	MD	226.3
MITSUI SUMITOMO INS CO OF AMER	NY	925.8
MOTORISTS MUTUAL INS CO	OH	1,375.1
NATIONAL CASUALTY CO	WI	402.1
NATIONWIDE MUTUAL FIRE INS CO	OH	6,045.9
PROPERTY-OWNERS INS CO	IN	257.1
SENTRY SELECT INS CO	WI	706.8
STATE FARM MUTUAL AUTOMOBILE INS CO	IL	143,802.0
TOA REINS CO OF AMERICA	DE	1,747.5
TRAVELERS INDEMNITY CO	CT	21,495.2
UNITED SERVICES AUTOMOBILE ASN	TX	32,870.8
USAA GENERAL INDEMNITY CO	TX	3,644.1
WESTERN AGRICULTURAL INS CO	IA	206.5

Alaska

INSURANCE COMPANY NAME	DOM. STATE	TOTAL ASSETS ($MIL)	INSURANCE COMPANY NAME	DOM. STATE	TOTAL ASSETS ($MIL)
Rating: A+					
BERKSHIRE HATHAWAY ASR CORP	NY	2,220.4			
MUNICIPAL ASR CORP	NY	1,125.1			
Rating: A					
SENTRY INS A MUTUAL CO	WI	7,458.5			
TOKIO MARINE AMERICA INS CO	NY	1,410.7			
Rating: A-					
CINCINNATI INDEMNITY CO	OH	123.8			
CINCINNATI INS CO	OH	11,749.4			
COUNTRY MUTUAL INS CO	IL	4,421.1			
ESSENT GUARANTY INC	PA	1,194.6			
GEICO CHOICE INS CO	NE	647.0			
GEICO SECURE INS CO	NE	436.8			
NATIONAL MORTGAGE INS CORP	WI	530.6			
TRAVELERS CASUALTY & SURETY CO	CT	16,398.0			
USAA CASUALTY INS CO	TX	9,860.1			
Rating: B+					
AMICA MUTUAL INS CO	RI	4,974.1			
COUNTRY CASUALTY INS CO	IL	83.4			
DAIRYLAND INS CO	WI	1,282.3			
FIRST COLONIAL INS CO	FL	370.3			
GEICO GENERAL INS CO	MD	226.3			
MITSUI SUMITOMO INS CO OF AMER	NY	925.8			
NATIONAL CASUALTY CO	WI	402.1			
NATIONWIDE MUTUAL FIRE INS CO	OH	6,045.9			
SENTRY SELECT INS CO	WI	706.8			
STATE FARM MUTUAL AUTOMOBILE INS CO	IL	143,802.0			
TOA REINS CO OF AMERICA	DE	1,747.5			
TRAVELERS INDEMNITY CO	CT	21,495.2			
UNITED SERVICES AUTOMOBILE ASN	TX	32,870.8			
USAA GENERAL INDEMNITY CO	TX	3,644.1			

Arizona

INSURANCE COMPANY NAME	DOM. STATE	TOTAL ASSETS ($MIL)	INSURANCE COMPANY NAME	DOM. STATE	TOTAL ASSETS ($MIL)
Rating: A+					
BERKSHIRE HATHAWAY ASR CORP	NY	2,220.4			
COPPERPOINT MUTUAL INS CO	AZ	3,573.1			
MUNICIPAL ASR CORP	NY	1,125.1			
Rating: A					
SENTRY INS A MUTUAL CO	WI	7,458.5			
TOKIO MARINE AMERICA INS CO	NY	1,410.7			
Rating: A-					
AUTO-OWNERS INS CO	MI	13,712.2			
CINCINNATI INDEMNITY CO	OH	123.8			
CINCINNATI INS CO	OH	11,749.4			
COUNTRY MUTUAL INS CO	IL	4,421.1			
ESSENT GUARANTY INC	PA	1,194.6			
GEICO CHOICE INS CO	NE	647.0			
GEICO SECURE INS CO	NE	436.8			
NATIONAL MORTGAGE INS CORP	WI	530.6			
OWNERS INS CO	OH	3,891.6			
TRAVELERS CASUALTY & SURETY CO	CT	16,398.0			
USAA CASUALTY INS CO	TX	9,860.1			
Rating: B+					
ACUITY A MUTUAL INS CO	WI	3,483.6			
ALL AMERICA INS CO	OH	280.0			
AMERICAN FAMILY MUT INS CO	WI	16,216.1			
AMERICAN STANDARD INS CO OF WI	WI	433.2			
AMICA MUTUAL INS CO	RI	4,974.1			
CENTURION CASUALTY CO	IA	157.1			
COUNTRY CASUALTY INS CO	IL	83.4			
DAIRYLAND INS CO	WI	1,282.3			
FARM BUREAU P&C INS CO	IA	2,379.2			
FARMERS AUTOMOBILE INS ASN	IL	1,283.7			
FIRST COLONIAL INS CO	FL	370.3			
GEICO GENERAL INS CO	MD	226.3			
HOLYOKE MUTUAL INS CO IN SALEM	MA	217.0			
MITSUI SUMITOMO INS CO OF AMER	NY	925.8			
NATIONAL CASUALTY CO	WI	402.1			
NATIONWIDE MUTUAL FIRE INS CO	OH	6,045.9			
PEKIN INS CO	IL	312.8			
SENTRY SELECT INS CO	WI	706.8			
STATE FARM MUTUAL AUTOMOBILE INS CO	IL	143,802.0			
TOA REINS CO OF AMERICA	DE	1,747.5			
TRAVELERS INDEMNITY CO	CT	21,495.2			
UNITED SERVICES AUTOMOBILE ASN	TX	32,870.8			
USAA GENERAL INDEMNITY CO	TX	3,644.1			
WESTERN AGRICULTURAL INS CO	IA	206.5			

Arkansas

INSURANCE COMPANY NAME	DOM. STATE	TOTAL ASSETS ($MIL)
Rating: A+		
BERKSHIRE HATHAWAY ASR CORP	NY	2,220.4
MUNICIPAL ASR CORP	NY	1,125.1
Rating: A		
SENTRY INS A MUTUAL CO	WI	7,458.5
TOKIO MARINE AMERICA INS CO	NY	1,410.7
Rating: A-		
AUTO-OWNERS INS CO	MI	13,712.2
CINCINNATI INDEMNITY CO	OH	123.8
CINCINNATI INS CO	OH	11,749.4
COUNTRY MUTUAL INS CO	IL	4,421.1
ESSENT GUARANTY INC	PA	1,194.6
GEICO CHOICE INS CO	NE	647.0
GEICO SECURE INS CO	NE	436.8
HOME-OWNERS INS CO	MI	2,106.0
NATIONAL MORTGAGE INS CORP	WI	530.6
OWNERS INS CO	OH	3,891.6
TRAVELERS CASUALTY & SURETY CO	CT	16,398.0
USAA CASUALTY INS CO	TX	9,860.1
Rating: B+		
ACUITY A MUTUAL INS CO	WI	3,483.6
ALL AMERICA INS CO	OH	280.0
AMICA MUTUAL INS CO	RI	4,974.1
COUNTRY CASUALTY INS CO	IL	83.4
DAIRYLAND INS CO	WI	1,282.3
FIRST COLONIAL INS CO	FL	370.3
GEICO GENERAL INS CO	MD	226.3
HOLYOKE MUTUAL INS CO IN SALEM	MA	217.0
MITSUI SUMITOMO INS CO OF AMER	NY	925.8
NATIONAL CASUALTY CO	WI	402.1
NATIONWIDE MUTUAL FIRE INS CO	OH	6,045.9
PROPERTY-OWNERS INS CO	IN	257.1
SENTRY SELECT INS CO	WI	706.8
STATE FARM MUTUAL AUTOMOBILE INS CO	IL	143,802.0
TOA REINS CO OF AMERICA	DE	1,747.5
TRAVELERS INDEMNITY CO	CT	21,495.2
UNITED SERVICES AUTOMOBILE ASN	TX	32,870.8
USAA GENERAL INDEMNITY CO	TX	3,644.1
WESTERN AGRICULTURAL INS CO	IA	206.5

California

INSURANCE COMPANY NAME	DOM. STATE	TOTAL ASSETS ($MIL)
Rating:	**A+**	
BERKSHIRE HATHAWAY ASR CORP	NY	2,220.4
MUNICIPAL ASR CORP	NY	1,125.1
Rating:	**A**	
SENTRY INS A MUTUAL CO	WI	7,458.5
TOKIO MARINE AMERICA INS CO	NY	1,410.7
Rating:	**A-**	
CINCINNATI INDEMNITY CO	OH	123.8
CINCINNATI INS CO	OH	11,749.4
COUNTRY MUTUAL INS CO	IL	4,421.1
ESSENT GUARANTY INC	PA	1,194.6
NATIONAL MORTGAGE INS CORP	WI	530.6
TRAVELERS CASUALTY & SURETY CO	CT	16,398.0
USAA CASUALTY INS CO	TX	9,860.1
Rating:	**B+**	
ALL AMERICA INS CO	OH	280.0
AMICA MUTUAL INS CO	RI	4,974.1
CENTURION CASUALTY CO	IA	157.1
GEICO GENERAL INS CO	MD	226.3
INTERINS EXCHANGE	CA	9,074.7
MERCURY INS CO	CA	1,600.5
MITSUI SUMITOMO INS CO OF AMER	NY	925.8
MOTORISTS MUTUAL INS CO	OH	1,375.1
NATIONAL CASUALTY CO	WI	402.1
NATIONWIDE MUTUAL FIRE INS CO	OH	6,045.9
SENTRY SELECT INS CO	WI	706.8
STATE FARM MUTUAL AUTOMOBILE INS CO	IL	143,802.0
TOA REINS CO OF AMERICA	DE	1,747.5
TRAVELERS INDEMNITY CO	CT	21,495.2
UNITED SERVICES AUTOMOBILE ASN	TX	32,870.8
USAA GENERAL INDEMNITY CO	TX	3,644.1

Colorado

INSURANCE COMPANY NAME	DOM. STATE	TOTAL ASSETS ($MIL)
Rating: A+		
BERKSHIRE HATHAWAY ASR CORP	NY	2,220.4
MUNICIPAL ASR CORP	NY	1,125.1
Rating: A		
SENTRY INS A MUTUAL CO	WI	7,458.5
TOKIO MARINE AMERICA INS CO	NY	1,410.7
Rating: A-		
AUTO-OWNERS INS CO	MI	13,712.2
CINCINNATI INDEMNITY CO	OH	123.8
CINCINNATI INS CO	OH	11,749.4
COUNTRY MUTUAL INS CO	IL	4,421.1
ESSENT GUARANTY INC	PA	1,194.6
GEICO CHOICE INS CO	NE	647.0
GEICO SECURE INS CO	NE	436.8
HOME-OWNERS INS CO	MI	2,106.0
NATIONAL MORTGAGE INS CORP	WI	530.6
OWNERS INS CO	OH	3,891.6
TRAVELERS CASUALTY & SURETY CO	CT	16,398.0
USAA CASUALTY INS CO	TX	9,860.1
Rating: B+		
ACUITY A MUTUAL INS CO	WI	3,483.6
ALL AMERICA INS CO	OH	280.0
AMERICAN FAMILY MUT INS CO	WI	16,216.1
AMERICAN STANDARD INS CO OF WI	WI	433.2
AMICA MUTUAL INS CO	RI	4,974.1
CENTURION CASUALTY CO	IA	157.1
COUNTRY CASUALTY INS CO	IL	83.4
DAIRYLAND INS CO	WI	1,282.3
FIRST COLONIAL INS CO	FL	370.3
GEICO GENERAL INS CO	MD	226.3
HOLYOKE MUTUAL INS CO IN SALEM	MA	217.0
MITSUI SUMITOMO INS CO OF AMER	NY	925.8
NATIONAL CASUALTY CO	WI	402.1
NATIONWIDE MUTUAL FIRE INS CO	OH	6,045.9
SENTRY SELECT INS CO	WI	706.8
STATE FARM MUTUAL AUTOMOBILE INS CO	IL	143,802.0
TOA REINS CO OF AMERICA	DE	1,747.5
TRAVELERS INDEMNITY CO	CT	21,495.2
UNITED SERVICES AUTOMOBILE ASN	TX	32,870.8
USAA GENERAL INDEMNITY CO	TX	3,644.1
WESTERN AGRICULTURAL INS CO	IA	206.5

Connecticut

INSURANCE COMPANY NAME	DOM. STATE	TOTAL ASSETS ($MIL)	INSURANCE COMPANY NAME	DOM. STATE	TOTAL ASSETS ($MIL)
Rating: A+					
BERKSHIRE HATHAWAY ASR CORP	NY	2,220.4			
MUNICIPAL ASR CORP	NY	1,125.1			
Rating: A					
SENTRY INS A MUTUAL CO	WI	7,458.5			
TOKIO MARINE AMERICA INS CO	NY	1,410.7			
Rating: A-					
CINCINNATI INDEMNITY CO	OH	123.8			
CINCINNATI INS CO	OH	11,749.4			
COUNTRY MUTUAL INS CO	IL	4,421.1			
ESSENT GUARANTY INC	PA	1,194.6			
GEICO CHOICE INS CO	NE	647.0			
GEICO SECURE INS CO	NE	436.8			
NATIONAL MORTGAGE INS CORP	WI	530.6			
TRAVELERS CASUALTY & SURETY CO	CT	16,398.0			
USAA CASUALTY INS CO	TX	9,860.1			
Rating: B+					
ALL AMERICA INS CO	OH	280.0			
AMICA MUTUAL INS CO	RI	4,974.1			
CENTURION CASUALTY CO	IA	157.1			
COUNTRY CASUALTY INS CO	IL	83.4			
DAIRYLAND INS CO	WI	1,282.3			
FARM FAMILY CASUALTY INS CO	NY	1,160.0			
FIRST COLONIAL INS CO	FL	370.3			
GEICO GENERAL INS CO	MD	226.3			
HOLYOKE MUTUAL INS CO IN SALEM	MA	217.0			
MITSUI SUMITOMO INS CO OF AMER	NY	925.8			
MOTORISTS MUTUAL INS CO	OH	1,375.1			
NATIONAL CASUALTY CO	WI	402.1			
NATIONWIDE MUTUAL FIRE INS CO	OH	6,045.9			
SENTRY SELECT INS CO	WI	706.8			
STATE FARM MUTUAL AUTOMOBILE INS CO	IL	143,802.0			
TOA REINS CO OF AMERICA	DE	1,747.5			
TRAVELERS INDEMNITY CO	CT	21,495.2			
UNITED SERVICES AUTOMOBILE ASN	TX	32,870.8			
USAA GENERAL INDEMNITY CO	TX	3,644.1			

Delaware

INSURANCE COMPANY NAME	DOM. STATE	TOTAL ASSETS ($MIL)
Rating: **A+**		
BERKSHIRE HATHAWAY ASR CORP	NY	2,220.4
MUNICIPAL ASR CORP	NY	1,125.1
Rating: **A**		
SENTRY INS A MUTUAL CO	WI	7,458.5
TOKIO MARINE AMERICA INS CO	NY	1,410.7
Rating: **A-**		
CINCINNATI INDEMNITY CO	OH	123.8
CINCINNATI INS CO	OH	11,749.4
COUNTRY MUTUAL INS CO	IL	4,421.1
ESSENT GUARANTY INC	PA	1,194.6
GEICO CHOICE INS CO	NE	647.0
GEICO SECURE INS CO	NE	436.8
NATIONAL MORTGAGE INS CORP	WI	530.6
TRAVELERS CASUALTY & SURETY CO	CT	16,398.0
USAA CASUALTY INS CO	TX	9,860.1
Rating: **B+**		
ACUITY A MUTUAL INS CO	WI	3,483.6
AMICA MUTUAL INS CO	RI	4,974.1
CENTURION CASUALTY CO	IA	157.1
COUNTRY CASUALTY INS CO	IL	83.4
DAIRYLAND INS CO	WI	1,282.3
FARM FAMILY CASUALTY INS CO	NY	1,160.0
FIRST COLONIAL INS CO	FL	370.3
GEICO GENERAL INS CO	MD	226.3
MITSUI SUMITOMO INS CO OF AMER	NY	925.8
MOTORISTS MUTUAL INS CO	OH	1,375.1
NATIONAL CASUALTY CO	WI	402.1
NATIONWIDE MUTUAL FIRE INS CO	OH	6,045.9
SENTRY SELECT INS CO	WI	706.8
STATE FARM MUTUAL AUTOMOBILE INS CO	IL	143,802.0
TOA REINS CO OF AMERICA	DE	1,747.5
TRAVELERS INDEMNITY CO	CT	21,495.2
UNITED SERVICES AUTOMOBILE ASN	TX	32,870.8
USAA GENERAL INDEMNITY CO	TX	3,644.1

District Of Columbia

INSURANCE COMPANY NAME	DOM. STATE	TOTAL ASSETS ($MIL)	INSURANCE COMPANY NAME	DOM. STATE	TOTAL ASSETS ($MIL)
Rating: A+					
BERKSHIRE HATHAWAY ASR CORP	NY	2,220.4			
MUNICIPAL ASR CORP	NY	1,125.1			
Rating: A					
SENTRY INS A MUTUAL CO	WI	7,458.5			
TOKIO MARINE AMERICA INS CO	NY	1,410.7			
Rating: A-					
CINCINNATI INDEMNITY CO	OH	123.8			
CINCINNATI INS CO	OH	11,749.4			
ESSENT GUARANTY INC	PA	1,194.6			
GEICO CHOICE INS CO	NE	647.0			
GEICO SECURE INS CO	NE	436.8			
NATIONAL MORTGAGE INS CORP	WI	530.6			
TRAVELERS CASUALTY & SURETY CO	CT	16,398.0			
USAA CASUALTY INS CO	TX	9,860.1			
Rating: B+					
AMICA MUTUAL INS CO	RI	4,974.1			
BUILDERS MUTUAL INS CO	NC	736.0			
FIRST COLONIAL INS CO	FL	370.3			
GEICO GENERAL INS CO	MD	226.3			
MITSUI SUMITOMO INS CO OF AMER	NY	925.8			
NATIONAL CASUALTY CO	WI	402.1			
NATIONWIDE MUTUAL FIRE INS CO	OH	6,045.9			
SENTRY SELECT INS CO	WI	706.8			
STATE FARM MUTUAL AUTOMOBILE INS CO	IL	143,802.0			
TOA REINS CO OF AMERICA	DE	1,747.5			
TRAVELERS INDEMNITY CO	CT	21,495.2			
UNITED SERVICES AUTOMOBILE ASN	TX	32,870.8			
USAA GENERAL INDEMNITY CO	TX	3,644.1			

Florida

INSURANCE COMPANY NAME	DOM. STATE	TOTAL ASSETS ($MIL)	INSURANCE COMPANY NAME	DOM. STATE	TOTAL ASSETS ($MIL)
Rating: A+					
BERKSHIRE HATHAWAY ASR CORP	NY	2,220.4			
CITIZENS PROPERTY INS CORP	FL	12,538.0			
MUNICIPAL ASR CORP	NY	1,125.1			
Rating: A					
SENTRY INS A MUTUAL CO	WI	7,458.5			
TOKIO MARINE AMERICA INS CO	NY	1,410.7			
Rating: A-					
AUTO-OWNERS INS CO	MI	13,712.2			
CINCINNATI INDEMNITY CO	OH	123.8			
CINCINNATI INS CO	OH	11,749.4			
ESSENT GUARANTY INC	PA	1,194.6			
NATIONAL MORTGAGE INS CORP	WI	530.6			
OWNERS INS CO	OH	3,891.6			
TRAVELERS CASUALTY & SURETY CO	CT	16,398.0			
USAA CASUALTY INS CO	TX	9,860.1			
Rating: B+					
AMERICAN FAMILY MUT INS CO	WI	16,216.1			
AMICA MUTUAL INS CO	RI	4,974.1			
BUILDERS MUTUAL INS CO	NC	736.0			
CENTURION CASUALTY CO	IA	157.1			
DAIRYLAND INS CO	WI	1,282.3			
FIRST COLONIAL INS CO	FL	370.3			
GEICO GENERAL INS CO	MD	226.3			
INTERINS EXCHANGE	CA	9,074.7			
MITSUI SUMITOMO INS CO OF AMER	NY	925.8			
NATIONAL CASUALTY CO	WI	402.1			
NATIONWIDE MUTUAL FIRE INS CO	OH	6,045.9			
SENTRY SELECT INS CO	WI	706.8			
SOUTHERN-OWNERS INS CO	MI	695.8			
STATE FARM MUTUAL AUTOMOBILE INS CO	IL	143,802.0			
TOA REINS CO OF AMERICA	DE	1,747.5			
TRAVELERS INDEMNITY CO	CT	21,495.2			
UNITED SERVICES AUTOMOBILE ASN	TX	32,870.8			
USAA GENERAL INDEMNITY CO	TX	3,644.1			

Georgia

INSURANCE COMPANY NAME	DOM. STATE	TOTAL ASSETS ($MIL)
Rating: A+		
BERKSHIRE HATHAWAY ASR CORP	NY	2,220.4
MUNICIPAL ASR CORP	NY	1,125.1
Rating: A		
SENTRY INS A MUTUAL CO	WI	7,458.5
TOKIO MARINE AMERICA INS CO	NY	1,410.7
Rating: A-		
AUTO-OWNERS INS CO	MI	13,712.2
CINCINNATI INDEMNITY CO	OH	123.8
CINCINNATI INS CO	OH	11,749.4
COUNTRY MUTUAL INS CO	IL	4,421.1
ESSENT GUARANTY INC	PA	1,194.6
GEICO CHOICE INS CO	NE	647.0
GEICO SECURE INS CO	NE	436.8
HOME-OWNERS INS CO	MI	2,106.0
NATIONAL MORTGAGE INS CORP	WI	530.6
OWNERS INS CO	OH	3,891.6
TRAVELERS CASUALTY & SURETY CO	CT	16,398.0
USAA CASUALTY INS CO	TX	9,860.1
Rating: B+		
ACUITY A MUTUAL INS CO	WI	3,483.6
ALFA MUTUAL GENERAL INS CO	AL	103.4
ALL AMERICA INS CO	OH	280.0
AMERICAN FAMILY MUT INS CO	WI	16,216.1
AMICA MUTUAL INS CO	RI	4,974.1
BUILDERS MUTUAL INS CO	NC	736.0
COUNTRY CASUALTY INS CO	IL	83.4
DAIRYLAND INS CO	WI	1,282.3
FIRST COLONIAL INS CO	FL	370.3
GEICO GENERAL INS CO	MD	226.3
HOLYOKE MUTUAL INS CO IN SALEM	MA	217.0
MITSUI SUMITOMO INS CO OF AMER	NY	925.8
MOTORISTS MUTUAL INS CO	OH	1,375.1
NATIONAL CASUALTY CO	WI	402.1
NATIONWIDE MUTUAL FIRE INS CO	OH	6,045.9
PROPERTY-OWNERS INS CO	IN	257.1
SENTRY SELECT INS CO	WI	706.8
STATE FARM MUTUAL AUTOMOBILE INS CO	IL	143,802.0
TOA REINS CO OF AMERICA	DE	1,747.5
TRAVELERS INDEMNITY CO	CT	21,495.2
UNITED SERVICES AUTOMOBILE ASN	TX	32,870.8
USAA GENERAL INDEMNITY CO	TX	3,644.1

Hawaii

INSURANCE COMPANY NAME	DOM. STATE	TOTAL ASSETS ($MIL)
Rating: A+		
BERKSHIRE HATHAWAY ASR CORP	NY	2,220.4
MUNICIPAL ASR CORP	NY	1,125.1
Rating: A		
SENTRY INS A MUTUAL CO	WI	7,458.5
TOKIO MARINE AMERICA INS CO	NY	1,410.7
Rating: A-		
CINCINNATI INDEMNITY CO	OH	123.8
CINCINNATI INS CO	OH	11,749.4
ESSENT GUARANTY INC	PA	1,194.6
NATIONAL MORTGAGE INS CORP	WI	530.6
TRAVELERS CASUALTY & SURETY CO	CT	16,398.0
USAA CASUALTY INS CO	TX	9,860.1
Rating: B+		
AMICA MUTUAL INS CO	RI	4,974.1
CENTURION CASUALTY CO	IA	157.1
FIRST COLONIAL INS CO	FL	370.3
GEICO GENERAL INS CO	MD	226.3
INTERINS EXCHANGE	CA	9,074.7
MITSUI SUMITOMO INS CO OF AMER	NY	925.8
NATIONAL CASUALTY CO	WI	402.1
NATIONWIDE MUTUAL FIRE INS CO	OH	6,045.9
SENTRY SELECT INS CO	WI	706.8
STATE FARM MUTUAL AUTOMOBILE INS CO	IL	143,802.0
TOA REINS CO OF AMERICA	DE	1,747.5
TRAVELERS INDEMNITY CO	CT	21,495.2
UNITED SERVICES AUTOMOBILE ASN	TX	32,870.8
USAA GENERAL INDEMNITY CO	TX	3,644.1

Idaho

INSURANCE COMPANY NAME	DOM. STATE	TOTAL ASSETS ($MIL)
Rating: A+		
BERKSHIRE HATHAWAY ASR CORP	NY	2,220.4
MUNICIPAL ASR CORP	NY	1,125.1
Rating: A		
SENTRY INS A MUTUAL CO	WI	7,458.5
TOKIO MARINE AMERICA INS CO	NY	1,410.7
Rating: A-		
AUTO-OWNERS INS CO	MI	13,712.2
CINCINNATI INDEMNITY CO	OH	123.8
CINCINNATI INS CO	OH	11,749.4
COUNTRY MUTUAL INS CO	IL	4,421.1
ESSENT GUARANTY INC	PA	1,194.6
GEICO CHOICE INS CO	NE	647.0
GEICO SECURE INS CO	NE	436.8
NATIONAL MORTGAGE INS CORP	WI	530.6
OWNERS INS CO	OH	3,891.6
TRAVELERS CASUALTY & SURETY CO	CT	16,398.0
USAA CASUALTY INS CO	TX	9,860.1
Rating: B+		
ACUITY A MUTUAL INS CO	WI	3,483.6
ALL AMERICA INS CO	OH	280.0
AMERICAN FAMILY MUT INS CO	WI	16,216.1
AMERICAN STANDARD INS CO OF WI	WI	433.2
AMICA MUTUAL INS CO	RI	4,974.1
CENTURION CASUALTY CO	IA	157.1
COUNTRY CASUALTY INS CO	IL	83.4
DAIRYLAND INS CO	WI	1,282.3
FARM BUREAU P&C INS CO	IA	2,379.2
FIRST COLONIAL INS CO	FL	370.3
GEICO GENERAL INS CO	MD	226.3
HOLYOKE MUTUAL INS CO IN SALEM	MA	217.0
MITSUI SUMITOMO INS CO OF AMER	NY	925.8
NATIONAL CASUALTY CO	WI	402.1
NATIONWIDE MUTUAL FIRE INS CO	OH	6,045.9
SENTRY SELECT INS CO	WI	706.8
STATE FARM MUTUAL AUTOMOBILE INS CO	IL	143,802.0
TOA REINS CO OF AMERICA	DE	1,747.5
TRAVELERS INDEMNITY CO	CT	21,495.2
UNITED SERVICES AUTOMOBILE ASN	TX	32,870.8
USAA GENERAL INDEMNITY CO	TX	3,644.1
WESTERN AGRICULTURAL INS CO	IA	206.5

Illinois

INSURANCE COMPANY NAME	DOM. STATE	TOTAL ASSETS ($MIL)
Rating: **A+**		
BERKSHIRE HATHAWAY ASR CORP	NY	2,220.4
MUNICIPAL ASR CORP	NY	1,125.1
OGLESBY REINS CO	IL	4,277.3
Rating: **A**		
SENTRY INS A MUTUAL CO	WI	7,458.5
TOKIO MARINE AMERICA INS CO	NY	1,410.7
Rating: **A-**		
AUTO-OWNERS INS CO	MI	13,712.2
CINCINNATI INDEMNITY CO	OH	123.8
CINCINNATI INS CO	OH	11,749.4
COUNTRY MUTUAL INS CO	IL	4,421.1
ESSENT GUARANTY INC	PA	1,194.6
GEICO CHOICE INS CO	NE	647.0
GEICO SECURE INS CO	NE	436.8
HOME-OWNERS INS CO	MI	2,106.0
NATIONAL MORTGAGE INS CORP	WI	530.6
OWNERS INS CO	OH	3,891.6
TRAVELERS CASUALTY & SURETY CO	CT	16,398.0
USAA CASUALTY INS CO	TX	9,860.1
Rating: **B+**		
ACUITY A MUTUAL INS CO	WI	3,483.6
ALL AMERICA INS CO	OH	280.0
AMERICAN FAMILY MUT INS CO	WI	16,216.1
AMERICAN STANDARD INS CO OF WI	WI	433.2
AMICA MUTUAL INS CO	RI	4,974.1
CENTURION CASUALTY CO	IA	157.1
COUNTRY CASUALTY INS CO	IL	83.4
DAIRYLAND INS CO	WI	1,282.3
FARMERS AUTOMOBILE INS ASN	IL	1,283.7
FIRST COLONIAL INS CO	FL	370.3
GEICO GENERAL INS CO	MD	226.3
HOLYOKE MUTUAL INS CO IN SALEM	MA	217.0
MITSUI SUMITOMO INS CO OF AMER	NY	925.8
MOTORISTS MUTUAL INS CO	OH	1,375.1
NATIONAL CASUALTY CO	WI	402.1
NATIONWIDE MUTUAL FIRE INS CO	OH	6,045.9
PEKIN INS CO	IL	312.8
PROPERTY-OWNERS INS CO	IN	257.1
SENTRY SELECT INS CO	WI	706.8
STATE FARM MUTUAL AUTOMOBILE INS CO	IL	143,802.0
TOA REINS CO OF AMERICA	DE	1,747.5
TRAVELERS INDEMNITY CO	CT	21,495.2
UNITED SERVICES AUTOMOBILE ASN	TX	32,870.8
USAA GENERAL INDEMNITY CO	TX	3,644.1
WEST BEND MUTUAL INS CO	WI	2,456.0
WESTERN AGRICULTURAL INS CO	IA	206.5

Indiana

INSURANCE COMPANY NAME	DOM. STATE	TOTAL ASSETS ($MIL)	INSURANCE COMPANY NAME	DOM. STATE	TOTAL ASSETS ($MIL)
Rating: A+					
BERKSHIRE HATHAWAY ASR CORP	NY	2,220.4			
MUNICIPAL ASR CORP	NY	1,125.1			
Rating: A					
SENTRY INS A MUTUAL CO	WI	7,458.5			
TOKIO MARINE AMERICA INS CO	NY	1,410.7			
Rating: A-					
AUTO-OWNERS INS CO	MI	13,712.2			
CINCINNATI INDEMNITY CO	OH	123.8			
CINCINNATI INS CO	OH	11,749.4			
COUNTRY MUTUAL INS CO	IL	4,421.1			
ESSENT GUARANTY INC	PA	1,194.6			
GEICO CHOICE INS CO	NE	647.0			
GEICO SECURE INS CO	NE	436.8			
HOME-OWNERS INS CO	MI	2,106.0			
NATIONAL MORTGAGE INS CORP	WI	530.6			
OWNERS INS CO	OH	3,891.6			
TRAVELERS CASUALTY & SURETY CO	CT	16,398.0			
USAA CASUALTY INS CO	TX	9,860.1			
Rating: B+					
ACUITY A MUTUAL INS CO	WI	3,483.6			
ALL AMERICA INS CO	OH	280.0			
AMERICAN FAMILY MUT INS CO	WI	16,216.1			
AMERICAN STANDARD INS CO OF WI	WI	433.2			
AMICA MUTUAL INS CO	RI	4,974.1			
CENTURION CASUALTY CO	IA	157.1			
COUNTRY CASUALTY INS CO	IL	83.4			
DAIRYLAND INS CO	WI	1,282.3			
FARMERS AUTOMOBILE INS ASN	IL	1,283.7			
FIRST COLONIAL INS CO	FL	370.3			
GEICO GENERAL INS CO	MD	226.3			
MITSUI SUMITOMO INS CO OF AMER	NY	925.8			
MOTORISTS MUTUAL INS CO	OH	1,375.1			
NATIONAL CASUALTY CO	WI	402.1			
NATIONWIDE MUTUAL FIRE INS CO	OH	6,045.9			
PEKIN INS CO	IL	312.8			
PROPERTY-OWNERS INS CO	IN	257.1			
SENTRY SELECT INS CO	WI	706.8			
STATE FARM MUTUAL AUTOMOBILE INS CO	IL	143,802.0			
TOA REINS CO OF AMERICA	DE	1,747.5			
TRAVELERS INDEMNITY CO	CT	21,495.2			
UNITED SERVICES AUTOMOBILE ASN	TX	32,870.8			
USAA GENERAL INDEMNITY CO	TX	3,644.1			
WEST BEND MUTUAL INS CO	WI	2,456.0			
WESTERN AGRICULTURAL INS CO	IA	206.5			

Iowa

INSURANCE COMPANY NAME	DOM. STATE	TOTAL ASSETS ($MIL)
Rating: A+		
BERKSHIRE HATHAWAY ASR CORP	NY	2,220.4
MUNICIPAL ASR CORP	NY	1,125.1
Rating: A		
SENTRY INS A MUTUAL CO	WI	7,458.5
TOKIO MARINE AMERICA INS CO	NY	1,410.7
Rating: A-		
AUTO-OWNERS INS CO	MI	13,712.2
CINCINNATI INDEMNITY CO	OH	123.8
CINCINNATI INS CO	OH	11,749.4
COUNTRY MUTUAL INS CO	IL	4,421.1
ESSENT GUARANTY INC	PA	1,194.6
GEICO CHOICE INS CO	NE	647.0
GEICO SECURE INS CO	NE	436.8
HOME-OWNERS INS CO	MI	2,106.0
NATIONAL MORTGAGE INS CORP	WI	530.6
OWNERS INS CO	OH	3,891.6
TRAVELERS CASUALTY & SURETY CO	CT	16,398.0
USAA CASUALTY INS CO	TX	9,860.1
Rating: B+		
ACUITY A MUTUAL INS CO	WI	3,483.6
ALL AMERICA INS CO	OH	280.0
AMERICAN FAMILY MUT INS CO	WI	16,216.1
AMERICAN STANDARD INS CO OF WI	WI	433.2
AMICA MUTUAL INS CO	RI	4,974.1
CENTURION CASUALTY CO	IA	157.1
COUNTRY CASUALTY INS CO	IL	83.4
DAIRYLAND INS CO	WI	1,282.3
FARM BUREAU P&C INS CO	IA	2,379.2
FARMERS AUTOMOBILE INS ASN	IL	1,283.7
FIRST COLONIAL INS CO	FL	370.3
GEICO GENERAL INS CO	MD	226.3
MITSUI SUMITOMO INS CO OF AMER	NY	925.8
MOTORISTS MUTUAL INS CO	OH	1,375.1
NATIONAL CASUALTY CO	WI	402.1
NATIONWIDE MUTUAL FIRE INS CO	OH	6,045.9
PEKIN INS CO	IL	312.8
PROPERTY-OWNERS INS CO	IN	257.1
SENTRY SELECT INS CO	WI	706.8
STATE FARM MUTUAL AUTOMOBILE INS CO	IL	143,802.0
TOA REINS CO OF AMERICA	DE	1,747.5
TRAVELERS INDEMNITY CO	CT	21,495.2
UNITED SERVICES AUTOMOBILE ASN	TX	32,870.8
USAA GENERAL INDEMNITY CO	TX	3,644.1
WEST BEND MUTUAL INS CO	WI	2,456.0
WESTERN AGRICULTURAL INS CO	IA	206.5

Kansas

INSURANCE COMPANY NAME	DOM. STATE	TOTAL ASSETS ($MIL)	INSURANCE COMPANY NAME	DOM. STATE	TOTAL ASSETS ($MIL)
Rating: A+					
BERKSHIRE HATHAWAY ASR CORP	NY	2,220.4			
MUNICIPAL ASR CORP	NY	1,125.1			
Rating: A					
SENTRY INS A MUTUAL CO	WI	7,458.5			
TOKIO MARINE AMERICA INS CO	NY	1,410.7			
Rating: A-					
AUTO-OWNERS INS CO	MI	13,712.2			
CINCINNATI INDEMNITY CO	OH	123.8			
CINCINNATI INS CO	OH	11,749.4			
COUNTRY MUTUAL INS CO	IL	4,421.1			
ESSENT GUARANTY INC	PA	1,194.6			
GEICO CHOICE INS CO	NE	647.0			
GEICO SECURE INS CO	NE	436.8			
NATIONAL MORTGAGE INS CORP	WI	530.6			
OWNERS INS CO	OH	3,891.6			
TRAVELERS CASUALTY & SURETY CO	CT	16,398.0			
USAA CASUALTY INS CO	TX	9,860.1			
Rating: B+					
ACUITY A MUTUAL INS CO	WI	3,483.6			
AMERICAN FAMILY MUT INS CO	WI	16,216.1			
AMERICAN STANDARD INS CO OF WI	WI	433.2			
AMICA MUTUAL INS CO	RI	4,974.1			
CENTURION CASUALTY CO	IA	157.1			
COUNTRY CASUALTY INS CO	IL	83.4			
DAIRYLAND INS CO	WI	1,282.3			
FARM BUREAU P&C INS CO	IA	2,379.2			
FIRST COLONIAL INS CO	FL	370.3			
GEICO GENERAL INS CO	MD	226.3			
MITSUI SUMITOMO INS CO OF AMER	NY	925.8			
NATIONAL CASUALTY CO	WI	402.1			
NATIONWIDE MUTUAL FIRE INS CO	OH	6,045.9			
SENTRY SELECT INS CO	WI	706.8			
STATE FARM MUTUAL AUTOMOBILE INS CO	IL	143,802.0			
TOA REINS CO OF AMERICA	DE	1,747.5			
TRAVELERS INDEMNITY CO	CT	21,495.2			
UNITED SERVICES AUTOMOBILE ASN	TX	32,870.8			
USAA GENERAL INDEMNITY CO	TX	3,644.1			
WEST BEND MUTUAL INS CO	WI	2,456.0			
WESTERN AGRICULTURAL INS CO	IA	206.5			

Kentucky

INSURANCE COMPANY NAME	DOM. STATE	TOTAL ASSETS ($MIL)
Rating: A+		
BERKSHIRE HATHAWAY ASR CORP	NY	2,220.4
MUNICIPAL ASR CORP	NY	1,125.1
Rating: A		
SENTRY INS A MUTUAL CO	WI	7,458.5
TOKIO MARINE AMERICA INS CO	NY	1,410.7
Rating: A-		
AUTO-OWNERS INS CO	MI	13,712.2
CINCINNATI INDEMNITY CO	OH	123.8
CINCINNATI INS CO	OH	11,749.4
COUNTRY MUTUAL INS CO	IL	4,421.1
ESSENT GUARANTY INC	PA	1,194.6
GEICO CHOICE INS CO	NE	647.0
GEICO SECURE INS CO	NE	436.8
HOME-OWNERS INS CO	MI	2,106.0
NATIONAL MORTGAGE INS CORP	WI	530.6
OWNERS INS CO	OH	3,891.6
TRAVELERS CASUALTY & SURETY CO	CT	16,398.0
USAA CASUALTY INS CO	TX	9,860.1
Rating: B+		
ACUITY A MUTUAL INS CO	WI	3,483.6
ALL AMERICA INS CO	OH	280.0
AMICA MUTUAL INS CO	RI	4,974.1
CENTURION CASUALTY CO	IA	157.1
COUNTRY CASUALTY INS CO	IL	83.4
DAIRYLAND INS CO	WI	1,282.3
FIRST COLONIAL INS CO	FL	370.3
GEICO GENERAL INS CO	MD	226.3
MITSUI SUMITOMO INS CO OF AMER	NY	925.8
MOTORISTS MUTUAL INS CO	OH	1,375.1
NATIONAL CASUALTY CO	WI	402.1
NATIONWIDE MUTUAL FIRE INS CO	OH	6,045.9
PROPERTY-OWNERS INS CO	IN	257.1
SENTRY SELECT INS CO	WI	706.8
STATE FARM MUTUAL AUTOMOBILE INS CO	IL	143,802.0
TOA REINS CO OF AMERICA	DE	1,747.5
TRAVELERS INDEMNITY CO	CT	21,495.2
UNITED SERVICES AUTOMOBILE ASN	TX	32,870.8
USAA GENERAL INDEMNITY CO	TX	3,644.1
WEST BEND MUTUAL INS CO	WI	2,456.0

INSURANCE COMPANY NAME	DOM. STATE	TOTAL ASSETS ($MIL)

Louisiana

INSURANCE COMPANY NAME	DOM. STATE	TOTAL ASSETS ($MIL)
Rating: A+		
BERKSHIRE HATHAWAY ASR CORP	NY	2,220.4
MUNICIPAL ASR CORP	NY	1,125.1
Rating: A		
SENTRY INS A MUTUAL CO	WI	7,458.5
TOKIO MARINE AMERICA INS CO	NY	1,410.7
Rating: A-		
CINCINNATI INDEMNITY CO	OH	123.8
CINCINNATI INS CO	OH	11,749.4
ESSENT GUARANTY INC	PA	1,194.6
GEICO CHOICE INS CO	NE	647.0
GEICO SECURE INS CO	NE	436.8
NATIONAL MORTGAGE INS CORP	WI	530.6
TRAVELERS CASUALTY & SURETY CO	CT	16,398.0
USAA CASUALTY INS CO	TX	9,860.1
Rating: B+		
AMICA MUTUAL INS CO	RI	4,974.1
CENTURION CASUALTY CO	IA	157.1
FIRST COLONIAL INS CO	FL	370.3
GEICO GENERAL INS CO	MD	226.3
MITSUI SUMITOMO INS CO OF AMER	NY	925.8
NATIONAL CASUALTY CO	WI	402.1
NATIONWIDE MUTUAL FIRE INS CO	OH	6,045.9
SENTRY SELECT INS CO	WI	706.8
STATE FARM MUTUAL AUTOMOBILE INS CO	IL	143,802.0
TOA REINS CO OF AMERICA	DE	1,747.5
TRAVELERS INDEMNITY CO	CT	21,495.2
UNITED SERVICES AUTOMOBILE ASN	TX	32,870.8
USAA GENERAL INDEMNITY CO	TX	3,644.1

Maine

INSURANCE COMPANY NAME	DOM. STATE	TOTAL ASSETS ($MIL)
Rating: A+		
BERKSHIRE HATHAWAY ASR CORP	NY	2,220.4
MUNICIPAL ASR CORP	NY	1,125.1
Rating: A		
SENTRY INS A MUTUAL CO	WI	7,458.5
TOKIO MARINE AMERICA INS CO	NY	1,410.7
Rating: A-		
CINCINNATI INDEMNITY CO	OH	123.8
CINCINNATI INS CO	OH	11,749.4
COUNTRY MUTUAL INS CO	IL	4,421.1
ESSENT GUARANTY INC	PA	1,194.6
NATIONAL MORTGAGE INS CORP	WI	530.6
TRAVELERS CASUALTY & SURETY CO	CT	16,398.0
USAA CASUALTY INS CO	TX	9,860.1
Rating: B+		
ACUITY A MUTUAL INS CO	WI	3,483.6
ALL AMERICA INS CO	OH	280.0
AMICA MUTUAL INS CO	RI	4,974.1
CENTURION CASUALTY CO	IA	157.1
COUNTRY CASUALTY INS CO	IL	83.4
DAIRYLAND INS CO	WI	1,282.3
FARM FAMILY CASUALTY INS CO	NY	1,160.0
FIRST COLONIAL INS CO	FL	370.3
GEICO GENERAL INS CO	MD	226.3
HOLYOKE MUTUAL INS CO IN SALEM	MA	217.0
INTERINS EXCHANGE	CA	9,074.7
MITSUI SUMITOMO INS CO OF AMER	NY	925.8
MOTORISTS MUTUAL INS CO	OH	1,375.1
NATIONAL CASUALTY CO	WI	402.1
NATIONWIDE MUTUAL FIRE INS CO	OH	6,045.9
SENTRY SELECT INS CO	WI	706.8
STATE FARM MUTUAL AUTOMOBILE INS CO	IL	143,802.0
TOA REINS CO OF AMERICA	DE	1,747.5
TRAVELERS INDEMNITY CO	CT	21,495.2
UNITED SERVICES AUTOMOBILE ASN	TX	32,870.8
USAA GENERAL INDEMNITY CO	TX	3,644.1

INSURANCE COMPANY NAME	DOM. STATE	TOTAL ASSETS ($MIL)

Maryland

INSURANCE COMPANY NAME	DOM. STATE	TOTAL ASSETS ($MIL)
Rating: A+		
BERKSHIRE HATHAWAY ASR CORP	NY	2,220.4
MUNICIPAL ASR CORP	NY	1,125.1
Rating: A		
SENTRY INS A MUTUAL CO	WI	7,458.5
TOKIO MARINE AMERICA INS CO	NY	1,410.7
Rating: A-		
CINCINNATI INDEMNITY CO	OH	123.8
CINCINNATI INS CO	OH	11,749.4
COUNTRY MUTUAL INS CO	IL	4,421.1
ESSENT GUARANTY INC	PA	1,194.6
GEICO CHOICE INS CO	NE	647.0
GEICO SECURE INS CO	NE	436.8
NATIONAL MORTGAGE INS CORP	WI	530.6
TRAVELERS CASUALTY & SURETY CO	CT	16,398.0
USAA CASUALTY INS CO	TX	9,860.1
Rating: B+		
ALL AMERICA INS CO	OH	280.0
AMICA MUTUAL INS CO	RI	4,974.1
BUILDERS MUTUAL INS CO	NC	736.0
CENTURION CASUALTY CO	IA	157.1
COUNTRY CASUALTY INS CO	IL	83.4
DAIRYLAND INS CO	WI	1,282.3
FARM FAMILY CASUALTY INS CO	NY	1,160.0
FIRST COLONIAL INS CO	FL	370.3
GEICO GENERAL INS CO	MD	226.3
MITSUI SUMITOMO INS CO OF AMER	NY	925.8
MOTORISTS MUTUAL INS CO	OH	1,375.1
NATIONAL CASUALTY CO	WI	402.1
NATIONWIDE MUTUAL FIRE INS CO	OH	6,045.9
SENTRY SELECT INS CO	WI	706.8
STATE FARM MUTUAL AUTOMOBILE INS CO	IL	143,802.0
TOA REINS CO OF AMERICA	DE	1,747.5
TRAVELERS INDEMNITY CO	CT	21,495.2
UNITED SERVICES AUTOMOBILE ASN	TX	32,870.8
USAA GENERAL INDEMNITY CO	TX	3,644.1

Massachusetts

INSURANCE COMPANY NAME	DOM. STATE	TOTAL ASSETS ($MIL)
Rating: A+		
BERKSHIRE HATHAWAY ASR CORP	NY	2,220.4
MUNICIPAL ASR CORP	NY	1,125.1
Rating: A		
SENTRY INS A MUTUAL CO	WI	7,458.5
TOKIO MARINE AMERICA INS CO	NY	1,410.7
Rating: A-		
CINCINNATI INDEMNITY CO	OH	123.8
CINCINNATI INS CO	OH	11,749.4
COUNTRY MUTUAL INS CO	IL	4,421.1
ESSENT GUARANTY INC	PA	1,194.6
NATIONAL MORTGAGE INS CORP	WI	530.6
TRAVELERS CASUALTY & SURETY CO	CT	16,398.0
USAA CASUALTY INS CO	TX	9,860.1
Rating: B+		
ALL AMERICA INS CO	OH	280.0
AMICA MUTUAL INS CO	RI	4,974.1
CENTURION CASUALTY CO	IA	157.1
COUNTRY CASUALTY INS CO	IL	83.4
DAIRYLAND INS CO	WI	1,282.3
FARM FAMILY CASUALTY INS CO	NY	1,160.0
FIRST COLONIAL INS CO	FL	370.3
GEICO GENERAL INS CO	MD	226.3
HOLYOKE MUTUAL INS CO IN SALEM	MA	217.0
MITSUI SUMITOMO INS CO OF AMER	NY	925.8
MOTORISTS MUTUAL INS CO	OH	1,375.1
NATIONAL CASUALTY CO	WI	402.1
NATIONWIDE MUTUAL FIRE INS CO	OH	6,045.9
SENTRY SELECT INS CO	WI	706.8
STATE FARM MUTUAL AUTOMOBILE INS CO	IL	143,802.0
TOA REINS CO OF AMERICA	DE	1,747.5
TRAVELERS INDEMNITY CO	CT	21,495.2
UNITED SERVICES AUTOMOBILE ASN	TX	32,870.8
USAA GENERAL INDEMNITY CO	TX	3,644.1

Michigan

INSURANCE COMPANY NAME	DOM. STATE	TOTAL ASSETS ($MIL)
Rating: A+		
BERKSHIRE HATHAWAY ASR CORP	NY	2,220.4
MUNICIPAL ASR CORP	NY	1,125.1
Rating: A		
SENTRY INS A MUTUAL CO	WI	7,458.5
TOKIO MARINE AMERICA INS CO	NY	1,410.7
Rating: A-		
AUTO-OWNERS INS CO	MI	13,712.2
CINCINNATI INDEMNITY CO	OH	123.8
CINCINNATI INS CO	OH	11,749.4
COUNTRY MUTUAL INS CO	IL	4,421.1
ESSENT GUARANTY INC	PA	1,194.6
HOME-OWNERS INS CO	MI	2,106.0
NATIONAL MORTGAGE INS CORP	WI	530.6
OWNERS INS CO	OH	3,891.6
TRAVELERS CASUALTY & SURETY CO	CT	16,398.0
USAA CASUALTY INS CO	TX	9,860.1
Rating: B+		
ACUITY A MUTUAL INS CO	WI	3,483.6
ALL AMERICA INS CO	OH	280.0
AMICA MUTUAL INS CO	RI	4,974.1
COUNTRY CASUALTY INS CO	IL	83.4
DAIRYLAND INS CO	WI	1,282.3
FARMERS AUTOMOBILE INS ASN	IL	1,283.7
FIRST COLONIAL INS CO	FL	370.3
GEICO GENERAL INS CO	MD	226.3
INTERINS EXCHANGE	CA	9,074.7
MITSUI SUMITOMO INS CO OF AMER	NY	925.8
MOTORISTS MUTUAL INS CO	OH	1,375.1
NATIONAL CASUALTY CO	WI	402.1
NATIONWIDE MUTUAL FIRE INS CO	OH	6,045.9
PEKIN INS CO	IL	312.8
PROPERTY-OWNERS INS CO	IN	257.1
SENTRY SELECT INS CO	WI	706.8
SOUTHERN-OWNERS INS CO	MI	695.8
STATE FARM MUTUAL AUTOMOBILE INS CO	IL	143,802.0
TOA REINS CO OF AMERICA	DE	1,747.5
TRAVELERS INDEMNITY CO	CT	21,495.2
UNITED SERVICES AUTOMOBILE ASN	TX	32,870.8
USAA GENERAL INDEMNITY CO	TX	3,644.1
WEST BEND MUTUAL INS CO	WI	2,456.0
WESTERN AGRICULTURAL INS CO	IA	206.5

Minnesota

INSURANCE COMPANY NAME	DOM. STATE	TOTAL ASSETS ($MIL)	INSURANCE COMPANY NAME	DOM. STATE	TOTAL ASSETS ($MIL)
Rating: **A+**					
BERKSHIRE HATHAWAY ASR CORP	NY	2,220.4			
MUNICIPAL ASR CORP	NY	1,125.1			
Rating: **A**					
SENTRY INS A MUTUAL CO	WI	7,458.5			
TOKIO MARINE AMERICA INS CO	NY	1,410.7			
Rating: **A-**					
AUTO-OWNERS INS CO	MI	13,712.2			
CINCINNATI INDEMNITY CO	OH	123.8			
CINCINNATI INS CO	OH	11,749.4			
COUNTRY MUTUAL INS CO	IL	4,421.1			
ESSENT GUARANTY INC	PA	1,194.6			
NATIONAL MORTGAGE INS CORP	WI	530.6			
OWNERS INS CO	OH	3,891.6			
TRAVELERS CASUALTY & SURETY CO	CT	16,398.0			
USAA CASUALTY INS CO	TX	9,860.1			
Rating: **B+**					
ACUITY A MUTUAL INS CO	WI	3,483.6			
AMERICAN FAMILY MUT INS CO	WI	16,216.1			
AMERICAN STANDARD INS CO OF WI	WI	433.2			
AMICA MUTUAL INS CO	RI	4,974.1			
CENTURION CASUALTY CO	IA	157.1			
COUNTRY CASUALTY INS CO	IL	83.4			
DAIRYLAND INS CO	WI	1,282.3			
FARM BUREAU P&C INS CO	IA	2,379.2			
FIRST COLONIAL INS CO	FL	370.3			
GEICO GENERAL INS CO	MD	226.3			
HOLYOKE MUTUAL INS CO IN SALEM	MA	217.0			
MITSUI SUMITOMO INS CO OF AMER	NY	925.8			
NATIONAL CASUALTY CO	WI	402.1			
NATIONWIDE MUTUAL FIRE INS CO	OH	6,045.9			
SENTRY SELECT INS CO	WI	706.8			
STATE FARM MUTUAL AUTOMOBILE INS CO	IL	143,802.0			
TOA REINS CO OF AMERICA	DE	1,747.5			
TRAVELERS INDEMNITY CO	CT	21,495.2			
UNITED SERVICES AUTOMOBILE ASN	TX	32,870.8			
USAA GENERAL INDEMNITY CO	TX	3,644.1			
WEST BEND MUTUAL INS CO	WI	2,456.0			
WESTERN AGRICULTURAL INS CO	IA	206.5			

Mississippi

INSURANCE COMPANY NAME	DOM. STATE	TOTAL ASSETS ($MIL)
Rating: A+		
BERKSHIRE HATHAWAY ASR CORP	NY	2,220.4
MUNICIPAL ASR CORP	NY	1,125.1
Rating: A		
SENTRY INS A MUTUAL CO	WI	7,458.5
TOKIO MARINE AMERICA INS CO	NY	1,410.7
Rating: A-		
AUTO-OWNERS INS CO	MI	13,712.2
CINCINNATI INDEMNITY CO	OH	123.8
CINCINNATI INS CO	OH	11,749.4
ESSENT GUARANTY INC	PA	1,194.6
GEICO CHOICE INS CO	NE	647.0
GEICO SECURE INS CO	NE	436.8
NATIONAL MORTGAGE INS CORP	WI	530.6
OWNERS INS CO	OH	3,891.6
TRAVELERS CASUALTY & SURETY CO	CT	16,398.0
USAA CASUALTY INS CO	TX	9,860.1
Rating: B+		
ACUITY A MUTUAL INS CO	WI	3,483.6
ALFA MUTUAL GENERAL INS CO	AL	103.4
ALL AMERICA INS CO	OH	280.0
AMICA MUTUAL INS CO	RI	4,974.1
BUILDERS MUTUAL INS CO	NC	736.0
CENTURION CASUALTY CO	IA	157.1
DAIRYLAND INS CO	WI	1,282.3
FIRST COLONIAL INS CO	FL	370.3
GEICO GENERAL INS CO	MD	226.3
MITSUI SUMITOMO INS CO OF AMER	NY	925.8
NATIONAL CASUALTY CO	WI	402.1
NATIONWIDE MUTUAL FIRE INS CO	OH	6,045.9
SENTRY SELECT INS CO	WI	706.8
STATE FARM MUTUAL AUTOMOBILE INS CO	IL	143,802.0
TOA REINS CO OF AMERICA	DE	1,747.5
TRAVELERS INDEMNITY CO	CT	21,495.2
UNITED SERVICES AUTOMOBILE ASN	TX	32,870.8
USAA GENERAL INDEMNITY CO	TX	3,644.1

Missouri

INSURANCE COMPANY NAME	DOM. STATE	TOTAL ASSETS ($MIL)	INSURANCE COMPANY NAME	DOM. STATE	TOTAL ASSETS ($MIL)
Rating: A+					
BERKSHIRE HATHAWAY ASR CORP	NY	2,220.4			
MUNICIPAL ASR CORP	NY	1,125.1			
Rating: A					
SENTRY INS A MUTUAL CO	WI	7,458.5			
TOKIO MARINE AMERICA INS CO	NY	1,410.7			
Rating: A-					
AUTO-OWNERS INS CO	MI	13,712.2			
CINCINNATI INDEMNITY CO	OH	123.8			
CINCINNATI INS CO	OH	11,749.4			
COUNTRY MUTUAL INS CO	IL	4,421.1			
ESSENT GUARANTY INC	PA	1,194.6			
GEICO CHOICE INS CO	NE	647.0			
GEICO SECURE INS CO	NE	436.8			
HOME-OWNERS INS CO	MI	2,106.0			
NATIONAL MORTGAGE INS CORP	WI	530.6			
OWNERS INS CO	OH	3,891.6			
TRAVELERS CASUALTY & SURETY CO	CT	16,398.0			
USAA CASUALTY INS CO	TX	9,860.1			
Rating: B+					
ACUITY A MUTUAL INS CO	WI	3,483.6			
AMERICAN FAMILY MUT INS CO	WI	16,216.1			
AMERICAN STANDARD INS CO OF WI	WI	433.2			
AMICA MUTUAL INS CO	RI	4,974.1			
CENTURION CASUALTY CO	IA	157.1			
COUNTRY CASUALTY INS CO	IL	83.4			
DAIRYLAND INS CO	WI	1,282.3			
FARM BUREAU P&C INS CO	IA	2,379.2			
FARM FAMILY CASUALTY INS CO	NY	1,160.0			
FIRST COLONIAL INS CO	FL	370.3			
GEICO GENERAL INS CO	MD	226.3			
HOLYOKE MUTUAL INS CO IN SALEM	MA	217.0			
INTERINS EXCHANGE	CA	9,074.7			
MITSUI SUMITOMO INS CO OF AMER	NY	925.8			
MOTORISTS MUTUAL INS CO	OH	1,375.1			
NATIONAL CASUALTY CO	WI	402.1			
NATIONWIDE MUTUAL FIRE INS CO	OH	6,045.9			
PROPERTY-OWNERS INS CO	IN	257.1			
SENTRY SELECT INS CO	WI	706.8			
STATE FARM MUTUAL AUTOMOBILE INS CO	IL	143,802.0			
TOA REINS CO OF AMERICA	DE	1,747.5			
TRAVELERS INDEMNITY CO	CT	21,495.2			
UNITED SERVICES AUTOMOBILE ASN	TX	32,870.8			
USAA GENERAL INDEMNITY CO	TX	3,644.1			
WEST BEND MUTUAL INS CO	WI	2,456.0			
WESTERN AGRICULTURAL INS CO	IA	206.5			

Montana

INSURANCE COMPANY NAME	DOM. STATE	TOTAL ASSETS ($MIL)
Rating: A+		
BERKSHIRE HATHAWAY ASR CORP	NY	2,220.4
MUNICIPAL ASR CORP	NY	1,125.1
Rating: A		
SENTRY INS A MUTUAL CO	WI	7,458.5
TOKIO MARINE AMERICA INS CO	NY	1,410.7
Rating: A-		
CINCINNATI INDEMNITY CO	OH	123.8
CINCINNATI INS CO	OH	11,749.4
COUNTRY MUTUAL INS CO	IL	4,421.1
ESSENT GUARANTY INC	PA	1,194.6
GEICO CHOICE INS CO	NE	647.0
GEICO SECURE INS CO	NE	436.8
NATIONAL MORTGAGE INS CORP	WI	530.6
TRAVELERS CASUALTY & SURETY CO	CT	16,398.0
USAA CASUALTY INS CO	TX	9,860.1
Rating: B+		
ACUITY A MUTUAL INS CO	WI	3,483.6
AMERICAN FAMILY MUT INS CO	WI	16,216.1
AMERICAN STANDARD INS CO OF WI	WI	433.2
AMICA MUTUAL INS CO	RI	4,974.1
CENTURION CASUALTY CO	IA	157.1
COUNTRY CASUALTY INS CO	IL	83.4
DAIRYLAND INS CO	WI	1,282.3
FIRST COLONIAL INS CO	FL	370.3
GEICO GENERAL INS CO	MD	226.3
HOLYOKE MUTUAL INS CO IN SALEM	MA	217.0
MITSUI SUMITOMO INS CO OF AMER	NY	925.8
MOTORISTS MUTUAL INS CO	OH	1,375.1
NATIONAL CASUALTY CO	WI	402.1
NATIONWIDE MUTUAL FIRE INS CO	OH	6,045.9
SENTRY SELECT INS CO	WI	706.8
STATE FARM MUTUAL AUTOMOBILE INS CO	IL	143,802.0
TOA REINS CO OF AMERICA	DE	1,747.5
TRAVELERS INDEMNITY CO	CT	21,495.2
UNITED SERVICES AUTOMOBILE ASN	TX	32,870.8
USAA GENERAL INDEMNITY CO	TX	3,644.1
WESTERN AGRICULTURAL INS CO	IA	206.5

Nebraska

INSURANCE COMPANY NAME	DOM. STATE	TOTAL ASSETS ($MIL)	INSURANCE COMPANY NAME	DOM. STATE	TOTAL ASSETS ($MIL)
Rating: A+					
BERKSHIRE HATHAWAY ASR CORP	NY	2,220.4			
MUNICIPAL ASR CORP	NY	1,125.1			
Rating: A					
SENTRY INS A MUTUAL CO	WI	7,458.5			
TOKIO MARINE AMERICA INS CO	NY	1,410.7			
Rating: A-					
AUTO-OWNERS INS CO	MI	13,712.2			
CINCINNATI INDEMNITY CO	OH	123.8			
CINCINNATI INS CO	OH	11,749.4			
COUNTRY MUTUAL INS CO	IL	4,421.1			
ESSENT GUARANTY INC	PA	1,194.6			
GEICO CHOICE INS CO	NE	647.0			
GEICO SECURE INS CO	NE	436.8			
HOME-OWNERS INS CO	MI	2,106.0			
NATIONAL MORTGAGE INS CORP	WI	530.6			
OWNERS INS CO	OH	3,891.6			
TRAVELERS CASUALTY & SURETY CO	CT	16,398.0			
USAA CASUALTY INS CO	TX	9,860.1			
Rating: B+					
ACUITY A MUTUAL INS CO	WI	3,483.6			
AMERICAN FAMILY MUT INS CO	WI	16,216.1			
AMERICAN STANDARD INS CO OF WI	WI	433.2			
AMICA MUTUAL INS CO	RI	4,974.1			
CENTURION CASUALTY CO	IA	157.1			
COUNTRY CASUALTY INS CO	IL	83.4			
DAIRYLAND INS CO	WI	1,282.3			
FARM BUREAU P&C INS CO	IA	2,379.2			
FIRST COLONIAL INS CO	FL	370.3			
GEICO GENERAL INS CO	MD	226.3			
HOLYOKE MUTUAL INS CO IN SALEM	MA	217.0			
MITSUI SUMITOMO INS CO OF AMER	NY	925.8			
MOTORISTS MUTUAL INS CO	OH	1,375.1			
NATIONAL CASUALTY CO	WI	402.1			
NATIONWIDE MUTUAL FIRE INS CO	OH	6,045.9			
PROPERTY-OWNERS INS CO	IN	257.1			
SENTRY SELECT INS CO	WI	706.8			
STATE FARM MUTUAL AUTOMOBILE INS CO	IL	143,802.0			
TOA REINS CO OF AMERICA	DE	1,747.5			
TRAVELERS INDEMNITY CO	CT	21,495.2			
UNITED SERVICES AUTOMOBILE ASN	TX	32,870.8			
USAA GENERAL INDEMNITY CO	TX	3,644.1			
WEST BEND MUTUAL INS CO	WI	2,456.0			
WESTERN AGRICULTURAL INS CO	IA	206.5			

Nevada

INSURANCE COMPANY NAME	DOM. STATE	TOTAL ASSETS ($MIL)	INSURANCE COMPANY NAME	DOM. STATE	TOTAL ASSETS ($MIL)
Rating: A+					
BERKSHIRE HATHAWAY ASR CORP	NY	2,220.4			
MUNICIPAL ASR CORP	NY	1,125.1			
Rating: A					
SENTRY INS A MUTUAL CO	WI	7,458.5			
TOKIO MARINE AMERICA INS CO	NY	1,410.7			
Rating: A-					
AUTO-OWNERS INS CO	MI	13,712.2			
CINCINNATI INDEMNITY CO	OH	123.8			
CINCINNATI INS CO	OH	11,749.4			
COUNTRY MUTUAL INS CO	IL	4,421.1			
ESSENT GUARANTY INC	PA	1,194.6			
GEICO CHOICE INS CO	NE	647.0			
GEICO SECURE INS CO	NE	436.8			
HOME-OWNERS INS CO	MI	2,106.0			
NATIONAL MORTGAGE INS CORP	WI	530.6			
OWNERS INS CO	OH	3,891.6			
TRAVELERS CASUALTY & SURETY CO	CT	16,398.0			
USAA CASUALTY INS CO	TX	9,860.1			
Rating: B+					
ACUITY A MUTUAL INS CO	WI	3,483.6			
ALL AMERICA INS CO	OH	280.0			
AMERICAN FAMILY MUT INS CO	WI	16,216.1			
AMERICAN STANDARD INS CO OF WI	WI	433.2			
AMICA MUTUAL INS CO	RI	4,974.1			
CENTURION CASUALTY CO	IA	157.1			
COUNTRY CASUALTY INS CO	IL	83.4			
DAIRYLAND INS CO	WI	1,282.3			
FIRST COLONIAL INS CO	FL	370.3			
GEICO GENERAL INS CO	MD	226.3			
HOLYOKE MUTUAL INS CO IN SALEM	MA	217.0			
MITSUI SUMITOMO INS CO OF AMER	NY	925.8			
NATIONAL CASUALTY CO	WI	402.1			
NATIONWIDE MUTUAL FIRE INS CO	OH	6,045.9			
PROPERTY-OWNERS INS CO	IN	257.1			
SENTRY SELECT INS CO	WI	706.8			
STATE FARM MUTUAL AUTOMOBILE INS CO	IL	143,802.0			
TOA REINS CO OF AMERICA	DE	1,747.5			
TRAVELERS INDEMNITY CO	CT	21,495.2			
UNITED SERVICES AUTOMOBILE ASN	TX	32,870.8			
USAA GENERAL INDEMNITY CO	TX	3,644.1			
WESTERN AGRICULTURAL INS CO	IA	206.5			

New Hampshire

INSURANCE COMPANY NAME	DOM. STATE	TOTAL ASSETS ($MIL)
Rating: A+		
BERKSHIRE HATHAWAY ASR CORP	NY	2,220.4
MUNICIPAL ASR CORP	NY	1,125.1
Rating: A		
SENTRY INS A MUTUAL CO	WI	7,458.5
TOKIO MARINE AMERICA INS CO	NY	1,410.7
Rating: A-		
CINCINNATI INDEMNITY CO	OH	123.8
CINCINNATI INS CO	OH	11,749.4
COUNTRY MUTUAL INS CO	IL	4,421.1
ESSENT GUARANTY INC	PA	1,194.6
GEICO CHOICE INS CO	NE	647.0
GEICO SECURE INS CO	NE	436.8
NATIONAL MORTGAGE INS CORP	WI	530.6
TRAVELERS CASUALTY & SURETY CO	CT	16,398.0
USAA CASUALTY INS CO	TX	9,860.1
Rating: B+		
AMICA MUTUAL INS CO	RI	4,974.1
DAIRYLAND INS CO	WI	1,282.3
FARM FAMILY CASUALTY INS CO	NY	1,160.0
FIRST COLONIAL INS CO	FL	370.3
GEICO GENERAL INS CO	MD	226.3
HOLYOKE MUTUAL INS CO IN SALEM	MA	217.0
INTERINS EXCHANGE	CA	9,074.7
MITSUI SUMITOMO INS CO OF AMER	NY	925.8
MOTORISTS MUTUAL INS CO	OH	1,375.1
NATIONAL CASUALTY CO	WI	402.1
NATIONWIDE MUTUAL FIRE INS CO	OH	6,045.9
SENTRY SELECT INS CO	WI	706.8
STATE FARM MUTUAL AUTOMOBILE INS CO	IL	143,802.0
TOA REINS CO OF AMERICA	DE	1,747.5
TRAVELERS INDEMNITY CO	CT	21,495.2
UNITED SERVICES AUTOMOBILE ASN	TX	32,870.8
USAA GENERAL INDEMNITY CO	TX	3,644.1

New Jersey

INSURANCE COMPANY NAME	DOM. STATE	TOTAL ASSETS ($MIL)
Rating: **A+**		
BERKSHIRE HATHAWAY ASR CORP	NY	2,220.4
MUNICIPAL ASR CORP	NY	1,125.1
Rating: **A**		
SENTRY INS A MUTUAL CO	WI	7,458.5
TOKIO MARINE AMERICA INS CO	NY	1,410.7
Rating: **A-**		
CINCINNATI INDEMNITY CO	OH	123.8
CINCINNATI INS CO	OH	11,749.4
COUNTRY MUTUAL INS CO	IL	4,421.1
ESSENT GUARANTY INC	PA	1,194.6
GEICO CHOICE INS CO	NE	647.0
GEICO SECURE INS CO	NE	436.8
NATIONAL MORTGAGE INS CORP	WI	530.6
TRAVELERS CASUALTY & SURETY CO	CT	16,398.0
USAA CASUALTY INS CO	TX	9,860.1
Rating: **B+**		
ALL AMERICA INS CO	OH	280.0
AMICA MUTUAL INS CO	RI	4,974.1
CENTURION CASUALTY CO	IA	157.1
FARM FAMILY CASUALTY INS CO	NY	1,160.0
FIRST COLONIAL INS CO	FL	370.3
GEICO GENERAL INS CO	MD	226.3
HOLYOKE MUTUAL INS CO IN SALEM	MA	217.0
MITSUI SUMITOMO INS CO OF AMER	NY	925.8
MOTORISTS MUTUAL INS CO	OH	1,375.1
NATIONAL CASUALTY CO	WI	402.1
NATIONWIDE MUTUAL FIRE INS CO	OH	6,045.9
SENTRY SELECT INS CO	WI	706.8
STATE FARM MUTUAL AUTOMOBILE INS CO	IL	143,802.0
TOA REINS CO OF AMERICA	DE	1,747.5
TRAVELERS INDEMNITY CO	CT	21,495.2
UNITED SERVICES AUTOMOBILE ASN	TX	32,870.8
USAA GENERAL INDEMNITY CO	TX	3,644.1

New Mexico

INSURANCE COMPANY NAME	DOM. STATE	TOTAL ASSETS ($MIL)
Rating: A+		
BERKSHIRE HATHAWAY ASR CORP	NY	2,220.4
MUNICIPAL ASR CORP	NY	1,125.1
Rating: A		
SENTRY INS A MUTUAL CO	WI	7,458.5
TOKIO MARINE AMERICA INS CO	NY	1,410.7
Rating: A-		
AUTO-OWNERS INS CO	MI	13,712.2
CINCINNATI INDEMNITY CO	OH	123.8
CINCINNATI INS CO	OH	11,749.4
COUNTRY MUTUAL INS CO	IL	4,421.1
ESSENT GUARANTY INC	PA	1,194.6
GEICO CHOICE INS CO	NE	647.0
GEICO SECURE INS CO	NE	436.8
NATIONAL MORTGAGE INS CORP	WI	530.6
OWNERS INS CO	OH	3,891.6
TRAVELERS CASUALTY & SURETY CO	CT	16,398.0
USAA CASUALTY INS CO	TX	9,860.1
Rating: B+		
ACUITY A MUTUAL INS CO	WI	3,483.6
AMERICAN FAMILY MUT INS CO	WI	16,216.1
AMERICAN STANDARD INS CO OF WI	WI	433.2
AMICA MUTUAL INS CO	RI	4,974.1
CENTURION CASUALTY CO	IA	157.1
COUNTRY CASUALTY INS CO	IL	83.4
DAIRYLAND INS CO	WI	1,282.3
FARM BUREAU P&C INS CO	IA	2,379.2
FIRST COLONIAL INS CO	FL	370.3
GEICO GENERAL INS CO	MD	226.3
HOLYOKE MUTUAL INS CO IN SALEM	MA	217.0
INTERINS EXCHANGE	CA	9,074.7
MITSUI SUMITOMO INS CO OF AMER	NY	925.8
NATIONAL CASUALTY CO	WI	402.1
NATIONWIDE MUTUAL FIRE INS CO	OH	6,045.9
SENTRY SELECT INS CO	WI	706.8
STATE FARM MUTUAL AUTOMOBILE INS CO	IL	143,802.0
TOA REINS CO OF AMERICA	DE	1,747.5
TRAVELERS INDEMNITY CO	CT	21,495.2
UNITED SERVICES AUTOMOBILE ASN	TX	32,870.8
USAA GENERAL INDEMNITY CO	TX	3,644.1
WESTERN AGRICULTURAL INS CO	IA	206.5

New York

INSURANCE COMPANY NAME	DOM. STATE	TOTAL ASSETS ($MIL)
Rating: A+		
BERKSHIRE HATHAWAY ASR CORP	NY	2,220.4
MUNICIPAL ASR CORP	NY	1,125.1
Rating: A		
SENTRY INS A MUTUAL CO	WI	7,458.5
TOKIO MARINE AMERICA INS CO	NY	1,410.7
Rating: A-		
CINCINNATI INDEMNITY CO	OH	123.8
CINCINNATI INS CO	OH	11,749.4
COUNTRY MUTUAL INS CO	IL	4,421.1
ESSENT GUARANTY INC	PA	1,194.6
NATIONAL MORTGAGE INS CORP	WI	530.6
TRAVELERS CASUALTY & SURETY CO	CT	16,398.0
USAA CASUALTY INS CO	TX	9,860.1
Rating: B+		
ALL AMERICA INS CO	OH	280.0
AMICA MUTUAL INS CO	RI	4,974.1
DAIRYLAND INS CO	WI	1,282.3
FARM FAMILY CASUALTY INS CO	NY	1,160.0
FIRST COLONIAL INS CO	FL	370.3
GEICO GENERAL INS CO	MD	226.3
HOLYOKE MUTUAL INS CO IN SALEM	MA	217.0
MITSUI SUMITOMO INS CO OF AMER	NY	925.8
MOTORISTS MUTUAL INS CO	OH	1,375.1
NATIONAL CASUALTY CO	WI	402.1
NATIONWIDE MUTUAL FIRE INS CO	OH	6,045.9
SENTRY SELECT INS CO	WI	706.8
STATE FARM MUTUAL AUTOMOBILE INS CO	IL	143,802.0
TOA REINS CO OF AMERICA	DE	1,747.5
TRAVELERS INDEMNITY CO	CT	21,495.2
UNITED SERVICES AUTOMOBILE ASN	TX	32,870.8
USAA GENERAL INDEMNITY CO	TX	3,644.1

North Carolina

INSURANCE COMPANY NAME	DOM. STATE	TOTAL ASSETS ($MIL)
Rating: A+		
BERKSHIRE HATHAWAY ASR CORP	NY	2,220.4
MUNICIPAL ASR CORP	NY	1,125.1
Rating: A		
SENTRY INS A MUTUAL CO	WI	7,458.5
TOKIO MARINE AMERICA INS CO	NY	1,410.7
Rating: A-		
AUTO-OWNERS INS CO	MI	13,712.2
CINCINNATI INDEMNITY CO	OH	123.8
CINCINNATI INS CO	OH	11,749.4
COUNTRY MUTUAL INS CO	IL	4,421.1
ESSENT GUARANTY INC	PA	1,194.6
GEICO CHOICE INS CO	NE	647.0
GEICO SECURE INS CO	NE	436.8
NATIONAL MORTGAGE INS CORP	WI	530.6
OWNERS INS CO	OH	3,891.6
TRAVELERS CASUALTY & SURETY CO	CT	16,398.0
USAA CASUALTY INS CO	TX	9,860.1
Rating: B+		
ALL AMERICA INS CO	OH	280.0
AMERICAN FAMILY MUT INS CO	WI	16,216.1
AMERICAN STANDARD INS CO OF WI	WI	433.2
AMICA MUTUAL INS CO	RI	4,974.1
BUILDERS MUTUAL INS CO	NC	736.0
CENTURION CASUALTY CO	IA	157.1
DAIRYLAND INS CO	WI	1,282.3
FIRST COLONIAL INS CO	FL	370.3
GEICO GENERAL INS CO	MD	226.3
HOLYOKE MUTUAL INS CO IN SALEM	MA	217.0
MITSUI SUMITOMO INS CO OF AMER	NY	925.8
MOTORISTS MUTUAL INS CO	OH	1,375.1
NATIONAL CASUALTY CO	WI	402.1
NATIONWIDE MUTUAL FIRE INS CO	OH	6,045.9
SENTRY SELECT INS CO	WI	706.8
STATE FARM MUTUAL AUTOMOBILE INS CO	IL	143,802.0
TOA REINS CO OF AMERICA	DE	1,747.5
TRAVELERS INDEMNITY CO	CT	21,495.2
UNITED SERVICES AUTOMOBILE ASN	TX	32,870.8
USAA GENERAL INDEMNITY CO	TX	3,644.1

North Dakota

INSURANCE COMPANY NAME	DOM. STATE	TOTAL ASSETS ($MIL)
Rating: A+		
BERKSHIRE HATHAWAY ASR CORP	NY	2,220.4
MUNICIPAL ASR CORP	NY	1,125.1
Rating: A		
SENTRY INS A MUTUAL CO	WI	7,458.5
TOKIO MARINE AMERICA INS CO	NY	1,410.7
Rating: A-		
AUTO-OWNERS INS CO	MI	13,712.2
CINCINNATI INDEMNITY CO	OH	123.8
CINCINNATI INS CO	OH	11,749.4
COUNTRY MUTUAL INS CO	IL	4,421.1
ESSENT GUARANTY INC	PA	1,194.6
HOME-OWNERS INS CO	MI	2,106.0
NATIONAL MORTGAGE INS CORP	WI	530.6
OWNERS INS CO	OH	3,891.6
TRAVELERS CASUALTY & SURETY CO	CT	16,398.0
USAA CASUALTY INS CO	TX	9,860.1
Rating: B+		
ACUITY A MUTUAL INS CO	WI	3,483.6
AMERICAN FAMILY MUT INS CO	WI	16,216.1
AMERICAN STANDARD INS CO OF WI	WI	433.2
AMICA MUTUAL INS CO	RI	4,974.1
CENTURION CASUALTY CO	IA	157.1
COUNTRY CASUALTY INS CO	IL	83.4
DAIRYLAND INS CO	WI	1,282.3
FIRST COLONIAL INS CO	FL	370.3
GEICO GENERAL INS CO	MD	226.3
HOLYOKE MUTUAL INS CO IN SALEM	MA	217.0
MITSUI SUMITOMO INS CO OF AMER	NY	925.8
NATIONAL CASUALTY CO	WI	402.1
NATIONWIDE MUTUAL FIRE INS CO	OH	6,045.9
PROPERTY-OWNERS INS CO	IN	257.1
SENTRY SELECT INS CO	WI	706.8
STATE FARM MUTUAL AUTOMOBILE INS CO	IL	143,802.0
TOA REINS CO OF AMERICA	DE	1,747.5
TRAVELERS INDEMNITY CO	CT	21,495.2
UNITED SERVICES AUTOMOBILE ASN	TX	32,870.8
USAA GENERAL INDEMNITY CO	TX	3,644.1
WESTERN AGRICULTURAL INS CO	IA	206.5

Ohio

INSURANCE COMPANY NAME	DOM. STATE	TOTAL ASSETS ($MIL)	INSURANCE COMPANY NAME	DOM. STATE	TOTAL ASSETS ($MIL)
Rating: A+					
BERKSHIRE HATHAWAY ASR CORP	NY	2,220.4			
MUNICIPAL ASR CORP	NY	1,125.1			
Rating: A					
SENTRY INS A MUTUAL CO	WI	7,458.5			
TOKIO MARINE AMERICA INS CO	NY	1,410.7			
Rating: A-					
AUTO-OWNERS INS CO	MI	13,712.2			
CINCINNATI INDEMNITY CO	OH	123.8			
CINCINNATI INS CO	OH	11,749.4			
COUNTRY MUTUAL INS CO	IL	4,421.1			
ESSENT GUARANTY INC	PA	1,194.6			
GEICO CHOICE INS CO	NE	647.0			
GEICO SECURE INS CO	NE	436.8			
HOME-OWNERS INS CO	MI	2,106.0			
NATIONAL MORTGAGE INS CORP	WI	530.6			
OWNERS INS CO	OH	3,891.6			
TRAVELERS CASUALTY & SURETY CO	CT	16,398.0			
USAA CASUALTY INS CO	TX	9,860.1			
Rating: B+					
ACUITY A MUTUAL INS CO	WI	3,483.6			
ALL AMERICA INS CO	OH	280.0			
AMERICAN FAMILY MUT INS CO	WI	16,216.1			
AMERICAN STANDARD INS CO OF WI	WI	433.2			
AMICA MUTUAL INS CO	RI	4,974.1			
CENTURION CASUALTY CO	IA	157.1			
COUNTRY CASUALTY INS CO	IL	83.4			
DAIRYLAND INS CO	WI	1,282.3			
FARMERS AUTOMOBILE INS ASN	IL	1,283.7			
FIRST COLONIAL INS CO	FL	370.3			
GEICO GENERAL INS CO	MD	226.3			
INTERINS EXCHANGE	CA	9,074.7			
MITSUI SUMITOMO INS CO OF AMER	NY	925.8			
MOTORISTS MUTUAL INS CO	OH	1,375.1			
NATIONAL CASUALTY CO	WI	402.1			
NATIONWIDE MUTUAL FIRE INS CO	OH	6,045.9			
PEKIN INS CO	IL	312.8			
SENTRY SELECT INS CO	WI	706.8			
STATE FARM MUTUAL AUTOMOBILE INS CO	IL	143,802.0			
TOA REINS CO OF AMERICA	DE	1,747.5			
TRAVELERS INDEMNITY CO	CT	21,495.2			
UNITED SERVICES AUTOMOBILE ASN	TX	32,870.8			
USAA GENERAL INDEMNITY CO	TX	3,644.1			
WEST BEND MUTUAL INS CO	WI	2,456.0			
WESTERN AGRICULTURAL INS CO	IA	206.5			

Oklahoma

INSURANCE COMPANY NAME	DOM. STATE	TOTAL ASSETS ($MIL)
Rating: A+		
BERKSHIRE HATHAWAY ASR CORP	NY	2,220.4
MUNICIPAL ASR CORP	NY	1,125.1
Rating: A		
SENTRY INS A MUTUAL CO	WI	7,458.5
TOKIO MARINE AMERICA INS CO	NY	1,410.7
Rating: A-		
CINCINNATI INDEMNITY CO	OH	123.8
CINCINNATI INS CO	OH	11,749.4
COUNTRY MUTUAL INS CO	IL	4,421.1
ESSENT GUARANTY INC	PA	1,194.6
GEICO CHOICE INS CO	NE	647.0
GEICO SECURE INS CO	NE	436.8
NATIONAL MORTGAGE INS CORP	WI	530.6
TRAVELERS CASUALTY & SURETY CO	CT	16,398.0
USAA CASUALTY INS CO	TX	9,860.1
Rating: B+		
ACUITY A MUTUAL INS CO	WI	3,483.6
ALL AMERICA INS CO	OH	280.0
AMICA MUTUAL INS CO	RI	4,974.1
CENTURION CASUALTY CO	IA	157.1
COUNTRY CASUALTY INS CO	IL	83.4
FIRST COLONIAL INS CO	FL	370.3
GEICO GENERAL INS CO	MD	226.3
MITSUI SUMITOMO INS CO OF AMER	NY	925.8
MOTORISTS MUTUAL INS CO	OH	1,375.1
NATIONAL CASUALTY CO	WI	402.1
NATIONWIDE MUTUAL FIRE INS CO	OH	6,045.9
SENTRY SELECT INS CO	WI	706.8
STATE FARM MUTUAL AUTOMOBILE INS CO	IL	143,802.0
TOA REINS CO OF AMERICA	DE	1,747.5
TRAVELERS INDEMNITY CO	CT	21,495.2
UNITED SERVICES AUTOMOBILE ASN	TX	32,870.8
USAA GENERAL INDEMNITY CO	TX	3,644.1
WESTERN AGRICULTURAL INS CO	IA	206.5

Oregon

INSURANCE COMPANY NAME	DOM. STATE	TOTAL ASSETS ($MIL)
Rating:	**A+**	
BERKSHIRE HATHAWAY ASR CORP	NY	2,220.4
MUNICIPAL ASR CORP	NY	1,125.1
Rating:	**A**	
SENTRY INS A MUTUAL CO	WI	7,458.5
TOKIO MARINE AMERICA INS CO	NY	1,410.7
Rating:	**A-**	
AUTO-OWNERS INS CO	MI	13,712.2
CINCINNATI INDEMNITY CO	OH	123.8
CINCINNATI INS CO	OH	11,749.4
COUNTRY MUTUAL INS CO	IL	4,421.1
ESSENT GUARANTY INC	PA	1,194.6
GEICO CHOICE INS CO	NE	647.0
GEICO SECURE INS CO	NE	436.8
NATIONAL MORTGAGE INS CORP	WI	530.6
OWNERS INS CO	OH	3,891.6
TRAVELERS CASUALTY & SURETY CO	CT	16,398.0
USAA CASUALTY INS CO	TX	9,860.1
Rating:	**B+**	
ACUITY A MUTUAL INS CO	WI	3,483.6
AMERICAN FAMILY MUT INS CO	WI	16,216.1
AMERICAN STANDARD INS CO OF WI	WI	433.2
AMICA MUTUAL INS CO	RI	4,974.1
CENTURION CASUALTY CO	IA	157.1
COUNTRY CASUALTY INS CO	IL	83.4
DAIRYLAND INS CO	WI	1,282.3
FIRST COLONIAL INS CO	FL	370.3
GEICO GENERAL INS CO	MD	226.3
HOLYOKE MUTUAL INS CO IN SALEM	MA	217.0
MITSUI SUMITOMO INS CO OF AMER	NY	925.8
MOTORISTS MUTUAL INS CO	OH	1,375.1
NATIONAL CASUALTY CO	WI	402.1
NATIONWIDE MUTUAL FIRE INS CO	OH	6,045.9
SENTRY SELECT INS CO	WI	706.8
STATE FARM MUTUAL AUTOMOBILE INS CO	IL	143,802.0
TOA REINS CO OF AMERICA	DE	1,747.5
TRAVELERS INDEMNITY CO	CT	21,495.2
UNITED SERVICES AUTOMOBILE ASN	TX	32,870.8
USAA GENERAL INDEMNITY CO	TX	3,644.1

Pennsylvania

INSURANCE COMPANY NAME	DOM. STATE	TOTAL ASSETS ($MIL)
Rating: **A+**		
BERKSHIRE HATHAWAY ASR CORP	NY	2,220.4
MUNICIPAL ASR CORP	NY	1,125.1
Rating: **A**		
SENTRY INS A MUTUAL CO	WI	7,458.5
TOKIO MARINE AMERICA INS CO	NY	1,410.7
Rating: **A-**		
AUTO-OWNERS INS CO	MI	13,712.2
CINCINNATI INDEMNITY CO	OH	123.8
CINCINNATI INS CO	OH	11,749.4
COUNTRY MUTUAL INS CO	IL	4,421.1
ESSENT GUARANTY INC	PA	1,194.6
GEICO CHOICE INS CO	NE	647.0
GEICO SECURE INS CO	NE	436.8
HOME-OWNERS INS CO	MI	2,106.0
NATIONAL MORTGAGE INS CORP	WI	530.6
OWNERS INS CO	OH	3,891.6
TRAVELERS CASUALTY & SURETY CO	CT	16,398.0
USAA CASUALTY INS CO	TX	9,860.1
Rating: **B+**		
ACUITY A MUTUAL INS CO	WI	3,483.6
AMICA MUTUAL INS CO	RI	4,974.1
COUNTRY CASUALTY INS CO	IL	83.4
DAIRYLAND INS CO	WI	1,282.3
FARM FAMILY CASUALTY INS CO	NY	1,160.0
FIRST COLONIAL INS CO	FL	370.3
GEICO GENERAL INS CO	MD	226.3
INTERINS EXCHANGE	CA	9,074.7
MITSUI SUMITOMO INS CO OF AMER	NY	925.8
MOTORISTS MUTUAL INS CO	OH	1,375.1
NATIONAL CASUALTY CO	WI	402.1
NATIONWIDE MUTUAL FIRE INS CO	OH	6,045.9
SENTRY SELECT INS CO	WI	706.8
STATE FARM MUTUAL AUTOMOBILE INS CO	IL	143,802.0
TOA REINS CO OF AMERICA	DE	1,747.5
TRAVELERS INDEMNITY CO	CT	21,495.2
UNITED SERVICES AUTOMOBILE ASN	TX	32,870.8
USAA GENERAL INDEMNITY CO	TX	3,644.1

Rhode Island

INSURANCE COMPANY NAME	DOM. STATE	TOTAL ASSETS ($MIL)
Rating: A+		
BERKSHIRE HATHAWAY ASR CORP	NY	2,220.4
MUNICIPAL ASR CORP	NY	1,125.1
Rating: A		
SENTRY INS A MUTUAL CO	WI	7,458.5
TOKIO MARINE AMERICA INS CO	NY	1,410.7
Rating: A-		
CINCINNATI INDEMNITY CO	OH	123.8
CINCINNATI INS CO	OH	11,749.4
COUNTRY MUTUAL INS CO	IL	4,421.1
ESSENT GUARANTY INC	PA	1,194.6
GEICO CHOICE INS CO	NE	647.0
GEICO SECURE INS CO	NE	436.8
NATIONAL MORTGAGE INS CORP	WI	530.6
TRAVELERS CASUALTY & SURETY CO	CT	16,398.0
USAA CASUALTY INS CO	TX	9,860.1
Rating: B+		
AMICA MUTUAL INS CO	RI	4,974.1
CENTURION CASUALTY CO	IA	157.1
COUNTRY CASUALTY INS CO	IL	83.4
DAIRYLAND INS CO	WI	1,282.3
FARM FAMILY CASUALTY INS CO	NY	1,160.0
FIRST COLONIAL INS CO	FL	370.3
GEICO GENERAL INS CO	MD	226.3
HOLYOKE MUTUAL INS CO IN SALEM	MA	217.0
MITSUI SUMITOMO INS CO OF AMER	NY	925.8
MOTORISTS MUTUAL INS CO	OH	1,375.1
NATIONAL CASUALTY CO	WI	402.1
NATIONWIDE MUTUAL FIRE INS CO	OH	6,045.9
SENTRY SELECT INS CO	WI	706.8
STATE FARM MUTUAL AUTOMOBILE INS CO	IL	143,802.0
TOA REINS CO OF AMERICA	DE	1,747.5
TRAVELERS INDEMNITY CO	CT	21,495.2
UNITED SERVICES AUTOMOBILE ASN	TX	32,870.8
USAA GENERAL INDEMNITY CO	TX	3,644.1

South Carolina

INSURANCE COMPANY NAME	DOM. STATE	TOTAL ASSETS ($MIL)	INSURANCE COMPANY NAME	DOM. STATE	TOTAL ASSETS ($MIL)
Rating: A+					
BERKSHIRE HATHAWAY ASR CORP	NY	2,220.4			
MUNICIPAL ASR CORP	NY	1,125.1			
Rating: A					
SENTRY INS A MUTUAL CO	WI	7,458.5			
TOKIO MARINE AMERICA INS CO	NY	1,410.7			
Rating: A-					
AUTO-OWNERS INS CO	MI	13,712.2			
CINCINNATI INDEMNITY CO	OH	123.8			
CINCINNATI INS CO	OH	11,749.4			
COUNTRY MUTUAL INS CO	IL	4,421.1			
ESSENT GUARANTY INC	PA	1,194.6			
GEICO CHOICE INS CO	NE	647.0			
GEICO SECURE INS CO	NE	436.8			
HOME-OWNERS INS CO	MI	2,106.0			
NATIONAL MORTGAGE INS CORP	WI	530.6			
OWNERS INS CO	OH	3,891.6			
TRAVELERS CASUALTY & SURETY CO	CT	16,398.0			
USAA CASUALTY INS CO	TX	9,860.1			
Rating: B+					
ALL AMERICA INS CO	OH	280.0			
AMERICAN FAMILY MUT INS CO	WI	16,216.1			
AMERICAN STANDARD INS CO OF WI	WI	433.2			
AMICA MUTUAL INS CO	RI	4,974.1			
BUILDERS MUTUAL INS CO	NC	736.0			
CENTURION CASUALTY CO	IA	157.1			
DAIRYLAND INS CO	WI	1,282.3			
FIRST COLONIAL INS CO	FL	370.3			
GEICO GENERAL INS CO	MD	226.3			
HOLYOKE MUTUAL INS CO IN SALEM	MA	217.0			
MITSUI SUMITOMO INS CO OF AMER	NY	925.8			
MOTORISTS MUTUAL INS CO	OH	1,375.1			
NATIONAL CASUALTY CO	WI	402.1			
NATIONWIDE MUTUAL FIRE INS CO	OH	6,045.9			
PROPERTY-OWNERS INS CO	IN	257.1			
SENTRY SELECT INS CO	WI	706.8			
STATE FARM MUTUAL AUTOMOBILE INS CO	IL	143,802.0			
TOA REINS CO OF AMERICA	DE	1,747.5			
TRAVELERS INDEMNITY CO	CT	21,495.2			
UNITED SERVICES AUTOMOBILE ASN	TX	32,870.8			
USAA GENERAL INDEMNITY CO	TX	3,644.1			
WESTERN AGRICULTURAL INS CO	IA	206.5			

South Dakota

INSURANCE COMPANY NAME	DOM. STATE	TOTAL ASSETS ($MIL)	INSURANCE COMPANY NAME	DOM. STATE	TOTAL ASSETS ($MIL)
Rating: A+					
BERKSHIRE HATHAWAY ASR CORP	NY	2,220.4			
MUNICIPAL ASR CORP	NY	1,125.1			
Rating: A					
SENTRY INS A MUTUAL CO	WI	7,458.5			
TOKIO MARINE AMERICA INS CO	NY	1,410.7			
Rating: A-					
AUTO-OWNERS INS CO	MI	13,712.2			
CINCINNATI INDEMNITY CO	OH	123.8			
CINCINNATI INS CO	OH	11,749.4			
COUNTRY MUTUAL INS CO	IL	4,421.1			
ESSENT GUARANTY INC	PA	1,194.6			
HOME-OWNERS INS CO	MI	2,106.0			
NATIONAL MORTGAGE INS CORP	WI	530.6			
OWNERS INS CO	OH	3,891.6			
TRAVELERS CASUALTY & SURETY CO	CT	16,398.0			
USAA CASUALTY INS CO	TX	9,860.1			
Rating: B+					
ACUITY A MUTUAL INS CO	WI	3,483.6			
AMERICAN FAMILY MUT INS CO	WI	16,216.1			
AMERICAN STANDARD INS CO OF WI	WI	433.2			
AMICA MUTUAL INS CO	RI	4,974.1			
CENTURION CASUALTY CO	IA	157.1			
COUNTRY CASUALTY INS CO	IL	83.4			
DAIRYLAND INS CO	WI	1,282.3			
FARM BUREAU P&C INS CO	IA	2,379.2			
FIRST COLONIAL INS CO	FL	370.3			
GEICO GENERAL INS CO	MD	226.3			
HOLYOKE MUTUAL INS CO IN SALEM	MA	217.0			
MITSUI SUMITOMO INS CO OF AMER	NY	925.8			
MOTORISTS MUTUAL INS CO	OH	1,375.1			
NATIONAL CASUALTY CO	WI	402.1			
NATIONWIDE MUTUAL FIRE INS CO	OH	6,045.9			
PROPERTY-OWNERS INS CO	IN	257.1			
SENTRY SELECT INS CO	WI	706.8			
STATE FARM MUTUAL AUTOMOBILE INS CO	IL	143,802.0			
TOA REINS CO OF AMERICA	DE	1,747.5			
TRAVELERS INDEMNITY CO	CT	21,495.2			
UNITED SERVICES AUTOMOBILE ASN	TX	32,870.8			
USAA GENERAL INDEMNITY CO	TX	3,644.1			
WESTERN AGRICULTURAL INS CO	IA	206.5			

Tennessee

INSURANCE COMPANY NAME	DOM. STATE	TOTAL ASSETS ($MIL)
Rating: **A+**		
BERKSHIRE HATHAWAY ASR CORP	NY	2,220.4
MUNICIPAL ASR CORP	NY	1,125.1
Rating: **A**		
SENTRY INS A MUTUAL CO	WI	7,458.5
TOKIO MARINE AMERICA INS CO	NY	1,410.7
Rating: **A-**		
AUTO-OWNERS INS CO	MI	13,712.2
CINCINNATI INDEMNITY CO	OH	123.8
CINCINNATI INS CO	OH	11,749.4
COUNTRY MUTUAL INS CO	IL	4,421.1
ESSENT GUARANTY INC	PA	1,194.6
GEICO CHOICE INS CO	NE	647.0
GEICO SECURE INS CO	NE	436.8
NATIONAL MORTGAGE INS CORP	WI	530.6
OWNERS INS CO	OH	3,891.6
TRAVELERS CASUALTY & SURETY CO	CT	16,398.0
USAA CASUALTY INS CO	TX	9,860.1
Rating: **B+**		
ACUITY A MUTUAL INS CO	WI	3,483.6
ALL AMERICA INS CO	OH	280.0
AMERICAN FAMILY MUT INS CO	WI	16,216.1
AMICA MUTUAL INS CO	RI	4,974.1
BUILDERS MUTUAL INS CO	NC	736.0
CENTURION CASUALTY CO	IA	157.1
COUNTRY CASUALTY INS CO	IL	83.4
DAIRYLAND INS CO	WI	1,282.3
FIRST COLONIAL INS CO	FL	370.3
GEICO GENERAL INS CO	MD	226.3
MITSUI SUMITOMO INS CO OF AMER	NY	925.8
MOTORISTS MUTUAL INS CO	OH	1,375.1
NATIONAL CASUALTY CO	WI	402.1
NATIONWIDE MUTUAL FIRE INS CO	OH	6,045.9
SENTRY SELECT INS CO	WI	706.8
STATE FARM MUTUAL AUTOMOBILE INS CO	IL	143,802.0
TENNESSEE FARMERS ASR CO	TN	1,408.6
TENNESSEE FARMERS MUTUAL INS CO	TN	2,804.7
TOA REINS CO OF AMERICA	DE	1,747.5
TRAVELERS INDEMNITY CO	CT	21,495.2
UNITED SERVICES AUTOMOBILE ASN	TX	32,870.8
USAA GENERAL INDEMNITY CO	TX	3,644.1
WESTERN AGRICULTURAL INS CO	IA	206.5

Texas

INSURANCE COMPANY NAME	DOM. STATE	TOTAL ASSETS ($MIL)
Rating:	**A+**	
BERKSHIRE HATHAWAY ASR CORP	NY	2,220.4
MUNICIPAL ASR CORP	NY	1,125.1
OGLESBY REINS CO	IL	4,277.3
Rating:	**A**	
SENTRY INS A MUTUAL CO	WI	7,458.5
TOKIO MARINE AMERICA INS CO	NY	1,410.7
Rating:	**A-**	
CINCINNATI INDEMNITY CO	OH	123.8
CINCINNATI INS CO	OH	11,749.4
COUNTRY MUTUAL INS CO	IL	4,421.1
ESSENT GUARANTY INC	PA	1,194.6
GEICO CHOICE INS CO	NE	647.0
GEICO SECURE INS CO	NE	436.8
NATIONAL MORTGAGE INS CORP	WI	530.6
TRAVELERS CASUALTY & SURETY CO	CT	16,398.0
USAA CASUALTY INS CO	TX	9,860.1
Rating:	**B+**	
ACUITY A MUTUAL INS CO	WI	3,483.6
ALL AMERICA INS CO	OH	280.0
AMERICAN FAMILY MUT INS CO	WI	16,216.1
AMICA MUTUAL INS CO	RI	4,974.1
AUTO CLUB INDEMNITY CO	TX	27.2
CENTURION CASUALTY CO	IA	157.1
COUNTRY CASUALTY INS CO	IL	83.4
DAIRYLAND INS CO	WI	1,282.3
FIRST COLONIAL INS CO	FL	370.3
GEICO GENERAL INS CO	MD	226.3
HOLYOKE MUTUAL INS CO IN SALEM	MA	217.0
INTERINS EXCHANGE	CA	9,074.7
MITSUI SUMITOMO INS CO OF AMER	NY	925.8
MOTORISTS MUTUAL INS CO	OH	1,375.1
NATIONAL CASUALTY CO	WI	402.1
NATIONWIDE MUTUAL FIRE INS CO	OH	6,045.9
SENTRY SELECT INS CO	WI	706.8
STATE FARM MUTUAL AUTOMOBILE INS CO	IL	143,802.0
TEXAS FARM BUREAU CASUALTY INS CO	TX	1,179.5
TOA REINS CO OF AMERICA	DE	1,747.5
TRAVELERS INDEMNITY CO	CT	21,495.2
UNITED SERVICES AUTOMOBILE ASN	TX	32,870.8
USAA GENERAL INDEMNITY CO	TX	3,644.1
WESTERN AGRICULTURAL INS CO	IA	206.5

Utah

INSURANCE COMPANY NAME	DOM. STATE	TOTAL ASSETS ($MIL)	INSURANCE COMPANY NAME	DOM. STATE	TOTAL ASSETS ($MIL)
Rating: A+					
BERKSHIRE HATHAWAY ASR CORP	NY	2,220.4			
MUNICIPAL ASR CORP	NY	1,125.1			
Rating: A					
SENTRY INS A MUTUAL CO	WI	7,458.5			
TOKIO MARINE AMERICA INS CO	NY	1,410.7			
Rating: A-					
AUTO-OWNERS INS CO	MI	13,712.2			
CINCINNATI INDEMNITY CO	OH	123.8			
CINCINNATI INS CO	OH	11,749.4			
COUNTRY MUTUAL INS CO	IL	4,421.1			
ESSENT GUARANTY INC	PA	1,194.6			
GEICO CHOICE INS CO	NE	647.0			
GEICO SECURE INS CO	NE	436.8			
HOME-OWNERS INS CO	MI	2,106.0			
NATIONAL MORTGAGE INS CORP	WI	530.6			
OWNERS INS CO	OH	3,891.6			
TRAVELERS CASUALTY & SURETY CO	CT	16,398.0			
USAA CASUALTY INS CO	TX	9,860.1			
Rating: B+					
ACUITY A MUTUAL INS CO	WI	3,483.6			
AMERICAN FAMILY MUT INS CO	WI	16,216.1			
AMERICAN STANDARD INS CO OF WI	WI	433.2			
AMICA MUTUAL INS CO	RI	4,974.1			
CENTURION CASUALTY CO	IA	157.1			
DAIRYLAND INS CO	WI	1,282.3			
FARM BUREAU P&C INS CO	IA	2,379.2			
FIRST COLONIAL INS CO	FL	370.3			
GEICO GENERAL INS CO	MD	226.3			
HOLYOKE MUTUAL INS CO IN SALEM	MA	217.0			
MITSUI SUMITOMO INS CO OF AMER	NY	925.8			
MOTORISTS MUTUAL INS CO	OH	1,375.1			
NATIONAL CASUALTY CO	WI	402.1			
NATIONWIDE MUTUAL FIRE INS CO	OH	6,045.9			
PROPERTY-OWNERS INS CO	IN	257.1			
SENTRY SELECT INS CO	WI	706.8			
STATE FARM MUTUAL AUTOMOBILE INS CO	IL	143,802.0			
TOA REINS CO OF AMERICA	DE	1,747.5			
TRAVELERS INDEMNITY CO	CT	21,495.2			
UNITED SERVICES AUTOMOBILE ASN	TX	32,870.8			
USAA GENERAL INDEMNITY CO	TX	3,644.1			
WESTERN AGRICULTURAL INS CO	IA	206.5			

Vermont

INSURANCE COMPANY NAME	DOM. STATE	TOTAL ASSETS ($MIL)
Rating: A+		
BERKSHIRE HATHAWAY ASR CORP	NY	2,220.4
MUNICIPAL ASR CORP	NY	1,125.1
Rating: A		
SENTRY INS A MUTUAL CO	WI	7,458.5
TOKIO MARINE AMERICA INS CO	NY	1,410.7
Rating: A-		
CINCINNATI INDEMNITY CO	OH	123.8
CINCINNATI INS CO	OH	11,749.4
COUNTRY MUTUAL INS CO	IL	4,421.1
ESSENT GUARANTY INC	PA	1,194.6
NATIONAL MORTGAGE INS CORP	WI	530.6
TRAVELERS CASUALTY & SURETY CO	CT	16,398.0
USAA CASUALTY INS CO	TX	9,860.1
Rating: B+		
ACUITY A MUTUAL INS CO	WI	3,483.6
ALL AMERICA INS CO	OH	280.0
AMICA MUTUAL INS CO	RI	4,974.1
DAIRYLAND INS CO	WI	1,282.3
FARM FAMILY CASUALTY INS CO	NY	1,160.0
FIRST COLONIAL INS CO	FL	370.3
GEICO GENERAL INS CO	MD	226.3
HOLYOKE MUTUAL INS CO IN SALEM	MA	217.0
INTERINS EXCHANGE	CA	9,074.7
MITSUI SUMITOMO INS CO OF AMER	NY	925.8
MOTORISTS MUTUAL INS CO	OH	1,375.1
NATIONAL CASUALTY CO	WI	402.1
NATIONWIDE MUTUAL FIRE INS CO	OH	6,045.9
SENTRY SELECT INS CO	WI	706.8
STATE FARM MUTUAL AUTOMOBILE INS CO	IL	143,802.0
TOA REINS CO OF AMERICA	DE	1,747.5
TRAVELERS INDEMNITY CO	CT	21,495.2
UNITED SERVICES AUTOMOBILE ASN	TX	32,870.8
USAA GENERAL INDEMNITY CO	TX	3,644.1

Virginia

INSURANCE COMPANY NAME	DOM. STATE	TOTAL ASSETS ($MIL)
Rating: A+		
BERKSHIRE HATHAWAY ASR CORP	NY	2,220.4
MUNICIPAL ASR CORP	NY	1,125.1
Rating: A		
SENTRY INS A MUTUAL CO	WI	7,458.5
TOKIO MARINE AMERICA INS CO	NY	1,410.7
Rating: A-		
AUTO-OWNERS INS CO	MI	13,712.2
CINCINNATI INDEMNITY CO	OH	123.8
CINCINNATI INS CO	OH	11,749.4
COUNTRY MUTUAL INS CO	IL	4,421.1
ESSENT GUARANTY INC	PA	1,194.6
GEICO CHOICE INS CO	NE	647.0
GEICO SECURE INS CO	NE	436.8
HOME-OWNERS INS CO	MI	2,106.0
NATIONAL MORTGAGE INS CORP	WI	530.6
OWNERS INS CO	OH	3,891.6
TRAVELERS CASUALTY & SURETY CO	CT	16,398.0
USAA CASUALTY INS CO	TX	9,860.1
Rating: B+		
ACUITY A MUTUAL INS CO	WI	3,483.6
ALL AMERICA INS CO	OH	280.0
AMERICAN FAMILY MUT INS CO	WI	16,216.1
AMICA MUTUAL INS CO	RI	4,974.1
BUILDERS MUTUAL INS CO	NC	736.0
CENTURION CASUALTY CO	IA	157.1
DAIRYLAND INS CO	WI	1,282.3
FARM FAMILY CASUALTY INS CO	NY	1,160.0
FIRST COLONIAL INS CO	FL	370.3
GEICO GENERAL INS CO	MD	226.3
INTERINS EXCHANGE	CA	9,074.7
MITSUI SUMITOMO INS CO OF AMER	NY	925.8
MOTORISTS MUTUAL INS CO	OH	1,375.1
NATIONAL CASUALTY CO	WI	402.1
NATIONWIDE MUTUAL FIRE INS CO	OH	6,045.9
PROPERTY-OWNERS INS CO	IN	257.1
SENTRY SELECT INS CO	WI	706.8
STATE FARM MUTUAL AUTOMOBILE INS CO	IL	143,802.0
TOA REINS CO OF AMERICA	DE	1,747.5
TRAVELERS INDEMNITY CO	CT	21,495.2
UNITED SERVICES AUTOMOBILE ASN	TX	32,870.8
USAA GENERAL INDEMNITY CO	TX	3,644.1
WESTERN AGRICULTURAL INS CO	IA	206.5

Washington

INSURANCE COMPANY NAME	DOM. STATE	TOTAL ASSETS ($MIL)	INSURANCE COMPANY NAME	DOM. STATE	TOTAL ASSETS ($MIL)
Rating: A+					
BERKSHIRE HATHAWAY ASR CORP	NY	2,220.4			
MUNICIPAL ASR CORP	NY	1,125.1			
Rating: A					
SENTRY INS A MUTUAL CO	WI	7,458.5			
TOKIO MARINE AMERICA INS CO	NY	1,410.7			
Rating: A-					
AUTO-OWNERS INS CO	MI	13,712.2			
CINCINNATI INDEMNITY CO	OH	123.8			
CINCINNATI INS CO	OH	11,749.4			
COUNTRY MUTUAL INS CO	IL	4,421.1			
ESSENT GUARANTY INC	PA	1,194.6			
GEICO CHOICE INS CO	NE	647.0			
GEICO SECURE INS CO	NE	436.8			
NATIONAL MORTGAGE INS CORP	WI	530.6			
OWNERS INS CO	OH	3,891.6			
TRAVELERS CASUALTY & SURETY CO	CT	16,398.0			
USAA CASUALTY INS CO	TX	9,860.1			
Rating: B+					
ACUITY A MUTUAL INS CO	WI	3,483.6			
AMERICAN FAMILY MUT INS CO	WI	16,216.1			
AMERICAN STANDARD INS CO OF WI	WI	433.2			
AMICA MUTUAL INS CO	RI	4,974.1			
CENTURION CASUALTY CO	IA	157.1			
COUNTRY CASUALTY INS CO	IL	83.4			
DAIRYLAND INS CO	WI	1,282.3			
FIRST COLONIAL INS CO	FL	370.3			
GEICO GENERAL INS CO	MD	226.3			
HOLYOKE MUTUAL INS CO IN SALEM	MA	217.0			
MITSUI SUMITOMO INS CO OF AMER	NY	925.8			
NATIONAL CASUALTY CO	WI	402.1			
NATIONWIDE MUTUAL FIRE INS CO	OH	6,045.9			
SENTRY SELECT INS CO	WI	706.8			
STATE FARM MUTUAL AUTOMOBILE INS CO	IL	143,802.0			
TOA REINS CO OF AMERICA	DE	1,747.5			
TRAVELERS INDEMNITY CO	CT	21,495.2			
UNITED SERVICES AUTOMOBILE ASN	TX	32,870.8			
USAA GENERAL INDEMNITY CO	TX	3,644.1			

West Virginia

INSURANCE COMPANY NAME	DOM. STATE	TOTAL ASSETS ($MIL)	INSURANCE COMPANY NAME	DOM. STATE	TOTAL ASSETS ($MIL)
Rating: A+					
BERKSHIRE HATHAWAY ASR CORP	NY	2,220.4			
MUNICIPAL ASR CORP	NY	1,125.1			
Rating: A					
SENTRY INS A MUTUAL CO	WI	7,458.5			
TOKIO MARINE AMERICA INS CO	NY	1,410.7			
Rating: A-					
CINCINNATI INDEMNITY CO	OH	123.8			
CINCINNATI INS CO	OH	11,749.4			
COUNTRY MUTUAL INS CO	IL	4,421.1			
ESSENT GUARANTY INC	PA	1,194.6			
GEICO CHOICE INS CO	NE	647.0			
GEICO SECURE INS CO	NE	436.8			
NATIONAL MORTGAGE INS CORP	WI	530.6			
TRAVELERS CASUALTY & SURETY CO	CT	16,398.0			
USAA CASUALTY INS CO	TX	9,860.1			
Rating: B+					
ACUITY A MUTUAL INS CO	WI	3,483.6			
AMICA MUTUAL INS CO	RI	4,974.1			
CENTURION CASUALTY CO	IA	157.1			
DAIRYLAND INS CO	WI	1,282.3			
FARM FAMILY CASUALTY INS CO	NY	1,160.0			
FIRST COLONIAL INS CO	FL	370.3			
GEICO GENERAL INS CO	MD	226.3			
MITSUI SUMITOMO INS CO OF AMER	NY	925.8			
MOTORISTS MUTUAL INS CO	OH	1,375.1			
NATIONAL CASUALTY CO	WI	402.1			
NATIONWIDE MUTUAL FIRE INS CO	OH	6,045.9			
SENTRY SELECT INS CO	WI	706.8			
STATE FARM MUTUAL AUTOMOBILE INS CO	IL	143,802.0			
TOA REINS CO OF AMERICA	DE	1,747.5			
TRAVELERS INDEMNITY CO	CT	21,495.2			
UNITED SERVICES AUTOMOBILE ASN	TX	32,870.8			
USAA GENERAL INDEMNITY CO	TX	3,644.1			

Wisconsin

INSURANCE COMPANY NAME	DOM. STATE	TOTAL ASSETS ($MIL)
Rating: A+		
BERKSHIRE HATHAWAY ASR CORP	NY	2,220.4
MUNICIPAL ASR CORP	NY	1,125.1
Rating: A		
SENTRY INS A MUTUAL CO	WI	7,458.5
TOKIO MARINE AMERICA INS CO	NY	1,410.7
Rating: A-		
AUTO-OWNERS INS CO	MI	13,712.2
CINCINNATI INDEMNITY CO	OH	123.8
CINCINNATI INS CO	OH	11,749.4
COUNTRY MUTUAL INS CO	IL	4,421.1
ESSENT GUARANTY INC	PA	1,194.6
GEICO CHOICE INS CO	NE	647.0
GEICO SECURE INS CO	NE	436.8
HOME-OWNERS INS CO	MI	2,106.0
NATIONAL MORTGAGE INS CORP	WI	530.6
OWNERS INS CO	OH	3,891.6
TRAVELERS CASUALTY & SURETY CO	CT	16,398.0
USAA CASUALTY INS CO	TX	9,860.1
Rating: B+		
ACUITY A MUTUAL INS CO	WI	3,483.6
ALL AMERICA INS CO	OH	280.0
AMERICAN FAMILY MUT INS CO	WI	16,216.1
AMERICAN STANDARD INS CO OF WI	WI	433.2
AMICA MUTUAL INS CO	RI	4,974.1
BUILDERS MUTUAL INS CO	NC	736.0
CENTURION CASUALTY CO	IA	157.1
COUNTRY CASUALTY INS CO	IL	83.4
DAIRYLAND INS CO	WI	1,282.3
FARM BUREAU P&C INS CO	IA	2,379.2
FARMERS AUTOMOBILE INS ASN	IL	1,283.7
FIRST COLONIAL INS CO	FL	370.3
GEICO GENERAL INS CO	MD	226.3
MITSUI SUMITOMO INS CO OF AMER	NY	925.8
MOTORISTS MUTUAL INS CO	OH	1,375.1
NATIONAL CASUALTY CO	WI	402.1
NATIONWIDE MUTUAL FIRE INS CO	OH	6,045.9
PEKIN INS CO	IL	312.8
PROPERTY-OWNERS INS CO	IN	257.1
SENTRY SELECT INS CO	WI	706.8
STATE FARM MUTUAL AUTOMOBILE INS CO	IL	143,802.0
TOA REINS CO OF AMERICA	DE	1,747.5
TRAVELERS INDEMNITY CO	CT	21,495.2
UNITED SERVICES AUTOMOBILE ASN	TX	32,870.8
USAA GENERAL INDEMNITY CO	TX	3,644.1
WEST BEND MUTUAL INS CO	WI	2,456.0
WESTERN AGRICULTURAL INS CO	IA	206.5

Wyoming

INSURANCE COMPANY NAME	DOM. STATE	TOTAL ASSETS ($MIL)	INSURANCE COMPANY NAME	DOM. STATE	TOTAL ASSETS ($MIL)
Rating: A+					
BERKSHIRE HATHAWAY ASR CORP	NY	2,220.4			
MUNICIPAL ASR CORP	NY	1,125.1			
Rating: A					
SENTRY INS A MUTUAL CO	WI	7,458.5			
TOKIO MARINE AMERICA INS CO	NY	1,410.7			
Rating: A-					
CINCINNATI INDEMNITY CO	OH	123.8			
CINCINNATI INS CO	OH	11,749.4			
COUNTRY MUTUAL INS CO	IL	4,421.1			
ESSENT GUARANTY INC	PA	1,194.6			
GEICO CHOICE INS CO	NE	647.0			
GEICO SECURE INS CO	NE	436.8			
NATIONAL MORTGAGE INS CORP	WI	530.6			
TRAVELERS CASUALTY & SURETY CO	CT	16,398.0			
USAA CASUALTY INS CO	TX	9,860.1			
Rating: B+					
ACUITY A MUTUAL INS CO	WI	3,483.6			
AMERICAN FAMILY MUT INS CO	WI	16,216.1			
AMERICAN STANDARD INS CO OF WI	WI	433.2			
AMICA MUTUAL INS CO	RI	4,974.1			
CENTURION CASUALTY CO	IA	157.1			
COUNTRY CASUALTY INS CO	IL	83.4			
DAIRYLAND INS CO	WI	1,282.3			
FIRST COLONIAL INS CO	FL	370.3			
GEICO GENERAL INS CO	MD	226.3			
HOLYOKE MUTUAL INS CO IN SALEM	MA	217.0			
MITSUI SUMITOMO INS CO OF AMER	NY	925.8			
NATIONAL CASUALTY CO	WI	402.1			
NATIONWIDE MUTUAL FIRE INS CO	OH	6,045.9			
SENTRY SELECT INS CO	WI	706.8			
STATE FARM MUTUAL AUTOMOBILE INS CO	IL	143,802.0			
TOA REINS CO OF AMERICA	DE	1,747.5			
TRAVELERS INDEMNITY CO	CT	21,495.2			
UNITED SERVICES AUTOMOBILE ASN	TX	32,870.8			
USAA GENERAL INDEMNITY CO	TX	3,644.1			
WESTERN AGRICULTURAL INS CO	IA	206.5			

Section VI

All Companies
Listed by Rating

A list of all rated and unrated

U.S. Property and Casualty Insurers.

Companies are ranked by Weiss Safety Rating
and then listed alphabetically within each rating category.

Section VI Contents

This section sorts all companies by their Safety Rating and then lists them alphabetically within each rating category. The purpose of this section is to provide in one place all of those companies receiving a given rating. Companies with the same rating should be viewed as having the same relative financial strength regardless of their order in this table.

1. Insurance Company Name

The legally registered name, which can sometimes differ from the name that the company uses for advertising. An insurer's name can be very similar to that of another, so verify the company's exact name and state of domicile to make sure you are looking at the correct company.

2. Domicile State

The state which has primary regulatory responsibility for the company. It may differ from the location of the company's corporate headquarters. You do not have to be living in the domicile state to purchase insurance from this firm, provided it is licensed to do business in your state.

3. Total Assets

All assets admitted by state insurance regulators in millions of dollars. This includes investments and current business assets such as receivables from agents and reinsurers.

INSURANCE COMPANY NAME	DOM. STATE	TOTAL ASSETS ($MIL)	INSURANCE COMPANY NAME	DOM. STATE	TOTAL ASSETS ($MIL)
Rating: A+			TOA REINS CO OF AMERICA	DE	1,747.5
BERKSHIRE HATHAWAY ASR CORP	NY	2,220.4	TRAVELERS INDEMNITY CO	CT	21,495.2
CITIZENS PROPERTY INS CORP	FL	12,538.0	UNITED SERVICES AUTOMOBILE ASN	TX	32,870.8
COPPERPOINT MUTUAL INS CO	AZ	3,573.1	USAA GENERAL INDEMNITY CO	TX	3,644.1
MUNICIPAL ASR CORP	NY	1,125.1	WEST BEND MUTUAL INS CO	WI	2,456.0
OGLESBY REINS CO	IL	4,277.3	WESTERN AGRICULTURAL INS CO	IA	206.5
Rating: A			**Rating: B**		
SENTRY INS A MUTUAL CO	WI	7,458.5	21ST CENTURY ADVANTAGE INS CO	MN	29.3
TOKIO MARINE AMERICA INS CO	NY	1,410.7	21ST CENTURY ASR CO	DE	70.1
Rating: A-			21ST CENTURY CASUALTY CO	CA	12.4
AUTO-OWNERS INS CO	MI	13,712.2	21ST CENTURY CENTENNIAL INS CO	PA	587.9
CINCINNATI INDEMNITY CO	OH	123.8	21ST CENTURY INDEMNITY INS CO	PA	67.2
CINCINNATI INS CO	OH	11,749.4	21ST CENTURY INS CO	CA	940.0
COUNTRY MUTUAL INS CO	IL	4,421.1	21ST CENTURY NATIONAL INS CO INC	NY	24.5
ESSENT GUARANTY INC	PA	1,194.6	21ST CENTURY NORTH AMERICA INS	NY	577.2
GEICO CHOICE INS CO	NE	647.0	21ST CENTURY PACIFIC INS	CO	44.5
GEICO SECURE INS CO	NE	436.8	21ST CENTURY PINNACLE INS CO	NJ	42.9
HOME-OWNERS INS CO	MI	2,106.0	21ST CENTURY PREFERRED INS CO	PA	41.9
NATIONAL MORTGAGE INS CORP	WI	530.6	21ST CENTURY SECURITY INS CO	PA	198.7
OWNERS INS CO	OH	3,891.6	ACCIDENT FUND GENERAL INS CO	MI	264.2
TRAVELERS CASUALTY & SURETY CO	CT	16,398.0	ACCIDENT FUND NATIONAL INS CO	MI	271.3
USAA CASUALTY INS CO	TX	9,860.1	ALASKA NATIONAL INS CO	AK	916.1
Rating: B+			ALFA ALLIANCE INS CORP	VA	28.8
ACUITY A MUTUAL INS CO	WI	3,483.6	ALFA GENERAL INS CORP	AL	95.0
ALFA MUTUAL GENERAL INS CO	AL	103.4	ALFA INS CORP	AL	97.0
ALL AMERICA INS CO	OH	280.0	ALFA MUTUAL FIRE INS CO	AL	715.5
AMERICAN FAMILY MUT INS CO	WI	16,216.1	ALFA MUTUAL INS CO	AL	1,251.2
AMERICAN STANDARD INS CO OF WI	WI	433.2	ALFA SPECIALTY INS CORP	VA	51.1
AMICA MUTUAL INS CO	RI	4,974.1	ALFA VISION INS CORP	VA	96.5
AUTO CLUB INDEMNITY CO	TX	27.2	ALLIED P&C INS CO	IA	402.1
BUILDERS MUTUAL INS CO	NC	736.0	ALLIED WORLD SPECIALTY INS CO	DE	837.0
CENTURION CASUALTY CO	IA	157.1	ALLSTATE COUNTY MUTUAL INS CO	TX	14.7
COUNTRY CASUALTY INS CO	IL	83.4	ALLSTATE INDEMNITY CO	IL	128.5
DAIRYLAND INS CO	WI	1,282.3	ALLSTATE INS CO	IL	43,881.3
FARM BUREAU P&C INS CO	IA	2,379.2	ALLSTATE NJ INS CO	IL	2,550.9
FARM FAMILY CASUALTY INS CO	NY	1,160.0	ALLSTATE P&C INS CO	IL	249.7
FARMERS AUTOMOBILE INS ASN	IL	1,283.7	ALLSTATE TEXAS LLOYDS	TX	17.3
FIRST COLONIAL INS CO	FL	370.3	ALLSTATE VEHICLE & PROPERTY INS CO	IL	52.6
GEICO GENERAL INS CO	MD	226.3	ALPHA P&C INS CO	WI	30.9
HOLYOKE MUTUAL INS CO IN SALEM	MA	217.0	AMERICAN AGRICULTURAL INS CO	IN	1,247.8
INTERINS EXCHANGE	CA	9,074.7	AMERICAN BANKERS INS CO OF FL	FL	1,972.7
MERCURY INS CO	CA	1,600.5	AMERICAN CAPITAL ASR CORP	FL	121.0
MITSUI SUMITOMO INS CO OF AMER	NY	925.8	AMERICAN CONTRACTORS INDEMNITY CO	CA	298.8
MOTORISTS MUTUAL INS CO	OH	1,375.1	AMERICAN EQUITY SPECIALTY INS CO	CT	78.8
NATIONAL CASUALTY CO	WI	402.1	AMERICAN FAMILY INS CO	OH	34.5
NATIONWIDE MUTUAL FIRE INS CO	OH	6,045.9	AMERICAN MERCURY INS CO	OK	368.8
PEKIN INS CO	IL	312.8	AMERICAN MERCURY LLOYDS INS CO	TX	6.5
PROPERTY-OWNERS INS CO	IN	257.1	AMERICAN MODERN PROPERTY & CASUALTY	OH	20.7
SENTRY SELECT INS CO	WI	706.8	AMERICAN MODERN SURPLUS LINES INS CO	OH	70.6
SOUTHERN-OWNERS INS CO	MI	695.8	AMERICAN NATIONAL GENERAL INS CO	MO	103.6
STATE FARM MUTUAL AUTOMOBILE INS CO	IL	143,802.0	AMERICAN NATIONAL LLOYDS INS CO	TX	86.7
TENNESSEE FARMERS ASR CO	TN	1,408.6	AMERICAN NATIONAL PROPERTY & CAS CO	MO	1,292.6
TENNESSEE FARMERS MUTUAL INS CO	TN	2,804.7	AMERICAN NATL COUNTY MUT INS CO	TX	22.3
TEXAS FARM BUREAU CASUALTY INS CO	TX	1,179.5	AMERICAN RELIABLE INS CO	AZ	273.8
			AMERICAN STANDARD INS CO OF OH	OH	9.6

INSURANCE COMPANY NAME	DOM. STATE	TOTAL ASSETS ($MIL)	INSURANCE COMPANY NAME	DOM. STATE	TOTAL ASSETS ($MIL)
Rating: B (Continued)			ECONOMY PREMIER ASR CO	IL	84.5
AMERICAN STATES INS CO OF TX	TX	12.2	EMPLOYERS COMPENSATION INS CO	CA	1,063.5
AMERICAN STATES LLOYDS INS CO	TX	3.6	ENCOMPASS INDEMNITY CO	IL	30.2
AMERIPRISE INS CO	WI	48.6	ENDURANCE ASR CORP	DE	1,801.5
AMEX ASSURANCE CO	IL	265.9	ERIE INS CO OF NEW YORK	NY	110.3
AMICA TEXAS INS CO	TX	77.8	ERIE INS EXCHANGE	PA	14,449.8
ANPAC LOUISIANA INS CO	LA	126.4	ESSENT GUARANTY OF PA INC	PA	85.8
ANSUR AMERICA INS CO	MI	111.4	EULER HERMES NORTH AMERICA INS CO	MD	423.1
ARCH MORTGAGE GUARANTY CO	WI	51.7	EXECUTIVE RISK INDEMNITY INC	DE	3,093.7
ARCH SPECIALTY INS CO	MO	515.4	FAIR AMERICAN INS & REINS CO	NY	255.8
ASI ASR CORP	FL	129.5	FAIR AMERICAN SELECT INS CO	DE	53.7
AUTO CLUB INS ASSN	MI	3,921.9	FARM BU TOWN & COUNTRY INS CO OF MO	MO	384.3
AUTOMOBILE INS CO OF HARTFORD CT	CT	1,034.2	FARM BUREAU GENERAL INS CO OF MI	MI	661.8
AXIS INS CO	IL	1,528.9	FARM BUREAU INS OF NC INC	NC	9.6
BARNSTABLE COUNTY MUTUAL INS CO	MA	101.3	FARM BUREAU MUTUAL INS CO OF AR	AR	399.9
BCS INS CO	OH	287.0	FARM BUREAU MUTUAL INS CO OF ID	ID	458.5
BEAR RIVER MUTUAL INS CO	UT	247.7	FARM BUREAU MUTUAL INS CO OF MI	MI	725.2
BITCO GENERAL INS CORP	IL	844.8	FARMERS & MECH MUTUAL INS CO	PA	5.6
BITCO NATIONAL INS CO	IL	501.0	FARMERS INS CO OF OREGON	OR	1,713.8
BRETHREN MUTUAL INS CO	MD	250.6	FARMERS INS HAWAII INC	HI	99.5
BROTHERHOOD MUTUAL INS CO	IN	553.8	FARMERS MUTUAL INS CO OF NE	NE	624.1
CALIFORNIA AUTOMOBILE INS CO	CA	640.6	FARMINGTON CASUALTY CO	CT	1,033.6
CALIFORNIA GENERAL UNDERWRITERS INS	CA	22.5	FARMLAND MUTUAL INS CO	IA	566.1
CANAL INDEMNITY CO	SC	46.8	FEDERAL INS CO	IN	30,306.0
CANAL INS CO	SC	800.7	FEDERATED MUTUAL INS CO	MN	5,260.8
CASTLE KEY INDEMNITY CO	IL	11.7	FEDERATED RURAL ELECTRIC INS EXCH	KS	531.4
CATERPILLAR INS CO	MO	690.3	FINANCIAL PACIFIC INS CO	CA	234.1
CENTRAL MUTUAL INS CO	OH	1,468.5	FIRST FLORIDIAN AUTO & HOME INS CO	FL	275.9
CENTURY-NATIONAL INS CO	CA	485.4	FIRST NATIONAL INS CO OF AMERICA	NH	57.5
CHARTER INDEMNITY CO	TX	12.0	FIRSTCOMP INS CO	NE	296.0
CHARTER OAK FIRE INS CO	CT	944.7	FLORIDA FARM BUREAU GENERAL INS CO	FL	10.1
CHESAPEAKE EMPLOYERS INS CO	MD	2,168.9	FOREMOST INS CO	MI	2,292.9
CHUBB INDEMNITY INS CO	NY	408.4	FORTUITY INS CO	MI	41.4
CHUBB INS CO OF NJ	NJ	76.5	FRANKENMUTH MUTUAL INS CO	MI	1,242.1
CHUBB LLOYDS INS CO OF TX	TX	39.1	FRANKLIN MUTUAL INS CO	NJ	824.4
CHUBB NATIONAL INS CO	IN	342.0	FREEDOM SPECIALTY INS CO	OH	57.0
CHURCH MUTUAL INS CO	WI	1,566.3	GARRISON P&C INS CO	TX	1,779.1
CINCINNATI CASUALTY CO	OH	391.5	GEICO INDEMNITY CO	MD	7,092.5
CINCINNATI SPECIALTY UNDERWRITER	DE	669.5	GENWORTH MORTGAGE REINS CORP	NC	14.5
CITIZENS INS CO OF AM	MI	1,545.0	GEORGIA FARM BUREAU CASUALTY INS CO	GA	3.5
COLONIAL COUNTY MUTUAL INS CO	TX	168.4	GERMANIA SELECT INS CO	TX	209.0
CONNECTICUT MEDICAL INS CO	CT	493.4	GNY CUSTOM INS CO	AZ	58.5
CONTRACTORS BONDING & INS CO	IL	209.9	GOODVILLE MUTUAL CAS CO	PA	237.7
COPIC INS CO	CO	690.9	GOVERNMENT EMPLOYEES INS CO	MD	23,562.9
COUNTRY PREFERRED INS CO	IL	237.3	GOVERNMENTAL INTERINS	IL	67.4
COURTESY INS CO	FL	785.7	GRANGE MUTUAL CAS CO	OH	2,258.8
COVINGTON SPECIALTY INS CO	NH	107.1	GREAT MIDWEST INS CO	TX	200.2
CRESTBROOK INS CO	OH	127.9	GREAT NORTHERN INS CO	IN	1,666.2
CUMIS INS SOCIETY INC	IA	1,789.0	GREAT WEST CASUALTY CO	NE	2,008.2
CUMIS SPECIALTY INS CO INC	IA	54.1	GREEN MOUNTAIN INS CO	VT	11.7
DAIRYLAND COUNTY MUTUAL INS CO OF TX	TX	13.5	GUARANTEE CO OF NORTH AMERICA USA	MI	209.3
DENTISTS INS CO	CA	328.6	GUIDEONE MUTUAL INS CO	IA	1,249.1
DRYDEN MUTUAL INS CO	NY	191.6	GUIDEONE P&C INS CO	IA	456.3
EAGLESTONE REINS CO	PA	6,494.1	GUIDEONE SPECIALTY MUTUAL INS CO	IA	269.5
ECONOMY PREFERRED INS CO	IL	40.3	HANOVER INS CO	NH	6,972.7
			HARTFORD ACCIDENT & INDEMNITY CO	CT	11,729.7

INSURANCE COMPANY NAME	DOM. STATE	TOTAL ASSETS ($MIL)	INSURANCE COMPANY NAME	DOM. STATE	TOTAL ASSETS ($MIL)
Rating: B (Continued)			METROPOLITAN GROUP PROP & CAS INS CO	RI	673.2
HARTFORD CASUALTY INS CO	IN	2,370.8	MIAMI MUTUAL INS CO	OH	55.7
HARTFORD FIRE INS CO	CT	25,602.1	MIDDLESEX INS CO	WI	719.1
HARTFORD INS CO OF IL	IL	3,931.9	MIDDLESEX MUTUAL ASR CO	CT	193.6
HARTFORD INS CO OF THE MIDWEST	IN	633.3	MIDWEST BUILDERS CASUALTY MUTUAL CO	KS	83.1
HARTFORD INS CO OF THE SOUTHEAST	CT	184.8	MILWAUKEE CASUALTY INS CO	WI	105.9
HARTFORD LLOYDS INS CO	TX	73.1	MINNESOTA LAWYERS MUTUAL INS CO	MN	174.3
HARTFORD SM BOIL INSPECTION & INS	CT	1,179.3	MMG INS CO	ME	252.2
HARTFORD SM BOIL INSPECTION IC OF CT	CT	74.4	MMIC INS INC	MN	704.6
HARTFORD UNDERWRITERS INS CO	CT	1,651.2	MOTOR CLUB INS CO	RI	46.8
HASTINGS MUTUAL INS CO	MI	862.9	MOTORISTS COMMERCIAL MUTUAL INS CO	OH	354.2
HIGH POINT P&C INS CO	NJ	345.1	MUTUAL INS CO OF AZ	AZ	1,032.8
HOMELAND INS CO OF DE	DE	52.0	MUTUAL OF ENUMCLAW INS CO	OR	738.6
HORACE MANN INS CO	IL	456.9	NATIONAL BUILDERS INS CO	DE	84.6
HORACE MANN P&C INS CO	IL	284.5	NATIONAL INDEMNITY CO	NE	163,246.0
HOUSING AUTHORITY PROP A MUTUAL CO	VT	169.0	NATIONAL PUBLIC FINANCE GUAR CORP	NY	4,754.2
HSB SPECIALTY INS CO	CT	53.5	NATIONWIDE AFFINITY INS CO OF AMER	OH	419.2
HUDSON EXCESS INS CO	DE	66.0	NATIONWIDE LLOYDS	TX	44.9
ICI MUTUAL INS CO A RRG	VT	353.4	NATIONWIDE MUTUAL INS CO	OH	36,667.7
IMT INS CO	IA	344.8	NAVIGATORS INS CO	NY	2,764.8
INDIANA FARMERS MUTUAL INS CO	IN	408.5	NCMIC INS CO	IA	731.1
INFINITY INS CO	IN	2,018.9	NEW JERSEY RE-INS CO	NJ	548.6
INS CO OF ILLINOIS	IL	20.9	NEW YORK SCHOOLS INS RECIPROCAL	NY	257.6
IOWA AMERICAN INS CO	IA	25.3	NJ MANUFACTURERS INS CO	NJ	6,882.1
IOWA MUTUAL INS CO	IA	99.7	NLC MUTUAL INS CO	VT	326.2
JEWELERS MUTUAL INS CO	WI	380.0	NORTH CAROLINA FARM BU MUTUAL INS CO	NC	1,860.2
KANSAS MEDICAL MUTUAL INS CO	KS	153.3	NORTHLAND CASUALTY CO	CT	109.4
KEMPER INDEPENDENCE INS CO	IL	91.1	NORTHLAND INS CO	CT	1,211.3
KENTUCKY FARM BUREAU MUTUAL INS CO	KY	2,373.1	OKLAHOMA ATTORNEYS MUTUAL INS CO	OK	55.0
KINSALE INS CO	AR	442.4	OLD REPUB INS CO	PA	2,868.4
KNIGHT SPECIALTY INS CO	DE	81.3	OLD REPUB UNION INS CO	IL	59.4
LAMMICO	LA	408.4	OLD REPUBLIC GENERAL INS CORP	IL	1,992.7
LANCER INS CO	IL	661.1	OLD REPUBLIC LLOYDS OF TX	TX	2.2
LIBERTY LLOYDS OF TX INS CO	TX	6.6	OLD REPUBLIC SURETY CO	WI	118.5
LIBERTY MUTUAL INS CO	MA	42,340.6	OMNI INDEMNITY CO	IL	76.6
LIBERTY MUTUAL PERSONAL INS CO	MA	6.9	OPHTHALMIC MUTUAL INS CO RRG	VT	274.6
LION INS CO (FL)	FL	253.2	OTSEGO MUTUAL FIRE INS CO	NY	117.2
LOUISIANA FARM BUREAU CAS INS CO	LA	10.9	P&C INS CO OF HARTFORD	IN	240.0
LOUISIANA FARM BUREAU MUTUAL INS CO	LA	219.4	PACIFIC INDEMNITY CO	WI	6,797.0
LUBA CASUALTY INS CO	LA	226.1	PACIFIC INS CO LTD	CT	661.0
MARKEL GLOBAL REINS CO	DE	1,649.7	PACIFIC PROPERTY & CASUALTY CO	CA	82.0
MEDICAL INS EXCHANGE OF CALIFORNIA	CA	413.4	PATRIOT GENERAL INS CO	WI	26.1
MEDICAL MUTUAL INS CO OF MAINE	ME	275.0	PEAK P&C INS CORP	WI	45.7
MEDICAL PROTECTIVE CO	IN	2,726.3	PENNSYLVANIA LUMBERMENS MUTUAL INS	PA	467.2
MENDAKOTA INS CO	MN	11.6	PHARMACISTS MUTUAL INS CO	IA	278.4
MERCURY CASUALTY CO	CA	1,905.1	PHOENIX INS CO	CT	4,300.2
MERCURY COUNTY MUTUAL INS CO	TX	12.3	PIONEER STATE MUTUAL INS CO	MI	526.4
MERCURY INDEMNITY CO OF GEORGIA	GA	15.5	PREFERRED MUTUAL INS CO	NY	526.3
MERCURY INS CO OF GA	GA	21.1	PREFERRED PHYSICIANS MEDICAL RRG	MO	214.6
MERCURY INS CO OF IL	IL	36.1	PREFERRED PROFESSIONAL INS CO	NE	307.3
MERCURY NATIONAL INS CO	IL	16.5	PREMIER INS CO OF MA	CT	280.7
MET LLOYDS INS CO OF TX	TX	108.6	PROTECTIVE INS CO	IN	763.4
METROPOLITAN CASUALTY INS CO	RI	197.5	PROTECTIVE SPECIALTY INS CO	IN	67.3
METROPOLITAN DIRECT PROP & CAS INS	RI	136.3	QBE REINS CORP	PA	1,212.7
METROPOLITAN GENERAL INS CO	RI	43.0	QUINCY MUTUAL FIRE INS CO	MA	1,536.0
			RED SHIELD INS CO	WA	38.6

INSURANCE COMPANY NAME	DOM. STATE	TOTAL ASSETS ($MIL)	INSURANCE COMPANY NAME	DOM. STATE	TOTAL ASSETS ($MIL)
Rating: B (Continued)			TRAVELERS PERSONAL INS CO	CT	210.0
			TRAVELERS PERSONAL SECURITY INS CO	CT	213.7
RETAILFIRST INS CO	FL	295.4	TRAVELERS PROPERTY CAS OF AMERICA	CT	840.3
RIVERPORT INS CO	IA	115.6	TRAVELERS PROPERTY CASUALTY INS CO	CT	256.6
RLI INS CO	IL	1,808.7	TRI-STATE CONSUMER INS CO	NY	98.0
RURAL COMMUNITY INS CO	MN	3,260.3	TRINITY UNIVERSAL INS CO	TX	1,921.2
SAFECO INS CO OF IL	IL	186.2	TRUMBULL INS CO	CT	230.3
SAFECO INS CO OF INDIANA	IN	15.1	TWIN CITY FIRE INS CO	IN	690.2
SAFECO INS CO OF OREGON	OR	13.9	UFB CASUALTY INS CO	IN	8.7
SCOTTSDALE INDEMNITY CO	OH	93.0	UMIA INS INC	OR	245.6
SCOTTSDALE SURPLUS LINES INS CO	AZ	50.1	UNION NATIONAL FIRE INS CO	LA	10.1
SECURIAN CASUALTY CO	MN	228.6	UNITED CASUALTY INS CO OF AMERICA	IL	11.7
SECURITY NATIONAL INS CO	DE	1,174.9	UNITED FARM FAMILY INS CO	NY	42.7
SELECTIVE AUTO INS CO OF NJ	NJ	356.3	UNITED FARM FAMILY MUTUAL INS CO	IN	1,037.9
SELECTIVE CASUALTY INS CO	NJ	413.4	UNITED FIRE & CAS CO	IA	1,863.5
SELECTIVE F&C INS CO	NJ	180.5	UNITED SPECIALTY INS CO	DE	143.7
SELECTIVE INS CO OF AM	NJ	2,216.9	UNITED SURETY & INDEMNITY CO	PR	99.4
SELECTIVE INS CO OF NY	NY	413.5	UNITRIN COUNTY MUTUAL INS CO	TX	31.8
SELECTIVE INS CO OF SC	IN	614.0	UNITRIN DIRECT INS CO	IL	12.5
SELECTIVE INS CO OF THE SOUTHEAST	IN	474.9	UNITRIN DIRECT PROPERTY & CAS CO	IL	15.1
SELECTIVE WAY INS CO	NJ	1,264.9	UNITRIN SAFEGUARD INS CO	WI	27.0
SENTINEL INS CO LTD	CT	250.6	USAA TEXAS LLOYDS CO	TX	372.7
SENTRY CASUALTY CO	WI	287.5	UTICA LLOYDS OF TX	TX	7.5
SENTRY LLOYDS OF TX	TX	7.0	VALLEY P&C INS CO	OR	12.3
SERVICE INS CO (FL)	FL	49.9	VANLINER INS CO	MO	385.6
SFM MUTUAL INS CO	MN	547.6	VERMONT ACCIDENT INS CO	VT	8.5
SHELTER MUTUAL INS CO	MO	3,210.5	VIGILANT INS CO	NY	519.2
SOCIETY INS A MUTUAL CO	WI	398.5	VIRGINIA SURETY CO INC	IL	1,231.9
SOMPO JAPAN INS CO OF AM	NY	1,236.8	WESTERN HERITAGE INS CO	AZ	137.4
SOUTHERN FIDELITY INS CO	FL	207.3	WILSON MUTUAL INS CO	WI	93.2
ST PAUL FIRE & MARINE INS CO	CT	18,479.2	**Rating: B-**		
STANDARD FIRE INS CO	CT	3,665.0	21ST CENTURY PREMIER INS CO	PA	281.7
STARR INDEMNITY & LIABILITY CO	TX	4,391.4	360 INS CO	WY	27.3
STATE FARM FIRE & CAS CO	IL	37,184.7	ACCIDENT FUND INS CO OF AMERICA	MI	3,099.4
STATE FARM GENERAL INS CO	IL	7,064.0	ACE AMERICAN INS CO	PA	12,643.3
STATE FARM INDEMNITY CO	IL	2,231.1	ACE P&C INS CO	PA	8,959.9
STATE FARM LLOYDS	TX	3,331.5	AEGIS SECURITY INS CO	PA	120.9
STATE VOLUNTEER MUTUAL INS CO	TN	1,203.2	AFFILIATES INS RECIPROCAL A RRG	VT	7.1
SUNAPEE MUTL FIRE INS CO	NH	4.2	AGRICULTURAL WORKERS MUT AUTO INS CO	TX	89.1
TEACHERS INS CO	IL	342.6	AIX SPECIALTY INS CO	DE	55.8
TEXAS PACIFIC INDEMNITY CO	TX	7.7	ALAMANCE FARMERS MUTUAL INS CO	NC	8.2
TNUS INS CO	NY	62.8	ALLIED WORLD NATL ASR CO	NH	330.4
TRANS PACIFIC INS CO	NY	68.7	ALLSTATE NORTHBROOK INDEMNITY CO	IL	44.1
TRANSATLANTIC REINS CO	NY	14,151.9	ALTERRA AMERICA INS CO	DE	454.4
TRANSGUARD INS CO OF AMERICA INC	IL	250.0	AMERICAN EUROPEAN INS CO	NH	132.3
TRAVCO INS CO	CT	229.5	AMERICAN HALLMARK INS CO OF TX	TX	427.2
TRAVELERS CASUALTY CO OF CONNECTICUT	CT	327.5	AMERICAN INTERSTATE INS CO	NE	1,291.5
TRAVELERS CASUALTY INS CO OF AMERICA	CT	1,984.9	AMERICAN INTERSTATE INS CO OF TEXAS	TX	69.0
TRAVELERS COMMERCIAL CASUALTY CO	CT	337.5	AMERICAN MINING INS CO	IA	37.5
TRAVELERS COMMERCIAL INS CO	CT	362.9	AMERICAN SECURITY INS CO	DE	1,506.1
TRAVELERS EXCESS & SURPLUS LINES CO	CT	214.8	AMERICAN STATES PREFERRED INS CO	IN	21.8
TRAVELERS HOME & MARINE INS CO	CT	401.7	AMERISURE INS CO	MI	821.3
TRAVELERS INDEMNITY CO OF AMERICA	CT	631.1	AMERISURE MUTUAL INS CO	MI	2,192.8
TRAVELERS INDEMNITY CO OF CT	CT	1,098.3	AMTRUST INS CO OF KANSAS INC	KS	91.6
TRAVELERS LLOYDS INS CO	TX	27.8	ANCHOR P&C INS CO	FL	70.8
TRAVELERS LLOYDS OF TEXAS INS CO	TX	24.1			

INSURANCE COMPANY NAME	DOM. STATE	TOTAL ASSETS ($MIL)	INSURANCE COMPANY NAME	DOM. STATE	TOTAL ASSETS ($MIL)
Rating: B- (Continued)			ERIE & NIAGARA INS ASSN	NY	199.2
			ERIE INS CO	PA	944.4
ARAG INS CO	IA	79.4	ERIE INS P&C CO	PA	102.0
ARCH INDEMNITY INS CO	MO	62.7	EVEREST REINS CO	DE	9,863.2
ARISE BOILER INSPECT & INS CO RRG	KY	4.1	EXECUTIVE RISK SPECIALTY INS CO	CT	299.7
ARMED FORCES INS EXCHANGE	KS	145.1	FACTORY MUTUAL INS CO	RI	16,582.9
ARROW MUTUAL LIABILITY INS CO	MA	49.1	FALLS LAKE NATIONAL INS CO	OH	325.6
ASI HOME INS CORP	FL	18.8	FARM CREDIT SYS ASSOC CAPTIVE INS CO	CO	112.6
ASI PREFERRED INS CORP	FL	109.7	FARMERS & MECHANICS MUTUAL IC OF WV	WV	63.1
ASPEN AMERICAN INS CO	TX	606.7	FARMERS ALLIANCE MUTUAL INS CO	KS	319.8
ATHENS FINANCIAL INS CO	OK	2.3	FARMERS INS CO OF WA	WA	557.5
ATLANTIC CASUALTY INS CO	NC	254.4	FARMERS MUTUAL F I C OF SALEM CTY	NJ	142.5
ATLANTIC CHARTER INS CO	MA	190.7	FARMERS MUTUAL HAIL INS CO OF IA	IA	792.3
ATLANTIC SPECIALTY INS CO	NY	2,256.9	FARMERS SPECIALTY INS CO	MI	58.4
ATLANTIC STATES INS CO	PA	740.8	FARMERS UNION MUTUAL INS CO	ND	112.6
AUTO CLUB INS CO OF FL	FL	369.7	FEDERATED SERVICE INS CO	MN	470.4
AUTO CLUB SOUTH INS CO	FL	116.1	FINANCIAL INDEMNITY CO	IL	90.7
BAY STATE INS CO	MA	453.0	FIRST GUARD INS CO	AZ	27.5
BEAZLEY INS CO	CT	310.6	FLORIDA FAMILY INS CO	FL	105.7
BENCHMARK INS CO	KS	234.6	FLORIDA FARM BU CASUALTY INS CO	FL	559.1
BENEFIT SECURITY INS CO	IL	8.2	FMH AG RISK INS CO	IA	293.6
BERKLEY INS CO	DE	17,317.1	FMI INS CO	NJ	47.2
BONDEX INS CO	NJ	7.1	FORTRESS INS CO	IL	133.3
BRIDGEFIELD EMPLOYERS INS CO	FL	125.9	FRANDISCO P&C INS CO	GA	104.2
CALIFORNIA CAPITAL INS CO	CA	588.7	GEICO ADVANTAGE INS CO	NE	1,177.8
CALIFORNIA INS CO	CA	775.7	GEICO MARINE INS CO	MD	134.9
CAMBRIDGE MUTUAL FIRE INS CO	MA	848.0	GENERAL STAR NATIONAL INS CO	DE	212.1
CANOPIUS US INS INC	DE	217.3	GEORGIA FARM BUREAU MUTUAL INS CO	GA	674.5
CAROLINA MUTUAL INS INC	NC	88.5	GERMAN AMERICAN FARM MUTUAL	TX	4.3
CASTLE KEY INS CO	IL	388.5	GERMANTOWN MUTUAL INS CO	WI	104.8
CENTENNIAL CASUALTY CO	AL	110.2	GOVT TECHNOLOGY INS CO RRG INC	NV	1.5
CHUBB CUSTOM INS CO	NJ	396.9	GRANGE INS ASSN	WA	282.4
CO-OPERATIVE INS COS	VT	128.2	GREAT AMERICAN INS CO	OH	6,188.9
COLUMBIA MUTUAL INS CO	MO	380.8	GREATER NEW YORK MUTUAL INS CO	NY	971.5
CONCORD GENERAL MUTUAL INS CO	NH	449.3	GRINNELL MUTUAL REINS CO	IA	1,078.2
CONSUMERS INS USA INC	TN	70.2	GUIDEONE TEXAS INS CO	TX	3.3
COPPERPOINT GENERAL INS CO	AZ	15.1	HALLMARK SPECIALTY INS CO	OK	219.4
COPPERPOINT WESTERN INS CO	AZ	9.0	HAMILTON SPECIALTY INS CO	DE	85.4
CRUSADER INS CO	CA	119.7	HARCO NATIONAL INS CO	IL	338.9
CSAA INS EXCHANGE	CA	6,651.6	HARFORD MUTUAL INS CO	MD	404.4
CUMBERLAND INS CO	NJ	103.8	HAULERS INS CO	TN	73.4
CUMBERLAND MUTUAL FIRE INS CO	NJ	273.3	HCC SPECIALTY INS CO	OK	20.6
DEALERS ASR CO	OH	103.7	HEALTH PROVIDERS INS RECIPROCAL RRG	HI	79.4
DEPOSITORS INS CO	IA	309.3	HIGH POINT PREFERRED INS CO	NJ	251.0
DIAMOND STATE INS CO	IN	133.3	HIGH POINT SAFETY & INS CO	NJ	62.5
DOCTORS CO AN INTERINS	CA	4,063.5	HISCOX INS CO	IL	218.8
DONEGAL MUTUAL INS CO	PA	451.0	HM CASUALTY INS CO	PA	24.8
DONGBU INS CO LTD US GUAM BRANCH	GU	62.7	HORACE MANN LLOYDS	TX	5.8
ECONOMY FIRE & CAS CO	IL	486.0	HOSPITALITY MUTUAL INS CO	MA	60.8
EMCASCO INS CO	IA	482.2	HOUSING AUTHORITY RISK RET GROUP INC	VT	307.2
EMPIRE BONDING & INS CO	NY	3.5	HOUSTON CASUALTY CO	TX	3,769.6
EMPLOYERS INS CO OF NV	NV	839.8	HOUSTON SPECIALTY INS CO	TX	482.7
EMPLOYERS INS OF WAUSAU	WI	5,526.4	HYUNDAI MARINE & FIRE INS CO LTD	CA	97.6
EMPLOYERS MUTUAL CAS CO	IA	3,116.3	IDS PROPERTY CASUALTY INS CO	WI	1,765.1
ENCOMPASS HOME & AUTO INS CO	IL	20.1	INFINITY ASSURANCE INS CO	OH	7.1
ENCOMPASS INDEPENDENT INS CO	IL	7.3	INFINITY CASUALTY INS CO	OH	7.5

INSURANCE COMPANY NAME	DOM. STATE	TOTAL ASSETS ($MIL)	INSURANCE COMPANY NAME	DOM. STATE	TOTAL ASSETS ($MIL)
Rating: B- (Continued)			NEVADA CAPITAL INS CO	NV	105.5
INFINITY SELECT INS CO	IN	6.7	NEW ENGLAND MUTUAL INS CO	MA	45.3
INTEGRITY MUTUAL INS CO	WI	94.5	NEW HAMPSHIRE EMPLOYERS INS CO	NH	4.0
IRONSHORE INDEMNITY INC	MN	429.5	NEW HOME WARRANTY INS CO RRG	DC	19.9
ISLAND INS CO LTD	HI	340.6	NEW LONDON COUNTY MUTUAL INS CO	CT	114.5
ISMIE MUTUAL INS CO	IL	1,482.7	NEW MEXICO EMPLOYERS ASR CO	NM	6.2
KENTUCKY EMPLOYERS MUTUAL INS	KY	917.8	NEW YORK CENTRAL MUTUAL FIRE INS CO	NY	1,054.2
KESWICK GUARANTY INC	VI	4.9	NEW YORK MARINE & GENERAL INS CO	NY	1,274.9
LACKAWANNA AMERICAN INS CO	PA	85.7	NEW YORK MUNICIPAL INS RECIPROCAL	NY	156.2
LACKAWANNA CASUALTY CO	PA	227.0	NGM INS CO	FL	2,412.3
LAFAYETTE INS CO	LA	198.8	NODAK MUTUAL INS CO	ND	256.4
LAWYERS MUTUAL INS CO	CA	318.3	NORCAL MUTUAL INS CO	CA	1,623.1
LAWYERS MUTUAL LIAB INS CO OF NC	NC	101.6	NORCAL SPECIALTY INS CO	PA	264.8
LIBERTY MUTUAL FIRE INS CO	WI	5,500.1	NORTH LIGHT SPECIALTY INS CO	IL	90.3
LIGHTNING ROD MUTUAL INS CO	OH	267.4	NORTH STAR MUTUAL INS CO	MN	684.9
LITITZ MUTUAL INS CO	PA	253.2	OASIS RECIPROCAL RRG	VT	13.5
LM GENERAL INS CO	IL	10.9	OCEAN HARBOR CASUALTY INS CO	FL	231.7
LYNDON SOUTHERN INS CO	DE	142.9	OHIO BAR LIABILITY INS CO	OH	38.6
MAG MUTUAL INS CO	GA	1,748.4	OHIO FARMERS INS CO	OH	2,815.4
MAIDEN RE NORTH AMERICA INC	MO	1,319.8	OHIO MUTUAL INS CO	OH	268.7
MDOW INS CO	TX	18.9	OKLAHOMA FARM BUREAU MUTUAL INS CO	OK	299.7
MEDICAL LIABILITY ALLIANCE	MO	77.5	OLD AMERICAN INDEMNITY CO	KY	16.1
MEDICAL MUTUAL INS CO OF NC	NC	516.9	OLD DOMINION INS CO	FL	35.3
MEDICAL MUTUAL LIAB INS SOC OF MD	MD	811.1	OMNI INS CO	IL	149.2
MEDICAL PROFESSIONAL MUTUAL INS CO	MA	2,998.9	OMS NATIONAL INS CO RRG	IL	391.4
MEDICUS INS CO	TX	69.9	PACIFIC EMPLOYERS INS CO	PA	3,697.7
MEDMAL DIRECT INS CO	FL	40.0	PEERLESS INS CO	NH	13,004.0
MEMBERSELECT INS CO	MI	485.4	PEMCO MUTUAL INS CO	WA	721.3
MERASTAR INS CO	IL	33.2	PENN NATIONAL SECURITY INS CO	PA	950.7
MERCHANTS BONDING CO (MUTUAL)	IA	172.9	PENNSYLVANIA NTL MUTUAL CAS INS CO	PA	1,268.3
MERCHANTS MUTUAL INS CO	NY	505.7	PHENIX MUTUAL FIRE INS CO	NH	65.8
MERCHANTS NATIONAL INS CO	NH	127.1	PHILADELPHIA CBSP FOR INS OF HOUSES	PA	312.6
MERCHANTS PREFERRED INS CO	NY	70.9	PHILADELPHIA CONTRIBUTIONSHIP INS CO	PA	205.7
MERRIMACK MUTUAL FIRE INS CO	MA	1,409.3	PHILADELPHIA INDEMNITY INS CO	PA	7,811.8
METROPOLITAN P&C INS CO	RI	5,739.6	PHYSICIANS INS A MUTL CO	WA	499.8
MID AMERICAN FIRE & CAS CO	NH	8.3	PIH INS CO A RECIP RRG	HI	17.6
MID-CENTURY INS CO	CA	4,005.3	PLYMOUTH ROCK ASR CORP	MA	571.3
MID-CENTURY INS CO OF TX	TX	38.5	PRIVILEGE UNDERWRITERS RECIP EXCH	FL	376.8
MIDWEST FAMILY MUTUAL INS CO	IA	210.7	PROASSURANCE CASUALTY CO	MI	1,074.4
MILLERS CAPITAL INS CO	PA	126.9	PROFESSIONALS ADVOCATE INS CO	MD	133.4
MISSISSIPPI FARM BUREAU CAS INS CO	MS	414.9	PROGRESSIVE CASUALTY INS CO	OH	7,375.3
MO EMPLOYERS MUTUAL INS CO	MO	637.0	PROGRESSIVE GARDEN STATE INS CO	NJ	354.8
MOUNTAIN STATES MUTUAL CAS CO	NM	148.9	PROTECTIVE P&C INS CO	MO	375.3
MOUNTAIN WEST FARM BU MUTUAL INS CO	WY	391.0	PROVIDENCE MUTUAL FIRE INS CO	RI	189.2
MSA INS CO	SC	18.6	PURE INS CO	FL	279.0
MUTUAL BENEFIT INS CO	PA	215.0	QBE INS CORP	PA	2,608.9
NATIONAL LIABILITY & FIRE INS CO	CT	2,341.1	RAM MUTUAL INS CO	MN	105.5
NATIONAL LLOYDS INS CO	TX	225.9	RED CLAY RRG INC	SC	8.3
NATIONAL SECURITY FIRE & CAS CO	AL	77.8	RENAISSANCE RE US INC	MD	1,600.5
NATIONWIDE AGRIBUSINESS INS CO	IA	567.3	REPUBLIC INDEMNITY CO OF AMERICA	CA	2,274.5
NATIONWIDE ASR CO	WI	144.8	REPUBLIC-VANGUARD INS CO	AZ	24.6
NATIONWIDE GENERAL INS CO	OH	415.0	ROCKINGHAM INS CO	VA	125.4
NATIONWIDE INS CO OF AM	WI	453.4	RURAL MUTUAL INS CO	WI	448.9
NATIONWIDE P&C INS CO	OH	688.5	SAFE AUTO INS CO	OH	400.0
NAVIGATORS SPECIALTY INS CO	NY	178.2	SAFECO INS CO OF AMERICA	NH	4,349.5
			SAFECO LLOYDS INS CO	TX	13.1

INSURANCE COMPANY NAME	DOM. STATE	TOTAL ASSETS ($MIL)	INSURANCE COMPANY NAME	DOM. STATE	TOTAL ASSETS ($MIL)
Rating: B- (Continued)			WESTERN NATIONAL MUTUAL INS CO	MN	929.6
SAFECO NATIONAL INS CO	NH	15.5	WESTERN PACIFIC MUT INS CO RISK RET	CO	137.6
SAFEPOINT INS CO	FL	117.8	WESTERN RESERVE MUTUAL CAS CO	OH	187.1
SAFETY INS CO	MA	1,455.7	WESTFIELD INS CO	OH	2,634.5
SAFEWAY INS CO	IL	464.8	WESTFIELD NATIONAL INS CO	OH	634.5
SAGAMORE INS CO	IN	156.4	WESTPORT INS CORP	MO	4,890.9
SCOTTSDALE INS CO	OH	2,561.9	WINTHROP PHYSICIANS RECIP RRG	VT	3.0
SECURA INS A MUTUAL CO	WI	1,066.5	WISCONSIN MUTUAL INS CO	WI	146.9
SECURITY FIRST INS CO	FL	226.7	ZURICH AMERICAN INS CO	NY	30,823.4
SENTRUITY CASUALTY CO	TX	188.3	**Rating: C+**		
SERVICE LLOYDS INS CO	TX	306.0	1ST CHOICE AUTO INS CO	PA	20.1
SHELTER REINS CO	MO	437.6	ACSTAR INS CO	IL	61.0
SIGMA RRG INC	DC	16.7	ADDISON INS CO	IA	116.8
SILVER OAK CASUALTY INC	NE	249.0	ADVANTAGE WORKERS COMP INS CO	IN	484.6
SOUTHERN FARM BUREAU CAS INS CO	MS	2,152.0	AETNA INS CO OF CT	CT	15.9
SOUTHERN TRUST INS CO	GA	44.8	AGENCY INS CO OF MD INC	MD	131.6
ST PAUL MERCURY INS CO	CT	328.3	AGSECURITY INS CO	OK	57.7
ST PAUL PROTECTIVE INS CO	CT	520.9	AIG ASR CO	PA	33.9
STANDARD GUARANTY INS CO	DE	342.2	AIG INS CO - PR	PR	143.2
STARR SURPLUS LINES INS CO	IL	372.4	AIG SPECIALTY INS CO	IL	104.9
STATE AUTO INS CO OF WI	WI	18.3	AIOI NISSAY DOWA INS CO OF AMERICA	NY	133.6
STATE FARM FLORIDA INS CO	FL	2,073.8	AIU INS CO	NY	87.6
STATE NATIONAL INS CO	TX	321.6	ALABAMA MUNICIPAL INS CORP	AL	105.6
STERLING INS CO	NY	169.1	ALLEGANY CO-OP INS CO	NY	52.3
STILLWATER INS CO	CA	336.8	ALLIANCE INDEMNITY CO	KS	10.5
STRATFORD INS CO	NH	146.1	ALLIED EASTERN INDEMNITY CO	PA	91.1
SUNLAND RRG INC	TN	7.0	ALLIED WORLD ASR CO (US) INC	DE	365.1
SURETEC INS CO	TX	225.5	ALLMERICA FINANCIAL ALLIANCE INS CO	NH	20.0
TITAN INDEMNITY CO	TX	239.2	ALLMERICA FINANCIAL BENEFIT INS CO	MI	37.7
TITAN INS CO	MI	108.9	ALLSTATE F&C INS CO	IL	224.6
TOPA INS CO	CA	175.8	ALPS PROPERTY & CASUALTY INS CO	MT	113.1
TRANSAMERICA CASUALTY INS CO	OH	378.1	AMALGAMATED CASUALTY INS CO	WA	54.4
TRIPLE S PROPIEDAD INC	PR	288.8	AMCO INS CO	IA	940.5
TRITON INS CO	TX	418.3	AMERICA FIRST INS CO	NH	14.6
TRUSTGARD INS CO	OH	116.2	AMERICAN AGRI BUSINESS INS CO	TX	1,052.9
TUSCARORA WAYNE INS CO	PA	100.0	AMERICAN COMMERCE INS CO	OH	345.4
UMIALIK INS CO	AK	59.9	AMERICAN ECONOMY INS CO	IN	67.9
UNION MUTUAL FIRE INS CO	VT	202.3	AMERICAN FAMILY HOME INS CO	FL	562.9
UNITED EDUCATORS INS A RECIP RRG	VT	866.1	AMERICAN FREEDOM INS CO	IL	53.8
UNITED FINANCIAL CASUALTY CO	OH	2,805.0	AMERICAN GUARANTEE & LIABILITY INS	NY	286.9
UNITED GUARANTY CREDIT INS CO	NC	25.3	AMERICAN MODERN HOME INS CO	OH	1,295.2
UNITED OHIO INS CO	OH	308.6	AMERICAN MODERN INS CO OF FLORIDA	FL	35.7
UNIVERSAL INS CO (PR)	PR	851.6	AMERICAN PLATINUM PROP & CAS INS CO	FL	20.5
US SPECIALTY INS CO	TX	1,844.9	AMERICAN ROAD INS CO	MI	663.4
UTICA FIRST INS CO	NY	268.9	AMERICAN SOUTHERN INS CO	KS	114.2
UTICA MUTUAL INS CO	NY	2,292.1	AMERICAN STATES INS CO	IN	132.1
VERLAN FIRE INS CO	NH	26.2	AMERICAN SUMMIT INS CO	TX	48.4
VERMONT MUTUAL INS CO	VT	794.0	AMERICAN ZURICH INS CO	IL	348.7
VETERINARY PET INS CO	OH	139.9	AMERIHEALTH CASUALTY INS CO	DE	293.6
VICTORIA AUTOMOBILE INS CO	OH	31.6	AMERISURE PARTNERS INS CO	MI	79.5
VICTORIA SELECT INS CO	OH	25.3	ARBELLA MUTUAL INS CO	MA	1,399.1
VIRGINIA FARM BUREAU MUTUAL INS CO	VA	392.4	ARBELLA PROTECTION INS CO	MA	330.3
WESCO INS CO	DE	1,794.7	ARCH MORTGAGE INS CO	WI	451.7
WESTERN COMMUNITY INS CO	ID	40.1	ARECA INS EXCHANGE	AK	28.4
WESTERN MUTUAL FIRE INS CO	MN	7.6	ASSOCIATED INDUSTRIES OF MA MUT INS	MA	583.3

INSURANCE COMPANY NAME	DOM. STATE	TOTAL ASSETS ($MIL)	INSURANCE COMPANY NAME	DOM. STATE	TOTAL ASSETS ($MIL)
Rating: C+ (Continued)			DISCOVER SPECIALTY INS CO	CT	109.2
			DRIVE NEW JERSEY INS CO	NJ	206.7
ASURE WORLDWIDE INS CO	MI	40.7	EAGLE WEST INS CO	CA	123.7
AUTO CLUB GROUP INS CO	MI	336.6	EASTERN ADVANTAGE ASR CO	PA	51.6
AVATAR P&C INS CO	FL	51.0	ELECTRIC INS CO	MA	1,643.4
AVEMCO INS CO	MD	83.9	EMC REINS CO	IA	465.6
AXIS REINS CO	NY	3,136.3	EMPIRE FIRE & MARINE INS CO	NE	46.6
BADGER MUTUAL INS CO	WI	176.1	EMPIRE INDEMNITY INS CO	OK	60.1
BELL UNITED INS CO	NV	37.6	ENCOMPASS INS CO OF AM	IL	20.5
BERKLEY REGIONAL INS CO	DE	723.4	ENCOMPASS INS CO OF NJ	IL	30.1
BERKSHIRE HATHAWAY HOMESTATE INS	NE	2,128.3	ENCOMPASS PROP & CAS INS CO OF NJ	IL	13.8
BERKSHIRE HATHAWAY SPECIALTY INS CO	NE	3,479.8	ENCOMPASS PROPERTY & CASUALTY CO	IL	10.7
BLOOMINGTON COMP INS CO	MN	17.9	ENDEAVOUR INS CO	MA	6.1
BRITISH AMERICAN INS CO	TX	55.6	ENDURANCE AMERICAN INS CO	DE	1,660.6
BROADLINE RRG INC	VT	85.9	ENDURANCE AMERICAN SPECIALTY INS CO	DE	404.1
BUCKEYE STATE MUTUAL INS CO	OH	65.4	ENDURANCE RISK SOLUTIONS ASR CO	DE	254.9
CA CASUALTY COMP INS CO	CA	73.0	ENUMCLAW P&C INS CO	OR	8.5
CALIFORNIA CASUALTY INDEMNITY EXCH	CA	575.5	EVEREST NATIONAL INS CO	DE	884.3
CALIFORNIA CASUALTY INS CO	OR	105.4	EVERETT CASH MUTUAL INS CO	PA	118.4
CALIFORNIA HEALTHCARE INS CO INC RRG	HI	122.7	EXACT PROPERTY & CASUALTY CO INC	CA	279.3
CALLICOON CO-OPERATIVE INS CO	NY	30.2	FARMERS & MERCHANTS MUTUAL FIRE I C	MI	29.1
CAMERON MUTUAL INS CO	MO	81.4	FARMERS INS CO	KS	301.0
CAMPMED CAS & INDEM CO INC OF MD	NH	20.8	FARMERS INS CO OF AZ	AZ	44.1
CAPITOL CASUALTY CO	NE	28.7	FARMERS INS CO OF FLEMINGTON	NJ	64.1
CAPITOL SPECIALTY INS CORP	WI	135.1	FARMERS INS CO OF IDAHO	ID	198.5
CATLIN SPECIALTY INS CO	DE	656.3	FARMERS INS OF COLUMBUS INC	OH	272.1
CENTER MUTUAL INS CO	ND	54.4	FARMERS NEW CENTURY INS CO	IL	195.5
CENTRAL STATES INDEMNITY CO OF OMAHA	NE	395.5	FARMERS TEXAS COUNTY MUTUAL INS CO	TX	165.8
CHUNG KUO INS CO LTD GUAM BRANCH	GU	39.5	FARMERS UNION MUTUAL INS CO	MT	58.2
CITATION INS CO (MA)	MA	258.2	FCCI INS CO	FL	1,915.8
CITIZENS INS CO OF IL	IL	4.8	FIDELITY & DEPOSIT CO OF MARYLAND	MD	227.8
CIVIC PROPERTY & CASUALTY CO INC	CA	280.2	FIDELITY & GUARANTY INS	WI	156.0
CIVIL SERVICE EMPLOYEES INS CO	CA	212.6	FIDELITY & GUARANTY INS CO	IA	21.5
CLEAR BLUE SPECIALTY INS CO	NC	64.4	FIDELITY MOHAWK INS CO	NJ	17.0
CMIC RRG	DC	5.2	FINGER LAKES FIRE & CASUALTY CO	NY	38.5
COLONIAL AMERICAN CAS & SURETY CO	MD	30.2	FIRE DISTRICTS OF NY MUT INS CO INC	NY	83.5
COLORADO CASUALTY INS CO	NH	24.5	FIRE INS EXCHANGE	CA	2,431.5
COLUMBIA INS CO	NE	19,039.1	FIREMANS FUND INDEMNITY CORP	NJ	16.2
COLUMBIA NATIONAL INS CO	NE	91.6	FIREMANS FUND INS CO OF HI INC	HI	13.0
CONTINENTAL CASUALTY CO	IL	43,522.7	FIRST LIBERTY INS CORP	IL	22.8
CONTINENTAL DIVIDE INS CO	CO	15.7	FIRSTLINE NATIONAL INS CO	MD	87.6
CONTROLLED RISK INS CO OF VT RRG	VT	105.7	FITCHBURG MUTUAL INS CO	MA	119.3
CONVENTUS INTER-INS	NJ	88.8	FLAGSHIP CITY INS CO	PA	54.2
COOPERATIVA D SEGUROS MULTIPLES D PR	PR	509.1	FLORIDA LAWYERS MUTUAL INS CO	FL	82.3
COPPERPOINT AMERICAN INS CO	AZ	6.9	FOREMOST COUNTY MUTUAL INS CO	TX	94.9
COPPERPOINT CASUALTY INS CO	AZ	6.8	FOREMOST LLOYDS OF TEXAS	TX	68.1
COPPERPOINT PREMIER INS CO	AZ	19.6	FOREMOST P&C INS CO	MI	66.4
CSE SAFEGUARD INS CO	CA	91.5	FOREMOST SIGNATURE INS CO	MI	69.8
CYPRESS INS CO	CA	1,363.6	GENERAL REINS CORP	DE	15,099.1
CYPRESS P&C INS CO	FL	100.2	GERMANIA INS CO	TX	75.3
DAILY UNDERWRITERS OF AMERICA	PA	42.0	GERMANTOWN INS CO	PA	93.6
DAKOTA TRUCK UNDERWRITERS	SD	109.5	GRANGE P&C INS CO	OH	69.8
DE SMET FARM MUTUAL INS CO OF SD	SD	28.7	GRANITE MUTUAL INS CO	VT	4.5
DIRECT GENERAL INS CO	IN	411.0	GRANITE STATE INS CO	IL	34.7
DIRECT NATIONAL INS CO	AR	16.8	GRAPHIC ARTS MUTUAL INS CO	NY	144.5
DISCOVER P&C INS CO	CT	135.3	GRAY INS CO	LA	284.0

INSURANCE COMPANY NAME	DOM. STATE	TOTAL ASSETS ($MIL)	INSURANCE COMPANY NAME	DOM. STATE	TOTAL ASSETS ($MIL)
Rating: C+ (Continued)			NAMIC INS CO	IN	55.3
GREAT AMERICAN ASR CO	OH	19.6	NATIONAL AMERICAN INS CO	OK	189.9
GUIDEONE AMERICA INS CO	IA	13.0	NATIONAL GENL PREMIER INS CO	CA	20.4
GUIDEONE ELITE INS CO	IA	32.4	NATIONAL INDEMNITY CO OF THE SOUTH	FL	353.8
GUIDEONE NATIONAL INS CO	IA	54.1	NATIONAL INS CO OF WI	WI	20.1
GULFSTREAM P&C INS CO	FL	117.9	NATIONAL INTERSTATE INS CO	OH	1,237.9
HANOVER LLOYDS INS CO	TX	6.0	NATIONAL SPECIALTY INS CO	TX	78.0
HAWAIIAN INS & GUARANTY CO LTD	HI	26.9	NATIONWIDE INDEMNITY CO	OH	3,004.2
HERITAGE INDEMNITY CO	CA	158.0	NATIONWIDE INS CO OF FL	OH	316.9
HERITAGE P&C INS CO	FL	663.9	NEIGHBORHOOD SPIRIT PROP & CAS CO	CA	283.2
HINGHAM MUTUAL FIRE INS CO	MA	62.0	NEW JERSEY CASUALTY INS CO	NJ	560.1
HOUSING ENTERPRISE INS CO	VT	73.2	NEW JERSEY INDEMNITY INS CO	NJ	78.6
IL STATE BAR ASSOC MUTUAL INS CO	IL	74.2	NEW MEXICO MUTUAL CASUALTY CO	NM	366.2
ILLINOIS CASUALTY CO	IL	99.4	NEW MEXICO PREMIER INS CO	NM	3.7
ILLINOIS EMCASCO INS CO	IA	356.7	NORFOLK & DEDHAM MUTUAL FIRE INS CO	MA	383.8
ILLINOIS FARMERS INS CO	IL	253.3	NORTHFIELD INS CO	IA	395.1
ILLINOIS NATIONAL INS CO	IL	42.0	NOVA CASUALTY CO	NY	95.2
INDEPENDENCE AMERICAN INS CO	DE	119.6	OBI NATIONAL INS CO	PA	13.1
INDEPENDENT MUTUAL FIRE INS CO	IL	44.6	OKLAHOMA SPECIALTY INS CO	OK	20.3
INFINITY SAFEGUARD INS CO	OH	5.1	OLD GUARD INS CO	OH	435.1
INS CO OF GREATER NY	NY	119.7	PACIFIC SPECIALTY INS CO	CA	328.2
INTERNATIONAL FIDELITY INS CO	NJ	205.8	PALMETTO CASUALTY INS CO	SC	7.0
JAMES RIVER CASUALTY CO	VA	32.2	PARTNERRE AMERICA INS CO	DE	398.9
KEYSTONE NATIONAL INS CO	PA	16.9	PEERLESS INDEMNITY INS CO	IL	189.3
LACKAWANNA NATIONAL INS CO	PA	36.8	PENINSULA INS CO	MD	89.4
LAKEVIEW INS CO	FL	34.6	PERSONAL SERVICE INS CO	PA	39.2
LE MARS INS CO	IA	63.9	PLATEAU CASUALTY INS CO	TN	42.2
LEAGUE OF WI MUNICIPALITIES MUT INS	WI	69.9	PLAZA INS CO	IA	72.2
LIGHTHOUSE PROPERTY INS CORP	LA	76.4	PODIATRY INS CO OF AM	IL	303.0
MADISON MUTUAL INS CO	IL	64.6	PROASSURANCE INDEMNTIY CO INC	AL	1,394.4
MADISON MUTUAL INS CO	NY	13.5	PROFESSIONAL SECURITY INS CO	AZ	85.6
MANUFACTURING TECHNOLOGY MUT INS CO	MI	54.5	PROGRESSIVE NORTHERN INS CO	WI	1,556.6
MAPFRE INS CO OF NY	NY	154.2	PROGRESSIVE NORTHWESTERN INS CO	OH	1,516.9
MARYSVILLE MUTUAL INS CO	KS	45.1	RAINIER INS CO	AZ	25.6
MASSACHUSETTS BAY INS CO	NH	65.0	REPUBLIC-FRANKLIN INS CO	OH	104.5
MEDICAL SECURITY INS CO	NC	18.5	ROCKFORD MUTUAL INS CO	IL	77.3
MEMIC CASUALTY CO	NH	45.0	RSUI INDEMNITY CO	NH	3,423.5
MERCED PROPERTY & CASUALTY CO	CA	22.3	SAFETY INDEMNITY INS CO	MA	122.0
MICHIGAN INS CO	MI	141.0	SAFEWAY INS CO OF LA	LA	120.8
MICHIGAN PROFESSIONAL INS EXCHANGE	MI	100.3	SAN FRANCISCO REINS CO	CA	3,220.1
MID-CONTINENT CAS CO	OH	516.6	SECURA SUPREME INS CO	WI	134.9
MID-CONTINENT EXCESS & SURPLUS INS	DE	17.6	SECURITY MUTUAL INS CO	NY	102.0
MIDSTATE MUTUAL INS CO	NY	41.1	SENECA SPECIALTY INS CO	DE	49.3
MIDWEST EMPLOYERS CAS CO	DE	155.7	SEQUOIA INDEMNITY CO	NV	14.2
MILBANK INS CO	IA	606.8	SHEBOYGAN FALLS INS CO	WI	33.6
MILLVILLE MUTUAL INS CO	PA	80.2	SHELTER GENERAL INS CO	MO	131.4
MISSOURI HOSPITAL PLAN	MO	180.6	SIRIUS AMERICA INS CO	NY	1,444.0
MITSUI SUMITOMO INS USA INC	NY	135.5	SLAVONIC MUTUAL FIRE INS ASN	TX	29.5
MODERN USA INS CO	FL	45.1	SOMPO JAPAN FIRE & MAR INS CO AMER	NY	77.6
MONTEREY INS CO	CA	82.8	SOUTHERN FIDELITY P&C INC	FL	109.5
MOUNT VERNON SPECIALTY INS CO	NE	33.6	SOUTHERN INS CO OF VA	VA	143.5
MUNICH REINS AMERICA INC	DE	17,460.2	SOUTHERN MUTUAL CHURCH INS CO	SC	60.5
MUNICIPAL MUTUAL INS CO	WV	34.4	SOUTHERN MUTUAL INS CO	GA	17.0
MUTUAL RRG INC	HI	117.7	SOUTHERN STATES INS EXCHANGE	VA	48.4
MUTUALAID EXCHANGE	KS	27.7	SOUTHWEST MARINE & GEN INS CO	AZ	119.3
			ST PAUL GUARDIAN INS CO	CT	76.0

INSURANCE COMPANY NAME	DOM. STATE	TOTAL ASSETS ($MIL)
Rating: C+ (Continued)		
STANDARD CASUALTY CO	TX	38.0
STATE AUTOMOBILE MUTUAL INS CO	OH	2,449.7
STATE FARM CTY MUTUAL INS CO OF TX	TX	214.2
STEADFAST INS CO	DE	674.1
STILLWATER P&C INS CO	NY	121.7
STONEWOOD INS CO	NC	84.1
SUBLIMITY INS CO	OR	38.2
SURETEC INDEMNITY CO	CA	21.7
SURETY BONDING CO OF AMERICA	SD	7.6
SWISS REINS AMERICA CORP	NY	13,573.0
TEACHERS AUTO INS CO	NJ	22.5
TERRA INS CO (A RRG)	VT	35.2
TEXAS FARMERS INS CO	TX	357.3
THE INS CO	LA	211.8
TOKIO MILLENNIUM RE AG (US BRANCH)	NY	931.4
TOYOTA MOTOR INS CO	IA	505.3
TRAVELERS CASUALTY & SURETY CO OF AM	CT	4,564.3
TRAVELERS CASUALTY CO	CT	208.7
TRAVELERS CONSTITUTION STATE INS CO	CT	208.2
TRIANGLE INS CO	OK	90.9
TRUCK INS EXCHANGE	CA	2,206.8
UNITED FIRE & INDEMNITY CO	TX	52.5
UNITED FIRE LLOYDS	TX	30.6
UNITED GUAR RESIDENTIAL INS CO OF NC	NC	407.8
UNITED GUARANTY INS CO	NC	124.0
UNITED GUARANTY MORTGAGE INDEM CO	NC	431.1
UNITED GUARANTY MORTGAGE INS CO	NC	122.4
UNITED GUARANTY MTG INS CO OF NC	NC	124.8
UNITED NATIONAL SPECIALTY INS CO	WI	55.6
UNITED P&C INS CO	FL	575.3
UNITED STATES SURETY CO	MD	67.6
UNITED WISCONSIN INS CO	WI	395.1
UNIVERSAL INS CO OF NORTH AMERICA	FL	118.9
UNIVERSAL UNDERWRITERS INS CO	IL	404.7
UNIVERSAL UNDERWRITERS OF TX	IL	12.0
USPLATE GLASS INS CO	IL	27.7
UTICA NATIONAL INS CO OF OHIO	OH	15.3
VA FARM BUREAU TOWN & COUNTRY INS CO	VA	69.0
VOYAGER INDEMNITY INS CO	GA	123.6
WAWANESA GENERAL INS CO	CA	605.1
WAYNE MUTUAL INS CO	OH	69.4
WEST BRANCH MUTL INS CO	PA	1.1
WESTCHESTER FIRE INS CO	PA	1,753.9
WESTGUARD INS CO	PA	884.7
WI LAWYERS MUTUAL INS CO	WI	31.8
WINDSOR MOUNT JOY MUTUAL INS CO	PA	74.5
WISCONSIN COUNTY MUTUAL INS CORP	WI	86.1
ZALE INDEMNITY CO	TX	51.0
ZENITH INS CO	CA	1,902.7
ZURICH AMERICAN INS CO OF IL	IL	47.5
Rating: C		
1ST AUTO & CASUALTY INS CO	WI	29.3
ACADIA INS CO	NH	167.0
ACCESS INS CO	TX	181.7

INSURANCE COMPANY NAME	DOM. STATE	TOTAL ASSETS ($MIL)
ACCREDITED SURETY & CAS CO INC	FL	26.3
ACE FIRE UNDERWRITERS INS CO	PA	115.2
ACE INS CO OF THE MIDWEST	IN	97.8
ADM INS CO	AZ	222.3
ADMIRAL INDEMNITY CO	DE	61.3
ADMIRAL INS CO	DE	732.7
ADRIATIC INS CO	ND	84.0
AFFILIATED FM INS CO	RI	2,889.7
AGENT ALLIANCE INS CO	AL	50.5
AGRI INS EXCHANGE RRG	IN	17.0
AIG PROPERTY CASUALTY CO	PA	4,187.6
ALASKA TIMBER INS EXCHANGE	AK	15.6
ALLEGHENY CASUALTY CO	NJ	37.8
ALLIANCE INS CO	KS	26.2
ALLIANZ GLOBAL RISKS US INS CO	IL	8,012.3
ALLIED INS CO OF AMERICA	OH	39.4
ALLIED WORLD INS CO	NH	1,802.4
ALLIED WORLD SURPLUS LINES INS	AR	284.7
ALLSTATE NJ P&C INS CO	IL	66.2
AMERICA FIRST LLOYD'S INS CO	TX	6.7
AMERICAN ALTERNATIVE INS CORP	DE	518.5
AMERICAN AUTOMOBILE INS CO	MO	124.7
AMERICAN BUILDERS INS CO	DE	130.5
AMERICAN CASUALTY CO OF READING	PA	141.6
AMERICAN COASTAL INS CO	FL	329.6
AMERICAN COLONIAL INS CO	FL	46.5
AMERICAN COUNTRY INS CO	IL	93.5
AMERICAN EMPIRE INS CO	OH	49.3
AMERICAN EMPIRE SURPLUS LINES INS CO	DE	381.3
AMERICAN FARMERS & RANCHERS MUTUAL	OK	141.7
AMERICAN FEDERATED INS CO	MS	43.6
AMERICAN HOME ASR CO	NY	29,633.5
AMERICAN INTEGRITY INS CO OF FL	FL	218.9
AMERICAN INTER FIDELITY EXCHANGE RRG	IN	69.2
AMERICAN MODERN LLOYDS INS CO	TX	9.1
AMERICAN MODERN SELECT INS CO	OH	329.2
AMERICAN SAFETY INS CO	GA	18.1
AMERICAN SELECT INS CO	OH	244.7
AMERICAN SENTINEL INS CO	PA	36.3
AMERICAN SOUTHERN HOME INS CO	FL	182.1
AMERICAN STRATEGIC INS CO	FL	999.2
AMERICAN SURETY CO	IN	14.1
AMERICAN TRADITIONS INS CO	FL	50.7
AMERICAN WEST INS CO	ND	18.5
AMERICAN WESTERN HOME INS CO	OK	180.4
AMERICAS INS CO	DC	22.2
AMGUARD INS CO	PA	569.6
AMICA P&C INS CO	RI	83.2
ANCHOR GENERAL INS CO	CA	108.6
ANCHOR SPECIALTY INS CO	TX	18.5
APPALACHIAN INS CO	RI	320.8
ARBELLA INDEMNITY INS CO	MA	50.1
ARCH INS CO	MO	3,619.7
ARCHITECTS & ENGINEERS INS CO RRG	DE	21.5
ARGONAUT INS CO	IL	1,616.4
ARK ROYAL INS CO	FL	114.2

INSURANCE COMPANY NAME	DOM. STATE	TOTAL ASSETS ($MIL)	INSURANCE COMPANY NAME	DOM. STATE	TOTAL ASSETS ($MIL)
Rating: C (Continued)			CIM INS CORP	MI	17.7
ARTISAN & TRUCKERS CASUALTY CO	WI	324.4	CITIES & VILLAGES MUTUAL INS CO	WI	51.9
ASOC DE SUSCRIPCION CONJUNTA DEL SEG	PR	169.7	CITIZENS INS CO OF OHIO	OH	15.8
ASPEN SPECIALTY INS CO	ND	374.7	CITIZENS INS CO OF THE MIDWEST	IN	51.5
ASSN CASUALTY INS CO	TX	46.7	CLARENDON NATIONAL INS CO	IL	814.8
ASSOCIATED EMPLOYERS INS CO	MA	5.3	CLEAR BLUE INS CO	IL	18.0
ASSOCIATED INDEMNITY CORP	CA	122.0	CLERMONT INS CO	IA	26.0
ASSOCIATED LOGGERS EXCHANGE	ID	33.3	CM REGENT INS CO	PA	170.8
ASSOCIATED MUTUAL INS CO	NY	26.9	COFACE NORTH AMERICA INS CO	MA	157.9
ATAIN INS CO	TX	80.8	COLONIAL SURETY CO	PA	55.5
ATAIN SPECIALTY INS CO	MI	351.5	COLONY INS CO	VA	1,450.9
ATRADIUS TRADE CREDIT INS CO	MD	110.6	COLORADO FARM BUREAU MUTUAL INS CO	CO	86.7
AUTO CLUB FAMILY INS CO	MO	113.3	COLUMBIA CASUALTY CO	IL	236.2
AUTO CLUB PROPERTY & CASUALTY INS CO	MI	85.3	COLUMBIA LLOYDS INS CO	TX	51.9
AUTOMOBILE CLUB INTERINSURANCE EXCH	MO	419.5	COMMERCE & INDUSTRY INS CO	NY	482.6
AXA ART INS CORP	NY	25.7	COMMERCE INS CO	MA	2,244.5
AXIS SURPLUS INS CO	IL	480.5	COMMERCE WEST INS CO	CA	173.5
BANKERS INDEPENDENT INS CO	PA	26.5	COMMERCIAL ALLIANCE INS CO	TX	76.7
BANKERS INS CO	FL	146.1	COMMUNITY BLOOD CENTERS EXCHANGE RRG	IN	20.7
BANKERS SPECIALTY INS CO	LA	58.3	COMMUNITY HOSPITAL ALTERNATIVE RRG	VT	266.1
BANKERS STANDARD FIRE & MARINE CO	PA	203.0	COMMUNITY INS CORP	WI	8.7
BANKERS STANDARD INS CO	PA	502.6	COMP OPTIONS INS CO	FL	115.1
BAR PLAN MUTUAL INS CO	MO	44.2	COMPTRUST AGC MUT CAPTIVE INS CO	GA	32.8
BAR PLAN SURETY & FIDELITY CO	MO	5.5	COMPWEST INS CO	CA	258.3
BARNSTABLE COUNTY INS CO	MA	23.2	CONSOLIDATED INS CO	IN	13.4
BEARING MIDWEST CASUALTY CO	KS	6.2	CONSTITUTION INS CO	NY	24.8
BERKLEY NATIONAL INS CO	IA	111.7	CONTINENTAL HERITAGE INS CO	FL	7.5
BERKLEY REGIONAL SPECIALTY INS CO	DE	60.6	CONTINENTAL INDEMNITY CO	IA	177.9
BLUE RIDGE INDEMNITY CO	WI	8.4	CONTINENTAL INS CO	PA	1,685.8
BREMEN FARMERS MUTUAL INS CO	KS	42.7	CONTINENTAL INS CO OF NJ	NJ	18.4
BRIAR CREEK MUTUAL INS CO	PA	13.3	CONTINENTAL WESTERN INS CO	IA	230.0
BRICKSTREET MUTUAL INS CO	WV	1,931.4	COPPERPOINT INDEMNITY INS CO	AZ	10.9
BRIDGEFIELD CASUALTY INS CO	FL	65.1	COPPERPOINT NATIONAL INS CO	AZ	6.6
BROOME CO OPERATIVE INS CO	NY	20.6	CORNERSTONE NATIONAL INS CO	MO	31.7
BUILDERS INS (A MUTUAL CAPTIVE CO)	GA	546.3	COUNTRYWAY INS CO	NY	27.9
BUILDERS PREMIER INS CO	NC	11.8	COVENANT INS CO	CT	91.4
BUNKER HILL INS CO	MA	56.8	CROSSFIT RRG INC	MT	6.8
BUS ALLIANCE INS CO	CA	24.2	CSAA AFFINITY INS CO	AZ	212.4
BUSINESSFIRST INS CO	FL	41.1	CSAA FIRE & CASUALTY INS CO	IN	106.5
CALIFORNIA CAS GEN INS CO OF OREGON	OR	108.2	CSAA GENERAL INS CO	IN	296.4
CALIFORNIA CASUALTY & FIRE INS CO	CA	66.4	CUMIS MORTGAGE REINS CO	WI	11.3
CAMICO MUTUAL INS CO	CA	91.4	DAKOTA FIRE INS CO	ND	231.0
CAPITOL COUNTY MUTUAL FIRE INS CO	TX	11.7	DANBURY INS CO	MA	11.8
CAPITOL INDEMNITY CORP	WI	508.9	DENTISTS BENEFITS INS CO	OR	17.3
CARIBBEAN AMERICAN PROPERTY INS CO	PR	42.3	DEVELOPERS SURETY & INDEMNITY CO	IA	130.9
CARING COMMUNITIES RECIP RRG	DC	81.4	DIRECT INS CO	TN	84.3
CAROLINA CASUALTY INS CO	IA	181.1	DOCTORS DIRECT INS INC	IL	14.2
CASCO INDEMNITY CO	ME	29.8	DORCHESTER INS CO LTD	VI	21.3
CATLIN INDEMNITY CO	DE	124.3	DORCHESTER MUTUAL INS CO	MA	85.7
CATLIN INS CO	TX	250.6	DTRIC INS CO LTD	HI	100.4
CELINA MUTUAL INS CO	OH	70.3	DTRIC INS UNDERWRITERS LTD	HI	11.7
CENSTAT CASUALTY CO	NE	23.2	EASTERN DENTISTS INS CO RRG	VT	54.8
CHAUTAUQUA PATRONS INS CO	NY	21.4	EASTERN MUTUAL INS CO	NY	24.3
CHEROKEE INS CO	MI	469.7	ECHELON P&C INS CO	IL	15.5
CHICAGO INS CO	IL	101.5	ECOLE INS CO	AZ	11.3
			EDISON INS CO	FL	39.3

INSURANCE COMPANY NAME	DOM. STATE	TOTAL ASSETS ($MIL)
Rating: C (Continued)		
ELEMENTS PROPERTY INS CO	FL	62.3
ELEPHANT INS CO	VA	162.2
EMC PROPERTY & CASUALTY CO	IA	122.8
EMPLOYERS ASSURANCE CO	FL	489.8
EMPLOYERS PREFERRED INS CO	FL	1,089.3
ENCOMPASS INS CO	IL	9.6
ENCOMPASS INS CO OF MA	MA	6.5
EQUITY INS CO	TX	82.0
ESSENTIA INS CO	MO	80.3
ESURANCE INS CO	WI	195.2
ESURANCE INS CO OF NJ	WI	14.5
EVANSTON INS CO	IL	4,264.1
EVER-GREENE MUTUAL INS CO	PA	5.8
EVEREST INDEMNITY INS CO	DE	167.1
EVEREST SECURITY INS CO	GA	39.9
EVERGREEN NATIONAL INDEMNITY CO	OH	45.2
EXCELSIOR INS CO	NH	36.3
EXCESS SHARE INS CORP	OH	51.7
EXPLORER INS CO	CA	336.6
FAIRMONT FARMERS MUTUAL INS CO	MN	32.9
FALLS LAKE GENERAL INS CO	OH	6.6
FAMILY SECURITY INS CO	HI	33.3
FARM BUREAU CNTY MUTUAL INS CO OF TX	TX	19.9
FARMERS FIRE INS CO	PA	26.3
FARMERS INS EXCHANGE	CA	16,189.6
FARMERS MUTUAL F I C OF OKARCHE OK	OK	18.2
FARMERS MUTUAL FIRE INS CO OF MARBLE	PA	29.4
FARMERS MUTUAL INS CO	WV	14.8
FARMERS MUTUAL OF TENNESSEE	TN	23.1
FARMERS REINS CO	CA	591.9
FD INS CO	FL	43.9
FEDERATED NATIONAL INS CO	FL	500.7
FFVA MUTUAL INS CO	FL	335.1
FINANCIAL CASUALTY & SURETY INC	TX	24.0
FIREMANS FUND INS CO	CA	2,208.8
FIREMANS FUND INS CO OF OH	OH	53.3
FIREMENS INS CO OF WASHINGTON DC	DE	102.5
FIRST ACCEPTANCE INS CO	TX	269.3
FIRST ACCEPTANCE INS CO OF GEORGIA	GA	90.4
FIRST ACCEPTANCE INS CO OF TN INC	TN	30.4
FIRST AMERICAN PROP & CAS INS CO	CA	99.5
FIRST AMERICAN SPECIALTY INS CO	CA	115.7
FIRST COMMUNITY INS CO	FL	101.2
FIRST DAKOTA INDEMNITY CO	SD	43.9
FIRST F&C INS OF HI INC	HI	9.1
FIRST INDEMNITY INS OF HI INC	HI	7.4
FIRST INS CO OF HI LTD	HI	653.7
FIRST MEDICAL INS CO RRG	VT	92.2
FIRST PROFESSIONALS INS CO INC	FL	270.6
FIRST SECURITY INS OF HI INC	HI	5.5
FIRST SPECIALTY INS CORP	MO	212.6
FLORIDA PENINSULA INS CO	FL	346.1
FLORIDA SPECIALTY INS CO	FL	59.3
FLORISTS INS CO	IL	6.7

INSURANCE COMPANY NAME	DOM. STATE	TOTAL ASSETS ($MIL)
FORESTRY MUTUAL INS CO	NC	59.5
FOUNDERS INS CO (IL)	IL	155.2
FOUNDERS INS CO (NJ)	NJ	6.5
FRANKLIN INS CO	PA	28.7
GEICO COUNTY MUTUAL INS CO	TX	88.9
GEMINI INS CO	DE	128.7
GENERAL AUTOMOBILE INS CO	OH	101.1
GENERAL CASUALTY CO OF WI	WI	1,086.9
GENERAL INS CO OF AM	NH	108.3
GENERAL STAR INDEMNITY CO	DE	749.0
GENESIS INS CO	DE	176.7
GENWORTH MORTGAGE INS CORP	NC	2,817.4
GENWORTH MTG INS CORP OF NC	NC	342.0
GEORGIA CASUALTY & SURETY CO	GA	40.9
GEOVERA SPECIALTY INS CO	DE	108.1
GERMANIA FIRE & CASUALTY CO	TX	30.6
GOLDEN BEAR INS CO	CA	133.4
GOLDEN EAGLE INS CORP	NH	58.7
GOTHAM INS CO	NY	223.9
GRAIN DEALERS MUTUAL INS CO	IN	9.8
GRANGE INDEMNITY INS CO	OH	106.0
GRANGE INS CO OF MI	OH	74.1
GRANITE RE INC	OK	47.0
GRANWEST P&C	WA	21.6
GRAY CASUALTY & SURETY CO	LA	17.3
GREAT AMERICAN ALLIANCE INS CO	OH	30.1
GREAT AMERICAN E & S INS CO	DE	47.1
GREAT AMERICAN FIDELITY INS CO	DE	47.2
GREAT AMERICAN INS CO OF NEW YORK	NY	47.7
GREAT AMERICAN PROTECTION INS CO	OH	21.9
GREAT AMERICAN SECURITY INS CO	OH	15.2
GREAT AMERICAN SPIRIT INS CO	OH	16.8
GREAT DIVIDE INS CO	ND	246.2
GREAT LAKES CASUALTY INS CO	MI	17.4
GREAT PLAINS CASUALTY INC	IA	18.2
GREENWICH INS CO	DE	1,118.6
GRINNELL SELECT INS CO	IA	38.4
GUARDIAN INS CO	VI	32.4
GULF GUARANTY INS CO	MS	4.4
HALLMARK COUNTY MUTUAL INS CO	TX	5.9
HALLMARK NATIONAL INS CO	AZ	84.4
HAMILTON MUTUAL INS CO	IA	86.3
HANOVER AMERICAN INS CO	NH	30.2
HARLEYSVILLE INS CO	PA	153.1
HARLEYSVILLE INS CO OF NEW YORK	PA	77.8
HARLEYSVILLE LAKE STATES INS CO	MI	62.7
HARTLAND MUTUAL INS CO	ND	13.1
HAWAII EMPLOYERS MUTUAL INS CO	HI	376.8
HAWKEYE-SECURITY INS CO	WI	13.7
HDI GLOBAL INS CO	IL	329.9
HEALTH CARE INDEMNITY INC	CO	438.3
HEALTHCARE UNDERWRITERS GRP MUT OH	OH	91.2
HEREFORD INS CO	NY	199.4
HIGHMARK CASUALTY INS CO	PA	452.5
HILLSTAR INS CO	IN	3.6
HOCHHEIM PRAIRIE CASUALTY INS CO	TX	73.8

INSURANCE COMPANY NAME	DOM. STATE	TOTAL ASSETS ($MIL)	INSURANCE COMPANY NAME	DOM. STATE	TOTAL ASSETS ($MIL)
Rating: C (Continued)			LIBERTY INS UNDERWRITERS INC	IL	192.6
HOME & FARM INS CO	IN	10.0	LIBERTY MUTUAL MID ATLANTIC INS CO	MA	20.1
HOME STATE COUNTY MUTUAL INS CO	TX	291.9	LIBERTY NORTHWEST INS CORP	OR	54.6
HOMELAND INS CO OF NY	NY	114.8	LIBERTY PERSONAL INS CO	NH	16.8
HOMESITE INDEMNITY CO	KS	56.2	LIBERTY SURPLUS INS CORP	NH	164.9
HOMESITE INS CO	CT	154.1	LIVINGSTON MUTUAL INS CO	PA	2.9
HOMESITE INS CO OF CA	CA	51.7	LM INS CORP	IL	118.5
HOMESITE INS CO OF FL	IL	13.5	LUTHERAN MUTUAL FIRE INS CO	IL	10.5
HOMESITE INS CO OF GA	GA	19.0	MA EMPLOYERS INS CO	MA	4.3
HOMESITE INS CO OF IL	IL	12.9	MAIN STREET AMERICA ASR CO	FL	43.3
HOMESITE INS CO OF NY	NY	30.8	MAISON INS CO	LA	51.6
HOMESITE INS CO OF THE MIDWEST	ND	426.6	MAPFRE INS CO	NJ	79.5
HOSPITALITY INS CO	MA	12.2	MAPFRE INS CO OF FLORIDA	FL	104.4
HOUSING & REDEVELOPMENT INS EXCH	PA	47.6	MAPFRE PAN AMERICAN INS CO	PR	24.2
HOUSING SPECIALTY INS CO	VT	17.3	MAPLE VALLEY MUTUAL INS CO	WI	13.4
ILLINOIS INS CO	IA	46.5	MARKEL AMERICAN INS CO	VA	364.7
ILLINOIS UNION INS CO	IL	408.6	MARKEL INS CO	IL	1,525.8
IMPERIAL F&C INS CO	LA	100.2	MASSACHUSETTS HOMELAND INS CO	MA	8.9
INDEMNITY CO OF CA	CA	21.2	MAXUM CASUALTY INS CO	DE	52.1
INDEMNITY INS CO OF NORTH AMERICA	PA	462.8	MAXUM INDEMNITY CO	DE	280.8
INDEMNITY NATIONAL INS CO	MS	23.1	MCMILLAN WARNER MUTUAL INS CO	WI	16.2
INDIANA INS CO	IN	69.8	MDADVANTAGE INS CO OF NJ	NJ	364.6
INDIANA LUMBERMENS MUTUAL INS CO	IN	57.4	MEDMARC CASUALTY INS CO	VT	276.4
INDIANA OLD NATIONAL INS CO	VT	2,150.0	MEEMIC INS CO	MI	249.2
INFINITY AUTO INS CO	OH	9.7	MEMIC INDEMNITY CO	NH	425.5
INFINITY COUNTY MUTUAL INS CO	TX	39.3	MENNONITE MUTUAL INS CO	OH	26.2
INFINITY INDEMNITY INS CO	IN	6.0	MENTAL HEALTH RISK RETENTION GROUP	VT	28.2
INFINITY PREFERRED INS CO	OH	4.9	MERCER INS CO	PA	263.7
INFINITY SECURITY INS CO	IN	6.0	MERCER INS CO OF NJ INC	NJ	88.4
INFINITY STANDARD INS CO	IN	7.0	MERCHANTS NATIONAL BONDING INC	IA	29.0
INLAND INS CO	NE	250.8	MERCURY INS CO OF FL	FL	44.6
INS CO OF NORTH AMERICA	PA	898.7	MERIDIAN SECURITY INS CO	IN	123.3
INS CO OF THE STATE OF PA	PA	222.7	MERITPLAN INS CO	CA	14.6
INS CO OF THE WEST	CA	2,066.2	MESA UNDERWRITERS SPECIALTY INS CO	NJ	320.0
INTEGON CASUALTY INS CO	NC	40.0	MGA INS CO	TX	254.5
INTEGON GENERAL INS CORP	NC	37.0	MHA INS CO	MI	561.1
INTEGON INDEMNITY CORP	NC	101.9	MIC GENERAL INS CORP	MI	42.1
INTEGON NATIONAL INS CO	NC	2,215.7	MIC P&C INS CORP	MI	97.2
INTEGON PREFERRED INS CO	NC	70.2	MID-CONTINENT INS CO	OH	20.4
INTEGRAND ASR CO	PR	118.0	MID-HUDSON CO-OPERTIVE INS CO	NY	23.9
INTERSTATE FIRE & CAS CO	IL	109.2	MIDSOUTH MUTUAL INS CO	TN	26.2
IRONSHORE SPECIALTY INS CO	AZ	1,111.8	MIDWEST INS CO	IL	88.7
ISLAND PREMIER INS CO LTD	HI	10.3	MIDWESTERN INDEMNITY CO	NH	27.7
JAMES RIVER INS CO	OH	556.3	MONROE GUARANTY INS CO	IN	51.6
JEFFERSON INS CO	NY	85.7	MONTGOMERY MUTUAL INS CO	MA	51.7
KEY RISK INS CO	IA	50.5	MOUNT VERNON FIRE INS CO	PA	555.8
KINGSTONE INS CO	NY	116.4	MOUNTAIN LAUREL ASR CO	OH	162.8
LAMORAK INS CO	PA	26.0	MOUNTAIN STATES INDEMNITY CO	NM	51.2
LANCER INDEMNITY CO	NY	28.0	MT HAWLEY INS CO	IL	924.7
LANDCAR CASUALTY CO	UT	40.1	MT WASHINGTON ASR CORP	NH	6.7
LANDMARK AMERICAN INS CO	OK	402.9	MUTUAL OF WAUSAU INS CORP	WI	23.7
LAWYERS MUTUAL INS CO OF KENTUCKY	KY	24.0	NATIONAL CONTINENTAL INS CO	NY	141.6
LEATHERSTOCKING COOP INS CO	NY	32.0	NATIONAL FARMERS UNION PROP & CAS CO	WI	182.7
LEBANON VALLEY INS CO	PA	25.2	NATIONAL FIRE & CASUALTY CO	IL	7.9
LEXINGTON INS CO	DE	25,270.1	NATIONAL FIRE & MARINE INS CO	NE	8,533.9
			NATIONAL FIRE INS CO OF HARTFORD	IL	115.8

INSURANCE COMPANY NAME	DOM. STATE	TOTAL ASSETS ($MIL)
Rating: C (Continued)		
NATIONAL GENERAL ASR CO	MO	43.2
NATIONAL GENERAL INS CO	MO	57.2
NATIONAL GENERAL INS ONLINE INC	MO	41.0
NATIONAL INDEMNITY CO OF MID-AMERICA	IA	236.5
NATIONAL MORTGAGE RE INC ONE	WI	43.6
NATIONAL MUTUAL INS CO	OH	75.4
NATIONAL SERVICE CONTRACT INS CO RRG	DC	13.2
NATIONAL SURETY CORP	IL	133.6
NATIONAL TRUST INS CO	IN	36.3
NATIONAL UNION FIRE INS CO OF PITTSB	PA	27,169.5
NAU COUNTRY INS CO	MN	1,291.9
NAUTILUS INS CO	AZ	264.0
NETHERLANDS INS CO	NH	92.0
NEW CENTURY INS CO	TX	9.2
NEW HAMPSHIRE INS CO	IL	213.0
NEW MEXICO FOUNDATION INS CO	NM	23.4
NEW SOUTH INS CO	NC	52.8
NOETIC SPECIALTY INS CO	VT	123.0
NORTH AMERICAN CAPACITY INS CO	NH	99.2
NORTH AMERICAN ELITE INS CO	NH	124.2
NORTH AMERICAN SPECIALTY INS CO	NH	462.5
NORTH COUNTRY INS CO	NY	27.1
NORTH PACIFIC INS CO	OR	7.9
NORTHERN MUTUAL INS CO	MI	33.6
NORTHERN SECURITY INS CO	VT	8.5
NORTHSTONE INS CO	PA	57.5
NORTHWEST DENTISTS INS CO	WA	21.3
OAK RIVER INS CO	NE	606.1
ODYSSEY REINS CO	CT	7,394.0
OHIO CASUALTY INS CO	NH	5,600.3
OHIO INDEMNITY CO	OH	151.0
OKLAHOMA SURETY CO	OH	16.5
OLD UNITED CAS CO	KS	566.2
OMEGA ONE INS CO	AL	12.4
ONTARIO INS CO	NY	17.1
OOIDA RISK RETENTION GROUP INC	VT	96.4
OREGON AUTOMOBILE INS CO	OR	7.8
OSWEGO COUNTY MUTUAL INS CO	NY	25.4
PACIFIC INDEMNITY INS CO	GU	33.1
PACIFIC STAR INS CO	WI	13.1
PACO ASR CO INC	IL	73.5
PALISADES SAFETY & INS ASSOC	NJ	1,159.7
PALMETTO SURETY CORP	SC	11.2
PARTNER REINSURANCE CO OF THE US	NY	5,025.4
PARTNERRE INS CO OF NY	NY	126.5
PATRIOT INS CO	ME	112.0
PATRONS MUTUAL INS CO OF CT	CT	53.6
PATRONS OXFORD INS CO	ME	21.6
PENINSULA INDEMNITY CO	MD	11.5
PENN CHARTER MUTL INS CO	PA	14.1
PENN MILLERS INS CO	PA	118.5
PENN-AMERICA INS CO	PA	148.6
PENN-PATRIOT INS CO	VA	21.6
PENN-STAR INS CO	PA	132.5

INSURANCE COMPANY NAME	DOM. STATE	TOTAL ASSETS ($MIL)
PENNSYLVANIA INS CO	IA	58.8
PENNSYLVANIA MANUFACTURERS ASN INS	PA	876.8
PENNSYLVANIA MANUFACTURERS IND CO	PA	205.3
PERMANENT GEN ASR CORP OF OHIO	OH	200.4
PETROLEUM CAS CO	TX	37.8
PHYSICIANS PROFESSIONAL LIABILTY RRG	VT	36.4
PILGRIM INS CO	MA	79.9
PINNACLEPOINT INS CO	WV	60.9
PLANS LIABILITY INS CO	OH	76.1
PLATTE RIVER INS CO	NE	136.4
POSITIVE PHYSICIANS INS	PA	53.7
PRAETORIAN INS CO	PA	658.9
PRE-PAID LEGAL CAS INC	OK	19.9
PREFERRED EMPLOYERS INS CO	CA	102.1
PREMIER GROUP INS CO	TN	62.9
PRIME INS CO	IL	79.0
PRIME P&C INS INC	IL	19.9
PRINCETON EXCESS & SURPLUS LINES INS	DE	147.6
PRINCETON INS CO	NJ	667.4
PRIORITY ONE INS CO	TX	20.0
PROASSURANCE SPECIALTY INS CO INC	AL	48.6
PRODUCERS AGRICULTURE INS CO	TX	734.5
PRODUCERS LLOYDS INS CO	TX	6.4
PROGRESSIVE ADVANCED INS CO	OH	462.3
PROGRESSIVE AMERICAN INS CO	OH	472.8
PROGRESSIVE BAYSIDE INS CO	OH	152.2
PROGRESSIVE CLASSIC INS CO	WI	401.7
PROGRESSIVE COUNTY MUTUAL INS CO	TX	551.8
PROGRESSIVE DIRECT INS CO	OH	6,529.2
PROGRESSIVE EXPRESS INS CO	OH	237.6
PROGRESSIVE FREEDOM INS CO	NJ	4.0
PROGRESSIVE GULF INS CO	OH	269.4
PROGRESSIVE HAWAII INS CORP	OH	197.7
PROGRESSIVE MARATHON INS CO	MI	510.9
PROGRESSIVE MAX INS CO	OH	482.5
PROGRESSIVE MICHIGAN INS CO	MI	528.2
PROGRESSIVE MOUNTAIN INS CO	OH	294.5
PROGRESSIVE PALOVERDE INS CO	IN	150.6
PROGRESSIVE PREFERRED INS CO	OH	774.8
PROGRESSIVE PREMIER INS CO OF IL	OH	270.8
PROGRESSIVE SECURITY INS CO	LA	286.3
PROGRESSIVE SELECT INS CO	OH	642.7
PROGRESSIVE SOUTHEASTERN INS CO	IN	178.0
PROGRESSIVE SPECIALTY INS CO	OH	979.7
PROGRESSIVE UNIVERSAL INS CO	WI	375.6
PROGRESSIVE WEST INS CO	OH	134.2
PROSELECT INS CO	MA	95.8
QUALITAS INS CO	CA	42.8
REDWOOD FIRE & CAS INS CO	NE	1,512.1
REGENT INS CO	WI	90.8
RELIABLE LLOYDS INS CO	TX	17.8
RELIAMAX SURETY CO	SD	52.3
REPUBLIC FIRE & CASUALTY INS CO	OK	9.1
REPUBLIC INDEMNITY OF CA	CA	32.0
REPUBLIC LLOYDS	TX	12.2
REPUBLIC MORTGAGE INS CO OF FLORIDA	FL	24.1

INSURANCE COMPANY NAME	DOM. STATE	TOTAL ASSETS ($MIL)	INSURANCE COMPANY NAME	DOM. STATE	TOTAL ASSETS ($MIL)
Rating: C (Continued)			TOKIO MARINE PACIFIC INS LTD	GU	117.4
REPUBLIC UNDERWRITERS INS CO	TX	712.4	TOKIO MARINE SPECIALTY INS CO	DE	563.1
RESTORATION RRG INC	VT	77.2	TOWER HILL SELECT INS CO	FL	75.6
RETAILERS CASUALTY INS CO	LA	79.8	TRADEWIND INS CO LTD	HI	12.5
ROCHE SURETY & CASUALTY INC	FL	24.2	TRANS CITY CASUALTY INS CO	AZ	18.0
ROCKHILL INS CO	AZ	171.0	TRANSPORTATION INS CO	IL	80.1
ROCKINGHAM CASUALTY CO	VA	30.7	TRI-CENTURY INS CO	PA	30.9
RVI AMERICA INS CO	CT	106.2	TRI-STATE INS CO OF MN	IA	48.7
SAFE HARBOR INS CO	FL	83.5	TRIUMPHE CASUALTY CO	OH	61.9
SAFETY FIRST INS CO	IL	71.9	TUDOR INS CO	NH	262.5
SAFETY NATIONAL CASUALTY CORP	MO	6,043.9	UNIGARD INDEMNITY CO	WI	10.6
SAFETY P&C INS CO	MA	45.1	UNIGARD INS CO	WI	494.9
SAFEWAY INS CO OF AL	IL	60.1	UNION INS CO	IA	133.0
SAFEWAY INS CO OF GA	GA	60.8	UNION INS CO OF PROVIDENCE	IA	88.6
SEAVIEW INS CO	CA	23.1	UNION STANDARD LLOYDS	TX	2.7
SELECT RISK INS CO	PA	41.9	UNITED FRONTIER MUTUAL INS CO	NY	15.9
SEQUOIA INS CO	CA	197.0	UNITED GUARANTY RESIDENTIAL INS CO	NC	3,161.8
SEVEN SEAS INS CO	FL	19.1	UNITED NATIONAL INS CO	PA	461.8
SIMED	PR	159.8	UNITED STATES FIDELITY & GUARANTY CO	CT	3,700.2
SONNENBERG MUTUAL INS CO	OH	24.6	UNIVERSAL NORTH AMERICA INS CO	TX	200.3
SOUTH CAROLINA FARM BU MUTUAL INS CO	SC	107.9	UNIVERSAL SURETY CO	NE	184.9
SOUTHERN COUNTY MUTUAL INS CO	TX	34.3	UNIVERSAL SURETY OF AMERICA	SD	14.6
SOUTHERN FIRE & CASUALTY CO	WI	7.7	UPLAND MUTUAL INS INC	KS	27.7
SOUTHERN INS CO	TX	38.5	US FIRE INS CO	DE	3,914.8
SOUTHERN OAK INS CO	FL	130.3	US LIABILITY INS CO	PA	886.0
SOUTHERN PILOT INS CO	WI	12.4	US UNDERWRITERS INS CO	ND	165.7
SOUTHERN PIONEER PROP & CAS INS CO	AR	44.3	UTICA NATIONAL ASR CO	NY	63.7
SOUTHERN UNDERWRITERS INS CO	OK	5.4	UTICA NATIONAL INS CO OF TX	TX	34.4
SOUTHERN VANGUARD INS CO	TX	24.5	VALLEY FORGE INS CO	PA	71.6
SPARTA AMERICAN INS CO	CA	33.0	VERSANT CASUALTY INS CO	MS	39.5
SPARTAN PROPERTY INS CO	SC	28.6	VICTORIA FIRE & CASUALTY CO	OH	133.7
ST PAUL SURPLUS LINES INS CO	DE	641.4	VIKING INS CO OF WI	WI	413.6
STANDARD MUTUAL INS CO	IL	53.1	VIRGINIA FARM BUREAU FIRE & CAS INS	VA	58.6
STAR INS CO	MI	862.8	WADENA INS CO	IA	5.4
STARNET INS CO	DE	236.0	WASHINGTON INTL INS CO	NH	104.3
STARSTONE NATIONAL INS CO	DE	274.7	WAUSAU BUSINESS INS CO	WI	35.4
STATE AUTO P&C INS CO	IA	2,404.1	WAUSAU UNDERWRITERS INS CO	WI	109.0
STATE FARM GUARANTY INS CO	IL	36.8	WAYNE COOPERATIVE INS CO	NY	29.9
STATE MUTUAL INS CO (ME)	ME	2.5	WEA P&C INS CO	WI	17.0
STATE NATIONAL FIRE INS CO	LA	2.4	WELLINGTON INS CO	TX	41.7
STONETRUST COMMERCIAL INS CO	LA	147.3	WESTCHESTER SURPLUS LINES INS CO	GA	354.8
STRATHMORE INS CO	NY	54.8	WESTERN HOME INS CO	MN	71.7
SU INS CO	WI	16.1	WESTERN NATIONAL ASR CO	MN	65.7
SUMMITPOINT INS CO	WV	42.5	WESTERN PROTECTORS INS CO	OR	9.7
SUSSEX INS CO	SC	758.6	WESTERN SELECT INS CO	IL	17.4
SUTTER INS CO	CA	37.8	WESTERN SURETY CO	SD	1,962.4
TANK OWNER MEMBERS INS CO	TX	27.4	WESTERN WORLD INS CO	NH	905.5
TDC NATIONAL ASR CO	OR	304.0	WESTMINSTER AMERICAN INS CO	MD	27.7
TDC SPECIALTY INS CO	DC	67.1	WESTON INS CO	FL	81.5
TECHNOLOGY INS CO	NH	2,351.4	WHITE PINE INS CO	MI	41.5
TEXAS FARM BUREAU UNDERWRITERS	TX	57.2	WISCONSIN MUNICIPAL MUTUAL INS CO	WI	54.4
TEXAS HERITAGE INS CO	TX	22.1	WISCONSIN REINS CORP	WI	91.1
TEXAS INS CO	TX	28.6	WOLVERINE MUTUAL INS CO	MI	56.2
TEXAS LAWYERS INS EXCHANGE	TX	87.6	WORTH CASUALTY CO	TX	18.4
THAMES INS CO	CT	28.3	WRIGHT NATIONAL FLOOD INS CO	TX	32.3
			XL INS AMERICA INC	DE	742.2

INSURANCE COMPANY NAME	DOM. STATE	TOTAL ASSETS ($MIL)	INSURANCE COMPANY NAME	DOM. STATE	TOTAL ASSETS ($MIL)
Rating: C (Continued)			CBIA COMP SERVICES INC	CT	24.5
XL REINS AMERICA INC	NY	5,935.1	CENTAURI SPECIALTY INS CO	FL	118.6
XL SPECIALTY INS CO	DE	846.2	CENTRAL CO-OPERATIVE INS CO	NY	16.0
YEL CO INS	FL	16.8	CENTRAL PA PHYSICIANS RRG INC	SC	58.7
YORK INS CO OF MAINE	ME	47.0	CENTURY MUTUAL INS CO	NC	9.3
YOSEMITE INS CO	IN	156.4	CENTURY SURETY CO	OH	561.5
ZNAT INS CO	CA	68.6	CLEARFIELD CTY GRNGE MUT FIRE INS CO	PA	2.9
Rating: C-			CLOISTER MUTL CAS INS CO	PA	9.6
ACCEPTANCE INDEMNITY INS CO	NE	269.7	COASTAL AMERICAN INS CO	MS	8.3
ACCESS HOME INS CO	LA	44.8	COASTAL SELECT INS CO	CA	108.3
ADIRONDACK INS EXCHANGE	NY	252.9	COLLEGE RRG INC	VT	20.9
AFFINITY MUTUAL INS CO	OH	14.2	COMMUNITIES OF FAITH RRG INC	SC	14.6
AGRI GENERAL INS CO	IA	112.3	CONEMAUGH VALLEY MUTUAL INS CO	PA	8.6
ALAMANCE INS CO	IL	485.5	CONSOLIDATED INS ASSN	TX	3.0
ALINSCO INS CO	TX	62.2	COREPOINTE INS CO	MI	101.4
ALLIANCE OF NONPROFITS FOR INS RRG	VT	94.2	CPA MUTL INS CO OF AM (A RRG)	VT	18.5
ALLIANCE UNITED INS CO	CA	519.6	CSAA MID-ATLANTIC INS CO	AZ	35.5
ALLIANZ UNDERWRITERS INS CO	IL	91.5	CSAA MID-ATLANTIC INS CO OF NJ	NJ	50.3
ALLIED PROFESSIONALS INS CO RRG	AZ	49.7	CYPRESS TEXAS INS CO	TX	50.6
AMERICAN ASSOC OF ORTHODONTIST RRG	AZ	45.3	DE SMET INS CO OF SD	SD	15.1
AMERICAN BUS & MERCANTILE INS MUT	DE	65.1	DEALERS CHOICE MUTUAL INS INC	NC	24.7
AMERICAN EXCESS INS EXCHANGE RRG	VT	325.9	DELTA FIRE & CAS INS CO	GA	7.3
AMERICAN FIRE & CASUALTY CO	NH	40.6	DIRECT GENERAL INS CO OF LA	LA	25.9
AMERICAN INDEPENDENT INS CO	PA	56.3	DIRECT GENERAL INS CO OF MS	MS	36.9
AMERICAN INS CO	OH	140.2	DORINCO REINS CO	MI	1,575.2
AMERICAN MILLENNIUM INS CO	NJ	35.1	DUBOIS MEDICAL RRG	DC	11.7
AMERICAN MUTUAL SHARE INS CORP	OH	255.4	EASTERN ATLANTIC INS CO	PA	66.8
AMERITRUST INS CORP	MI	115.2	EMERGENCY MEDICINE PROFESSIONAL ASR	NV	19.4
ANTHRACITE MUTUAL FIRE INS CO	PA	3.9	EMERGENCY PHYSICIANS INS RRG	VT	31.5
ANTILLES INS CO	PR	72.2	ESURANCE P&C INS CO	WI	98.0
APOLLO MUTUAL FIRE INS CO	PA	3.9	FALCON INS CO	IL	36.3
APPLIED MEDICO LEGAL SOLUTIONS RRG	AZ	134.3	FARM BUREAU NEW HORIZONS INS CO MO	MO	45.8
ARCH MORTGAGE REINS CO	WI	20.8	FARMERS & MECHANICS FIRE & CAS INS	WV	11.3
ARCH REINS CO	DE	1,963.4	FARMERS MUTUAL F I C OF MCCANDLESS	PA	10.2
ARIZONA AUTOMOBILE INS CO	AZ	23.0	FCCI COMMERCIAL INS CO	FL	14.6
ARKANSAS MUTUAL INS CO	AR	5.7	FHM INS CO	FL	83.9
ASPIRE GENERAL INS CO	CA	15.8	FINANCIAL AMERICAN PROP & CAS INS CO	TX	22.4
ASSOCIATED INDUSTRIES INS CO INC	FL	290.4	FIRE DISTRICTS INS CO	NY	14.2
ASSOCIATED INTL INS CO	IL	213.7	FIRST FINANCIAL INS CO	IL	557.6
ASSURED GUARANTY CORP	MD	3,022.8	FIRST MERCURY INS CO	DE	162.5
ATTORNEYS INS MUTUAL	DC	11.6	FIRST NONPROFIT INS CO	DE	127.4
AXA INS CO	NY	226.4	FIRST SURETY CORP	WV	10.3
BALBOA INS CO	CA	99.8	FLORISTS MUTUAL INS CO	IL	128.7
BATTLE CREEK MUTUAL INS CO	NE	9.6	FRANK WINSTON CRUM INS CO	FL	69.8
BEDFORD GRANGE MUTUAL INS CO	PA	8.9	FREDERICK MUTUAL INS CO	MD	46.1
BERKLEY ASR CO	IA	68.7	FRIENDS COVE MUTUAL INS CO	PA	5.5
BLOOMFIELD MUTUAL INS CO	MN	11.4	GEICO CASUALTY CO	MD	2,755.4
BRIERFIELD INS CO	MS	13.1	GEM STATE INS CO	ID	11.2
BRISTOL WEST PREFERRED INS CO	MI	24.6	GENERAL CASUALTY INS CO	WI	13.6
BUNKER HILL INS CAS CO	MA	15.3	GENERAL SECURITY NATIONAL INS CO	NY	344.5
BURLINGTON INS CO	IL	367.0	GENERALI - US BRANCH	NY	63.9
CAMERON NATIONAL INS CO	MO	12.1	GERMANIA FARM MUTUAL INS ASN	TX	393.8
CAPITOL PREFERRED INS CO	FL	58.9	GREAT LAKES MUTUAL INS CO	MI	11.0
CAROLINA FARMERS MUTUAL INS CO	NC	9.1	GREAT NORTHWEST INS CO	MN	19.8
CASTLEPOINT NATIONAL INS CO	CA	355.2	GREENVILLE CASUALTY INS CO INC	SC	10.6
			GUILFORD INS CO	IL	385.7

INSURANCE COMPANY NAME	DOM. STATE	TOTAL ASSETS ($MIL)	INSURANCE COMPANY NAME	DOM. STATE	TOTAL ASSETS ($MIL)
Rating: C- (Continued)			OLD RELIABLE CAS CO	MO	6.0
GUTHRIE RRG	SC	47.2	OLYMPUS INS CO	FL	91.0
HARLEYSVILLE INS CO OF NJ	NJ	99.8	OMEGA INS CO	FL	42.8
HARLEYSVILLE PREFERRED INS CO	PA	136.2	ONTARIO REINS CO LTD	GA	26.5
HARLEYSVILLE WORCESTER INS CO	PA	206.9	OREGON MUTUAL INS CO	OR	221.1
HEALTH CARE INS RECPL	MN	27.6	PACIFIC COMPENSATION INS CO	CA	324.8
HLTHCR PROVIDERS INS CO	SC	77.3	PALOMAR SPECIALTY INS CO	OR	114.5
HOMEOWNERS CHOICE PROP & CAS INS CO	FL	396.2	PANHANDLE FARMERS MUT INS CO OF WV	WV	4.8
HOMESITE LLOYDS OF TEXAS	TX	31.7	PARATRANSIT INS CO A MUTUAL RRG	TN	23.7
HOMESTEAD MUTUAL INS CO	WI	8.9	PARTNERS MUTUAL INS CO	WI	44.2
HOOSIER INS CO	IN	8.9	PEOPLES TRUST INS CO	FL	255.5
HOSPITALS INS CO	NY	1,559.0	PERMANENT GENERAL ASR CORP	OH	351.0
HUDSON INS CO	DE	1,138.5	PETROLEUM MARKETERS MGMT INS CO	IA	32.0
ID COUNTIES RISK MGMT PROGRAM UNDW	ID	64.8	PHYSICIANS INS PROGRAM	PA	27.0
IMPERIUM INS CO	TX	380.7	PHYSICIANS REIMBURSEMENT FUND RRG	VT	31.5
INDIAN HARBOR INS CO	DE	161.3	PIONEER SPECIALTY INS CO	MN	66.3
INDIANA HEALTHCARE RECIPROCAL RRG	VT	36.1	PLICO INC	OK	94.5
INLAND MUTUAL INS CO	WV	6.7	POINT GUARD INS CO	PR	63.5
INSURORS INDEMNITY LLOYDS	TX	4.9	PREPARED INS CO	FL	69.4
KANSAS MUTUAL INS CO	KS	13.5	PRIMERO INS CO	NV	15.8
LAUNDRY OWNERS MUTUAL LIAB INS ASN	PA	16.5	PROCENTURY INS CO	MI	170.0
LEXON INS CO	TX	212.1	PROFESSIONAL CASUALTY ASSN	PA	46.0
LIBERTY COUNTY MUTUAL INS CO	TX	7.1	PROFESSIONAL SOLUTIONS INS CO	IA	23.1
LIBERTY INS CORP	IL	245.6	QBE SPECIALTY INS CO	ND	447.4
MAIDSTONE INS CO	NY	64.5	REDPOINT COUNTY MUTUAL INS CO	TX	13.4
MANUFACTURERS ALLIANCE INS CO	PA	195.4	RESIDENCE MUTUAL INS CO	CA	122.8
MAPFRE PRAICO INS CO	PR	433.1	RESPONSE INDEMNITY CO OF CA	CA	7.3
MEDPRO RRG	DC	84.3	RESPONSE INS CO	IL	38.1
MFS MUTUAL INS CO	IA	3.9	RESPONSIVE AUTO INS CO	FL	27.0
MIC REINS CORP	WI	2.6	ROCHDALE INS CO	NY	390.6
MIC REINS CORP OF WI	WI	2.7	ROCKWOOD CASUALTY INS CO	PA	250.3
MICHIGAN COMMERCIAL INS MUTUAL	MI	76.2	RURAL TRUST INS CO	TX	20.1
MICHIGAN MILLERS MUTUAL INS CO	MI	173.3	RUTGERS CASUALTY INS CO	NJ	21.4
MIDDLE STATES INS CO	OK	5.7	SAFETY SPECIALTY INS CO	MO	70.2
MILLVILLE INS CO OF NY	NY	3.1	SAMARITAN RRG INC	SC	31.8
MOUNT BEACON INS CO	FL	33.5	SAMSUNG FIRE & MARINE INS CO LTD US	NY	190.8
MT MORRIS MUTUAL INS CO	WI	34.1	SAUQUOIT VALLEY INS CO	NY	4.6
NATIONAL FIRE & INDEMNITY EXCHANGE	MO	11.1	SAVERS P&C INS CO	MO	223.9
NATIONAL GUARDIAN RRG INC	HI	11.4	SCOR REINS CO	NY	2,929.1
NATIONAL INDEPENDENT TRUCKERS IC RRG	SC	14.0	SCRUBS MUTUAL ASR CO RRG	NV	16.4
NATIONAL INTERSTATE INS CO OF HAWAII	OH	54.8	SELECTIVE INS CO OF NEW ENGLAND	NJ	182.6
NATIONS INS CO	CA	35.5	SOUTHERN GUARANTY INS CO	WI	14.5
NAZARETH MUTUAL INS CO	PA	13.7	ST JOHNS INS CO	FL	133.5
NCMIC RRG INC	VT	6.7	STARSTONE SPECIALTY INS CO	DE	180.8
NEW JERSEY SKYLANDS INS CO	NJ	53.0	STATE AUTO INS CO OF OH	OH	34.0
NEW MEXICO ASR CO	NM	5.9	STEADPOINT INS CO	TN	24.9
NEW MEXICO SOUTHWEST CASUALTY CO	NM	17.9	SUN SURETY INS CO	SD	19.6
NHRMA MUTUAL INS CO	IL	32.8	TEXAS FARM BUREAU MUTUAL INS CO	TX	713.0
NORTH POINTE INS CO	PA	39.6	TITAN INS CO INC A RRG	SC	58.5
NORTH RIVER INS CO	NJ	1,050.7	TOWER HILL SIGNATURE INS CO	FL	120.1
NUTMEG INS CO	CT	770.2	UNITED INS CO	UT	35.9
OCCIDENTAL FIRE & CAS CO OF NC	NC	554.7	UNIVERSAL FIRE & CASUALTY INS CO	IN	15.3
OCEAN MARINE INDEMNITY INS CO	LA	11.9	US LLOYDS INS CO	TX	27.2
OHIO SECURITY INS CO	NH	15.8	USA UNDERWRITERS	MI	9.6
OLD GLORY INS CO	TX	22.9	VERTERRA INS CO	TX	69.0
			VICTORIA SPECIALTY INSURANCE CO	OH	20.2

INSURANCE COMPANY NAME	DOM. STATE	TOTAL ASSETS ($MIL)
Rating: C- (Continued)		
WARRANTY UNDERWRITERS INS CO	TX	34.4
WEST AMERICAN INS CO	IN	46.4
WEST VIRGINIA FARMERS MUT INS ASSOC	WV	7.4
WEST VIRGINIA INS CO	WV	51.5
WESTERN MUTL INS CO (CA)	CA	82.8
WILLIAMSBURG NATIONAL INS CO	MI	118.1
WILSHIRE INS CO	NC	244.7
WINDHAVEN NATIONAL INS CO	TX	6.7
WOODLANDS INS CO	TX	12.5
XL INS CO OF NY INC	NY	213.2
YOUNG AMERICA INS CO	TX	55.2
ZEPHYR INS CO	HI	114.7
Rating: D+		
1ST ATLANTIC SURETY CO	NC	3.8
ACIG INS CO	IL	474.3
AGCS MARINE INS CO	IL	383.8
AGIC INC	FL	2.6
AIOI NISSAY DOWA INS CO LTD	GU	30.9
AMERICAN ACCESS CASUALTY CO	IL	308.3
AMERICAN FOREST CASUALTY CO RRG	VT	9.0
AMERICAN PROPERTY INS	NJ	18.2
AMERICAN RISK INS CO	TX	33.1
AMERICAN SAFETY RRG INC	VT	8.3
AMERICAN STEAMSHIP O M PROT & IND AS	NY	302.0
AMERICAN UNDERWRITERS INS CO	AR	6.1
APOLLO CASUALTY CO	IL	19.1
ARGONAUT GREAT CENTRAL INS CO	IL	42.7
ARROWOOD INDEMNITY CO	DE	1,294.8
ASI LLOYDS	TX	205.7
ASSURANCEAMERICA INS CO	SC	51.8
ASSURED GUARANTY MUNICIPAL CORP	NY	5,665.6
AUTO CLUB COUNTY MUTUAL INS CO	TX	91.3
BAR VERMONT RRG INC	VT	25.0
BEDFORD PHYSICIANS RRG INC	VT	52.7
BEDIVERE INS CO	PA	268.7
BRISTOL WEST CASUALTY INS CO	OH	18.0
BRISTOL WEST INS CO	OH	134.0
BUILD AMERICA MUTUAL ASR CO	NY	485.9
CARE RRG INC	DC	20.9
CASUALTY UNDERWRITERS INS CO	UT	4.5
CENTER VALLEY MUTUAL FIRE INS CO	PA	2.5
CENTRE COUNTY MUTUAL FIRE INS CO	PA	5.6
CENTURY CASUALTY CO	GA	5.5
COAST NATIONAL INS CO	CA	603.8
COLONIAL LLOYDS	TX	8.8
COLONIAL MORTGAGE INS CO	TX	3.0
COLONY SPECIALTY INS CO	OH	62.4
COLUMBIA FEDERAL INS CO	DC	3.1
COMMUNITY MUTUAL INS CO	NY	2.7
CONSUMER SPECIALTIES INS CO RRG	VT	4.6
COVERYS RRG INC	DC	9.2
CRUM & FORSTER INDEMNITY CO	DE	51.0
CRUM & FORSTER INS CO	NJ	50.2
CRUM & FORSTER SPECIALTY INS CO	DE	64.5

INSURANCE COMPANY NAME	DOM. STATE	TOTAL ASSETS ($MIL)
DELTA LLOYDS INS CO OF HOUSTON	TX	6.8
DISCOVERY INS CO	NC	24.3
EASTGUARD INS CO	PA	127.6
ELLINGTON MUTUAL INS CO	WI	6.0
FDM PREFERRED INS CO	NY	9.9
FINIAL REINS CO	CT	1,226.1
FIRST FOUNDERS ASR CO	NJ	5.1
FIRST MUTUAL INS CO	NC	6.2
FORT WAYNE MEDICAL ASR CO RRG	AZ	4.6
FREEDOM ADVANTAGE INS CO	PA	11.0
GENERAL SECURITY IND CO OF AZ	AZ	374.2
GENEVA INS CO	IN	4.2
GEORGIA MUNICIPAL CAPTIVE INS CO	GA	10.5
GEOVERA INS CO	CA	85.2
GLOBAL REINS CORP OF AM	NY	279.0
GRANGE MUTUAL FIRE INS CO	PA	4.4
GREAT CENTRAL FIRE INS CO	LA	3.9
HALLMARK INS CO	AZ	307.9
HANNAHSTOWN MUTUAL INS CO	PA	4.2
HANOVER FIRE & CASUALTY INS CO	PA	5.4
HARBOR INS CO	OK	11.7
HEALTHCARE PROFESSIONAL INS CO INC	NY	242.6
HEARTLAND HEALTHCARE RECIPROCAL RRG	VT	14.6
HUDSON SPECIALTY INS CO	NY	360.9
INS CO OF THE SOUTH	GA	36.6
INSURORS INDEMNITY CO	TX	30.2
JUNIATA MUTUAL INS CO	PA	8.5
LAMMICO RRG INC	DC	5.8
LENDERS PROTECTION ASR CO RRG	NE	2.5
LOYA CASUALTY INS CO	CA	119.5
LOYA INS CO	TX	274.5
MARATHON FINANCIAL INS INC RRG	DE	8.1
MEDICAL ALLIANCE INS CO	IL	9.8
MEDICAL LIABILITY MUTUAL INS CO	NY	5,539.7
MEDICAL PROVIDERS MUTUAL INS CO RRG	DC	7.1
MENDOTA INS CO	MN	121.2
MGIC INDEMNITY CORP	WI	139.1
MGIC MORTGAGE REINS CORP	WI	5.1
MGIC REINS CORP	WI	5.8
MGIC RESIDENTIAL REINSURANCE CORP	WI	5.1
MIDROX INS CO	NY	7.9
MIDWESTERN EQUITY TITLE INS CO	IN	3.5
MISSOURI VALLEY MUTUAL INS CO	SD	6.0
MORTGAGE GUARANTY INS CORP	WI	4,375.5
MOUND PRAIRIE MUTUAL INS CO	MN	7.1
MOUNT CARROLL MUTUAL INS CO	IL	6.7
MOWER COUNTY FARMERS MUT INS CO	MN	5.3
MULTINATIONAL INS CO	PR	33.1
MUTUAL FIRE INS CO OF S BEND TOWNSHP	PA	3.5
NATIONAL ASSISTED LIVING RRG INC	DC	8.2
NATIONAL HERITAGE INS CO	IL	3.6
NATIONAL MEDICAL PROFESSIONAL RRG	SC	3.6
NEVADA GENERAL INS CO	NV	16.2
NEVADA MUTUAL INS CO	NV	31.0
NEW JERSEY PHYS UNITED RECIP EXCH	NJ	30.9
NEW JERSEY SKYLANDS INS ASSN	NJ	71.9

INSURANCE COMPANY NAME	DOM. STATE	TOTAL ASSETS ($MIL)	INSURANCE COMPANY NAME	DOM. STATE	TOTAL ASSETS ($MIL)
Rating: D+ (Continued)			AMERICAN ALLIANCE CASUALTY CO	IL	21.0
NEW MEXICO SAFETY CASUALTY CO	NM	5.2	AMERICAN COMPENSATION INS CO	MN	74.9
NEW MEXICO SECURITY INS CO	NM	3.6	AMERICAN HEARTLAND INS CO	IL	17.6
NORMANDY INS CO	FL	40.3	AMERICAN PET INS CO	NY	47.2
PALISADES INS CO	NJ	29.0	AMERICAN RESOURCES INS CO INC	OK	23.9
PALLADIUM RRG INC	VT	79.4	AMERICAN SERVICE INS CO	IL	156.6
PATRONS MUTUAL FIRE INS CO OF IN PA	PA	2.8	AMERIGUARD RRG INC	VT	14.9
PHYSICIANS CASUALTY RRG INC	NV	12.1	AMFED CASUALTY INS CO	MS	5.7
PHYSICIANS INS CO	FL	12.8	APPLIED UNDERWRITERS CAPTIVE RISK	IA	952.8
PHYSICIANS PROACTIVE PROTECTION INC	SC	90.9	ARGONAUT-MIDWEST INS CO	IL	22.1
PIEDMONT MUTUAL INS CO	NC	4.5	ARGONAUT-SOUTHWEST INS CO	IL	18.2
PROFESSIONAL INS EXCHANGE MUTUAL	UT	8.1	ARI INS CO	PA	108.3
PYMATUNING MUTUAL FIRE INS CO	PA	3.3	ARIZONA HOME INS CO	AZ	26.2
RADIAN GUARANTY INC	PA	3,805.1	ASI SELECT INS CORP	DE	22.5
RADIAN INS INC	PA	22.6	ASSN OF CERTIFIED MTG ORIG RRG	NV	2.5
RADIAN MORTGAGE INS INC	PA	2.8	ATLANTIC BONDING CO	MD	9.8
RANCHERS & FARMERS MUTUAL INS CO	TX	35.3	ATTORNEYS INS MUTUAL RRG	HI	15.6
REAMSTOWN MUTUAL INS CO	PA	8.1	ATTORNEYS LIAB ASR SOCIETY INC RRG	VT	2,096.8
REPUBLIC CREDIT INDEMNITY CO	IL	65.3	BALDWIN MUTUAL INS CO	AL	12.1
RIDER INS CO	NJ	41.4	BOND SAFEGUARD INS CO	SD	81.8
RUTGERS ENHANCED INS CO	NJ	11.6	BONDED BUILDERS INS CO RRG	NV	3.1
SAINT LUKES HEALTH SYSTEM RRG	SC	15.2	BROADWAY INS & SURETY CO	NJ	2.2
SECURITY AMERICA RRG INC	VT	5.2	CALIFORNIA MUTUAL INS CO	CA	14.5
SECURITY NATIONAL INS CO	FL	121.2	CAPACITY INS CO	FL	21.4
SENECA INS CO	NY	202.3	CAPSON PHYSICIANS INS CO	TX	24.8
SPARTA INS CO	CT	319.8	CARE WEST INS CO	CA	127.9
SPARTAN INS CO	TX	6.9	CAREGIVERS UNITED LIAB INS CO RRG	SC	41.2
SPECIALTY RISK OF AMERICA	IL	14.2	CASSATT RISK RETENTION GROUP INC	VT	13.4
SPRINGFIELD INS CO	CA	93.1	CASTLEPOINT FLORIDA INS	FL	10.0
STAR CASUALTY INS CO	FL	12.5	CATASTROPHE REINS CO	TX	1,953.6
SYNERGY INS CO	NC	62.6	CEM INS CO	IL	33.6
TERRAFIRMA RRG LLC	VT	7.0	CENTURION MEDICAL LIAB PROTECT RRG	AZ	22.8
TEXAS HOSPITAL INS EXCHANGE	TX	35.3	CHERRY VALLEY COOPERATIVE INS CO	NY	1.7
TITLE INDUSTRY ASR CO RRG	VT	7.2	CIRCLE STAR INS CO A RRG	VT	7.8
TRADERS INS CO	MO	67.7	CITIZENS UNITED RECIP EXCH	NJ	88.3
UNITED CASUALTY & SURETY CO INC	MA	8.2	CLAIM PROFESSIONALS LIAB INS CO RRG	VT	4.3
UNITED EQUITABLE INS CO	IL	22.3	CLEARWATER SELECT INS CO	CT	1,223.4
UNITED HERITAGE PROP & CAS CO	ID	40.8	COASTAL INS CO	AL	40.7
UNITRIN AUTO & HOME INS CO	NY	81.8	COMCARE PRO INS RECIPROCAL RRG	VT	4.5
UNITRIN PREFERRED INS CO	NY	24.0	CONIFER INS CO	MI	83.1
UPMC HEALTH BENEFITS INC	PA	151.5	CONSUMERS COUNTY MUTUAL INS CO	TX	187.8
WEST VIRGINIA NATIONAL AUTO INS CO	WV	6.7	CONTINENTAL MUTUAL INS CO	PA	1.6
WESTERN GENERAL INS CO	CA	72.1	CONTRACTORS INS CO OF NORTH AMER RRG	HI	37.2
WILMINGTON INS CO	DE	5.5	CROWN CAPTIVE INS CO	GA	1.5
WRM AMERICA INDEMNITY CO	NY	15.5	CROWN CAPTIVE INS CO INC	DC	5.3
Rating: D			CRUDEN BAY RRG INC	VT	15.7
A CENTRAL INS CO	NY	104.9	DELAWARE GRANGE MUTUAL FIRE INS CO	DE	1.4
A-ONE COMM INS RRG GROUP INC	TN	11.0	DELAWARE PROFESSIONAL INS CO	DE	5.1
ACCC INS CO	TX	315.4	DELPHI CASUALTY CO	IL	2.6
ACCEPTANCE CASUALTY INS CO	NE	73.6	DIRECT AUTO INS CO	IL	45.1
ADVANCED PHYSICIANS INS RRG INC	AZ	1.6	DISTRICTS MUTUAL INS	WI	21.3
AGENTS MUTUAL INS CO	AR	3.9	DOCTORS CO RRG A RECIPROCAL	DC	12.9
AGRINATIONAL INS CO	VT	658.6	DONGBU INS CO LTD	HI	248.3
ALLEGHENY SURETY CO	PA	3.8	EAGLE POINT MUTUAL INS CO	WI	4.9
ALLIED PREMIER INS A RRG	CT	6.4	EASTERN ALLIANCE INS CO	PA	302.9
			EMERGENCY CAP MGMT LLC A RRG	VT	6.9

INSURANCE COMPANY NAME	DOM. STATE	TOTAL ASSETS ($MIL)	INSURANCE COMPANY NAME	DOM. STATE	TOTAL ASSETS ($MIL)
Rating: D (Continued)			MOUNTAIN VALLEY INDEMNITY CO	NY	41.9
EQUITABLE LIABILITY INS CO	DC	2.8	MPM INS CO OF KS	KS	4.2
ETHIO-AMERICAN INS CO	GA	10.2	MUTUAL INS CO OF LEHIGH CTY	PA	2.7
EXCELA RECIPROCAL RRG	VT	9.9	MUTUAL SAVINGS FIRE INS CO	AL	4.9
FAIRWAY PHYSICIANS INS CO RRG	DC	22.0	NARRAGANSETT BAY INS CO	RI	227.7
FARMERS & MECH MU I ASN OF CECIL CTY	MD	1.1	NASW RRG INC	DC	7.8
FARMERS UNION MUTUAL INS CO	AR	4.7	NATIONAL BUILDERS & CONTRACTORS INS	NV	3.0
FIRST BENEFITS INS MUTUAL INC	NC	43.3	NATIONAL DIRECT INS CO	NV	5.1
FIRST CHICAGO INS CO	IL	72.7	NATIONAL UNITY INS CO	TX	50.3
FIRST CHOICE CASUALTY INS CO	NV	17.6	NORGUARD INS CO	PA	716.4
FIRST INDEMNITY OF AMERICA INS CO	NJ	8.8	NORTH CAROLINA GRANGE MUTUAL INS CO	NC	29.7
FIRST NET INS CO	GU	19.5	NORTH EAST INS CO	ME	35.9
FRANKLIN CASUALTY INS CO RRG	VT	10.7	ORANGE COUNTY MEDICAL RECIP INS RRG	AZ	5.9
FREDERICKSBURG PROFESSIONAL RISK EXC	VT	20.3	OTSEGO COUNTY PATRONS CO-OP F R ASN	NY	1.9
FREMONT INS CO	MI	139.7	PACE RRG INC	VT	5.8
FULMONT MUTUAL INS CO	NY	4.0	PACIFIC PIONEER INS CO	CA	26.6
GATEWAY INS CO	MO	62.4	PALISADES P&C INS CO	NJ	14.2
GENESEE PATRONS COOP INS	NY	8.9	PARAMOUNT INS CO	MD	7.5
GEORGIA TRANSPORTATION CAPTIVE INS	GA	2.9	PCH MUTUAL INS CO INC RRG	DC	7.4
GLOBAL LIBERTY INS CO OF NY	NY	67.7	PEACE CHURCH RRG INC	VT	22.5
GOAUTO INS CO	LA	43.1	PEACHTREE CASUALTY INS CO	FL	22.6
GREAT FALLS INS CO	ME	9.9	PELICAN INS RRG	VT	17.2
GROWERS AUTOMOBILE INS ASN	IN	6.3	PENN RESERVE INS CO LTD	PA	1.9
HAY CREEK MUTUAL INS CO	MN	5.8	PHYSICIANS IND RRG INC	NV	5.4
HEALTH CARE CASUALTY RRG INC	DC	14.3	PHYSICIANS SPECIALTY LTD RRG	SC	12.7
HEALTH CARE INDUSTRY LIAB RECIP INS	DC	47.0	PIA PROFESSIONAL LIABILITY INS RRG	MT	2.1
HEALTHCARE UNDERWRITING CO RRG	VT	166.0	PONCE DE LEON LTC RRG INC	FL	7.5
HOMEOWNERS OF AMERICA INS CO	TX	46.0	PREFERRED AUTO INS CO	TN	8.3
HUTTERIAN BRETHREN MUTUAL INS CORP	IL	3.2	PRIMEONE INS CO	MI	15.7
INDEPENDENCE CASUALTY INS CO	MA	4.6	PROFESSIONAL EXCHANGE ASR CO (A RRG)	HI	10.6
INTEGRA INS INC	MN	1.9	PROFESSIONALS RRG INC	MT	4.1
INTEGRITY P&C INS CO	WI	22.9	PUERTO RICO MED DEFENSE MUT INS CO	PR	17.0
INTERBORO INS CO	NY	78.4	QBE SEGUROS	PR	74.1
IQS INS RRG INC	VT	1.7	QUALITY CASUALTY INS CO	AL	1.5
IU HEALTH RRG INC	SC	14.7	RADIAN GUARANTY REINS INC	PA	6.9
KENSINGTON INS CO	NY	13.3	REAL LEGACY ASR CO INC	PR	143.5
KENTUCKY HOSPITAL INS CO RRG	KY	20.8	RED ROCK RISK RETENTION GROUP INC	AZ	6.4
KENTUCKY NATIONAL INS CO	KY	30.9	RELIAMAX INS CO	SD	15.5
KEY INS CO	KS	30.8	REPUBLIC MORTGAGE INS CO OF NC	NC	169.5
KNIGHTBROOK INS CO	DE	221.1	REPWEST INS CO	AZ	316.9
LAKE STREET RRG INC	VT	2.1	RETAILERS INS CO	MI	21.4
LANCET IND RRG INC	NV	19.0	RVOS FARM MUTUAL INS CO	TX	79.1
LIGHTHOUSE CASUALTY CO	IL	24.7	SAFE INS CO	WV	10.9
LITTLE BLACK MUTUAL INS CO	WI	6.1	SAFECARD SERVICES INS CO	ND	1.9
LONE STAR ALLIANCE INC A RRG	DC	9.0	SAGE RRG INC	NV	2.6
MAKE TRANSPORTATION INS INC RRG	DE	5.2	SAWGRASS MUTUAL INS CO	FL	39.2
MBIA INS CORP	NY	752.7	SECURITY PLAN FIRE INS CO	LA	7.8
MD RRG INC	MT	23.9	SELECT MD RRG INC	MT	2.7
MED MAL RRG INC	TN	3.6	SERVICE INS CO (NJ)	NJ	13.7
MEMBERS INS CO	NC	29.0	SFM SELECT INS CO	MN	4.0
MERCURY INDEMNITY CO OF AMERICA	FL	60.0	SOMERSET CASUALTY INS CO	PA	39.1
MIDWEST INS GROUP INC RRG	VT	6.5	SOMPO JAPAN NIPPONKOA INS INC	GU	7.0
MOTORS INS CORP	MI	2,054.9	SOUTH CAROLINA FARM BUREAU INS	SC	3.4
MOUNTAIN LAKE RRG INC	VT	1.7	SOUTHERN GENERAL INS CO	GA	44.7
MOUNTAIN STATES HEALTHCARE RECIP RRG	MT	119.1	SOUTHWEST GENERAL INS CO	NM	2.5
			SPIRIT MOUNTAIN INS CO RRG INC	DC	6.1

INSURANCE COMPANY NAME	DOM. STATE	TOTAL ASSETS ($MIL)
Rating: D (Continued)		
SPRING VALLEY MUTUAL INS CO	MN	4.3
STICO MUTUAL INS CO RRG	VT	23.7
STONEGATE INS CO	IL	17.6
SUNDERLAND MARINE INS CO LTD	AK	10.2
SYNERGY COMP INS CO	PA	32.8
TEXAS MEDICAL INS CO	TX	48.9
TOWER BONDING & SURETY CO	PR	3.7
TOWER HILL PREFERRED INS CO	FL	106.0
TOWER HILL PRIME INS CO	FL	191.9
TRANSIT GENERAL INS CO	IL	27.1
TWIN LIGHTS INS CO	NJ	8.5
UNDERWRITERS AT LLOYDS	KY	185.9
UNDERWRITERS AT LLOYDS (IL)	IL	322.9
UNIQUE INS CO	IL	96.3
UNITED GROUP CAPTIVE INS CO	GA	1.3
UNITED HOME INS CO	AR	34.0
UNITRIN ADVANTAGE INS CO	NY	3.3
UNIVERSAL INS CO	NC	34.5
UNIVERSAL P&C INS CO	FL	967.3
UPMC WORK ALLIANCE INC	PA	4.9
URGENT CARE ASR CO RRG INC	NV	5.1
US COASTAL INS CO	NY	27.4
US INS CO OF AMERICA	IL	6.1
US LEGAL SERVICES INC	TN	2.9
USA INS CO	MS	15.0
UV INS RRG INC	HI	1.3
VASA SPRING GARDEN MUTUAL INS CO	MN	5.0
VIRGINIA PHYSICIANS RRG INC	MT	2.2
WASHINGTON COUNTY CO-OPERATIVE INS	NY	8.0
WEST VIRGINIA MUTUAL INS CO	WV	166.7
WORK FIRST CASUALTY CO	DE	40.1
WORKMENS AUTO INS CO	CA	41.0
XL SELECT INS CO	DE	135.6
YELLOWSTONE INS EXCHANGE	VT	18.8
Rating: D-		
AEGIS HEALTHCARE RRG INC	DC	5.5
AMERICAN CONTRACTORS INS CO RISK RET	TX	60.2
AMFED NATIONAL INS CO	MS	72.8
ATTPRO RRG RECIPROCAL RRG	DC	2.7
AUSTIN MUTUAL INS CO	MN	55.3
CASUALTY CORP OF AMERICA	OK	10.1
CENTURY INS CO GUAM LTD	GU	22.7
CGB INS CO	IN	337.6
CLEARWATER INS CO	DE	1,129.5
COLLEGE LIAB INS CO LTD RRG	HI	15.2
COUNTRY-WIDE INS CO	NY	250.0
CRYSTAL RUN RECIPROCAL RRG	VT	24.7
DIAMOND INS CO	IL	46.1
FARMERS ALLIANCE MUTUAL INS CO	MI	2.0
FARMERS MUTUAL INS CO OF ELLINWOOD	KS	4.0
GEISINGER INS CORP RRG	VT	12.3
GEORGIA DEALERS INS CO	GA	12.6
GERMAN MUTUAL INS CO	OH	41.5
GLOBAL HAWK INS CO RRG	VT	44.3

INSURANCE COMPANY NAME	DOM. STATE	TOTAL ASSETS ($MIL)
GOOD SHEPHERD RECIPROCAL RRG	SC	9.1
GREEN HILLS INS CO A RRG	VT	10.7
HALIFAX MUTUAL INS CO	NC	7.9
HEALTH CARE MUT CAPTIVE INS CO	GA	13.0
HEARTLAND MUTUAL INS CO	MN	7.0
HOCHHEIM PRAIRIE FARM MUT INS ASN	TX	117.9
IRONSHORE RRG (DC) INC	DC	3.2
ISLAND HOME INS CO	GU	26.7
LONE STAR NATIONAL INS CO	IN	6.5
MACHINERY INS INC	FL	2.3
MGIC REINS CORP OF WI	WI	543.4
MIDVALE INDEMNITY CO	IL	13.9
MOUNTAIN LAUREL RRG INC	VT	18.5
NATIONAL CATHOLIC RRG	VT	63.5
NORTHWEST GF MUTUAL INS CO	SD	18.2
OCEANUS INS CO A RRG	SC	54.2
ONYX INS CO INC A RRG	TN	26.0
ORTHOFORUM INS CO	SC	19.7
PHYSICIANS INS EXCHANGE RESOURCE RRG	VT	2.9
PINE TREE INS RECIPROCAL RRG	VT	10.6
SEABRIGHT INS CO	TX	31.2
STAR & SHIELD INS EXCHANGE	FL	14.3
STATES SELF-INSURERS RISK RET GROUP	VT	24.0
STERLING CASUALTY INS CO	CA	14.4
TRANSIT MUTUAL INS CORP OF WI	WI	14.9
UNITED BUS INS CO	GA	10.3
UPPER HUDSON NATIONAL INS CO	NY	2.8
UTAH BUSINESS INS CO	UT	19.4
VISION INS CO	TX	31.5
WELLSPAN RRG	VT	31.1
WHITECAP SURETY CO	MN	1.5
Rating: E+		
AMERICAN TRANSIT INS CO	NY	311.8
AMERICAN TRUCKING & TRANSP INS RRG	MT	34.3
ASCENDANT COMMERCIAL INS INC	FL	45.8
DOCTORS & SURGEONS NATL RRG IC	VT	9.1
ELITE TRANSPORTATION RRG INC	VT	12.6
FAITH AFFILIATED RRG INC	VT	9.3
GOLDEN INS CO A RRG	NV	12.8
GRANADA INS CO	FL	31.0
GUARANTEE INS CO	FL	367.6
HEALTHCARE PROVIDERS INS EXCH	PA	55.1
HERMITAGE INS CO	NY	167.6
JM WOODWORTH RRG INC	NV	8.1
KOOKMIN BEST INS CO LTD US BR	NY	351.7
LEXINGTON NATIONAL INS CORP	FL	58.7
MAYA ASR CO	NY	17.2
NATIONAL BUILDING MATERIAL ASR CO	IN	6.3
NEW YORK HEALTHCARE INS CO INC RRG	DC	26.1
NORTHWESTERN NATL INS CO SEG ACCNT	WI	26.0
OLD AMERICAN CTY MUTUAL FIRE INS CO	TX	83.3
STONINGTON INS CO	PA	34.2
VICTORY INS CO	MT	10.9
WINDHAVEN INS CO	FL	184.4

INSURANCE COMPANY NAME	DOM. STATE	TOTAL ASSETS ($MIL)
Rating: E		
ACADEMIC MEDICAL PROFESSIONALS RRG	VT	4.2
ACCIDENT INS CO	SC	119.0
ALLEGIANT INS CO INC A RRG	HI	23.5
ALLIANCE NATIONAL INS CO	NY	48.3
ALLIED SERVICES RRG	SC	6.6
AMBAC ASSURANCE CORP	WI	5,367.0
AMERICAN LIBERTY INS CO	UT	10.6
ARCOA RRG INC	NV	15.9
AVIATION ALLIANCE INS RRG INC	MT	3.6
BUILDING INDUSTRY INS ASSN INC	VA	17.8
CALIFORNIA MEDICAL GROUP INS CO RRG	AZ	16.5
CAPITOL INS CO	PA	15.3
CARECONCEPTS INS INC A RRG	MT	3.8
CASTLEPOINT INS CO	NY	178.4
CHEROKEE GUARANTEE CO INC A RRG	AZ	14.3
COLUMBIA NATIONAL RRG INC	VT	1.8
COMMONWEALTH CASUALTY CO	AZ	12.6
CONTINUING CARE RRG INC	VT	4.8
DIST-CO INS CO INC RRG	HI	3.4
EMERGENCY MEDICINE RRG INC	SC	7.4
FARMINGTON MUTUAL INS CO	WI	7.9
FINANCIAL GUARANTY INS CO	NY	2,419.3
GABLES RRG INC	VT	10.1
GALEN INS CO	MO	14.0
GUARDIAN INDEMNITY INC	MT	6.2
IFA INS CO	NJ	13.2
INNOVATIVE PHYSICIAN SOLUTIONS RRG	VT	6.2
INSUREMAX INS CO	IN	5.0
KENTUCKIANA MEDICAL RRG & INS CO INC	KY	50.3
KEYSTONE MUTUAL INS CO	MO	2.6
MISSOURI DOCTORS MUTUAL INS CO	MO	6.5
MISSOURI PROFESSIONALS MUTUAL INS CO	MO	17.2
NOVANT HEALTH RRG INC	SC	9.8
OHA INS SOLUTIONS INC	OH	40.6
ORISKA INS CO	NY	34.8
PACIFIC SPECIALTY PROPERTY & CAS CO	TX	5.1
PARAMOUNT INS CO	NY	38.0
PARK INS CO	NY	26.8
PHOEBE RECIPROCAL RRG	SC	6.2
PHYSICIANS INS MUTUAL	MO	3.7
PREFERRED CONTRACTORS INS CO RRG LLC	MT	102.6
PREMIER PHYSICIANS INS CO INC A RRG	NV	10.8
PUBLIC SERVICE INS CO	IL	295.8
PUBLIC UTILITY MUTUAL INS CO RRG	VT	7.1
SENTINEL ASR RRG INC	HI	17.0
SPIRIT COMMERCIAL AUTO RRG INC	NV	70.7
ST CHARLES INS CO RRG	SC	15.0
ST LUKES HEALTH NETWORK INS CO RRG	VT	64.7
SUNZ INS CO	FL	88.0
SYNCORA CAPITAL ASR INC	NY	444.1
TRINITY RISK SOLUTIONS RECIP INS RRG	DC	8.4
UNITED AUTOMOBILE INS CO	FL	339.0
UNITED CENTRAL PA RRG	VT	20.8

INSURANCE COMPANY NAME	DOM. STATE	TOTAL ASSETS ($MIL)
VFH CAPTIVE INS CO	GA	5.5
WASHINGTON CASUALTY CO	WA	28.7
WESTERN CATHOLIC INS CO RRG	VT	4.5
WORKERS COMPENSATION EXCHANGE	ID	7.4
Rating: E-		
ACADEMIC HLTH PROFESSIONALS INS ASSO	NY	312.0
AF&L INS CO	PA	141.3
FIDUCIARY INS CO OF AMERICA	NY	90.7
INS PLACEMENT FACILITY OF PA	PA	8.8
PHYSICIANS RECIPROCAL INSURERS	NY	1,301.4
SENIOR AMERICAN INS CO	PA	13.9
SYNCORA GUARANTEE INC	NY	1,282.2
TEXAS FAIR PLAN ASSN	TX	80.8
Rating: F		
ACCEPTANCE INS CO	NE	15.0
AFFIRMATIVE CASUALTY INS CO	LA	35.4
AFFIRMATIVE DIRECT INS CO	NY	5.3
AFFIRMATIVE INS CO	IL	179.4
ARGUS FIRE & CASUALTY INS CO	FL	3.6
COMMERCIAL MUT INS CO	GA	0.0
CORNERSTONE MUTUAL INS CO	GA	0.0
FLORIDA SELECT INS CO	FL	0.0
GULF BUILDERS RRG INC	SC	0.0
HIGHLANDS INS CO	TX	0.0
HOME VALUE INS CO	OH	0.0
HOSPITALITY MUT CAPT INS CO	GA	0.0
INTERSTATE BANKERS CASUALTY CO	IL	0.0
LEMIC INS CO	LA	0.0
LIBERTY FIRST RRG INS CO	UT	0.0
LINCOLN GENERAL INS CO	PA	65.6
LUMBER MUTUAL INS CO	MA	0.0
LUMBERMENS UNDERWRITING ALLIANCE	MO	354.2
MANHATTAN RE-INS CO	DE	0.0
MILLERS CLASSIFIED INS CO	IL	2.7
MILLERS FIRST INS CO	IL	7.8
NATIONAL INS CO	PR	0.0
NORTHWESTERN NTL INS CO MILWAUKEE	WI	26.3
PAFCO GENERAL INS CO	IN	0.0
PHOENIX FUND INC	NC	0.0
PMI INS CO	AZ	109.7
PMI MORTGAGE INS CO	AZ	918.5
PROAIR RRG INC	NV	0.5
REGIS INS CO	PA	0.6
REPUB MORTGAGE INS CO	NC	695.3
SAN ANTONIO INDEMNITY CO	TX	0.0
SHELBY INS CO	TX	0.0
TRIAD GUARANTY ASR CORP	IL	0.0
TRIAD GUARANTY INS CORP	IL	0.0
UNION MUTUAL INS CO	OK	3.6
UNIVERSAL INS EXCHANGE	TX	0.0
VESTA INS CORP	TX	0.0
Rating: U		
21ST CENTURY AUTO INS CO OF NJ	NJ	25.5
21ST CENTURY INS CO OF THE SW	TX	6.1

INSURANCE COMPANY NAME	DOM. STATE	TOTAL ASSETS ($MIL)	INSURANCE COMPANY NAME	DOM. STATE	TOTAL ASSETS ($MIL)
Rating: **U** **(Continued)**			CENTRE INS CO	DE	89.0
21ST CENTURY SUPERIOR INS CO	CA	30.8	CENTURY INDEMNITY CO	PA	708.4
7710 INS CO	SC	9.3	CHARITABLE SERVICE PROVIDERS RRG	AZ	3.5
ACA FINANCIAL GUARANTY CORP	MD	316.4	CHUBB INS CO OF PR	PR	141.9
AFFILIATES INS CO	IN	62.5	CHURCH INS CO	NY	24.7
AFFIRMATIVE INS CO OF MI	MI	9.4	CINCINNATI EQUITABLE INS CO	OH	3.1
AIG STRUCTURED MORTGAGE INS CO	NC	10.1	CLAVERACK CO-OPERATIVE INS CO	NY	3.4
AIMCO MUTUAL INS CO	NC	8.1	CLINIC MUTUAL INS CO RRG	HI	4.1
ALEA NORTH AMERICA INS CO	NY	99.4	CM VANTAGE SPECIALTY INS CO	WI	53.3
ALLIED TRUST INS CO	TX	10.4	CODAN INS CO LTD	NY	2.1
ALLSTATE NORTH AMERICAN INS CO	IL	10.7	COLISEUM REINS CO	DE	295.8
AMBAC ASR CORP SEGREGATED ACCT	WI	11.0	COMMERCIAL CASUALTY INS CO	CA	113.6
AMERICAN BUILDERS INS CO RRG INC	MT	0.8	COMMERCIAL GUARANTY INS CO	DE	33.6
AMERICAN EQUITY INS CO	AZ	102.7	COMMERCIAL HIRECAR INS CO RRG	TN	2.0
AMERICAN FARMERS & RANCHERS INS CO	OK	8.8	COMMONWEALTH INS CO OF AMERICA	DE	11.2
AMERICAN FEED INDUSTRY INS CO RRG	IA	1.5	COMMUNITY CARE RRG INC	DC	5.0
AMERICAN HEALTHCARE INDEMNITY CO	OK	22.1	COMMUNITY HEALTH ALLIANCE RECIP RRG	VT	57.9
AMERICAN MEDICAL ASR CO	IL	3.3	COMPASS INS CO	NY	12.2
AMERICAN PACIFIC INS CO	HI	11.6	COMPASS SPCLTY INS RRG INC	TN	1.6
AMERICAN PHYSICIANS ASR CORP	MI	344.1	COMPSOURCE MUTUAL INS CO	OK	0.0
AMERICAN RISK MGMT RRG INC	TN	2.0	COMPUTER INS CO	RI	23.5
AMERICAN SPECIAL RISK INS CO	DE	0.8	CONSOLIDATED LLOYDS	TX	1.6
AMFIRST SPECIALTY INS CO	MS	2.0	CONTINENTAL RISK UNDERWRITERS RRG IN	NV	0.4
AMSHIELD INS CO	MO	4.6	COPIC A RRG	DC	0.7
ARCH EXCESS & SURPLUS INS CO	MO	65.1	COUNTY HALL INS CO INC A RRG	HI	1.0
ARCH MORTGAGE ASR CO	WI	15.0	COVENTRY INS CO	RI	1.6
ARGONAUT LTD RISK INS CO	IL	11.7	COVERYS SPECIALTY INS CO	NJ	61.8
ARI CASUALTY CO	NJ	8.1	CUBE INS CO	OH	21.6
ARROWOOD SURPLUS LINES INS CO	DE	91.3	DAN RRG INC	SC	2.2
ASHLAND MUTUAL FIRE INS CO OF PA	PA	0.5	DANIELSON NATIONAL INS CO	CA	6.0
ASHMERE INS CO	IL	9.4	DOCTORS PROF LIAB RRG INC	NC	1.1
ASPEN SPECIALTY RRG INC	DC	0.7	ELIZABETHTOWN INS CO	DE	3.9
ASSET PROTECTION PROGRAM RRG INC	SC	1.2	EMPIRE INS CO	NY	24.4
ATLANTA INTERNATIONAL INS CO	NY	42.5	EMPLOYERS FIRE INS CO	PA	13.1
ATRIUM INS CORP	NY	1.7	ENCOMPASS FLORIDIAN INDEMNITY CO	IL	4.9
AUTO CLUB CASUALTY CO	TX	2.9	ENCOMPASS FLORIDIAN INS CO	IL	4.9
AUTO-OWNERS SPECIALTY INS CO	DE	28.5	EVERGREEN USA RRG INC	VT	9.4
AVIVA INS CO OF CANADA (US BR)	NY	18.0	EVERSPAN FINANCIAL GUARANTEE CORP	WI	227.6
AWBURY INS CO	DE	1.0	EXCALIBUR NATIONAL INS CO	LA	8.6
AXIS SPECIALTY INS CO	CT	66.4	EXCALIBUR REINS CORP	PA	9.0
BALTIMORE EQUITABLE SOCIETY	MD	151.3	EXECUTIVE INS CO	NY	1.7
BAY INS RRG INC	SC	0.7	EXPLORER AMERICAN INS CO	CA	2.7
BEACONHARBOR MUTUAL RRG	ME	1.0	FACILITY INS CORP	TX	101.2
BERKSHIRE HATHATWAY DIRECT INS CO	NE	123.7	FALLS LAKE FIRE & CASUALTY CO	CA	17.9
BLACK DIAMOND INS CO	NV	0.0	FB INS CO	KY	1.3
BLUE HILL SPECIALTY INS CO	IL	15.6	FBALLIANCE INS CO	IL	49.2
BLUESHORE INS CO	CO	77.5	FBALLIANCE INS INC	VA	4.5
BOSTON INDEMNITY CO INC	SD	7.8	FCCI ADVANTAGE INS CO	FL	7.2
BROOKWOOD INS CO	IA	7.4	FIRST JERSEY CASUALTY INS CO INC	NJ	5.9
BTTS INS RRG GROUP INC	SC	0.7	FIRST PROTECTIVE INS CO	FL	264.9
BUCKS COUNTY CONTRIBUTIONSHIP	PA	6.4	FIRST STATE INS CO	CT	199.8
CAMBRIA COUNTY MUTUAL INS CO	PA	0.5	FIRST WASHINGTON INS CO	DC	1.2
CAR RRG INC	TN	1.1	FOUNDERS INS CO OF MI	MI	6.0
CATAWBA INS CO	SC	6.1	FRANKLIN HOMEOWNERS ASSR CO	DE	75.7
CATTLEMANS INS CO A RRG	MT	0.6	FRONTLINE INS UNLIMITED CO	IL	31.9
			GENWORTH FINANCIAL ASR CORP	NC	7.5

INSURANCE COMPANY NAME	DOM. STATE	TOTAL ASSETS ($MIL)	INSURANCE COMPANY NAME	DOM. STATE	TOTAL ASSETS ($MIL)
Rating: U (Continued)			MMIC RRG INC	DC	0.7
GLOBAL HAWK PROPERTY CAS INS CO	DE	6.5	MONARCH NATIONAL INS CO	FL	35.6
GLOBAL INS CO	GA	3.5	MONTOUR MUTUAL INS CO	PA	0.9
GOLDSTREET INS CO	NY	5.6	MOUNTAIN STATES COMM INS CO	NM	1.1
GOVERNMENT ENTITIES MUTUAL INC	DC	74.0	MOUNTAINPOINT INS CO	AZ	12.0
GRACO RRG INC	SC	1.4	MUNICIPAL PROPERTY INS CO	WI	14.5
GRAY INS CO OF LOUISIANA	LA	6.1	MYCOMPASS INC	IA	5.0
GREAT AMERICAN CASUALTY INS CO	OH	10.8	NATIONAL AMERICAN INS CO OF CA	CA	32.1
GREAT AMERICAN CONTEMPORARY INS CO	OH	10.5	NATIONAL BAIL & SURETY CO	FL	2.1
GREAT AMERICAN LLOYDS INS CO	TX	1.5	NATIONAL HOME INS CO RRG	CO	20.2
GREEN TREE PERPETUAL ASR CO	PA	0.2	NATIONAL INS ASSN	IN	13.6
GUILDERLAND REINS CO	NY	3.5	NEVADA DOCS MEDICAL RRG INC	NV	2.6
GULF UNDERWRITERS INS CO	CT	51.1	NEW ENGLAND GUARANTY INS CO INC	VT	44.3
HAMDEN ASR RRG INC	VT	89.4	NEW ENGLAND INS CO	CT	37.6
HAMILTON INS CO	DE	24.5	NEW ENGLAND REINS CORP	CT	38.6
HANOVER NATIONAL INS CO	NH	12.4	NEW MEXICO PROPERTY & CASUALTY CO	NM	1.7
HANOVER NJ INS CO	NH	31.9	NEW YORK TRANSPORTATION INS CORP	NY	0.0
HERITAGE CASUALTY INS CO	KS	65.3	NEWPORT BONDING & SURETY CO	PR	4.3
HOME CONSTRUCTION INS CO RRG	NV	5.3	NEWPORT INS CO	AZ	12.0
HOMEOWNERS CHOICE ASR CO INC	AL	1.9	NORTH STAR GENERAL INS CO	MN	4.3
HOMESHIELD FIRE & CASUALTY INS CO	OK	1.1	NUCLEAR ELECTRIC INS LTD	DE	4,761.0
HOMESTEAD INS CO	PA	4.5	OAKWOOD INS CO	TN	66.9
HORIZON MIDWEST CASUALTY CO	KS	2.6	OBI AMERICA INS CO	PA	15.9
HOUSTON GENERAL INS EXCH	TX	5.2	OBSTETRICIANS & GYNECOLOGISTS RRG	MT	0.5
HOW INS CO A RRG	VA	0.4	OHIC INS CO	OH	95.0
HPIC RRG	SC	1.3	OKLAHOMA P&C INS CO	OK	3.4
INS CO OF THE AMERICAS	FL	7.4	OLD ELIZABETH MUTUAL FIRE INS CO	PA	0.6
INTREPID INS CO	MI	35.0	OLD REPUBLIC SECURITY ASR CO	IL	1,067.4
ISMIE INDEMNITY CO	IL	52.7	OMAHA INDEMNITY CO	WI	14.4
KAMMCO CASUALTY CO	KS	5.0	ONE ALLIANCE INS CORP	PR	12.3
KEMPER FINANCIAL INDEMNITY CO	IL	20.3	ONECIS INS CO	IL	23.6
LCTA CASUALTY INS CO	LA	77.5	ORDINARY MUTUAL A RRG CORP	VT	2.6
LEGAL MUTUAL LIAB INS SOCIETY OF MD	MD	0.5	P&S INS RRG INC	SC	0.9
LEON HIX INS CO	SC	3.4	PALADIN REINS CORP	NY	1.3
LIBERTY AMERICAN INS CO	FL	8.7	PASSPORT INS CO	ND	2.0
LIBERTY AMERICAN SELECT INS CO	FL	8.3	PAWTUCKET INS CO	RI	7.0
LM P&C INS CO	IN	67.5	PELEUS INS CO	VA	125.3
LOCUST MUTUAL FIRE INS CO	PA	1.2	PENNSYLVANIA PHYSICIANS RECIP INS	PA	8.2
LR INS INC	DE	1.5	PHILADELPHIA REINS CORP	PA	6.8
LVHN RRG	SC	58.8	PLATINUM TRANSPORT INS RRG INC	HI	2.9
MADA INS EXCHANGE	MN	0.4	POLICYHOLDERS MUTUAL INS CO	WI	0.3
MAIN STREET AMER PROTECTION INS CO	FL	15.7	POTOMAC INS CO	PA	10.7
MCIC VERMONT INC RRG	VT	1,772.1	PREFERRED PROFESSIONAL RRG	DC	1.0
MEDCHOICE RRG INC	VT	2.9	PREMIER INS EXCHANGE RRG	VT	7.8
MEDSTAR LIABILITY LTD INS CO INC RRG	DC	3.7	PREVISOR INS CO	CO	8.6
MENDAKOTA CASUALTY CO	IL	36.5	PROASSURANCE AMER MUTL A RRG	DC	10.5
MERCHANTS PROPERTY INS CO OF IN	IN	76.5	PROBUILDERS SPECIALTY INS CO RRG	DC	13.5
METROMILE INS CO	DE	14.9	PROFESSIONAL QUALITY LIABILITY INS	VT	2.1
MGIC ASSURANCE CORP	WI	6.7	PROGRESSIVE CHOICE INS CO	OH	7.9
MGIC CREDIT ASR CORP	WI	8.4	PROGRESSIVE COMMERCIAL CASUALTY CO	OH	8.2
MICA RRG INC	DC	0.8	PROSELECT NATIONAL INS CO INC	AZ	13.8
MICHIGAN AUTO INS PLACEMENT FACILITY	MI	0.0	PROTECTION MUTUAL INS CO	PA	0.6
MICO INS CO	OH	10.9	PROVIDENCE PLANTATIONS INS CO	RI	1.2
MIDSTATES REINS CORP	IL	82.5	PROVIDENCE WASHINGTON INS CO	RI	213.9
MISSOURI PHYSICIANS ASSOCIATES	MO	1.9	QUANTA INDEMNITY CO	CO	39.4
			QUEEN CITY ASR INC	VT	2,480.4

INSURANCE COMPANY NAME	DOM. STATE	TOTAL ASSETS ($MIL)
Rating: U (Continued)		
R&Q REINS CO	PA	165.7
RADIAN INVESTOR SURETY INC	PA	5.0
RADIAN MORTGAGE ASR INC	PA	8.7
RADIAN MORTGAGE GUARANTY INC	PA	19.9
RADIAN REINS INC	PA	467.9
RADNOR SPECIALTY INS CO	NE	26.1
RAMPART INS CO	NY	31.2
RECREATION RRG INC	VT	3.1
REPUBLIC RRG	SC	1.7
RESPONSE WORLDWIDE DIRECT AUTO INS	IL	6.9
RESPONSE WORLDWIDE INS CO	IL	11.3
ROMULUS INS RRG INC	SC	2.6
ROOT INS CO	OH	4.0
RPX RRG INC	HI	4.9
SAFECO SURPLUS LINES INS CO	NH	42.2
SALEM COUNTY MUTUAL FIRE INS CO	NJ	0.0
SAN DIEGO INS CO	CA	68.0
SAUCON MUTUAL INS CO	PA	19.0
SEAWAY MUTUAL INS CO	PA	2.1
SELECT INS CO	TX	78.0
SELECT MARKETS INS CO	IL	15.8
SFM SAFE INS CO	MN	3.2
SLAVONIC INS CO OF TEXAS	TX	4.7
SOMPO JAPAN CANOPIUS RE AG	DE	25.2
SOUTHERN FARM BUREAU PROPERTY	MS	58.0
SOUTHLAND LLOYDS INS CO	TX	0.0
SOUTHWEST PHYSICIANS RRG INC	SC	65.9
SPECIALTY SURPLUS INS CO	IL	17.2
SPINNAKER INS CO	IL	35.4
ST CLAIR INS CO	NY	1.3
STATE INS FUND	NY	0.0
STATE INS FUND DISABILITY BENEFITS	NY	0.0
STERLING INS COOP INC	NY	0.5
STONE VALLEY MUTUAL FIRE INS CO	PA	0.8
SUBURBAN HEALTH ORG RRG LLC	SC	0.9
SUECIA INS CO	NY	46.0
TEXAS BUILDERS INS CO	TX	12.1
THIRD COAST INS CO	IL	18.9
TIG INS CO	CA	1,868.9
TM SPECIALTY INS CO	AZ	39.5
TRANSPORT INS CO	OH	39.5
TRANSPORTATION INS SVCS RRG	SC	0.9
TRAVEL AIR INS CO (KS)	KS	5.0
TRENWICK AMERICA REINSURANCE CORP	CT	61.4
TRUSTSTAR INS CO	MD	0.6
TYPTAP INS CO	FL	25.5
UFG SPECIALTY INS CO	IA	42.9
UNDERWRITERS AT LLOYDS (VI)	VI	73.3
UNITED AMERICAS INS CO	NY	5.8
UNITED GUARANTY COML INS CO OF NC	NC	69.0
UNITED HOME INS CO A RRG	VT	1.5
UNITED INTERNATIONAL INS CO	NY	4.8
UNITED SECURITY HEALTH & CASUALTY	IL	2.8
URGENT MD RRG INC	VT	7.6

INSURANCE COMPANY NAME	DOM. STATE	TOTAL ASSETS ($MIL)
US COASTAL P&C INS CO	FL	26.9
USAA COUNTY MUTUAL INS CO	TX	5.7
UTICA SPECIALTY RISK INS CO	TX	32.1
VANTAGE CASUALTY INS CO	IN	81.0
VANTAPRO SPECIALTY INS CO	AR	23.8
VEHICULAR SERVICE INS CO RRG	OK	2.6
VELOCITY INS CO A RRG	SC	1.5
VICTORIA NATIONAL INS CO	OH	3.5
WALL ROSE MUTUAL INS CO	PA	0.9
WARNER INS CO	IL	12.1
WATFORD INS CO	NJ	23.0
WATFORD SPECIALTY INS CO	NJ	62.1
WAUSAU GENERAL INS CO	WI	15.1
WESCAP INS CO	CO	3.8
WESTERN PROFESSIONAL INS CO	WA	13.7

Section VII

Rating Upgrades
and Downgrades

A list of all

U.S. Property and Casualty Insurers

receiving a rating upgrade or downgrade
during the current quarter.

Section VII Contents

This section identifies those companies receiving a rating change since the previous edition of this publication, whether it is a rating upgrade, rating downgrade, newly rated company or the withdrawal of a rating. A rating may be withdrawn due to a merger, dissolution, or liquidation. A rating upgrade or downgrade may entail a change from one letter grade to another, or it may mean the addition or deletion of a plus or minus sign within the same letter grade previously assigned to the company. Ratings are normally updated once each quarter of the year. In some instances, however, a company's rating may be downgraded outside of the normal updates due to overriding circumstances.

Unlike other rating agencies, Weiss ratings are reviewed each and every quarter to ensure that the company's current rating reflects the most recent information available. This allows us to react more promptly and with greater flexibility to changing conditions as they occur. In addition, we are not inhibited to upgrade or downgrade a company as soon as its financial condition warrants the change. You should therefore consider the magnitude of the rating change along with the meaning of the new rating when evaluating the significance of a rating upgrade or downgrade.

1. Insurance Company Name — The legally-registered name, which can sometimes differ from the name that the company uses for advertising. An insurer's name can be very similar to that of another, so verify the company's exact name and state of domicile to make sure you are looking at the correct company.

2. Domicile State — The state which has primary regulatory responsibility for the company. It may differ from the location of the company's corporate headquarters. You do not have to be living in the domicile state to purchase insurance from this firm, provided it is licensed to do business in your state.

3. Total Assets — All assets admitted by state insurance regulators in millions of dollars. This includes investments and current business assets such as receivables from agents and reinsurers.

4. New Safety Rating — The rating assigned to the company as of the date of this Guide's publication. Our rating is measured on a scale from A to F and considers a wide range of factors. Highly-rated companies are, in our opinion, less likely to experience financial difficulties than lower-rated firms. See *About Weiss Safety Ratings* for more information.

5. Previous Safety Rating — The rating assigned to the company prior to its most recent change.

6. Date of Change — The date that the rating upgrade or downgrade officially occurred. Normally, all rating changes are put into effect on a single day each quarter of the year. In some instances, however, a rating may have been changed outside of this normal update.

Withdrawn Ratings

INSURANCE COMPANY NAME	DOM. STATE	TOTAL ASSETS ($MIL)	NEW RATING	PREVIOUS RATING	DATE OF CHANGE
2-10 HOME BUYERS WARRANTY OF VA	VA	0.0	U	U	10/12/16
AMERICAN INTERNATIONAL OVERSEAS LTD		0.0	U	U	10/12/16
AMERICAN SAFETY CASUALTY INS CO	OK	153.1	U	C-	10/12/16
AMERICAN SAFETY INDEMNITY CO	OK	191.4	U	D	10/12/16
AQUAGUARDIAN INS CO	AZ	0.0	U	U	10/12/16
ARTISAN CONTRACTORS INS CO RRG LLC	MT	0.0	U	U	10/12/16
AVERA PROPERTY INS INC	SD	0.0	U	U	10/12/16
AZTEC INS CO	FL	0.0	U	U	10/12/16
BEACON MUTUAL INS CO	RI	387.1	U	U	10/12/16
BOLD LEGAL DEFENSE INS INC	FL	0.0	U	U	10/12/16
CASTLE HILL INS CO	RI	0.0	U	U	10/12/16
CHATTAHOCHEE RRG CAPTIVE INS CO	GA	0.0	U	U	10/12/16
CIFG ASR NORTH AMERICA INC	NY	730.2	U	E	10/12/16
CIMARRON INS EXCH RRG	VT	0.0	U	U	10/12/16
CLTIC RRG	DC	0.0	U	U	10/12/16
COMPANION CAPTIVE INS CO	SC	0.0	U	U	10/12/16
COOP OF AMER PHYS INS CO RRG	HI	0.0	U	U	10/12/16
DISTRIBUTORS INS CO	TN	0.0	U	U	10/12/16
DRIVERS INS CO	NY	2.3	U	F	10/12/16
ESSEX INS CO	DE	1,335.0	U	C	10/12/16
FIRST AMERICAN HOME BUYERS PRO CORP	CA	0.0	U	U	10/12/16
HERITAGE WARRANTY INS RRG INC	SC	0.5	U	U	10/12/16
HOMESURE OF VIRGINIA INC	VA	0.0	U	U	10/12/16
IDAHO STATE INS FUND	ID	0.0	U	U	10/12/16
INTERMODAL INS CO	DC	0.0	U	U	10/12/16
JOLIET AREA RRG CAPTIVE INS CO	GA	0.0	U	U	10/12/16
LION INS CO (NY)	NY	0.0	U	F	10/12/16
LOUISIANA WORKERS COMPENSATION CORP	LA	1,576.2	U	U	10/12/16
MAINE EMPLOYERS MUTUAL INS CO	ME	813.8	U	U	10/12/16
MANAGED CARE MUT CAPTIVE INS CO	GA	0.0	U	U	10/12/16
MICHIGAN BASIC PROPERTY INS ASN	MI	0.0	U	U	10/12/16
NEW JERSEY CAR RRG	DC	0.0	U	U	10/12/16
OHIO FAIR PLAN UNDERWRITING ASN	OH	0.0	U	U	10/12/16
PENNSYLVANIA PROFESSIONAL LIAB JUA	PA	279.4	U	U	10/12/16
PINELANDS INS CO RRG INC	DC	3.4	U	F	10/12/16
PINNACOL ASR CO	CO	2,094.0	U	U	10/12/16
PREFERRED MANAGED RISK LTD	DC	0.0	U	U	10/12/16
PRESERVER INS CO	NJ	121.1	U	D	10/12/16
SAIF CORP	OR	4,802.9	U	U	10/12/16
SOUTHEAST EMPLOYERS MUT CAP INS CO	GA	0.0	U	U	10/12/16
STATE COMPENSATION INS FUND	CA	19,387.8	U	U	10/12/16
STATE WORKERS INS FUND	PA	0.0	U	U	10/12/16
STEWARD RRG	DC	0.0	U	U	10/12/16
SYSTEMS PROTECTION ASR RRG INC	MT	0.0	U	U	10/12/16
TEXAS MEDICAL LIAB INS UNDWRG ASN	TX	293.1	U	U	10/12/16
TEXAS MUTUAL INS CO	TX	5,660.4	U	U	10/12/16
TEXAS WINDSTORM INS ASSN	TX	0.0	U	U	10/12/16
TIFT AREA CAPTIVE INS CO	GA	0.0	U	U	10/12/16

Withdrawn Ratings (Continued)

INSURANCE COMPANY NAME	DOM. STATE	TOTAL ASSETS ($MIL)	NEW RATING	PREVIOUS RATING	DATE OF CHANGE
TITLE REINS CO	VT	0.0	U	U	10/12/16
TOWER INS CO OF NY	NY	437.8	U	D-	10/12/16
TOWER NATIONAL INS CO	MA	22.9	U	E+	10/12/16
TPA CAPTIVE INS CO	GA	0.0	U	U	10/12/16
UNIONE ITALIANA REINS CO OF AMERICA	NY	62.5	U	U	10/12/16
VIRGINIA SENIOR CARE RRG	DC	0.0	U	U	10/12/16
WISCONSIN HEALTH CARE LIAB INS PLAN	WI	0.0	U	U	10/12/16
WORKERS COMPENSATION FUND OF UTAH	UT	1,701.1	U	U	10/12/16

Rating Upgrades

ALFA ALLIANCE INS CORP was upgraded to B from B- in October 2016 based on an increase in the stability index from a 3.80(fair) to 4.30(fair).

ARCH MORTGAGE REINS CO was upgraded to C- from D+ in October 2016 based on an increase in the stability index from a 2.70(weak) to 3.10(fair), profitability index from a 2.80(weak) to 2.90(fair), and capitalization index from a 9.80(excellent) to 9.90(excellent).

ATLANTIC SPECIALTY INS CO was upgraded to B- from C+ in October 2016 based on an increase in the stability index from a 4.50(fair) to 4.70(fair).

AUTO CLUB SOUTH INS CO was upgraded to B- from C+ in October 2016 based on an increase in the stability index from a 3.50(fair) to 3.60(fair).

CGB INS CO was upgraded to D- from E+ in October 2016 based on an increase in the stability index from a 0.50(weak) to 1.00(weak). Other factors: The company's net asset base increased during the period by 13.8%, from $296.8 million to $337.6 million.

EMPLOYERS INS CO OF NV was upgraded to B- from C+ in October 2016 based on an increase in the capitalization index from a 5.00(good) to 5.10(good). Other factors: Capital and surplus increased during the period by 6.0%, from $436.6 million to $462.9 million.

ESURANCE INS CO OF NJ was upgraded to C from C- in October 2016 based on an increase in the stability index from a 2.90(fair) to 3.00(fair).

ESURANCE P&C INS CO was upgraded to C- from D+ in October 2016 based on an increase in the stability index from a 2.70(weak) to 3.20(fair).

FARMERS UNION MUTUAL INS CO was upgraded to B- from C+ in October 2016 based on an increase in the stability index from a 3.50(fair) to 3.60(fair).

FLORIDA FAMILY INS CO was upgraded to B- from C+ in October 2016 based on an increase in the profitability index from a 5.60(good) to 8.40(excellent) and stability index from a 3.50(fair) to 3.60(fair). Other factors: Capital and surplus increased during the period by 7.1%, from $54.1 million to $57.9 million.

FRANK WINSTON CRUM INS CO was upgraded to C- from D+ in October 2016 based on an increase in the capitalization index from a 2.10(weak) to 2.80(weak). Other factors: Capital and surplus increased during the period by 38.6%, from $14.1 million to $19.5 million.

GEORGIA FARM BUREAU MUTUAL INS CO was upgraded to B- from C+ in October 2016 based on the overall strength of the index ratios.

GREAT LAKES MUTUAL INS CO was upgraded to C- from D+ in October 2016 based on the overall strength of the index ratios.

HEALTH CARE INS RECPL was upgraded to C- from D+ in October 2016 based on the overall strength of the index ratios.

HOMESTEAD MUTUAL INS CO was upgraded to C- from D+ in October 2016 based on an increase in the profitability index from a 6.20(good) to 6.40(good). Other factors: The company's net asset base increased during the period by 6.2%, from $8.4 million to $8.9 million. Capital and surplus increased during the period by 7.6%, from $6.5 million to $7.0 million.

MGIC REINS CORP OF WI was upgraded to D- from E+ in October 2016 based on an increase in the stability index from a 0.70(weak) to 1.20(weak). Other factors: The company's net asset base increased during the period by 17.0%, from $464.4 million to $543.4 million.

MICHIGAN MILLERS MUTUAL INS CO was upgraded to C- from D+ in October 2016 based on an increase in the stability index from a 2.80(weak) to 3.00(fair). Other factors: The company's net asset base increased during the period by 5.1%, from $164.9 million to $173.3 million.

MIDWEST FAMILY MUTUAL INS CO was upgraded to B- from C+ in October 2016 based on an increase in the profitability index from a 6.50(good) to 6.70(good) and stability index from a 3.50(fair) to 3.60(fair). Other factors: Capital and surplus increased during the period by 5.0%, from $55.7 million to $58.5 million.

NEW YORK MUNICIPAL INS RECIPROCAL was upgraded to B- from C+ in October 2016 based on an increase in the stability index from a 3.50(fair) to 3.60(fair).

NUTMEG INS CO was upgraded to C- from D+ in October 2016 based on an increase in the stability index from a 2.40(weak) to 2.90(fair).

PROFESSIONAL SOLUTIONS INS CO was upgraded to C- from D+ in October 2016 based on an increase in the profitability index from a 2.30(weak) to 2.40(weak). Other factors: The company's net asset base increased during the period by 5.8%, from $21.9 million to $23.1 million.

ST JOHNS INS CO was upgraded to C- from D+ in October 2016 based on an increase in the capitalization index from a 2.90(fair) to 3.10(fair) and stability index from a 2.70(weak) to 2.90(fair).

WELLSPAN RRG was upgraded to D- from E+ in October 2016 based on an increase in the stability index from a 0.50(weak) to 0.90(weak) and capitalization index from a 7.20(excellent) to 7.30(excellent). Other factors: Capital and surplus increased during the period by 30.3%, from $6.4 million to $8.3 million.

Rating Downgrades

AMERICAN INS CO was downgraded to C- from C in October 2016 based on a decrease in the profitability index from a 3.00(fair) to 1.90(weak) and stability index from a 3.80(fair) to 3.10(fair). Other factors: The company's net asset base decreased during the period by 6.4%, from $149.1 million to $140.2 million.

ASI LLOYDS was downgraded to D+ from C in October 2016 based on a decrease in the stability index from a 3.60(fair) to 2.70(weak), profitability index from a 3.40(fair) to 2.90(fair), and capitalization index from a 9.50(excellent) to 9.10(excellent). Other factors: Capital and surplus decreased during the period by 19.2%, from $90.8 million to $76.1 million.

CAPITOL INS CO was downgraded to E from E+ in October 2016 based on a decrease in the stability index from a 0.50(weak) to 0.10(weak), profitability index from a 0.80(weak) to 0.50(weak), and capitalization index from a 0.20(weak) to 0.00(weak). Other factors: Capital and surplus decreased during the period by 25.6%, from $1.9 million to $1.5 million.

CHEROKEE GUARANTEE CO INC A RRG was downgraded to E from E+ in October 2016 based on a decrease in the profitability index from a 3.90(fair) to 2.50(weak) and capitalization index from a 3.30(fair) to 3.00(fair). Other factors: Capital and surplus decreased during the period by 47.8%, from $3.5 million to $2.4 million.

CONTINUING CARE RRG INC was downgraded to E from D+ in October 2016 based on a decrease in the stability index from a 1.90(weak) to 0.10(weak), capitalization index from a 4.90(good) to 3.30(fair), and profitability index from a 1.50(weak) to 0.90(weak). Other factors: The company's net asset base decreased during the period by 50.3%, from $7.2 million to $4.8 million. Capital and surplus decreased during the period by 109.5%, from $2.4 million to $1.2 million.

HAMILTON SPECIALTY INS CO was downgraded to B- from B in October 2016 based on a decrease in the stability index from a 4.40(fair) to 3.50(fair), capitalization index from a 8.30(excellent) to 8.20(excellent), and profitability index from a 2.80(weak) to 2.70(weak).

INSUREMAX INS CO was downgraded to E from D- in October 2016 based on a decrease in the stability index from a 0.80(weak) to 0.00(weak), capitalization index from a 2.60(weak) to 2.20(weak), and profitability index from a 0.50(weak) to 0.40(weak). Other factors: The company's net asset base decreased during the period by 25.4%, from $6.3 million to $5.0 million. Capital and surplus decreased during the period by 36.7%, from $1.7 million to $1.3 million.

LEXINGTON INS CO was downgraded to C from C+ in October 2016 based on a decrease in the stability index from a 2.90(fair) to 2.80(weak) and capitalization index from a 7.80(excellent) to 7.70(excellent). Other factors: Capital and surplus decreased during the period by 5.7%, from $6649.6 million to $6289.3 million.

NEVADA GENERAL INS CO was downgraded to D+ from C in October 2016 based on a decrease in the capitalization index from a 7.80(excellent) to 7.20(excellent), stability index from a 3.00(fair) to 2.60(weak), and profitability index from a 1.70(weak) to 1.40(weak). Other factors: The company's net asset base decreased during the period by 26.2%, from $20.5 million to $16.2 million. Capital and surplus decreased during the period by 84.9%, from $11.6 million to $6.3 million.

PALOMAR SPECIALTY INS CO was downgraded to C- from C in October 2016 based on a decrease in the capitalization index from a 2.40(weak) to 2.10(weak) and profitability index from a 3.70(fair) to 3.60(fair).

REPUBLIC UNDERWRITERS INS CO was downgraded to C from C+ in October 2016 based on a decrease in the profitability index from a 4.00(fair) to 2.80(weak) and capitalization index from a 8.20(excellent) to 7.80(excellent). Other factors: Capital and surplus decreased during the period by 55.7%, from $247.5 million to $158.9 million.

SAMSUNG FIRE & MARINE INS CO LTD US was downgraded to C- from C in October 2016 based on a decrease in the capitalization index from a 4.40(fair) to 4.00(fair), stability index from a 3.30(fair) to 2.90(fair), and profitability index from a 1.90(weak) to 1.70(weak). Other factors: The company's net asset base decreased during the period by 11.5%, from $212.7 million to $190.8 million. Capital and surplus decreased during the period by 15.4%, from $48.2 million to $41.7 million.

SWISS REINS AMERICA CORP was downgraded to C+ from B- in October 2016 based on a decrease in the capitalization index from a 5.30(good) to 4.90(good) and stability index from a 3.50(fair) to 3.20(fair). Other factors: Capital and surplus decreased during the period by 14.4%, from $3575.8 million to $3124.8 million.

UNITED AUTOMOBILE INS CO was downgraded to E from D- in October 2016 based on a decrease in the capitalization index from a 3.80(fair) to 2.80(weak), stability index from a 0.90(weak) to 0.10(weak), and profitability index from a 1.80(weak) to 1.50(weak). Other factors: Capital and surplus decreased during the period by 38.1%, from $58.4 million to $42.3 million.

Appendix

State Guaranty Associations

The states have established insurance guaranty associations to help pay claims to policyholders of failed insurance companies. However, there are several cautions which you must be aware of with respect to this coverage:

1. Most of the guaranty associations do not set aside funds in advance. Rather, states assess contributions from other insurance companies after an insolvency occurs.

2. There can be an unacceptably long delay before claims are paid.

3. Each state has different levels and types of coverage, often governed by legislation unique to that state that can sometimes conflict with coverage of other states. Generally speaking, most property and casualty lines of business written by licensed insurers are covered by guaranty associations subject to the conditions and limitations set forth in the various acts. The Guaranty Funds do not cover non-admitted carriers (except in the state of New Jersey). Most state guaranty funds will not cover title, surety, credit, mortgage guarantee or ocean marine insurance.

The table on the following page is designed to help you sort out these issues. However, it is not intended to handle all of them. If your carrier has failed and you need a complete answer, we recommend you contact your State Insurance Official.

Following is a brief explanation of each of the columns in the table.

1.	**Maximum Per Claim**	The maximum amount payable by the State Guaranty Fund on a single covered claim, with the exception of workers' compensation claims, which are paid in full in most states.
2.	**Workers' Comp. Paid in Full**	"Yes" indicates that there is no cap on the amount paid for workers' compensation claims.
3.	**Net Worth Provision**	A net worth provision gives the association the right to seek reimbursement from an insured if the insured's net worth exceeds $50 million, essentially excluding certain large organizations from coverage by the guaranty association. Roughly half of the states have a net worth provision. If a state has a provision, marked "yes", there are other conditions applicable; contact your local department of insurance for further information.
4.	**Guaranty Fund Trigger**	The action that triggers the guaranty fund process.

COVERAGE OF STATE GUARANTY FUNDS

STATE	MAXIMUM PER CLAIM	WORKERS' COMP. PAID IN FULL	NET WORTH PROVISION	GUARANTY FUND TRIGGER		
				FINAL ORDER OF LIQUIDATION WITH FINDING OF INSOLVENCY	FINDING OF INSOLVENCY ONLY	OTHER
Alabama	$150,000	Yes	Yes	X		(16)
Alaska	$500,000	Yes	None	X		
Arizona	$300,000	(8)	None	X		(16)
Arkansas	$300,000	(9)	Yes		X	
California	$500,000	Yes	None	X		
Colorado	$300,000	Yes	Yes	X		(16)
Connecticut	$400,000	Yes	Yes		X	
Delaware	$300,000	Yes	Yes	X		(16)
Dist. of Colombia	$300,000	Yes	Yes	X		(16)
Florida	$300,000 (1)	(10)	None	X		(17)
Georgia	$300,000	Yes	Yes	X		(16)
Hawaii	$300,000	Yes	Yes	X		
Idaho	$300,000	Yes	None	X		
Illinois	$500,000	Yes	Yes	X		(17)
Indiana	$300,000	Yes	Yes	X		(17)
Iowa	$500,000	Yes	yes (15)	X		
Kansas	$300,000	Yes	None	X		
Kentucky	$300,000	Yes	Yes	X		
Louisiana	$500,000	Yes	Yes	X		(18)
Maine	$300,000	Yes	Yes	X		
Maryland	$300,000 (2)	Yes	Yes	X		
Massachusetts	$300,000	Yes	Yes		X	
Michigan	(3)	Yes	Yes	X		(19)
Minnesota	$300,000	Yes	Yes	X		
Mississippi	$300,000	Yes	None	X		(16)
Missouri	$300,000	Yes	Yes	X		(16)
Montana	$300,000	Yes	Yes	X		
Nebraska	$300,000	Yes	None	X		
Nevada	$300,000	Yes	Yes	X		(20)
New Hampshire	$300,000	Yes	Yes	X		(21)
New Jersey	$300,000 (2)	(10)	Yes			(22)
New Mexico	$100,000	Yes	None	X		(16)
New York	$1,000,000 (4)	(10)	None			(23)
North Carolina	$300,000	Yes	Yes	X		(16)
North Dakota	$300,000	(11)	Yes	X		
Ohio	$300,000	(11)	Yes			(24)
Oklahoma	$150,000 (6)	Yes	Yes	X		
Oregon	$300,000	Yes	Yes	X		
Pennsylvania	$300,000	(10)	Yes	X		
Puerto Rico	$300,000	(12)	None	X		(16)
Rhode Island	$500,000	Yes	Yes	X		
South Carolina	$300,000	Yes	Yes		X	(25)
South Dakota	$300,000	Yes	Yes	X		
Tennessee	$100,000	Yes	Yes	X		
Texas	$300,000	Yes	Yes		X	(26)
Utah	$300,000	Yes	Yes			(22)
Vermont	$500,000	Yes	None	X		
Virgin Island	$50,000	(9)	None		X	
Virginia	$300,000	Yes	Yes			(22)
Washington	$300,000	(13)	None			(24)
West Virginia	$300,000	Yes	None			(24)
Wisconsin	$300,000 (5)	(12)	yes			(24)
Wyoming	$300,000 (2)	Yes	None	X		

NOTES

1. Limit of $100,000 per residential unit for policies covering condominium associations or homeowners' associations. Policies providing coverage for homeowner's insurance shall provide for an additional 200,000 for the portion of covered claim which relates only to the damage to the structure and contents.

2. Maximum claim per occurrence is $300,000.

3. $5,000,000 – Subject to Consumer Price Index.

4. $100,000 – Per claim or claimant

5. $1,000,000/Claim; $5,000,000/Policy (non residents)

6. $150,000 limit per claimant for each covered claim.

7. $300,000 is the limit on a sinlge risk, loss or life.

8. Workers' compensation claims of insolvent insurers paid by Arizona's state fund.

9. Workers' compensation payments subject only to maximu claim amount.

10. Workers' compensation not covered, workers' compensation claims covered by a separate workers' compensation security fund.

11. Workers' compensation insurance written exclusively through monopolistic state fund.

12. Workers' compensation payments subject to both deductible and maximum claim amount.

13. Workers compensation not covered except Longshore Harbor workers'. Workers' compensation insurance written exclusively through monopolistic state fund.

14. Covered clain does not include any claim that would otherwise be a covered clain under this part that has been rejected by any other state guaranty fund on the grounds that an insured's net worth is greater than that allowed under that state's guaranty fund law.

15. Iowa does not cover claim of person whose net worth is greater than that allowed by guaranty fund law of his or her state of residence.

16. Order not stayed or subject to supersedeas.

17. Liquidation order not final until there is no further right of appeal.

18. Associated also obligatd to pay claims of an insurer in rehabilitation upon joint motion of association and receiver; order not stayed or subject to supersedeas.

19. All appeals exhausted

20. Also triggered if the insolvent insurer is involved in a court proceeding to determine its status of solvency, rehabilitation or liquidation, and the court has prohibited the insurer from paying claims for more than thirty days.

21. A new act (NH Act of 2004) was enacted for insolvencies occurring after 8-6-2004 and defines an insolvent insurer as a licensed insurer against whom a final order of liquidation has been entered with a finding of insolvency by a court of competent jurisdiction in the insurer's state of domicile. The prior act requires a finding of insolvency only.

22. Order of liquidation with finding of insolvency.

23. Insolvency of Insurer.

24. Triggered by finding of insolvency and liquidation order.

25. Fails to meet obligation to policyholders and state.

26. Requires separate impairment order.

Although the NCIGF has made every effort to produce the most complete, up-to-date and accurate law summaries possible, this work is meant to be used for reference purposes only. It is not meant as a substitute for an official version of a state statue or for legal advice.

Information provided in the Coverage of State Guaranty Funds chart was obtained from the National Conference of Insurance Guaranty Funds (NCIGF).

State Insurance Commissioners'
Departmental Contact Information

State	Official's Title	Website Address	Phone Number
Alabama	Commissioner	www.aldoi.org	(334) 269-3550
Alaska	Director	https://www.commerce.alaska.gov/web/ins/	(800) 467-8725
Arizona	Director	https://insurance.az.gov/	(602) 364-2499
Arkansas	Commissioner	www.insurance.arkansas.gov	(800) 282-9134
California	Commissioner	www.insurance.ca.gov	(800) 927-4357
Colorado	Commissioner	https://www.colorado.gov/dora/division-insurance	(800) 886-7675
Connecticut	Commissioner	http://www.ct.gov/cid/site/default.asp	(800) 203-3447
Delaware	Commissioner	http://delawareinsurance.gov/	(800) 282-8611
Dist. of Columbia	Commissioner	http://disb.dc.gov/	(202) 727-8000
Florida	Commissioner	www.floir.com/	(850) 413-3140
Georgia	Commissioner	www.oci.ga.gov/	(800) 656-2298
Hawaii	Commissioner	http://cca.hawaii.gov/ins/	(808) 586-2790
Idaho	Director	www.doi.idaho.gov	(800) 721-3272
Illinois	Director	www.insurance.illinois.gov/	(866) 445-5364
Indiana	Commissioner	www.in.gov/idoi/	(317) 232-2385
Iowa	Commissioner	www.iid.state.ia.us	(877) 955-1212
Kansas	Commissioner	www.ksinsurance.org	(800) 432-2484
Kentucky	Commissioner	http://insurance.ky.gov/	(800) 595-6053
Louisiana	Commissioner	www.ldi.la.gov/	(800) 259-5300
Maine	Superintendent	www.maine.gov/pfr/insurance/	(800) 300-5000
Maryland	Commissioner	http://insurance.maryland.gov/Pages/default.aspx	(800) 492-6116
Massachusetts	Commissioner	www.mass.gov/ocabr/government/oca-agencies/doi-lp/	(877) 563-4467
Michigan	Director	http://www.michigan.gov/difs	(877) 999-6442
Minnesota	Commissioner	http://mn.gov/commerce/	(651) 539-1500
Mississippi	Commissioner	http://www.mid.ms.gov/	(601) 359-3569
Missouri	Director	www.insurance.mo.gov	(800) 726-7390
Montana	Commissioner	http://csimt.gov/	(800) 332-6148
Nebraska	Director	www.doi.nebraska.gov/	(402) 471-2201
Nevada	Commissioner	www.doi.nv.gov/	(888) 872-3234
New Hampshire	Commissioner	www.nh.gov/insurance/	(800) 852-3416
New Jersey	Commissioner	www.state.nj.us/dobi/	(800) 446-7467
New Mexico	Superintendent	www.osi.state.nm.us/	(855) 427-5674
New York	Superintendent	www.dfs.ny.gov/	(800) 342-3736
North Carolina	Commissioner	www.ncdoi.com	(800) 546-5664
North Dakota	Commissioner	www.nd.gov/ndins/	(800) 247-0560
Ohio	Lieutenant Governor	www.insurance.ohio.gov/	(800) 686-1526
Oklahoma	Commissioner	www.ok.gov/oid/	(800) 522-0071
Oregon	Insurance Commissioner	www.oregon.gov/dcbs/insurance/Pages/index.aspx	(888) 877-4894
Pennsylvania	Commissioner	www.insurance.pa.gov/	(877) 881-6388
Puerto Rico	Commissioner	www.ocs.gobierno.pr	(787) 304-8686
Rhode Island	Superintendent	www.dbr.state.ri.us/divisions/insurance/	(401) 462-9500
South Carolina	Director	www.doi.sc.gov	(803) 737-6160
South Dakota	Director	http://dlr.sd.gov/insurance/default.aspx	(605) 773-3563
Tennessee	Commissioner	www.tn.gov/insurance/	(615) 741-2241
Texas	Commissioner	www.tdi.texas.gov/	(800) 252-3439
Utah	Commissioner	www.insurance.utah.gov	(800) 439-3805
Vermont	Commissioner	www.dfr.vermont.gov/	(802) 828-3301
Virgin Islands	Lieutenant Governor	http://ltg.gov.vi/division-of-banking-and-insurance.html	(340) 774-7166
Virginia	Commissioner	www.scc.virginia.gov/boi/	(804) 371-9741
Washington	Commissioner	www.insurance.wa.gov	(800) 562-6900
West Virginia	Commissioner	www.wvinsurance.gov	(888) 879-9842
Wisconsin	Commissioner	oci.wi.gov	(800) 236-8517
Wyoming	Commissioner	http://doi.wyo.gov/	(800) 438-5768

Risk-Adjusted Capital for Property and Casualty Insurers in Weiss Rating Model

Among the most important indicators used in the analysis of an individual company are our two risk-adjusted capital ratios, which are useful tools in determining exposure to investment, liquidity and insurance risk in relation to the capital the company has to cover those risks.

The first risk-adjusted capital ratio evaluates the company's ability to withstand a moderate loss scenario. The second ratio evaluates the company's ability to withstand a severe loss scenario.

In order to calculate these Risk-Adjusted Capital Ratios, we follow these steps:

1. **Capital Resources**

    First, we find out how much capital a company actually has by adding the company's resources which could be used to cover unexpected losses. These resources are primarily composed of stock issued by the company (capital) and accumulated funds from prior year profits (retained earnings or surplus). Additional credit can also be given for conservative reserving practices and other "hidden capital" where applicable.

    Conservative policy reserves can be an important source of capital and can contribute significantly to the financial strength of a company. Companies that set aside more than is necessary in their reserves year after year are less likely to be over run with claims and forced to dip into capital to pay them. Conversely, a company that understates its reserves year after year will be forced to routinely withdraw from capital to pay claims. Accordingly, we give companies credit for consistent over- reserving and penalize companies for consistent under-reserving.

2. **Target Capital**

    Next, we determine how much capital the company should have to cover moderate losses based upon the company's level of risk in both its insurance business and its investment portfolio. We examine each of the company's risk areas and determine how much capital is needed for each area, based on how risky it is and how much exposure it has in that area. Then we combine these amounts to arrive at a total risk figure.

    Credit is given for the company's diversification, since it is unlikely that "the worst" will happen in all areas at once.

3. **Risk-Adjusted Capital Ratio #1**

    We compare the results of Step 1 with those of Step 2. Specifically, we divide the "capital resources" by the "target capital" and express it in terms of a ratio. This ratio is called RACR #1.

    If a company has a Risk-Adjusted Capital Ratio of 1.0 or more, it means the company has all of the capital we believe it requires to withstand potential losses which could be inflicted by a moderate economic decline. If the company has a ratio of less than 1.0, it does not currently have all of the capital resources we think it needs. During times of financial distress, companies often have access to additional capital through contributions from a parent or holding company, current profits or reductions in dividends. Therefore, we make an allowance for firms with Risk-Adjusted Capital Ratios of somewhat less than 1.0.

4. **Risk-Adjusted Capital Ratio #2**   We repeat Steps 2 and 3 but now assume a severe loss scenario. This ratio is called RACR #2.

5. **Risk-Adjusted Capital Index**   We convert RACR #1 and #2 into an index. It is measured on a scale of zero to ten, with ten being the best and seven or better considered strong. A company whose capital resources exactly equal its target capital will have a Risk-Adjusted Capital Ratio of 1.0 and a Risk-Adjusted Capital Index of 7.0.

How We Determine Target Capital

The basic procedure for determining target capital is to identify the risk areas where the company is exposed to loss such as: (1) the risk of receiving more claims than expected; (2) the risk of not being able to collect from reinsurers or others who owe the company money; (3) the risk of losses on investments and (4) the risk of having inadequate reserves. Then we ask questions, such as:

- What is the breakdown of the company's investment portfolio? What types of policies does the company offer? Who owes the company money and how likely are they to pay? What losses has the company experienced on its underwriting (when claims and expenses exceeded premiums)? How accurate have reserve estimates been? What exposure does the company have to catastrophic property losses, such as Hurricane Andrew or the Los Angeles earthquake? What exposure does the company have to catastrophic liability losses such as asbestos pollution?

- For each category, what are the potential losses which could be incurred in both a moderate loss and a severe loss scenario?

- In order to cover those potential losses, how much in capital resources does the company need? It stands to reason that more capital is needed as a cushion for losses on high-risk investments, such as junk bonds, than on low-risk investments, such as AAA-rated utility bonds.

Amounts from each separate risk area are added together and adjustments are made to take into account the low likelihood that all risk areas would suffer severe losses at the same time. Finally, target capital is adjusted for the company's spread of risk in the diversification of its investment portfolio, the size and number of the policies it writes and the diversification of its business.

Table 1 on the next page shows target capital percentages used by the National Association of Insurance Commissioners (NAIC) in relation to Weiss Ratings Risk-Adjusted Capital Ratios #1 and #2 (RACR #1 and RACR #2).

The percentages shown in the table answer the question: How much should the firm hold in capital resources for every $100 it has committed to each category? Several of the items in Table 1 are expressed as ranges. The actual percentages used in the calculation of target capital for an individual company are determined by the levels of risk in the operations, investments or policy obligations of that specific company.

Table 1. Target Capital Percentages

Invested Asset Risk	Weiss Ratings		NAIC
	RACR#1	RACR#2	
Bonds	(%)	(%)	(%)
Government guaranteed bonds	0	0	0
Class 1	.5-.75	1-1.5	0.3
Class 2	2	5	1
Class 3	5	15	2
Class 4	10	30	4.5
Class 5	20	60	10
Class 6	20	60	30
Preferred Stock	7	9.1	2.3-30
Common Stock			
Unaffiliated	25	33	15
Affiliated	25-100	33-100	N/A
Mortgages	5	15	5
Real Estate	10	33	10
Short-term investment	0.5	1	0.3
Collateral loans	2	5	5
Other invested assets	5	10	20
Credit Risk			
Agents' Balances	0.5	1	
Premium Notes	2	5	
Receivable Investment Income	2	3	5
Misc. Non-invested Assets	5	10	5
Reinsurance Recov. Current	1	1.5	10
30 to 90 Days Overdue	2	3	10
90 to 180 Days Overdue	5	7.5	10
More Than 180 Days Overdue	10	15	10
Rein Recov on Unpaid Losses	5	7.5	10
Rein Recov on IBNR	10	15	10
Rein Recov on UEP	5	7.5	10
Off Balance Sheet RBC			
Noncontrolled assets	1	2	1
Guarantee for affiliates	2	5	1
Contingent Liabilities	2	5	1
Reserve Risk*			
Homeowner Reserves	19-152	22-176	19-154
Private Auto Reserves	10-80	14-108	13-107
Commercial Auto Reserves	11-88	14-108	14-108
Worker's Comp Reserves	8-60	21-168	6-48
Commercial Multiple Peril Res.	19-152	22-176	19-153
Medical Malpractice Res.	26-208	39-312	26-201
Special Liability Res.	13-100	15-120	13-102
Other Liability Res.	24-192	26-208	24-190
International Reserves	16-128	19-152	16-127
Product Liability Reserves	24-192	39-312	24-192
Health Lines Reserves	15-116	23-180	20-157
Other Lines Reserves	20-156	25-196	20-157
Premium Risk*			
Homeowners NPW	29-260	43-260	43-260
Auto Liability NPW	34-304	35-319	52-304
Worker's Comp NPW	34-303	40-363	50-303
Commercial Multiperil NPW	30-272	39-347	45-272
Medical Malpractice NPW	53-478	79-478	80-478
Special Liabilities NPW	29-266	32-281	44-266
Other Liabilities NPW	38-342	49-441	57-342
International NPW	41-373	43-388	62-373
Product Liabilities NPW	41-365	52-464	61-365
Other Lines NPW	24-220	26-234	27-220

* All numbers are shown for illustrative purposes. Figures actually used in the formula vary annually based on industry experience.

Investment Class

Description

Government guaranteed bonds

Guaranteed bonds issued by U.S. and other governments which receive the top rating of state insurance commissioners

Bonds	Class 1	Investment grade bonds rated AAA, AA or A by Moody's or Standard & Poor's or deemed AAA - A equivalent by state insurance regulators
	Class 2	Investment grade bonds with some speculative elements rated BBB or equivalent
	Class 3	Noninvestment grade bonds, rated BB or equivalent
	Class 4	Noninvestment grade bonds, rated B or equivalent
	Class 5	Noninvestment grade bonds, rated CCC, C, C- or equivalent
	Class 6	Noninvestment grade bonds, in or near default

Preferred Stock

Common Stock

Unaffiliated common stock
Affiliated common stock

Mortgages

Real Estate

Company occupied and other investment properties

Short-term Investments

All investments whose maturities at the time of acquisition were one year or less

Collateral Loans

Loans made to a company or individual where the underlying security is in the form of bonds, stocks or other marketable securities

Other Invested Assets

Any invested assets that do not fit under the main categories above

Credit Risk

Agents' Balances

Amounts which have been booked as written and billed to agents

Premium Notes

Loans to policyholders for payments of premiums

Receivable Interest Income

Interest income due but not yet received

Misc. Noninvested Income

Misc. income that is not related to invested assets

Reinsurance Recov. Current

Current receivables from reinsurers for their portion of the recorded losses

    30 to 90 Days Overdue

Receivables from reinsurers 30 - 90 days overdue

    90 to 180 Days Overdue

Receivables from reinsurers 90 - 180 days overdue

    More Than 180 Days Overdue

Receivables from reinsurers more than 180 days overdue

Rein. Recov. on Unpaid Losses

Receivables from reinsurers for unpaid losses

Rein. Recov. on IBNR

Receivables from reinsurers for incurred but not reported losses

Rein. Recov. on UEP

Receivables from reinsurers for unearned premium

Off Balance Sheet Risk

Noncontrolled Assets

Assets not subject to complete insurer control

Guarantee for Affiliates

Guarantees on behalf of affiliates

Contingent Liabilities

Liabilities that are likely to happen but are not certain

Table 2. Bond Default Rates - potential losses as a percent of bond portfolio

	(1)	(2)	(3)	(4)	(5)	(6)	(7)	(8)
	Moody's	Moody's		3 Cum.	Weiss Ratings	Assumed	Losses	RACR
	15 Yr	12 Yr	Worst	Recession	15 Year	Loss	as % of	#2
Bond	Rate	Rate	Year	Years	Rate	Rate	Holdings	Rate
Rating	(%)	(%)	(%)	(%)	(%)	(%)	(%)	(%)
Aaa	2.80	1.60	0.10	0.30	1.89	50	0.95	1.00
Aa	2.00	1.60	0.20	0.60	2.19	50	1.09	1.00
A	3.30	2.50	0.40	1.20	3.67	55	2.02	1.00
Baa	7.20	5.50	1.10	3.26	8.58	60	5.15	5.00
Ba	20.10	17.90	8.40	23.08	36.47	65	23.71	15.00
B	33.70	32.50	21.60	50.80	62.24	70	43.57	30.00

Comments on Target Capital Percentages

The factors in the RACR calculations can be grouped into five categories: (1) Investment Risks; (2) Credit Risks; (3) Off Balance Sheet Risks; (4) Reserve Risks and (5) Premium Risks. Each of these has numerous subcomponents. The five categories are discussed below along with specific comments on some of the most important subcomponents.

Investment Risks:

Bonds

Target capital percentages for bonds are derived from a model that factors in historical cumulative bond default rates from the last twenty years and the additional loss potential during a prolonged economic decline. The continuance of post-World War II prosperity is by no means certain. Realistic analysis of potential losses must factor in the possibility of a severe economic recession.

Table 2 shows how this was done for each bond rating classification. A 15-year cumulative default rate is used (column 1). These are historical default rates for 1970-1990 for each bond class, taken from Moody's Studies of Loss Potential of Life Insurance Assets.

To factor in the additional loss potential of a severe three-year-long economic decline, we reduced the base to Moody's 12-year rate (column 2), determined the worst single year experience (column 3), spread that experience over three years (column 4) and added the historical 12-year rate to the 3-year projection to derive Weiss Ratings 15-year default rate (column 5). Note: Due to the shrinking base of nondefaulted bonds in each year, column 4 may be somewhat less than three times column 3; and column 5 may be somewhat less than the sum of column 2 and column 4.

The next step was to determine the losses that could be expected from these defaults. This would be equivalent to the capital a company should have to cover those losses. Loss rates were assigned for each bond class (column 6), based on the fact that higher rated issues generally carry less debt and the fact that the debt is also better secured, leading to higher recovery rates upon default.

Column 7 shows losses as a percent of holdings for each bond class. Column 8 shows the target capital percentages that are used in RACR #2 (Table 1, RACR #2 column, Bonds -classes 1 to 6).

Regulations limiting junk bond holdings of insurers to a set percent of assets are a tacit acknowledgement that the maximum reserve requirements used by State Insurance Commissioners (Table 1, NAIC column, Bonds — classes 4, 5 and 6) are inadequate. If the figure adequately represented full loss potential, there would be no need to limit holdings through legislation since an adequate loss reserve would provide sufficient capital to absorb potential losses.

Affiliate Common Stock

These stocks are often only "paper" assets, difficult to sell, and not truly available to pay insurance claims. The appropriate value of the stock may also be difficult to determine unless the stock is publicly traded.

The target capital rate on affiliate common stock for RACR #2 can vary between 33% and 100% (Table 1, RACR #2 column, Common stock — Affiliated), depending on the financial strength of the affiliate and the prospects for obtaining capital from the affiliate should the need arise.

Credit Risk

This category refers to the financial risk faced if the company cannot collect funds it is owed. These include funds owed to the company by its agents and funds owed to the company by its reinsurers.

Off Balance Sheet Risk

A miscellaneous category of risk that is developed from data not found on the company's balance sheet. It includes risks associated with rapid premium growth, unsettled lawsuits against the company, guarantees to affiliates and investment risks such as interest rate swaps.

Reserve Risk   The risk that reserve estimates are too low to pay all outstanding claims. Target capital percentages used for each line of business are based on the historical experience of both the company and industry, for that line.

Rather than basing our figures solely on the company's average experience over the last nine years, as is done in the NAIC formula, we factor in the company's worst results over the same period. We believe that this gives a more realistic appraisal of the company's loss potential. Of two companies with identical averages, one may have greater ups and downs than the other. Under the NAIC formula, the companies would have the same target capital, while our formula would require more target capital from the company with the more volatile history.

Target capital requirements have been reduced for each line of business in order to reflect the time value of money. As claims are generally paid months or years after premiums are received, insurers invest those premium funds, accumulating investment income until the claims must be paid. The discount given varies from 9% for private auto liability, a "short-tail" line where claims are paid shortly after receipt of premiums, to 21% for medical malpractice, a "long-tail" line where claims are generally paid many years after receipt of premiums.

Premium Risk   The risk that premium levels are not sufficient to pay claims and related expenses. Individual target capital percentages are used for each line of business based on the riskiness of the line and the company's own experience with reserve risk. Target capital requirements are reduced to account for the time value of money, using a technique similar to that used for reserve risk.

Risky Lines of Business and Catastrophic Losses   These include fire, earthquake, multiple peril (including storm damage) and similar personal and commercial property coverages. Even excluding Hurricane Andrew, the insured losses from natural disasters since 1989 have been far greater than in previous decades. Yet, too many insurance companies are basing their risk calculations on the assumption that losses will return to more normal levels. They are not ready for the possibility that the pattern of increasing disasters might be a real, continuing trend.

Also considered high risk lines are medical malpractice, general liability, product liability and other similar liability coverages. Court awards for damages often run into the millions. These settlement amounts can be very difficult to predict. This uncertainty hinders an insurer's ability to accurately assess how much to charge policyholders and how much to set aside to pay claims. Of special concern are large, unexpected liabilities related to environmental damages such as asbestos. Similar risk may lie hidden in coverage for medical equipment and procedures, industrial wastes, carcinogens and other substances found in products previously viewed as benign.

RECENT INDUSTRY FAILURES

2016

Institution	Headquarters	Industry	Date of Failure	Total Assets ($Mil)	Safety Rating
				At Date of Failure	
Consumers Choice Health Ins Co	South Carolina	Health	01/06/16	92.4	D (Weak)
Moda Health Plan Inc	Oregon	Health	01/28/16	445.5	D+ (Weak)
Family Health Hawaii MBS	Hawaii	Health	04/07/16	5.5	D (Weak)
Health Republic Ins of NY Corp	New York	Health	04/22/16	525.3	D (Weak)
HealthyCT Inc	Connecticut	Health	07/01/16	112.3	D+ (Weak)
Land of Lincoln Mut Health Ins Co	Illinois	Health	07/14/16	107.8	D+ (Weak)
Excalibur Reins Corp	Pennsylvania	P&C	07/18/16	9.0	U (Unrated)
Castlepoint National Ins Co	California	P&C	07/28/16	355.1	C- (Fair)
Freelancers Consumer Operated	New Jersey	Health	09/12/16	135.3	D+ (Weak)

2015

Institution	Headquarters	Industry	Date of Failure	At Date of Failure	
				Total Assets ($Mil)	Safety Rating
Millers Classified Ins Co	Illinois	P&C	01/20/15	2.7	E (Very Weak)
Eveready Ins Co	New York	P&C	01/29/15	10.6	E- (Very Weak)
Jordan Funeral and Ins Co, Inc	Alabama	L&H	02/17/15	1.1	U (Unrated)
Drivers Insurance Co	New York	P&C	03/12/15	3.0	E- (Very Weak)
Lumbermens Underwriting Alliance	Missouri	P&C	05/19/15	354.3	E- (Very Weak)
Pinelands Ins Co RRG, Inc	District of Columbia	P&C	08/25/15	4.9	E (Very Weak)
Louisiana Health Cooperative, Inc	Louisiana	Health	09/01/15	59.5	E (Very Weak)
Affirmative Ins Co	Illinois	P&C	09/16/15	181.2	E (Very Weak)
Affirmative Casualty Ins Co	Louisiana	P&C	10/05/15	32.6	D+ (Weak)
Affirmative Direct Ins Co	New York	P&C	10/05/15	5.3	U (Unrated)
Nevada Health Co-op	Nevada	Health	10/14/15	47.9	E- (Very Weak)
WINHealth Partners	Wyoming	Health	10/21/15	34.0	D (Weak)
Kentucky Health Cooperative Inc	Kentucky	Health	10/29/15	189.5	D+ (Weak)
Meritus Mutual Health Partners	Arizona	Health	10/30/15	45.8	D (Weak)
Meritus Health Partners	Arizona	Health	10/30/15	43.0	D+ (Weak)
Regis Ins Co	Pennsylvania	P&C	10/30/15	.6	E- (Very Weak)
Arches Mutual Ins Co	Utah	Health	11/02/15	77.2	D (Weak)
Lincoln General Ins Co	Pennsylvania	P&C	11/05/15	65.6	E- (Very Weak)
Advantage Health Solutions Inc	Indiana	Health	11/06/15	64.2	E (Very Weak)
Colorado Health Ins Coop Inc	Colorado	Health	11/10/15	108.7	D+ (Weak)
Consumers Mutual Ins of Michigan	Michigan	Health	11/13/15	60.4	E- (Very Weak)

2014

Institution	Headquarters	Industry	Date of Failure	At Date of Failure	
				Total Assets ($Mil)	Safety Rating
Union Mutual Ins Co	Oklahoma	P&C	01/24/14	5.1	E+ (Very Weak)
Commonwealth Ins Co	Pennsylvania	P&C	03/20/14	1.1	E (Very Weak)
LEMIC Ins Co	Louisiana	P&C	03/31/14	51.6	D (Weak)
Interstate Bankers Casualty Co	Illinois	P&C	04/16/14	16.2	D+ (Weak)
Freestone Ins Co	Delaware	P&C	04/28/14	421.2	D- (Weak)
Alameda Alliance For Health	California	Health	05/05/14	176.3	D (Weak)
Sunshine State Ins Co	Florida	P&C	06/03/14	22.9	E+ (Very Weak)
Physicians United Plan Inc	Florida	Health	06/09/14	110.7	E (Very Weak)
Red Rock Ins Co	Oklahoma	P&C	08/01/14	28.5	E+ (Very Weak)
DLE Life Ins co	Louisiana	L&H	10/02/14	39.3	D+ (Weak)
Mothe Life Ins Co	Louisiana	L&H	10/02/14	15.2	E- (Very Weak)
First Keystone RRG Inc	South Carolina	P&C	10/21/14	13.6	E+ (Very Weak)
SeeChange Health Ins Co	California	Health	11/19/14	23.4	D (Weak)
PROAIR Risk Retention Grp Inc	Nevada	P&C	11/12/14	0.5	U (Unrated)
Florida Healthcare Plus, Inc	Florida	Health	12/10/14	11.1	U (Unrated)
CoOportunity Health, Inc	Iowa	Health	12/23/14	195.7	U (Unrated)

2013

Institution	Headquarters	Industry	Date of Failure	Total Assets ($Mil)	Safety Rating
				At Date of Failure	
Partnership Health Plan Inc	Wisconsin	Health	01/18/13	27.1	D (Weak)
Driver's Insurance Co	Oklahoma	P&C	02/21/13	33.1	D+ (Weak)
Lewis & Clark LTC RRG	Nevada	P&C	02/28/13	16.4	E (Very Weak)
Pride National Ins Co	Oklahoma	P&C	03/08/13	17.1	E+ (Very Weak)
Santa Fe Auto	Texas	P&C	03/08/13	22.9	E (Very Weak)
Ullico Casualty Co	Delaware	P&C	03/11/13	327.7	D (Weak)
Builders Ins Co Inc	Nevada	P&C	03/15/13	15.0	U (Unrated)
Nevada Contractors Ins Co Inc	Nevada	P&C	03/15/13	49.0	U (Unrated)
Universal Health Care Ins Co Inc	Florida	Health	03/22/13	106.1	C (Fair)
Universal Health Care Inc	Florida	Health	03/25/13	109.0	D (Weak)
Universal HMO of Texas	Texas	Health	04/18/13	15.3	C- (Fair)
Universal Health Care of NV Inc	Nevada	Health	06/03/13	1.9	D+ (Weak)
Liberty First RRG Ins Co	Utah	P&C	08/06/13	2.5	E (Very Weak)
United Contrs Ins Co Inc, RRG	Delaware	P&C	08/22/13	17.0	E (Very Weak)
Advance Physicians Ins RRG, Inc	Arizona	P&C	08/29/13	1.9	D (Weak)
Georgia Mutual Ins Co	Georgia	P&C	09/10/13	3.3	D (Weak)
Ocean Risk Retention Group	D.C.	P&C	09/06/13	7.9	E (Very Weak)
Gertrude Geddes Willis Life Ins Co	Louisiana	L&H	10/24/13	4.9	U (Unrated)
San Antonio Indemnity Co	Texas	P&C	10/31/13	2.8	E+ (Very Weak)
Higginbotham Burial Ins Co	Arkansas	L&H	11/04/13	1.3	U (Unrated)
Indemnity Ins Corp RRG	Delaware	P&C	11/07/13	83.2	D- (Weak)
Concert Health Plan Ins Co	Illinois	L&H	12/10/13	1.8	D- (Weak)
ICM Insurance Co	New York	P&C	12/23/13	5.0	E+ (Very Weak)

2012

Institution	Headquarters	Industry	Date of Failure	Total Assets ($Mil)	Safety Rating
				At Date of Failure	
Autoglass Ins Co	New York	P&C	01/09/12	29.7	E+ (Very Weak)
Hlth Facilities of CA Mut I C RRG	Nevada	P&C	01/10/12	1.9	U (Unrated)
Republic Mortgage Ins Co	North Carolina	P&C	01/19/12	1.41	E (Very Weak)
CAGC Ins Co	North Carolina	P&C	01/26/12	11.8	U (Unrated)
First Sealord Surety Inc	Pennsylvania	P&C	02/08/12	15.2	U (Unrated)
Scaffold Industry Ins Co RRG Inc	D.C.	P&C	05/01/12	5.1	E+ (Very Weak)
Financial Guaranty Ins Co	New York	P&C	06/11/12	2054.0	E- (Very Weak)
Global Health Plan & Ins Co	Puerto Rico	Health	06/13/12	1.1	U (Unrated)
Garden State Indemnity Co, Inc	New Jersey	P&C	06/22/12	2.93	E- (Very Weak)
AvaHealth Inc	Florida	HMO	06/27/12	3.3	E (Very Weak)
American Manufacturers Mutual	Illinois	P&C	07/02/12	10.3	E+ (Very Weak)
Lumbermens Mutual Casualty Co	Illinois	P&C	07/02/12	789.4	E (Very Weak)
Millers First Ins Co	Illinois	P&C	07/24/12	23.0	E (Very Weak)
American Motorists Ins Co	Illinois	P&C	08/16/12	19.7	D (Weak)
Home Value Ins Co	Ohio	P&C	08/31/12	3.5	U (Unrated)
Northern Plains Ins Co	South Dakota	P&C	09/18/12	1.4	D (Weak)
Jamestown Ins Co RRG	South Carolina	P&C	09/24/12	5.9	E+ (Very Weak)
Interstate Auto Ins Co	Maryland	P&C	10/11/12	4.6	D (Weak)
Regional Health Ins Co, RRG	D.C.	P&C	10/18/12	0.6	U (Unrated)
DC Chartered Health Plan Inc	D.C.	HMO	10/19/12	65.4	E- (Very Weak)
American Fellowship Mut Ins Co	Michigan	P&C	10/29/20	50.0	D (Weak)
Gramercy Ins Co	Texas	P&C	12/04/12	41.8	D (Weak)
Triad Guaranty Ins Corp	Illinois	P&C	12/11/12	766.7	E (Very Weak)
Triad Guaranty ASR Corp	Illinois	P&C	12/11/12	16.1	B (Good)

2011

Institution	Headquarters	Industry	Date of Failure	At Date of Failure	
				Total Assets ($Mil)	Safety Rating
Comm. Ins. Alliance Reciprocal	Florida	P&C	01/26/11	N/A	N/A
Aequicap Ins Co	Florida	P&C	02/28/11	29.7	E+ (Very Weak)
US Rail Ins Co a RRG	Vermont	P&C	03/04/11	3.2	E (Very Weak)
Seminole Casualty Ins Co	Florida	P&C	03/15/11	35.6	D (Weak)
Qualicare Self-Insurance Trust	Georgia	HMO	04/21/11	N/A	N/A
Majestic Insurance Co	California	P&C	04/21/11	313.1	D+ (Weak)
Reinsurance Co of America Inc	Illinois	P&C	04/27/11	7.1	D (Weak)
National Insurance Co	Puerto Rico	P&C	05/24/11	79.4	D+ (Weak)
Argus Fire & Casualty Ins Co	Florida	P&C	05/27/11	33.8	D (Weak)
Security Pacific Ins Co	Delaware	P&C	06/15/11	N/A	N/A
Great Republic Life Ins Co	Washington	L&H	07/07/11	16.9	E+ (Very Weak)
National Group Ins Co	Florida	P&C	08/01/11	9.53	E- (Very Weak)
Federal Motors Carriers RRG Inc	Delaware	P&C	08/18/11	11.9	E (Very Weak)
PMI Insurance Co	Arizona	P&C	08/19/11	436.9	D (Weak)
PMI Mortgage Ins Co	Arizona	P&C	08/19/11	2841.2	D (Weak)
Western Insurance Co	Utah	P&C	08/25/11	21.66	U (Unrated)
Homewise Preferred Ins Co	Florida	P&C	09/02/11	11.1	E (Very Weak)
American Sterling Ins Co	California	P&C	09/26/11	15.4	D (Weak)
Quality Health Plans Inc	Florida	HMO	10/17/11	45.0	E+ (Very Weak)
HomeWise Ins Co	Florida	P&C	11/18/11	84.7	D (Weak)
Minnesota Surety & Trust Co	Minnesota	P&C	12/02/11	1.5	E(Very Weak)
Southern Eagle Ins Co	Florida	P&C	12/06/11	18.6	D (Weak)

Glossary

This glossary contains the most important terms used in this publication.

Admitted Assets

The total of all investments and business interests which are acceptable under statutory accounting rules.

Asset/Liability Matching

Management of cash flows so that investments pay interest or mature at just the right time to meet the need for cash to pay claims and expenses.

Average Recession

A recession involving a decline in real GDP which is approximately equivalent to the average of the postwar recessions of 1957-58, 1960, 1970, 1974-75, 1980 and 1981-82. It is assumed, however, that in today's market, the financial losses suffered from a recession of that magnitude would be greater than those experienced in previous decades. (See also "Severe Recession.")

Capital

Strictly speaking, capital refers to funds raised through the sale of common and preferred stock. Mutual companies have capital in the form of retained earnings. In a more general sense, the term capital is commonly used to refer to a company's equity or net worth, that is, the difference between assets and liabilities (i.e., capital and surplus as shown on the balance sheet).

Capital Resources

The sum of various resources which serve as a capital cushion to losses, including capital and surplus.

Cash and Demand Deposits

Includes cash on hand and on deposit. A negative figure indicates that the company has more checks outstanding than current funds to cover those checks. This is not an unusual situation for an insurance company.

Common and Preferred Stocks

See "Stocks".

Direct Premiums Written

Premiums derived from policies issued directly by the company. This figure excludes the impact of reinsurance.

Safety Rating

Weiss Safety Ratings grade insurers on a scale from A (Excellent) to F (Failed). Ratings for property and casualty insurers are based on five major factors: liquidity, reserve adequacy, capitalization, profitability, and stability of operations.

Five-Year Profitability Index

See "Profitability Index".

Government Securities

Securities issued and/or guaranteed by U.S. and foreign governments which are rated as highest quality (class 1) by state insurance commissioners. Included in this category are bonds issued by governmental agencies and guaranteed with the full faith and credit of the government. Regardless of the issuing entity, they are viewed as being relatively safer than the other investment categories.

Interest Rate Risk

The risk that, due to changes in interest rates, investment income will not meet the needs of policy commitments. This risk can be reduced by effective asset/liability matching.

Invested Assets

The total size of the firm's investment portfolio.

Investments in Affiliates

Includes bonds, preferred stocks and common stocks, as well as other vehicles which many insurance companies use to invest in—and establish a corporate link with—affiliated companies.

Line of Business

Types of insurance coverage such as fire, inland marine, group accident and health, auto physical damage and auto liability. Statutory accounting uses over 30 different lines of business. A particular insurer may write coverage in any or all of these lines.

Liquidity Index

An index, expressed on a scale of zero to ten, with seven or higher considered excellent, that measures a company's ability to raise the necessary cash to settle claims. It is possible for a company to have the resources to pay claims on paper, but be unable to raise the cash. This can occur when a company is owed a great deal of money by its agents or reinsurers, or when it cannot sell its investments at the anticipated price.

Our liquidity tests examine how the company might fare under various cash flow scenarios.

Long/Short-Tail Lines

Time periods over which claims are paid out. For example, auto physical damage is considered a short-tail line, since claims are generally paid within one year of an accident. On the other hand, medical malpractice is considered a long-tail line as claims are typically paid five years or more after the occurrence of the incident giving rise to the claim.

For the insurer, the risks associated with long-tail lines are greater than with short-tail lines because the period of uncertainty in which unexpected claims can arise is longer.

Moderate Loss Scenario

Possible future events that would result in loss levels comparable to those experienced in recent history. (Compare with "Severe Loss Scenario.")

Net Premiums Written

The dollar volume of premiums retained by the company. This figure is equal to direct premiums written, plus reinsurance assumed, less reinsurance ceded to other companies.

Noninvestment Grade Bonds

Low-rated issues, commonly known as "junk bonds," which carry a high risk as defined by the state insurance commissioners. These include bond classes 3 - 6.

Other Investments

Items not included in any of the other categories, such as premium notes, collateral loans, short-term investments and other miscellaneous items.

Premium Risk

The risk that, for a particular group of policies, premiums will not be sufficient to meet the level of claims and related expenses.

Profitability Index

An index, expressed on a scale of zero to ten, with seven or higher considered excellent, that measures the soundness of the company's operations and the contribution of profits to the company's fiscal strength. The Profitability Index is a composite of five factors: (1) gain or loss on underwriting (core insurance business); (2) gain or loss on overall operations; (3) consistency of operating results; (4) impact of operating results on surplus and (5) expenses in relation to industry averages for the types of policies that the company offers.

Real Estate

Direct real estate investments, including property (a) occupied by the company; (b) acquired through foreclosure of a mortgage and (c) purchased as an investment.

Reinsurance Assumed

Insurance risk acquired by taking on partial or full responsibility for claims on policies written by other companies. (See "Reinsurance Ceded.")

Reinsurance Ceded

Insurance risk sold to another company. When there is a claim on a reinsured policy, the original company generally pays the claim and then is reimbursed by its reinsurer.

Reserve Adequacy Index

An index, expressed on a scale of zero to ten with seven or higher considered excellent, that measures the adequacy of the company's reserves over the last five years. Companies that have a history of inadequate reserves will receive a low score. Reserves are company estimates of unsettled claims in each year, including both claims that have been received but not yet settled, as well as claims that the company expects to receive. A company that underestimates its claims inflates profits and capital. Additionally, chronically deficient reserves call into question the company's ability to manage its policy risk effectively.

Risk-Adjusted Capital

The capital resources that would be needed to deal with unexpected claims or other adverse developments (same as "Target Capital").

Risk-Adjusted Capital Ratio #1

The capital resources which a company currently has, expressed as a ratio, to the resources that would be needed to deal with a moderate loss scenario. (See "Moderate Loss Scenario.")

Risk-Adjusted Capital Ratio #2	The capital resources which a company currently has, expressed as a ratio, to the resources that would be needed to deal with a severe loss scenario. (See "Severe Loss Scenario.")
Severe Loss Scenario	Possible future events that could result in loss levels that are somewhat higher than recent experience. These levels are developed from examination of current trends. (Compare with "Moderate Loss Scenario.")
Severe Recession	A prolonged economic slowdown in which the single worst year of the postwar period is extended for a period of three years. (See also "Average Recession.")
Short-Tail Lines	See "Long/Short-Tail Lines".
Stability Index	An index, measured on a scale of zero to ten, integrating a wide variety of factors that reflect the company's stability and diversification of risk.
State of Domicile	Although most insurance companies are licensed to do business in many states, they have only one state of domicile. This is the state which has primary regulatory responsibility for the company. Use the state of domicile to make absolutely sure that you have the correct company. Bear in mind, however, that this need not be the state where the company's main offices are located.
State Guaranty Funds	Funds that are designed to raise cash from existing insurance carriers to cover policy claims of bankrupt insurance companies.
Stocks	Common and preferred equities, including stocks in affiliates.
Surplus	Accumulated funds from prior years' profits (retained earnings) plus additional amounts paid-in by a parent or other corporation. The term "surplus" is also sometimes used broadly to include capital such as common stock.
Target Capital	See "Risk-Adjusted Capital."
Total Assets	Total admitted assets, including investments and other business assets. (See "Admitted Assets.")